Canadian Edition

NUTRITION

for Healthy Living

WENDY J. SCHIFF, MS, RD
St. Louis Community College

MATTHEW DURANT, PhD, PDt, MEd, CDE
Acadia University

With Contributions from

GORDON M. WARDLAW, PhD, RD
Formerly of *The Ohio State University*

SOBIA KHAN, MSc, RD
George Brown College

The McGraw·Hill Companies

Nutrition for Healthy Living
Canadian Edition

ISBN-13: 978-0-07-007344-9
ISBN-10: 0-07-007344-9

1 2 3 4 5 6 7 8 9 0 TCP 1 9 8 7 6 5 4 3 2 1

Printed and bound in Canada.

Vice-President and Editor-in-Chief: Joanna Cotton
Publisher: Cara Yarzab
Sponsoring Editor: Marcia Siekowski
Marketing Manager: Stacey Metz
Developmental Editors: Jennifer Cressman and My Editor, Inc.
Supervising Editor: Kara Stahl
Photo/permission Research: My Editor, Inc.
Senior Editorial Associate: Stephanie Hess
*i*Learning Sales Specialist: Joanne Barnett
Copy Editor: Michael Kelly
Production Coordinators: Jennifer Hall and Tammy Mavroudi
Cover Design: Katherine Strain
Cover Image Credit: Eriko Koga/Getty Images (RF)
Interior Design: Greg Nettles/Squarecrow Creative
Page Layout: Michelle Losier
Printer: Transcontinental Printing Group

Library and Archives Canada Cataloguing in Publication

Schiff, Wendy
Nutrition for healthy living / Wendy J. Schiff, Matthew Durant. -- Canadian ed.

Includes bibliographical references and index.
ISBN 978-0-07-007344-9

1. Nutrition--Textbooks. I. Durant, Matthew A II. Title.

QP141.S3435 2011 612.3 C2010-904690-0

Meet the Authors

Wendy J. Schiff, MS, RD, received her BS in biological health/medical dietetics and MS in human nutrition from The Pennsylvania State University. She has taught introductory food and nutrition courses at the University of Missouri–Columbia as well as nutrition, human biology, and personal health courses at St. Louis Community College–Meramec. She has worked as a public health nutritionist at the Allegheny County Health Department (Pittsburgh, Pennsylvania) and State Food and Nutrition Specialist for Missouri Extension at Lincoln University in Jefferson City, Missouri. In addition to authoring *Nutrition for Healthy Living*, Wendy has co-authored a college-level personal health textbook and authored many other nutrition-related educational manuals and supplements. She is a registered dietitian and a member of the American Dietetic Association.

Matthew Durant, PhD, earned his PhD at Dalhousie University in interdisciplinary studies related to community health and epidemiology, health and human performance, and nutrition as it influences youth obesity. He received a master's degree in educational psychology and human relations at Mount Saint Vincent University. Matthew is currently an associate professor in the School of Nutrition and Dietetics at Acadia University, where his areas of research and teaching include introductory nutrition, medical nutrition therapy for acute and chronic disease, nutrition in long-term care, and advanced topics in youth and adult obesity. Matthew also works as a registered dietitian and certified diabetes educator and has been actively involved with Dietitians of Canada, having served a three-year term on the Board of Directors representing the Atlantic region.

Brief Contents

Appendices Available on *Connect* at www.mcgrawhillconnect.ca

Contents

8 Vitamins 224

9 Water and Minerals 274

Part 3 Applying Your Nutrition Knowledge

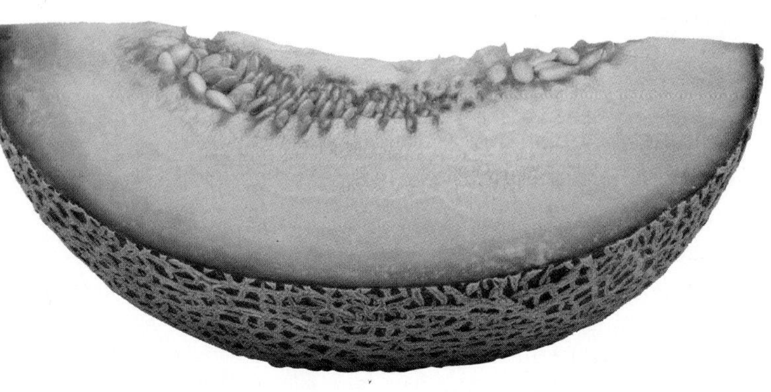

Preface

We think of ourselves as consumers when we purchase homes, cars, computers, and food. We are also consumers of nutrition-related information. Nearly every day, we are bombarded with media messages concerning nutrition, foods, and health. Much of this information is unreliable and designed to promote sales of products or services. Nevertheless, we may use the information when making decisions about which foods or nutrition-related products to buy. Why? Many consumers lack the knowledge and skills needed to analyze such information critically and decide whether to apply it to their decision-making process.

Helping students become better informed consumers, particularly in the areas of food and nutrition, is the foundation of *Nutrition for Healthy Living*, Canadian Edition. This major theme flows throughout the textbook by providing students with practical information, critical-thinking skills, and the scientific foundation needed to make more informed choices about their diet and health. By reading *Nutrition for Healthy Living*, Canadian Edition, students not only will learn basic principles of nutrition but will also be able to evaluate various sources of nutrition information critically and apply sound nutrition practices to improve their lives.

Who Is This Book Written For?

Nutrition for Healthy Living, Canadian Edition, is intended for students who are interested in learning about nutrition for personal reasons, as well as for students considering majoring in nutrition, nursing, or other health- and science-related fields. Students from a wide variety of academic backgrounds often enroll in introductory nutrition courses, and in many instances, they have not taken university-level science courses prior to this course. With this in mind, *Nutrition for Healthy Living*, Canadian Edition, was written with the understanding that an introductory textbook must appeal to students who represent a broad range of interests and academic backgrounds—from English majors to nursing majors. An introductory course, along with this textbook, can spark students' interest in adopting healthier dietary practices and possibly even inspire them to consider nutrition as a major.

The *Nutrition for Healthy Living* Difference Is *ABC*

This text was written as an alternative to established nutrition textbooks, while maintaining a focus on concepts that are fundamental to introductory nutrition courses. It was our vision to create a textbook that would be fun to read, engage students' interest, be well organized, and have features that contribute to the pedagogy without being distracting. We gathered feedback from numerous instructors, and the advantages that the new textbook would offer took shape—what we refer to as the "**ABCs of *Nutrition for Healthy Living*.**"

A = Accessible Science

Nutrition is an "offspring" science that requires a basic understanding of certain chemical and physiological concepts, terms, and scientific principles. Ignorance about chemistry and physiology contributes to food faddism and health quackery. By providing a solid scientific foundation, nutrition educators can more easily dispel commonly held but inaccurate beliefs, such as "When you're inactive, muscle turns into fat," and "Cellulite is a special type of body fat."

Becoming knowledgeable about nutrition requires a certain level of understanding of important scientific principles. *Nutrition for Healthy Living*, Canadian Edition, recognizes the importance of introducing such principles in a manner that every college and university student can understand.

The primary goal for students who use this textbook is the same as it is for the introductory nutrition courses we teach—to aim for students to complete the course with a basic understanding of nutritional science so that they can make intelligent, practical choices that can result in improved nutrition and health.

Chapter 4 (Body Basics) presents basic principles of chemistry and human physiology as they apply to the study of nutrition at a level students can easily understand. This chapter introduces and defines terms that relate to nutrition and foods such as *acid*, *basic*, *enzyme*, and *solvent*. Students and courses vary in the depth of scientific foundation required; therefore, this chapter features some flexibility. The chapter is divided into two main sections, chemistry and human physiology, so professors can choose to skip the chemistry section if they prefer.

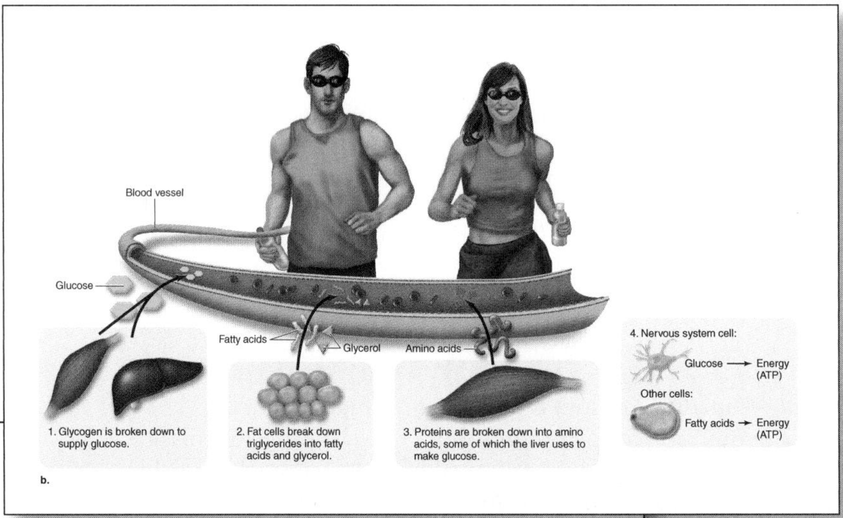

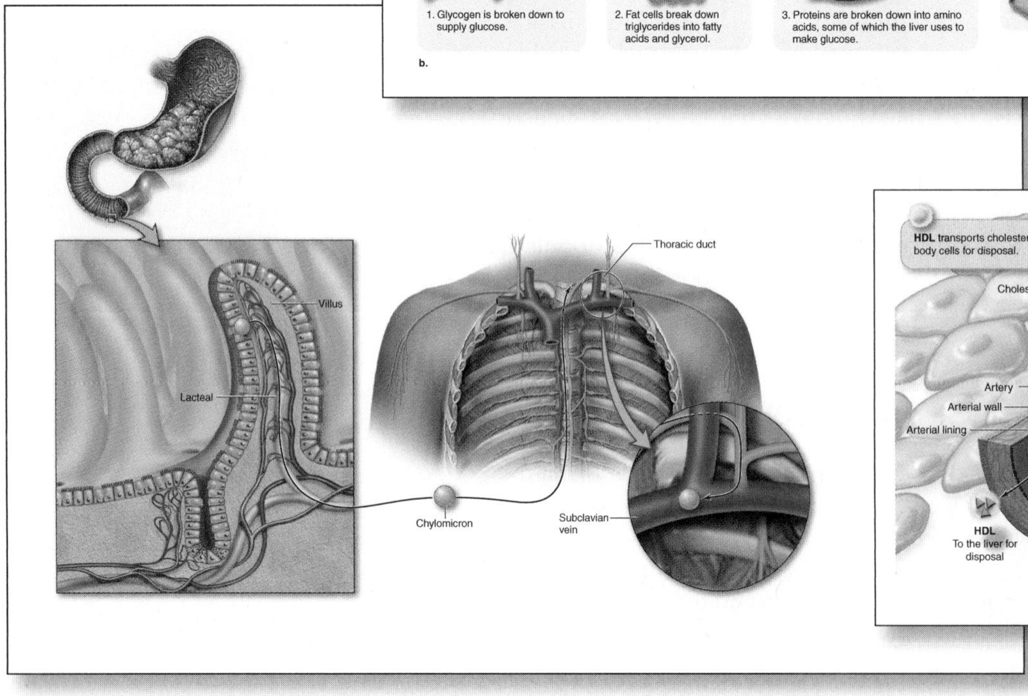

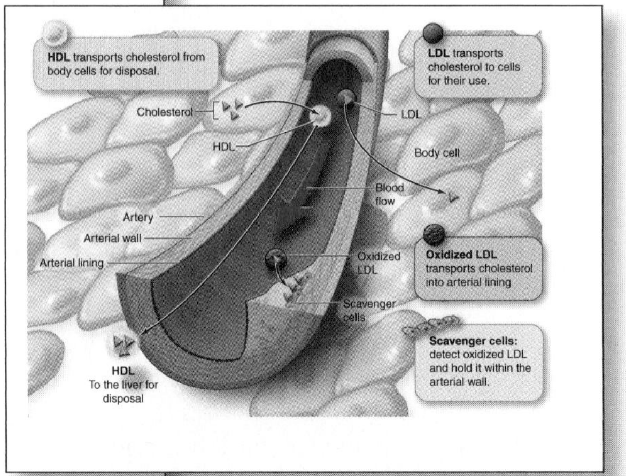

B = Brief Organization

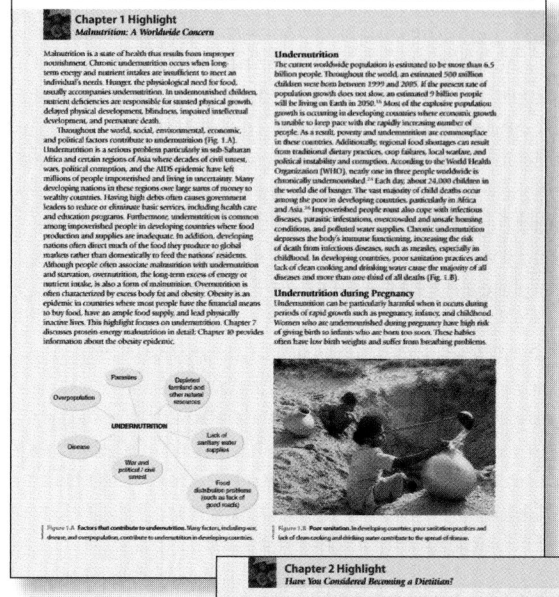
Chapter 1 Highlight
Malnutrition: A Worldwide Concern

Undernutrition

Undernutrition during Pregnancy

Chapter 2 Highlight
Have You Considered Becoming a Dietitian?

In developing the structure of this book, a new approach emerged; instructors often do not have the time to cover all the material in their textbooks. Based upon their feedback, the core content was organized into 13 chapters. This organization makes teaching introductory nutrition more manageable and fits the time frame of most courses better than textbooks that include 15 or more chapters. Some topics were important to cover, but they did not warrant a full chapter. Thus, topics such as global nutrition concerns, alcohol and alcohol abuse, and eating disorders are presented in a "Highlight" feature at the end of chapters. Chapter 13 is devoted entirely to nutrition during the life cycle. Furthermore, key aspects of world nutrition and life-cycle nutrition are also incorporated into relevant chapters throughout the book.

Nutrition for Healthy Living, Canadian Edition, covers the core material that instructors need in a format that is logical and practical for nearly all introductory nutrition courses:

- Chapter 1 introduces students to nutrition and nutrients and presents key nutrition concepts, such as "Most naturally occurring foods are mixtures of nutrients," and "Eating a variety of foods can help ensure the nutritional adequacy of a diet." There is a new section on the Canadian Healthy Living Strategy, information on how Canadians' eating habits have changed in the past two generations, and data concerning undernutrition in Canada, along with some of the obstacles that hinder the ability of Canadian families to select nutritionally adequate diets.
- Chapter 2 presents basic information about scientific methodology as it relates to nutrition research and provides tips for becoming a more wary consumer of nutrition- and health-related information. Tips and Web links for Canadian organizations will help students to find reliable health and nutrition information on the Internet, along with information on becoming an accredited dietician in Canada.
- Chapter 3 provides a brief history of Canadian food guides, as well as an introduction to the current *Eating Well with Canada's Food Guide;* discussion of the four major food groups; and age- and gender-specific dietary guidelines for Canadians. This chapter discusses dietary standards and guidelines, food groups and guides, and how to use information provided on nutrient labels. Chapter 3 also introduces the EATracker tool, developed by Dietitians of Canada, which allows individuals to track their daily food and activity choices and compare them to guidelines set forth by Health Canada.
- Chapter 4 introduces basic chemical and physiological concepts and key terms that relate to the science of nutrition.
- Chapters 5, 6, 7, 8, and 9 present basic and practical information about nutrients, such as their major functions in the body, food sources, and roles in health, along with mention of the Canadian Diabetes Association (CDA) in a discussion about diabetes, and a Web link provided for students to access the diabetes risk checklist on the CDA's Web site. Discussions include Health Canada's labelling regulations for trans fat in manufactured foods, recommendations for lipid intake, recommendations for protein intake based on *Eating Well with Canada's Food Guide*, and expanded coverage of vitamin D deficiency, with recommendations from the Canadian Paediatric Society and Health Canada for vitamin D consumption.
- Chapters 10, 11, 12, and 13 focus on applying basic nutrition information for special needs and important concerns. Chapter 10 covers weight management; Chapter 12 features information about food-borne illness and information about Health Canada's legislation on food additives; Chapter 13 covers daily food plans based on *Eating Well with Canada's Food Guide* for each major life stage, including pregnant and lactating women.

Nutrition for Healthy Living, Canadian Edition, follows a more traditional approach to the study of nutrition in that the textbook's organization focuses on nutrients rather than certain tissues or diseases. Additionally, the textbook integrates health information within each chapter where it is appropriate, rather than relegating it to a single chapter at the end of the textbook. For example, the chapters that discuss nutrients provide fundamental information first and then present applications, including the nutrient-related health effects of certain lifestyle practices, particularly dietary choices. Additionally, the quantity and length of boxed features in the chapters are limited, as they tend to disrupt the flow of content and students often skip reading them.

C = Consumer Focus

Regardless of their background, students are consumers of nutrition information from a wide variety of sources, including popular magazines, diet books, infomercials, and the Internet. Often, these students arrive in class with many misconceptions about diet and health. As nutrition educators, we seek to identify these beliefs and to impart sound, reliable nutrition and health information. We also strive to equip our students with the tools they need to make intelligent, informed food and nutrition-related decisions beyond the classroom. Chapter 2 (Evaluating Nutrition Information) presents a practical introduction to becoming an informed consumer of nutrition and nutrition-related information. This unique chapter provides basic information concerning scientific research and a thorough discussion of how to evaluate nutrition- and health-related sources and messages. The consumer emphasis is also integrated into the narrative and in pedagogical tools throughout the text.

In addition to devoting an entire chapter to the topic of evaluating nutrition-related information and ways of becoming a more wary consumer of nutrition information, the consumer emphasis is integrated throughout the book.

Gelatin is an animal protein that dissolves in boiled water. As it cools, gelatin holds the water and thickens, forming a gel, a solution that takes the shape of its container. Pineapple, papaya, kiwifruit, and guava naturally contain enzymes that break down gelatin. Therefore, when using gelatin in recipes, don't add fresh or frozen forms of these fruits, because the enzymes will break down gelatin and the mixture won't gel. Heating destroys these enzymes, thus you can make a moulded gelatin salad or dessert that contains canned pineapple. (Foods undergo heating during the canning process.)

- **Food & Nutrition Tips:** Interspersed throughout the chapters, these tip boxes present practical suggestions that apply to chapter content and provide students with information they can use every day. Examples include tips for adding calcium to your diet, staying hydrated, and keeping foods safe to eat.

- **Real People, Real Stories**: Appearing in Chapters 4, 5, 7, and 9, these features narrate real-life cases about people who have recovered from or who are currently living with nutrition-related conditions. These stories will help students recognize the challenges of living with such conditions and the roles that diet and physical activity play in managing health.

REAL *people*

REAL *stories*

Dallas C.

Dallas C. is an energetic teenager who loves mountain bike and road bike racing, downhill skiing, wrestling, and climbing ropes and trees. Not only is he athletic, he is also smart—his marks place him at the top of his class. According to his proud parents, Dallas is the perfect son—"a nice boy." Dallas *is* a special young man, but he also needs a special diet. Dallas was born with phenylketonuria (PKU).

A few days after birth, Dallas underwent standard newborn blood testing. The results of the test indicated that the level of phenylalanine in his blood was about 40 times higher than the normal amount, a sign of the inherited disorder PKU. To avoid developing severe brain damage and other physiological effects of PKU, the infant needed to receive the care of a physician who specializes in treating children with the disorder. The primary treatment for PKU is a low-phenylalanine diet.

Most foods that are rich sources of protein, especially high-quality animal proteins, contain more phenylalanine than people with PKU can tolerate. Thus, from the time Dallas was a week old, he has consumed a formula that does not contain the amino acid. In addition to the formula, Dallas eats special foods that resemble "regular" foods but are not available in supermarkets. To obtain low-phenylalanine foods, his parents order them from companies that manufacture such products. Dallas can eat limited amounts of grain products and most fruits and vegetables. To determine whether the diet is working, Dallas must have the level of phenylalanine in his blood checked weekly.

Dallas' parents and his two younger sisters do not have PKU. At home, he eats the low-phenylalanine foods, while the other members of his family consume regular foods. Foods that are eaten away from home can present problems for people with PKU. In Dallas' case, his mother provides his school with a supply of low-phenylalanine foods for the teen's lunches. When the family visits restaurants, Dallas usually orders french fries, which are allowed in his diet. Dallas is so accustomed to his special diet that he thinks meat looks "gross."

In the past, children with PKU were often allowed to eat regular foods after they were about 6 years of age. However, the importance of continuing the low-phenylalanine diet became evident when many of the children experienced learning and behavioural problems as they matured. Dallas is aware of the consequences that can occur if he does not limit his phenylalanine intake, and he accepts the need to follow the special diet for the rest of his life. According to Dallas, "Being on a strict diet has not only made me disciplined, it has taught me to do whatever is needed to always take good care of myself. I have learned that we are all different, anyway. So, accept who you are!"

REAL *people*

REAL *stories*

Lisa G.

Late in 1999, Lisa G. began experiencing painful abdominal cramps followed by frequent bouts of diarrhea. It seemed that whatever she ate would pass through her digestive tract and be eliminated quickly. When over-the-counter diarrhea remedies didn't work, Lisa sensed her ailment was not a self-limiting intestinal tract infection. Before the illness struck, Lisa weighed 57 kg (125 lbs.)—a healthy weight for a person who is 157 cm (5'2"). She was physically active and strong. Four weeks after developing the digestive tract problems, she had lost about 5.5 kg (12 lbs.) and become noticeably weaker.

Lisa's physician suspected a form of inflammatory bowel disease (IBD) was responsible for her condition. She was admitted into a local hospital and treated with prednisone, a steroid medication that helps reduce inflammation. When her weight stabilized, her physician prescribed additional medications that are specific for treating IBD. Her special diet included foods that were easily digested. She soon learned which foods she could eat without suffering from diarrhea. For example, she couldn't eat raw carrots, but she could tolerate cooked carrots. Because IBD damaged the ileum, the site for vitamin B-12 absorption, Lisa had to have injections of vitamin B-12 regularly. Within a few weeks, Lisa was well enough to leave the hospital, but she remained on the medication.

- **Recipes for Healthy Living**: This practical application of nutrition and food information will appeal to most college and university students. Each chapter includes at least one easy-to-make, kitchen-tested recipe. Each recipe presents information about the energy and key nutrients per serving, as well as a pie chart displaying the percentages of energy provided by the meal from carbohydrate, protein, and fat. This feature demonstrates that preparing nutritious foods can be fun and economical. By trying the recipes, students can develop basic food preparation skills and may be inspired to cook more foods "from scratch." As a result, they may rely less on vending machines and fast-food outlets.

Recipes for Healthy Living

Trendy Black Beans

You've probably eaten ordinary canned baked beans as an accompaniment to hot dogs and hamburgers. If you're interested in eating a more trendy kind of bean, try this recipe for black beans. Although canned black beans are more convenient to use in recipes than dried black beans, the canned products generally contain a lot of salt.

This black bean recipe makes about four ½-cup servings. Each serving supplies approximately 120 kcal, 8 g protein, less than 1 g fat, 7.5 g fibre, 2 mg iron, 340 mg potassium, 70 mg sodium, and 130 mcg folate (a B vitamin). To make the beans a complementary protein source, serve them wrapped in a soft burrito or on cooked rice.

INGREDIENTS:

1 cup dried black beans
¼ cup coarsely chopped green pepper
¼ cup peeled, chopped yellow onion
1 large clove garlic, peeled and minced
⅛ tsp ground black pepper
⅛ tsp salt
3–5 drops hot pepper sauce (optional)

PREPARATION STEPS:

27%
3%
70%
Fat
Protein
Carbohydrate

1. Rinse dried beans in cold water, draining excess water.
2. Place the beans in a saucepan and add 1¾ cups of water.
3. Heat beans and water on high heat until mixture boils. Boil for 2 minutes, then turn off heat, and remove saucepan from the burner. Cover saucepan and allow beans to remain in the hot water for 1 hour. While beans are soaking, prepare green pepper, onion, and garlic.
4. Do not drain water from beans. Simmer beans on low heat, in the covered saucepan, for 45 minutes. Stir occasionally.
5. Add green pepper, onion, garlic, black pepper, and salt. Simmer for an additional 15 minutes.
6. Serve hot. Cooked beans can be frozen.

Hummus

Hummus may have originated in the Middle East, but it's become popular in this country as a dip for vegetables or bread. Hummus is a good source of protein, monounsaturated fat, fibre, the minerals potassium and iron, and the B vitamin folate. This hummus recipe makes about eight ¼-cup servings. If you don't have a blender, you can mash the chickpeas and garlic with a fork before you add the other ingredients. To make hummus a complementary protein source, serve it with whole-grain crackers, tortilla chips, or pita bread. Each serving (with no added salt) supplies about 130 kcal, 3 g protein, 8 g fat, 3 g fibre, 0.8 mg iron, 120 mg potassium, 4 mg sodium, and 70 mcg folate.

INGREDIENTS:

2 cups unsalted, cooked garbanzo beans (chickpeas)
1 Tbsp lemon juice
1 medium clove garlic, peeled
¼ cup cold water
¼ cup olive oil pinch salt and paprika (optional)

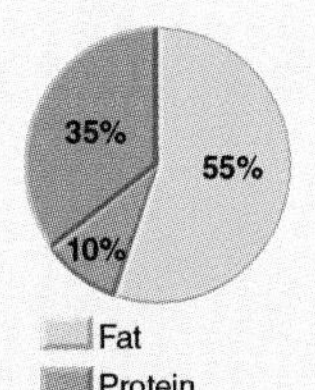

PREPARATION STEPS:

1. Drain beans. Place the beans, lemon juice, garlic clove, oil, and water in a blender. Blend until the mixture is smooth.
2. Serve in a bowl. If desired, sprinkle paprika on top of hummus.

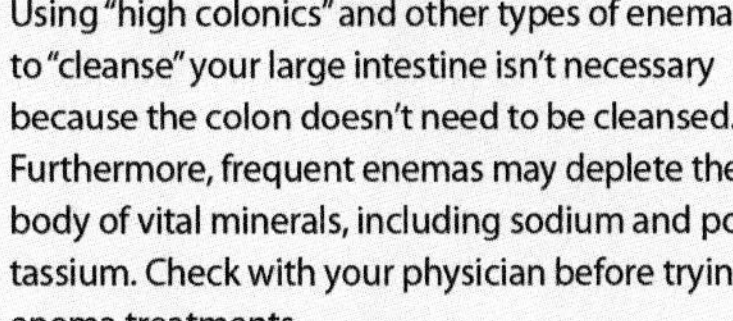

Did You Know?

Using "high colonics" and other types of enemas to "cleanse" your large intestine isn't necessary because the colon doesn't need to be cleansed. Furthermore, frequent enemas may deplete the body of vital minerals, including sodium and potassium. Check with your physician before trying enema treatments.

Did You Know?

Despite information provided in commercials or advertisements, you cannot "feed" your hair, nails, or skin by using shampoos, conditioners, or lotions containing proteins or other nutrients. Hair, nails, and the outermost layer of skin are not living. By eating a nutritious diet, you'll provide your body with the nutrients it needs to make healthy hair, nails, and skin.

- **Did You Know?** These brief boxes relay interesting nutrition-related tidbits that relate to information presented in the text. A number of "Did You Know?" boxes present facts that dispel common misconceptions about food and nutrition.

Readability and Style for Today's Student

A key pedagogical element of any college or university textbook is readability. As each chapter was written, priority was given to maintaining a balance between having a clear, technically accurate narrative and an engaging, easy-to-read writing style. Examples that students can relate to were carefully chosen, and tools are provided for applying healthy nutritional practices to their own lives. Additionally, to ensure accuracy, the content has been extensively researched with in-text citations and references listed in Appendix E.

Another way the McGraw-Hill Ryerson editorial team and the authors sought to appeal to today's students is by creating beautiful, pedagogically based illustrations and creative page layouts. Keeping in mind that many students are visual learners, we selected vibrant photos and rendered illustrations that are visually appealing as well as instructional, for a deliciously beautiful book. It is important to note the use of products in photos are for example representation only and do not constitute an endorsement.

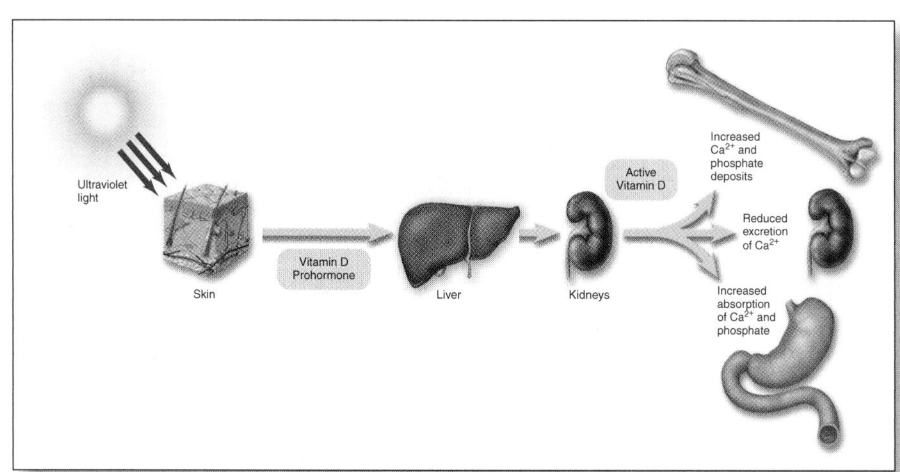

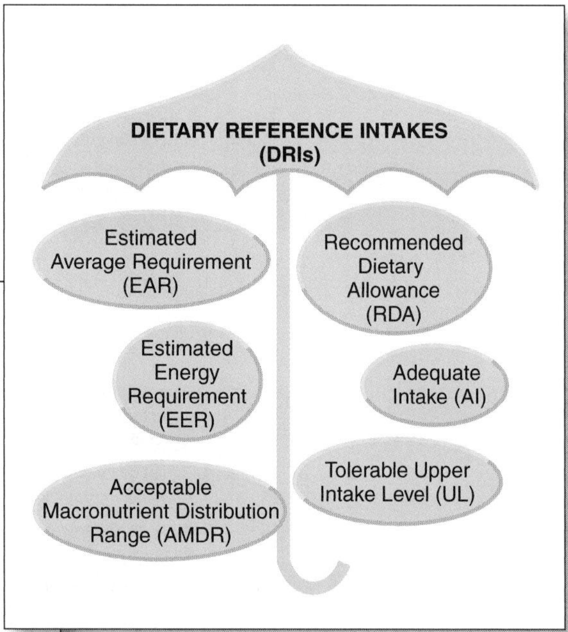

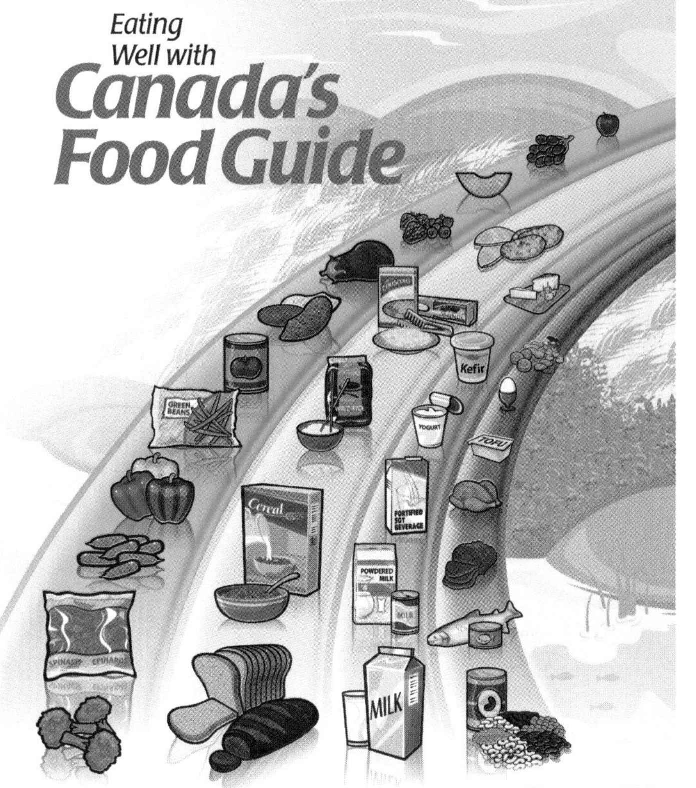
Eating
Well with
Canada's
Food Guide
Canada
Vegetables and Fruit
Spinach Pears
Squash Prunes
Potatoes Peaches
Tomatoes Avocados
Lettuce Cantaloupes
Lima beans Bananas
Grain Products
Whole-wheat bread
Whole-grain products
Milk and Alternatives
Milk
Yogourt
Cottage cheese
Ricotta cheese
Meat and Alternatives
Meat
Chicken
Fish
Shrimp
Beans

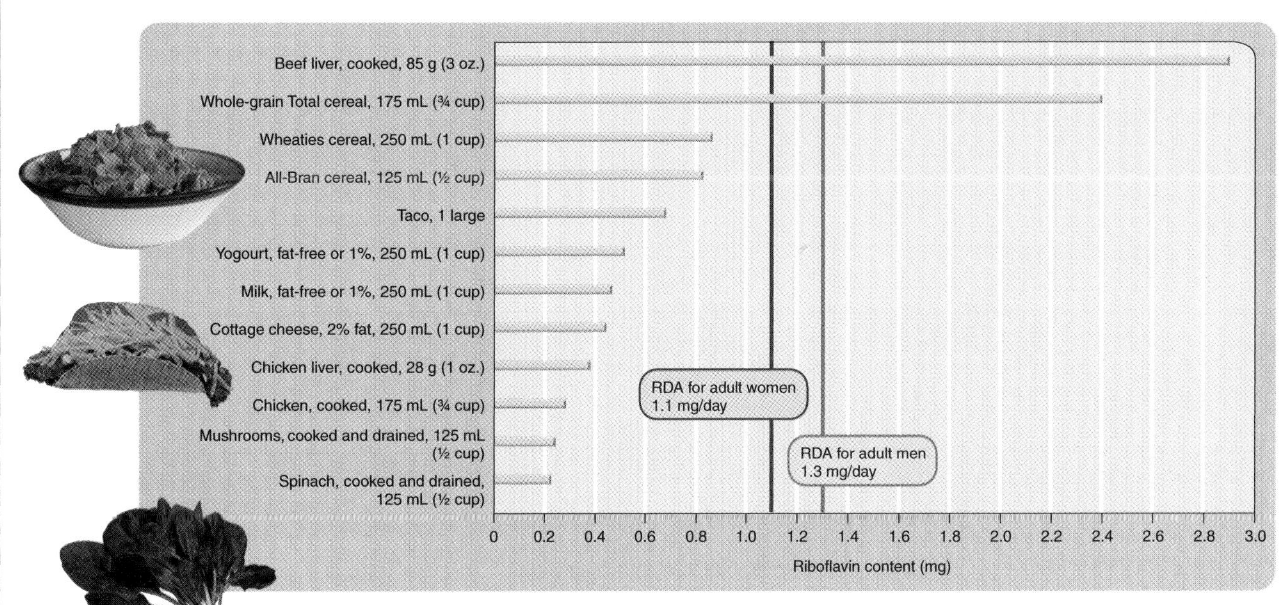
Beef liver, cooked, 85 g (3 oz.)
Whole-grain Total cereal, 175 mL (¾ cup)
Wheaties cereal, 250 mL (1 cup)
All-Bran cereal, 125 mL (½ cup)
Taco, 1 large
Yogourt, fat-free or 1%, 250 mL (1 cup)
Milk, fat-free or 1%, 250 mL (1 cup)
Cottage cheese, 2% fat, 250 mL (1 cup)
Chicken liver, cooked, 28 g (1 oz.)
Chicken, cooked, 175 mL (¾ cup)
Mushrooms, cooked and drained, 125 mL (½ cup)
Spinach, cooked and drained, 125 mL (½ cup)
RDA for adult women 1.1 mg/day
RDA for adult men 1.3 mg/day
0 0.2 0.4 0.6 0.8 1.0 1.2 1.4 1.6 1.8 2.0 2.2 2.4 2.6 2.8 3.0
Riboflavin content (mg)

Assessing and Evaluating Student Progress

Chapter Learning Outcomes

After reading Chapter 1, you should be able to:

1. Define the terms diet, nutrition, nutrient, essential nutrient, macronutrient, micronutrient, kilocalorie, and phytochemical.
2. Identify factors that influence personal food choices.
3. Identify lifestyle factors that contribute to the leading causes of death in Canada.
4. List the six classes of nutrients and identify a major role of each class of nutrient in the body.
5. Identify basic units of the metric system often used in nutrition.
6. Explain the concept of energy density and identify energy dense foods.
7. Use the caloric values of energy-yielding nutrients to estimate the amount of energy (kcal) in a food.
8. Identify key basic nutrition concepts, such as the importance of eating a variety of foods and that no food supplies all nutrients.

One of our primary goals as nutrition educators is to ensure that our students leave their introductory nutrition course with a better understanding of the nutrition principles and concepts needed to improve their diet and health. In order to assess how well faculty are achieving that goal, many colleges and universities are implementing Student Learning Outcomes as a way to measure what students have learned upon completing an introductory nutrition course. Student Learning Outcomes can also be used to help instructors identify content areas that need more refined teaching methods. *Nutrition for Healthy Living*, Canadian Edition, has been developed around the following course-wide outcomes.

Student Learning Outcomes

1. Identify functions and sources of nutrients.
2. Demonstrate basic knowledge of digestion, absorption, and metabolism.
3. Apply current dietary guidelines and nutrition recommendations.
4. Analyze and evaluate nutrition information scientifically.
5. Relate the roles of nutrients in good health, optimal fitness, and chronic diseases.
6. Summarize basic concepts of nutrition throughout the lifespan.
7. Evaluate a personal diet record using a computer database.

Additionally, each chapter is structured around five to ten Chapter Learning Outcomes. Listed on the chapter-opening pages, these Chapter Learning Outcomes can help students focus their studying and guide instructors with their teaching and assessment. The Chapter Learning Outcomes help students prepare for reading the chapter and also clarify major concepts they are expected to learn. These measurable outcomes are further supported by assessment methods and study aids found within the chapters.

Quiz YOURSELF

Take the following quiz to test your basic nutrition knowledge; the answers are on page 27.

1. There are four classes of nutrients: proteins, lipids, sugars, and vitamins. ______T ______F
2. Proteins are the most essential class of nutrients. ______T ______F
3. All nutrients must be supplied by the diet, because they cannot be made by the body. ______T ______F
4. Vitamins are a source of energy. ______T ______F
5. Milk, carrots, and bananas are examples of "perfect" foods that contain all nutrients. ______T ______F

- **Quiz Yourself:** This pre-test is comprised of five true-or-false questions, which appear at the beginning of each chapter and serve to stimulate readers in the subsequent content; answers to the quiz are provided on the last page of the chapter. By taking the quiz, students may be surprised to learn how little or how much they know about the chapter's contents.

CRITICAL THINKING

1. Identify at least six factors that influence your food selections. Which of these factors is the most important? Explain why.
2. Consider your current eating habits. Explain why you think your diet is nutritionally adequate or not.
3. "Everything in moderation." Explain what this statement means in terms of diet.
4. If you are at risk of developing a chronic health condition that could be prevented by changing your diet, would you make the necessary changes? Explain why or why not.
5. Have you ever used food to treat or prevent illnesses? If you have, describe the situations and discuss which foods were used.
6. What actions have you taken or can you take to help hungry or food-insecure people obtain adequate nutrition?

- **Critical Thinking:** "Critical Thinking" involves higher-level cognitive skills, including applying, analyzing, synthesizing, and evaluating information. This assessment features a series of thought-provoking questions at the end of the chapter. The questions can help students develop higher-level cognitive skills using nutrition-related content. Acquiring and/or sharpening these skills can help students become better consumers of nutrition-related information.

- **Concept Checkpoint:** At the end of each major section of a chapter, Concept Checkpoints pose two to ten review questions, many of which involve critical-thinking skills. Students can access the answers to these questions within *Connect* at www.mcgrawhillconnect.ca.

Concept **Checkpoint**

1. Identify at least three of the ten leading causes of death that are diet related.
2. List the six major classes of nutrients.
3. What is the smallest functional structural unit in the body?
4. What are three key factors that determine whether a substance is an essential nutrient?
5. What is a phytochemical?
6. Define dietary supplement.
7. Which Canadian agency regulates drug and dietary supplement manufacturers?
8. Identify at least four factors that influence your eating habits.

PRACTICE TEST

Select the best answer.

1. Diet is a
   a. practice of restricting energy intake.
   b. typical pattern of food choices.
   c. method of reducing portion sizes.
   d. technique to reduce carbohydrate intake.
2. Which of the following conditions is not a leading cause of death in Canada?
   a. tuberculosis
   b. cancer
   c. heart disease
   d. stroke
3. The nutrients that provide energy are
   a. carbohydrates, vitamins, and lipids.
   b. lipids, proteins, and minerals.
   c. vitamins, minerals, and proteins.
   d. proteins, fats, and carbohydrates.

- **Practice Test:** Each chapter ends with a series of ten or more multiple-choice questions that test students' comprehension and recall of information presented in the chapter. Students can access these same tests in an online format with automatic grading within *Connect* at www.mcgrawhillconnect.ca. The multiple-choice questions prepare students for classroom exams because they are similar in type and format to those provided in the test bank for *Nutrition for Healthy Living*, Canadian Edition. In many instances, the test questions are correlated to the course-wide Student Learning Outcomes and Chapter Learning Outcomes.

kilocalorie or **Calorie** heat energy needed to raise the temperature of 1 litre of water 1° Celsius; measure of food energy

macronutrients nutrients needed in gram amounts daily and that provide energy; carbohydrates, proteins, and fats

micronutrients vitamins and minerals

- **Key Terms and Pronunciation Guide:** Key terms are indicated throughout the chapters using bold font, with definitions provided in the margins. Many terms also have pronunciations provided within the text where the term is first introduced. A full glossary of key terms is provided at the end of the book.

- **End-of-Chapter Content:** In addition to the aforementioned Practice Tests, the chapter is summarized with a brief recap of the chapter's main points.

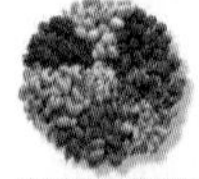

SUMMARY

Lifestyle choices, including poor eating habits and lack of physical activity, contribute to the development of leading causes of premature deaths for Canadian adults—heart disease, cancer, and stroke. You may be able to extend your lifespan and improve your quality of life by applying what you learn about nutrition and the role of diet and health.

- **References:** *Nutrition for Healthy Living*, Canadian Edition, includes in-text citations and extensive lists of references in Appendix E. References provide readers with access to sources of information for more in-depth understanding or for topics of particular interest.

Chapter 4

1. Saladin KS: *Anatomy & physiology 4th ed.* Boston: McGraw-Hill Publisl Company, 2007.
2. Seeley RR and others: *Essentials of anatomy & physiology* 6th ed. Bos McGraw-Hill Publishing Company, 2007.
3. Widmaier E and others: *Vander's human physiology* 10th ed. Bos McGraw-Hill Publishing Company, 2006.
4. Prescott LM and others: *Microbiology* 6th ed. Boston: McGraw-Hill I lishing Company, 2005.
5. Reid G and others: Potential uses of probiotics in clinical practice. *C cal Microbiology Reviews* 16(4):658, 2003.
6. Adolfsson O and others: Yogurt and gut function. *American Journ Clinical Nutrition* 80(2):245, 2004.

- **Personal Dietary Analysis:** Many chapters include an end-of-chapter activity for analyzing personal eating habits. Most of these activities require the use of a dietary analysis software program, such as McGraw-Hill Ryerson's NutritionCalc Plus. Students can gain insight into their eating behaviours by completing this activity.

Personal Dietary Analysis

1. Refer to the three-day food log from the Personal Dietary Analysis feature in Chapter 3. Calculate your average protein intake by adding the grams of protein eaten each day, dividing the total by three, and rounding the figure to the nearest whole number.

Sample Calculation:

Day 1 76 g
Day 2 55 g
Day 3 103 g
Total grams 234 g ÷ 3 days = **78** g of protein/day

Your Calculation:

Day 1 _____ g
Day 2 _____ g
Day 3 _____ g
Total grams _____ ÷ 3 days = _____ g/day
My average daily protein intake was _____ g.

2. The RDA for protein is based on body weight. Using the RDA of 0.8 g of protein/kg of body weight, calculate the amount of protein that you need to consume daily to meet the recommendation. To determine your body weight in kilograms, divide your weight (pounds) by 2.2, multiply this number by 0.8 to obtain your RDA for protein, and then round the figure to the nearest whole number.

My weight in pounds _____ ÷ 2.2 = _____ kg
My weight in kg _____ × 0.8 = _____ g
My RDA for protein = _____ g

   a. Did your average intake of protein meet or exceed your RDA level that was calculated in step 1? _____ yes _____ no
   b. If your answer to 2a is "yes," which foods contributed the most to your protein intake?

Teaching and Learning Supplements

McGraw-Hill Ryerson *Connect*™ (www.mcgrawhillconnect.ca) is an online teaching and learning platform developed and supported in Canada for Canadian institutions, their faculty, and students. *Connect* was inspired by multiple student and instructor research initiatives, including a quantitative usage and attitude study that captured insights from more than 1400 students across Canada.

Connect embraces diverse study behaviours and preferences with breakthrough features that help students master course content and achieve better results. The powerful course management tool in *Connect* also offers a wide range of exclusive features that help instructors spend less time managing and more time teaching.

For the Student

Connect features:

- **An Interactive and Searchable eBook:** Seamless view—includes digital tool box with highlighting and sticky note features.
- **Flexible Study Plan Options:** Self-assessment quizzes identify knowledge gaps and suggest study exercises and resources. Students can also access and customize content to create their own study plan within *Connect*.
- **Accessibility:** *Connect* with eBook is included with all new *Connect* textbooks at no extra charge.

Within *Connect*, students can access and/or add the following resources to their study plan:

- Practice multiple-choice and true/false quizzes
- Health- and nutrition-related Web links
- Animations illustrating nutrition and biological processes
- Answers to Concept Checkpoint and Practice Test questions from the textbook
- Bonus Appendices: Amino Acids, Vitamins Involved in Energy Metabolism, Body Mass Index-for-Age Percentiles

For the Instructor

Connect features:

- **An Interactive and Searchable eBook:** Seamless view—includes digital tool box with highlighting and sticky note features.
- **A Step-by-Step Assignment Builder:** Instructors can easily create assignments with a range of questions, including end-of-chapter questions and Test Bank material.
- **A Personalized Teaching Plan:** Instructors can access resources, build their teaching plan, and share with associates all within *Connect*.
- **An At-a-Glance Grade Book:** Instructors can monitor student or group performance, and easily export grade reports into Blackboard, Desire2Learn, Moodle, and WebCT.
- **Turn-Key Instructor Set-Up:** Support programs are available to help instructors easily set up their course with ongoing support.

Within *Connect*, instructors can access, download, or add the following resources to their teaching plan:

- **Instructor's Manual:** The Instructor's Manual includes an Overview, detailed Chapter Outline, and various teaching ideas for each chapter.
- **Microsoft® PowerPoint® Presentations:** Detailed PowerPoint® slides begin with Learning Outcomes and present the key points for each chapter, integrating many of the illustrations and tables from the textbook.
- **Computerized Test Bank:** The Test Bank contains approximately 780 multiple-choice questions, each aligned with a Learning Outcome and page reference from the text. Test items are also available in Word format (rich text format). For secure online testing, exams created in EZ Test can be exported to WebCT and Blackboard.
- **Image Bank:** The Image Bank contains a digital copy of each photo, illustration, and table from the textbook. These jpeg files can be used to create customized lectures, visually enhance tests and quizzes, or design compelling course Web sites.

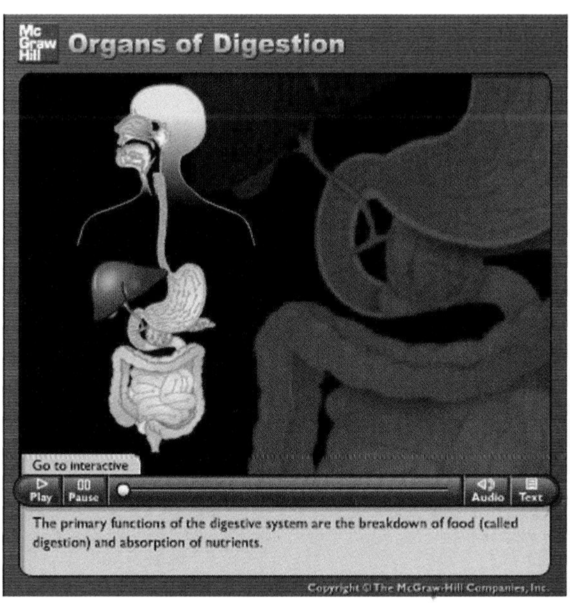

NutritionCalc Plus™

NutritionCalc Plus™ is a suite of powerful dietary self-assessment tools available on CD and online. This newest release features approximately 27 000 foods from the ESHA Research Nutrient Database and a new user-friendly interface that makes creating a personal diet analysis even easier. Users now have the ability to add up to three profiles and to create their own recipes. The program functions are supported by detailed Help documents and helpful cautionary notes that warn the user of possible entry errors.

Please contact your *i*Learning Sales Specialist for more information.

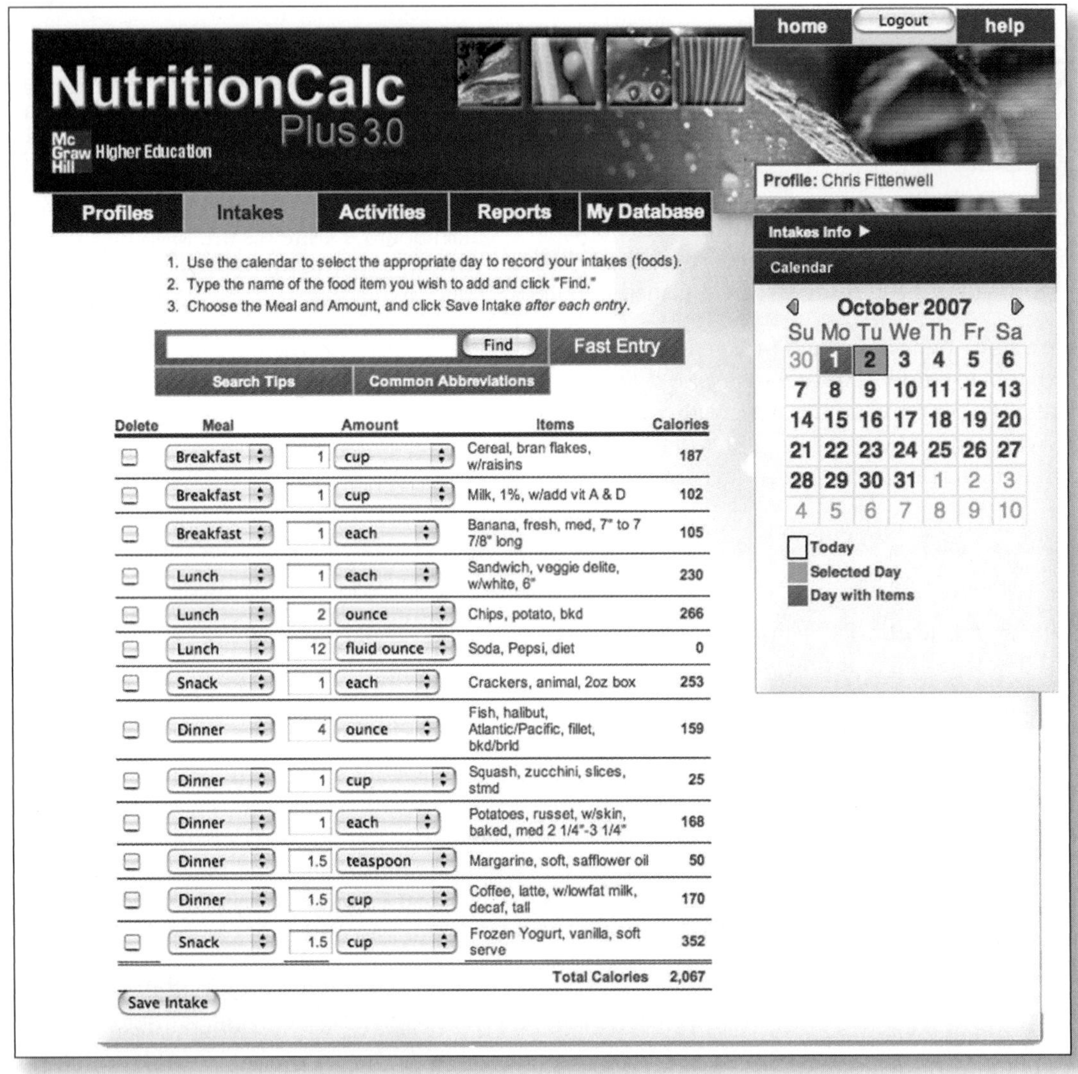

Acknowledgements

The development of an accurate and current manuscript for *Nutrition for Healthy Living*, Canadian Edition, was facilitated by the input of numerous college and university instructors and emeriti. These individuals reviewed draft chapters and contributed encouraging comments and constructive suggestions concerning content and pedagogy. Moreover, several reviewers were asked to contribute additional input on specific sections of the manuscript. Their willingness to provide suggestions for developing content was gratifying.

The authoring team offer our sincere thanks to the following colleagues who provided a wide range of valuable input, including manuscript reviews, class-testing chapters, serving on our Advisory Board, and preparing supplement materials:

Reviewers

Olasunkanmi Adegoke, *York University*

Emily Agard, *Ryerson University*

Ken Anderson, *Douglas College*

Nick Bellissimo, *Mount Saint Vincent University*

Manuela Brachlow, *Niagara College*

Eithne Dunbar, *St. Lawrence College*

Barb Dunlop, *George Brown College*

Jo-Ann Fullerton, *Centennial College*

Donna J. Hennyey, *University of Toronto*

Richard A. Jarrell, *York University*

Vineet Johnson, *Capilano University*

Elizabeth Johnston, *Acadia University*

Kathy Keiver, *University of the Fraser Valley*

Sobia Khan, *George Brown College*

Paul LeBlanc, *Brock University*

Mary McKenna, *University of New Brunswick, Fredericton*

Norman Naisbitt, *Fanshawe College*

Donna Pegg, *Durham College*

Csilla Reszegi, *George Brown College*

Amandio Vieira, *Simon Fraser University*

Many McGraw-Hill Ryerson employees invested a great deal of time and effort into the development and production of *Nutrition for Healthy Living*, Canadian Edition. Without their help, making the transition from raw manuscript to finished textbook would have been impossible. My sincerest thanks is extended to all the members of the McGraw-Hill Ryerson editorial, design, production, and marketing teams for their enthusiastic support and encouragement. While writing this textbook, the team consulted me when making important decisions that directly affected the textbook's features, design, and pedagogy. It was a pleasure to work with people who were willing to listen to my concerns and incorporate many of my suggestions. I also want to thank my sponsoring editor, Marcia Siekowski, for recognizing my potential as a nutrition textbook author during the signing for this project. Additionally, publisher, Cara Yarzab, and vice-president, editor-in-chief, Joanna Cotton, were instrumental in making certain McGraw-Hill Ryerson provided ample financial support for the production of a superior textbook. Last, but not least, my developmental editors, Jennifer Cressman and Katherine Goodes; supervising editor, Kara Stahl; and copy editor, Michael Kelly, deserve my heartfelt gratitude for the hard work, long hours, and extraordinary dedication they invested in this endeavour. Without their expertise, creativity, and cooperation, working on this textbook would not have been such an enjoyable experience.

Matthew Durant

Chapter **1**

The Basics of Nutrition

Chapter Learning Outcomes

After reading Chapter 1, you should be able to:

1. Define the terms diet, nutrition, nutrient, essential nutrient, macronutrient, micronutrient, kilocalorie, and phytochemical.
2. Identify factors that influence personal food choices.
3. Identify lifestyle factors that contribute to the leading causes of death in Canada.
4. List the six classes of nutrients and identify a major role of each class of nutrient in the body.
5. Identify basic units of the metric system often used in nutrition.
6. Explain the concept of energy density and identify energy dense foods.
7. Use the caloric values of energy-yielding nutrients to estimate the amount of energy (kcal) in a food.
8. Identify key basic nutrition concepts, such as the importance of eating a variety of foods and that no food supplies all nutrients.
9. Discuss factors that contribute to malnutrition in the world.
10. Understand the difference between hunger and appetite and explain from an evolutionary perspective why Canadians struggle to control their body weights.

When you were a young child, your parents or caregivers were the "gatekeepers" of your food; they chose what you ate and prepared it, and you probably ate most of it. If you balked at eating broccoli or meatloaf, they may have told you, "Eat your vegetables if you expect to get dessert," or "Finish that meat; people in other parts of the world are starving!" As you grew older, your **diet**, your typical pattern of food choices, became increasingly under your control.

Today your diet is composed of foods that you enjoy as well as can afford, and probably those you can prepare easily or obtain quickly. Your family's ethnic and cultural background may also play a role in determining what you eat regularly. For example, do you eat plantain, moon cakes, goat, or wild game because you ate these foods as a child? Numerous other factors influence your food choices including friends, food advertising, as well as your beliefs and moods (Fig. 1.1).

Food is a basic human need for survival. You become hungry and search for something to eat when your body needs **nutrients**, the life-sustaining substances in food. Nutrients are necessary for the growth, maintenance, and repair of your body's cells. However, you have no instinctual drive that enables you to select the appropriate mix of nutrients your body requires for proper functioning. To eat well, you need to learn about the nutritional value of foods and the effects that your diet can have on your health.

Simply having information about nutrients and foods and their effects on health may not be enough for people to change ingrained food-related behaviours—a person must be motivated to make such changes. Some people become motivated to improve their diets because they want to lose or gain weight. Others are so concerned about their health that they are motivated to change their eating habits in specific ways, such as by eating fewer salty or fatty foods. Many Canadians struggle to consistently make the healthiest choices when it comes to their lifestyle. Despite having the knowledge of what constitutes healthy versus less healthy dietary choices, many Canadians make unhealthy dietary choices frequently. In general, many Canadians eat too much in relation to their level of physical activity. Obesity rates for Canadian children and adults have increased dramatically in the past decades.[1,2]

Why should you care about your diet? In Canada, poor eating habits are associated with 8 of the 10 leading causes of death: heart disease; pulmonary disease; some types of cancer including lung, colon, and breast cancer, and lymphoma; stroke; and type 2 diabetes.[3] Consuming more fruits, vegetables, whole-grain cereals, nuts, and low-fat or skim milk and milk products, as well as exercising regularly, may reduce your chances of developing serious chronic (long-lasting) diseases, such as heart disease, diabetes, certain cancers, and excess body fat.[4] Physical inactivity, excessive caloric intake, and a diet of primarily animal foods may increase your risks of these chronic health problems.

Are you concerned about the nutritional quality of your diet? The fact that you are taking a nutrition course indicates you have a strong interest in nutrition and a desire to learn more about the topic. A major objective of this textbook is to provide you with the basic information you need to better understand how your diet can influence your health. Managing your diet is your responsibility. We will not tell you what to eat to guarantee optimal health—no one can make that promise. After reading this textbook and learning about foods and the nutrients they contain, you can use the information to make informed decisions concerning the foods you eat. Furthermore, you will be able to evaluate your diet and decide if it needs to be changed.

Each chapter of this textbook begins with "Quiz Yourself," a brief true or false quiz to test your knowledge of the material covered in the chapter. At the end of each chapter, you will find the answers to this quiz, as well as a group of multiple choice questions that test your understanding of the material in the chapter.

Quiz YOURSELF

Take the following quiz to test your basic nutrition knowledge; the answers are on page 27.

1. There are four classes of nutrients: proteins, lipids, sugars, and vitamins. ______T ______F
2. Proteins are the most essential class of nutrients. ______T ______F
3. All nutrients must be supplied by the diet, because they cannot be made by the body. ______T ______F
4. Vitamins are a source of energy. ______T ______F
5. Milk, carrots, and bananas are examples of "perfect" foods that contain all nutrients. ______T ______F

Figure 1.1 What influences your eating practices? Numerous factors influence food choices including food advertising, peers, income, moods, food availability, and personal beliefs.

diet typical pattern of food choices

nutrients life-sustaining substances in food

nutrition scientific study of nutrients, chemicals that are in food that are necessary for life, and how the body uses them

chemistry study of the composition and characteristics of matter and changes that can occur to it

biology study of living organisms

anthropology within the context of nutrition, the study of how communities and cultures use food as part of daily life and religious or spiritual celebrations

Nutrition: The Basics

Nutrition is a science based on many other scientific disciplines and involves the study of nutrients, chemicals necessary for proper body functioning, and how the body uses them. Understanding nutrition requires learning about chemistry. **Chemistry** is the study of the composition and characteristics of matter, and changes that can occur to it. Even your body consists of matter. "There are chemicals in our food!" This statement may sound frightening, but it is true. Food is matter; therefore it contains chemicals, some of which are nutrients.

The study of nutrition also involves **biology**, **anthropology**, and **psychology**. To truly understand how our bodies use nutrients, we must understand how the body and the cells within it work; this is the realm of biology. In addition, we must understand how people use food in their lives. Anthropologists study how communities and cultures use food as part of daily life and religious or spiritual celebrations. A new area of research related to nutrition is psychology, or the study of the brain and human behaviour. If we hope to assist people to make healthy decisions regarding their diet and lifestyle, we must understand what influences the decisions they make.

There are six classes of nutrients: carbohydrates, fats and other lipids, proteins, vitamins, minerals, and water. Your body is comprised of these nutrients (Fig. 1.2). Although an average healthy young man and woman have similar amounts of vitamins, minerals, and carbohydrates in their bodies, the young woman has less water and protein, and considerably more fat.

Table 1.1 presents major roles of nutrients in your body. In general, your body uses certain nutrients for energy and regulation of chemical changes (reactions), particularly processes involved in growth, repair, and maintenance of cells. A **cell** is the smallest functioning structural unit in a living organism, such as a human being. There are hundreds of different types of cells in your body. Cells do not need food to survive, but they need the nutrients in food to carry out their metabolic activities. **Metabolism** is the total of all chemical processes that occur in living cells, including chemical reactions involved in generating energy, making proteins, and eliminating waste products. Chapters 5 (Carbohydrates), 6 (Fats and Other Lipids), 7 (Proteins), 8 (Vitamins), and 9 (Water and Minerals) provide more information about the functions of nutrients in the body.

Understanding nutrition also involves learning about **human physiology**, the study of how the body functions. Chapter 4 (Body Basics) prepares you for the study of nutrition by presenting basic information about chemistry and human physiology. Subsequent chapters provide in-depth information about each class of nutrients. Chapter 5, for example, discusses roles of carbohydrates in the body and identifies rich food sources of "carbs," including sugars and starches.

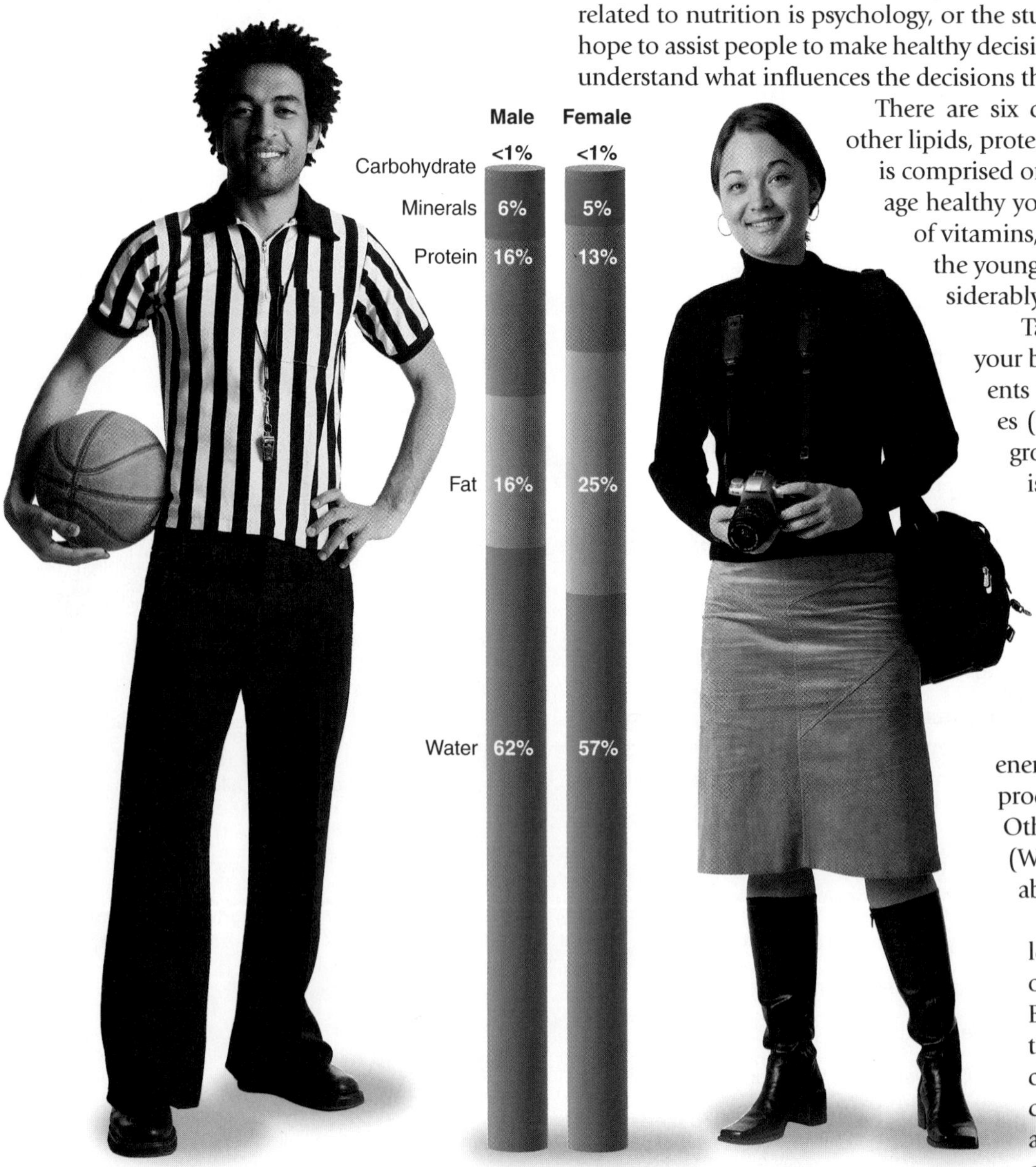

	Male	Female
Carbohydrate	<1%	<1%
Minerals	6%	5%
Protein	16%	13%
Fat	16%	25%
Water	62%	57%

Figure 1.2 Comparing composition. These illustrations present the approximate percentages of nutrients that comprise the bodies of a healthy young man and woman. Note that the amount of vitamins in the human body is so small, it is not shown.

TABLE 1.1 *Major Functions of Nutrients in the Body*

Nutrient	Major Functions
Carbohydrates	Energy
Lipids	Energy (fat)
	Cellular development, physical growth, and maintenance
	Regulation of body processes (certain chemical messengers, for example)
	Absorption of certain vitamins
Proteins	Production of structural components, such as cell membranes, and functional components, such as enzymes
	Cellular development, growth, and maintenance
	Regulation of body processes (certain chemical messengers, for example)
	Energy
Vitamins	Regulation of body processes, including cell metabolism
	Maintenance of immune function, production and maintenance of tissues, and protection against agents that can damage cellular components
Minerals	Regulation of body processes, including fluid balance and metabolism
	Formation of certain chemical messengers
	Structural and functional components of various substances and tissues
	Necessary for physical growth, maintenance, and development
Water	Maintenance of fluid balance
	Regulation of body temperature
	Elimination of wastes
	Transportation of substances
	Participant in many chemical reactions

Essential Nutrients and Nonnutrients

The body can synthesize (make) many nutrients, such as the lipids cholesterol and fat, but about 50 nutrients are dietary essentials. An **essential nutrient** must be supplied by food, because the body does not synthesize the nutrient or make enough to meet its needs. Water is the most essential nutrient.

There are three key features that help identify an essential nutrient:

- If a nutrient is missing from the diet, a **deficiency disease** occurs as a result. The deficiency disease is a state of health characterized by certain abnormal physiological changes, referred to as signs of disease. Symptoms are subjective complaints of ill health that are difficult to observe and measure, such as dizziness, fatigue, and headache.
- When the missing nutrient is added to the diet, the abnormal physiological changes are corrected. As a result, signs and symptoms of the deficiency disorder resolve as normal functioning is restored and the condition is cured.
- After scientists identify the nutrient's specific roles in the body, they can explain why the abnormalities occurred when the substance was missing from the diet.

If you wanted to test your body's need for vitamin C, for example, you could avoid consuming foods or vitamin supplements that contain the vitamin. When the amount of vitamin C in your cells becomes too low for them to function normally, you would develop physical signs of *scurvy*, the vitamin C deficiency disease. Early in the course of the deficiency, tiny red spots that are actually signs of bleeding under the skin (bruises) would appear where the elastic casings of your clothing applied pressure. When you brushed your teeth, your gums would bleed from the pressure of the toothbrush. If you cut

psychology study of the brain and human behaviour, which helps us understand what influences the decisions people make regarding diet and lifestyle

cell smallest functioning structural unit in a living organism

metabolism chemical processes that take place in living cells

human physiology the study of how the body functions

essential nutrient nutrient that must be supplied by food or we will perish

deficiency disease state of health that occurs when a nutrient is missing from the diet

TABLE 1.2

Essential Nutrients for Humans

Water	**Possibly Essential Minerals:**
Vitamins:	Arsenic
A	Lithium
B vitamins	Nickel
Thiamine	Silicon
Riboflavin	Boron
Niacin	Vanadium
Pantothenic acid	**Fats that contain linoleic and alpha-linolenic acids**
Biotin	**The following amino acids are generally recognized as essential:**
Folic acid (folate)	Histidine
B-6	Leucine
B-12	Isoleucine
Choline #	Lysine
C	Methionine
D*	Phenylalanine
E	Threonine
K	Tryptophan
Glucose †	Valine
Minerals:	
Calcium	
Chloride	
Chromium	
Copper	
Iodide	
Iron	
Magnesium	
Manganese	
Molybdenum	
Phosphorus	
Potassium	
Selenium	
Sodium	
Sulphur	
Zinc	

* The body makes vitamin D after exposure to sunlight, but a dietary source of the vitamin is usually necessary.

Generally classified as a vitamin.

† A source of glucose (carbohydrate) is needed to supply the nervous system with energy and body protein from being used as an energy source.

yourself, the wound would heal slowly or not at all. If you once again started consuming foods containing vitamin C, the deficiency signs and symptoms would disappear within a few days as your body recovers. By reading about vitamin C in Chapter 8, you will learn that one of the physiological roles of vitamin C is maintaining a substance in your body that literally holds cells together. This substance is also needed to produce scar tissue for wound healing. When the vitamin is lacking, the tiniest blood vessels in your skin begin to leak blood where the skin is compressed, and even minor cuts have difficulty healing. Thus, vitamin C meets all the required features of an essential nutrient.

Table 1.2 lists nutrients that are generally considered to be essential. Fortunately, the human body is designed to obtain these substances from a wide variety of foods. The recommended way to obtain all nutrients is to build a core diet comprised of minimally processed foods including whole grains; peas, beans, and nuts; fruits and vegetables; low-fat or skim milk and milk products; lean meats, fish, and poultry; and small amounts of eggs and vegetable oils.

Nonnutrients

Some foods, particularly those from plants, contain substances that are not essential nutrients, yet they have healthful benefits. For example, plants are sources of dietary **fibre**. Although humans cannot digest fibre, the plant material still provides some health benefits. Chapter 5 provides information about fibre. Plants also make hundreds of **phytochemicals** (*phyto* means plant), some of which may reduce risks of heart disease and certain cancers. Many phytochemicals are antioxidants. An **antioxidant** protects cells and their components from being damaged or destroyed by exposure to certain environmental factors. Not all phytochemicals, however, have beneficial effects on the body; some are toxic or can interfere with the absorption of nutrients. Scientific research that explores the effects of phytochemicals on the body is ongoing. Table 1.3 lists phytochemicals that are currently under scientific investigation, their biological effects on the body, and possible health benefits.

What Are Dietary Supplements?

Dietary supplements, also known as nutrition supplements or food supplements, are products that contain one or more ingredients such as vitamins, minerals, or phytochemicals provided in a capsule, tablet, powder, or formula that is not a conventional food product. In Canada, dietary supplements are now included in a class of products called natural health products (NHPs) as outlined by the Health Products and Food Branch of Health Canada.[5] These products are typically more similar to medications than to foods and are defined as

- a mineral;
- a vitamin;
- a plant or plant material, alga, bacterium, fungus, or non-human animal material;
- an extract or isolate of the above;

Figure 1.3 Echinacea flower and pills. The results of scientific testing do not support health-related claims that many popular herbal products are useful. For example, the herbal supplement echinacea is generally not useful for preventing colds or reducing the duration of colds. More studies, however, are needed to confirm these findings.

- an amino acid;
- an essential fatty acid;
- a synthetic duplicate of any of the above; or
- a pre- or probiotic.

It is important to recognize that despite not requiring a doctor's prescription to buy them, many dietary supplements are powerful pharmacological agents and can have significant influence on your health and well being, often causing adverse affects.

Many Canadians purchase dietary supplements to improve their appearance or health. According to scientific evidence, some herbs have beneficial effects on health; in other instances, scientific testing indicates that many popular herbal products are not helpful, or more research is needed to determine the product's health benefits. Many Canadians, for example, take the herbal supplement echinacea to prevent colds and other infections (Fig. 1.3). However, the results of studies generally do not support the use of echinacea for preventing colds or reducing the duration of colds.[6] Consumers need to be aware that certain medicinal herbs are poisonous, and they may interact with prescription

fibre group of substances made by plants that humans do not digest but that still provide some health benefits

phytochemicals compounds made by plants that are not nutrients

antioxidant substance that protects other compounds from being damaged or destroyed by certain environmental factors

dietary supplements products that contain one or more ingredients such as vitamins, minerals, or phytochemicals provided in a capsule, tablet, powder, or formula that is not a conventional food product

TABLE 1.3 *Phytochemicals of Scientific Interest*

Classification	Rich Food Source	Biological Effects/Possible Health Benefits
Carotenoids		
Alpha-carotene, beta-carotene, lutein, lycopene, zeaxanthin	Orange, red, yellow fruits and vegetables; egg yolks	May reduce risk of certain cancers
Phenolics		
Quercetin	Apples, tea, red wine, onions, olives, raspberries, cocoa	Antioxidant activity, may inhibit cancer growth, may reduce risk of heart disease
Catechins	Green and black tea, chocolate, plums, apples, berries, pecans	
Naringenin, hesperidin	Citrus fruits	
Anthocyanins	Red, blue, or purple fruits and vegetables	
Resveratrol	Red wine, purple grapes and grape juice	
Isoflavonoids	Soybeans and other legumes	
Lignans	Flaxseed, berries, whole grains, nuts	
Tannins, ellagic acid	Tea, coffee, walnuts, berries, grapes, pomegranates, apples	
Organosulfides		
Isothiocyanates, indoles, allylic sulphur compounds	Garlic, onions, leeks, cruciferous vegetables (broccoli, cauliflower, cabbage, kale, bok choy, collard and mustard greens)	Antioxidant effects; may improve immune system functioning and reduce the risk of heart disease
Alkaloids		
Caffeine	Coffee, tea, kola nuts, cocoa	Stimulant effects
Glycosides		
Saponins	Chickpeas, beans, oats, grapes, olives, spinach, garlic, quinoa	May kill certain microbes, inhibit certain cancers, and reduce risk of heart disease
Monoterpenes		
	Oranges, lemons, grapefruit, cherries	May inhibit certain cancers
Capsaicinoids		
Capsaicin	Chili peppers	May provide some pain relief
Fructooligosaccharides		
	Onions, bananas, asparagus, wheat	May stimulate the growth of beneficial bacteria in the human intestinal tract

or over-the-counter medications as well as other herbs, producing unwanted and even dangerous side effects. It is often difficult to determine if a dietary supplement is right for you. Canadians have access to a food supply unprecedented in many parts of the world that is quite comprehensive and safe. The many foods we choose in our diet have unique nutrient profiles, and the surest way to collect a full spectrum of essential nutrients in the diet is by choosing a variety of foods each day. While dietary supplements can provide certain nutrients, they should not take the place of whole, natural foods. Individuals who are suffering from some disorders as well as women who are pregnant or are thinking of becoming pregnant are well served to take some dietary supplements, such as folic acid.

Although consumers often believe advertising claims that certain supplements can prevent or treat common ailments, many people are simply wasting their money on these products—money that could be better spent on natural sources of nutrients and phytochemicals, particularly fruits, vegetables, and whole-grain cereals.[7] However, a more serious concern occurs when a truly ill person uses dietary supplements to treat a life-threatening disease instead of seeking conventional medical care that has proven value. Chapter 2 (Evaluating Nutrition Information) presents tips for becoming a more careful consumer of nutrition-related information, including how to evaluate claims about the health benefits of dietary supplements.

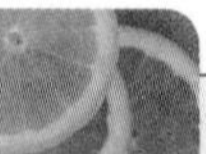

Did You Know?

Your genetic makeup influences the effects of diet on your health as well as disease susceptibility. *Nutritional genomics* or *nutragenomics* is a relatively new area of nutrition research that explores complex interactions among gene functioning, diet and other lifestyle choices, and the environment.

Concept Checkpoint

1. Identify at least three of the ten leading causes of death that are diet related.
2. List the six major classes of nutrients.
3. What is the smallest functional structural unit in the body?
4. What are three key factors that determine whether a substance is an essential nutrient?
5. What is a phytochemical?
6. Define dietary supplement.
7. Which Canadian agency regulates drug and dietary supplement manufacturers?
8. Identify at least four factors that influence your eating habits.

By eating more fruit and vegetables, Canadians may dramatically reduce their risk of cancer.

Factors that Influence Your Health

A **risk factor** is a personal characteristic that increases your chances of developing a chronic disease. For example, your genetic background or family history is an important risk factor for the major causes of death and disability. If your father's father had a stroke before he was 55 years old and your mother is being treated for hypertension (chronic high blood pressure), your family history indicates you have a higher than average risk of having elevated blood pressure and a stroke. For many people, however, having a family history of a chronic disease does not mean that they definitely will develop the condition. Other risk factors that contribute to health are age; environmental conditions; psychological factors; access to health care and a secure, healthy food supply; and lifestyle practices.

Lifestyle is a way of living that includes dietary practices; physical activity habits; use of drugs such as tobacco, alcohol, and narcotics; and other typical patterns of behaviour. Your lifestyle may increase or reduce your chances of developing a chronic disease or delay its occurrence for years, even decades. Poor diet and cigarette smoking, for example, are risk factors that increase the likelihood of heart disease, stroke, and many cancers. Cigarette smoking is the primary cause of preventable cancer deaths, but dietary habits and physical activity patterns also contribute to the development of certain types of cancer.[8] Additionally, poor diet and physical inactivity can result in **obesity**, a condition characterized by the accumulation of too much body fat. Obesity is a risk factor for numerous health problems, including heart disease, hypertension, and type 2 diabetes.

Canadians may dramatically reduce their risk of heart disease, cancer, and other serious chronic diseases by exercising regularly, maintaining a healthy body weight, avoiding tobacco exposure, limiting alcohol intake, and eating plenty of fruits, vegetables, and whole-grain cereals.[4,8] Chapter 5 discusses diabetes, and Chapter 6 explains the role of diet and other lifestyle factors in the development of heart disease and hypertension. The highlight for Chapter 8 takes a closer look at the diet and cancer connection. Chapter 10 (Energy Balance and Weight Control) provides information about obesity and ways to prevent this common condition.

risk factor personal characteristic that increases a person's chances of developing a disease

lifestyle way of living

obesity condition characterized by excess body fat

Our Changing Eating Habits

Canadian dietary habits have changed considerably over the past 35 years.[1,9] Today, we eat less red meat and eggs, and more fish and poultry than past generations. Our diet supplies more grain and cereal products, but refined grain foods, especially white bread and pasta, make up the majority of these products. Compared to past years, Canadians are eating additional servings of fruit, but not enough to meet recommended amounts.[10] When examining changes in North American dietary intake from 1970 to 2000, the U.S. Centers for Disease Control and Prevention concluded that North Americans consumed larger quantities of food in 2000 than in 1970. Over the past 30 years, average daily intake increased by 335 and 168 calories for women and men respectively. Even more surprising was that North Americans were consuming an average of 1,775 pounds of food per year, up from 1,497 pounds in 1970. Some changes were positive, such as an increased consumption of fruits and vegetables, which have fewer calories from fat. However, overall intake was greater for all food groups, as well as fats and oils. Although increases in

TABLE 1.4 *Average Daily Consumption of Selected Beverages, by Age Group and Gender, Total Household Population Aged 19 or Older, Canada, Excluding Territories, 2004*

	19 to 30		31 to 50		51 to 70		71 or older	
	Men	Women	Men	Women	Men	Women	Men	Women
	Grams							
Total beverage consumption	2,610	2,056	2,345	2,206	2,051	1,891	1,584	1,532
Water	1,045	1,000	861	1,065	705	840	500	654
Coffee	227	183	451	375	474	364	365	270
Tea	105	136	131	178	174	227	246	262
Regular soft drinks	304	142	193	97	115	62	37	29
Diet soft drinks	32	44	61	69	53	55	39	13
Beer	300	54	232	49	174	36	69	9
Wine	19	18	28	36	52	34	27	20
Spirits and liquor	8	8	7	6	8	2	7	2
Milk	201	178	158	154	133	120	166	136
Milk-based beverages	42	30	17	16	11	18	6	8
Fruit juice	176	136	108	86	98	80	76	84
Vegetable juice	10	10	15	12	20	13	12	8
Fruit drinks	135	107	77	55	31	34	31	32

Note: Fruit and vegetable juice and coolers are included in total beverage consumption.

Source: Statistics Canada, *2004 Canadian Community Health Survey - Nutrition*, Table 1. http://www.statcan.gc.ca/pub/82-003-x/2008004/article/10716/t/6500247-eng.htm. Accessed: July 20, 2010.

Did You Know?

Overweight and obesity rates in Canada are increasing among most age groups, but are escalating most rapidly among Canadian children and youth.

protein and carbohydrate intake made the relative intake of calories from fats and oils appear lower, consumption of fats and oils increased from 56 pounds per year in 1970 to 77 pounds per year in 2000. Also, it is estimated that nearly one-third of the 88 pounds per year per person increase in North American vegetable intake can be attributed to iceberg lettuce, French fries, and potato chips.

Sugar-sweetened soft drinks may contribute to unwanted weight gain[11] and replace more nutrient-rich beverages in diets. However, water and coffee remain the most frequently consumed beverages respectively among Canadian adults (see Table 1.4).[12]

Today, many Canadians consume more food energy, fat, and sugar than in 1970. If a person's energy intake is more than needed, especially for physical activity, his or her body fat increases. Surveys indicate that Canadians are fatter than in previous decades. Dietary practices, however, should not receive all the blame for this unhealthy finding; during the same period, we have become increasingly dependent on various labour-saving gadgets and machines that make our lives easier but also reduce the amount of energy we need to expend. Chapter 10 examines weight management in detail.

Canadian Healthy Living Strategy

Making healthy lifestyle choices are affected by where you live, work, learn, and spend your recreational time. Keeping informed about positive lifestyle opportunities within your environment is an important first step toward improving your health and well-being (Fig. 1.4). Health Canada advocates for Canadians to live healthy. Healthy living means making healthy choices that improve your personal mental, physical, and spiritual health. These choices include the following:

- Eating a variety of nutritious foods from all of the food groups outlined by *Eating Well with Canada's Food Guide*.
- Creating a circle of social contacts that creates a supportive, healthy environment of people who care for you and respect you.
- Staying physically active to keep your body strong, reduce stress, and improve your energy level.
- Choosing not to use tobacco.
- Putting an end to other negative lifestyle practices such as excessive intake of alcohol or use of narcotics.

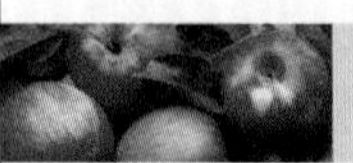

Concept **Checkpoint**

9. What is a risk factor?
10. Explain how your lifestyle can affect your health.
11. Discuss how Canadians' eating habits have changed in the past two generations.
12. Identify at least one main component of the Canadian Healthy Living Strategy.

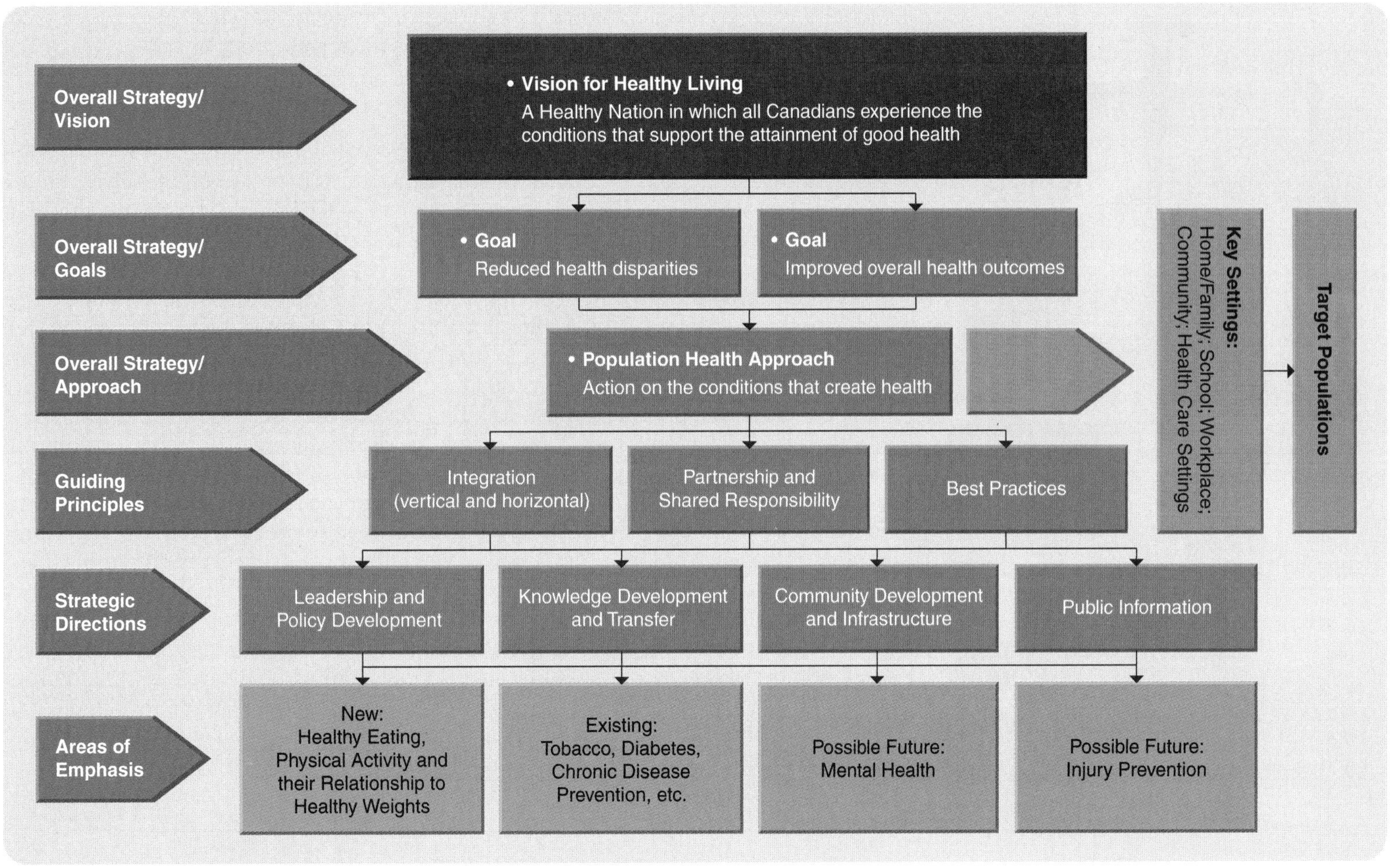

Overall Strategy/ Vision

• **Vision for Healthy Living**
A Healthy Nation in which all Canadians experience the conditions that support the attainment of good health

Overall Strategy/ Goals

• **Goal**
Reduced health disparities

• **Goal**
Improved overall health outcomes

Overall Strategy/ Approach

• **Population Health Approach**
Action on the conditions that create health

Key Settings:
Home/Family; School; Workplace; Community; Health Care Settings

Target Populations

Guiding Principles

Integration (vertical and horizontal)

Partnership and Shared Responsibility

Best Practices

Strategic Directions

Leadership and Policy Development

Knowledge Development and Transfer

Community Development and Infrastructure

Public Information

Areas of Emphasis

New: Healthy Eating, Physical Activity and their Relationship to Healthy Weights

Existing: Tobacco, Diabetes, Chronic Disease Prevention, etc.

Possible Future: Mental Health

Possible Future: Injury Prevention

Figure 1.4 The Integrated Pan-Canadian Healthy Living Strategy Framework.
Source: Public Works and Government Services Canada, modified November 14, 2005. http://www.phac-aspc.gc.ca/hl-vs-strat/hl-vs/diagram_bg-eng.php. Accessed: July 20, 2010.

Metrics for Nutrition

Scientists classify specific nutrients according to their chemical composition and major functions in the body. Nutrients can also be classified based on how much of them are in food. Although you may refer to amounts of food in familiar household measures (e.g., teaspoons, tablespoons, cups), scientists generally use metric values to report length (*metre*), weight (*gram*), and volume (*litre*). The following section provides a basic review of the metric system.

TABLE 1.5 *Common Metric Prefixes in Nutrition*

kilo- (k) = one thousand
deci- (d) = one-tenth (0.1)
centi- (c) = one-hundredth (0.01)
milli- (m) = one-thousandth (0.001)
micro- (mc or μ) = one-millionth

Metric Basics

The metric prefixes *micro, milli, deci, centi,* and *kilo* indicate whether a measurement is a fraction or multiples of a metre (m), gram (g), or litre (l or L) (Table 1.5).

There are approximately 2.54 centimetres (cm) per inch. To obtain your approximate height in centimetres, multiply your height in inches by 2.54. For example, a person who is 5′5″ in height (65″) measures about 165.1 cm (65 × 2.54) in length. There are approximately 28 g in an ounce and 454 g in a pound. A kilogram (*kilo* = 1,000) equals 1,000 g or about 2.2 pounds. To determine your weight in kilograms (kg), divide your weight in pounds by 2.2. A person who weighs 130 pounds, for example, weighs about 59 kg.

Assume that a small raisin weighs 1 gram. If you cut this raisin into 1,000 equal pieces, then each piece weighs 1 milligram (*milli* = 1,000). Thus, 1,000 milligrams (mg)

equal 1 gram (g). Imagine cutting a small raisin into one million equal pieces. Each piece of raisin would weigh 1-millionth of a gram, or a microgram (mcg or μg).

What's a Calorie?

Running, sitting, studying—your body uses energy even while sleeping. Every cell in your body needs energy to carry out its various activities. As long as you are alive, you are constantly using energy. You are probably familiar with the term calorie, the unit that describes the energy content of food. A calorie is the heat energy necessary to raise the temperature of 1 g (1 mL) of water 1° Celsius (C). A calorie is such a small unit of measurement, so the amount of energy in food is reported in 1,000-calorie units called kilocalories or Calories. Thus, a **kilocalorie** (kcal) or **Calorie** is the heat energy needed to raise the temperature of 1,000 g (a litre) of water 1°Celsius (C). A small apple, for example, supplies 40,000 calories or 40 kcal or 40 Calories. If no number of kilocalories is specified, it is appropriate to use "calories." In this textbook, the term "kilocalories" (kcal) is interchangeable with "food energy" or simply "energy." To convert calories to kilojoules, simply multiply each calorie by 4.2 kJ, for example 4.18 or 4.2 kJ = 1 calorie.

A gram of carbohydrate and a gram of protein each supply about 4 kcal; a gram of fat provides about 9 kcal. Although alcohol is not a nutrient, it does provide energy; a gram of pure alcohol furnishes 7 kcal. If you know how many grams of carbohydrate, protein, fat, and/or alcohol are in a food, you can estimate the number of kilocalories it provides. For example, if a food contains 10 g of carbohydrate and 5 g of fat, multiply 10 by 4 (the number of kcal each gram of carbohydrate supplies). Then multiply 5 by 9 (the number of kcal each gram of fat supplies). By adding the two values (40 kcal from carbohydrate and 45 kcal from fat), you will determine that this food provides 85 kcal. Fats and alcohol have the greatest amount of food energy per gram with fat at 37 kJ, and alcohol at 29 kJ. Protein and carbohydrates are a bit lower at 17 kJ.

Macronutrients and Micronutrients

Carbohydrates, fats, and proteins are referred to as **macronutrients** because the body needs relatively large amounts (grams) of these nutrients daily. Vitamins and minerals are **micronutrients**, because the body needs very small amounts (milligrams or micrograms) of them to function properly. In general, a serving of food supplies grams of carbohydrate, fat, and protein, and milligram or microgram quantities of vitamins and minerals. It is important to understand that macronutrients supply energy for cells, whereas micronutrients do not. Although the body requires large amounts of water, this nutrient provides no energy and is not classified as a macronutrient.

Amounts of nutrients present in different foods vary widely, and even the same food from the same source can contain different amounts of nutrients. Therefore, food composition tables and nutrient analysis software generally indicate average amounts of nutrients in foods. By using these tools, however, you can obtain approximate values for each nutrient measured and estimate your nutrient intake.

kilocalorie or **Calorie** heat energy needed to raise the temperature of 1 litre of water 1° Celsius; measure of food energy

macronutrients nutrients needed in gram amounts daily and that provide energy; carbohydrates, proteins, and fats

micronutrients vitamins and minerals

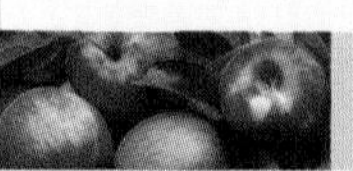

Concept Checkpoint

13. Scientists generally use which metric values to report volume, weight, and length?

14. A person weighs 154 pounds. How many kilograms does this person weigh?

15. A slice of whole-wheat bread supplies approximately 13 g of carbohydrate, 1 g of fat, 3 g of protein, and 11 g of water. Based on this information, estimate the number of kilocalories this food provides.

16. Which nutrients are classified as macronutrients? Which are classified as micronutrients?

Key Nutrition Concepts

Before learning about the nutrients and their roles in health, it is important to grasp some key basic nutrition concepts (Table 1.6). The content in the chapters that follow will build upon these key concepts and can help you make more informed choices concerning your dietary practices.

TABLE 1.6

Key Basic Nutrition Concepts

- Most naturally occurring foods are mixtures of nutrients.
- Eating a variety of foods can help ensure the nutritional adequacy of a diet.
- There are no "good" or "bad" foods.
- Enjoy eating all foods in moderation.
- For each nutrient, there is a range of safe intake.
- Food is the best source of nutrients and phytochemicals.
- There is no "one size fits all" approach to planning a nutritionally adequate diet.
- Foods and the nutrients they contain are not cure-alls.
- Malnutrition includes undernutrition as well as overnutrition.
- Nutrition is a dynamic science.

Concept 1: Most Naturally Occurring Foods Are Mixtures of Nutrients

Which foods do you think of when you hear the words "protein" or "carbohydrate"? You probably identify meat, milk, and eggs as sources of protein, and potatoes, bread, and candy as sources of carbohydrate. Most naturally occurring foods, however, are mixtures of nutrients. In many instances, water is the major nutrient in foods. For example, a 237-mL (8-fl.-oz.) serving of skim milk is about 91% water by weight, but it is an excellent source of protein and supplies carbohydrate, very little fat, and several vitamins and minerals. A 227-g (6-oz.) plain white potato baked in its skin is 75% water and only about 23% carbohydrate by weight. The baked potato also supplies iron and potassium (minerals) and vitamin C and the B-vitamin niacin. About half the weight of a slice of whole-wheat bread is carbohydrate, but slightly over one-third of its weight is water. The bread also contains protein, fat, and some vitamins and minerals.

You may be surprised to learn that many sweet snacks are sources of nutrients other than sugar, a carbohydrate. Although sugar comprises about 44% of the weight of a chocolate with almonds candy bar, over one-third of the sweet snack's energy is from fat. The candy bar also contains small amounts of protein, iron, calcium, vitamin A, and the B-vitamin riboflavin. Figure 1.5 compares the energy, water, protein, carbohydrate, fat, and calcium contents of a 227-g (6-oz.) baked potato, a slice of whole-wheat bread, 237 mL (8 fl. oz.) of skim milk, and a 41-g (1.45-oz.) chocolate and almond candy bar.

Concept 2: Eating a Variety of Foods Can Help Ensure the Nutritional Adequacy of a Diet

No natural food is "perfect" in that it contains all nutrients in amounts that are needed by the body. By eating a variety of foods, especially fruits, vegetables, and minimally processed grains, you can increase the likelihood that your diet is nutritionally adequate and contains beneficial phytochemicals. Furthermore, you can make menu planning more interesting and dishes more appealing by trying unfamiliar foods and new recipes for preparing your usual fare. Chapter 3 (Planning Nutritious Diets) provides information about dietary guidelines, such as the Dietary Reference Intakes that represent the recommended intake levels of energy and nutrients for Canadians, and practical menu-planning tools, such as EATracker.ca developed and hosted by Dietitians of Canada. The EATracker.ca online tool allows you to track your daily food and activity choices and compares them to guidelines set forth by Health Canada. The EATracker.ca tool can be found at http://www.dietitians.ca/public/content/eat_well_live_well/english/eatracker/.

Concept 3: There Are No "Good" or "Bad" Foods

Are some foods "good" and others "bad" for your body? If you think there are such foods, which ones are good and which are bad? Do you sometimes feel guilty about eating "junk foods"? What is a junk food? Should pizza, chips, candy, doughnuts, ice cream,

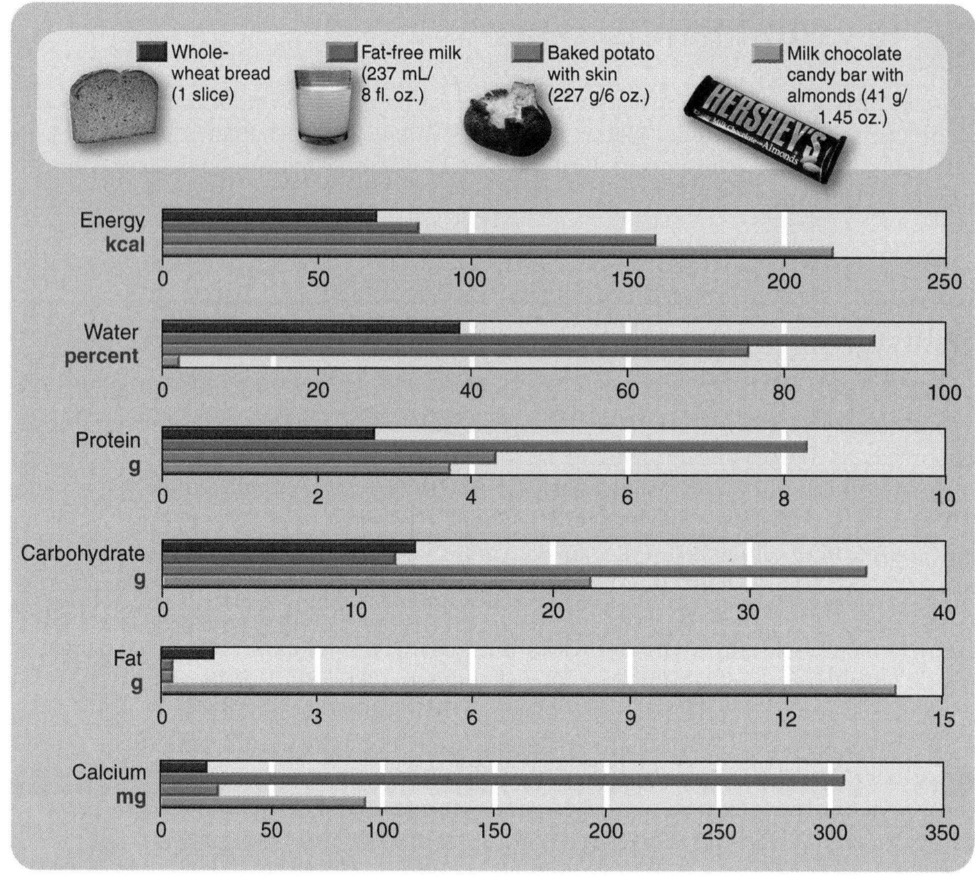

Figure 1.5 Energy and nutrient comparison. These foods contribute very different amounts of energy, water, protein, carbohydrate, fat, and calcium to diets.

Pumpkin pie is a good source of food energy, protein, iron, and beta-carotene, a substance the body can convert to vitamin A.

and sugar-sweetened soft drinks be classified as junk food? No food deserves the label of "bad" or "junk," because all foods have nutritional value. For example, many people think pumpkin pie is a junk food. Pumpkin pie, however, is a good source of protein, the mineral iron, and the phytochemical beta-carotene that the body can convert to vitamin A. Even sugar-sweetened soft drinks provide water and the carbohydrate sugar, a source of energy. Although pies, doughnuts, and ice cream contain a lot of fat and sugar, these foods also supply small amounts of protein, vitamins, and minerals to diets.

Some foods and beverages, such as bacon, candy, pastries, snack chips, and alcoholic or sugar-sweetened drinks, are described as empty calories. An **empty-calorie** food contributes a large portion of its energy from fat, sugar, and/or alcohol in relation to its supply of micronutrients. Consuming too much food energy in relation to one's needs can result in obesity. Furthermore, eating too many empty-calorie foods may displace more nutritious foods from the diet and may contribute to weight gain.

Certain foods are more nutritious than others. A **nutrient-dense** food contains more vitamins and minerals in relation to its fat, sugar, and/or alcohol contents. Broccoli, leafy greens, skim milk, orange juice, lean meats, and whole-grain cereals are examples of nutrient-dense foods. Figure 1.6 compares the nutritional values of 237-mL (8-fl.-oz.) servings of a cola-type soft drink and skim milk. Note that the milk supplies water, protein, and certain vitamins and minerals, whereas cola supplies water and carbohydrate but is a poor source of protein and micronutrients. A nutritionally balanced diet contains a variety of nutrient-dense foods. Therefore, you should focus on eating nutrient-dense foods to improve the nutrient content of your diet.

Energy density describes the energy value of a food in relation to the food's weight. For example, a chocolate, cake-type frosted doughnut

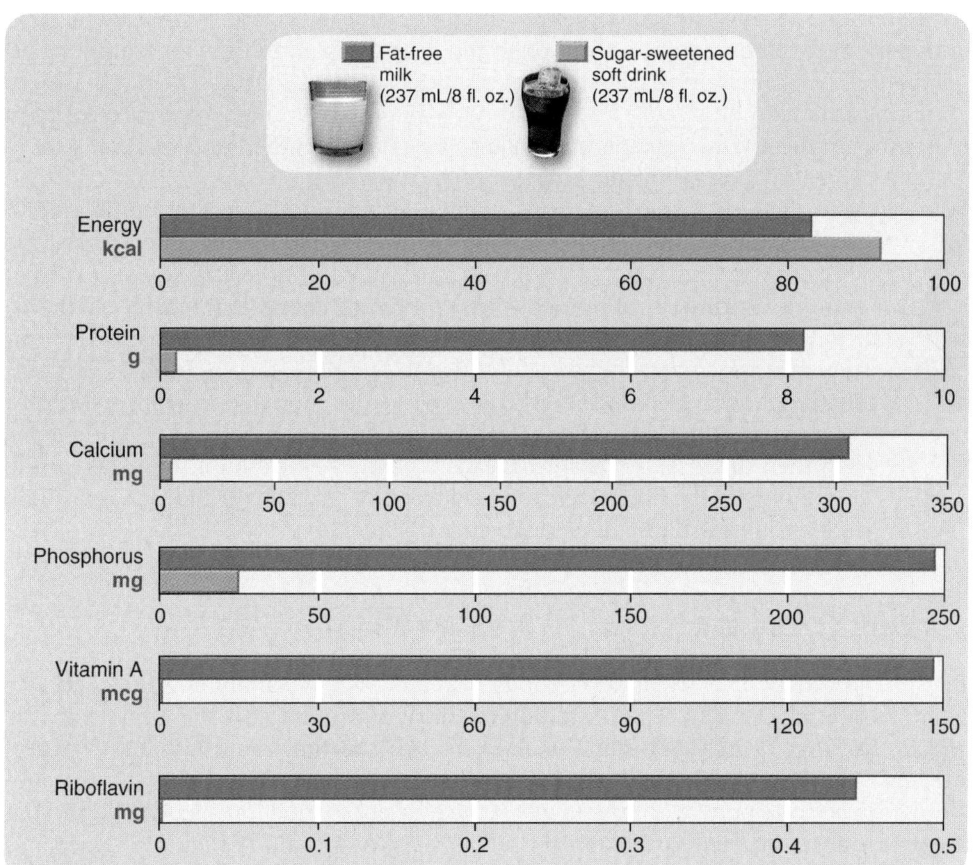

Figure 1.6 Comparing foods. This graph compares energy contents and amounts of key nutrients in 237-mL (8-fl.-oz.) servings of skim milk and sugar-sweetened soft drink. Although the two beverages have similar calorie contents, milk contains vitamin A and the B-vitamin riboflavin and considerably more protein, calcium, and phosphorus (minerals).

that weighs about 57 g (2 oz.) provides 242 kcal; 5 medium strawberries also weigh about 57 g (2 oz.), but they provide only 19 kcal. You would have to eat nearly 64 of the strawberries to obtain the same amount of food energy that is in the chocolate doughnut. Therefore, the doughnut is an energy-dense food in comparison to the berries. In general, high-fat foods such as doughnuts are energy dense because they are concentrated sources of energy. Most fruits are not energy dense, because they contain far more water than fat.

Figure 1.7 compares a group of foods that supply similar amounts of calories but differ in their energy densities. It is important to note that not all energy-dense foods are empty-calorie foods. Nuts, for example, are high in fat and, therefore, energy dense. However, nuts are also nutrient-dense because they contribute protein, vitamins, minerals, and fibre to diets.

A food *is* bad for you if it is unsafe to eat. You have probably suffered from a food-borne illness at least once. Food-borne illnesses result from eating foods that are contaminated with certain bacteria, viruses, or microscopic animals. The abdominal cramps, nausea, vomiting, and diarrhea that usually accompany a food-borne illness occur within a few hours or days after eating the contaminated food. Chapter 12 (Food Safety Concerns) focuses on food safety concerns, including major types of food-borne illnesses and how to prevent them.

empty-calorie describes food or beverage that is a poor source of micronutrients in relation to its energy value

nutrient-dense describes food or beverage that has more vitamins and minerals in relation to its energy value

energy density energy value of a food in relation to the food's weight

moderation obtaining adequate amounts of nutrients while balancing calorie intake with calorie expenditure

Concept 4: Enjoy Eating All Foods in Moderation

Dietary **moderation** involves obtaining enough nutrients from food to meet one's needs while avoiding excessive amounts, and balancing calorie intake with calorie expenditure, primarily by physical activity. This can be accomplished by choosing nutrient-dense

When a diet meets nutritional needs, including some empty-calorie items adds enjoyment when such foods are consumed in moderation.

foods, limiting serving sizes, and incorporating moderate- to vigorous-intensity physical activities into your daily routine. Although moderation requires time for planning and preparing meals and setting aside time for physical activity daily, it can help you achieve your health and fitness goals. If, for example, you overeat during a meal or snack, you can regain dietary moderation and balance by eating less food and exercising more intensely during the following 24 hours.

The diets of many Canadians contain excessive amounts of empty-calorie foods in relation to nutrient-dense foods. However, eliminating all empty-calorie foods from your diet is not generally recommended or necessary. If your core diet is comprised primarily of nutrient-dense foods and meets your nutritional needs, including some empty-calorie items adds enjoyment to living when they are consumed in moderation. Physically active individuals, such as athletes in training programs, often find it difficult to consume enough energy from foods to sustain healthy body weights, unless they include some empty-calorie items in their diets. Eating healthy means making the healthiest food choices the majority of the time, while truly enjoying treats when we choose to consume foods with low-nutrient and high-energy content.

Concept 5: For Each Nutrient, There Is a Range of Safe Intake

By eating a variety of nutrient-dense foods, you are likely to obtain adequate and safe amounts of each nutrient. The **physiological dose** of a nutrient is the amount that is within the range of safe intake and enables the body to function optimally. Consuming less than the physiological dose can result in marginal nutritional status. In other words, the person's body has just enough of the nutrient to function adequately, but that amount is not sufficient to overcome the added stress of infection or injury. If a person's nutrient intake falls below the marginal level, the individual is at risk of developing the nutrient's deficiency disease. For example, the recommended amounts of the B-vitamin niacin are 16 mg for men and 14 mg for women. People whose diets contain little or no niacin are at risk of developing *pellagra*, the vitamin's deficiency disease.

physiological dose amount of a nutrient that is within the range of safe intake and enables the body to function optimally

megadose generally defined as 10 times the recommended amount of a vitamin or mineral

Most people require physiological amounts of micronutrients. In rare cases, a person is born with an inherited defect that greatly increases his or her body's need for a particular vitamin. These individuals must take megadoses of the vitamin to avoid developing the nutrient's deficiency disease. A **megadose** is generally defined as an amount of a vitamin or mineral that is at least 10 times the recommended amount of the nutrient.[13] When taken in high amounts, many vitamins behave like drugs and can produce unpleasant and even toxic (poisonous) side

Figure 1.7 Energy density. Although each of these portions of food supplies about 200 kcal, they differ in their energy densities. For example, you would need to eat over 4 cups of whole strawberries to consume the same amount of energy in an 85-g (3-oz.) hamburger patty.

effects. For example, physicians sometimes use megadoses of the B-vitamin niacin to treat high blood cholesterol levels, but such amounts may cause painful facial flushing and liver damage. Megadoses of vitamin C can cause intestinal upsets and diarrhea; consuming extremely high amounts of vitamin A can even be deadly. Minerals have very narrow ranges of safe intakes.

Many consumers take megadoses of vitamin and mineral supplements without consulting physicians because they think the micronutrients will prevent or treat ailments such as the common cold or heart disease. For most people, consuming amounts of nutrients that exceed what is necessary for good health is economically wasteful and could be harmful to the body. "More is not always better," when it relates to optimal nutrition. Eating from a wide variety of food sources and including foods from all food groups in the *Eating Well with Canada's Food Guide* likely means taking a multivitamin supplement is unnecessary if you are in good health. Many of the nutrients found in a multivitamin supplement will simply be lost in the urine and not remain stored in the body, meaning these supplements are often a waste of money.

In their natural states, most commonly eaten foods do not contain toxic levels of vitamins and minerals. You probably do not need to worry about consuming toxic levels of vitamins or minerals, unless you are taking megadoses of vitamin/mineral supplements or eating large amounts of foods that are fortified with these nutrients regularly. The diagram shown in Figure 1.8 illustrates the general concept of deficient, safe, and toxic intake ranges for nutrients such as vitamins and minerals. Chapters 8 and 9 provide more information about micronutrients, including deficiencies and toxicities.

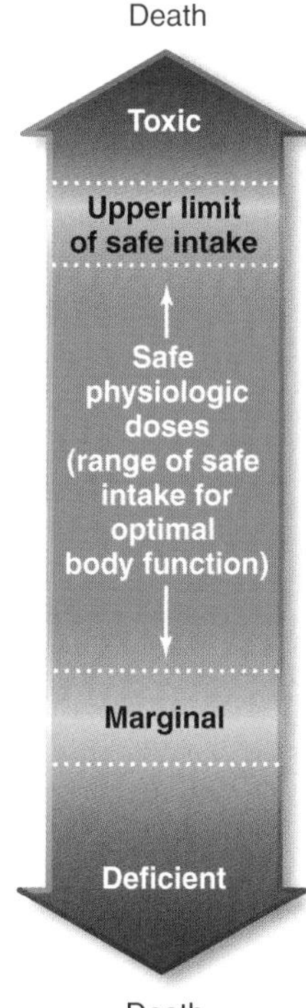

Figure 1.8 Intake continuum. For each nutrient, there is a range of safe intake.

Concept 6: Food Is the Best Source of Nutrients and Phytochemicals

Basing your diet on a variety of minimally processed foods is the most natural, reliable, and economical way to obtain nutrients and nonnutrients. Plant foods naturally contain a variety of nutrients and phytochemicals, but processing the foods often removes some of the most healthful parts. In general, the more refined a food is, the more processing it has undergone before it reaches your plate; as a result, it loses micronutrients and other beneficial substances. For example, a whole-wheat kernel is stripped of its nutrient-rich germ and phytochemical-rich outer hull during refinement into white flour (Fig. 1.9). By including unrefined grain foods in your diet, you can increase the likelihood of obtaining a wide variety of micronutrients and phytochemicals.

In addition to eating food, many people take nutrient supplements in the form of pills, powders, bars, wafers, or beverages. People who use dietary supplements may increase their intake of certain nutrients to unsafe levels and, as a result, create nutrient imbalances and overdoses. The human body is designed to obtain nutrients and nonnutrient phytochemicals from foods, not supplements. In some instances, nutrients from food are more available, that is, more easily digested and absorbed, than those in supplements.

It is important to understand that nutrient supplements do not contain everything one needs for optimal nutrition. For example, they do not contain the wide variety of phytochemicals found in plant foods. Although supplements that contain phytochemicals are available, they may not provide the same healthful benefits as consuming the

plants that contain these compounds. Why? Nutrients and phytochemicals may need to be consumed together to provide the desirable effects in the body. Food naturally contains combinations of these chemicals in very small amounts and certain proportions. There is nothing "natural" about gulping down handfuls of supplements.

A few individuals have increased needs for certain nutrients, particularly vitamins. People who have chronic illnesses, digestive disorders that interfere with nutrient absorption, and certain inherited disorders may need supplemental nutrients. Additionally, many elderly people may need higher amounts of vitamins than those found in food. Because it is often difficult to plan and eat nutritious menus each day, taking a supplement that contains a variety of vitamins may be advisable, even for healthy older adults.[14] In general, there appears to be little danger in regularly taking a daily multiple vitamin supplement that provides 100% of recommended amounts of the micronutrients.[15] However, healthy adults should consider taking a vitamin supplement as an "insurance policy" and not a substitute for eating a variety of nutrient-dense foods.

Concept 7: There Is No "One Size Fits All" Approach to Planning a Nutritionally Adequate Diet

malnutrition state of health that occurs when the body is improperly nourished

Healthy adults can generally meet their nutritional needs by eating a variety of nutrient-dense foods. By using food guides presented in Chapter 3, you can individualize your diet so that it is nutritionally adequate and also suits your food likes and dislikes, budget, and lifestyle. Individualizing a diet does not mean only eating foods that "match" your blood type, hair colour, personality, or shoe size. If someone promotes a diet based on such personal traits, steer clear of the diet and the promoter. Consider this: Human beings would not have survived as a species for thousands of years if their diets had to be matched to physical characteristics or personalities.

Physicians often prescribe special diets, sometimes referred to as medical nutrition therapies, for people with chronic health conditions. Even the nutritional needs of healthy people vary during different stages of their lives. Chapter 13 (Nutrition for a Lifetime) provides information about the importance of diet during pregnancy, childhood, and other stages of the life cycle.

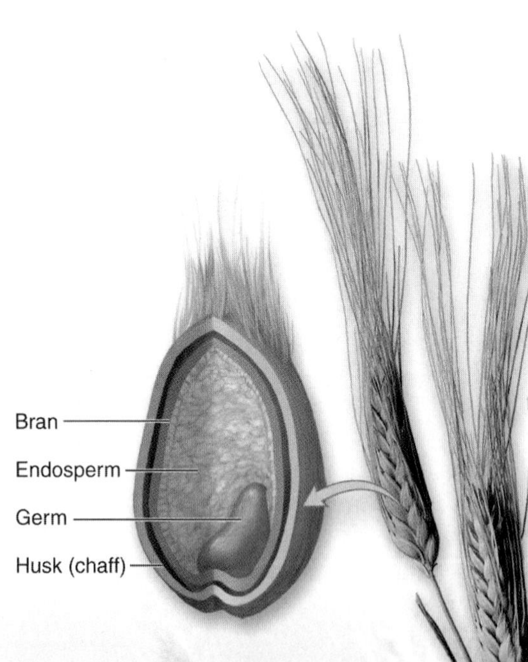

Figure 1.9 Sources of fibre in a wheat kernel. During refinement, a wheat kernel is stripped of its nutrient-rich germ and phytochemical-rich bran. The endosperm that remains contains starch and some protein.

Concept 8: Foods and the Nutrients They Contain Are Not Cure-Alls

Although specific nutrient deficiency diseases, such as scurvy, can be cured by eating foods that contain the nutrient that is missing or in short supply, nutrients do not "cure" other ailments. Diet is only one aspect of a person that influences his or her health. By making certain dietary changes, however, a person may be able to prevent or forestall the development of certain diseases and illnesses, or possibly lessen their severity if they occur.

Concept 9: Malnutrition Includes *Under*nutrition as well as *Over*nutrition

Malnutrition is a state of health that occurs when the body is improperly nourished. Everyone must consume food and water to stay alive, yet despite the abundance and variety of nutritious foods, many Canadians choose nutritionally poor diets and suffer from malnutrition as a result. Some people select nutritionally inadequate diets because they lack knowledge about nutritious foods or the importance of nutrition to health. Low-income people, however, are at risk for malnutrition because they have limited financial resources for making wise food purchases. In Canada, especially in the winter, buying fresh fruits and vegetables can be expensive. Thus, low-income families and individuals often find it less expensive to purchase foods that lack nutrient density, such as potato chips and pop, rather than buying fruits, vegetables, and low-fat milk products. Other people who are at risk of malnutrition include those who have severe eating disorders, are addicted to drugs such as alcohol, or have certain serious medical problems. It is also important to recognize that many Canadians select nutritionally inadequate diets despite having the knowledge about foods and nutrition. Human behaviour is a dynamic and complex topic and much is still unknown about what motivates individual lifestyle choices, especially regarding diet and physical activity.

You may be surprised to learn that overnutrition is more common in Canada than undernutrition. Obesity, a sign of overnutrition, is a prevalent nutrition-related health problem in many nations (Fig. 1.10). The Chapter 1 Highlight discusses the international problem of obesity and other forms of malnutrition.

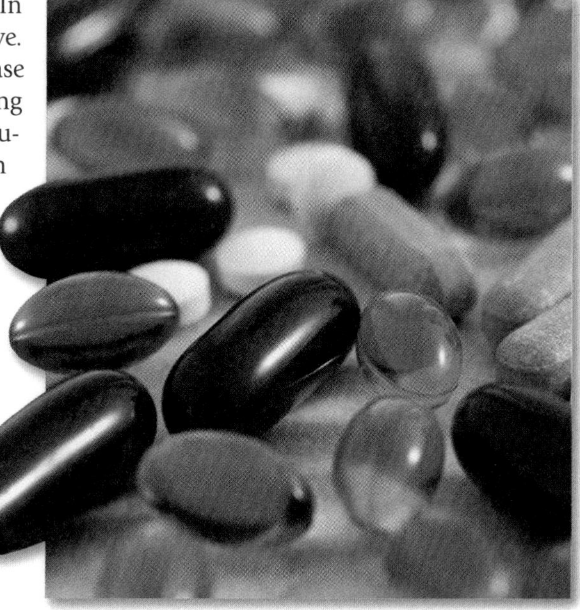

Vitamin/mineral supplements should not be considered substitutes for nutrient-dense food.

Concept 10: Nutrition Is a Dynamic Science

As researchers continue to explore the complex relationships between diets and health, nutrition information constantly evolves. As a result, dietary practices and recommendations undergo revision as new scientific evidence becomes available and is reviewed and accepted by nutrition experts. Unfortunately such changes can be confusing to the general public, who expect medical researchers to provide definite answers to their nutrition-related questions and rigid advice concerning optimal dietary practices.

Even nutrition educators find it difficult to keep up with the vast amount of research articles published in scientific journals. Chapter 2 explains how nutrition research is conducted using scientific methods. Furthermore, Chapter 2 provides information to help you become a better consumer of nutrition and health information that appears in popular sources such as magazines and infomercials.

Concept **Checkpoint**

17. Identify at least five of the key nutrition-related concepts presented in this section.
18. What is the difference between empty-calorie food and nutrient-dense food?
19. What is the difference between a physiological dose and a megadose of a nutrient?

Figure 1.10 Obesity. Obesity is a prevalent nutrition-related health problem in many nations.

Chapter 1 Highlight

Malnutrition: A Worldwide Concern

Malnutrition is a state of health that results from improper nourishment. Chronic undernutrition occurs when long-term energy and nutrient intakes are insufficient to meet an individual's needs. Hunger, the physiological need for food, usually accompanies undernutrition. In undernourished children, nutrient deficiencies are responsible for stunted physical growth, delayed physical development, blindness, impaired intellectual development, and premature death.

Throughout the world, social, environmental, economic, and political factors contribute to undernutrition (Fig. 1.A). Undernutrition is a serious problem particularly in sub-Saharan Africa and certain regions of Asia where decades of civil unrest, wars, political corruption, and the AIDS epidemic have left millions of people impoverished and living in uncertainty. Many developing nations in these regions owe large sums of money to wealthy countries. Having high debts often causes government leaders to reduce or eliminate basic services, including health care and education programs. Furthermore, undernutrition is common among impoverished people in developing countries where food production and supplies are inadequate. In addition, developing nations often direct much of the food they produce to global markets rather than domestically to feed the nations' residents. Although people often associate malnutrition with undernutrition and starvation, overnutrition, the long-term excess of energy or nutrient intake, is also a form of malnutrition. Overnutrition is often characterized by excess body fat and obesity. Obesity is an epidemic in countries where most people have the financial means to buy food, have an ample food supply, and lead physically inactive lives. This highlight focuses on undernutrition. Chapter 7 discusses protein-energy malnutrition in detail; Chapter 10 provides information about the obesity epidemic.

Parasites
Depleted farmland and other natural resources
Overpopulation
UNDERNUTRITION
Lack of sanitary water supplies
Disease
War and political / civil unrest
Food distribution problems (such as lack of good roads)

Figure 1.A Factors that contribute to undernutrition. Many factors, including war, disease, and overpopulation, contribute to undernutrition in developing countries.

Undernutrition

The current worldwide population is estimated to be more than 6.5 billion people. Throughout the world, an estimated 500 million children were born between 1999 and 2005. If the present rate of population growth does not slow, an estimated 9 billion people will be living on Earth in 2050.[1A] Most of the explosive population growth is occurring in developing countries where economic growth is unable to keep pace with the rapidly increasing number of people. As a result, poverty and undernutrition are commonplace in these countries. Additionally, regional food shortages can result from traditional dietary practices, crop failures, local warfare, and political instability and corruption. According to the World Health Organization (WHO), nearly one in three people worldwide is chronically undernourished.[2A] Each day, about 24,000 children in the world die of hunger. The vast majority of child deaths occur among the poor in developing countries, particularly in Africa and Asia.[3A] Impoverished people must also cope with infectious diseases, parasitic infestations, overcrowded and unsafe housing conditions, and polluted water supplies. Chronic undernutrition depresses the body's immune functioning, increasing the risk of death from infectious diseases, such as measles, especially in childhood. In developing countries, poor sanitation practices and lack of clean cooking and drinking water cause the majority of all diseases and more than one-third of all deaths (Fig. 1.B).

Undernutrition during Pregnancy

Undernutrition can be particularly harmful when it occurs during periods of rapid growth such as pregnancy, infancy, and childhood. Women who are undernourished during pregnancy have high risk of giving birth to infants who are born too soon. These babies often have low birth weights and suffer from breathing problems.

Figure 1.B Poor sanitation. In developing countries, poor sanitation practices and lack of clean cooking and drinking water contribute to the spread of disease.

Furthermore, low-birth-weight infants have a high risk of dying during their first year of life. Each year, more than 20 million low-birth-weight infants (nearly 16% of all births) are born in the world.[4A] The vast majority of low-birth-weight infants are born in developing countries. Chapter 13 provides more information about the importance of adequate nutrition during pregnancy.

Undernutrition during Infancy

As explained in Chapter 13, breast milk is the best food for infants because it is sanitary, is nutritionally adequate, and provides infants with immunity to some infectious diseases. Infant formulas, on the other hand, are generally more expensive than breast milk. To extend infant formulas, poor parents in developing countries often add excessive amounts of water. This practice dilutes the nutritional value of the formula and increases the likelihood of contaminating it with disease-causing microbes. In infants, the diarrhea that results from drinking formula mixed with unsanitary water can rapidly cause loss of body water (dehydration) and death.

Dietitians recommend that infants be breast-fed exclusively for the first six months of life. Ideally, babies should continue to receive breast milk in addition to solid foods well into their second year.[5A] In developing countries, signs and symptoms of protein malnutrition typically occur soon after impoverished children are weaned abruptly from breast milk and introduced to far less nourishing solid foods.

Figure 1.C Chronic undernutrition. Chronically undernourished children are underweight, do not grow normally, and tend to be shorter—if they survive to adulthood. This photograph shows a group of malnourished children outside a Nigerian orphanage during the late 1960s.

Undernutrition during the Preschool Years

The brain grows rapidly during the first five years of life. When undernutrition occurs during this period, the effects can be devastating to the child's brain and result in permanent learning disabilities. Additionally, chronically undernourished children are underweight, do not grow normally, and tend to be shorter if they survive to adulthood (Fig. 1.C). In Canada and other developed countries, children are usually well nourished and vaccinated against common childhood diseases such as measles. In poorer nations, however, many children are malnourished and not protected from the virus that causes measles. Measles often is a life-threatening illness for malnourished children because their immune systems do not function normally.

Undernutrition in Canada

Undernutrition occurs in wealthy, developed nations such as Canada. In some instances, undernutrition is not due to poverty in these countries. For example, many people suffering from anorexia nervosa and chronic alcoholism are undernourished despite having the financial resources to purchase food. Nevertheless, people with low incomes have a higher risk of malnutrition than people in higher income categories. Although by most global standards Canada is an affluent nation, it is also a country where the health of citizens is compromised by poor dietary intake. Within the Canadian population, even after transfers and tax adjustments, the poorest 20% of the Canadian population receive only 7% of the national income, while the most affluent 20% of the Canadian population receive 36% of the national income.[6A]

Food insecurity affects individuals or families who are concerned about running out of food or not having enough money to buy more food. People who are unemployed, work in low-paying

Figure 1.D Feeding the hungry. In many cities, charities and churches operate food banks and soup kitchens to feed hungry people.

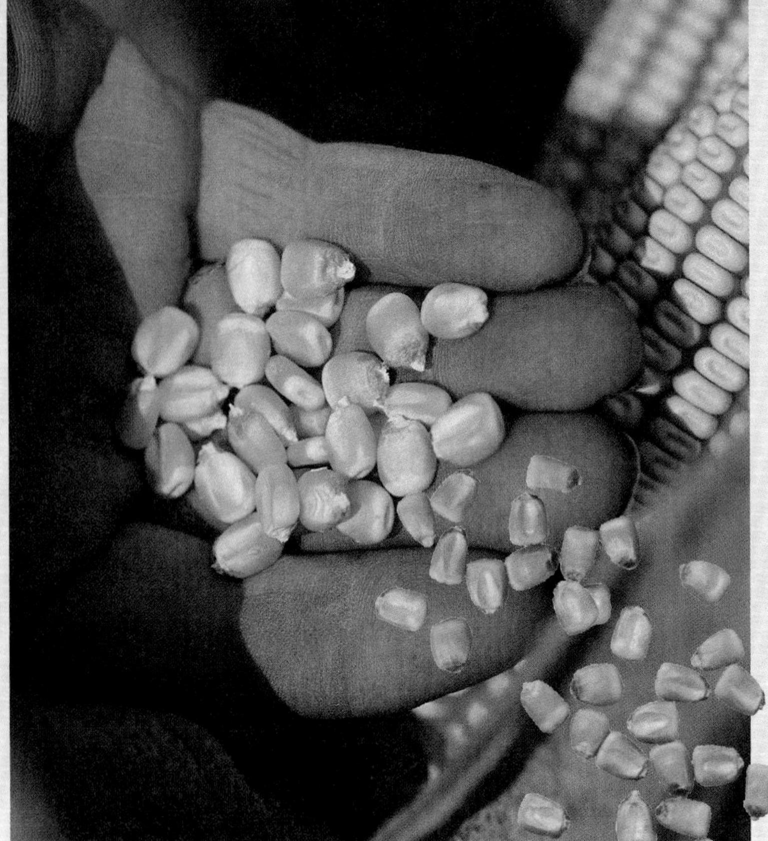

Figure 1.E Genetically modified corn. This seed corn is the result of genetic engineering.

jobs, or have excessive living expenses often experience food insecurity. Food insecurity may also affect elderly Canadians who live on fixed incomes/pensions, especially if they live alone and have high housing expenses.

In 2004, food insecurity affected nearly one in ten Canadian households, or more than 2.3 million Canadians.[7A,8A] Charities and churches in many communities operate food banks and soup kitchens to feed the hungry (Fig. 1.D).

Solutions

Biotechnology involves the use of living things—plants, animals, bacteria—to manufacture improved products. As a result of various biotechnological advances, food production has improved. Biotechnology in agriculture has led to the development of more nutritious fruits and grains; dairy cattle that produce more milk; and crops that supply higher yields, resist pests, or are tolerant of drought conditions. One form of biotechnology, **genetic modification**, involves altering an animal or plant's hereditary material (*genes* or DNA) scientifically. For example, genes that produce a desirable trait are transferred from one organism into the DNA of a second organism, altering its genes. Although these *genetically modified organisms (GMOs)* are used for feeding livestock, many processed foods manufactured for human consumption also contain ingredients from GMOs (Fig. 1.E).

food insecurity situation in which individuals or families are concerned about running out of food or not having enough money to buy more food

genetic modification techniques that alter an organism's DNA

According to Dr. J. Craig Venter, geneticist and founder of the Institute for Genomic Research, the safety of genetically engineered crops destined for human consumption has been tested extensively.[9A] Some scientists, however, have raised concerns that GMOs introduce new proteins into the food chain, creating the potential for environmental harm. Moreover, people consuming foods that contain the modified genetic material may experience unexpected side effects. For example, altering DNA produces proteins that are unfamiliar to the immune systems of animals and humans. When foods containing these foreign proteins are introduced into the human body, they may elicit allergic responses that could be annoying for some people and life threatening for others. Despite these concerns, experts think currently approved varieties of genetically engineered foods are safe for human consumption. In the near future, farmers may find it difficult to sustain a high degree of agricultural productivity as crops and livestock reach their maximum capacity to produce food, particularly as water for irrigation becomes scarce and farmland is used for other purposes, such as housing for the ever-expanding population. Biotechnological advances in agriculture may help reduce the prevalence of undernutrition by increasing livestock production and crop yields in many parts of the world.

Poverty and hunger have always plagued humankind; the causes of poverty and hunger are complex and, therefore, difficult to eliminate. Nevertheless, certain social, political, economic, and agricultural changes can reduce the number of people who are chronically hungry. In the short run, wealthy countries can provide food aid to keep people in developing countries from starving to death and lobby for equity in the global marketplace through advocacy of fair trade practices. Families and small farmers in these nations need to learn new and more efficient methods of growing, processing, preserving, and distributing nutritious regional food products. Additionally, governments can support programs that fortify locally grown or commonly consumed foods with vitamins and minerals that are often deficient in local diets.

As people deplete the earth's resources, population control is critical. In developing countries, impoverished parents often have many children because they expect only a few to survive and reach adulthood. When people are financially secure, adequately nourished, and well educated, they tend to have fewer children. Thus, long-term ways to slow population growth include providing well-paying jobs, improving public education, and increasing access to health care services.

Although waging a battle against worldwide hunger may seem like a daunting prospect, there are actions you can take to help relieve the problem in your community. You can stimulate student interest by researching the extent of food insecurity in the area and then writing an article about the situation for the campus newspaper. You can help food-insecure people directly by volunteering to prepare or serve food at a community kitchen or homeless shelter in your community. You can initiate and coordinate a canned food drive on your campus to benefit a local food bank.

References for Chapter 1 Highlight

1A. United Nations (UN): *World population to reach 9.1 billion in 2050, UN projects.* UN News Service, 2005. www.un.org/apps/news. Accessed: February 25, 2005.

2A. World Health Organization (WHO): *Turning the tide of malnutrition: Responding to the challenge of the 21st century.* Geneva: WHO, 2000. www.who.int/nut/documents/nhd_brochure.pdf. Accessed: February 25, 2005.

3A. World Health Organization (WHO): Surviving the first five years of life. *The World Health Report.* Geneva: WHO, 2003. www.who.int/whr/2003/chapter1/en/index2.html. Accessed: March 1, 2005.

4A. United Nations Children's Fund and World Health Organization: *Low birthweight: Country, regional and global estimates.* New York: UNICEF, 2004. www.who.int/reproductive-health/publications/low_birthweight/index.html. Accessed: March 1, 2005.

5A. Rutstein SO: Factors associated with trends in infant and child mortality in developing countries during the 1990s. *Bulletin of the World Health Organization* 78(10):1256, 2000.

6A. Ross DP, Roberts P: Income and child well-being: A new perspective on the poverty debate. *Canadian Council on Social Development.* www.ccsd.ca/pubs/inckids/2.htm. Accessed: September 1, 2005.

7A. Kirkpatrick SA, Tarasuk V: Food insecurity in Canada: considerations for monitoring. *Canadian Journal of Public Health* 99(4):324–7, 2008.

8A. Power EM: Economic abuse and intra-household inequities in food security. *Canadian Journal of Public Health,* 97(3):258–60, 2006.

9A. Thomson JA: Genetically modified crops—Playing a positive role in sustainable development in Africa. *South African Medical Journal* 96(6):509, 2006.

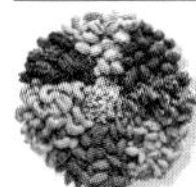

SUMMARY

Lifestyle choices, including poor eating habits and lack of physical activity, contribute to the development of leading causes of premature deaths for Canadian adults—heart disease, cancer, and stroke. You may be able to extend your lifespan and improve your quality of life by applying what you learn about nutrition and the role of diet and health.

There are six classes of nutrients: carbohydrates, lipids, proteins, vitamins, minerals, and water. The body uses certain nutrients for energy and regulation of chemical reactions, particularly processes involved in growth, repair, and maintenance of cells. The body can synthesize many nutrients, but about 50 nutrients are dietary essentials that must be supplied by food because the body does not synthesize the nutrient or make enough to meet its needs.

Plant foods naturally contain a variety of phytochemicals, substances that are not classified as nutrients yet may have healthful benefits. Many phytochemicals are antioxidants that protect cells from being damaged or destroyed by exposure to certain environmental factors. However, some phytochemicals are toxic.

A risk factor is a personal characteristic such as family history and lifestyle practices that increases a person's chances of developing diseases. In many instances, people can live longer and healthier by modifying their diets, increasing their physical activity, and altering other aspects of their lifestyles.

Scientists generally use metric values when measuring volume, weight, and length. The metric prefixes *micro* -, *milli* -, *deci* -, *centi* -, and kilo - indicate whether a measurement is a fraction or multiples of a metre, gram, or litre. Approximately 28 grams are in an ounce and 454 grams are in a pound; a kilogram equals 1,000 grams or about 2.2 pounds. Each gram equals one thousand milligrams or one million micrograms.

Every cell needs energy to carry out its various activities. A Calorie is the heat energy needed to raise the temperature of 1 litre of water 1° Celsius (C). Calories or kilocalories (kcal) are used to indicate the energy value in food. If no number of kilocalories is specified, it is appropriate to use "calories."

Carbohydrates, fats, and proteins are referred to as macronutrients because the body needs relatively large amounts of these nutrients daily. Vitamins and minerals are micronutrients, because the body needs very small amounts. Although the body

requires large amounts of water, this nutrient provides no energy and is not usually classified as a macronutrient.

There are several key points to understanding nutrition. Most naturally occurring foods are mixtures of nutrients, but no food contains all the nutrients needed for optimal health. Thus, eating a variety of foods can help ensure the nutritional adequacy of a diet. Instead of classifying foods as "good" or "bad," people can focus on eating all foods in moderation. For each nutrient, there is a range of safe intake. Healthy people should rely on eating a variety of food to meet their nutrient needs instead of taking dietary supplements. Although nutrients are vital to good health, foods and the nutrients they contain are not cure-alls. There is no "one size fits all" approach to planning a nutritionally adequate diet. Malnutrition is not simply starvation; the term includes overnutrition as well as undernutriton. Finally, nutrition is a dynamic science; new scientific information about nutrients and their roles in health is constantly emerging. Therefore, ways the science of nutrition is applied, such as dietary recommendations, also change.

Recipe for Healthy Living

Food Preparation Basics (Yes, You Can Cook!)

By learning how to prepare dishes, experimenting with recipe ingredients, and using a variety of spices and herbs as seasonings, home-cooked meals can be more tasty, appealing, and lower in fat, sugar, salt, and calories than the usual choices at fast food restaurants. Additionally, you can save money by making your meals and snacks instead of purchasing them from restaurants and vending machines. At the end of each chapter, you'll find the "Recipe for Healthy Living," a collection of nutritious, easy-to-prepare recipes. Each recipe includes a list of ingredients, instructions, and some information concerning the energy and selected nutrient contents in a serving of the product.

Even if you've had little or no cooking experience, you can learn the basics of preparing foods. Some cooks don't measure ingredients; they know from experience how to estimate amounts of foods and seasonings to add when preparing dishes. Until you feel confident with your food preparation skills, it is best to follow recipes and measure ingredients carefully.

You'll need some basic food preparation equipment to get started. You don't have to spend a lot of money, but buy well-made stainless steel (rust-proof) cooking utensils and mixing bowls that will last for decades. Baking pans should also be stainless steel. A square or rectangular tempered-glass baking dish can be used for a variety of cooking needs, including heating foods in a toaster oven or microwave oven.

Understanding how to use household measurements is a good place to begin when learning how to cook. Purchase a set of metal measuring spoons that include ⅛ teaspoon (tsp), ¼ tsp, ½ tsp, 1 tsp, and 1 tablespoon (Tbsp) measures. You'll also need a set of plastic or metal measuring cups that include the following measures: ¼ cup, ⅓ cup, ½ cup, and 1 cup. These cups are used to measure dry ingredients such as flour or sugar. Finally, purchase a 500-mL (2-cup) glass or clear-plastic measuring pitcher that is marked to indicate fluid ounces. This pitcher is used for measuring liquid ingredients such as water, milk, and oil.

To measure dry ingredients, fill the appropriate measuring cup or spoon to the top, and skim off the excess with the straight edge of a knife. To measure liquid ingredients, use a liquid measuring pitcher. Fill the pitcher to the desired amount, and place it on a level surface. Kneel down so that you are eye-level with the fluid's level, and then carefully add or remove fluid as necessary.

Household Units

Common household units often used for measuring food ingredients and their commonly used abbreviations are listed below. Ounces (oz) are a measure of weight; *fluid* ounces are a measure of volume. Appendix A at the back of the text provides information about English–metric conversions and metric to household units.

Common Household Units for Measuring Food Ingredients

1 tsp = 5 mL	½ cup = 125 mL
1 Tbsp = 15 mL	1 cup = 250 mL
3 tsp = 1 Tbsp	1 cup = 8 fluid ounces (oz)
4 Tbsp = ¼ cup	2 cups = 1 pint
8 Tbsp = ½ cup	4 cups or 2 pints = 1 quart
16 Tbsp = 1 cup	4 quarts = 1 gallon

Cornbread

The following cornbread recipe is simple and will give you an opportunity to practise measuring dry and liquid ingredients. This recipe makes 16 cornbread squares (2″ × 2″). Each square supplies approximately 135 kcal, 2.3 g protein, 5.2 g fat, 73 mg calcium, and 245 mg sodium.

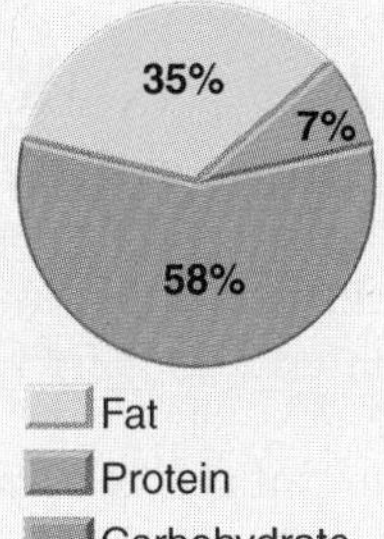

INGREDIENTS:

- Vegetable oil cooking spray
- 250 mL (1 cup) yellow cornmeal
- 250 mL (1 cup) all-purpose enriched flour
- 140 mL (½ cup + 1 Tbsp) white sugar
- 5 mL (1 tsp) salt
- 15 mL (1 Tbsp) baking powder
- 1 large raw egg
- 250 mL (1 cup) skim milk
- 80 mL (⅓ cup) vegetable oil

PREPARATION STEPS:

1. Preheat oven to 200° C (400° F).
2. Spray vegetable oil cooking spray lightly on the inside bottom and sides of an 8″ × 8″ cooking pan that has sides 2″ deep.
3. Measure the amount of each dry ingredient called for in the list of ingredients, place in a small mixing bowl, and stir dry ingredients until they are well blended.
4. Crack raw egg in a cup or small bowl. Discard eggshell. Using a fork, swirl and beat the egg to blend the white and yolk thoroughly.
5. Measure the amount of each liquid ingredient called for in the list of ingredients and place in a separate small mixing bowl.
6. Add beaten egg to the liquid ingredients and stir.
7. Add liquid ingredients to the dry ingredients and stir with a large spoon until well blended.
8. Pour batter into the oiled baking pan. Place in hot oven.
9. Bake for 22 to 25 minutes. To check for doneness, insert a clean toothpick into the centre of the baked bread. Bread is finished baking if the toothpick doesn't have any batter sticking to it when removed from the bread.
10. Use potholders to protect your hands when removing the bread from the oven.
11. Turn off the oven. Serve the bread while it is hot.

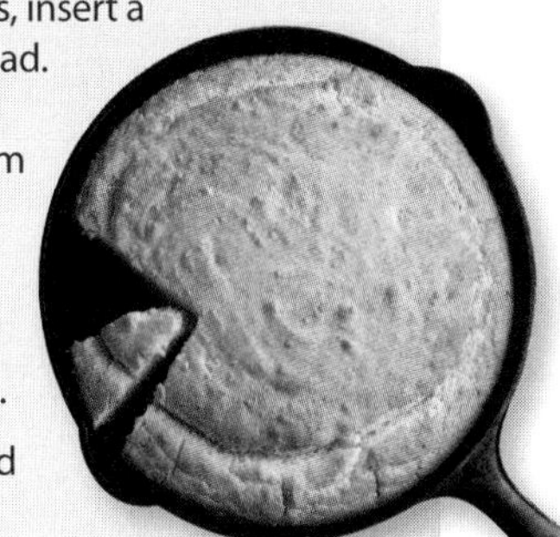

Tip: For easier cleanup, soak the bowl that contained the batter in cold, soapy water.

Personal Dietary Analysis

1. For a week, keep grocery and convenience store receipts.
   a. How much money did you spend on foods purchased at these markets?
   b. Which foods were the most expensive items purchased?
   c. How much money did you spend on empty-calorie foods such as salty snacks, cookies, soft drinks, and candy? ______
   d. What percentage of your food dollars were spent on empty-calorie foods? ______ (Divide the amount of money spent on empty-calorie foods by the total cost of food for the week. Move the decimal point over two places to the right and place a percent sign after the number.)
   e. How much money did you spend on nutrient-dense foods such as whole-grain products, fruits, and vegetables? ______
   f. What percentage of your food dollars were spent on nutrient-dense foods? ______ (Divide the amount of money spent on nutrient-dense foods by the total cost of food for the week. Move the decimal point over two places to the right and place a percent sign after the number.)
2. For one week, keep a detailed log of your usual vending machine purchases, including the item(s) purchased and amount of money spent for each purchase.
   a. What types of foods and beverages did you buy from the machines?
   b. How many soft drinks did you consume each day? ______
   c. How much money did you spend on vending machine foods and beverages? ______
   d. Based on this week's vending machine expenditures, estimate how much money you spend on such purchases in a year. ______
3. For one week, keep a detailed log of your usual fast food consumption practices, including fast food purchases at convenience stores. List the types of food and beverages you purchased and amount of money you spent.
   a. According to your weekly record, how often do you eat at fast food places? ______
   b. What types of foods did you usually buy?
   c. How much money did you spend on fast foods? ______
   d. Based on this week's expenditures, estimate how much money you spend on fast food purchases in a year. ______

CRITICAL THINKING

1. Identify at least six factors that influence your food selections. Which of these factors is the most important? Explain why.
2. Consider your current eating habits. Explain why you think your diet is nutritionally adequate or not.
3. "Everything in moderation." Explain what this statement means in terms of diet.
4. If you are at risk of developing a chronic health condition that could be prevented by changing your diet, would you make the necessary changes? Explain why or why not.
5. Have you ever used food to treat or prevent illnesses? If you have, describe the situations and discuss which foods were used.
6. What actions have you taken or can you take to help hungry or food-insecure people obtain adequate nutrition?

PRACTICE TEST

Select the best answer.

1. Diet is a
   a. practice of restricting energy intake.
   b. typical pattern of food choices.
   c. method of reducing portion sizes.
   d. technique to reduce carbohydrate intake.
2. Which of the following conditions is not a leading cause of death in Canada?
   a. tuberculosis
   b. cancer
   c. heart disease
   d. stroke
3. The nutrients that provide energy are
   a. carbohydrates, vitamins, and lipids.
   b. lipids, proteins, and minerals.
   c. vitamins, minerals, and proteins.
   d. proteins, fats, and carbohydrates.
4. ______ refers to chemical processes that occur in living cells.
   a. Physiology
   b. Catabolism
   c. Anatomy
   d. Metabolism
5. Phytochemicals
   a. are essential nutrients.
   b. may have healthful benefits.
   c. are toxic and should be avoided.
   d. none of the above

6. Dietary supplements
   a. may act as drugs.
   b. are scientifically proven to provide health benefits.
   c. must be safe for long-term human consumption before being marketed.
   d. are nutritionally complete replacements for foods.
7. Which of the following foods is a rich source of phytochemicals?
   a. hamburger c. peaches
   b. fish d. chicken
8. Which of the following conditions is a chronic disease?
   a. heart disease c. cancer
   b. stroke d. all of the above
9. In Canada, the primary cause of preventable cancer deaths is
   a. physical inactivity.
   b. tobacco use.
   c. high-fat diet.
   d. excessive alcohol intake.
10. Compared to 35 years ago, the typical Canadian
    a. eats less fruit.
    b. drinks more milk.
    c. consumes a lower percentage of energy from fat.
    d. eats more eggs.
11. Joe weighs 165 pounds. What is his weight in kilograms?
    a. 75 kg c. 82 kg
    b. 7.5 kg d. 8.2 kg
12. A serving of food contains 10 g carbohydrate, 2 g protein, and 4 g fat. The total kilocalories per serving of this food is
    a. 64. c. 84.
    b. 74. d. 94.
13. A serving of food supplies 20 g carbohydrate, 4 g protein, 10 g fat, and 50 g water. Which of the following statements is true about a serving of the food?
    a. Fat provides the most food energy.
    b. Carbohydrate provides the most food energy.
    c. Water provides the most food energy.
    d. Fat provides about 25% of total calories.
14. Which of the following foods is the most nutrient-dense?
    a. potato chips c. butter
    b. broccoli d. chocolate chip cookie
15. Which of the following statements is false?
    a. A megadose is 10 times the recommended amount of a nutrient.
    b. Megadoses of nutrients may behave like drugs in the body.
    c. In general, megadoses of nutrients are safe to consume.
    d. A physiologic dose of a vitamin is less than a megadose of the vitamin.

Answers to Chapter 1 Quiz Yourself

1. There are four classes of nutrients: proteins, lipids, sugars, and vitamins. **False.** (p. 4)
2. Proteins are the most essential class of nutrients. **False.** (p. 5)
3. All nutrients must be supplied by the diet, because they cannot be made by the body. **False.** (p. 5)
4. Vitamins are a source of energy. **False.** (p. 5)
5. Milk, carrots, and bananas are examples of "perfect" foods that contain all nutrients. **False.** (p. 13)

Please visit Connect at

www.mcgrawhillconnect.ca

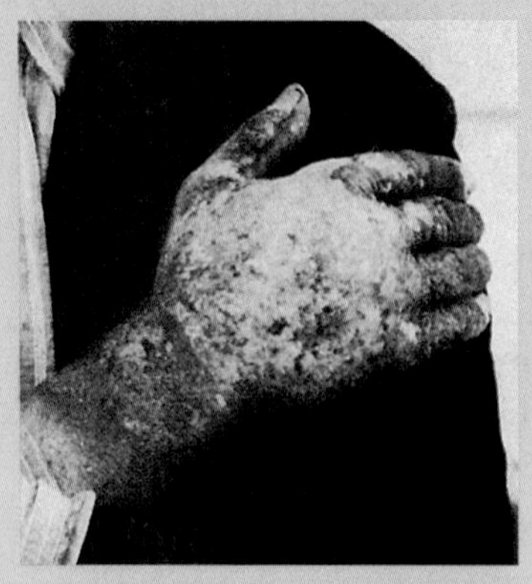

Chapter **2**

Evaluating Nutrition Information

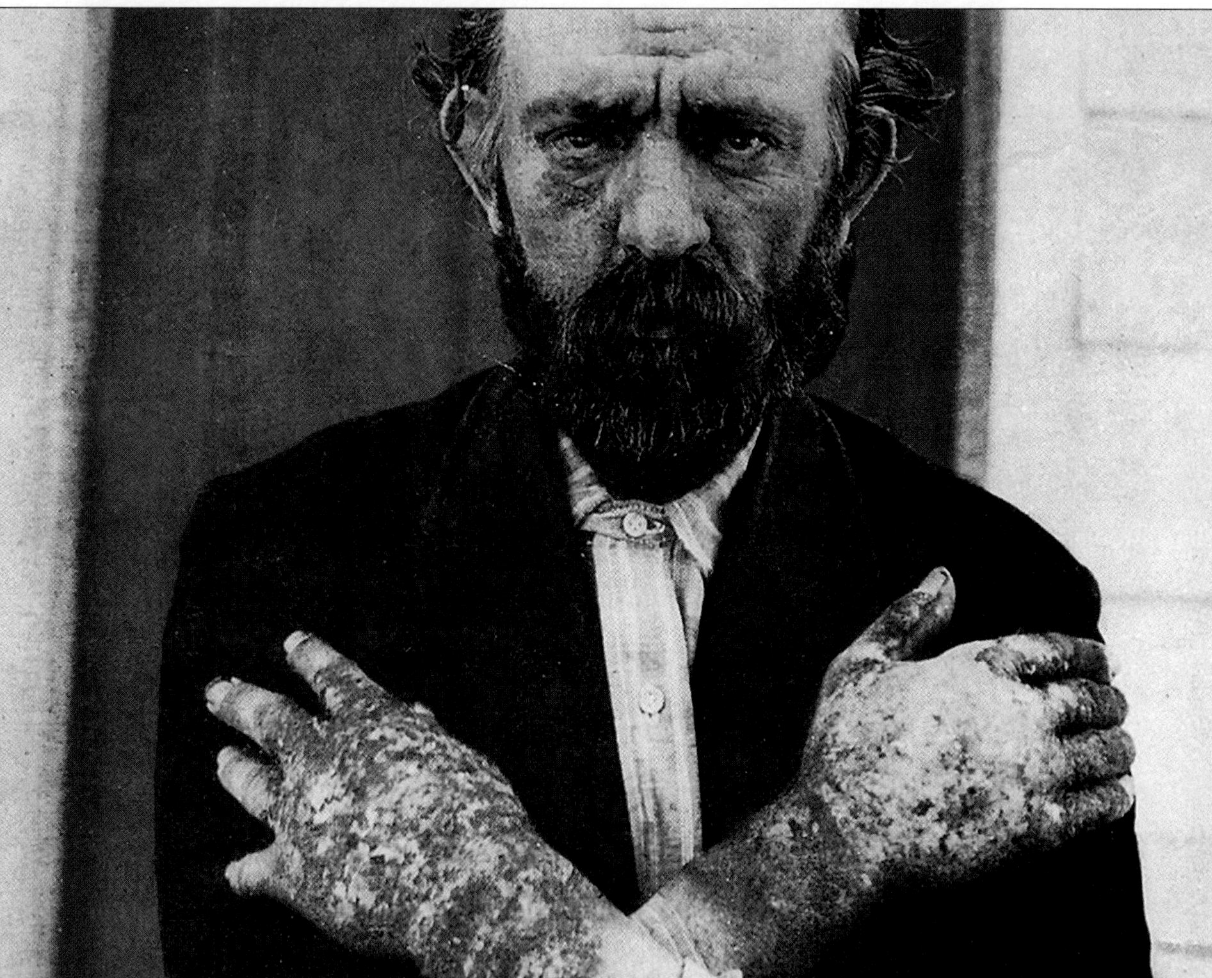

Chapter Learning Outcomes

After reading Chapter 2, you should be able to:

1. Define the terms anecdote, variable, epidemiology, placebo, placebo effect, peer review, and quackery.
2. Explain the basis of the scientific method as it is used in developing hypotheses and conducting research in the field of nutrition.
3. Explain the importance of having controls when performing experiments.
4. Define research bias.
5. Describe how to identify questionable sources of nutrition information.
6. Identify reliable sources of nutrition information.

In the early 1900s, the disease pellagra was widespread in the United States, especially in southern states. Individuals with pellagra were weak, and they developed diarrhea, a skin rash, and mental confusion. Each year, thousands of Americans died from this dreaded illness. In 1914 the U.S. surgeon general assigned Joseph Goldberger, a physician who worked in a federal government laboratory, to study pellagra. Most medical experts thought pellagra was an infectious disease because it often occurred where people lived in close quarters, such as prisons, orphanages, and mental health institutions.

Goldberger knew from his previous research that infectious diseases usually spread through a population by close physical contact. While investigating factors associated with pellagra, Goldberger observed that not everyone who was exposed to people suffering from pellagra developed the condition. For example, many prisoners had pellagra, but none of their guards or prison administrators suffered from the disease, even though they associated closely with the affected inmates. Based on his observations, Goldberger rejected the medical establishment's notion that pellagra was an infectious disease.

Dr. Goldberger also noted that prisoners ate a diet that was typically eaten by other people with pellagra. The diet emphasized cornbread, hominy grits (a corn product), molasses, potatoes, cabbage, and rice. At the time, this monotonous low-protein diet was associated with poverty throughout the southern United States. He also observed that people who did not develop pellagra had higher incomes and ate more meat, milk, and fresh vegetables. Goldberger developed the hypothesis that pellagra resulted from the lack of something in poor people's diet. A **hypothesis** is a possible explanation for an observation that guides scientific research. Goldberger hypothesized that the missing dietary factor was in meat, milk, and other foods eaten regularly by people with high incomes. To test his hypothesis, Goldberger gave these foods to children in two Mississippi orphanages and patients in a Georgia mental institution who were suffering from pellagra, and they were cured of the disease. Despite the results of Goldberger's experiment, many members of the medical establishment rejected his finding that a poor diet was the cause of pellagra, and they continued to think pellagra was an infectious disease.

To satisfy his critics, Goldberger enrolled a group of healthy, Mississippi prison inmates in an experiment that involved consuming the corn- and molasses-based diet commonly eaten in the southern U.S. at the time. After a few months, more than half of the inmates developed cases of pellagra, confirmed by medical experts who were not associated with Goldberger. Once again, however, many of Goldberger's critics rejected his finding that poor diet was the cause of pellagra.

In 1916, Dr. Goldberger decided to end the controversy by experimenting on himself and some volunteers during what they called a "filth party." The group applied secretions taken from inside the nose and throat of a patient with pellagra into their noses and throats; they also swallowed pills made with flakes of skin scraped from the rashes of people with the disease. Additionally, Goldberger and one of his colleagues gave each other an injection of blood from a person who had pellagra. If pellagra were infectious, filth party participants should have contracted the disease—but none of them did. Despite the results of Dr. Goldberger's extraordinary experiment, a few physicians still resisted the idea that pellagra was associated with diet.[1]

Dr. Goldberger died in 1929—eight years before Dr. Conrad Elvehjem and his team of scientists at the University of Wisconsin isolated a form of the B-vitamin niacin from liver extracts. Elvehjem and his colleagues discovered niacin cured "black tongue," a condition affecting dogs that was similar to pellagra.[2] Not long after Elvehjem's findings were published, niacin was determined to be effective in treating pellagra, and the medical establishment finally accepted the fact that the disease was the result of a dietary deficiency.

Quiz YOURSELF

Before reading the rest of Chapter 2, test your knowledge of scientific methods and reliable sources of nutrition information by taking the following quiz. The answers are on page 49.

1. Scientists generally do not raise questions about or criticize the conclusions of their colleagues' research data, even when they disagree with those conclusions. ______T______F
2. Popular health-related magazines typically publish articles that have been peer-reviewed. ______T______F
3. By conducting a prospective epidemiological study, medical researchers can determine risk factors that influence health outcomes. ______T______F
4. A placebo contains ingredients that provide no measurable effects. ______T______F
5. In general, registered dietitians are reliable sources of food and nutrition information. ______T______F

hypothesis possible explanation about an observation that guides scientific research

Today, the idea that something missing in diets can cause a nutrient deficiency disease is widely accepted. A hundred years ago, however, it was a novel idea that most medical experts dismissed because they thought only "germs" caused disease. It is interesting to note that raw corn actually contains niacin, but it is in a form the body cannot digest. Furthermore, consuming meat and milk helps prevent pellagra because these foods contain tryptophan, an essential amino acid that the body can convert to niacin.

A more recent example of the time and effort it takes to gain support for a medical hypothesis that opposes established beliefs is the case of the mysterious microbe. In the mid-1950s, the medical community generally accepted the cause of peptic ulcers (stomach sores) as stress and poor diet. Monkeys and rodents living under stressful conditions and humans recovering from severe burns often developed such ulcers. In 1982, Australian physicians Barry Marshall and Robin Warren isolated a type of bacteria from the stomachs of patients with gastritis, inflammation of the stomach lining that can result in peptic ulcers.[3] Marshall and Warren hypothesized that this microbe might be related to the development of gastritis and peptic ulcers, and they suggested treating the conditions with antibiotics. Initially other physicians were skeptical about Marshall and Warren's hypothesis because it challenged traditional medical beliefs and treatment practices. Traditional treatment for gastritis and peptic ulcers generally included antacids and a bland diet, not antibiotics. To provide support for his idea, Marshall actually swallowed some of the bacteria and developed severe stomach inflammation as a result. Then other researchers published articles that confirmed the presence of a type of bacteria that was capable of living in human stomachs and likely responsible for certain chronic stomach ailments. Within a few years, the medical profession accepted the idea that the bacterium (*Helicobacter pylori or H. pylori*) was a primary cause of gastritis and peptic ulcers (Fig. 2.1). Today people with peptic ulcers who test positive for *H. pylori* in their stomachs are treated with antibiotics that kill the bacterium. In 2005, Marshall and Warren received the Nobel Prize in medicine for their groundbreaking research and scientific contribution to medical care.

These experiences are just two of many fascinating examples that illustrate how researchers use scientific methods to solve medical mysteries relating to nutrition and health. As in these cases, it is not unusual for scientists to refrain from making quick judgments about a novel nutrition hypothesis until it undergoes repeated testing. Thus it often takes many years before a scientific discovery becomes widely accepted by other experts in the nutrition field. How do nutrition scientists determine facts about foods, nutrients, and diets? Why do nutrition scientists seem to contradict themselves so much? How can you evaluate the reliability of nutrition information? Where can you obtain up-to-date, accurate nutrition information? Chapter 2 will provide answers to these questions and help you become a more critical, educated, and careful consumer.

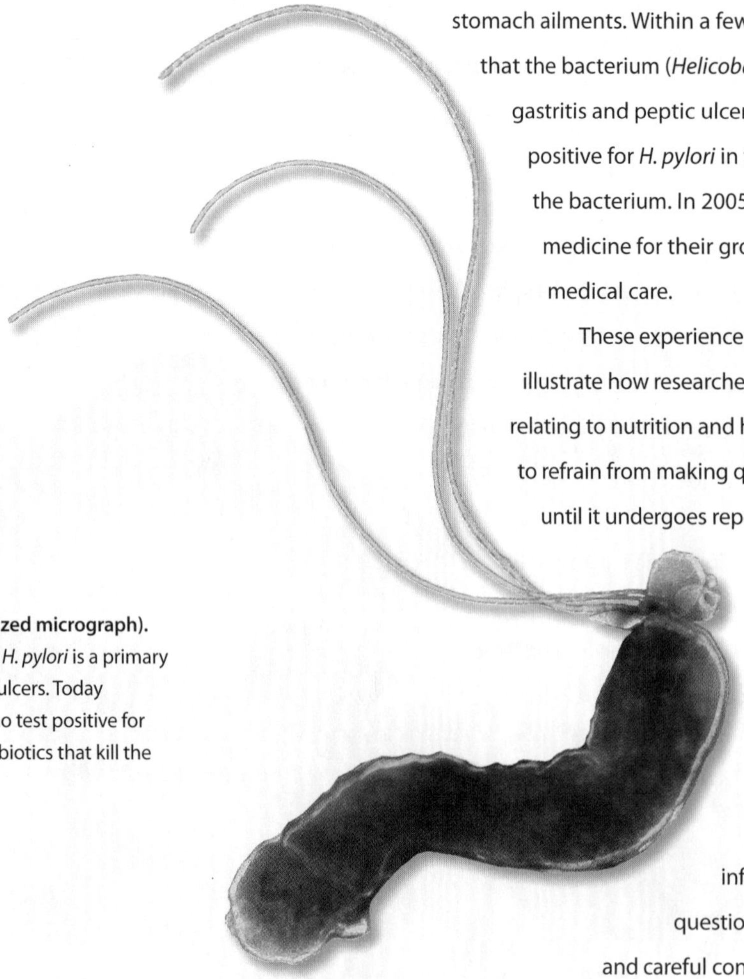

Figure 2.1 ***H. pylori*** **(colourized micrograph).** Infection with the bacterium *H. pylori* is a primary cause of gastritis and peptic ulcers. Today people with peptic ulcers who test positive for *H. pylori* are treated with antibiotics that kill the bacterium.

Understanding the Scientific Method

Scientists ask questions about the natural world and follow generally accepted, standardized methods to obtain answers to these questions. In the past, nutrition facts and dietary practices were often based on intuition, common sense, "conventional wisdom" (tradition), or **anecdotes** (personal reports of experiences). Today, dietitians and other nutrition experts discard conventional beliefs, explanations, and practices when the results of current scientific research no longer support them.

Nutrition researchers generally rely on scientific methods that may involve making observations, asking questions and developing hypotheses, performing tests, and collecting and analyzing data (information) to find relationships between variables. A **variable** is a factor such as a person's age, weight, or environment that can change and influence an outcome. After analyzing data, researchers draw conclusions from the information and report and disseminate the findings. Other scientists can test the findings to support or refute them. Figure 2.2 presents the general steps nutrition researchers take when conducting scientific investigations. The following sections take a closer look at some common methods that scientists use to collect nutrition information and establish nutrition facts.

SCIENTIFIC METHOD

1. Make observations that generate questions
2. Formulate hypotheses to explain events
3. Design studies, perform tests, and collect data
4. Analyze data and draw conclusions based on the results
5. Share results with peers (report findings)
6. Conduct more research, the results of which may confirm or refute previous findings

Figure 2.2 Nutrition science: Scientific method. Nutrition scientists generally follow these steps when conducting research.

Epidemiological Studies

For decades, medical researchers have noted differences in rates of chronic diseases and causes of death among various populations. Type 2 diabetes, for example, occurs more frequently among Native North Americans and non-Hispanic adults of African descent than among white Canadian adults.[4] Additionally, breast cancer is more common among non-Hispanic white females than females who are members of other North American racial or ethnic groups.[5] **Epidemiology** is the study of disease rates among different population groups, factors associated with the occurrence of diseases, and how diseases spread in a population. Epidemiologists often rely on physical examinations of people to obtain health data (Fig. 2.3). Additionally, they may collect information by conducting surveys, the use of questionnaires that ask people about their attitudes and practices.

anecdotes personal reports of experiences

variable personal characteristic or other factor that changes and can influence an outcome

epidemiology study of disease rates among different population groups

case-control study type of study in which individuals who have a health condition are compared with individuals who have similar characteristics but do not have the condition

Designing Epidemiological Studies

Epidemiological studies often have case-control, prospective, or retrospective designs. Such investigations can provide epidemiologists with clues about the causes, progression, and prevention of the disease. In a **case-control study**, individuals with a health condition (cases) such as stomach cancer are matched to persons with similar characteristics who do not have the condition. By analyzing the results of case-control studies, scientists may be able to identify dietary factors that differ between the two groups, such as long-term fruit and vegetable intakes. Dr. Goldberger's efforts to determine the cause of pellagra involved comparing cases of the disease with people who lived in the same area but were healthy.

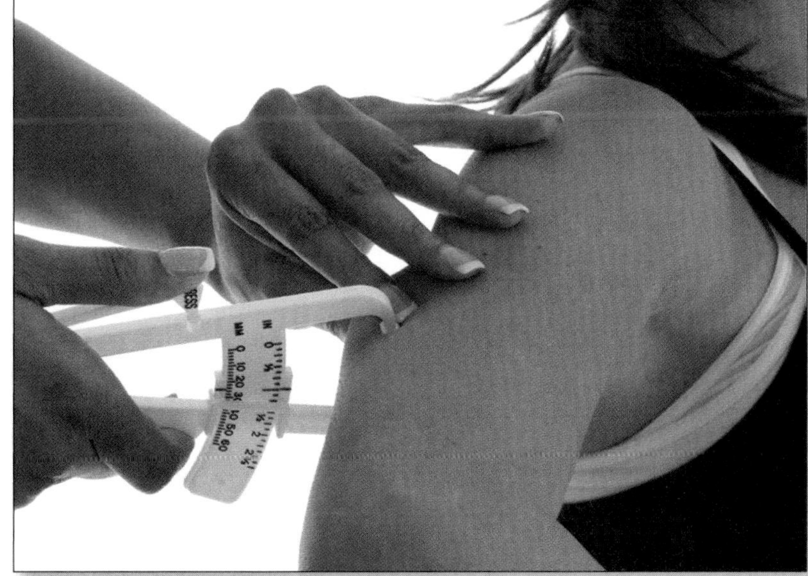

Figure 2.3 Collecting nutrition-related information. Epidemiologists and dietitians often rely on physical examinations of people to obtain health data.

prospective study type of study that follows a group of healthy people over time to determine characteristics associated with the development of diseases

treatment or **experimental group** group being studied that receives a treatment

control group group being studied whose treatment differs from that of a treatment group, such as not receiving any treatment or receiving a placebo

retrospective study type of study that determines factors that may have contributed to the development of disease

A **prospective study** follows a large group of healthy people over time to determine whether those with a certain characteristic develop a disease and those without that characteristic remain disease-free. (Prospective means "to look forward.") The Framingham Study that began in 1949 in Framingham, Massachusetts, is one of the most well-known prospective studies. At the beginning of the study, more than 5200 healthy participants (men and women) underwent extensive physical examinations and questioning about their family and personal medical histories as well as their lifestyle practices. Over the following years, a group of medical researchers periodically collected data concerning each participant's health and, if the person died, cause of death. The scientists analyzed this information and found relationships between a variety of personal characteristics and health outcomes. Findings from the Framingham Study identified numerous risk factors for heart disease, including elevated blood cholesterol levels, cigarette smoking, and hypertension (chronic high blood pressure). Today, medical researchers are still collecting information from the original Framingham Study participants as well as their descendants.

In some prospective studies, researchers perform an intervention, such as a specific dietary or behavioural change, on a group of people (the **treatment** or **experimental group**), and the results of the intervention are monitored over a long period. Data collected from the treatment group are compared to a population with similar characteristics who has not made the specific change during the same period (the **control group**). If the data indicate that the health of the treatment group differs from the health of the control group, the researchers may associate the difference with the intervention. A team of researchers, for example, gives a dietary supplement that contains an extract made from the bark of a tree that grows in South America to a group of healthy people and monitors their blood cholesterol levels. At the end of the treatment period, the team compares cholesterol levels of the treatment group to cholesterol levels of a group of healthy people with similar characteristics who did not take the tree bark supplement. The results of this study may indicate whether the supplement affects blood cholesterol levels.

To conduct a **retrospective study**, researchers identify a group of people who already suffer from a disease and compare them, particularly their past lifestyle practices, to a group of people with similar characteristics who do not have the disease. (Retrospective means to "look back.") The results may identify long-term factors that may have been responsible for the illness. For example, researchers compare the dietary histories of a group of people suffering from hypertension to the dietary histories of a group of people with similar characteristics but healthy blood pressures. By comparing the dietary data collected from the two groups, researchers can identify foods that may be associated with the development of hypertension.

Limitations of Epidemiological Studies

By studying differences in dietary practices and disease occurrences among populations, epidemiologists may establish nutritional hypotheses for the prevalence of certain diseases. If one group of people is more likely to develop a certain health disorder than another group, and the two populations consume very different diets, scientists can speculate about the role diet plays in this difference. For example, results of several epidemiological studies indicate that the incidence of breast cancer is higher among women in Western countries than women in Asian countries, and Western women generally have lower intakes of soy products than women with Asian ancestry.[6,7,8] Based on this information, you might conclude that eating a low-soy diet *causes* breast cancer, but is your conclusion valid?

Although it appears that a low-soy diet increases the risk of breast cancer in females, epidemiological studies cannot establish causation, that is, whether a practice is responsible for an effect. When two different natural events occur simultaneously within a population, it does not necessarily mean they are correlated. A **correlation** is a relationship between variables. A correlation occurs when two variables change over the same period, such as when a country's percentage of overweight people increases as its population's intake of sugar-sweetened soft drinks also increases. In this case, the correlation is *direct* or *positive* because the two variables—body weight and regular soft drink consumption—are changing in the same direction; they are both increasing. An *inverse* or *negative* correlation occurs when one variable increases and the other one decreases. An example of an inverse correlation is the relationship between diet and hypertension; as a population's fresh fruit consumption increases, the prevalence of hypertension in that population tends to decrease.

correlation relationship between variables

What appears to be a correlation between a behaviour and an outcome could be a coincidence, that is, a chance happening, and not an indication of a *cause-and-effect* relationship between the two variables. For example, in a survey of iced tea consumption in Ontario over a 10-year period, we might observe that fewer people drank iced tea during winter months than during summer months. In a survey of snow skiing accidents in Ontario during the same 10-year period, we might also find that snow skiing accidents were more likely to occur in winter than in summer. Thus, as iced tea consumption declined, snow skiing accidents increased. Does this mean iced tea consumption is inversely correlated to skiing accidents, and people who do not drink iced tea have a greater risk of having a skiing accident at this time of year? It is more likely that the relationship between snow skiing and iced tea drinking is coincidental, because both activities are associated with seasonal weather conditions. Although this example is obviously far-fetched, it illustrates the problems scientists can have when analyzing results of epidemiological studies.

In cases involving chronic diseases such as cancer, it is difficult to determine a single variable that is responsible for the development of the condition. Multiple factors, including a person's genetic susceptibility (inherited proneness) to develop the disease, usually influence whether the chronic disease occurs. For example, many environmental, physiological, and lifestyle variables are responsible for the development of breast cancer in women. According to results of epidemiological studies, body weight, red meat consumption, and age are some of the variables that influence a woman's risk of breast cancer.[9] Therefore, it is possible that variables besides soy intake account for the different rates of breast cancer observed between Western and Asian women.

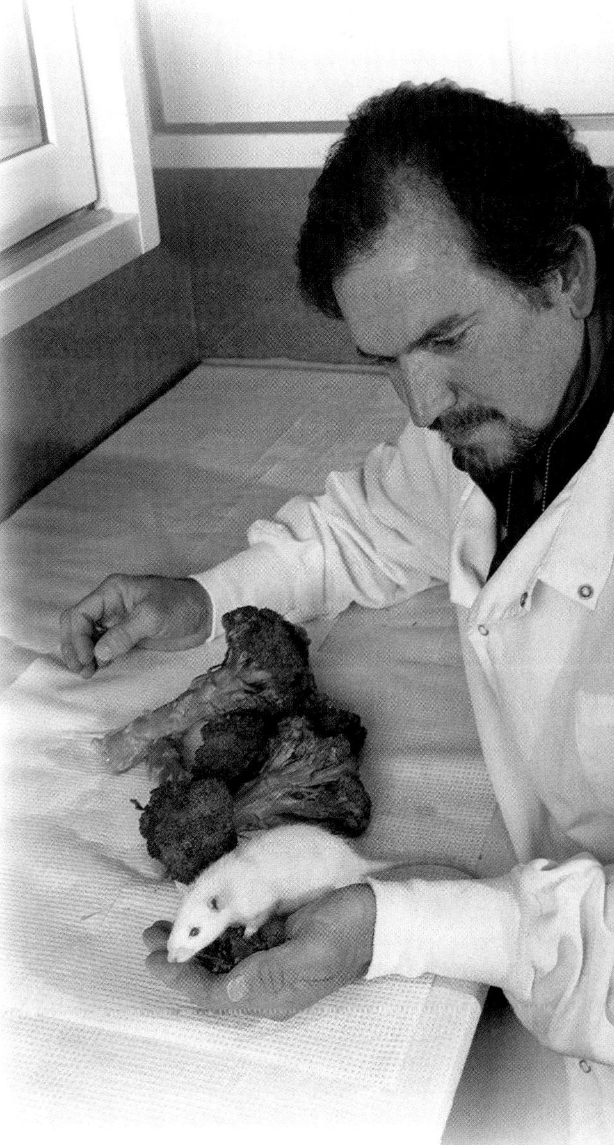

Figure 2.4 Rodents for research. Nutrition scientists often conduct in vivo experiments on small rodents that are raised for experimentation purposes. In this photo, a nutritionist holds a laboratory rat and a sample of selenium-enriched broccoli.

Experimentation

Many variables may influence the outcome of an epidemiological study. Thus, scientists performing research to determine the effect or effects of a single variable need to *control* the influence of other variables. Such testing is often done in laboratory settings. Nutrition researchers can perform controlled laboratory experiments on components derived from living organisms (in vitro or "test tube" experiments) or on whole living organisms (in vivo experiments). Nutrition scientists often conduct in vivo experiments on small mammals, particularly mice or rats that are raised for experimentation purposes. These rodents are inexpensive to house in laboratories, and their food and other living conditions can be carefully controlled (Fig. 2.4). Because of the physiological differences between humans and other mammals, medical researchers must be careful when applying the results of animal studies to people. Nevertheless, scientists are often able to determine the safety and effectiveness of treatments by conducting research on laboratory animals before engaging in similar testing on humans.

The findings of research involving a group of human subjects are more likely to be generalized to other people; however, conducting experiments on humans can be costly and often involves ethical concerns. Furthermore, people are not likely to enroll in clinical studies. Clinical

placebo fake treatment, such as a sham pill, injection, or medical procedure

studies may require living in tightly controlled settings such as the nutrition research unit of a major university's medical school for a few days or weeks. Such participation would likely restrict people's lifestyles too much. Nutrition scientists recognize that valuable information can be collected from recruiting subjects who are able to go about their usual routines. Thus, researchers can design studies to allow subjects to maintain their lifestyle practices, except for the variable being studied.

Reviewing the Scientific Literature

Before nutrition scientists design studies, they perform a review of literature that involves a search of scientific articles previously published on their topic of interest. For example, a team of scientists plans to conduct a 5-year intervention study to determine the effects of adding 15 grams of soy per day to the diets of women who have higher than average risks of breast cancer. The scientists read articles concerning research that examined the effects of soy intake on breast cancer risk to learn what is known about them. Additionally, the findings and conclusions of the previous research may raise questions that can be explored in a new study. The goal of a comprehensive review of literature is to identify gaps in the current body of knowledge in a particular area, to inform future research design.

Developing a Hypothesis

After performing the literature review, our team of scientists can develop one or more hypotheses, such as, "Increasing soy intake to 15 grams daily reduces the risk of breast cancer in Canadian women." Another hypothesis might be, "Daily consumption of wafers that provide a total of 15 grams of soy reduces the risk of breast cancer in women." The results of analyzing data gathered from this study may support or refute each hypothesis.

Conducting Human Research

To reduce the likelihood that the results of the soy study occur by chance, the researchers enroll a large group of healthy women (2000, for example) who have higher than average risk of breast cancer in the study. Subjects are randomly assigned into two groups; 1000 are in the treatment group, and 1000 are in the control group. Random assignment helps ensure that the members of the experimental and control groups have similar variables, such as age and other characteristics.

The investigative team provides a supply of wafers to the treatment group's participants and instructions concerning their daily consumption. By following these instructions, each treatment group member will consume 15 grams of soy per day. Members of the control group are also given a supply of wafers, but their wafers are **placebos** that do not contain soy. Placebos are not simply "sugar pills"; they are a fake treatment, such as a sham pill, injection, or medical procedure. A placebo wafer looks, smells, and tastes like the wafer that actually contains soy, except its ingredients are *inert*, that is, they are not known to produce any measurable physical changes in the people eating them. Both groups are given the same instructions concerning their food intake, dietary record-keeping, and health care reporting for the duration of the study.

Why do scientists often use placebos? Some people report positive or negative reactions to a treatment even though they received the placebo. If a patient believes a medical treatment will improve his or her health, the patient is more likely to report positive results for the therapy. Such wishful thinking is called the **placebo effect**. Providing placebos to members of the control group enables scientists to compare the extent of the treatment's response with that of the placebo.

People who take herbal products or use unconventional medical therapies to prevent or treat diseases are often convinced the products and treatments are effective despite the general lack of scientific evidence to support their beliefs. For some people, placebos can produce beneficial physiological and psychological changes, particularly in conditions that involve pain or depression.[11] Because subjects in the control group believe they are receiving a real treatment, their faith in the "treatment" can stimulate the release of chemicals in the brain that alters pain perception, reducing their discomfort. Therefore, when people report that a treatment was beneficial, they may not have been imagining the response, even when they were taking a placebo.

placebo effect response to a placebo

double-blind study experimental design in which neither the participants nor the researchers are aware of each participant's assignment

peer review expert critical analysis of a research article prior to its publication

Reviewing Human Subject Research Design Scientists must follow the Medical Research Council of Canada guidelines when performing research involving human subjects as outlined in the *Tri-Council Policy Statement: Ethical Conduct for Research Involving Humans.*[10] Before conducting this type of research, scientists must have the study design scrutinized by their institution's human subjects' ethics review committee. To pass the review, a study generally should avoid causing physical and psychological harm or discomfort to subjects beyond that which may be encountered in daily life or during a routine physical examination. Additionally, adult subjects must provide legally obtained informed consent indicating they are aware of the benefits and risks of the research effort and are willing participants.

Double-blind Studies Randomized human studies are usually **double-blind**—that is, both the investigators and subjects are not aware of the subjects' group assignments. Codes are used to identify a subject's group membership, and this information is not revealed until the end of the study. Maintaining such secrecy is important during the course of a human study involving placebos because researchers and subjects may try to predict group assignments based on their expectations. If the investigators who interview the participants are aware of their individual group assignments during the study, they may unwittingly convey clues to each subject, perhaps in the form of body language, that could influence the subject's belief about being in the experimental or control group. Subjects who suspect they are in the control group and taking a placebo may report no changes in their condition because they expect a placebo should have no effect on them. On the other hand, subjects who think they are in the treatment group could insist that they feel better or have more stamina as a result of the treatment, even though the treatment may not have produced any measurable changes in their bodies. Ideally, subjects should not be able to figure out their group assignment while researchers are collecting information from them.

Analyzing Data, Drawing Conclusions, and Reporting Findings

Nutrition researchers use a variety of statistical methods to analyze data collected from observations and experiments. These methods may enable the researchers to find relationships between the variables and health outcomes that were studied. As a result, scientists can determine whether their hypotheses are supported by the data. According to results of our example study investigating the effects of soy intake on breast cancer risk, the rate of new cases of breast cancer was 3/1000 among members of the experimental group and 25/1000 among the members of the control group. Based on their analyses, the scientists concluded that eating at least 15 grams of soy daily for 5 years may reduce the risk of breast cancer in women who have high risk of the disease.

When an experiment or study is completed and the results analyzed, researchers summarize the findings and seek to publish articles with information about their investigation in scientific journals. Before articles are accepted for publication, they undergo **peer review**, a critical analysis conducted by a group of peers. Peers are investigators who were not part of the study but are experts involved in related research. If peers agree that a study was well conducted, its results are fairly represented, and

Examples of peer-reviewed medical and nutrition journals include the *Canadian Medical Association Journal, Canadian Journal of Dietetic Practice and Research, American Journal of Clinical Nutrition, New England Journal of Medicine, Journal of the American Medical Association,* and *Canadian Journal of Public Health.*

the research is of interest to the journal's readers, these scientists are likely to recommend that the journal's editors publish the article.

Research Bias Scientists expect other researchers to avoid relying on their personal attitudes and biases when collecting and analyzing data, and to evaluate and report their results objectively and honestly. This process is important because much of the scientific research that is conducted in Canada is supported financially by the federal or provincial government, non-profit foundations, and other private industries. Some funding sources can have certain expectations or biases about research outcomes, and as a result, they are likely to finance studies of scientists whose research efforts support their interests. The beef industry, for example, might not fund scientific investigations to find connections between high intakes of beef and the risk of certain cancers. On the other hand, the beef industry might be interested in supporting a team of scientists whose research indicates a high-protein diet that contains plenty of beef is useful for people who are trying to lose weight.

Peer-reviewed journals usually require authors of articles to disclose their affiliations and sources of financial support. Such disclosers may appear on the first page or at the end of the article. By having this information, readers can decide on the reliability of the findings. Although peer review helps ensure that the scientists are as ethical and objective as possible, it is impossible to eliminate all research bias.

Spreading the News

After the results of a study are published in a nutrition-related journal or reported to health professionals attending a meeting of a nutrition or medical society, the media (e.g., newspapers, magazines, Internet news sources) may receive notice of the findings. If the information is simplistic and sensational, such as a finding that drinking green tea can result in permanent weight loss, it is more likely to be reported in the popular press. In many instances, you learn about the study's results when they are reported in a television or radio news broadcast as a 15- or 30-second sound bite. Such sources generally provide very little information concerning the way the study was conducted or how the data were collected and analyzed.

Popular sources of nutrition information, such as magazines and newspapers, generally do not subject articles to peer review or other scientific scrutiny, and as a result, they may feature articles and columns with faulty, biased information. Some newspapers, magazines, and Internet news sites contain brief articles or columns that summarize research conclusions extracted from scientific journal articles. Although these secondary sources may contain accurate information, they may provide an unbalanced review of the research if they reflect the biases of the summaries' authors. For example, a health news column in a popular magazine may report findings from a few nutrition journal articles that support the use of garlic supplements for reducing blood cholesterol levels. However, you may conclude that the column is biased if it excludes results of other studies that do not indicate such benefits.

You can often distinguish a peer-reviewed scientific journal from a popular magazine simply by looking at their covers and skimming their pages. Compared to scientific journals, magazines typically have more colourful, attractive covers and photographs, and their articles are shorter and easier for the average person to read (Fig. 2.5).

It is important to keep in mind that sensational media coverage of a medical "breakthrough" is not necessarily an indication of the value or quality of research that resulted in the news story, magazine article, or newspaper column. More research is often necessary for scientists to determine whether the results of a widely reported study are valid and can be generalized to other populations.

Figure 2.5 Judging by the cover. Consumers can be trained to look for features, such as covers, that distinguish a peer-reviewed scientific journal from a popular magazine.

Following Up with More Research

The results of one study are rarely enough to gain widespread acceptance for new or unusual findings or to provide a basis for nutritional recommendations. Thus, the findings obtained by one research team must be supported by those generated in other studies. If the results of several scientific investigations conducted under similar conditions confirm the original researcher's conclusions, then these findings are more likely to be accepted by other nutrition scientists.

Confusion and Conflict One day the news highlights dramatic health benefits from eating garlic, dark chocolate, or whole grains. A few weeks later, the news includes reports of more recent scientific investigations that do not support the earlier findings. When consumers become aware of conflicting results generated by nutrition studies, they often become confused and disappointed. As a result, some people may mistrust the scientific community and think nutrition scientists do not know what they are doing.

Consumers need to recognize that conflicting findings often result from differences in the ways various studies are designed. Even when investigating the same question, different groups of scientists often conduct their studies and analyze the results differently. For example, the numbers, ages, and physical conditions of subjects; the type and length of the study; the amount of the treatment provided; and the statistical tests used to analyze results typically vary among studies. Additionally, individual genetic differences often contribute to a person's response to a treatment. Not only are people genetically different, they also have different lifestyles, and they typically recall dietary information and follow instructions concerning health care practices differently. These and other factors can influence the results of nutrition research involving human subjects.

The science of nutrition is constantly evolving; old beliefs and practices are discarded when they are not supported by more recent scientific evidence, and new principles and practices emerge from the new findings. By now you should understand that science involves asking questions, developing and testing hypotheses, gathering and analyzing data, drawing conclusions from data, and sometimes, accepting change.

Concept Checkpoint

1. What is epidemiology?
2. Explain the importance of having a control group when conducting experimental research.
3. What is the major difference between a prospective study and a retrospective study?
4. What is a placebo? Why are placebos often used in studies involving human subjects?
5. What is a double-blind study?
6. What is a peer-reviewed article?
7. Explain why results of similar studies may provide different findings.

Nutrition Information: Fact or Fiction?

While channel surfing one afternoon, you stop and watch the host of a televised home-shopping program promote FatMegaMelter, his company's brand of a dietary supplement for losing weight. According to the host, the supplement contains a chemical derived from a plant that grows naturally in South Africa. This amazing chemical reduces the appetite for fattening foods, enabling an overweight person taking FatMegaMelter to lose up to 30 pounds in 30 days, without the need to exercise more or eat less. The host interviews an attractive young actress who claims to have lost a lot of weight after she started taking FatMegaMelter pills. A few days later, a friend mentions that she has lost three pounds since she began taking this product a week ago. You would like to lose a few pounds without resorting to restricting your food intake or exercising. Should you take FatMegaMelter? The supplement helped the actress and your friend; will it help you?

testimonial personal endorsement of a product

Although the actress's health history appears to be compelling evidence that the weight-loss supplement is effective, her information is a **testimonial**, a personal endorsement of a product. People are usually paid to provide their testimonials for advertisements, therefore their remarks may be biased (slanted) in favour of the product. Your friend's experience with taking the same weight-loss product is intriguing, but it is an anecdote and not *proof* that FatMegaMelter promotes weight loss. When your source of nutrition information is a testimonial, anecdote, or advertisement, you cannot be sure that the information is based on scientific facts and, therefore, reliable.

Be Skeptical of Claims

People may think they have learned facts about nutrition and dietary supplements by reading popular magazine articles, newspaper columns, or best-selling books; visiting Internet Web sites; or watching television news, infomercials, or home-shopping programs. In many instances, however, they have been misinformed. It is prudent to be skeptical and not believe what you read or hear about nutrition-related topics without investigating the credibility of their sources. As a consumer, you are responsible for questioning and researching the accuracy of nutrition information as well as the credentials of the people making nutrition-related claims.

Promoters of worthless nutrition products and services often use sophisticated marketing methods to lure consumers. For example, some promoters of dietary supplements claim their products are "scientifically tested" or they include citations to what appear to be scientific journal articles in their ads or articles. Consumers, however, cannot be certain the information is true. Few dietary supplements have been thoroughly evaluated by reputable scientists. In some instances, these products have been scientifically tested, but the bulk of the research has shown that most dietary supplements provide little or no measurable health benefits. Nevertheless, promoters of dietary supplements usually ignore the scientific evidence and continue to sell their goods to an unsuspecting trusting public. Consumers also need to be alert for promoters' use of **pseudoscience**, the presentation of information masquerading as factual and obtained by scientific methods. In many instances, pseudoscientific nutrition or physiology information is presented with complex scientific-sounding terms, such as "enzymatic therapy" or "colloidal extract." Such terms are designed to convince people without science backgrounds that the nutrition-related information is true. Often, promoters of nutrition misinformation try to confuse people by weaving false information with facts into their claims, making the untrue material seem credible too.

pseudoscience presentation of information masquerading as factual and obtained by scientific methods

Although people's lives have improved as a result of scientific advancements in medicine, the general public tends to mistrust scientists, medical professionals, and the pharmaceutical industry. Promoters of nutrition misinformation exploit this mistrust to sell their products and services. For example, they may tell consumers that physicians rely on costly diagnostic methods and treatments for serious diseases because they are more interested in making money than doing what is best for their patients, such as recommending a dietary supplement. It is true that physicians need income to support themselves and their families, and drug companies strive to make profits and recover the large amounts of money they spend on testing new drugs for safety and usefulness. However, people who tell you that the "medical/scientific establishment and drug companies are hiding information about natural cures from you just to make money from your misery…" are using *scare tactics* to build mistrust in the medical establishment. People's lives have been improved by contributions of medical researchers, such as physicians Salk and Sabin who developed vaccines for preventing polio and Marshall and Warren who determined that a bacterium was responsible for most peptic ulcers (Fig. 2.6). By discovering effective ways to prevent or treat serious diseases, medical researchers are likely to enjoy considerable positive worldwide recognition for their efforts, such as the Nobel Prize in medicine. Additionally, physicians have much to gain from treating their patients kindly and effectively. Consider this: If you follow a physician's advice and have positive results, are you likely to be that doctor's patient for a long time and recommend the practitioner to others?

What are the motives of the person who sponsors a nutrition-related Web site or promotes a nutrition-related book, supplement, or device? Do you think they are simply in the business of providing information and promoting their products because they care more about consumers' health than making profits? Dietary supplement manufacturers, promoters, and sales outlets make considerable money as a result of consumer expectations in the health-promoting powers of their products. Sales of vitamins and dietary supplements in Canada totalled approximately $866 million in 2008.[12]

Not all dietary supplement manufacturers or their promoters provide misleading or dishonest nutrition information. Nevertheless, some of these products may be harmful or a waste of money. Therefore, consumers must be careful when deciding whether to purchase dietary supplements.

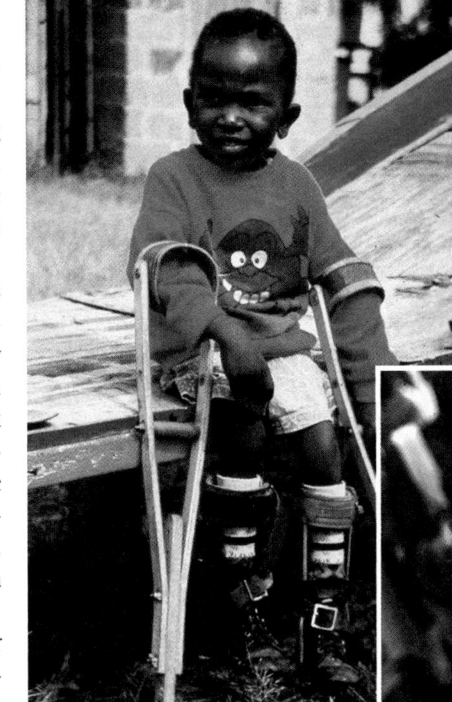

Figure 2.6 Applying results of scientific research. Our lives have been improved by contributions of medical researchers, such as physicians Salk and Sabin who developed vaccines for preventing polio. The child on the left has polio. Today polio rarely occurs in Canada because Canadian children routinely receive polio vaccines.

Ask Questions

If you are like most people, you do not want to waste your money on things you do not need, or that are useless or potentially harmful. How can you become a more careful, critical consumer of nutrition-related information? The following questions should help you evaluate various sources of nutrition information:

- *What motivates the authors, promoters, or sponsors to provide the information? Do you think they are more interested in your health and well-being or selling their products?* Salespeople often have favourable biases toward the things they sell, and therefore they may not be reliable sources of information about these products. A clerk in a health food store, for example, may wear a white lab coat and look as though he or she has a science or medical educational background, but you should keep in mind that the clerk was hired to

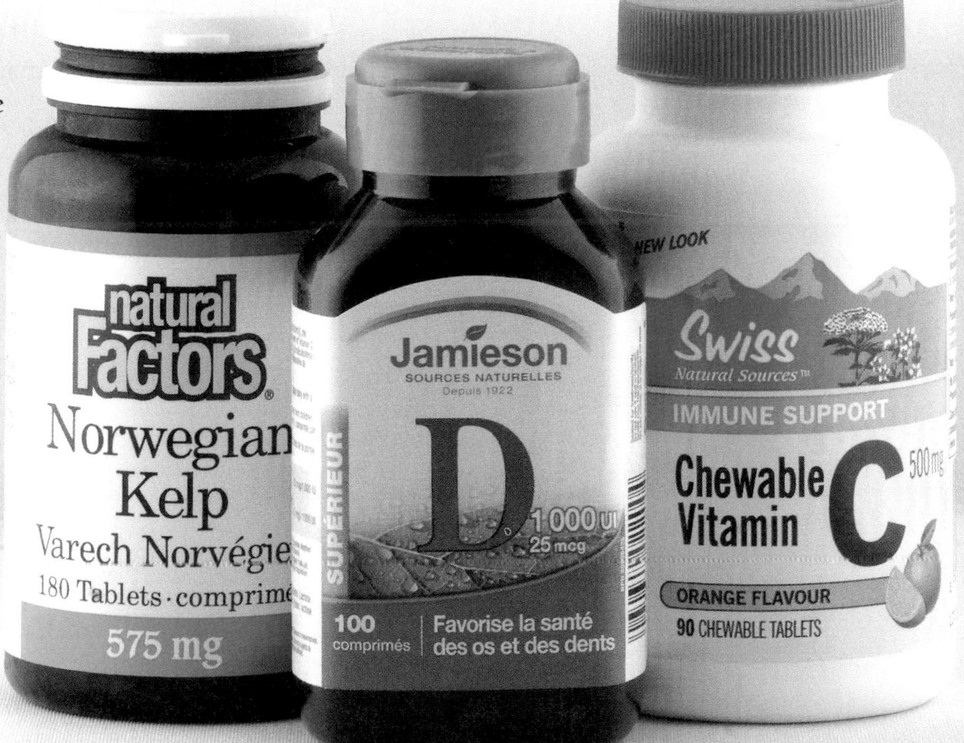

Many Canadians take dietary supplements regularly. Many of these supplements remain unregulated and should only be taken after consultation with a professional dietitian or physician.

sell dietary supplements and may have little or no scientific training. Furthermore, salespeople who work in health food stores may be unwilling to inform customers about the potential health hazards of taking certain products, particularly if they earn a commission from each sale.

- *Does the promoter or advertisement rely on anecdotes or testimonials?* As mentioned earlier, these sources of information are unreliable. Reliable nutrition information is research- or evidence-based.
- *Does the article or ad claim the product caused dramatic positive results, such as miraculous cures for serious diseases or extraordinary weight losses?* These claims are rarely true. Remember, if the claim sounds too good to be true, it probably is not true.
- *Is the product touted as a new scientific breakthrough that has been kept "secret" by the medical or pharmaceutical "establishment"? Are there statements that attack the credibility and motives of conventional medical practitioners?* Such statements indicate bias against the pharmaceutical industry or medical community. As a group, dietitians and physicians are dedicated to improving their patients' health and saving lives. Dietitians and physicians have nothing to gain from concealing a cure from the public. They strive to diagnose and treat diseases using scientifically tested and approved techniques. Moreover, a physician may face a malpractice lawsuit if he or she fails to diagnose and treat a condition effectively.
- *Does the source of information have disclaimers such as, "These results are not typical. Your results may vary."?* Disclaimers are clues that the product may not live up to your expectations or the manufacturer's claims.
- *Is the source scientific, such as an article from a peer-reviewed nutrition journal?* In general, popular sources of nutrition information such as articles in magazines are not peer-reviewed. Additionally, radio or TV programs that promote nutrition information may actually be advertisements for nutrition-related products.
- *If a study is cited, how was the research conducted? Did the study involve humans or animals? If people participated in the study, how many subjects were involved in the research? Who sponsored the study?* As mentioned earlier in this chapter, epidemiological studies are not useful for finding cause-and-effect relationships. Additionally, the results of studies involving large numbers of human subjects are more reliable than studies of animals. Sponsors may influence the outcomes of the studies they fund. To keep their readers more fully informed, many editors routinely disclose sponsors of the research articles published in their scientific journals.
- *To provide scientific support for claims, does the source cite respected nutrition or medical journals or mention reliable experts?* Be careful if you see citations to references in nutrition or medical journals. Promoters of nutrition misinformation may refer to scientific-appearing citations from phony medical journals to convince people that their information is reliable. Furthermore, be wary of nutrition experts introduced or identified as "Doctor" because they may not be physicians or persons with medical or nutrition/dietetics training. A so-called nutrition expert who is referred to as "Doctor" may have a doctorate degree (PhD) in any subject area. Furthermore, someone with a PhD may have obtained his or her degree simply by purchasing it through an Internet or mail-order outlet, without having graduated from an accredited university or college.

quackery promotion of useless medical treatments

Practising medicine without the proper training and licensing is illegal. However, providing nutrition information and advice without the proper training and licensing is unfortunately legal. **Quackery** involves promoting useless medical treatments. To obtain information about a nutrition expert's credentials, enter the person's name at an Internet search engine and evaluate the results, or visit www.quackwatch.org and submit an "Ask a Question" e-mail to the site's sponsors.

Did You Know?

In order to call yourself a dietitian in Canada you must complete a university degree from a program accredited by Dietitians of Canada with significant emphasis on nutrition, as well as having completed a similarly accredited dietetic internship or practicum program. Once this education is complete, dietitians must seek registration with a provincial regulatory body in order to practise. Professional dietitians in Canada may use RD or RDt (registered dietitian), or PDt (professional dietitian) depending on the province in which they practise, or Dt (diététiste professionnel) in Quebec. In many provinces, "nutritionist" is not a legally protected title like dietitian, and thus some individuals with questionable education and training may still legally refer to themselves as nutritionists. If you have a problem with your car's functioning, you probably would want people who have the training, tools, and equipment to determine the problem and repair it. If you think something is wrong with your body, it is prudent to seek information and opinions from medical professionals who have the training and experience to diagnose and treat human health problems. Before purchasing and using a dietary supplement or nutrition-related device or service, check with a dietitian or your physician. Some products may interfere with conventional treatments, including prescription and over-the-counter medicines; others may be dangerous to take.

- *Are only the benefits of using the product highlighted, whereas potentially harmful side effects ignored?* Anything you consume, even water, can be toxic in high doses. Beware of any source of information that fails to mention the possible side effects of using a dietary supplement or other nutrition-related product.

Look for Red Flags

To become a skeptical consumer of nutrition information, you need to be aware of *red flags*, clues that indicate a source of nutrition information is unreliable. Common red flags include the following:

1. **Promises of quick and easy remedies for health-related problems:** "Our product helps you lose weight without exercise or dieting."
2. **Claims that sound too good to be true:** "Our all-natural product blocks fat and calories from being absorbed, so you can eat everything you like and still lose weight," or "Why eat food when you'll get all the nutrients you need by taking our supplements?"
3. **Scare tactics that include frightening, false, or misleading statements about a food, dietary practice, or nutrition-related health condition:** "Dairy products cause cancer," or "Children who eat meat and drink milk mature too early because of the hormones and chemical additives in these foods," or "More Canadians have cancer than ever before."
4. **Attacks on conventional scientists and health care practitioners:** "Physicians and drug company researchers don't want you to know about natural remedies for cancer, diabetes, and heart disease because it will dry up their profits."
5. **Statements about the superiority of natural dietary supplements and unconventional medical practices:** "For centuries, Asians have been drinking green tea to control their weight," or "For decades, Russian scientists have known about the countless health benefits of Siberian ginseng, but the North American medical community ignores these findings."
6. **Testimonials and anecdotes as evidence of effectiveness:** "I lost 50 pounds in 30 days using this product," or "I rubbed this vitamin E–containing lotion on my scar and it disappeared in days."

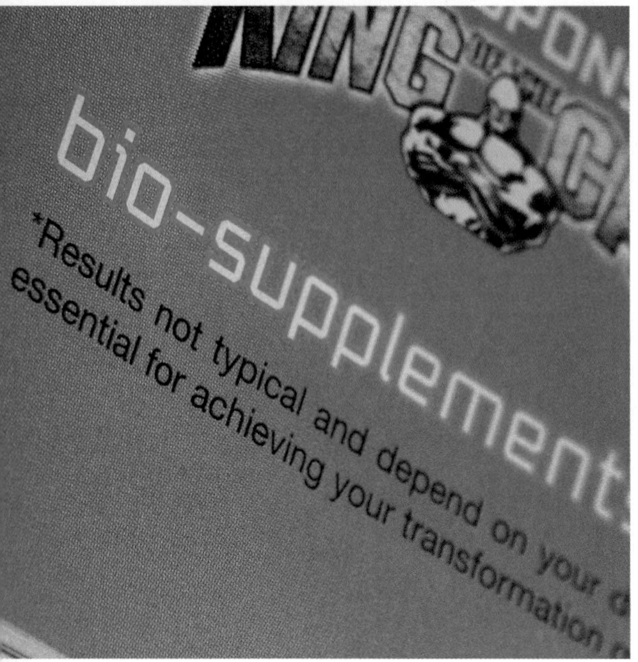

Figure 2.7 Disclaimer. This disclaimer may be a red flag indicating the product has limited effectiveness, despite its promoter's claims.

7. **Information that promotes a product's benefits while overlooking its risks:** "Our supplement boosts your metabolism naturally so it won't harm your system," or "One hundred percent of the people who used our product to treat diabetes had excellent results."
8. **Vague, meaningless, or scientific-sounding terms to confuse consumers:** "Our *all-natural, patented, chelated* dietary supplement works best when compared to our competitors' supplements," or "The typical vegetable grown in Canada lacks high-grade nutrients because conventional farming methods have *devitalized* the soil."
9. **Simplistic conclusions drawn from complex studies:** "Eating yogourt prevents gastrointestinal problems," or "Fish oil supplements prevent attention deficit disorder."
10. **Sensational statements without citing complete references of sources:** "Clinical research performed at a major university and published in a distinguished medical journal indicates food manufacturers have added ingredients to products that make you hungry and fat," or "Millions of Canadians suffer from nutritional deficiencies."
11. **Recommendations based on a single study:** "Research conducted at our private health facility proves coffee enemas can cure cancer."
12. **Information concerning nutrients or human physiology that are not supported by reliable scientific evidence:** "This book explains how to combine certain foods based on your blood type," or "Most diseases are caused by undigested food that gets stuck in your guts," or "People with alkaline bodies don't develop cancer."
13. **Sensational or frightening descriptions of commonly eaten foods:** "White foods, such as sugar, milk, and refined flour, are toxic," or "Eating processed foods causes cancer."
14. **References to natural cures that the medical establishment, pharmaceutical industry, and government agencies are concealing from the public:** "For years it has been known that cider vinegar is a natural cure for cancer, but Health Canada suppresses this information because it wants consumers to buy patent medications to support the pharmaceutical industry."
15. **Dramatic generalizations:** "Our dietary supplement cured Mary's diabetes; it can cure you too."
16. **Disclaimers, usually in small or difficult-to-read print:** "Results may vary," or "Results aren't typical" (Fig. 2.7).

If you're looking for a recipe for guacamole, cranberry chutney, or sweet and sour cabbage, simply use the Internet—it's like having a cookbook at your fingertips. Recipes for nearly every food and from various countries and ethnic groups are available on the Internet, and you can also find menu planning and cooking tips from this vast resource.

When searching the Web for recipes, you need to recognize that many food manufacturers use the sites to promote their products in recipes. If the brand name of a product is mentioned in the recipe, you can usually substitute another company's product. Additionally, recipes do not always provide information about the nutrients and calories in a serving of food, and you cannot be certain that the recipes have been tested for quality. Therefore, it's a good idea to check more than one site for a recipe and compare the information.

Using the Internet Wisely

You can find abundant sources of information about nutrition and the benefits of dietary supplements on the Internet. However, you must be careful and consider the sources. Who or what organization sponsors the site? Is the information intended to promote sales? Be wary if the site discusses benefits of dietary supplements and enables you to purchase these products online. Furthermore, a site is likely to be unreliable if it includes comprehensive disclaimers such as, "The manufacturer is not responsible or obligated to verify statements." Also avoid sites that publish disclaimers such as, "The nutrition and health information at this site is provided for educational purposes only and not as a substitute for the advice of a physician or dietitian. The author and owner of this site are not liable for personal actions taken as a result of the site's contents."

Be wary of Web sites that are authored or sponsored by one person, or sites that promote or sell products for profit (*.com) because such sources of information may be biased. In general, Web sites sponsored by nationally recognized health associations such as Dietitians of Canada (www.dietitians.ca) and non-profit organizations such as the Canadian Diabetes Association (www.diabetes.ca) are reliable sources of nutrition information. Additionally, government agencies (*.gc.ca or *.gov) and nationally accredited colleges and universities (*.edu) are excellent sources of credible nutrition information. Table 2.1 presents some tips for using the Internet to obtain reliable nutrition information.

TABLE 2.1
Tips for Searching Nutrition Information on the Internet

To be a careful consumer of Internet sources of information:

1. Use multiple sites, especially government sites, such as Health Canada (www.hc-sc.gc.ca), the Centers for Disease Control and Prevention (www.cdc.gov), and the Canadian Food Inspection Agency (www.inspection.gc.ca), as well as the sites of nationally recognized nutrition- or health-related associations such as Dietitians of Canada (www.dietitians.ca) and the Canadian Heart and Stroke Foundation (www.heartandstroke.ca).
2. Rely primarily on sites that are managed or reviewed by a group of qualified health professionals. Blogs might be fun and interesting to read, but they are not necessarily reliable.
3. Look for the Health on the Net symbol at the bottom of the main page of the Web site. The Health on the Net Foundation is a non-profit, international organization that promotes the HONcode, a set of principles for standardizing the reliability of health information on the Internet. Currently, Web site sponsors are not required to follow HONcode standards. For more information about HONcode, you can visit the organization's Web site (www.hon.ch).
4. Do not trust information at a site that does not indicate valid sources, such as well-respected peer-reviewed scientific journals or nationally recognized universities or medical centres. Contributing authors and their credentials should be identified; when they are, perform an online search of the scientific journals, as well as the authors' names and credentials to determine their validity.
5. Do not trust a site that includes attacks on the trustworthiness of the medical or scientific establishment.
6. Avoid sites that provide online diagnoses and treatments.
7. Be wary of commercial sites (*.com) with links to government sites or the sites of well-known medical, nutrition, or scientific associations. An unreliable *.com site can be linked to reliable sites without having received their endorsements.
8. Avoid providing your personal information at the site because its confidentiality may not be protected.

In addition to the Dietitians of Canada Web site, you can find reliable nutrition and health information at the following:

Health Canada—Food & Nutrition: http://www.hc-sc.gc.ca/fn-an/index-eng.php

Canadian Diabetes Association: www.diabetes.ca

Canadian Heart and Stroke Foundation: www.heartandstroke.ca

Canadian Council of Food and Nutrition: www.nin.ca

Centers for Disease Control and Prevention: www.cdc.gov

Quackwatch: www.quackwatch.org

Canadian Food Inspection Agency: www.inspection.gc.ca

HONcode symbol. The Health on the Net Foundation (HON) is a non-profit, international organization that promotes the HONcode, a set of principles for standardizing the reliability of health information on the Internet. © Health on the Net Foundation.

Concept Checkpoint

8. What is the difference between a testimonial and an anecdote?
9. List at least three red flags that may indicate a questionable source of nutrition information.
10. List at least three tips for using the Internet as a reliable source of nutrition information.

Why Consult a Registered Dietitian?

If you have questions about food or nutrition, where do you find the answers? Although some provinces protect the term nutritionist, you cannot always rely on someone who refers to him- or herself as "nutritionist" or "nutritionalist" for reliable nutrition information, because there are no standard legal definitions for these descriptors. Should you ask a physician for nutrition advice? In general, physicians are not necessarily the best sources of nutrition information; most doctors do not have extensive university coursework in the subject.

To obtain reliable answers to your nutrition, foods, and dietary questions, you should consult a registered dietitian (RD). Registered dietitians are university-trained professionals who have extensive knowledge of foods, nutrition, and *dietetics*, the application of nutrition and food information to treat many health-related conditions. The title *registered dietitian* is legally protected in Canada.

Many dietitians provide dietary counselling for patients in hospitals or other clinical settings. Some dietitians provide nutrition advice for clients who obtain preventive health care from local government sources, such as health departments in their communities. Other dietitians manage food systems for hospitals, school districts, or large corporations. If your university or college has a nutrition or dietetics department, you are likely to find registered dietitians who are faculty members. Otherwise, you can locate registered dietitians by consulting the yellow pages of telephone directories, contacting your local provincial dietetic regulatory association, calling the dietary department of a local hospital, or visiting the Dietitians of Canada Web site (www.dietitians.ca) and using the "Find a Dietitian" search tool. Make sure the person has the credentials "RD" after his or her name. The Chapter 2 Highlight provides more information about registered dietitians, including university courses that are required for students who major in nutrition and dietetics.

Concept **Checkpoint**

11. What is the difference between a nutritionist and a registered dietitian?
12. List three ways of locating registered dietitians.

Chapter 2 Highlight
Have You Considered Becoming a Dietitian?

Are you interested in science? Would you like to learn how diets can be altered to treat disease? Would you like a challenging career as a health professional? If you answered "yes" to each of these questions, you may want to consider becoming a registered dietitian (RD). There are three major professional divisions for registered dietitians—clinical dietetics, community nutrition, and food service systems management. Clinical dietitians can work as members of medical teams in hospitals or clinics. Registered dietitians can also work as community nutritionists in public health settings or as dietary counsellors in private practice or with wellness programs. Food service systems management dietitians direct food systems in hospitals, schools, or other settings. Although most registered dietitians work in health care settings, some are educators or researchers.

An RD has completed a baccalaureate degree program accredited by Dietitians of Canada. As undergraduate students, dietetics majors are required to take a wide variety of courses, including food and nutrition sciences, organic chemistry, biochemistry, biology, physiology, psychology, microbiology, food service systems management, business, and communication. If you are attending a major university, you can check the course or program catalogue at your school to determine whether an accredited dietetics program is offered.

After completion of an accredited undergraduate nutrition program, students wishing to pursue a career as a dietitian must complete an accredited internship or practicum program. The internship experience consists of hands-on training in hospital, community, and management settings. Dietetic internship programs are typically offered in either an integrated or graduate model. Integrated dietetic interns typically complete their internship rotations between semesters of the final years of their undergraduate degrees, while graduate internship programs typically accept only students who have completed the requirements of their undergraduate degree programs. After completing a dietetic internship or practicum program, students are eligible to write the national examination to become registered dietitians. To maintain their certification, registered dietitians must continually update their knowledge in the field of dietetics and obtain continuing education credits.

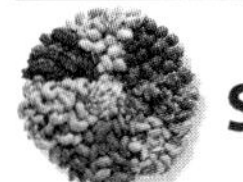

SUMMARY

Scientists ask questions about the natural world and follow generally accepted methods to obtain answers to these questions. Nutrition research relies on scientific methods that may involve making observations, asking questions and developing possible explanations, performing tests, collecting and analyzing data, drawing conclusions from data, and reporting on the findings. Other scientists can test the findings to confirm or reject them.

Epidemiology is the study of disease rates among different population groups, factors associated with the occurrence of diseases, and ways to control the spread of diseases in a population. By studying differences in dietary practices and disease occurrences among populations, epidemiologists can suggest nutrition-related hypotheses for the prevalence of certain diseases. Epidemiologists often conduct case-control, prospective, and retrospective studies to provide clues about the causes, progression, and prevention of the disease. Epidemiological studies, however, cannot indicate whether two variables are correlated, because the relationship could be a coincidence.

When an experiment or study is completed and the results analyzed, researchers summarize the findings and seek to publish articles with information about their investigations in scientific journals. Before articles are accepted for publication, they undergo peer review. Scientists generally do not accept a hypothesis or the results of a study until they are supported by considerable research evidence. Thus, researchers often face stiff criticism and rejection from members of the medical establishment when their hypotheses or findings contradict accepted nutrition principles. Media coverage of a medical breakthrough is not necessarily an indication of the value or quality of research that resulted in the news story. More research is often necessary for scientists to determine whether the results are valid and can be generalized.

Consumers may think scientists do not know what they are doing when conflicting research findings are reported in the media. However, consumers need to recognize that conflicting findings often result because different teams of researchers use different study designs when investigating the same hypothesis. Furthermore, each team of scientists may analyze the results differently. Other factors, such as genetic and lifestyle differences, can also influence the results of nutrition research involving human subjects. The science of nutrition is constantly evolving.

Although testimonials and anecdotes are often used to promote nutrition-related products and services, consumers cannot be sure that this information is reliable or based on scientific facts. Personal observations are not evidence of a cause-and-effect relationship because many factors, such as lifestyle and environment, can influence outcomes.

Popular magazine articles, best-selling trade books, Internet Web sites, television news reports, and other forms of media are often unreliable sources of nutrition information. Consumers need to be skeptical and question the reliability of such sources. Few dietary supplements have been thoroughly evaluated by reputable scientists, and many supplements that have been scientifically tested do not provide measurable health benefits. Nevertheless, promoters of dietary supplements often ignore results of scientific research that indicate their products are not effective. Furthermore, they often use consumer mistrust of the scientific and medical establishment to sell their products and services.

Consumers need to become more knowledgeable about the basics of human nutrition and physiology, and they need to be skeptical about the reliability of the nutrition information that is so readily available in the news media, in magazines, and on the Internet. To determine whether a source of information is reliable, consumers need to ask questions to determine the author's reasons for promoting the information. Consumers should also look for red flags, such as scare tactics and claims that sound too good to be true.

Much of the nutrition information that is on the Internet is unreliable and intended to promote sales. Web sites sponsored by non-profit organizations, nationally recognized health associations, government agencies, and nationally accredited colleges and universities are generally reliable sources of information.

Although some provinces protect the title nutritionist, there is no standard legal definition for "nutritionist" in Canada. For reliable food, nutrition, and dietary information, consumers can consult registered dietitians. Consumers can locate registered dietitians at many universities and colleges or by consulting the yellow pages of telephone directories, contacting local dietetic associations, calling the dietary departments of local hospitals, or visiting the Dietitians of Canada Web site.

Recipe for Healthy Living

Grandma's Chicken Soup

Long before the advent of over-the-counter antihistamines and cough syrups, there was chicken soup. People have used chicken soup as a cold remedy for centuries. Chicken soup is not a cure for the common cold. However, results of a laboratory study indicated that chicken soup contains substances that can subdue the body's inflammatory response to upper respiratory tract infections.* This inflammatory response typically results in common cold symptoms such as cough and excess nasal discharge. Although the soup's specific actions on cold-causing microbes still need to be determined, consuming a soothing, warm bowl of chicken soup contributes to the sick person's fluid and other nutrient intake at a time when he or she may not feel like eating anything else. Even if you don't have a cold, the following chicken soup recipe is delicious and easy to make. You can freeze the soup in small covered plastic containers for future meals.

This recipe makes approximately 6 to 8 cups of soup. A 1-cup serving of the soup supplies approximately 90 kcal, 6 g of protein, 3 g fat, 340 mg sodium, 250 mg potassium, and 3.8 mg niacin.

Note: When you reheat the soup, you can also add your favourite soup ingredients, such as corn kernels, frozen peas or string beans, broccoli florets, fine noodles, or cooked brown rice.

* Rennard BO and others: Chicken soup inhibits neutrophil chemotaxis in vitro. *Chest* 118(4):1150, 2000.

INGREDIENTS:

1 package of raw chicken wings, approx. 1.4 to 1.8 kg (3 to 4 lbs.)
1 large onion, cut in wedges
4 large carrots, cleaned and cut into 7.5-cm (3-in.) lengths
⅛ tsp black pepper
1 chicken bouillon cube
3 celery stalks, cleaned and cut into 7.5-cm (3-in.) lengths
parsley sprigs
⅛ tsp paprika
⅛ tsp thyme
⅛ tsp curry seasoning

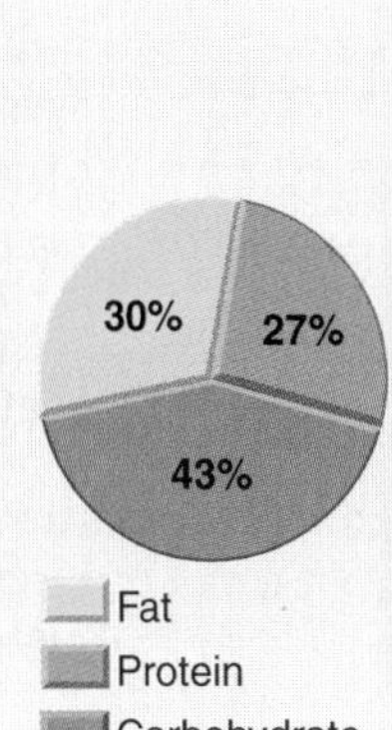

PREPARATION STEPS:

1. Place the raw chicken in a large cooking pot and add enough cold water (approximately 2 L) to cover chicken.
2. Add onion, carrots, celery, parsley, pepper, bouillon cube, and spices to chicken and water; turn burner on high. When mixture comes to a boil, reduce heat to medium and cover the pot with a lid. Soup should boil for at least an hour.
3. Turn off the heat, remove chicken wings from the soup, and place them in a bowl. Cover and refrigerate.
4. Cover soup and refrigerate for 12 hours.
5. Skim chicken fat from top of soup. Remove skin from the wings, separate the meat from the bones, and add the meat to the soup. Reheat soup before eating.
6. Cover and store leftover soup in refrigerator for up to 3 days, or freeze.

CRITICAL THINKING

1. A news broadcaster reports the results of a study in which people who took daily fish oil and vitamin E supplements did not reduce their risk of heart attack. Moreover, the researchers stopped the study when they determined the supplements increased the subjects' risk of stroke! Explain how you would determine whether this information is reliable.
2. Explain how you can verify the reliability of advice about vitamins provided at an Internet Web site.
3. Design a study that involves observing nutrition-related practices of university students and share your idea with the class. Your study should be designed so that it is ethical and does not harm subjects physically or psychologically.
4. Results from one scientific study often suggest a new set of questions for researchers to investigate. Chapter 2 described current research that suggests a relationship between soy foods and the risk of breast cancer. Think of two questions this finding is likely to generate that could be answered by further scientific investigation.
5. Browse through popular health-related magazines to find an article or advertisement that relates to nutrition, and make a copy of the article or advertisement. Analyze each sentence or line of the article or advertisement for signs of unreliability. Is the article or advertisement a reliable source of information? Explain why it is or why it is not.

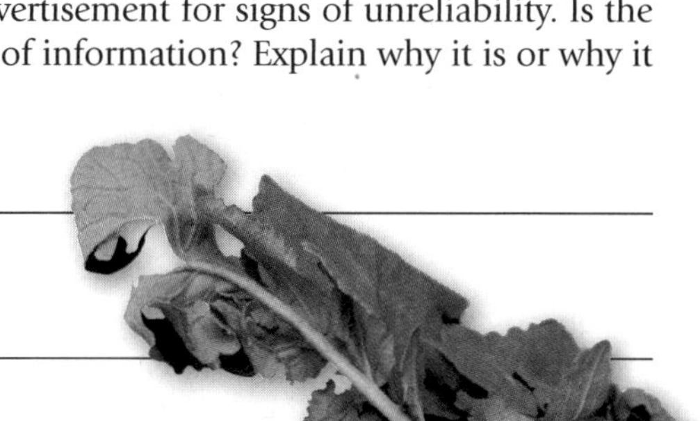

PRACTICE TEST

Select the best answer.

1. The first step of the scientific method usually involves
   a. gathering data.
   b. developing a hypothesis.
   c. identifying relationships between variables.
   d. making observations.
2. A group of scientists observe a group of university students over four years to determine which of their characteristics leads to weight gain. This study is an example of
   a. a case-control study.
   b. a prospective study.
   c. a retrospective study.
   d. an experimental study.

3. ______ includes the study of disease rates among different population groups.
   a. Epidemiology
   b. Technobiology
   c. Diseasiology
   d. Censusology

4. Comparing characteristics of individuals with iron-deficiency anemia to individuals who match the characteristics but are healthy would be an example of
   a. a prospective study.
   b. an anecdotal study.
   c. a retrospective study.
   d. a case-control study.
5. Generally, epidemiological studies
   a. establish causation.
   b. prove correlations.
   c. cannot determine cause-and-effect relationships.
   d. are experimental-based research between two variables.
6. Which of the following journals does not have peer-reviewed articles?
   a. *Canadian Journal of Dietetic Practice and Research*
   b. *American Journal of Clinical Nutrition*
   c. *Canadian Journal of Public Health*
   d. none of the above
7. Peer-reviewed journals publish research findings only after the journal article has been reviewed by a specialist in the field to ensure the methodology research findings are legitimate.
   a. true
   b. false
8. A testimonial is
   a. an unbiased report about a product's value.
   b. a scientifically valid claim.
   c. a personal endorsement of a product.
   d. a form of scientific evidence.
9. Which of the following Web sites is most likely to provide biased and unreliable nutrition information?
   a. the site of a nationally recognized health association (*.ca or *.org)
   b. a site that promotes or sells dietary supplements (*.com)
   c. the site of a Canadian government agency (*.gc.ca)
   d. an accredited college or university's site (*.edu)
10. A fake treatment is a(n)
    a. anecdote.
    b. double-blind study.
    c. pseudoscience experiment.
    d. placebo.

Answers to Chapter 2 Quiz Yourself

1. Scientists generally do not raise questions about or criticize the conclusions of their colleagues' research data, even when they disagree with these conclusions. **False.** (p. 35)
2. Popular health-related magazines typically publish articles that have been peer-reviewed. **False.** (p. 36)
3. By conducting a prospective epidemiological study, medical researchers can determine risk factors that influence health outcomes. **True.** (p. 32)
4. A placebo contains ingredients that provide no measurable effects. **True.** (p. 34)
5. In general, registered dietitians are generally reliable sources of food and nutrition information. **True.** (p. 44)

Please visit Connect at

www.mcgrawhillconnect.ca

Chapter **3**

Planning Nutritious Diets

Chapter Learning Outcomes

After reading Chapter 3, you should be able to:

1. Identify the Dietary Reference Intake standards and explain how they can be used.
2. Access the Health Canada Web site to find age- and gender-specific dietary guidelines for Canadians based on the *Eating Well with Canada's Food Guide* recommendations.
3. List major food groups and identify foods that are typically classified in each group.
4. Use *Eating Well with Canada's Food Guide* to develop nutritionally adequate daily menus.
5. Use the Nutrition Facts table to make more nutritious food choices.
6. Identify nutrition-related claims that Health Canada allows on food and supplement labels.

When you shop for groceries, do you sometimes feel overwhelmed by the vast array of foods that are available? If your answer is yes, your response is not surprising, considering the average grocery store offers tens of thousands of unique items.[1] Every time you enter a grocery store, you are likely to find food items that were not on the shelves during your last visit to the store. In fact, many grocery stores will stock items that consumers request.

Chapter 1 introduced some key concepts concerning nutritious foods and diets, including the need for moderation and variety. In Chapter 2, we described how you can become a more careful consumer of nutrition information. However, you are also a consumer of food. With so many grocery items from which to choose, what are the primary factors that influence your food purchases? Do you select foods simply because they taste good, are reasonably priced, or are easy to prepare? Do you ever consider the effects that certain foods may have on your health before you purchase them?

Your lifestyle reflects your health-related behaviours, including your dietary practices and physical activity habits. Canadians of all ages may reduce their risk of chronic disease by adopting nutritious diets and engaging in regular physical activity. However, consumers need practical advice to help them make decisions that can promote more healthy lifestyles.

This chapter discusses how dietary standards are established and used. The information in this chapter also presents practical ways to plan nutritionally adequate diets using tools such as the *Eating Well with Canada's Food Guide* recommendations and the EATracker dietary analysis tool offered by Dietitians of Canada via its Web site (www.dietitians.ca/public/content/eat_well_live_well/english/eatracker). Additionally in this chapter, we explain how to interpret nutrition-related information that appears on food labels.

Quiz YOURSELF

Before reading the rest of Chapter 3, test your knowledge of dietary standards, recommendations, and guides, as well as nutrient labels, by taking the following quiz. The answers are found on page 83.

1. According to the *Eating Well with Canada's Food Guide*, vegetables and fruit are combined into one food group. _____T _____F
2. According to Health Canada recommendations, it is acceptable for certain adults to consume moderate amounts of alcoholic beverages. _____T _____F
3. Last week, Colin didn't consume the recommended amount of vitamin C for a couple of days. Nevertheless, he is unlikely to develop scurvy, the vitamin C deficiency disease. _____T _____F
4. According to the *Eating Well with Canada's Food Guide* recommendations, an adult 40-year-old male should consume three to four servings of vegetables and fruit each day. _____T _____F
5. The Nutrition Facts table on a food label provides information concerning amounts of energy, fibre, and cholesterol that are in a serving of the food. _____T _____F

From Requirements to Standards

By using research methods discussed in Chapter 2, scientists have been able to estimate the amount of each nutrient required by the body. A **requirement** is the smallest amount of a nutrient that maintains a defined level of nutritional health.[2] In general, this amount fulfills the needs of certain cells for the nutrient or prevents the nutrient's deficiency disease. The requirement for each nutrient varies to some degree from person to person. Your age, sex, general health status, physical activity level, and use of medications and drugs are among factors that influence your nutrient requirements. Scientists use information about nutrient requirements to establish specific dietary recommendations.

Simply obtaining required amounts of nutrients does not result in optimal nutritional status. If intake of a nutrient just meets the requirements, your body has no extra supply available to use in case your food intake becomes limited. Many nutrients are stored in the body, and for optimal nutrition, you need to consume amounts of those nutrients that maintain storage levels. Your body uses its nutrient stores much like you use a savings account to help manage your money. When you have some extra cash, it is wise to place the money in a savings account so that you can withdraw some of the reserves to meet future needs without going into debt. When your consumption of certain nutrients is more than enough to meet your needs, the body stores the excess, primarily in the liver, body fat, and/or bones. When your intake of a stored nutrient is low or needs for this nutrient become increased, such as during recovery from illness, your body withdraws some from storage. As a result, you may avoid or delay developing a deficiency of the nutrient.

requirement smallest amount of a nutrient that maintains a defined level of health

Dietary Reference Intakes (DRIs) A set of energy and nutrient reference intake standards for a healthy population of North Americans

Dietary Reference Intakes

Dietary Reference Intakes (DRIs) encompass a variety of energy and nutrient intake standards that nutrition experts in Canada use as references when making dietary recommendations (Fig. 3.1).[3] DRIs are intended to help people reduce their risk of nutrient deficiencies and excesses, prevent disease, and achieve optimal health.[4] These dietary standards include Estimated Average Requirement (EAR), Recommended Dietary Allowance

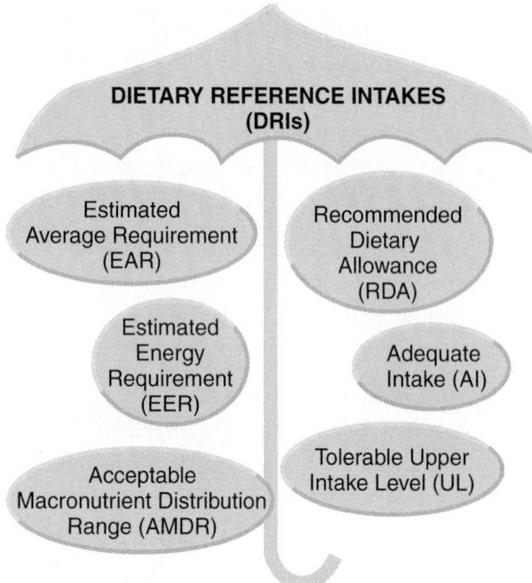

Figure 3.1 Dietary Reference Intakes. The Dietary Reference Intakes (DRIs) encompass a variety of terms that represent standards for nutrient and energy recommendations.

Food and Nutrition Board (FNB) group of nutrition scientists who develop DRIs

Estimated Average Requirement (EAR) amount of a nutrient that meets the needs of 50% of healthy people in a life stage/gender group

Recommended Dietary Allowances (RDA) standards for recommending daily intakes of several nutrients for most healthy individuals

(RDA), Adequate Intake (AI), and Tolerable Upper Intake Level (UL); for macronutrients the standards include Acceptable Macronutrient Distribution Ranges (AMDR) and Estimated Energy Requirement (EER).

A group of nutrition scientists from Canada and the United States form a panel with the **Food and Nutrition Board (FNB)** of the Institute of Medicine in the United States to develop the DRIs. Canadian scientists are appointed by Health Canada to represent Canada on these panels. Periodically, members of the Board adjust DRIs as new information concerning human nutritional needs and dietary adequacy becomes available. You can find tables for the latest DRIs at the back of this textbook. The following sections provide basic information about the various DRI standards. It is important to become familiar with these terms because we refer to them in the following chapters.

Estimated Average Requirement

An **Estimated Average Requirement (EAR)** is the amount of a nutrient that should meet the needs of 50% of healthy people who are in a particular *life stage/gender group*.[2] Life stage/gender groups classify people according to age and sex, as well as whether females are pregnant or lactating. The typical university student, for example, would be classified as male or female, between 19 and 30 years old.

To establish an EAR for a nutrient, researchers identify a physiological marker, a substance in the body that reflects proper functioning and can be measured. This marker indicates whether the level of a nutrient in the body is adequate. A marker for vitamin C, for example, is the amount of the vitamin in certain blood cells. When these cells contain nearly all the vitamin C they can hold, the body has an optimal supply of the vitamin. Thus, a physician can diagnose whether a patient is vitamin C deficient by taking a blood sample from the person and measuring the vitamin C content of certain blood cells.

Recommended Dietary Allowances

The **Recommended Dietary Allowances (RDAs)** are standards for recommending daily intakes of several nutrients. RDAs meet the nutrient needs of nearly all healthy individuals (about 97–98%) in a particular life stage/gender group. To establish an RDA for a nutrient, nutrition scientists first determine its EAR. Then scientists add a *margin of safety* amount to the EAR that allows for individual variations in nutrient needs and helps maintain tissue stores (Fig. 3.2). For example, the adult EAR for vitamin C is 60 mg for women who are not pregnant or breast-feeding and 75 mg for men.[2] However, the adult RDA for vitamin C is 15 mg higher than the EAR—75 mg for women who are not pregnant or breast-feeding and 90 mg for men. Because smoking cigarettes increases the need for vitamin C, smokers should add 30 mg to their RDA for the nutrient.

Life stage/gender groups classify people according to age, sex, and life stage (e.g., females who are pregnant or lactating).

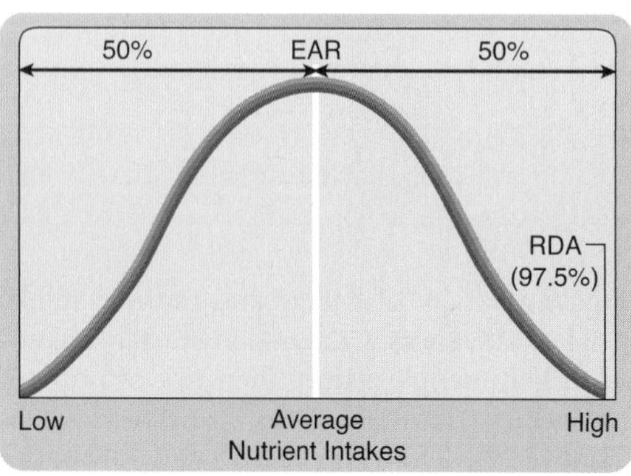

Figure 3.2 Establishing RDAs. To set an RDA, scientists add a margin of safety amount to the Estimated Average Requirement (EAR) that allows for individual variations in nutrient needs and helps maintain tissue stores. As a result, a nutrient's RDA is high enough to meet or exceed 97 to 98% of the healthy population's requirements for the nutrient. In other words, 97 to 98% of the population's needs for the nutrient will be met by just consuming the RDA amount.

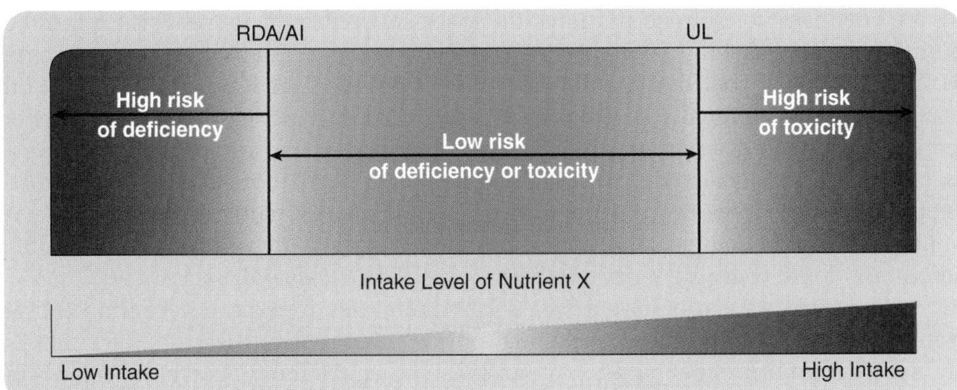

Figure 3.3 Establishing Adequate Intakes and Upper Limits. Nutrition scientists set an Adequate Intake (AI) for a nutrient if there is not enough information to determine an RDA. The Tolerable Upper Intake Level (UL) is the highest average amount of a nutrient that is unlikely to harm most people when the amount is consumed daily.

Adequate Intakes

In some instances, nutrition scientists are unable to develop RDAs for nutrients because there is not enough information to determine human requirements. Until such information becomes available, scientists set **Adequate Intakes (AIs)** for these nutrients. To establish an AI, scientists record eating patterns of a group of healthy people and estimate the group's average daily intake of the nutrient. If the population under observation shows no evidence of the nutrient's deficiency disorder, the researchers conclude that the average level of intake must be adequate and use that value as the AI (Fig. 3.3). Vitamin D and the mineral calcium are among the nutrients that have AIs instead of RDAs.

Adequate Intake (AI) standard established when sufficient scientific evidence is not available to establish an RDA; an AI can be used as a goal for usual intake by an individual

Tolerable Upper Intake Level (Upper Level or **UL)** standard representing the highest average amount of a nutrient that is unlikely to be harmful when consumed daily

Estimated Energy Requirement (EER) average daily energy intake that meets the needs of a healthy person maintaining his or her weight

Acceptable Macronutrient Distribution Ranges (AMDRs) macronutrient intake ranges that are nutritionally adequate and may reduce the risk of diet-related chronic diseases

Tolerable Upper Intake Level

Nutrition scientists also establish a **Tolerable Upper Intake Level (Upper Level** or **UL)** for many vitamins and minerals. The UL is the highest average amount of a nutrient that is unlikely to harm most people when the amount is consumed daily (see Fig. 3.3).[5,6] The risk of a toxicity disorder increases when a person regularly consumes amounts of a nutrient that exceed its UL. The UL for vitamin C, for example, is 2000 mg per day for adults.

Estimated Energy Requirement

The **Estimated Energy Requirement (EER)** is the average daily energy intake that meets the needs of a healthy person who is maintaining his or her weight. Dietitians can use EERs to evaluate an individual's energy intake. Compared to RDAs and AIs, the EER is more specific because it takes into account the person's physical activity level, height, and weight, as well as sex and life stage.[2,6] The EER, however, does not include an additional number of calories to serve as a margin of safety. Thus, some people have energy needs that are higher or lower than the EER. Chapter 10 provides formulas for calculating your EER.

Acceptable Macronutrient Distribution Ranges

The results of scientific research suggest that energy sources (macronutrients) are associated with the risk of certain diet-related chronic diseases, such as cardiovascular disease (CVD). **Acceptable Macronutrient Distribution Ranges (AMDRs)** indicate ranges of carbohydrate, fat, and protein intakes that provide adequate amounts of energy and may reduce the risk of diet-related chronic diseases.[4,6] The AMDR for carbohydrates is 45 to 65% of total energy intake, fat is 20 to 35%, and protein is 10 to 35%.

Applying Nutrient Standards

Dietitians refer to DRIs as standards for planning nutritious diets for groups of people and evaluating the nutritional adequacy of a population's diet. Nevertheless, RDAs and

AIs are often used to evaluate an individual's dietary practices.[4,5] Your diet is likely to be nutritionally adequate if your average daily intake for each nutrient meets the nutrient's RDA or AI value. If your diet consistently supplies less than the EAR for a nutrient, you may be at risk of eventually developing the nutrient's deficiency disorder. On the other hand, if your intake of a nutrient is consistently above its UL, you are at risk of developing that nutrient's toxicity disorder. Nutrient toxicity disorders are more likely to occur when people take high doses of individual nutrient supplements, particularly vitamins and minerals. If you do not take large doses of nutrient supplements and you eat reasonable amounts of food, your risk of developing a nutrient toxicity disorder is low.

Nutritional standards have a variety of commercial applications. Pharmaceutical companies refer to DRIs when developing formulas that replace breast milk for infants and special formulas for people who cannot consume regular foods. As a result, babies can thrive on commercially prepared formulas, and adults who are unable to swallow can survive for years on formula feedings administered through tubes inserted into their bodies.

For nutrition labelling purposes, Health Canada uses RDAs to develop a set of standards called Daily Values (DVs).[7] For adults, DVs are based on a standard diet that supplies 2000 kcal per day and certain dietary recommendations. Consumers may find DVs useful for comparing the nutritional contents of similar foods. The "Food and Supplement Labels" section later in this chapter provides more information about nutritional labelling, including DVs.

If you review the DRI tables, you are likely to be overwhelmed with the number of tables and confusing array of values. The information provided by DRIs is complex and not in a form that is practical for consumers to use when planning menus. To overcome these hurdles, nutrition experts develop dietary guides to help people make healthier food choices. As menu-planning tools, such food guides are not perfect, but they can help consumers add interest and variety to their diets while ensuring nutritional adequacy. We discuss dietary guides in further detail in subsequent sections of this chapter.

Grain products include foods made from wheat, rice, barley, oats, and many other grains.

Concept **Checkpoint**

1. What is the difference between an RDA and an AI?
2. Describe how scientists establish the RDA for a nutrient.
3. Explain how an EER differs from an RDA or AI.
4. Discuss how dietitians, pharmaceutical companies, and Health Canada use nutrient standards.

Major Food Groups

According to *Eating Well with Canada's Food Guide*, foods can be classified into the following major food groups according to their natural origins and key nutrients: Grain Products, Milk and Alternatives, Vegetables and Fruit, and Meat and Alternatives. In most instances, dietary guides also provide recommendations concerning amounts of foods from each group that should be eaten daily. The following points identify major food groups and summarize key features of each group.

- ***Grain Products:*** This group includes foods made from wheat, rice, and oats. For example, pasta, noodles, and flour tortillas are members of this group because wheat flour is their main ingredient. Although corn is a type of grain, it is often used as a vegetable in meals. Therefore, cornmeal and popcorn are usually grouped with grain products. In general, 1 serving of grain products is equivalent to 1 slice of bread, 175 mL (¾ cup) hot cereal, 30 g (1 oz.) of ready-to-eat cereal, or 125 mL (½ cup) of cooked rice or pasta.

Carbohydrate and protein are the primary macronutrients in grains. In Canada, most refined grain products are also good sources of several vitamins and minerals, because they have undergone enrichment or fortification. **Enrichment** is the addition of vitamins and minerals such as iron and certain B vitamins to cereal grain products such as flour and rice. In general, enrichment replaces some of the nutrients that were lost during processing or refinement. **Fortification** is the addition of supplementary nutrients to food, such as adding calcium to orange juice, vitamins A and D to milk, and numerous vitamins and minerals to ready-to-eat breakfast cereals.

enrichment addition of vitamins and minerals to food products to replace those lost during processing or refinement

fortification addition of supplementary nutrients to food

Dietary guides generally recommend choosing foods made with whole grains instead of refined grains. According to Health Canada, whole grains are defined as the dried seeds of various cereal species such as wheat, buckwheat, oats, corn, rice, wild rice, rye, barley, and millet, and these items must contain all of the original three parts of the seed: the germ, the bran, and the endosperm.[8] Compared to refined grain products, foods made from whole grains naturally contain more fibre as well as micronutrients that are not replaced during enrichment.

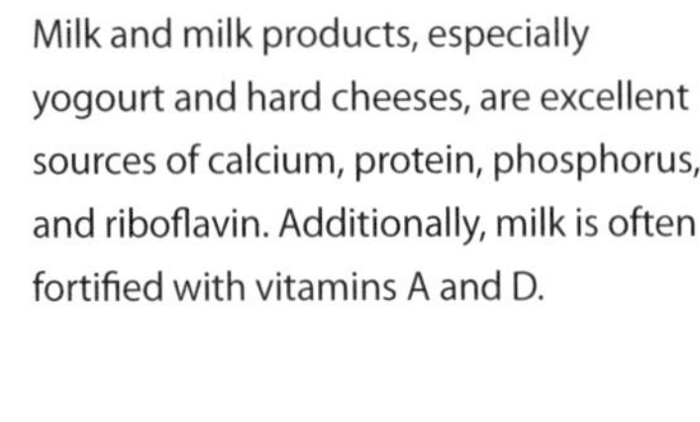

Milk and milk products, especially yogourt and hard cheeses, are excellent sources of calcium, protein, phosphorus, and riboflavin. Additionally, milk is often fortified with vitamins A and D.

- *Milk and Alternatives:* This food group includes milk and products made from milk that retain their content of the mineral calcium, such as yogourt and hard cheeses. Milk foods are also excellent sources of protein, phosphorus (a mineral), and riboflavin (a B vitamin). Additionally, most of the milk sold in Canada is fortified with vitamins A and D. Ice cream, pudding, frozen yogourt, and ice milk are often grouped with milk foods, even though they often have high sugar and fat contents. Although cream cheese, cream, and butter are milk products, they are not included in this group because they have little or no calcium and are high in fat.

  Most dietary guides recommend choosing milk products that have most of the fat removed, such as low-fat milk. Compared to whole milk, which is about 3.25% fat by weight, low-fat milk can be skim or 1% milk, the latter of which contains only 1% fat by weight.

  In general, 1 serving of milk and alternatives is equivalent to 250 mL (1 cup) of milk or fortified soy beverage, 187 mL (¾ cup) of yogourt or frozen yogourt, 125 mL (½ cup) of canned evaporated milk, or 50 g (1½ oz.) of natural cheese such as Swiss or cheddar. To obtain about the same amount of calcium and protein as in 1 cup of skim milk, you would have to eat almost 430 mL (1⅔ cups) of vanilla ice cream. This amount of ice cream provides 470 kcal and about 26 g of fat, whereas the same amount of skim milk supplies only 135 kcal and less than 1 g of fat.

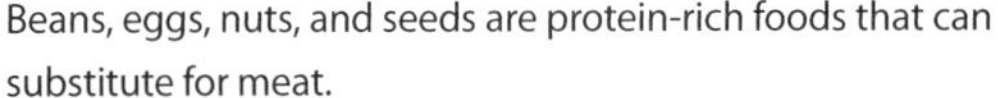

Beans, eggs, nuts, and seeds are protein-rich foods that can substitute for meat.

- *Meat and Alternatives:* This food group includes beef, pork, lamb, fish, shellfish, liver, and poultry. Beans, eggs, nuts, and seeds are included with this group because they are protein-rich foods that can substitute for meats. One serving of food from this group generally equals 75 g of meat, poultry, or fish; 175 mL (¾ cup) cooked legumes; 2 eggs; 30 mL (2 Tbsp) of peanut butter; or 60 mL (¼ cup) of nuts or seeds.

  Foods in the meat and alternatives group are rich sources of protein and micronutrients, especially iron, zinc, and B vitamins. In general, the body absorbs minerals, such as iron and zinc, more easily from animal foods than from plants. However, animal foods often contain a lot of saturated fat and cholesterol. Diets that supply high amounts of these lipids are associated with increased risk of heart and blood vessel diseases (cardiovascular disease or CVD).

  Some dietary guides use fat content to categorize meats and other protein-rich foods. According to these guides, low-fat cottage cheese and the white meat of turkey are very lean meats; ground beef that is not more than 15% fat by weight and tuna are lean meats. Pork sausage, bacon, salami, and hot dogs are examples of high-fat meats.

Did You Know?

Although cottage cheese is made from milk, 250 mL (1 cup) of low-fat (2%) cottage cheese contains only about half of the calcium that's in 250 mL (1 cup) of skim milk.

Oils are fats that are liquid at room temperature. Certain spreadable foods made from vegetable oils, such as mayonnaise, margarine, and salad dressing, are also classified as oils.

- ***Vegetables and Fruit:*** This food group includes 100% fruit juice and vegetables, as well as 100% vegetable juice. In general, 1 serving of food from this food group equals 125 mL (½ cup) fresh, frozen, or canned vegetables or fruit; 125 mL (½ cup) 100% vegetable or fruit juice; 1 piece of fruit; or 250 mL (1 cup) of leafy raw greens, such as salad greens.[9] Most fruits are low in fat and good sources of phytochemicals and micronutrients, especially the mineral potassium and vitamin C and the B-vitamin folate. Additionally, whole or cut-up fruit is a good source of fibre. Although 100% fruit juice is a source of phytochemicals and can count toward your fruit intake, the majority of your choices from this group should be whole or cut-up fruits.[10] Whole or cut-up fruits are healthier options than juices because they contain more dietary fibre. Many vegetables are good sources of micronutrients, fibre, and phytochemicals. Furthermore, many vegetables are naturally low in fat and energy.

Vegetables include fresh, frozen, and canned vegetables, or 100% vegetable juice.

Some dietary guides may also have a group for fats and oils, which include canola, corn, and olive oils, as well as other fats that are liquid at room temperature. Certain spreadable foods made from vegetable oils, such as mayonnaise, margarine, and salad dressing, are also classified as oils. Because nuts, olives, avocados, and some types of fish have high fat contents, a dietary guide may group these foods with oils.[11]

Dietary guides may also have a group for empty-calorie foods or beverages. Such items generally add a lot of sugar, alcohol, and/or solid fat to diets. Sugary foods ("sweets") include candy, regular soft drinks, jelly, and other foods that contain high amounts of sugar added during processing or preparation. Sugary foods and alcoholic beverages typically supply energy but little or no micronutrients. Solid fats, such as beef fat, butter, lard (pork fat), and shortening, are fairly hard at room temperature. Solid fats are often grouped with sweets and alcoholic beverages, because diets that contain high amounts of these fats are associated with increased risk of CVD. Chapter 6 discusses how dietary fats can affect health.

Fruit includes fresh, frozen, and canned, as well as 100% fruit juice.

It is important to note that the nutritional content of foods within each group often varies widely. For example, 100 g (3½ oz.) of fresh sliced apples and 100 g (3½ oz.) of fresh orange sections each supply about 48 kcal. However, the apples contribute 4 mg of vitamin C whereas oranges supply about 46 mg of the vitamin to diets (Fig. 3.4). Therefore, dietary guides generally recommend that people choose a variety of foods from each food group when planning daily meals and snacks.

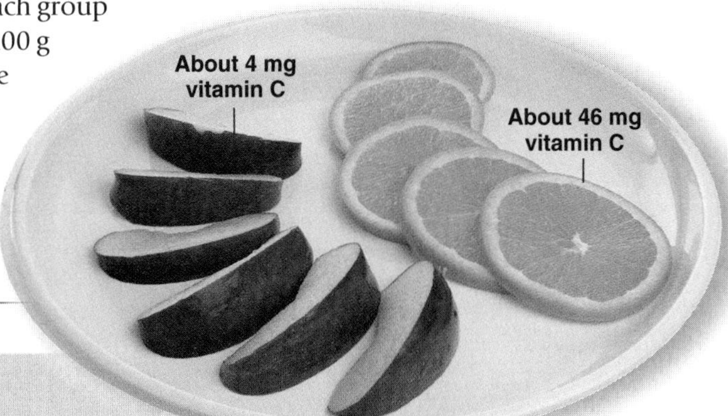

Figure 3.4 Comparing apples to oranges. The nutritional content of foods within each group often varies widely. For example, oranges supply more vitamin C than an equally sized portion of apples. Therefore, dietary guides generally recommend that people eat a variety of foods from each food group daily.

Concept Checkpoint

5. List at least three foods that are generally classified as grain products.
6. What is the difference between nutrient fortification and nutrient enrichment?
7. List at least four foods that are generally classified as milk or milk products.
8. Why are beans sometimes classified with meat and alternatives?
9. According to the information in this section, how many cups of dried apricots are nutritionally equivalent to 2 cups of fresh apricots?
10. Most dietary guides classify eggs and nuts with meat and alternatives. Why?
11. Identify at least two foods that are classified as solid fats.

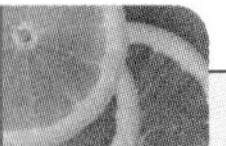

Did You Know?

To meet Canadian consumers' growing interest in nutrition and eating more healthy foods, manufacturers have responded by introducing a variety of new *functional foods* into the marketplace. Although there is no universally accepted definition, a functional food contains potentially healthful factors or ingredients other than the food's naturally occurring nutrients.[12] Fortified or enriched foods are functional foods because the nutrients that are added to them can improve the body's nutritional status. You can expect to see more functional foods in the marketplace in the future, particularly foods fortified with various vitamins and minerals.

Dietary Guidelines for Canadians—*Eating Well with Canada's Food Guide*

Cardiovascular disease (CVD), cancer, hypertension (chronically elevated blood pressure), and diabetes mellitus (commonly referred to as *diabetes*) are among the leading causes of disability and death among Canadians. According to a considerable amount of scientific evidence, risk of these diseases is strongly linked with certain lifestyles, particularly poor dietary choices and lack of regular physical activity. The goals of the dietary guidelines for Canadians are to reduce the burden of chronic diseases such as cardiovascular disease and obesity as well as to ensure that Canadians acquire all the nutrients they need to promote good health.

Dietary guidelines for Canadians were first issued as *Canada's Official Food Rules* during World War II in 1942 when food resources were relatively scarce and many Canadians struggled to secure a healthy food supply during a time of national food shortage. Since that time the Canadian government has released several sets of dietary guidelines to direct the dietary intake of Canadians. Most recently, *Eating Well with Canada's Food Guide* recommendations were released in 2007. To address the needs of the multi-cultural demographic in Canada, *Eating Well with Canada's Food Guide* is available in numerous languages in addition to French and English, including Arabic, Chinese, Farsi, Korean, Punjabi, Russian, Spanish, Tagalog, Tamil, and Urdu. Health Canada also produces a version for Canadians from the First Nations, Inuit, and Métis. Each of these sets of guidelines is presented with culturally appropriate food suggestions to address each of these diverse groups, as well as being printed in the Aboriginal languages. *Eating Well with Canada's Food Guide* recommendations can be individualized for Canadian men, women, and children and can be found online at http://www.hc-sc.gc.ca/fn-an/food-guide-aliment/index-eng.php.

Eating Well with Canada's Food Guide is a set of general dietary recommendations published by Health Canada.

Using the *Eating Well with Canada's Food Guide* Recommendations

The *Eating Well with Canada's Food Guide* rainbow has four arcs, each representing a food group. The outermost arc of the rainbow is green representing the *Vegetables and Fruit* group. This largest arc of the rainbow represents where the largest number of food servings should come from. As you move inward on the rainbow, the arcs get smaller, representing that fewer servings of foods should come from these food groups each day. The next arc of the rainbow, the yellow arc, represents the *Grain Products* group. The next arc, the blue arc represents the *Milk and Alternatives* group. Finally, the smallest arc, the red arc, represents the *Meat and Alternatives* group, and this is where the fewest number of food servings should come from each day.

Eating Well with Canada's Food Guide recommendations are provided by age and gender parameters. Figure 3.5 shows how many servings to choose from each food group each day based on your age and gender.

For the first time, Canada's dietary recommendations are tailored to specific age and gender groups. For children, the recommended number of servings from each food group is the same for both boys and girls in each age category. However, for teens and adults, the recommended number of food guide servings is often different for males and females. In addition, recommendations for children and adults are provided by specific age groupings. Children are categorized within the following groups: 2–3 years, 4–8 years, and 9–13 years. Teens are categorized in 14–18 years of age. Adults are categorized in groups of either 19–50 years or 51+ years. The more specific recommendations for Canadians by gender and age were developed to ensure that Canadians eat a nutritionally adequate diet that meets but does not exceed energy needs.

Serving Sizes

Many Canadians often struggle with what constitutes a serving from each of the *Eating Well with Canada's Food Guide* food groups. Figure 3.6 outlines what constitutes a serving of some commonly chosen foods from each of the four food groups. A quick summary of serving sizes from each of the four food groups is provided below:

Grain Products: 1 slice of bread
½ pita or hamburger bun or bagel
125 mL (½ cup) cooked rice or pasta noodles
30 g (1 oz.) of cold cereal

Milk and Alternatives: 250 mL (1 cup) milk or soy milk
50 g (1½ oz.) of cheese
175 mL (¾ cup) yogourt

Meat and Alternatives: 75 g (½ cup) lean meat, poultry, wild game, or fish
2 eggs
175 mL (¾ cup) cooked legumes
30 mL (2 Tbsp) peanut or nut butter

Vegetables and Fruit: 250 mL (1 cup) raw leafy greens
125 mL (½ cup) fresh, frozen, or canned vegetables or fruit
125 mL (½ cup) 100% vegetable or fruit juice

Figure 3.5 Recommended number of servings. From *Eating Well with Canada's Food Guide.*

Recommended Number of Food Guide Servings per Day

	Children			Teens		Adults			
Age in Years	2-3	4-8	9-13	14-18		19-50		51+	
Sex	Girls and Boys			Females	Males	Females	Males	Females	Males
Vegetables and Fruit	4	5	6	7	8	7-8	8-10	7	7
Grain Products	3	4	6	6	7	6-7	8	6	7
Milk and Alternatives	2	2	3-4	3-4	3-4	2	2	3	3
Meat and Alternatives	1	1	1-2	2	3	2	3	2	3

The chart above shows how many Food Guide Servings you need from each of the four food groups every day.

Having the amount and type of food recommended and following the tips in *Canada's Food Guide* will help:

- Meet your needs for vitamins, minerals and other nutrients.
- Reduce your risk of obesity, type 2 diabetes, heart disease, certain types of cancer and osteoporosis.
- Contribute to your overall health and vitality.

Figure 3.6 ***Eating Well with Canada's Food Guide.*** The current food guide provides Canadians with more than just recommended numbers of servings.

Make each Food Guide Serving count...
wherever you are – at home, at school, at work or when eating out!

- **Eat at least one dark green and one orange vegetable each day.**
  - Go for dark green vegetables such as broccoli, romaine lettuce and spinach.
  - Go for orange vegetables such as carrots, sweet potatoes and winter squash.
- **Choose vegetables and fruit prepared with little or no added fat, sugar or salt.**
  - Enjoy vegetables steamed, baked or stir-fried instead of deep-fried.
- **Have vegetables and fruit more often than juice.**

- **Make at least half of your grain products whole grain each day.**
  - Eat a variety of whole grains such as barley, brown rice, oats, quinoa and wild rice.
  - Enjoy whole grain breads, oatmeal or whole wheat pasta.
- **Choose grain products that are lower in fat, sugar or salt.**
  - Compare the Nutrition Facts table on labels to make wise choices.
  - Enjoy the true taste of grain products. When adding sauces or spreads, use small amounts.

- **Drink skim, 1%, or 2% milk each day.**
  - Have 500 mL (2 cups) of milk every day for adequate vitamin D.
  - Drink fortified soy beverages if you do not drink milk.
- **Select lower fat milk alternatives.**
  - Compare the Nutrition Facts table on yogurts or cheeses to make wise choices.

- **Have meat alternatives such as beans, lentils and tofu often.**
- **Eat at least two Food Guide Servings of fish each week.***
  - Choose fish such as char, herring, mackerel, salmon, sardines and trout.
- **Select lean meat and alternatives prepared with little or no added fat or salt.**
  - Trim the visible fat from meats. Remove the skin on poultry.
  - Use cooking methods such as roasting, baking or poaching that require little or no added fat.
  - If you eat luncheon meats, sausages or prepackaged meats, choose those lower in salt (sodium) and fat.

Enjoy a variety of foods from the four food groups.

Satisfy your thirst with water!

Drink water regularly. It's a calorie-free way to quench your thirst. Drink more water in hot weather or when you are very active.

* Health Canada provides advice for limiting exposure to mercury from certain types of fish. Refer to www.healthcanada.gc.ca for the latest information.

Advice for different ages and stages...

| **Figure 3.6** *(continued)*

Children

Following *Canada's Food Guide* helps children grow and thrive.

Young children have small appetites and need calories for growth and development.

- Serve small nutritious meals and snacks each day.
- Do not restrict nutritious foods because of their fat content. Offer a variety of foods from the four food groups.
- Most of all... be a good role model.

Women of childbearing age

All women who could become pregnant and those who are pregnant or breastfeeding need a multivitamin containing **folic acid** every day. Pregnant women need to ensure that their multivitamin also contains **iron**. A health care professional can help you find the multivitamin that's right for you.

Pregnant and breastfeeding women need more calories. Include an extra 2 to 3 Food Guide Servings each day.

Here are two examples:

- Have fruit and yogurt for a snack, or
- Have an extra slice of toast at breakfast and an extra glass of milk at supper.

Men and women over 50

The need for **vitamin D** increases after the age of 50.

In addition to following *Canada's Food Guide*, everyone over the age of 50 should take a daily vitamin D supplement of 10 µg (400 IU).

How do I count Food Guide Servings in a meal?

Here is an example:

Vegetable and beef stir-fry with rice, a glass of milk and an apple for dessert		
250 mL (1 cup) mixed broccoli, carrot and sweet red pepper	=	2 **Vegetables and Fruit** Food Guide Servings
75 g (2 ½ oz.) lean beef	=	1 **Meat and Alternatives** Food Guide Serving
250 mL (1 cup) brown rice	=	2 **Grain Products** Food Guide Servings
5 mL (1 tsp) canola oil	=	part of your **Oils and Fats** intake for the day
250 mL (1 cup) 1% milk	=	1 **Milk and Alternatives** Food Guide Serving
1 apple	=	1 **Vegetables and Fruit** Food Guide Serving

Figure 3.6 *(continued)*

Eat well and be active today and every day!

The benefits of eating well and being active include:

- Better overall health.
- Lower risk of disease.
- A healthy body weight.
- Feeling and looking better.
- More energy.
- Stronger muscles and bones.

Be active

To be active every day is a step towards better health and a healthy body weight.

Canada's Physical Activity Guide recommends building 30 to 60 minutes of moderate physical activity into daily life for adults and at least 90 minutes a day for children and youth. You don't have to do it all at once. Add it up in periods of at least 10 minutes at a time for adults and five minutes at a time for children and youth.

Start slowly and build up.

Eat well

Another important step towards better health and a healthy body weight is to follow *Canada's Food Guide* by:

- Eating the recommended amount and type of food each day.
- Limiting foods and beverages high in calories, fat, sugar or salt (sodium) such as cakes and pastries, chocolate and candies, cookies and granola bars, doughnuts and muffins, ice cream and frozen desserts, french fries, potato chips, nachos and other salty snacks, alcohol, fruit flavoured drinks, soft drinks, sports and energy drinks, and sweetened hot or cold drinks.

Read the label

- Compare the Nutrition Facts table on food labels to choose products that contain less fat, saturated fat, trans fat, sugar and sodium.
- Keep in mind that the calories and nutrients listed are for the amount of food found at the top of the Nutrition Facts table.

Nutrition Facts
Per 0 mL (0 g)

Amount	% Daily Value
Calories 0	
Fat 0 g	**0 %**
Saturates 0 g + Trans 0 g	**0 %**
Cholesterol 0 mg	
Sodium 0 mg	**0 %**
Carbohydrate 0 g	**0 %**
Fibre 0 g	**0 %**
Sugars 0 g	
Protein 0 g	

Vitamin A	0 %	Vitamin C	0 %
Calcium	0 %	Iron	0 %

Limit trans fat

When a Nutrition Facts table is not available, ask for nutrition information to choose foods lower in trans and saturated fats.

Take a step today...

✓ Have breakfast every day. It may help control your hunger later in the day.

✓ Walk wherever you can – get off the bus early, use the stairs.

✓ Benefit from eating vegetables and fruit at all meals and as snacks.

✓ Spend less time being inactive such as watching TV or playing computer games.

✓ Request nutrition information about menu items when eating out to help you make healthier choices.

✓ Enjoy eating with family and friends!

✓ Take time to eat and savour every bite!

For more information, interactive tools, or additional copies visit Canada's Food Guide on-line at: www.healthcanada.gc.ca/foodguide

or contact:

Publications
Health Canada
Ottawa, Ontario K1A 0K9
E-Mail: publications@hc-sc.gc.ca
Tel.: 1-866-225-0709
Fax: (613) 941-5366
TTY: 1-800-267-1245

Également disponible en français sous le titre :
Bien manger avec le Guide alimentaire canadien

This publication can be made available on request on diskette, large print, audio-cassette and braille.

 HC Pub.: 4651 Cat.: H164-38/1-2007E ISBN: 0-662-44467-1

What Should Guide Canadians' Food Choices?

Weight Management

Having too much body fat increases your risk of most major chronic nutrition-related diseases. If your weight is within a healthy range now, you should strive to maintain it. However, it is important to recognize that weight maintenance may become more difficult as you grow older. To avoid gaining unwanted weight over time, consider the following:

- Match your caloric intake from foods and beverages with the calories your body uses for its energy needs.
- Gradually reduce your energy intake, especially by eating fewer empty-calorie foods, such as sweets and fatty foods.
- Increase your physical activity level.

Physical Activity

Being physically active on a regular basis and spending less time being inactive (sedentary) promotes healthy body weight, psychological well-being, and overall good health. According to recent statistics, 63% of Canadian adults do not get sufficient physical activity.[13] Canadians should work to improve endurance, flexibility, and strength by performing at least 60 minutes of physical activity daily; the activity may be a combination of light, moderate, and vigorous.[13] You can achieve greater health benefits by engaging in physical activities that last longer or are more vigorous than moderate-intensity activities. Choose activities that you enjoy, and remember that the 60 minutes doesn't have to be done all at once. Break your activity up into shorter time periods if it assists you in achieving the goal of 60+ minutes per day. Table 3.1 presents some common physical activities and indicates their intensity levels.

TABLE 3.1 *Physical Activities Classified by Intensity*

Light Intensity
Light walking
Stretching
Light gardening/yard work
Moderate Intensity
Hiking
Dancing
Golf (walking while carrying clubs)
Bicycling (< 16km/hr)
Brisk walking (5 km/hr)
Weightlifting (general light workout)
Swimming (slow freestyle laps)
Vigorous Intensity
Running/jogging (8 km/hr)
Bicycling (> 16km/hr)
Fast swimming
Aerobic conditioning walking (7 km/hr)
Heavy yard work (chopping wood)
Weightlifting (vigorous effort)
Basketball (vigorous)

Source: Canada's Physical Activity Guide to Healthy Active Living; http://www.phac-aspc.gc.ca/hp-ps/hl-mvs/pag-gap/index-home-accueil-eng.php.

Food Groups to Encourage

Many Canadians do not eat enough fruit, vegetables, whole grains, and milk products each day. According to the *Eating Well with Canada's Food Guide* dietary guidelines, you should do the following:

- Consume adequate amounts of fruits and vegetables and include one dark green and one orange vegetable each day.
- Make sure at least half of your grain servings come from whole-grain sources such as 100% whole-grain breads and pastas. To meet this goal, eat whole-grain cereals such as oatmeal for breakfast or snacks and use 100% whole-grain or rye breads to make sandwiches.
- Choose low-fat milk and milk alternatives such as skim or 1% milk when possible.
- Frequently select meat alternatives such as beans, legumes, lentils, and soy-based products such as tofu. In addition, consume at least two servings of fish each week and use little if any added fats when preparing foods.
- Always try and enjoy a variety of foods from each of the four food groups and seek to quench your thirst with water.
- Limit butter, hard margarines, lard, and shortening. Choose soft margarines made with vegetable oils and select oils such as canola, soybean, and olive oils.

Canadians should aim for half of their grain servings to come from whole-grain sources such as 100% whole-grain bread.

Most kinds of cheese are rich sources of saturated fat and cholesterol.

Fats

Certain fats are healthier to eat than others. To reduce your risk of CVD, you should consider the following:

- Limit your total fat intake to between 20 to 35% of calories daily.
- Select foods that are rich sources of unsaturated fat, such as vegetable oils, fatty fish, and most nuts.
- Consume less than 10% of your total calories from saturated fat and limit added fats when preparing foods. Beef, butter, cheese, and whole milk are rich sources of saturated fat and cholesterol. At one time, dietitians recommended limiting egg consumption because egg yolks are a rich source of cholesterol. Results of research, however, indicate that eating eggs does not negatively affect blood lipid levels of most healthy people.[14] Therefore, dietary guides generally do not recommend that healthy people avoid eating eggs.
- Limit your trans fat intake by reading labels to determine whether this type of fat is in food products. Most of the trans fat in Canadian diets used to be from cakes, cookies, and crackers. However, due to mandatory labelling of trans fat in Canadian products beginning in 2005, the food supply has been rapidly changing and the trans fat content of many of these products has now been reduced.

Carbohydrates

Like fats, certain carbohydrates are healthier to eat than others. To increase your intake of healthy carbohydrates, do the following:

- Include fibre-rich fruits, vegetables, and whole-grain products in your daily diet.
- Choose and prepare foods and beverages with minimal amounts of added sugars, including caloric sweeteners, such as sugar, honey, and corn syrup.

Eating any form of carbohydrate can contribute to tooth decay (see Chapter 13), especially if the carbohydrates such as sugar are highly refined. Such forms of carbohydrate can stick to teeth and provide a food source for bacteria that contribute to dental decay. To reduce your risk of dental cavities, do the following:

- Practise good oral hygiene daily.
- Consume sugary and other highly refined carbohydrates infrequently.

Focus on Fruit

How many cups of fruit do you eat daily? Does your diet meet the amount of fruit recommended in your individualized *Eating Well with Canada's Food Guide* recommendation? Many kinds of fresh fruit make quick and easy snacks that can be carried in knapsacks, purses, and briefcases.

Fresh fruit such as apples, oranges, tangerines, kiwifruit, and grapes can be kept for a few days at room temperature in a fruit bowl. You can store fresh fruit for longer periods by placing them in the refrigerator. Banana peels, however, turn dark brown when the fruit is refrigerated, so it is best to store them at room temperature. The Recipe for Healthy Living later in this chapter features a fruit salad recipe that is easy to prepare.

Fresh fruit such as apples, oranges, tangerines, kiwifruit, and grapes can be kept at room temperature for a few days.

Protein

Similar to fats and carbohydrates, certain sources of protein are healthier to eat than others. Many Canadians consume more than the required amount of protein each day. It is important to note that there are small amounts of protein in many of the foods we eat. Grain products, while high in complex carbohydrates, often contain small amounts of protein. These small amounts of protein add up and contribute to our total daily intake of dietary protein. Some athletes often consume excessive amounts of protein assuming it will lead to greater muscle gain, but there is little scientific research to support this. To select healthy sources of dietary protein, consider the following:

- Choose wild game and lean cuts of poultry and fish before red meat, and choose lean cuts of beef and pork when choosing these foods.
- Frequently choose meat alternatives such as beans, legumes, and soy products rather than animal sources of protein.
- Snack on nuts and seeds as sources of protein.

Eating any form of energy can lead to unwanted weight gain, so limit protein intake according to the DRI to 0.8 g per kg of body weight and 10 to 35% of total energy daily. Do not attempt weight loss programs that advocate for high protein intake.

Sodium and Potassium

Sodium and potassium are mineral elements necessary for life, but high intakes of sodium and low intakes of potassium are associated with increased risk of hypertension. If untreated, hypertension can damage the heart and blood vessels. To reduce your risk of hypertension, do the following:

- Consume less than 1 teaspoon of salt (approximately 2300 mg of sodium) daily.
- Select low-sodium foods. Canned and processed foods, including many snack foods, often contain high amounts of salt.
- Prepare foods with little salt.
- Consume more potassium-rich foods, especially fruit and vegetables.

Alcoholic Beverages

When consumed in small amounts, alcohol can have beneficial effects on your body and well-being. Alcohol, however, is an addictive drug that can be harmful to individuals as well as society. If you choose to drink alcohol, drink sensibly and in moderation. To follow this dietary recommendation, consider the following:

- Recognize that moderate alcohol consumption is one standard drink per day for women and no more than two standard drinks per day for men. The Chapter 6 Highlight provides more information about alcohol, including the definition of a standard alcoholic drink.
- Be aware that certain people should not drink alcohol, including those who are under 19 years of age; are unable to limit their alcohol intake; are pregnant, breast-feeding, or likely to become pregnant; or are taking certain medications.
- Recognize that alcohol should not be consumed by people who drive, operate machinery, or perform other activities that require attention, skill, or physical coordination.

Food Safety

Suffering from a case of food poisoning (food-borne illness) is not only unpleasant; the experience can also be a deadly one. Chapter 12 provides more detailed information about food safety, but you can take these basic steps to avoid food-borne illness:

- Wash your hands and surfaces that come in contact with food such as fruits and vegetables before preparing them. When handling raw meat and poultry, be careful to avoid spreading bacteria from these items to other foods, a process called cross-contamination.
- Keep raw, cooked, and ready-to-eat foods separated.
- Cook foods to a temperature that kills bacteria and other microbes that can cause food-borne illness.
- Refrigerate perishable foods promptly and defrost foods properly.
- Avoid unpasteurized juices and milk products; raw or undercooked eggs, meat, and poultry; and raw sprouts.

Table 3.2 suggests ways you can apply the *Eating Well with Canada's Food Guide* recommendations to your usual food choices. However, making recommended dietary and other lifestyle changes does not always reduce risk factors for disease. For example, a man who has hypertension may find that his blood pressure remains dangerously elevated after several months of limiting his salt intake, exercising, and maintaining a healthy weight for his height. In this case, genetic factors may be influencing the man's health more than his lifestyle, and medication may be necessary to reduce his blood pressure.

TABLE 3.2 *Making Changes in Order to Eat Well with Canada's Food Guide*

If You Usually Eat:	Replace With:
White bread and rolls	100% whole-grain bread and rolls
Sugary breakfast cereals	Low-sugar high-fibre cereal sweetened with berries, bananas, peaches, or other fruit
Cheeseburger, french fries, and a regular (sugar-sweetened) soft drink	Roasted chicken or turkey sandwich, baked beans, skim or low-fat milk, or soy milk
Potato salad or cole slaw	Leafy greens or three-bean salad
Doughnuts, chips, or salty snack foods	Small bran muffin or whole-wheat bagel topped with peanut butter or soy nut butter, unsalted nuts, and dried fruit
Regular soft drinks	Water, diet soft drinks, skim or low-fat milk, or 100% fruit juice
Boiled vegetables	Raw or steamed vegetables (often retain more nutrients than boiled)
Breaded and fried meat, fish, or poultry	Broiled or roasted meat, fish, or poultry
Fatty meats such as barbequed ribs, sausage, and hot dogs	Chicken, turkey, or fish; lean meats such as ground round
Whole or 2% milk, cottage cheese with 4% fat, or yogourt made from whole milk	1% or skim milk, low-fat cottage cheese (1%), or low-fat yogourt
Ice cream	Frozen yogourt or ice milk
Cream cheese	Low-fat cottage cheese (mashed) or reduced-fat cream cheese
Creamy salad dressings or dips made with mayonnaise or sour cream	Oil and vinegar dressing, reduced-fat salad dressings, or dips made from low-fat sour cream or plain yogourt
Chocolate chip or cream-filled cookies	Fruit-filled bars, oatmeal cookies, or fresh fruit
Salt added to season foods	Herbs, spices, or lemon juice

Concept **Checkpoint**

Respond to the following points according to recommendations of the latest dietary guidelines.

12. What two steps can you take to eat a nutritionally adequate diet that meets your energy needs?
13. How much moderate-intensity physical activity should you add to your usual activities, and how often should you perform these activities?
14. What are the four *Eating Well with Canada's Food Guide* food groups?
15. Your diet can have as much as ______ % of total calories from fat.
16. Your diet can have as much as ______% of total calories from saturated fat.
17. List at least three foods you can eat to increase your intake of healthy carbohydrates.
18. Elevated salt intake is associated with an increased risk of which disorder?
19. How many standard alcoholic drinks per day represent moderate alcohol consumption for men and women?
20. What are two actions you can take to keep foods safe to eat?

 The "New" *Eating Well with Canada's Food Guide*

In 2007, Health Canada introduced the new *Eating Well with Canada's Food Guide* recommendations, a completely revamped version of the 1992 *Canada's Food Guide to Healthy Eating* (Fig. 3.7). There were initially some concerns regarding the 2007 *Eating Well with Canada's Food Guide* recommendations and some speculation that the suggested number of servings from each of the food groups may be *obesogenic*, meaning that it may promote weight gain. This is likely not the case. Canadian studies have determined that a significant proportion of the daily energy intake for Canadians comes from other foods that are high in calories, fat, and sugar, such as cakes, pastries, and cookies.[15] Thus, if energy intake from these foods remained high, and was coupled with the energy intake from the established four food groups, then generally Canadians would consume too much energy each day. Consequently, it is important for Canadians to limit their intake of other foods and obtain the majority of their daily caloric intake from the four food groups as outlined in the *Eating Well with Canada's Food Guide* serving recommendations based on age and gender.

EATracker Dietitians of Canada interactive Internet dietary analysis, menu planning, and physical activity tool

The EATracker

The **EATracker**[16] allows Canadians to assess their daily food and activity choices in comparison to the guidelines established by Health Canada. EATracker compares your daily food choices to the recommendations for energy intake and essential nutrients based on your age, gender, and activity level, and provides personalized feedback based on your daily intake and activity patterns. The EATracker program also allows for the determination of your body mass index (BMI) and provides guidance to assist you in achieving a healthy body weight. The program also allows Canadians to track dietary intake, activity, and progress over time.

The EATracker is not meant to replace the guidance of a dietitian or physician, but is designed to help Canadians over the age of 14 to better understand their eating and activity choices (Fig. 3.8). If Canadians desire more personalized and specific nutrition advice, it is wise to visit a registered dietitian (RD).

Figure 3.7 1992 *Canada's Food Guide to Healthy Eating*.

Figure 3.8 EATracker. To use the EATracker tool as a menu and dietary intake analyzer and planning and physical activity guide, you can visit the Dietitians of Canada interactive Web site at www.dietitians.ca/public/content/eat_well_live_well/english/eatracker.

Concept Checkpoint

21. Which *Eating Well with Canada's Food Guide* food group should we consume the largest number of servings from each day?
22. What is the name of the Dietitians of Canada online dietary intake and physical activity analyzer tool?
23. How many servings of meat and alternatives are represented by a 142-g (5-oz.) sirloin steak?
24. How many servings should a 19-year-old male consume each day from the grain products food group?

Figure 3.9 Nutrition Facts table. You can learn more about the energy and nutrient contents of packaged foods by reading the Nutrition Facts table on food labels.

Food and Supplement Labels

Consumers can use information on food labels to determine ingredients and compare energy and nutrient contents of packaged foods and beverages. In Canada, Health Canada regulates and monitors information that can be placed on food labels, including claims about the health benefits of ingredients.[7] Today nearly all foods and beverages sold in grocery stores must have labels that provide the product's name, manufacturer's name and address, and amount of product in the package. In Canada, the four main types of nutrition labelling are the Nutrition Facts table, list of ingredients, nutrient content claim, and health claim.

Nutrition Facts Table

You can find specific nutrition-related information about many packaged foods by reading their labels. To show this information, food labels must use a special format, the Nutrition Facts table (Fig. 3.9). The Nutrition Facts table indicates the amount of a serving size, in household units as well as grams. Serving sizes must be consistent among similar foods—for example, all brands of ice cream must use the same serving size (½ cup) in the Nutrition Facts table to describe the product's nutritional content. The table also must display the total amount of energy and energy from fat, indicated as numbers of calories, in a serving. The table uses grams (g) and milligrams (mg) to indicate amounts of fibre and nutrients in a serving of food, except for vitamins and minerals which list % Daily Value only. In Canada, it must also be bilingual with information in English and French.

The standard Nutrition Facts table must provide information about the food's energy (in calories) and 13 core nutrients: total fat, saturated fat, trans fat, cholesterol, sodium, total carbohydrate, fibre, sugars, protein, vitamin A, vitamin C, calcium, and iron.[7,17] Food manufacturers can also include amounts of polyunsaturated and monounsaturated fats, omega-3, omega-6, and vitamins and minerals in the Nutrition Facts table (Fig. 3.9). Listing these particular food components is required if the manufacturer has fortified the food with the nutrients or made claims about their health benefits.

Certain foods such as fresh fruits and vegetables, fish and shellfish, meats and poultry, alcoholic beverages (if an alcoholic content of more than 0.5%), and spices (with no nutrient value) and fresh herbs are not required to have Nutrition Facts table.[18] However, many large grocery store chains have voluntarily chosen to provide consumers with information about their products' nutritional content on posters or pamphlets displayed near the foods.

Daily Values

Daily Values (DVs) set of nutrient intake standards developed for labelling purposes

Nutrient standards such as the RDA and AI are gender, age, and life-stage specific. For example, the RDA for vitamin C is 90 mg per day and 75 mg per day for non-smoking 18-year-old males and females, respectively. Because the RDAs and AIs are so specific, it is not practical to provide nutrient information on food labels that refers to these complex standards. To help consumers evaluate the nutritional content of food products, Health Canada and the U.S. Food and Drug Administration (FDA) developed the **Daily Values (DVs)** for labelling purposes. Compared to the RDAs, the DVs are a more simplified and practical set of nutrient standards. The adult DV for a nutrient is based on a standard diet that supplies 2000 kcal per day. Not all nutrients have DVs, but they have been established for total fat, cholesterol, total carbohydrate, fibre, and several vitamins and minerals. There are no DVs for protein, sugars, and trans fat. Appendix C at the back of this textbook lists DVs. A set of DVs that applies to people over 4 years of age is used for foods and beverages that adults consume. Three other sets of DVs are used on labels of foods intended for infants, children between 1 and 4 years of age, and pregnant or breast-feeding women.

Although DVs are often the highest RDA or AI for a particular nutrient, in many instances, they are based on recommendations of public health experts. For example, the RDA for carbohydrate is 130 grams per day for people over 1 year of age. The DV for carbohydrate, however, is 300 grams per day. This amount reflects the general dietary recommendations that carbohydrate can contribute 60% of a person's total energy intake, or 1200 kcal (300 g × 4 kcal/g of carbohydrate) of a 2000 kcal per day diet. For people older than 1 year of age, no RDA or AI has been set for daily fat intake. However, the DV for fat is 65 grams per day. This amount meets the general recommendation that fat intake can be about 30% of a person's total energy intake for a 2000 kcal per day diet.

The % DVs can be quite confusing to use. When evaluating or planning nutritious menus, your goal is to obtain at least 100% of the DVs for fibre, vitamins, and minerals each day. On the other hand, you may need to limit your intake of foods that have high % DVs of total fat, cholesterol, and sodium. Reaching 100% of the DV is the upper limit of these nutrients and is not needed each day. Thus, you should not consume 100% of the DV for total fat, cholesterol, and sodium each day. The general rule of thumb: A food that supplies 5% DV or less of a nutrient is a low source of the nutrient; a food that provides 20% DV or more is a high source of the nutrient.[19]

Percents of DVs are designed to help consumers compare nutrient contents of packaged foods to make more healthful choices. However, most people do not eat just packaged foods. Fresh fruits and vegetables, as well as restaurant meals, do not have labels with information about % DVs per serving. Therefore, many consumers will underestimate their nutrient intakes if they do not consider the contribution that unlabelled foods make to their diets.

It is important to note the description of a serving size and the number of servings per container when using nutritional labelling information to estimate your intakes of energy, fibre, and nutrients in the food. A common mistake people make when using Nutrition Facts table is assuming that the information applies to the entire package. For example, the Nutrition Facts table on a package of ice cream indicates the nutrition information for one cone or serving. If you eat all the container's contents, you must multiply the information concerning calories, fat, and other food components by four (see Fig. 3.9). Why? Because there are actually four cones or servings and the nutritional information on the Nutrition Facts table applies to only one serving.

List of Ingredients

The list of ingredients is a mandatory nutrition label on pre-packaged foods. All ingredients are listed in descending order by weight. Ingredient lists provide consumers with allergy information by listing allergens such as soy or wheat. They highlight ingredients so that consumers with religious restrictions, allergies, or special diets can avoid such

Often, the only difference between a tablespoon of a light salad dressing, such as ranch or blue cheese, and regular salad dressing is the amount of water they contain. Instead of paying more for calorie-reduced bottled salad dressings, make your own light salad dressing by adding some water to regular salad dressing, then stir or shake the mixture.

products. Lastly, they also provide nutrition information for consumers looking for healthier products with lower fat, sugar, or salt.

Nutrient Content Claims

Health Canada permits labels to include claims about levels of nutrients in packaged foods.[17] Nutrient content claims can use terms such as "free," "high," or "low" to describe how much of a nutrient is in the product. Additionally, nutrient content claims can use terms such as "more" or "reduced" to compare amounts of nutrients in a product to those in a similar product. This claim is often used for an item that substitutes for a reference food, that is, a similar and more familiar food. For example, a "reduced-fat" salad dressing has considerably less fat than its *reference food*, regular salad dressing.

Table 3.3 lists some legal definitions for common nutrient content claims that may be used on labels. Note that a product may contain a small amount of a nutrient such as fat or sugar, yet the Nutrition Facts table can indicate the amount as "0 g." For example, the Nutrition Facts table may indicate that a serving of food supplies "0" grams of trans fat, even though the serving actually supplies less than 0.5 g of trans fat. Furthermore, products are allowed to claim that the product is "free" of the nutrient.

According to Health Canada, a *light* food has at least one-third fewer kilocalories or half the fat of the reference food.[18] For example, 15 mL (1 Tbsp) of light pancake syrup has one-third fewer kcal than a tablespoon of regular pancake syrup, and a tablespoon of light mayonnaise has less than half the fat of regular mayonnaise. The term *light* may also describe such properties as texture and colour, as long as the label explains the intent—for example, "light brown sugar." To include the term "natural" on the label, the food must not contain food colouring agents, synthetic flavours, or other unnatural substances.

Health Claims

To make their foods more appealing to consumers, manufacturers often promote products as having certain health benefits or high amounts of nutrients. A health claim describes

TABLE 3.3 *Legal Definitions for Common Nutrient Content Claims*

Sugar	• **Sugar free:** The product provides less than 0.5 g of sugar per serving. • **Reduced sugar:** The food contains at least 25% less sugar per serving than the reference food.
Calories	• **Calorie free:** The food provides fewer than 5 kcal per serving. • **Low calorie/Low energy:** The food supplies 40 kcal or less per serving. • **Reduced or fewer calories:** The food contains at least 25% fewer kcal per serving than the reference food.
Fat	• **Fat free:** The food provides less than 0.5 g of fat per serving. • **Low fat:** The food contains 3 g or less fat per serving. Two percent milk is not "low fat," because it has more than 3 g of fat per serving. The term reduced fat can be used to describe 2% milk. • **Reduced or less fat:** The food supplies at least 25% less fat per serving than the reference food.
Cholesterol	• **Cholesterol free:** The food contains less than 2 mg of cholesterol and 2 g or less of saturated fat per serving.
Fibre	• **High source of fibre:** The food contains 4 g or more fibre per serving. • **Source of fibre:** The food supplies 2 g or more of fibre per serving.
Meat and poultry products	• **Extra lean:** The food contains 7.5% or less fat. • **Lean:** The food contains 10% or less fat.

Source: Government of Canada: Regulations Amending the Food and Drug Regulations (Nutrition Labelling, Nutrient Content Claims and Health Claims). 2002; revised 2003. http://gazette.gc.ca/archives/p2/2003/2003-01-01/html/sor-dors11-eng.html. Accessed: December 18, 2009.

the relationship between a food, food ingredient, or dietary supplement and the reduced risk of a nutrition-related condition. Health Canada permits food manufacturers to include certain health claims on food labels (Fig. 3.10), and these guidelines are published in the *CFIA (Canadian Food Inspection Agency) Guide to Food Labelling and Advertising.*[18] For example, an allowable health claim may state, "A healthy diet with adequate calcium and vitamin D, and regular physical activity, help to achieve strong bones and may reduce the risk of osteoporosis" (Table 3.4).

Health Canada via the Canadian Food Inspection Agency controls food labelling claims through the implementation and enforcement of the *Food and Drugs Act.*[20]

Figure 3.10 Label claims. Health Canada permits food manufacturers to include certain health claims on food labels.

The *Food and Drugs Act* and the *Food and Drug Regulations*

The *Food and Drug Regulations,* as they apply to food, prescribe, among other things, the labelling of all prepackaged foods, including requirements for ingredient labelling, nutrition labelling, durable life dates, nutrient content claims, diet-related health claims, and foods for special dietary use. It also sets out bilingual labelling requirements.

The *Food and Drugs Act* prohibits the labelling, packaging, treating, processing, selling, or advertising of any food (at all levels of trade) in a manner that is false, misleading, or deceptive to consumers or is likely to create an erroneous message regarding the character, value, quantity, composition, merit, or safety of the product. Subsections prohibit health claims that might suggest that a food is a treatment, preventative, or cure for specified diseases or health conditions, *unless provided for in the regulations.*

Health Canada requires specific wording for certain health claims that are allowed on labels. For more information about health claims, visit Health Canada's Web site at www.hc-sc.gc.ca.

Health Canada will not approve health claims for foods that contain more than 13 g of fat, 4 g of saturated fat, 60 mg of cholesterol, or 480 mg of sodium per serving. For example, calcium is a mineral that strengthens bones and protects them from osteoporosis, a condition in which bones become brittle and break easily. Whole milk is a rich source of calcium. Nevertheless, the label on a carton of whole milk cannot include a health claim about calcium and osteoporosis, because the milk contains more than 4 g of saturated fat per serving. In addition, the product must meet specific conditions that relate to the health claim. For example, a claim regarding the benefits of eating a low-fat diet is allowed only if the product contains 3 g or less of fat per serving, which is Health Canada's standard definition of a low-fat food.

Another type of health claim is a *function* claim. A function claim describes the role a nutrient or dietary supplement plays in maintaining a structure, such as bone, or promoting a normal function, such as digestion. Health Canada allows function claims such as "Vitamin D is a factor in the formation and maintenance of bones and teeth," or "Protein helps build and repair body tissues." Function statements cannot claim that a nutrient, food, or dietary supplement can be used to prevent or treat a serious health

TABLE 3.4 *Examples of Permissible Health Claims for Food Labels*

Dietary Factor/Health Condition	Example of Permissible Health Claim
Heart disease	A diet low in saturated fat and trans fat, and the reduction of the risk of heart disease
Osteoporosis	A diet adequate in calcium and vitamin D, and the reduction of the risk of osteoporosis
High blood pressure (hypertension)	A diet low in sodium and high in potassium, and the reduction of the risk of hypertension
Cancer	A diet rich in vegetables and fruits, and the reduction of the risk of some types of cancer
Dental caries	Maximal fermentable carbohydrate in gum, hard candy or breath-freshening products, and the reduced risk of dental caries.

Source: Canadian Food Inspection Agency: Guide to Food Labelling and Advertising – Chapter 8. http://www.inspection.gc.ca/english/fssa/labeti/guide/ch8e.shtml#a8_4. Accessed: December 19, 2009.

condition. For example, Health Canada would not permit a claim that a product "promotes low blood pressure," because that claim implies the product has drug-like effects and can treat high blood pressure.

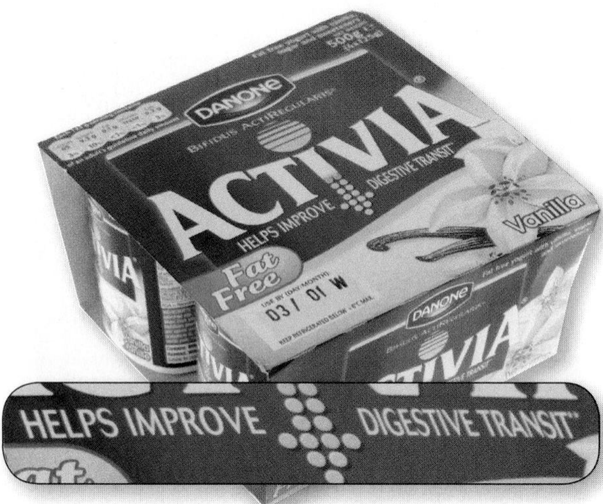

Figure 3.11 Function claim. Health Canada allows function claims such as "calcium builds strong bones" or "helps improve digestive transit." Function statements cannot claim that a nutrient, food, or dietary supplement can be used to prevent or treat a serious health condition.

Dietary Supplement Labels

Dietary supplements, such as vitamin pills and herbal extracts, have labels that are different than those used on food products. Instead of having a Nutrition Facts table, labels on dietary supplements display the ingredients and their amounts that are included in the supplement. When health claims appear on a supplement's label, the manufacturer of the product must be able to provide evidence that the statements are truthful and not misleading.

The Canadian Food Inspection Agency (CFIA) is responsible for taking action against any unsafe dietary supplement after it reaches the market. The agency receives and monitors reports from consumers and their health care providers concerning unwanted side effects that may have resulted from taking dietary supplements. The CFIA evaluates these reports to determine whether certain supplements pose a major or unreasonable health risk to consumers. If the evidence indicates that a dietary supplement is harmful, the CFIA may issue a consumer alert to warn people about potential hazards of using the product. In some cases, the agency orders dietary supplement manufacturers to stop distributing the product. If necessary, CFIA can take legal action against companies that do not comply with the agency's orders or regulations. For example, CFIA can seize dietary supplements that are unsafe, that contain unapproved substances, that have been labelled improperly, or that include information, such as package inserts, with claims that are not supported by scientific evidence.

organic foods foods produced without the use of antibiotics, hormones, synthetic fertilizers and pesticides, genetic improvements, or spoilage-killing radiation

Organic Foods

According to chemists, organic substances have the element carbon bonded to hydrogen (another element) in their chemical structures. Therefore, all foods are organic because they contain carbon bonded with hydrogen. The term "organic," however, also refers to certain farming methods. **Organic foods** are those produced without the use of antibiotics, hormones, synthetic fertilizers and pesticides, genetic improvements, or ionizing radiation. In Canada, organic food products are regulated by the Canadian Food Inspection Agency (CFIA) under the *Organic Product Regulations*. The new Canadian logo was approved in 2009 and was designed to protect consumers from false or misleading organic claims. Food products may only be referred to as organic if they come from a farm using practices that are considerate of the natural ecosystems in order to promote sustainable productivity and enhancement of biodiversity and water management. Farmers and food manufacturers in Canada must apply for certification and adhere to strict regulations in order to raise, produce, and sell organic food products. Multi-ingredient food products in Canada must contain 95% or greater organic product components to be sold as "organic," "organically grown," or "organically produced."[21]

Over the past 40 years, the popularity of organic foods increased in North America as many consumers became concerned about the environment and the effects of conventional farming methods on the safety and the nutritional value of the food supply. Sales of organic foods have increased steadily since the 1990s, even though these products are usually more expensive than the same foods produced by conventional farming methods.[22] The majority of people who purchased organically grown products thought they were better for their health than conventionally produced foods.

Although organic farming techniques can benefit the environment, crop yields are typically lower.[23] Results of some studies indicated organically grown vegetables had higher vitamin C content than conventionally grown vegetables. Nevertheless, more research is needed to determine whether there are health advantages to eating organic foods.[24]

Figure 3.12 Organic food logo. Foods that have been certified "organic" may use the CFIA symbol.

Concept **Checkpoint**

25. Identify at least one limitation of using % DVs to determine your nutrient intakes.
26. Explain how you can use nutritional information provided on food and dietary supplement labels to become a more careful consumer.
27. What is the difference between a Nutrition Facts table and list of ingredients?
28. Discuss the role of the CFIA in protecting consumers from false nutrition and health claims on food and dietary supplement labels.
29. Are there any risks in taking dietary supplements? Provide an explanation for your answer.
30. Explain how organic food production methods differ from conventional food production methods.

Because many plants have toxic parts, you can unintentionally poison yourself by taking herbal supplements. Comfrey, pennyroyal, sassafras, kava, lobelia, and ma huang are among the plants known to be highly toxic or cancer-causing. Plants may also contain chemicals that may interfere with or enhance the actions of prescribed or over-the-counter medications. Therefore, check with your physician before taking any dietary supplement. Pregnant women should always consult their physician before taking dietary supplements. Additionally, do not give an herbal or other dietary supplement to children without physician approval. This advice also applies to vitamin and mineral supplements, because nutrients are toxic when taken in excess.

Using Dietary Analysis Software

How much selenium, magnesium, and niacin are in an ounce of Swiss cheese? Have you ever wanted information about nutrients in a food that are not listed on the Nutrition Facts table? In the past, people relied on food composition tables, lists of commonly eaten foods that provide amounts of energy, fibre, macronutrients, and several micronutrients. Today, people can determine the energy and nutrient contents of their food choices by using a dietary analysis software program. Furthermore, people with Internet access can obtain the information from certain Web sites.

Dietary analysis software and Web sites can be quick and easy tools for determining nutrient and energy contents of a specific food. However, the values provided by these resources are not necessarily exact amounts. The same type of food may vary in nutrient content depending on hereditary factors, age, growing conditions, and production methods. Therefore, scientists generally analyze several samples of a food to determine their nutrient contents, and then the researchers average the results. For example, if the amount of energy in three Valencia oranges that each weigh about 120 g (4 oz.) were 55, 60, and 62 kcal, respectively, the value listed in the food composition table for a Valencia orange weighing 120 g (4 oz.) would be 59 kcal, the average of the three. In many instances, values for certain nutrients are missing. This occurs when accurate data concerning the complete nutrient analysis of the food are unavailable.

Valencia oranges may vary in nutrient content depending on various factors, including growing conditions.

What about Fast Foods?

Dietary analysis software may include energy and nutrient information about popular fast foods. Additionally, most major fast food restaurant chains provide information about the energy and nutrient content of their foods. The restaurants, however, may not display this information for their customers to see easily. To learn about the nutritional value of your favourite fast foods, ask the restaurant's manager for the company's brochure that includes a food composition table of their products. If such handouts are unavailable, visit the fast food chain's Web site to see if the information is posted.

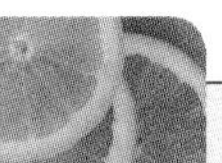

The original Hershey chocolate bar weighed about half an ounce in 1906, the same weight as today's Hershey "miniature" chocolate bar. The standard size Hershey chocolate bar weighs 1.45 ounces, making it almost three times heavier and more energy-dense than the original or miniature chocolate candy bar.[25]

Concept Checkpoint

31. Identify at least two reliable sources of information about the energy and nutrient contents of foods and beverages.

32. How can you obtain information about the energy and nutrient contents of fast food restaurant menu items?

Chapter 3 Highlight

The Multicultural Feast

Wherever you live or travel in Canada, you're likely to find restaurants that serve a wide variety of ethnic fare, such as Chinese, Indian, Italian, Thai, Vietnamese, or Middle Eastern dishes. Although your primary food selection and cooking habits probably reflect your own ethnic and religious heritage, you likely enjoy foods from other cultures and religious groups.

The Chapter 3 Highlight examines the influences that the dietary practices of certain cultures and ethnic groups have had on the Canadian diet and the possible effects of these practices on health. Traditional ethnic diets are often based on dishes containing small amounts of animal foods and larger amounts of locally grown fruits, vegetables, and unrefined grains. However, these foods are typically the first to be abandoned as immigrants adopt some Canadian dietary patterns over time. If an immigrant population becomes assimilated to the Canadian culture, the prevalence of chronic diseases such as cardiovascular disease (CVD), type 2 diabetes, and high blood pressure often increases among them, partly as a result of adopting less healthy North American eating practices.

Northwestern European Influences

Immigrants from northwestern European regions or countries such as the United Kingdom, Scandinavia, and Germany established the familiar "meat-and-potatoes" diet that features a large portion of beef or pork served with smaller portions of potatoes. In the past, the potatoes were either boiled or mashed; today they are usually fried. This mainstream Canadian diet, often referred to as a Western diet, provides large amounts of animal protein and fat, and lacks fruits, whole grains, and a variety of green vegetables. Such diets are associated with high rates of serious chronic diseases, particularly CVD and type 2 diabetes, which are discussed in later chapters of this textbook.

South Asian Influences

The South Asian population is now the largest minority group in the Canada. Many South Asians have migrated to Canada from all parts of South Asia, including India, Pakistan, Bangladesh, and Sri Lanka. The traditional South Asian diet includes mangoes, pomegranates, spices such as green chilis, herbs such as coriander, and legumes. Many grocery stores in Canada sell other plant foods that are often incorporated into South Asian meals, such as fresh okra, bitter melon, drumstick, and bitter gourd. Such fruits and vegetables add fibre and a variety of nutrients, phytochemicals, vivid colours, and interesting flavours to South Asian dishes.

Authentic South Asian meals are based primarily on rice, bread (*roti*), meat or vegetable curries, and legumes, depending on the region. To appeal to people with more Western food preferences, South Asian fast food restaurants in Canada often serve dishes that contain large portions of curries with added creams and oil or fried foods. Diets that contain high amounts of these fatty foods are associated with excess body fat, CVD, and type 2 diabetes.

Figure 3.A South Asian diet. Fresh fruits and vegetables, herbs and spices, and legumes add flavour, colour, and micronutrients to South Asian meals.

Italian Influences

The traditional Italian diet of pasta and other grain products, olive oil, fish, nuts, fruits, and vegetables is healthier than the Western diet. Pasta, a product made from wheat flour and water, is the core of the traditional Italian diet. To many North Americans, pasta is spaghetti topped with tomato sauce, meatballs, and grated Parmesan cheese. However, Italians eat a variety of different forms of pasta, such as penne, linguini, acini de pepe, and rotini along with sauces that are often meatless. Pizza, a dish from southern Italy, is one of the most frequently consumed foods in Canada. Unlike traditional Italian pizza that has a thin crust and is lightly covered with tomatoes, basil (a leafy herb), and mozzarella cheese, many Canadians choose thick-crust pizza topped with tomato sauce, plenty of shredded mozzarella cheese, and dotted with fatty pork sausage or pepperoni.

The typical Mediterranean dietary intake pattern is based on traditional dietary practices of Greece and southern Italy. In the new Mediterranean food pyramid, fruits, vegetables, grains, nuts, legumes, seeds, olives, and olive oils are grouped together to form the foundation of this diet. Herbs and spices also part of the pyramid because they add flavour and reduce the need for fat and salt when cooking. Red meat is rarely eaten. Main dishes often include seafood and poultry, and wine may be included with meals. Although this Mediterranean diet provides as much as 35% of total calories as fat in the diet, much of the fat is from olive oil. Olive oil is a rich source of a type of fat that reduces rather than increases the risk of CVD. Chapter 6 provides more information about oils and fats and their roles in health.

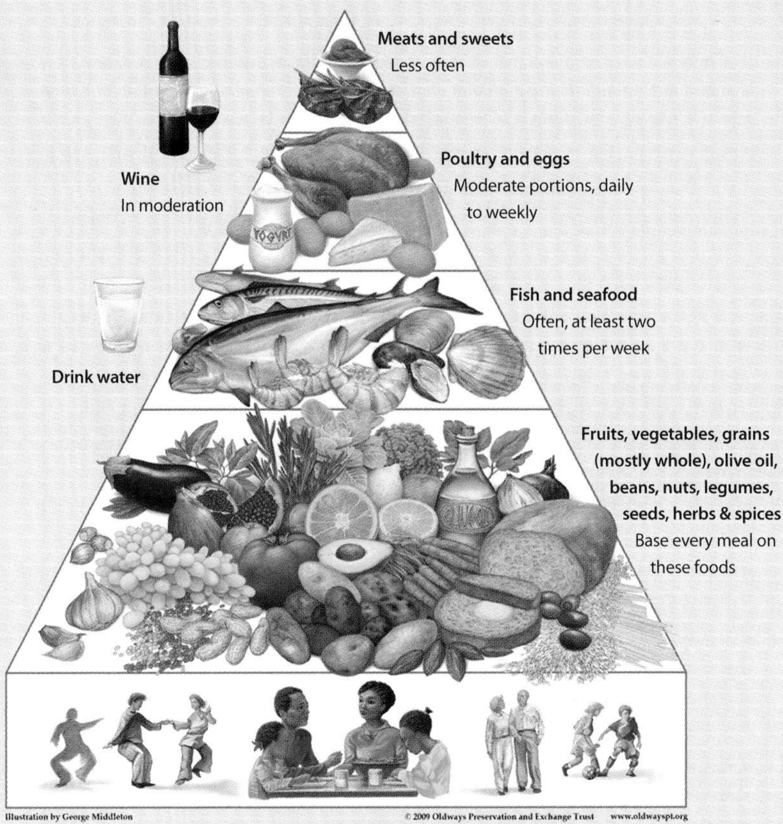

Figure 3.B Mediterranean diet pyramid. The Mediterranean diet emphasizes fruit and vegetable intake as well as healthy fats such as olive oil while limiting red meat intake.

African and West Indian Influences

The people who were forced to migrate from West Africa as slaves brought traditional foods such as sweet potatoes, okra, and peanuts from their homelands. West Indians have also brought foods such as scotch bonnet peppers, ackee, plantains, and cassava. Traditional African and West Indian Canadian cuisine has both health benefits and deficits. Although fruit, beans, and leafy vegetables provide fibre and a variety of vitamins and minerals, salt-cured pork and meat products like oxtail contribute undesirable levels of fat and sodium to the diet. Reliance on frying foods also increases fat intakes. High-fat diets are associated with obesity, and high-sodium diets raise the risk of hypertension. Obesity and hypertension are quite prevalent among African and West Indian Canadians. You will learn more about diet and blood pressure in Chapters 6 and 9.

Asian Influences

Traditional Asian foods, such as Chinese, Japanese, Vietnamese, Thai, and Korean cuisines, are similar and generally feature large amounts of vegetables, rice, or noodles combined with small amounts of meat, fish, or shellfish. The variety of vegetables used in Asian dishes adds colour, flavour, texture, phytochemicals, and nutrients to meals. Additionally, Asian dishes often include flavourful sauces and seasonings made from plants such as soy sauce, rice wine, ginger root, garlic, scallions, peppers, and sesame seeds. The Asian diet patterns generally provide inadequate amounts of calcium from milk and milk products. However, using calcium-fortified foods is one way to add the mineral to diets.

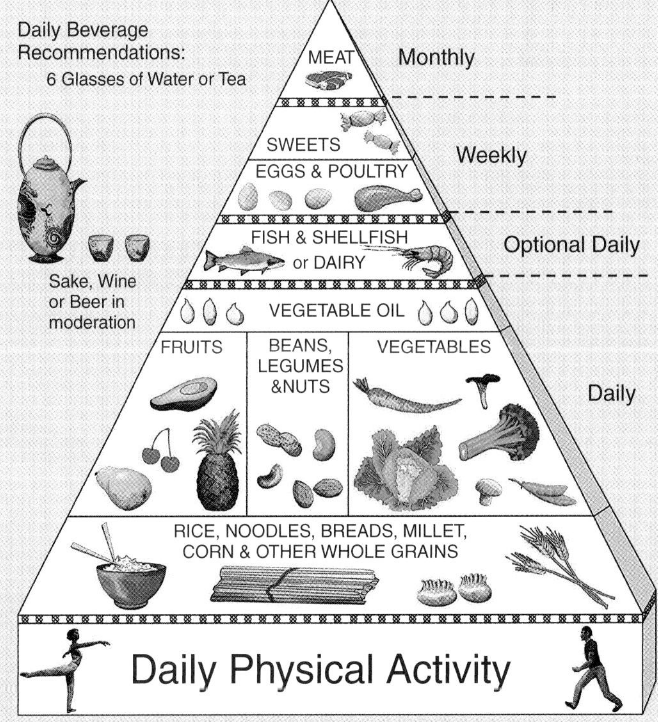

Figure 3.C Asian diet. A typical Asian diet features large amounts of rice, noodles, and vegetables, accented with small amounts of meat and fish.

Chinese foods are popular among Canadians. Many Canadians, however, do not favour dishes that feature seafood and contain large portions of vegetables and grains, because they believe meat should form the basis of a meal. Thus, North American Chinese restaurants that specialize in Cantonese, Szechwan, or Mandarin cuisines typically offer menu items that contain much larger portions of animal foods such as beef and chicken than authentic dishes. Furthermore, Canadian-Chinese foods are often prepared with far more fat than amounts used in true Chinese cooking.

Traditional Chinese food preparation methods, particularly steaming and stir-frying, tend to preserve the vitamins and minerals in fresh vegetables. Stir-frying involves cooking foods in a lightly oiled, very hot pan for a short period of time. Unlike Western methods of cooking vegetables, stir-fried vegetables remain crisp and colourful.

Rice is the staple food in the traditional Asian diet. Additionally, fish, poultry, pork, and foods made from soybeans provide protein in this diet. Japanese people eat sushi, small pieces of raw fish or shellfish that is usually served rolled in or pressed into rice and served with vegetables and seaweed. Canadian-Japanese restaurants often feature sushi, and many non-Japanese Canadians like to order the exotic dish.

Some of the oldest, healthiest people in the world reside on Okinawa, a tiny island south of the main Japanese islands. The traditional diet of fresh vegetables, minimal amounts of salt and animal protein (mainly from pork and fish), and moderate amounts of fat may protect the island's population from premature heart disease and stroke. Not all Japanese are as healthy as the Okinawans. The people living on the northern Japanese island of Honshu consume high amounts of salt, which is the principal dietary source of the mineral sodium. High-sodium intakes increase the risk of hypertension, and this disease is very common among the Honshu population.

Islamic Influences

Eating is a matter of faith for Muslims who follow the Islamic dietary laws termed *Halal*, which refers to all permitted foods. Muslims are allowed to eat what is pure, wholesome, nourishing, and pleasing to the taste—essentially everything that hasn't been specifically forbidden or prohibited by Allah—those items referred to as *haram*. Foods that are forbidden include pork, blood, intoxicating drinks, birds of prey, and meat from an already dead animal or an animal that has died from strangulation or blunt force. Thus, some Muslims will abstain from eating meat if they are unsure how the animal was killed. In addition, overindulgence or eating more than one's own share is discouraged.

Fasting is frequently practised regularly on Mondays and Thursdays, and on religious holidays such as Shawwal and the holy month of Ramadan. Typically fasting during Ramadan includes abstention from all forms of food and drink from sunrise to sunset each day, followed in the evening by a meal called *iftar*. The *Eid al-Fitr*, or "Festival of Breaking the Fast," marks the end of Ramadan.

Jewish Influences

Ancient religious laws dictate food handling and dietary practices for people who strictly follow the Jewish faith. According to these laws, a *kosher* food is "clean" and fit for consumption by Jews. Only cud-chewing, even-toed animals with hooves, such as cattle, sheep, and goats, and only fish with fins and scales can be eaten. Shellfish, pork, and foods made with pork by-products such as lard are forbidden. Additionally, animal blood is not kosher. After a kosher animal undergoes ritual butchering by a specially trained religious person, its raw meat or poultry is soaked and salted, then rinsed to remove blood. Some of the salt, however, remains after rinsing.

Jewish dietary laws also require keeping meat and poultry separate from milk products and having separate cooking and eating utensils for meat and dairy foods. Dairy products are not used to prepare foods that contain meat or poultry nor are they served with them. A cheeseburger, for example, is not kosher. Fruits, grains, and vegetables are "neutral" foods that can be eaten with meals that contain either meat or dairy products. However, vegetables cooked with meat become a "meat" food and cannot be served with milk; peaches served with cottage cheese become a "milk" food and cannot be eaten with meat or poultry. Today many Canadian Jews do not follow their religion's complex dietary laws as closely as their ancestors did.

Bagels with smoked salmon (lox), pickled herring, cream cheese, dill pickles, corned beef, and pastrami are popular among the Ashkenazi, the predominant group of Jews in North America. However, these traditional Ashkenazic foods may be too high in sodium and animal fat to be healthy.

The Role of Diet in Health

Diet is only one aspect of lifestyle that affects the health of a particular population. Physical activity habits also have a major influence on health. Today most Canadians enjoy and depend on a variety of labour-saving devices that make housework, occupations, and leisure time less physically demanding than these activities were 100 years ago. As immigrants and other members of the population become less physically active, they also tend to develop obesity, type 2 diabetes, and hypertension. Current recommendations for reducing the prevalence of these conditions generally include making specific dietary changes as well as increasing physical activity levels. Nevertheless, nutrition researchers need to learn more about the influence that traditional diets can have on the risk of chronic diseases.

Aboriginal Influences

In the past, many Aboriginal peoples were hunter-gatherers, depending on wild vegetation, fish, and game for food. Other Aboriginal peoples learned to grow vegetable crops, including tomatoes, corn, and squash. In general, the traditional Aboriginal diet was low in sodium and fat and high in fibre. During the last half of the twentieth century, many Aboriginal peoples have abandoned their traditional diets and adopted the typical Western diet. Today obesity and type 2 diabetes are extremely prevalent among Aboriginal peoples living in Canada, whereas in the past, these conditions rarely affected tribal members.

For example, the traditional Inuit diet was composed of fatty fish and sea mammals, game animals, and a few plants. Traditional Inuit who still follow traditional dietary practices have CVD rates that are lower than those in the general North American population, but those who switched to a more Western diet have developed type 2 diabetes and CVD at rates similar to those of the general population. To promote healthy eating among Canada's Aboriginal peoples, Health Canada modified the *Eating Well with Canada's Food Guide* in 2007 to reflect the traditions and food choices of First Nations, Inuit, and Métis.

SUMMARY

A requirement is the smallest amount of a nutrient that maintains a defined level of health. Numerous factors influence nutrient requirements. Scientists use information about nutrient requirements and storage capabilities to establish specific dietary recommendations. The Dietary Reference Intakes (DRIs) are standard values for nutrient recommendations. An Estimated Average Requirement (EAR) is the amount of the nutrient that meets the needs of 50% of healthy people in a particular life stage/gender group. The Recommended Dietary Allowances (RDAs) meet the needs of nearly all healthy individuals (97 to 98%) in a particular life stage/gender group. When nutrition scientists are unable to determine an RDA for a nutrient, they establish an Adequate Intake (AI) value. The Tolerable Upper Intake Level (UL) is the highest average amount of a nutrient that is unlikely to harm most people when the amount is consumed daily. Acceptable Macronutrient Distribution Ranges (AMDRs) indicate ranges of carbohydrate, fat, and protein intakes that provide adequate amounts of energy and may reduce the risk of diet-related chronic diseases. The Estimated Energy Requirement (EER) is used to evaluate a person's energy intake.

DRIs are various energy and nutrient intake standards for Canadians and Americans. DRIs can be used for planning nutritious diets for groups of people and evaluating the nutritional adequacy of a population's diet. RDAs and AIs are often used to evaluate an individual's dietary practices. For nutrition labelling purposes, Health Canada uses RDAs to develop Daily Values (DVs).

Dietary guides generally classify foods into groups according to their natural origins and key nutrients. Such guides usually feature major food groups. Some dietary guides also include a group for empty-calorie foods or beverages. *Eating Well with Canada's Food Guide* is a set of general nutrition-related lifestyle recommendations designed to promote adequate nutritional status, achieve good health, and reduce the risk of major chronic health conditions.

Consumers can use information on food labels to determine ingredients and compare nutrient contents of packaged foods and beverages. There are four types of nutrition labels in Canada: the Nutrition Facts table, list of ingredients, nutrient content claims, and health claims. Health Canada regulates and monitors information that can be placed on food labels, including claims about the product's health benefits. Health Canada permits food manufacturers to include certain health claims on food labels. However, the agency requires health claims meet certain guidelines, and in some instances, specific wording. Nearly all foods and beverages sold in grocery stores must be labelled with the product's name, manufacturer's name and address, amount of product in the package, and ingredients listed in descending order by weight. Furthermore, food labels must use a special format for listing specific information on the Nutrition Facts table.

The Daily Values (DVs) are a practical set of nutrient standards for labelling purposes. The nutrient content in a serving of food or dietary supplement is listed on the label as a percentage of the DV (% DV). Not all nutrients have DVs. A dietary goal is to obtain at least 100% of the DVs for fibre, vitamins, and minerals each day.

Organic foods are those produced without the use of antibiotics, hormones, synthetic fertilizers and pesticides, genetic improvements, or spoilage-killing radiation. Although organic farming techniques can benefit the environment, crop yields are typically lower. More research is needed to determine whether there are health advantages to eating organic foods.

Recipe for Healthy Living

Fresh Fruit Salad

The following recipe is for a simple fresh fruit salad. Fruits are so versatile, you can invent your own recipes by adding different ones, such as cherries, mangoes, and peaches, to this basic recipe. When selecting fruit, you should avoid fruits that are too hard or soft, because they may be under-ripe or too ripe. If you need help, ask a produce manager to show you how to choose the best quality fruit.

This recipe makes approximately six 250 mL (1-cup) servings. A serving of fresh fruit salad supplies about 84 kcal, 1 g protein, 0 g fat, 20 g carbohydrate, 2.3 g fibre, 150 mcg beta-carotene, 37 mg vitamin C, 290 mg potassium, and 3 mg sodium.

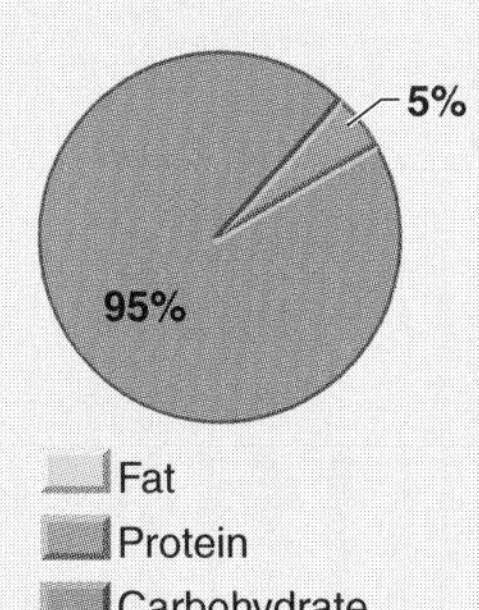

INGREDIENTS:

125 mL (½ cup) blueberries
1 slice of watermelon, about 1″ thick
250 mL (1 cup) red or purple seedless grapes
1 medium peach
2 medium kiwifruit, slightly firm
1 medium apple, with skin
125 mL (½ cup) orange juice

PREPARATION STEPS:

1. Wash fruit in cool water, including the watermelon peel. Drain blueberries, place in a bowl, and remove and discard stems and damaged berries. Dry other fruit with paper towels.
2. Remove green rind of watermelon and discard. Cut watermelon into cubes and add to the berries.
3. Slice each grape in half and add to watermelon.
4. Slice peach in half and discard seed. Cut into thin wedge-shaped segments and add to fruit.
5. Peel kiwifruit and slice into rounds that are about ¼″ thick. Add to fruit mixture.
6. Remove core and seeds from the apple. Cut fruit into small pieces and add to mixture.
7. Add orange juice to mixture and gently stir with a large spoon, coating fruit with juice.
8. Refrigerate.

CRITICAL THINKING

1. Your friend takes several dietary supplements daily, and as a result, his vitamin B-6 intake is 50 times higher than the RDA for the vitamin. You'd like to convince him to stop taking the supplements. To support your advice, which nutrient standards would you show him? Explain why.
2. Why is the *Eating Well with Canada's Food Guide* used to plan menus instead of the DRIs?
3. How do your fibre, sodium, and alcohol intakes compare to the recommendations of the latest dietary guidelines?
4. Examine Table 3.2. Which foods in the left-hand column do you eat regularly? Why are those foods listed in that column?
5. The ingredient list on a package of crackers includes vegetable oil. However, the Nutrition Facts table on the package's label indicates "0 g" fat is in the product, and a statement on the label claims the product is skim. Explain why this claim is permissible.
6. Discuss whether you use or would use one of the menu-planning tools described in Chapter 3 to plan your daily food intake.
7. According to a newspaper article, a 250-mL (1-cup) serving of skim milk contains 15 mcg of folate (a B vitamin). Another source of nutrition information indicates that a 250 mL (1-cup) serving of skim milk contains 12 mcg of folate. Explain why both sources of information can be correct.

Personal Dietary Analysis

I. Recordkeeping

A. 24-Hour Dietary Recall

1. Recall every food and beverage that you've eaten over the past 24 hours. Recall how much you consumed and how it was prepared.
   a. How easy or difficult was it to recall your food intake?

B. Three-Day Diet Record

1. Without changing your usual diet, keep a detailed log of your food and beverage intake for three days; one of the days should be Friday or Saturday. Use a separate log for each day.

II. Analysis

Using nutritional analysis software, analyze your daily food intakes and answer questions in Part III of this activity. Keep the record on file for future applications.

A. Computer-Generated Dietary Analysis

1. Load the software into the computer, or log on to a software Web site such as EATracker.
2. Choose the RDAs or related nutrient standard from the table inside the back cover of this book, based on your life stage, sex, height, and weight.
3. Enter the information from the three-day food-intake record. Be sure to enter each food and drink and the specific amounts.
4. The software program will give you the following results:
   a. The appropriate RDA (or related standard) for each nutrient
   b. The total amount of each nutrient and the kilocalories consumed for each day
   c. The percentage intake compared with the standard amount for each nutrient that you consumed each day
5. Keep this assessment for activities in other chapters.

III. Evaluation of Nutrient Intakes

Remember it is not necessary to consume the maximum of your nutrient recommendations every day. A general standard is meeting at least 70% of the standards averaged over several days. It is best not to exceed the Upper Level (if set) over the long term to avoid potential toxic effects of some nutrients.

A. For which nutrients did your average intake fall below the recommended amounts, that is, less than 70% of the RDA/AI?

B. For which nutrients did your average intake exceed the Upper Level (if an UL has been set)?

PRACTICE TEST

Select the best answer.

1. The amount of a nutrient that should meet the needs of half of the healthy people in a particular group is the
   a. Estimated Average Requirement (EAR).
   b. Recommended Dietary Allowance (RDA).
   c. Adequate Intake (AI).
   d. Tolerable Upper Intake Level (UL).

2. Which of the following statements is false?
   a. RDAs are standards for daily intakes of certain nutrients.
   b. RDAs meet the nutrient needs of nearly all healthy people.
   c. RDAs contain a margin of safety.
   d. RDAs are requirements for nutrients.
3. The Estimated Energy Requirement (EER)
   a. has a margin of safety.
   b. does not account for a person's height, weight, or physical activity level.
   c. is based on the average daily energy needs of a healthy person.
   d. reflects a person's actual daily energy needs.
4. A diet is likely to be safe and nutritionally adequate if
   a. average daily intakes for nutrients meet RDA or AI values.
   b. intakes of various nutrients are consistently less than EAR amounts.
   c. nutrient intakes are consistently above ULs.
   d. vitamin supplements are included.
5. Nutritional standards, such as the RDAs, are
   a. used to develop formula food products.
   b. the basis for establishing DVs.
   c. used to evaluate the nutritional adequacy of diets.
   d. all of the above
6. According to the *Eating Well with Canada's Food Guide* recommendations, which of the following foods is included in the Milk and Alternatives food group?
   a. cheese
   b. eggs
   c. butter
   d. all of the above
7. Protein-rich food sources that also contain saturated fat and cholesterol include
   a. peanut butter.
   b. dry beans.
   c. nuts.
   d. beef.
8. Fruit is generally a good source of all the following substances, except
   a. fibre.
   b. vitamin C.
   c. phytochemicals.
   d. protein.
9. Which of the following information is not provided by the Nutrition Facts table?
   a. percentage of calories from fat
   b. amount of carbohydrate per serving
   c. serving size
   d. amount of trans fat per serving
10. Daily Values are
   a. for people who consume 1200 to 1500 kilocalorie diets.
   b. based on the lowest RDA or AI for each nutrient.
   c. dietary standards developed for food-labelling purposes.
   d. used to evaluate the nutritional adequacy of a population's diet.
11. Organically grown foods are
   a. nutritionally superior to foods made from conventionally produced crops.
   b. produced without the use of antibiotics, pesticides, or genetic improvements.
   c. usually less expensive than conventionally produced foods.
   d. all of the above

Answers to Chapter 3 Quiz Yourself

1. According to the *Eating Well with Canada's Food Guide*, vegetables and fruit are combined into one food group. **True.** (p. 58)
2. According to Health Canada recommendations it is acceptable for certain adults to consume moderate amounts of alcoholic beverages. **True.** (p. 66)
3. Last week, Colin didn't consume the recommended amount of vitamin C for a couple of days. Nevertheless, he is unlikely to develop scurvy, the vitamin C deficiency disease. **True.** (p. 54)
4. According to the *Eating Well with Canada's Food Guide* recommendations, an adult 40-year-old male should consume three to four servings of vegetables and fruit each day. **False.** (p. 59)
5. The Nutrition Facts table on a food label provides information concerning amounts of energy, fibre, and cholesterol that are in a serving of the food. **True.** (p. 70)

Please visit Connect at

www.mcgrawhillconnect.ca

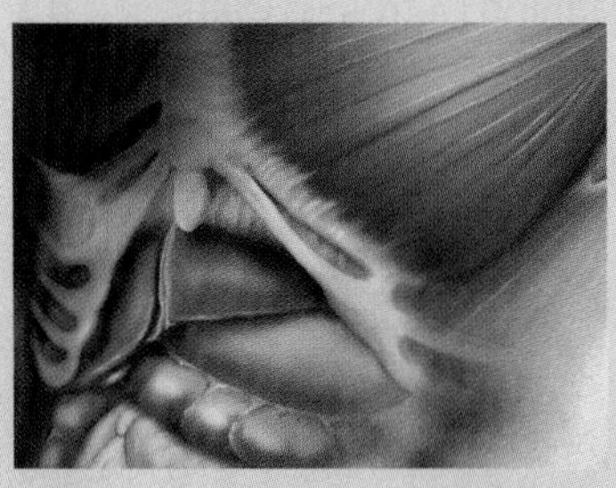

Chapter **4**

Body Basics

Chapter Learning Outcomes

After reading Chapter 4, you should be able to:

1. Define key basic chemistry terms, including atom, element, ion, chemical bond, solution, solvent, solute, acid, base, and enzyme.
2. Explain the basic function of an enzyme.
3. Define tissue, organ, and organ system.
4. Identify the organ systems and the major organs or tissues in each system, and describe primary functions of each system.
5. Discuss the overall processes of digestion and absorption.
6. Identify some common gastrointestinal health problems and discuss preventive measures and treatments for these conditions.

The human body is often compared to a complex machine, such as a car. Like a car, the body has numerous interrelated working parts and requires a source of fuel to operate. Additionally, the body has to be able to cool itself, eliminate waste products, and relies on lubrication to keep operating smoothly. Unlike most machines, however, the human body can make many of its spare parts, enabling the body to repair and maintain itself for long periods.

When the body functions properly, this wondrous machine may be taken for granted and expected to perform optimally. Nevertheless, the quality of the fuel that powers the human body can affect performance, much like the quality of gasoline that runs a car.

In Chapter 1, we defined chemistry as the study of the composition and characteristics of matter, and the changes that it can undergo. We also defined human physiology as the study of how the human body functions. Principles of chemistry and human physiology form the foundation for the scientific study of nutrition. The foods you eat and the air you breathe provide nutrients and oxygen, the raw materials (matter) that your cells need to survive and function. By reading Chapter 4, you will learn some basic chemistry concepts to help you understand how the matter in food becomes the raw materials for building, fuelling, and sustaining healthy bodies. Additionally, you will learn about body structures and functions so that you can understand the roles of nutrients in the body and why these particular chemicals are so important.

If you have taken general biology or human physiology courses in high school or university, much of the information in Chapter 4 will be a review for you. However, many students who enroll in nutrition classes do not have a strong science background, and they are likely to find the chapter's content interesting but possibly more challenging to understand. Parts of this chapter may seem to be filled with unfamiliar terms and their definitions, but learning the meaning of these terms can help you communicate more effectively with physicians and help you become a wiser consumer of health-related information.

Quiz YOURSELF

To test your knowledge of the material covered in Chapter 4, take the following quiz; the answers are on page 110.

1. The atom is the smallest living unit in the body. ______T ______F
2. The stomach produces hydrochloric acid. ______T ______F
3. Taste buds can be found in the lining of your mouth. ______T ______F
4. The human intestinal tract cannot digest certain combinations of foods, such as mixtures of simple carbohydrates and proteins. ______T ______F
5. Undigested food rots in your stomach, causing toxic materials to build up in your tissues. ______T ______F

Basic Chemistry Concepts

Do you or someone you know avoid eating foods that are not labelled organic because they contain chemicals such as additives, hormones, or pesticides? It is true that chemicals are in your food, but they are not necessarily harmful. Chemicals make up food as well as every other aspect of your environment; air, water, rocks, or any other form of matter contain chemicals. In fact, you are a complex collection of chemicals, much of which is organized into cells. The following sections provide basic information about some chemistry concepts that apply to the study of nutrition.

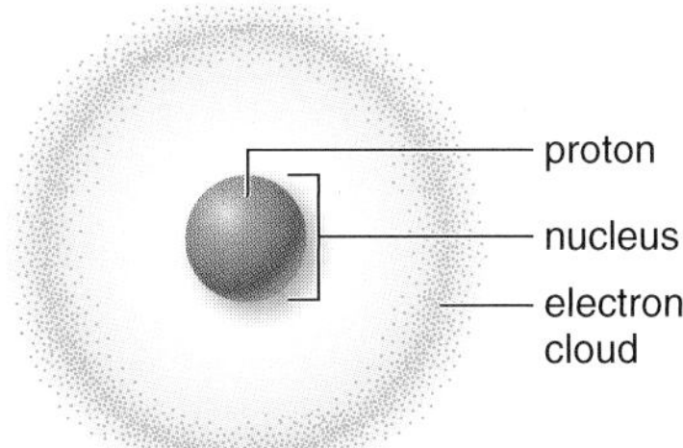

Figure 4.1 An atom. Matter is comprised of atoms that contain particles, including protons and electrons. The nucleus of this hydrogen atom contains one positively charged proton.

From Atoms to Compounds

Matter is comprised of atoms that contain protons and electrons (Fig. 4.1). **Protons** are positively charged particles in the nucleus, the central region of an atom. **Electrons** are small negatively charged particles that form a cloud surrounding the nucleus. The number of electrons surrounding the nucleus equals the number of protons within the nucleus. Thus, the negative and positive charges cancel out each other, making an atom neutral, which means it has no electrical charge.

More than 100 different types of atoms exist, and each type is an **element**, a substance that cannot be separated into simpler substances by ordinary chemical or physical means. Elements are the "building blocks" of matter. Table 4.1 lists elements, many of which are essential for human nutrition. An element is essential if the body cannot function normally without it and the element must be supplied by the diet. Note that chemists use letters as symbols to represent elements. For example, the symbols for carbon, nitrogen, and sodium are C, N, and Na, respectively.

protons positively charged particles in the nucleus of an atom

electrons small negatively charged particles that surround the nucleus of an atom

element each type of atom; substance that cannot be separated into simpler substances by ordinary chemical or physical means

minerals elements that are found in the earth's crust

chemical bond attraction that holds atoms together

molecule matter that forms when two or more atoms interact and are held together by a chemical bond

Minerals are elements, such as calcium, iron, and potassium, that are found in the earth's crust. Many minerals are essential nutrients. However, not every mineral is in living things or is necessary for life. Your external environment has natural and human-made forms of matter that may contain elements such as mercury (Hg), aluminum (Al), and cadmium (Cd). The human body does not need these minerals to function properly, and they can be quite toxic. Chapter 9 discusses the importance of various minerals to health.

Molecules

When atoms interact, they may share electrons and rearrange themselves, forming a **chemical bond**. A chemical bond is an attraction that holds atoms together and forms a **molecule**. When illustrating the structure of molecules, chemists often use straight lines to show the bonds (Fig. 4.2a). Some atoms form single bonds, but a few atoms can form multiple bonds. For example, each carbon atom (C) has four bonding sites, and as a result, carbon atoms can bond to each other by single, double (Fig. 4.2b), and even triple bonds (Fig. 4.2c). Carbon's ability to bond to other carbon atoms as well as form multiple bonds with a neighbouring carbon atom contributes to the formation of a vast array of organic (carbon-containing) compounds.

Molecules can contain the same element or different elements. For example, an oxygen molecule forms when two oxygen atoms bind together, whereas a water molecule forms when two hydrogen atoms bond to an oxygen atom. To identify a particular molecule without using lines to draw its chemical structure, chemists use a chemical formula. The chemical formula for an oxygen molecule is O_2; the subscript "2" indicates the presence of two oxygen atoms. The chemical formula for a water molecule is H_2O. The chemical formula for the simple sugar glucose is $C_6 H_{12} O_6$. Judging from its formula, how many carbon, hydrogen, and oxygen atoms are in a glucose molecule?

TABLE 4.1

Essential Elements in the Body

Element	Symbol
Hydrogen	H
Oxygen	O
Carbon	C
Nitrogen	N
Calcium	Ca
Phosphorus	P
Potassium	K
Sulphur	S
Sodium	Na
Chloride	Cl
Magnesium	Mg
Iron	Fe
Iodide	I
Copper	Cu
Zinc	Zn
Manganese	Mn
Cobalt	Co
Chromium	Cr
Selenium	Se
Molybdenum	Mo
Fluoride*	F
Tin	Sn
Silicon **	Si
Vanadium**	V
Nickel**	Ni
Boron**	B
Arsenic**	As

* Although fluoride is not essential, the mineral helps strengthen teeth and bones.

** When experimental animals are fed diets that are deficient in these mineral elements, they eventually develop deficiency symptoms. However, there have been no reports of widespread deficiencies of these minerals in human populations. Therefore, scientists have not established human requirements for them.

Solutions

Molecules that contain two or more different elements are called **compounds**. A **solution** is an evenly distributed mixture of two or more compounds. In living things, water is the **solvent**, the primary component of solutions. Your body, for example, is about 60% water. The lesser component in a solution is the **solute**. Many beverages and foods are solutions that have water as the solvent (Fig. 4.3a). A sports drink, for example, is a solution that is mostly water, the solvent. The drink has relatively small amounts of sugar, minerals, colourings, and flavourings (solutes) dissolved in the water.

The **solubility** of a compound describes how easily it dissolves, that is, forms a solution, in a liquid solvent. Many naturally occurring substances, including simple carbohydrates such as sugar and all mineral elements, dissolve in water. Other substances, such as fat, are insoluble and will not dissolve in water (Fig. 4.3b). Your blood has high water content, a characteristic that makes it easier for the body to transport and eliminate water-soluble substances than water-insoluble materials.

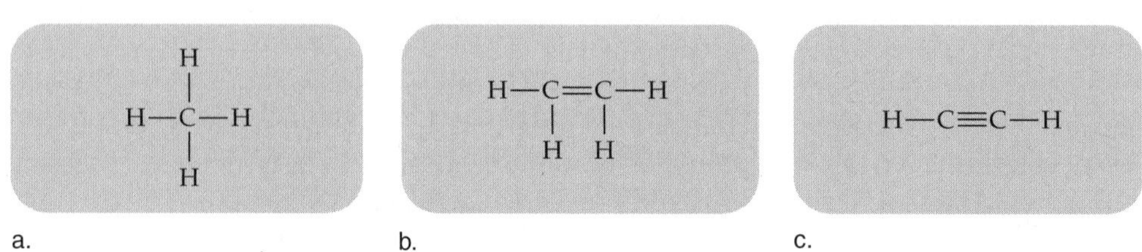

Figure 4.2 Chemical bonds. Some atoms form single bonds (a), but a few atoms can form multiple bonds. Carbon atoms can bond to each other by single, double (b), and even triple bonds (c).

Figure 4.3 Solubility. The solubility of a compound describes how easily it forms a solution in a liquid solvent. Many substances, including table sugar, dissolve in water. (*a*) Sports drinks are beverages in which sugar remains dissolved in water. Other substances, such as fat, are insoluble in water and will not dissolve in it. (*b*) Vinaigrette is an example of a food in which oil and water (balsamic vinegar) do not form a solution. In this particular product, note how the oil separates from the vinegar and forms a layer on top of the darker balsamic vinegar layer.

Ions

When an atom (or group of atoms) gains or loses one or more electrons, it has an electrical charge and is called an **ion** (Fig. 4.4). If an atom gains one electron, it becomes an ion with a negative charge, because electrons are negatively charged. If an atom loses an electron, it becomes an ion with a positive charge, because it has an extra proton and protons are positively charged. A negative charge is indicated with a minus sign ($^-$) and a positive charge is indicated with a plus sign ($^+$) after the chemical symbol or formula. For example, a molecule of ammonia is neutral, that is, has no electrical charge, because it has the same number of protons and electrons. If the molecule loses an electron, it becomes the positively charged ion, ammonium. The formula for the positively charged *hydrogen ion* is simply **H^+**.

When most mineral elements, including sodium and potassium, dissolve in water, they form solutions containing ions that can conduct electricity. Thus, sodium and potassium are called **electrolytes**. Electrolytes have many important functions in the body, including helping to maintain proper fluid balance.

compounds molecules that contain two or more different elements

solution evenly distributed mixture of two or more compounds

solvent primary component of a solution

solute lesser component of a solution that dissolves in solvent

solubility describes how easily a substance dissolves in a liquid solvent

ion atoms or group of atoms with a positive or negative charge, due to the loss or gain of one or more electrons

H^+ hydrogen ion chemical formula

electrolytes ions that conduct electricity when they are dissolved in a solution

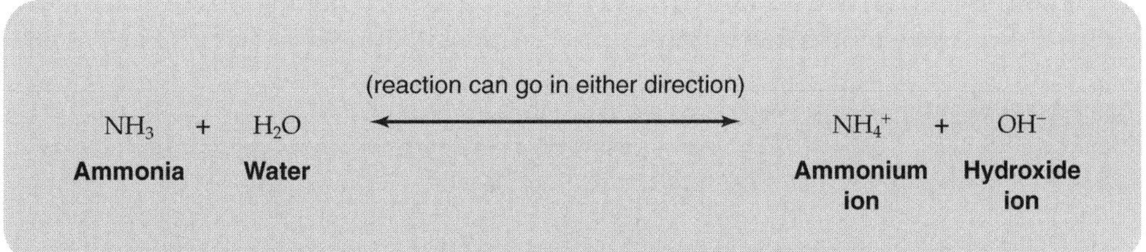

Figure 4.4 What is an ion? An ion is an atom or group of atoms that loses or gains one or more electrons and, as a result, has an electrical charge. In this reaction, ammonia and water react to form the positively charged ammonium ion and the negatively charged hydroxide ion.

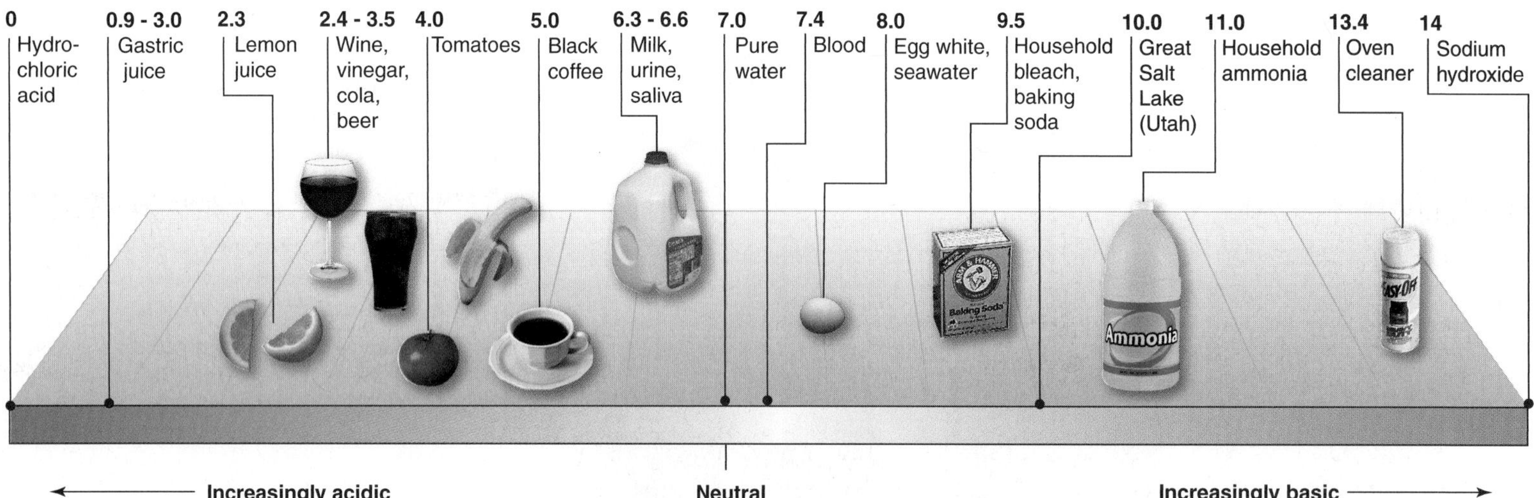

Figure 4.5 pH scale. Chemists measure the concentration of hydrogen ions in a watery solution by using the pH scale. This scale indicates the pH values of some substances, including foods. Substances with low pH values are more acidic than substances with high pH values (bases).

acids substances that donate hydrogen ions

bases substances that accept hydrogen ions

pH measure of the acidity or alkalinity of a solution

What Are Acids and Bases?

Acids are substances that lose H^+ when dissolved in water; **bases** are substances that remove and accept H^+ when dissolved in water. Many of the chemicals you encounter daily are either acidic or basic (alkaline). As you can tell by their names, phosphoric acid in soft drinks and ascorbic acid (better known as vitamin C) are acids. Baking soda and sodium hydroxide, an ingredient of many hair removal products, are bases.

Chemists measure the concentration of hydrogen ions (**pH**) in a watery solution by using the pH scale. The scale ranges from 0 to 14. With each whole number increase within the scale, the H^+ concentration decreases 10 times. Examine the pH scale shown in Figure 4.5. Note that black coffee has a pH of about 5.0 and tomatoes have a pH of about 4.0. Thus, tomatoes are 10 times more acidic than black coffee. Although it may seem confusing, a solution with a pH of 2.0 has a *higher* H^+ concentration and is *more* acidic than a solution with a pH of 12.0.

Pure water has equal concentrations of H^+ and OH^-, so it is neither acidic nor basic. Thus, pure water has a pH of 7 and is neutral. By combining an acid with a base, the pH of a solution can become 7.

Your body must maintain its *acid-base balance* to function properly. Under normal conditions, the pH of your blood ranges from 7.35 to 7.45, which is slightly alkaline. To control its pH within normal limits, blood contains buffers—ions or molecules that accept excess H^+ when necessary. Acids form naturally as by-products of cellular activity, but if the pH of blood begins to fall, the excess H^+ must be eliminated to prevent acidemia, a condition that can be deadly. The lungs remove excess H^+ from blood by releasing carbon dioxide (CO_2) and H_2O in exhaled air. Kidneys also participate in the buffering system by removing excess H^+ from the blood when forming urine. As a result, urine is an acidic fluid.

Common household products such as baking soda, household ammonia, and certain oven cleaners are bases.

Did You Know?

Blueberries, raspberries, red cabbage, and strawberries contain the pigment *anthocyanin*. This pigment is used as a natural dye for colouring yarns and can also be used as a crude pH meter. Anthocyanin is red when it is in solutions that have a pH of less than 4; this pigment loses its colour at higher pH values. Aside from being an interesting pigment, anthocyanin has antioxidant activity and may provide health benefits as a result (see Table 1.3 on page 7).

Figure 4.6 Chemical reaction. A chemical reaction occurs when vinegar (an acid) in the beaker combines with a tablespoon of baking soda (a base). This reaction forms sodium acetate, water, and carbon dioxide.

What's a Chemical Reaction?

Most molecules can undergo **chemical reactions**, processes that change the arrangement of atoms in the molecules. The elements that comprise the molecules that react are never destroyed, but they combine with other elements to form new molecules or compounds. When elements or compounds combine to form new substances, a synthetic reaction has occurred. The new substances often have physical and chemical characteristics (properties) that are quite different than the reactants. Decomposition reactions involve the breaking down of molecules. **Digestion**, the process by which large molecules in food are broken down into smaller ones that can be absorbed, requires decomposition reactions.

You can observe a simple chemical reaction by combining the reactants vinegar (an acid) and baking soda (a base). As soon as the vinegar makes contact with the soda, the powdery baking soda disappears and a fizzy liquid forms. This particular reaction produces carbon dioxide gas that forms bubbles in the fizzy liquid and sodium acetate. Thus, carbon dioxide and sodium acetate are two of the products that result when vinegar and baking soda react (Fig. 4.6). Sodium acetate is a **salt**, a substance that forms when an acid reacts with a base. Table salt (sodium chloride) is actually one type of salt. Sodium chloride forms when acid, such as hydrochloric acid (HCl), reacts with a base, such as sodium hydroxide (NaOH) (Fig. 4.7).

In recipes for baked goods that require baking soda, you will find an acid ingredient such as lemon juice, buttermilk, or cream of tartar (tartaric acid) included to react with the soda. The carbon dioxide gas that forms "raises" the mixture, giving it a light, airy structure after baking.

chemical reactions process that changes the atomic arrangements of molecules

digestion process by which large ingested molecules are mechanically and chemically broken down

salt substance that forms when an acid combines with a base

HCl	+	$NaOH$	$\longrightarrow$	$NaCl$	+	H_2O
Hydrochloric acid		**Sodium hydroxide**		**Sodium chloride (table salt)**		**Water**

Figure 4.7 What is a salt? A salt forms when an acid reacts with a base. For example, sodium chloride (NaCl) and H_2O form when hydrochloric acid (HCl) reacts with sodium hydroxide (NaOH).

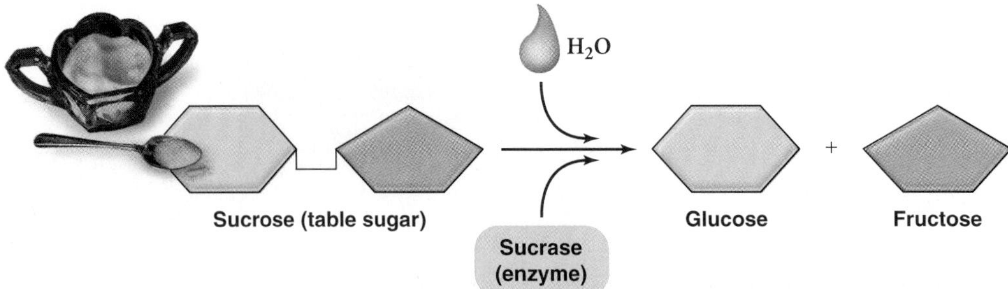

Figure 4.8 Enzyme action. Enzymes initiate or catalyze chemical reactions. Enzymes are recyclable; they do not become part of the products of a reaction, and as a result, one enzyme molecule can catalyze many reactions. In this reaction, the enzyme *sucrase* is necessary to break down sucrose into glucose and fructose.

metabolism the sum of all chemical reactions occurring in living cells

enzyme protein that speeds the rate of a chemical reaction but is not altered during the process

Metabolism refers to the sum of all chemical reactions that occur in living cells. *Catabolic* reactions involve breaking down molecules. Catabolism, for example, occurs during digestion. *Anabolic* reactions involve synthesizing new compounds. Repairing damaged muscle tissue after injury or exercise is an example of anabolism.

Enzymes

Living things contain thousands of chemicals, and life depends upon chemical reactions. However, many of these reactions occur slowly or do not occur spontaneously. Living cells produce **enzymes**, proteins that initiate or facilitate (catalyze) chemical reactions. Enzymes are recyclable; they do not become part of the products of a reaction, and as a result, one enzyme molecule can catalyze many reactions. Figure 4.8 illustrates an enzyme's action.

In general, the names of most enzymes end with *-ase*. Sucrase, for example, is the enzyme that catalyzes the reaction that breaks down the carbohydrate sucrose (table sugar) to its component simple sugars (see Fig. 4.8). Additionally, each enzyme usually has a specific action. For example, sucrase decomposes sucrose but does not affect lactose, the type of sugar in milk.

Enzymes are sensitive to environmental conditions, including pH, temperature, and the presence of certain vitamins and minerals. If the pH or temperature is too high or too low, the enzyme will not function. Raw food contains enzymes, but cooking food usually destroys them.

Food & Nutrition *tip*

Gelatin is an animal protein that dissolves in boiled water. As it cools, gelatin holds the water and thickens, forming a gel, a solution that takes the shape of its container. Pineapple, papaya, kiwifruit, and guava naturally contain enzymes that break down gelatin. Therefore, when using gelatin in recipes, don't add fresh or frozen forms of these fruits, because the enzymes will break down gelatin and the mixture won't gel. Heating destroys these enzymes, thus you can make a moulded gelatin salad or dessert that contains canned pineapple. (Foods undergo heating during the canning process.)

Concept **Checkpoint**

1. Define the following terms: electron, proton, element, chemical bond, molecule, compound, solution, solvent, and solute.
2. What is an ion?
3. Explain the difference between an acid and a base.
4. What is pH?
5. What is a chemical reaction?
6. What is an enzyme?
7. What factors can alter an enzyme's activity?

Basic Physiology Concepts

anatomy scientific study of cells and other body structures

physiology scientific study of the functioning of cells and other body structures

Anatomy is the scientific study of cells and other body structures; **physiology** is the scientific study of how cells and body structures function. The following section provides some basic information about human anatomy and physiology, including the organization of the body into systems. By learning about human anatomy and physiology, you may appreciate the complexity of your body and be amazed at the variety of metabolic activities that occur within you to keep you alive, physically active, mentally alert, and healthy.

The Cell

A cell is the smallest functioning structural unit in a living organism. Your body has about 100 trillion cells that can be classified into numerous cell types. Each type of cell has a specific function. For example, muscle cells are necessary for movement, red blood cells transport oxygen, and immune cells protect the body from disease-causing bacteria and viruses.

Most human cells contain several different types of **organelles**, structures that have specific functions (Fig. 4.9). The nucleus, for example, contains **DNA**, the molecule that provides coded instructions for synthesizing proteins. DNA enables the nucleus to control various cellular activities, including cell division and enzyme production. Mitochondria are organelles that play a major role in the generation of energy. Ribosomes are structures involved in the assembly of proteins. The nucleus, mitochondria, and the other organelles are surrounded by a watery fluid called cytoplasm. Many chemical reactions take place in the cytoplasm, including some reactions necessary to make proteins. Each human cell has a plasma membrane that defines the boundaries of the cell and holds the cytoplasm in place. The plasma membrane also controls the passage of materials into and out of the cell.

organelles structures in cells that perform specialized functions

DNA molecule that contains coded instructions for synthesizing proteins

tissues collection of cells that perform a specific function

epithelial tissue cells that line every body surface

connective tissue type of cells that hold together, protect, and support organs

From Cells to Systems

Cells that have similar characteristics and functions are usually joined together into larger masses called **tissues**. The cells that line every body surface, including skin and the inside of blood vessels, are **epithelial tissues**. Fat, bone, and blood are types of **connective tissue**.

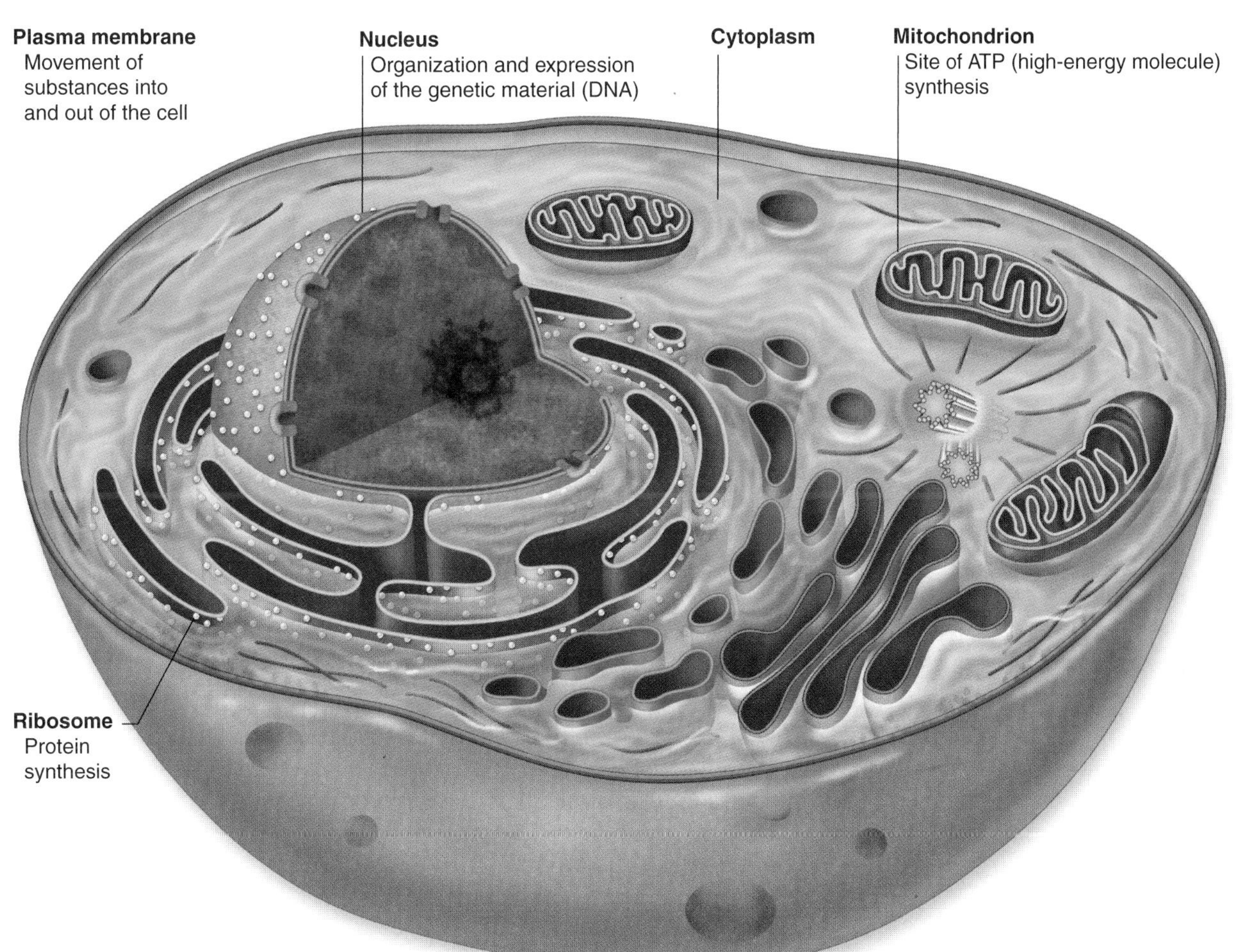

Figure 4.9 Typical human cell. A typical human cell contains certain structures and various organelles, including a nucleus, mitochondria, and ribosomes.

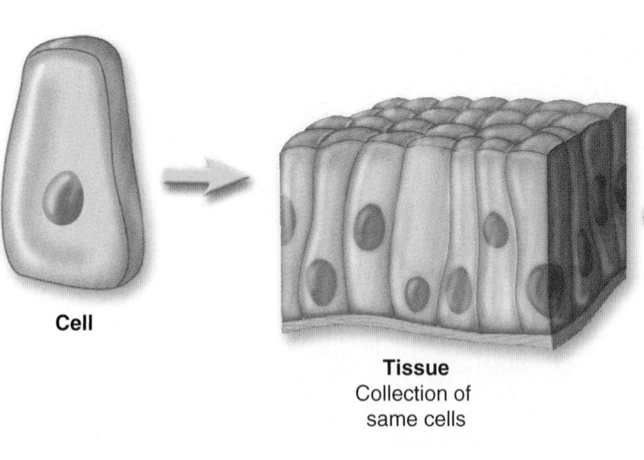

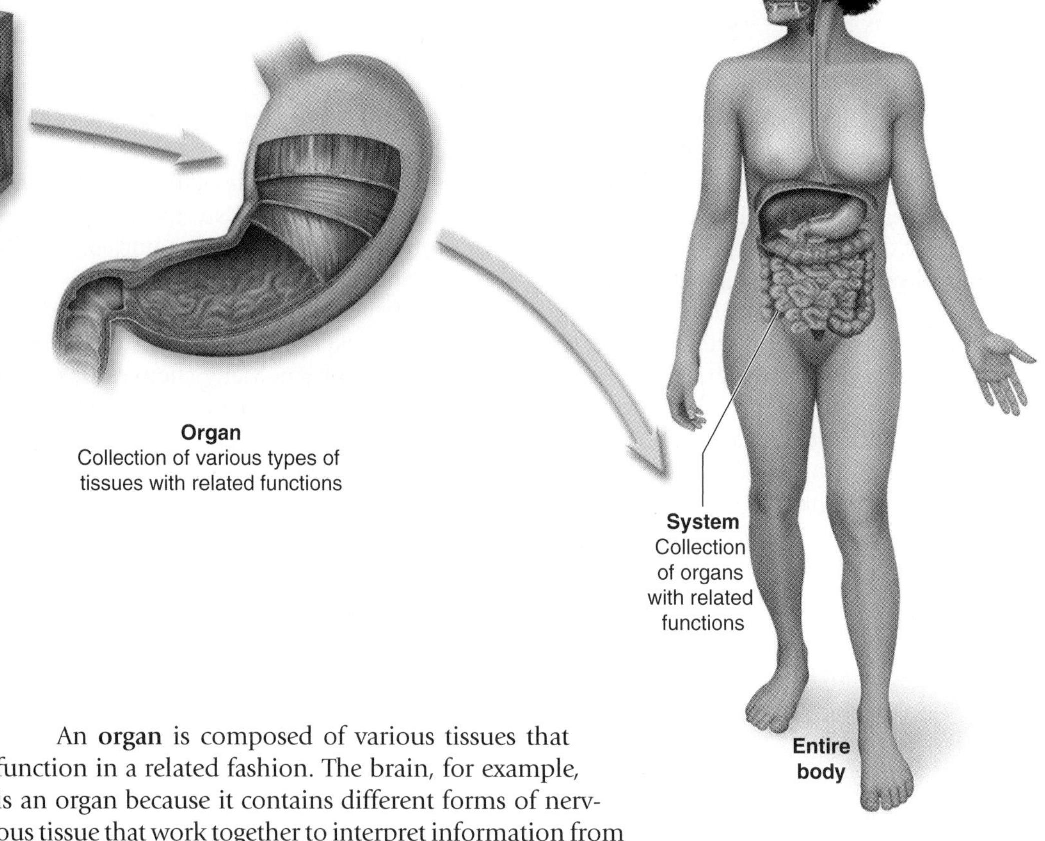

Figure 4.10 Organization of the human body. Cells in the body are organized into tissues, organs, and organ systems. A living organism is a complete individual comprised of organ systems that function together.

An **organ** is composed of various tissues that function in a related fashion. The brain, for example, is an organ because it contains different forms of nervous tissue that work together to interpret information from the environment, find meaning from this information, and signal responses, such as muscle movements. An **organ system** is a group of organs that work together for a similar purpose. The urinary system, for example, includes the kidneys and bladder. Two major functions of the urinary system are filtering blood and excreting wastes in urine. A living organism is a complete individual life form comprised of organ systems that function together. Figure 4.10 illustrates how cells in the body are organized into tissues, organs, and systems.

All systems in your body must work together in a coordinated manner to maintain good health. When one system fails to function correctly, the functioning of the other systems are soon affected. The body's ability to maintain **homeostasis**, a relatively constant internal chemical and physical environment, is critical for good health and even survival. Internal conditions such as body temperature and blood pressure normally fluctuate throughout the day, but the body strives to maintain such factors within fairly specific limits. Changes in the cell's internal and external environment can disrupt homeostasis, and sickness and even death can result if the abnormality persists. A healthy body, however, uses various mechanisms to regain its normal internal status. As you read about the nutrients, you will recognize how many play crucial roles in homeostasis, including maintaining proper body temperature, acid-base balance, and tissue fluid levels.

The following sections provide a brief description of each organ system's major organs or tissues and summarize their primary functions.

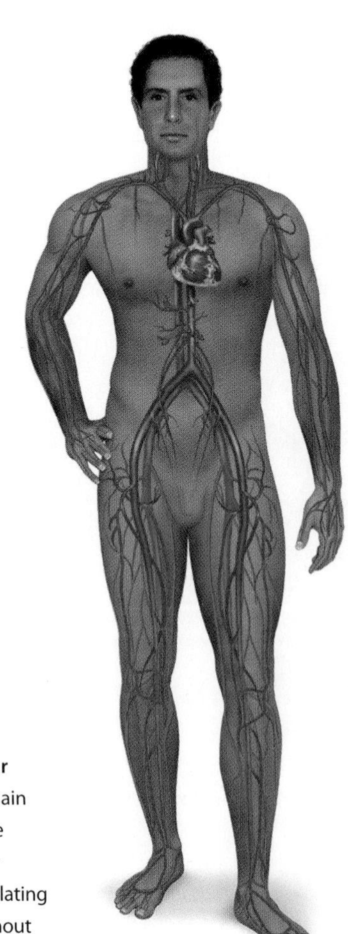

Figure 4.11 Cardiovascular system. The main function of the cardiovascular system is circulating blood throughout the body.

Cardiovascular System

The major components of the cardiovascular (*circulatory*) system are the heart, blood, and blood vessels (Fig. 4.11). The main function of the cardiovascular system is circulating blood throughout the body. The human heart is a four-chambered muscular pump that keeps blood moving through blood vessels. Blood contains red and white blood cells, nutrients, other substances, and plasma, the watery portion of the blood. Blood vessels form a network of tubes that help circulate blood throughout the body. **Arteries** carry blood away from the heart. Arteries branch into smaller and smaller vessels until they form **capillaries**, a network of tiny blood vessels with walls that are only one cell thick. The thin capillary walls enable nutrients and oxygen to move out of the blood and into cells, and carbon dioxide and other waste products to pass from cells and into the blood. After this exchange occurs, the deoxygenated (oxygen-poor) blood enters **veins** for the return trip to the heart.

After entering the right side of the heart, deoxygenated blood is pumped to the lungs via the pulmonary arteries (see Fig. 4.11). In the lungs, red blood cells release carbon dioxide, a cellular waste product, and pick up oxygen from inhaled air. Cells need oxygen to obtain energy. Hemoglobin, an iron-containing protein in red blood cells, carries most of the oxygen in blood. The oxygenated (oxygen-rich) blood then returns to the heart via the pulmonary veins so that it can be pumped to the rest of the body's cells.

organ collection of tissues that perform a specific function

organ system collection of organs that work together to perform a major function

homeostasis relatively constant internal environment in the body that is critical for good health and survival

arteries vessels that carry blood away from the heart

capillaries smallest blood vessels

veins vessels that return blood to the heart

lymph fluid in the lymphatic system

Respiratory System

Lungs, the primary structures of the respiratory system, enable the body to exchange gases, particularly oxygen and carbon dioxide (Fig. 4.12). As mentioned in the previous section, blood circulates through the lungs, picks up oxygen from inhaled air, and releases carbon dioxide, a waste product that forms when cells obtain energy. By exhaling, you eliminate carbon dioxide from your body.

Lymphatic System

The lymphatic system helps maintain fluid balance, absorb many fat-soluble nutrients, and defend the body against diseases. The system includes a network of lymphatic vessels (Fig. 4.13). As blood circulates in the body, some plasma leaks out of capillaries and into spaces between cells. The amount of fluid that surrounds cells must be limited, otherwise tissue swelling would occur. Under normal conditions, the extra fluid, called **lymph**, collects in tiny lymphatic capillaries and is transported by lymphatic system vessels that eventually drain into major veins near the heart, where it enters the general circulation. The lymphatic system does not have a special organ like the heart that circulates lymph. Muscles in the walls of the lymphatic vessels and skeletal muscle contractions that occur during normal body movements squeeze lymph through the lymphatic system.

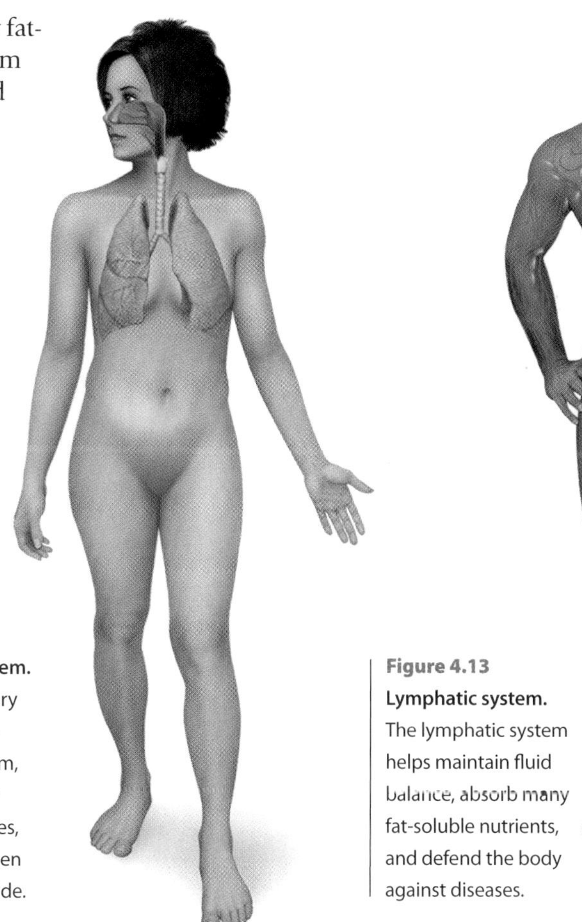

Figure 4.12
Respiratory system. Lungs, the primary structures of the respiratory system, enable the body to exchange gases, particularly oxygen and carbon dioxide.

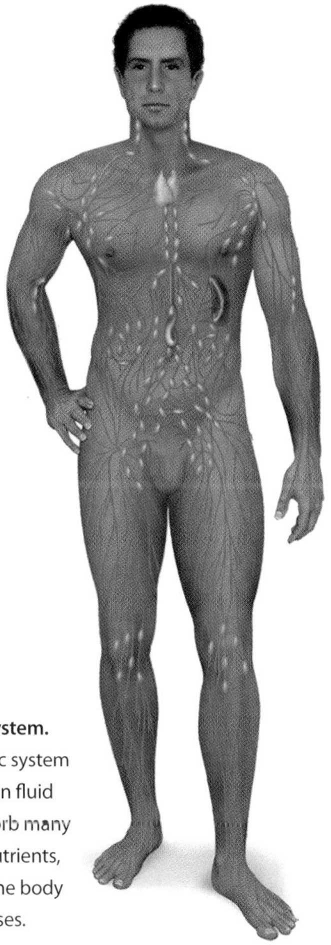

Figure 4.13
Lymphatic system. The lymphatic system helps maintain fluid balance, absorb many fat-soluble nutrients, and defend the body against diseases.

Urinary System

The urinary system includes the kidneys and bladder (Fig. 4.14). The major role of the kidneys is filtering unneeded substances from blood and maintaining proper fluid balance. As blood circulates, it passes through the kidneys, two bean-shaped organs that remove waste products as well as excess water and water-soluble nutrients from the bloodstream. This filtration process forms urine that moves from each kidney by a tube for storage in the bladder. Urine is mostly water, but it also contains dissolved substances such as urea, a by-product of protein metabolism, and excess minerals and water-soluble vitamins.

Muscular System

Muscles are the main organs of the muscular system (Fig. 4.15). Muscles enable movement to occur, and they also provide stability for the body. Furthermore, muscles generate heat that helps maintain normal body temperature.

Skeletal System

Bones, tendons, and ligaments are the principal organs of the skeletal system (Fig. 4.16). These structures provide support, movement, and protection for the body. Additionally, bones store excesses of several minerals and produce blood cells.

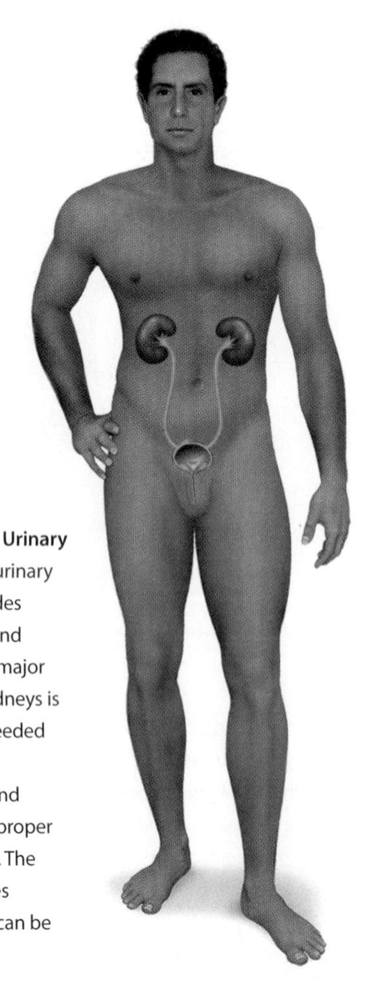

Figure 4.14 Urinary system. The urinary system includes the kidneys and bladder. The major role of the kidneys is filtering unneeded substances from blood and maintaining proper fluid balance. The bladder stores urine until it can be eliminated.

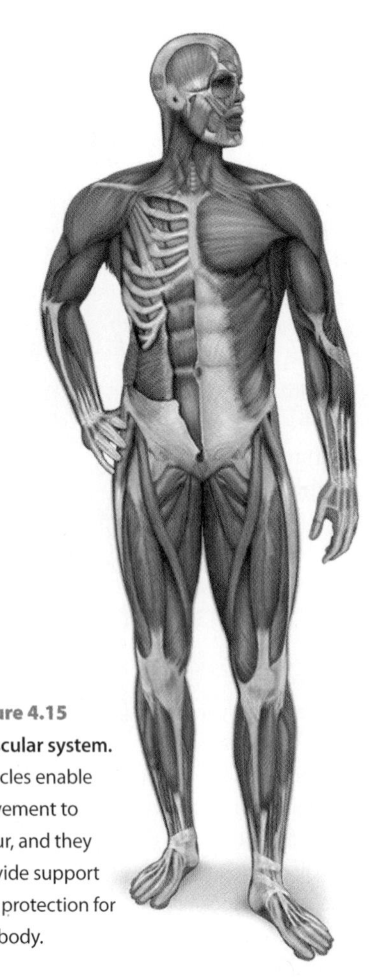

Figure 4.15 Muscular system. Muscles enable movement to occur, and they provide support and protection for the body.

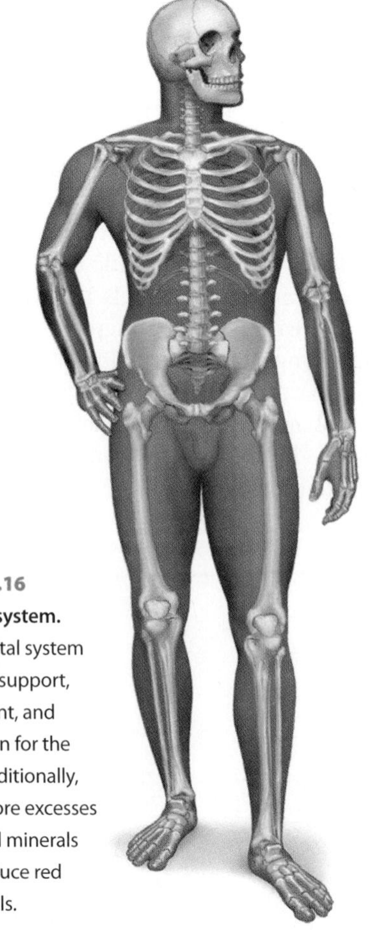

Figure 4.16 Skeletal system. The skeletal system provides support, movement, and protection for the body. Additionally, bones store excesses of several minerals and produce red blood cells.

Nervous System

The brain, spinal cord, and nerves throughout the rest of the body make up the nervous system (Fig. 4.17). The brain produces a variety of intellectual functions and emotional responses, including thoughts, memories, and emotions. The brain also controls and regulates many body functions, including hunger, muscle contractions, and physical responses to danger. Nervous system cells (*neurons*) transmit information and responses by electrical and chemical signals.

Endocrine System

The endocrine system is comprised of organs and tissues that produce a variety of chemical messengers called **hormones** (Fig. 4.18). When released into the bloodstream, a hormone conveys information to cells that are specially equipped to respond (target cells). Hormones regulate a variety of physiological activities, including metabolism, digestion, maintenance of fluid balance, and the maturation of reproductive organs that occurs during puberty.

hormones chemical messengers that convey information to target cells

Integumentary System

Hair, nails, and skin, the largest organ of your body, are structures of the integumentary system (Fig. 4.19). Skin protects against minor injuries and invading disease-causing agents, such as bacteria. Skin also helps maintain body temperature, primarily by perspiration.

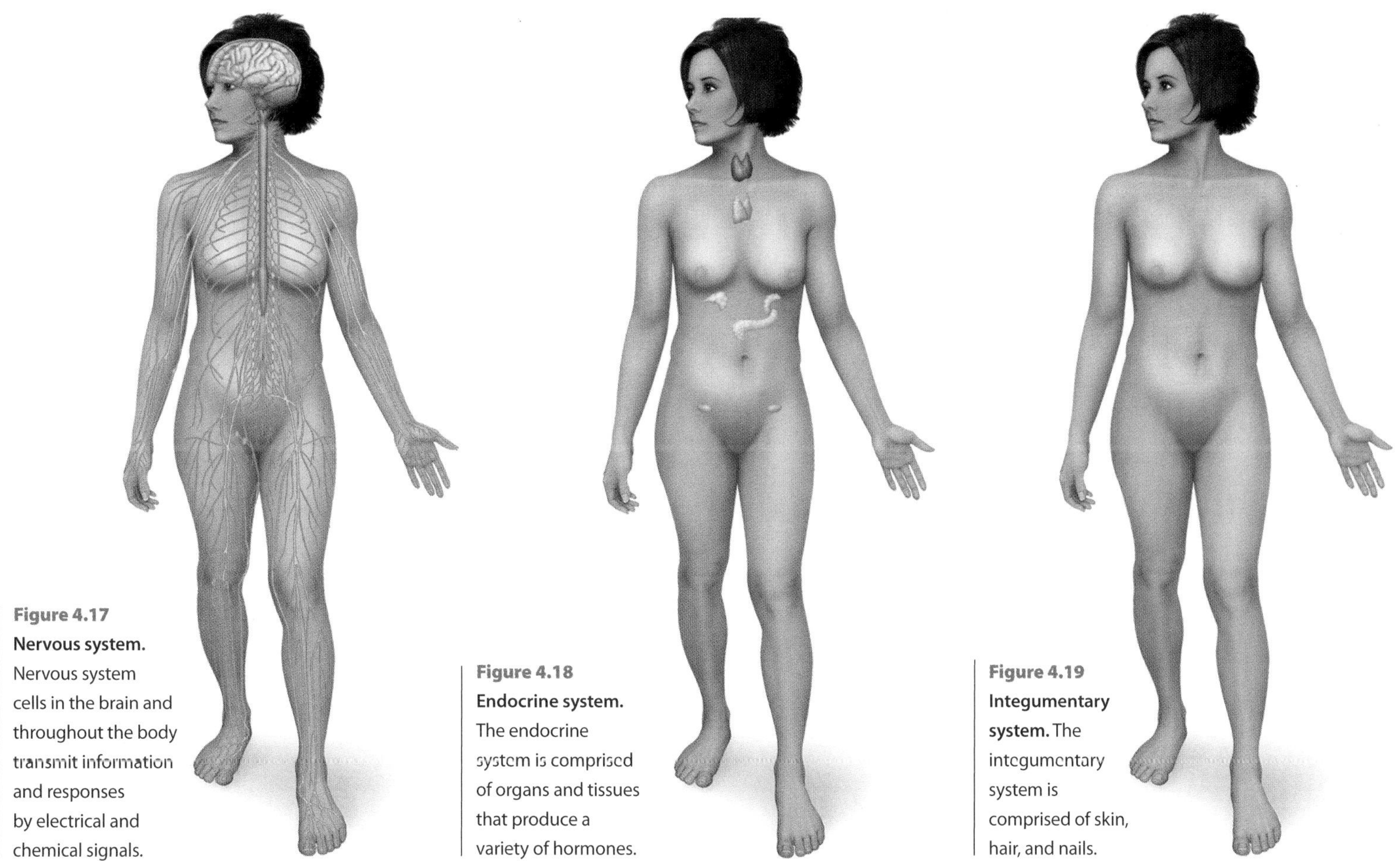

Figure 4.17
Nervous system. Nervous system cells in the brain and throughout the body transmit information and responses by electrical and chemical signals.

Figure 4.18
Endocrine system. The endocrine system is comprised of organs and tissues that produce a variety of hormones.

Figure 4.19
Integumentary system. The integumentary system is comprised of skin, hair, and nails.

Did You Know?

Beta-carotene is a yellow-orange plant pigment that the body can convert to vitamin A. Many fruits and vegetables, such as peaches, carrots, and pumpkin, are rich sources of beta-carotene. If you have light-colour skin, eating high amounts of such foods can make your skin appear yellowish. Your skin eventually will regain its normal colour when you reduce your intake of fruits and vegetables that are rich sources of the pigment.

absorption process by which substances are taken up from the GI tract and enter the bloodstream or the lymph

gastrointestinal (GI) tract muscular tube that extends from the mouth to the anus

bioavailability extent to which the digestive tract absorbs a nutrient and how well the body uses it

esophagus tubular structure of the GI tract that connects the pharynx with the stomach

Healthy skin needs many nutrients for its maintenance, including vitamin A, several types of B vitamins, and the mineral zinc. Each day, the dead cells that form the outermost layer of skin are shed and new skin cells form that will eventually replace them. Because new skin cells are constantly being produced, skin tissue has a high need for nutrients. Therefore, the early signs of many nutritional deficiency disorders often appear as skin abnormalities such as roughened, dry skin.

Reproductive System

The main function of the reproductive system is to produce children (Fig. 4.20). Adequate nutrition is essential for fertility, healthy pregnancies, and healthy newborns. Compared to women whose diets are nutritionally adequate before and during pregnancy, poorly nourished pregnant women have higher risks of miscarriage, stillbirths (infants who are born dead), as well as giving birth to babies with birth defects and low birth weights. During their first year of life, severely underweight infants are more likely to die than infants whose weights are normal.

Digestive System

Your cells do not need food to carry out their metabolic activities—they need nutrients that are in food. The primary roles of the digestive system are the breakdown of large food molecules into smaller components (nutrients) and the **absorption** of nutrients into the bloodstream or lymphatic system (Fig. 4.21). The following section focuses on the process of digestion and absorption.

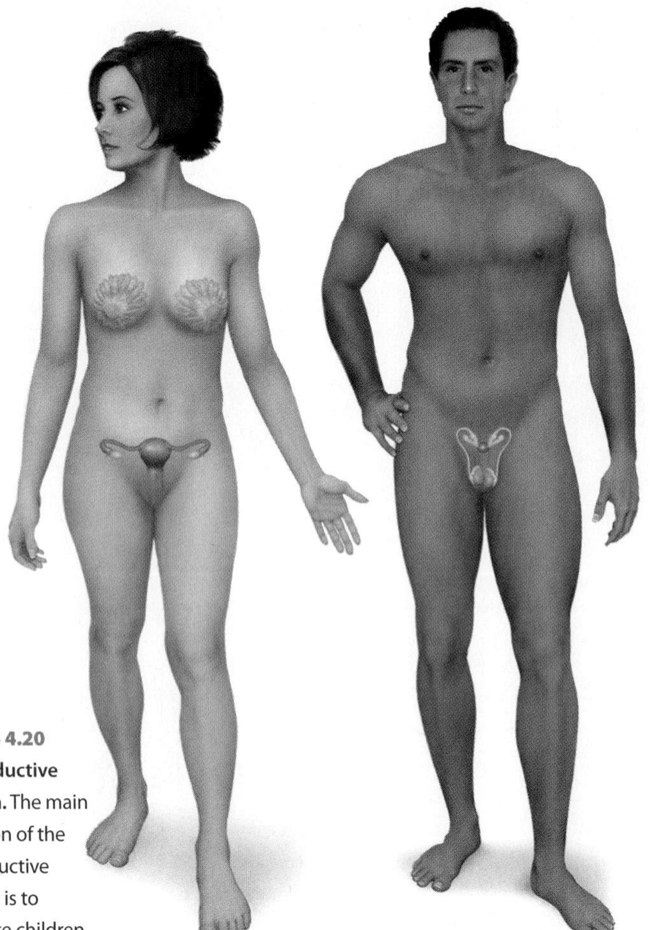

Figure 4.20 Reproductive system. The main function of the reproductive system is to produce children.

Concept Checkpoint

8. Define cell, organelle, DNA, and tissue.
9. Define homeostasis.
10. List at least six of the organ systems that comprise the human body and indicate at least one major function of each organ system listed.

Digestion and Absorption

The mouth, esophagus, stomach, and small and large intestines are the major structures of the **gastrointestinal (GI) tract**, a muscular tube that extends from the mouth to the anus (see Fig. 4.21). The liver, gallbladder, and pancreas are accessory organs that assist the GI tract in food digestion, nutrient absorption and distribution, and waste elimination.

It is important to recognize that many foods need to undergo some processing before they are eaten. Although some nutrients can be lost during food preparation, practices such as removing inedible parts or cooking raw foods often make them more digestible and safe to eat. Additionally, cooking food can enhance the absorption of its nutrients. **Bioavailability** refers to the extent to which the digestive tract absorbs a nutrient and how well the body uses it.

This section describes digestive system organs and their basic functions. More detailed information about digestion and absorption can be found in chapters that discuss specific classes of nutrients, such as Chapters 5, 6, and 7.

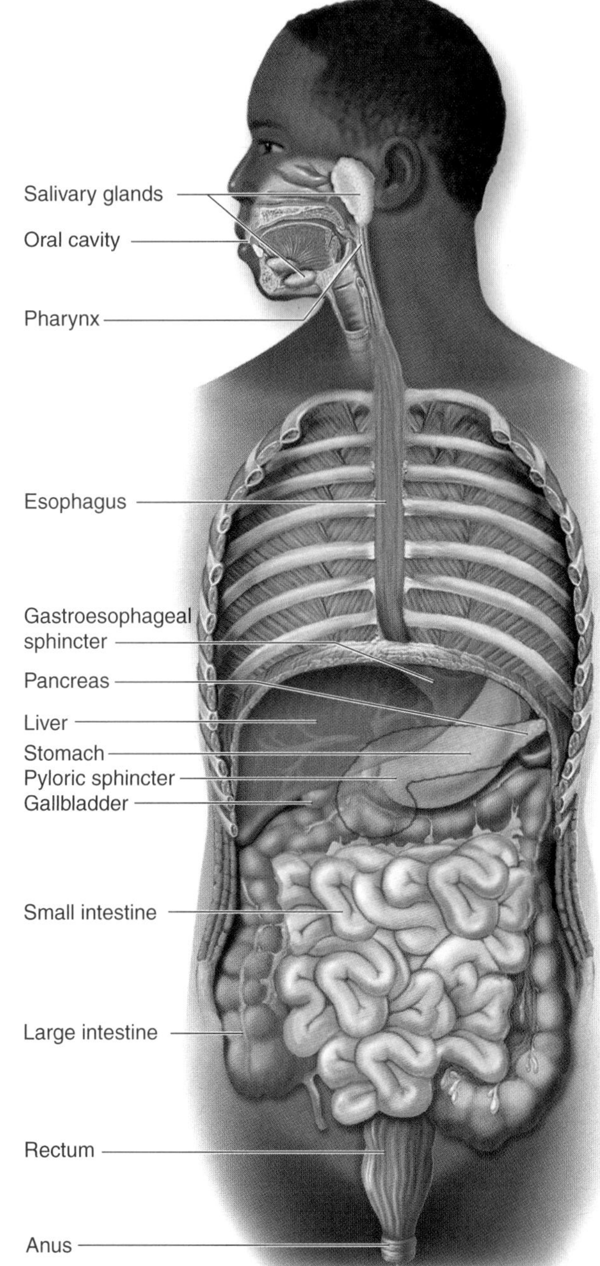

Figure 4.21 Digestive system. The primary roles of the digestive system are the digestion of food and the absorption of nutrients into the circulatory or lymphatic systems.

Mouth

Digestion actually begins in the mouth where mechanical digestion, such as the biting and grinding actions of teeth, break and mash chunks of food into smaller pieces that are easier to swallow. Mechanical digestion continues and muscular contractions mix and move food and its digestive products through the rest of the GI tract.

Chemical digestion refers to the chemical breakdown of foods by substances secreted into the GI tract. As you chew, saliva from salivary glands mixes with food and lubricates it. Saliva contains salivary amylase and lipase, enzymes that enable a minor amount of chemical digestion of starch and fat to occur in the mouth. The tongue helps direct food to the back of the mouth where it can be swallowed.

In addition to playing an important role in digestion, the mouth senses the taste and texture of foods. When food comes in contact with saliva, certain molecules in the food dissolve in the watery fluid. When these chemicals are in solution, they stimulate specialized sensory structures called taste buds on the tongue and in the lining of the mouth and throat. Taste buds relay information about the chemicals to a part of the brain that identifies the particular taste based on past experiences. The sense of taste is important for stimulating appetite and detecting nutrients or toxic substances in substances that enter the mouth.

The tongue has patches of specialized taste buds that help you distinguish sweet, sour, salty, bitter, and umami (*you-mom´-e*) tastes. What benefits do you gain from being able to detect these tastes? Foods that taste sweet usually contain carbohydrates, major energy sources for your cells, and the chemicals that elicit a bitter taste are often poisonous, so you are more likely to eat sweet-tasting foods and reject bitter-tasting ones. You may like foods that taste tart or sour, especially when they are teamed up with sweet ingredients. The sour taste can indicate the presence of ascorbic acid, more commonly known as vitamin C. Sodium ions stimulate your taste buds to detect a salty taste; a food that tastes salty may contain other mineral nutrients as well. The umami or savoury taste is often associated with meat and is detected when certain amino acids stimulate taste buds.[1] Foods that produce the umami taste may be protein-rich; protein is another important component of a healthy diet.

Did You Know?

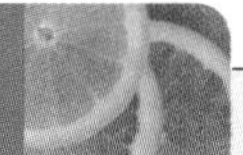

Children have more taste buds than adults, which may explain why they often reject strong-flavoured foods such as liver, cooked broccoli, and raw onion. As you age, the number of taste buds in your mouth declines, and as an older adult, you may find yourself adding more seasoning to food to improve its taste.

Esophagus

The **esophagus** (*e-sof´-ah-gus*) is a tube that extends about 25 cm (10 in.) from the back of the mouth, the pharynx, to the top of the stomach. The primary function of the esophagus is to transfer a mass of swallowed food into the stomach. The entrance to the

The tongue has patches of specialized taste buds that help you distinguish various tastes.

Food & Nutrition *tip*

Raw foods are not necessarily more nutritious or healthier for you than cooked foods. The human intestinal tract can more easily absorb the lycopene and beta-carotene that are in cooked rather than raw tomatoes and carrots. Lycopene and beta-carotene are among the growing list of phytochemicals that may provide health benefits (see Table 1.3 on page 7).

The sense of smell also contributes to your ability to sense the taste of food. As you chew food, it releases chemicals that become airborne and stimulate your nasal passages. Your brain combines such information with taste sensations from your mouth to identify foods' flavours. Thus, favourite foods may seem tasteless and unappealing when you have an upper respiratory tract infection and the inside of your nose is congested.

epiglottis flap of tissue that folds down over the windpipe to keep food from entering the respiratory system during swallowing

peristalsis muscular contractions of the gastrointestinal tract

gastroesophageal sphincter section of esophagus next to the stomach that controls the opening to the stomach

esophagus is near the voice box (larynx) and the opening of the windpipe (trachea). The **epiglottis** (*eh-pe-glot´-tis)* is a flap of tough tissue that prevents the food from entering the larynx and trachea (Fig. 4.22). When you swallow, breathing automatically stops and the food normally lands on the epiglottis, making it cover the opening of the larynx. These responses keep swallowed food from entering your trachea and choking you. Now you know why it is not a good idea to talk while you are eating!

Swallowing signals the GI tract that food is being eaten and stimulates **peristalsis** (*per´-e-stall´-sis*), waves of muscular activity that help propel material through the tract. In the esophagus, each muscular contraction is followed by a brief period of muscle relaxation. Peristalsis moves small amounts of food and beverage from the esophagus into the stomach and then through the intestines in a regulated manner (Fig. 4.23). Peristalsis is an involuntary response, which means the movements happen without the need to think about them. Peristaltic waves in the esophagus are so strong that you can swallow food even if you are standing on your head!

After food enters the stomach, the **gastroesophageal sphincter** (*gas´-tro-esof-ah-jee´-al sfink´-ter*) constricts, closing the opening between the esophagus and stomach. The gastroesophageal sphincter is the section of esophagus that is next to the stomach (see Fig. 4.21).[1] If this sphincter does not function properly and relaxes while food is still in

Figure 4.22
What happens when you swallow? The esophagus transfers food into the stomach. The epiglottis prevents the food from entering the larynx and trachea. When a person swallows, breathing automatically stops, and the food normally lands on the epiglottis, making it cover the opening of the larynx.

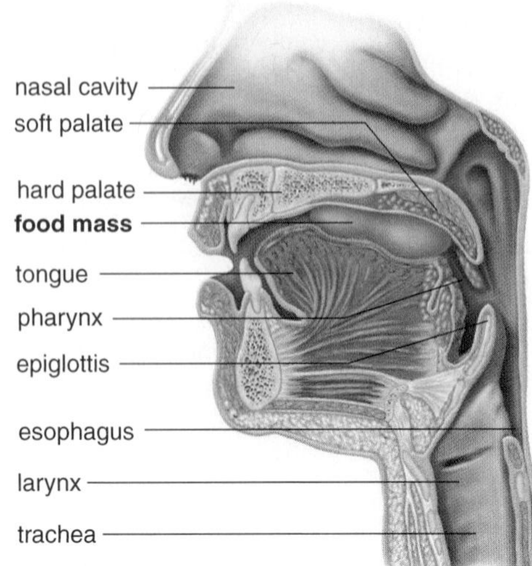

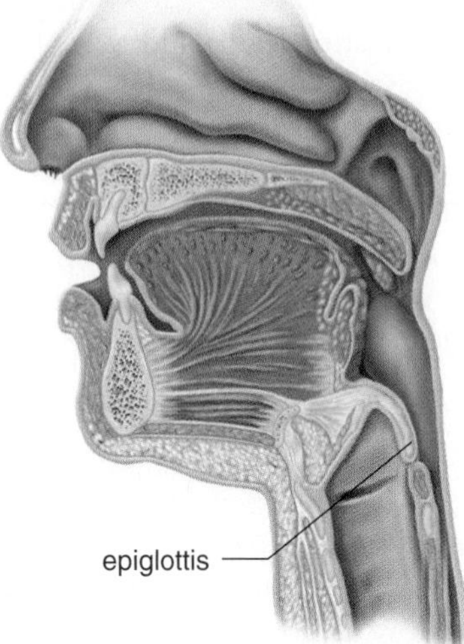

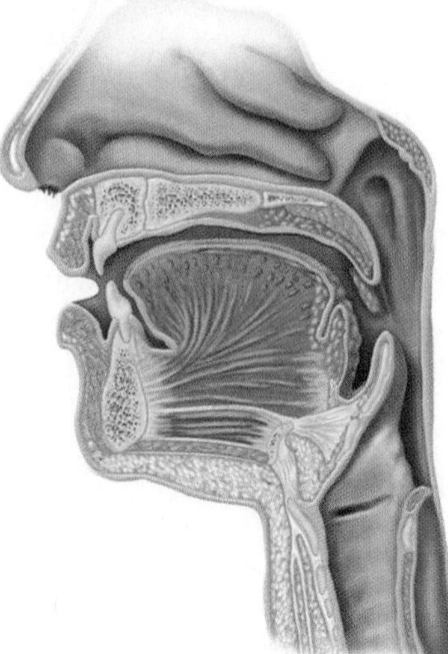

the stomach, *reflux*, the backflow of irritating stomach contents into the esophagus, can occur and cause **heartburn** or **gastroesophageal reflux disease (GERD)**. You can learn more about heartburn and other common gastrointestinal tract problems by reading the Chapter 4 Highlight, later in this chapter.

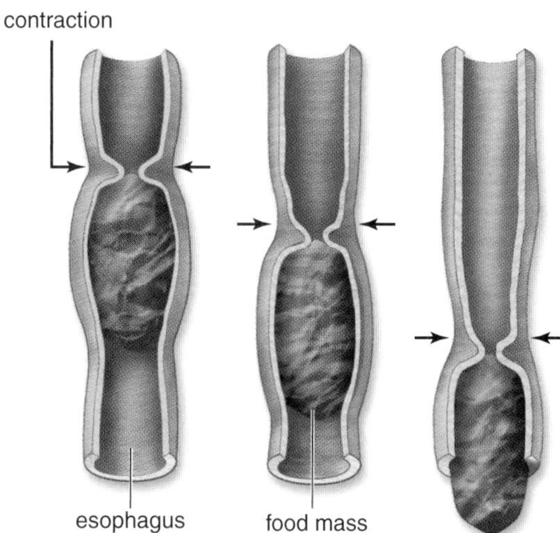

Figure 4.23 Peristalsis. Peristalsis moves small amounts of food and beverage from the esophagus, into the stomach, and then through the intestines in a regulated manner.

Stomach

The stomach is a large muscular sac that can expand and hold up to 4 cups of food for several hours. As food enters the stomach, the organ secretes gastric juice, a watery solution that contains hydrochloric acid (HCl) and some enzymes. HCl helps convert chemically inactive digestive enzymes to their active forms and makes proteins easier to digest. The acid also kills many dangerous disease-causing microorganisms that may be in food.

The churning movements of the stomach's muscles mix food with gastric juice, and as a result of this mechanical and chemical activity, some of the protein and fat in food breaks down. At this point, the stomach contents are a semisolid liquid called **chyme** (*kime*). Although the stomach absorbs very few nutrients from chyme, a few drugs, including some alcohol, can pass through the organ's walls and enter the bloodstream.

Stomach walls consist of muscle proteins—so how does the stomach avoid digesting itself? Special cells that line the inside of the stomach produce a thick layer of **mucus**. Mucus is a slippery alkaline substance that protects the stomach from its acid and digestive enzymes. If the layer of mucus breaks down, HCl and gastric enzymes can reach the stomach wall, destroying the tissue. Such destruction can cause one or more sores (ulcers) to form. For more information about factors that increase the risk of gastrointestinal tract ulcers, read the Chapter 4 Highlight, later in this chapter.

The pyloric (*pie-lor´-ic*) sphincter controls the rate at which chyme is released into the small intestine (see Fig. 4.21). This process is called gastric emptying. Following a meal, the stomach empties in about four hours, depending on the contents and size of the meal.[1] Watery meals such as soups spend less time in the stomach; fatty meals and those high in protein spend more time there. Obviously, larger meals take longer to empty from the stomach than smaller meals.

Small Intestine

The small intestine is a coiled hollow tube that extends from the stomach to the large intestine. The organ measures about 2 m (6½ ft.) in length. The small intestine is "small" because the tube's diameter is only about 2.5 cm (1 in.) wide, about half the width of the large intestine.

The small intestine has three sections. The first, the **duodenum** (*do-wahdee´-num*) is only about 25 cm (10 in.) long. Within the duodenum, the acidic stomach contents mix with alkaline intestinal fluids. This process neutralizes the acidity of chyme and enables enzymes that function in more alkaline conditions to work. The middle segment of the small intestine is the **jejunum** (*jeh-ju´-num*). Most digestion and nutrient absorption occurs in the jejunum.[1] The last portion of the small intestine is the **ileum** (*il´-lee-um*). The ileum connects the rest of the small intestine with the large intestine. Some nutrient absorption takes place in the ileum.[2]

heartburn or **gastroesophageal reflux disease (GERD)** backflow of irritating stomach contents into the esophagus

chyme mixture of gastric juice and partially digested food

mucus fluid that lubricates and protects certain cells

duodenum first segment of the small intestine

jejunum middle segment of the small intestine

ileum last segment of the small intestine

Did You Know?

When you eat foods or drink beverages, you swallow some air. Burping expels most of this air before it enters the stomach. If some air manages to enter your stomach and small intestine, it mixes with chyme and bubbles through it, often producing rather loud, gurgling sounds that can be embarrassing.

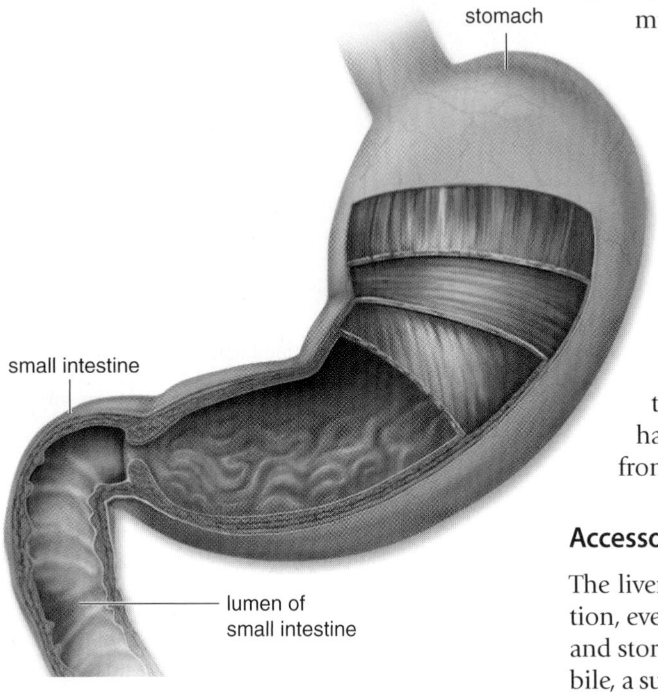

The **lumen** of the intestinal tract is the hollow space surrounded by the walls of the small and large intestines (Fig. 4.24). Each day, the small intestine secretes approximately 1½ litres (1500 mL) of watery fluids into the lumen. This fluid lubricates the intestinal walls, facilitating the passage of chyme. The cells lining the small intestine also produce mucus that protects the tissue from being damaged by chyme as it moves through the tract.[3]

Many of the major chemical reactions that occur during digestion are hydrolytic (*hydro* = water; *lytic* = breakdown), because water molecules are necessary for the reactions to occur. Water in intestinal fluid contributes H^+ and OH^- ions. These ions react with certain nutrients and become part of the products. Sucrose, for example, undergoes hydrolysis in the small intestine (see Fig. 4.8).

As chyme passes through the lumen of the small intestine, enzymes break down the large compounds in chyme and the intestinal cells into smaller fragments and individual nutrients that can be absorbed. The cells also contain enzymes that are added to chyme and contribute to the digestive process. By the time chyme reaches the middle part of the ileum, most of its nutrient contents have been digested and absorbed.[1] It takes about 3 to 10 hours for chyme to move from the duodenum to the end of the ileum.

stomach

small intestine

lumen of small intestine

Figure 4.24 Lumen of the small intestine. A lumen is a hollow space in an organ that is surrounded by walls. This illustration shows the lumen of the small intestine.

Accessory Organs

The liver, gallbladder, and pancreas are accessory organs that play major roles in digestion, even though chyme does not move through them (see Fig. 4.21). The liver processes and stores many nutrients. This organ also makes cholesterol and uses this lipid to make bile, a substance that prepares fat and fat-soluble vitamins for absorption. Bile flows from the liver into the gallbladder where it is stored until needed. When food and, particularly, fat are in the duodenum, the small intestine sends a hormonal signal to the gallbladder, and as a result, the gallbladder contracts, releasing bile into the duodenum.

The pancreas produces and secretes most of the enzymes that break down carbohydrates, protein, and fat in the GI tract. Additionally, the pancreas secretes bicarbonate ions (HCO^{3-}) that neutralize HCl in chyme when it enters the duodenum. This is a critical step in the digestion process because the enzymes that function in the small intestine do not work in acidic conditions.

In Canada, many adults develop gallstones within their gallbladders. Gallstones usually consist of cholesterol; they can be small and grainy, like particles of sand, or as large as a coin (Fig. 4.25). When a gallbladder that contains stones contracts or a gallstone lodges in one of the ducts that carries bile from the gallbladder to the small intestine, it causes considerable pain in the right upper part of the body. If the stone moves out of the duct, the discomfort ends, but in some cases, the duct remains blocked and bile backs up into the liver or pancreas. When this occurs, surgery to remove the diseased gallbladder is necessary to prevent damage to the liver or pancreas. After surgery, bile flows from the liver directly into the small intestine. Having excess body fat increases the risk of gallstones, so keeping your weight at a healthy level can reduce your chances of developing the condition.

When chyme is in the duodenum, its fat and protein content triggers the release of a hormone cholecystokinin (CCK) from small intestinal cells. CCK enters the bloodstream and circulates to the pancreas, where it stimulates the organ to secrete digestive enzymes into the duodenum. This hormone also signals the gallbladder to contract, releasing bile along with the pancreatic enzymes. Bile facilitates fat digestion and absorption (see Chapter 6).

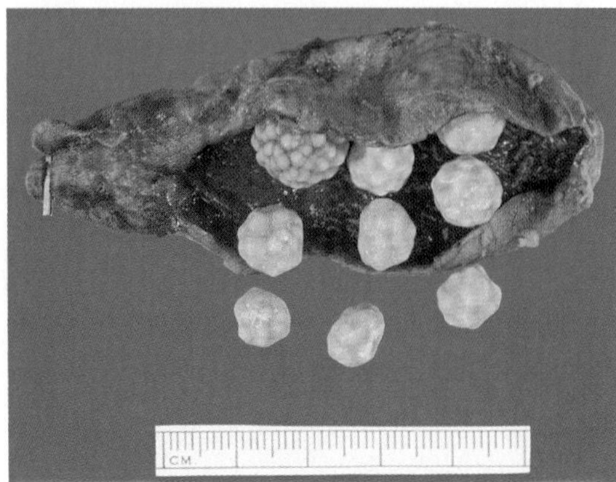

Figure 4.25 Gallstones. Gallstones form in the gallbladder. The stones usually consist of cholesterol.

Absorbing Nutrients

The lining of the small intestine is highly folded and covered by tiny, fingerlike projections called **villi** (singular, villus). Each villus has an outer layer of epithelial cells called absorptive cells (Fig. 4.26). Absorptive cells remove nutrients from chyme and transfer them into intestinal blood or lymph vessels. This process occurs in a variety of ways. Some nutrients require the help of transport proteins or pumping mechanisms within the absorptive cell's plasma membrane to enter the cell. Other kinds of nutrients can simply *diffuse* into these cells. Such diffusion usually happens when the concentration of a particular nutrient is higher in the lumen of the small intestine than in the absorptive cells. In a few instances, a segment of an absorptive cell's plasma membrane surrounds and "swallows" relatively large substances, such as entire protein molecules. This process, for example, enables an infant's intestinal tract to absorb whole proteins in human milk that provide immune benefits.

While digestion is occurring, absorptive cells are shed into the lumen and added to the contents of chyme. The old cells are digested along with chyme. Newly formed absorptive cells constantly replace those that have been shed. The new cells can absorb nutrients from the older cells and recycle some of their contents. However, the small intestine's high cell turnover rate leads to relatively high nutrient needs for these tissues. As a result, early signs and symptoms of nutrient deficiencies, such as diarrhea, often involve the intestinal tract.

After being absorbed, water-soluble nutrients enter the villus' capillary, and eventually the **portal vein**. This vein delivers nutrients directly to the liver where many undergo processing before they enter the general circulation. Most of the absorbed lipids are coated with a layer that contains protein, forming a **chylomicron**. Chylomicrons move into a **lacteal**, a type of lymphatic system structure in each villus similar in structure to a capillary (see Fig. 4.26). Chylomicrons are transported by lymph and eventually enter the bloodstream via the thoracic duct near the heart.

About 8 to 9 litres of water from ingested foods and beverages and the secretions of intestinal cells enter into the GI tract daily. Most of the water is absorbed along with other nutrients in the small intestine.[2] Any remaining water and the undigested material that reaches the end of the small intestine must pass through another sphincter called the *ileocecal valve* before entering the large intestine. This valve prevents the contents of the large intestine from re-entering the small intestine.

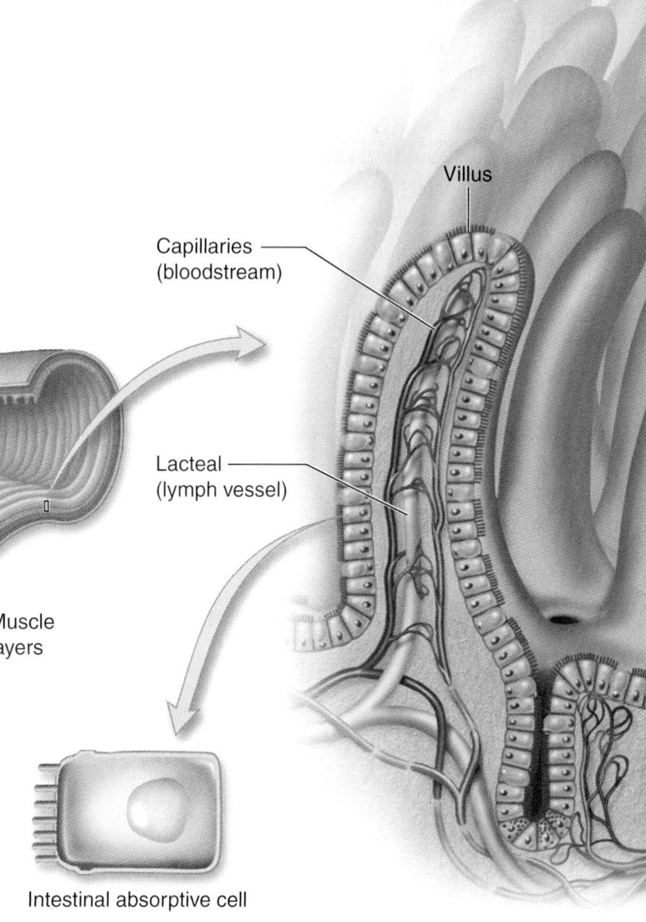

Figure 4.26 Small intestinal absorption. The lining of the small intestine is covered with villi, and the surface of each villus is covered with absorptive cells. Absorptive cells move nutrients from chyme into intestinal blood or lymph vessels.

Cystic Fibrosis and Inflammatory Bowel Disease Chronic diseases such as cystic fibrosis and inflammatory bowel disease affect the intestinal tract, disrupting digestion and nutrient absorption. In Canada, cystic fibrosis (CF) is an inherited incurable disease that is usually diagnosed in early childhood. In CF, certain cells produce thick sticky mucus that blocks passageways, particularly in the respiratory and digestive systems. People with CF often suffer from serious breathing problems and respiratory infections. The pancreatic ducts of an affected person may also become blocked by thick mucus. The mucus interferes with the organ's ability to deliver digestive enzymes to the small intestine. As a result, the digestion of nutrients, especially fat, is impaired. To overcome this problem, patients with cystic fibrosis can take capsules that contain pancreatic enzymes with their meals.

Inflammatory bowel disease (IBD) is the general name for a group of diseases that cause inflammation and swelling of the intestines. Crohn's disease and ulcerative colitis are the two most common forms of IBD. The Real People, Real Stories feature on page 102 highlights Lisa G., a woman who has Crohn's disease.

villi (singular, villus) tiny fingerlike projections of the small intestinal lining that participate in digesting and absorbing food

portal vein vein that collects nutrients from the intestinal tract and delivers them to the liver

chylomicron lipoprotein formed by intestinal cells

lacteal lymph vessel in villus that absorbs most lipids

Large Intestine

The large intestine is approximately 1.5 m (5 ft.) long (see Fig. 4.21). Under normal circumstances, very little carbohydrate, protein, and fat escape digestion and absorption in the small intestine and enter the large intestine. However, the large intestine has no villi, therefore little additional absorption other than some water and minerals takes place in this structure. The primary functions of the large intestine are to dehydrate the fecal waste before it is released to preserve body water and to store the feces until it can be released at an appropriate time. As the chyme passes through the large intestine, it becomes semi-solid and is called feces, bowel movements, or stools. In addition to containing relatively large amounts of water, feces consist of bacteria and other microorganisms that normally live in the large intestine; undigested fibre from plant foods; a small amount of fat; and some protein, mucus, and cells shed from the walls of the intestinal tract.

Feces remain in the **rectum**, a lower section of the large intestine, until muscular contractions move the material into the anal canal (see Fig. 4.21). The external anal sphincter is under voluntary control, so a healthy person can determine when to relax the sphincter and have a bowel movement. Young children must reach the stage of physical and emotional maturity in which they are able to relax or tighten their external anal sphincter voluntarily. The timing of this stage varies but generally occurs by 4 years of age.

Did You Know?

Using "high colonics" and other types of enemas to "cleanse" your large intestine isn't necessary because the colon doesn't need to be cleansed. Furthermore, frequent enemas may deplete the body of vital minerals, including sodium and potassium. Check with your physician before trying enema treatments.

rectum lower section of large intestine

Microbes in Your Digestive Tract

The small intestine of a healthy person usually has few microorganisms residing in its lumen, particularly in the duodenum and jejunum.[4] On the other hand, the large intestine is home to vast numbers of various *species* (types) of bacteria. Under normal conditions, the different bacterial populations maintain a balance with each other that is beneficial to their human hosts. Interestingly, the usual composition of the various bacterial species varies from person to person, because of dietary differences. Starvation and excessive emotional stress are among the factors that can upset the normal balance of intestinal bacteria and result in intestinal infections.[4]

Intestinal bacteria can metabolize undigested food, make vitamin K and the B-vitamin biotin that their human hosts can absorb, and produce substances that colon

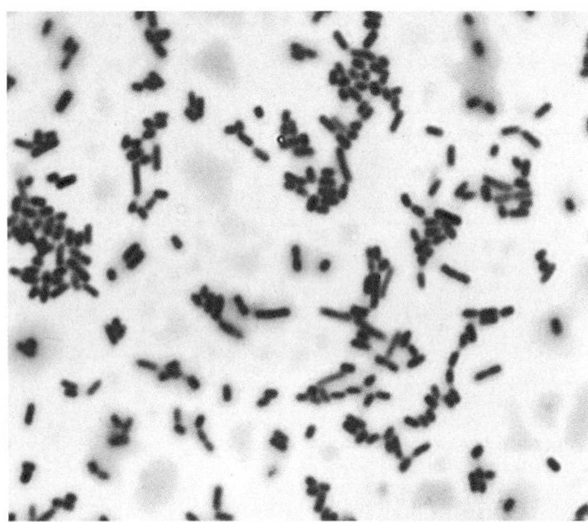

Certain types of *E. coli* bacteria normally live in the human intestinal tract without causing health problems for their host.

REAL *people* REAL *stories*

Lisa G.

Late in 1999, Lisa G. began experiencing painful abdominal cramps followed by frequent bouts of diarrhea. It seemed that whatever she ate would pass through her digestive tract and be eliminated quickly. When over-the-counter diarrhea remedies didn't work, Lisa sensed her ailment was not a self-limiting intestinal tract infection. Before the illness struck, Lisa weighed 57 kg (125 lbs.)—a healthy weight for a person who is 157 cm (5'2"). She was physically active and strong. Four weeks after developing the digestive tract problems, she had lost about 5.5 kg (12 lbs.) and become noticeably weaker.

Lisa's physician suspected a form of inflammatory bowel disease (IBD) was responsible for her condition. She was admitted into a local hospital and treated with prednisone, a steroid medication that helps reduce inflammation. When her weight stabilized, her physician prescribed additional medications that are specific for treating IBD. Her special diet included foods that were easily digested. She soon learned which foods she could eat without suffering from diarrhea. For example, she couldn't eat raw carrots, but she could tolerate cooked carrots. Because IBD damaged the ileum, the site for vitamin B-12 absorption, Lisa had to have injections of vitamin B-12 regularly. Within a few weeks, Lisa was well enough to leave the hospital, but she remained on the medication.

cells can use for energy. As a result of their metabolic activity, intestinal bacteria also produce gases that are expelled through the anus.

Large numbers of intestinal bacteria eventually become a major component of feces. Some species of these bacteria can be harmful if they enter other parts of the body or contaminate food. People should wash their hands after having bowel movements to reduce the likelihood of spreading dangerous microbes from their intestinal tract to others. Chapter 12 discusses microorganisms that cause common food-borne infections and ways to limit your exposure to them.

Your Adaptable Digestive Tract

Sometimes popular diet "experts" claim that eating certain combinations of foods, such as meats and fruits together, is unhealthy because the food "rots" in the intestinal tract or because one type of food interferes with the digestion of another type. Some people claim the human digestive tract is not designed for the consumption of animal foods, and the undigested food blocks the intestinal tract. According to some of these sources, the blockages can be the size of a young child, weighing 18 kg (40 lbs.)! Such information is simply not true.

A human being is an **omnivore**, an organism that can digest and absorb nutrients from plants, animals, fungi, and even bacteria. Additionally, the healthy human GI tract responds to dietary changes, such as alterations in the nutritional composition or amounts of food consumed, by increasing the production of various digestive enzymes. Consider this: How would people be able to survive in extreme environments, including deserts and permanently frozen regions, if they were unable to digest foods from a wide variety of sources? And finally, a healthy digestive tract does not become blocked by undigested food nor does it store large amounts of feces.

About six months after being released from hospital, Lisa experienced a major setback as her colon became severely inflamed, and she had to be rushed to hospital by ambulance. While in hospital, she was given special formula feedings administered through a vein, but she continued to lose weight and her condition deteriorated. At this point, Lisa's physician recommended she obtain treatment from a specialist at another local hospital.

While Lisa was in hospital, her physicians determined she had Crohn's disease, a form of IBD. Medical experts suspect Crohn's disease is an autoimmune disorder, a condition in which the body's immune system does not function properly and begins to attack normal cells. Rheumatoid arthritis and multiple sclerosis (MS) are autoimmune diseases. In Crohn's disease, certain immune system cells invade the intestinal lining and cause inflammation.

People who have autoimmune disorders often have genes that make them vulnerable to develop such conditions. Lisa eventually learned that she has a gene associated with increased risk of Crohn's disease. However, she was not aware of anyone in her family who also suffered from Crohn's disease or another autoimmune disorder.

The clinic's physicians treated Lisa with a medication specifically used to treat Crohn's disease. Within two days of starting treatment, Lisa began to feel better. After several days, her weight had risen to 40 kg (87 lbs.), and her physicians allowed her to return home, but she would need to return to the clinic every few weeks to receive the medication.

Today, Lisa is back at work and back to feeling "normal." She still has to obtain treatment for Crohn's disease, but her local hospital is able to provide the special medication she needs every eight weeks. Lisa continues to avoid eating certain foods, especially raw vegetables. She recommends that people be aware of autoimmune diseases such as Crohn's, because they are relatively common conditions. Furthermore, she says, "Follow your doctor's advice, take medicines as scheduled, and have an open and honest relationship with your doctor. The key to health and wellness is to listen to your body and keep a positive attitude."

Did You Know?

When you ingest antibiotics to kill bacteria responsible for an infection, you also destroy bacteria that normally reside in your colon, increasing the risk of diarrhea. The results of some studies indicate that you may be able to re-establish these bacteria by eating *probiotics*, such as yogourt, that contain live cultures of beneficial bacteria. Research has shown that certain probiotics can reduce the risk of diarrheal diseases, as well as bladder and urinary tract infections that commonly affect women.[5] Although yogourt is a nutritious food, more research is needed to determine its effects on GI health.[6]

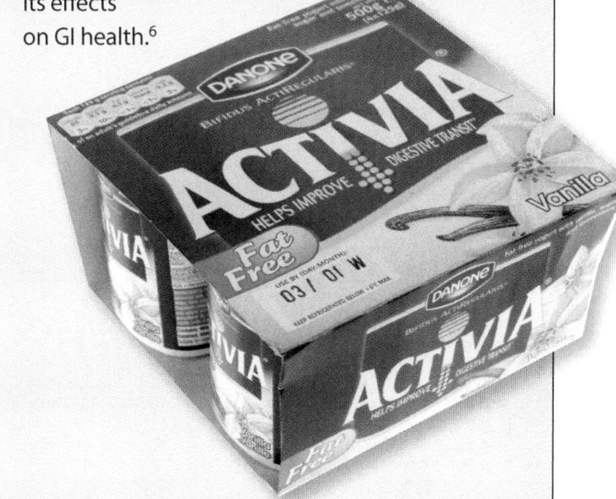

Some brands of yogourt are probiotics, because they contain live cultures of beneficial bacteria.

omnivore organism that can digest and absorb nutrients from plants, animals, fungi, and bacteria

Concept Checkpoint

11. Trace the path of a cheese sandwich as it enters your mouth. Name the organs or structures through which the sandwich passes and describe what happens to the food as it moves through the digestive tract.
12. Provide an example of mechanical digestion and chemical digestion.
13. Identify four different tastes.
14. Eliot choked on a piece of hot dog. Explain why choking can occur while eating.
15. Sara has been taking medication that has the side effect of reducing mucus production in the stomach. Based on this information, what common digestive system disorder is Sara at risk of developing?
16. What functional aspect of a healthy digestive system prevents food from becoming "stuck" in the tract?
17. What keeps stomach contents from re-entering the esophagus?
18. What are the three sections of the small intestine? Where does most digestion and nutrient absorption take place?
19. How would removal of the pancreas affect digestion?
20. Describe at least two different ways that nutrients can enter villi.
21. What is an omnivore?

Chapter 4 Highlight
Gut Reaction

Even though you may be healthy, you've probably experienced occasional bouts of constipation, vomiting, diarrhea, or heartburn. After being miserable and uncomfortable for awhile, you recovered and returned to your usual routine. This highlight provides general information about common intestinal problems, including peptic ulcers.

Constipation

Many Canadians, especially older adults, think they are constipated if they don't have a bowel movement at least once a day. Although the normal frequency of bowel movements varies individually, a healthy person should have at least three bowel movements a week.[1A] When bowel movements occur less frequently and are difficult to eliminate, the condition is called constipation.

Many factors influence the frequency of bowel movements. Lack of dietary fibre; low water intake; anxiety, depression, and other psychological disturbances; and changes in your typical routine, such as taking a long trip or having major surgery, can alter your usual pattern of bowel movements. Furthermore, constipation can result when people regularly ignore their normal bowel urges and avoid making a trip to the bathroom when it's not convenient. Even the use of certain pain medications can cause constipation in some individuals.

Although occasional constipation is a common health problem, chronic constipation can cause discomfort and may contribute to the development of hemorrhoids and diverticula. Hemorrhoids are swollen veins in the anal canal that can cause itching and bleeding. Diverticula are tiny pouches that can form in the lining of the large intestine. If diverticula become infected, antibiotics and, sometimes, surgery may be necessary to treat the condition (diverticulitis). Chapter 5 provides more information on these common conditions.

If you feel uncomfortable because your bowel habits have changed and you have hard, dry bowel movements that are difficult to eliminate, discuss the matter with your physician. In many instances, adding more fibre-rich foods to your diet is the first step to becoming more "regular." Chapter 5 provides information about dietary fibre, including rich food sources.

Diarrhea

Diarrhea is a condition characterized by frequent, loose bowel movements. Diarrhea occurs when more water than normal is secreted into the GI tract or the tract absorbs less water than normal. Most cases of diarrhea result from bacterial or viral infections of the intestinal tract. The infectious bacteria or viruses produce irritating or toxic substances that increase the movements (motility) of the GI tract. As a result, the GI tract propels chyme more rapidly through it, absorbing less water than normal in the process. Increased GI motility also enables the large intestine to eliminate the watery feces and the toxic material it contains rapidly.

Cases of severe diarrhea, however, require more immediate medical attention, because frequent watery bowel movements (stools) can deplete the body's fluid volume, causing dehydration and excessive losses of the minerals sodium and potassium. Therefore, treatment of severe diarrhea generally includes drinking replacement fluids that contain sodium, potassium, and simple sugars such as glucose. It's also prudent to avoid eating solid foods until the condition resolves. Prompt treatment of severe diarrhea—within 24 to 48 hours—is especially crucial for infants and the elderly, because they can become dehydrated quickly by the loss of body water. In adults, diarrhea that is accompanied by bloody stools or lasts more than seven days may be a sign of a serious intestinal disease, and a physician should be consulted.

Vomiting

Not long after eating something toxic or drinking too much alcohol, you begin to feel queasy or "sick to your stomach." You soon become well aware that your body has an effective way of removing the harmful food or beverage—vomiting. Although vomiting is an unpleasant experience, it prevents toxic substances from entering your small intestine where they can do more harm or be absorbed. Vomiting can also be a response to intense pain, head injury, swaying movements of the head (motion sickness), hormonal changes in pregnancy (morning sickness), and touching the back of the throat.[2A]

Vomiting occurs when the vomiting centre in the brain interprets information from various nervous system receptors concerning the physical and chemical conditions of the stomach, small intestine, and bloodstream. When a toxic chemical is detected, the centre initiates vomiting by contracting the abdominal muscles, expelling the contents of the stomach and duodenum forcefully out of the body via the mouth.

Vomiting generally does not last more than 24 hours. Repeated vomiting, however, can result in dehydration, especially if it's accompanied by diarrhea. Treatment includes avoiding solid food until the condition resolves. Additionally, sipping small amounts of water or clear liquids, including noncarbonated soft drinks such as sports drinks, can help prevent dehydration. If the affected person is able to retain small amounts of fluid, then he or she can try to drink increasing amounts of fluid until the vomiting subsides completely.

Adults should contact a physician if their vomiting lasts for more than a day and they have signs of dehydration such as increased thirst, decreased urination, and dry lips and mouth.[3A] Children who suffer from vomiting and/or diarrhea are likely to develop dehydration more rapidly than an adult who is suffering from these conditions. Signs of dehydration in young children include sunken eyes, dry lips and mouth, and decreased urination. Contact a physician if your child has vomiting and diarrhea that persists for more than a few hours and shows signs of dehydration.

Heartburn

About half of North American adults experience occasional heartburn, a gnawing pain or burning sensation generally felt in the upper chest, under the breastbone. Ten percent of the population has heartburn at least once a week.[4A] This discomfort is not the result of a heart problem but is caused by the passage of acidic contents from the stomach into the esophagus. Because the esophageal lining does not produce as much protective mucus as the stomach, the acid quickly destroys the tissue, causing pain and, sometimes, bleeding. Many factors can contribute to heartburn or worsen the condition, including being pregnant; smoking cigarettes; having excess body fat; drinking alcohol, caffeinated beverages, and citrus juices; overeating; and eating onions, chocolate, mints, greasy or spicy foods, or foods that contain tomatoes or vinegar.

Although many people think heartburn is a trivial health problem, frequent chronic heartburn can be a symptom of gastroesophageal reflux disease (GERD). Symptoms of GERD include frequent heartburn and may include nausea, gagging, coughing, or hoarseness. If not treated properly, GERD damages the lining of the esophagus and contributes to the development of esophageal ulcers (sores) (Fig. 4.A). Such ulcers can damage blood vessels in the wall of the esophagus, causing bleeding. Signs of bleeding from the esophagus

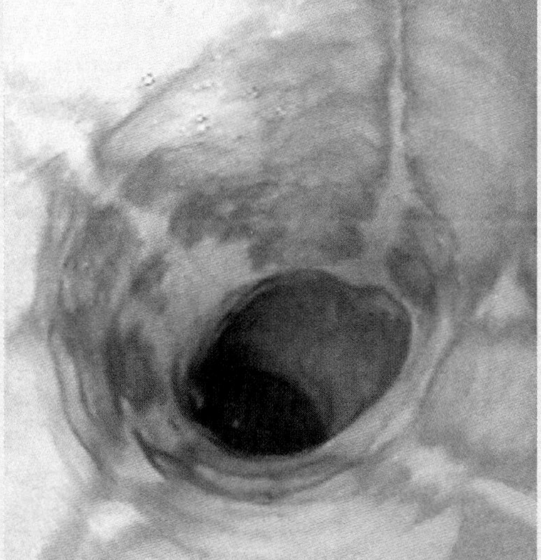

Figure 4.A Acid reflux damage. An endoscopic view of the esophagus near the opening to the stomach. The reddened areas are signs of damage caused by acid reflux.

and stomach include black, tarry bowel movements and iron deficiency anemia. In severe cases, the loss of blood from a bleeding ulcer can be deadly.

People who suffer from GERD have a higher risk of esophageal cancer than people who don't have a history of this condition. If you or someone you know suffers from GERD, typical dietary advice for treating the condition includes consuming smaller, more frequent meals that are low in fat; not overeating at mealtimes; and limiting intake of foods that relax the gastroesophageal sphincter, such as chili powder, onions, garlic, mint, peppermint, caffeine, alcohol, and chocolate. Additionally, you should wait about two hours after meals before lying down, because remaining upright reduces the likelihood that stomach contents will push against the gastroesophageal sphincter and force their way back up into your esophagus. Table 4.A lists these and other recommendations for reducing the risk of heartburn and managing GERD. Taking over-the-counter antacids can neutralize excess stomach acid and relieve the discomfort of heartburn within minutes, but these products don't prevent heartburn.[4A] People suffering from GERD can take other medications that inhibit stomach acid production, preventing heartburn.

Peptic Ulcer

A peptic ulcer is a sore that occurs in the lining of the stomach or the upper small intestine. The typical symptoms of a peptic ulcer are deep, dull upper abdominal pain and a feeling of fullness that occur about two hours after eating. The pain results when most of the chyme has left the stomach, and the HCl acid that remains comes in contact with and digests the lining of the organ, forming one or more sores. It's not unusual for the sores to damage the wall of a blood vessel, causing bleeding; thus, untreated gastrointestinal ulcers may result in iron-deficiency anemia. Furthermore, an ulcer may erode through the stomach or intestinal wall and allow GI contents to leak into the body cavities, resulting in a potentially life-threatening infection. Therefore, it's important to recognize ulcer symptoms and obtain treatment early.

Physicians detect peptic ulcers by performing a clinical examination called upper endoscopy.[5A] The first step of this procedure involves administering a medication that relaxes the patient. Then the physician inserts a special flexible scope into the mouth, down the esophagus, and into the stomach and upper small intestine. The scope is equipped with a video camera that transmits images of the lining of the esophagus, stomach, and upper small intestine to a screen that the physician views for the presence of ulcers, eroded areas, or cancerous tumours. The scope also enables the physician to use tools to treat areas of bleeding or remove pieces of tissue (biopsy) for microscopic examination.

At one time, medical experts thought excessive emotional stress caused peptic ulcers. By the 1990s, however, researchers determined that *Helicobacter pylori (H. pylori)*, a type of bacteria that can live in parts of the stomach, was responsible for the development of most stomach ulcers (see Fig. 2.1 on page 30). *H. pylori* infection makes the lining of the stomach more susceptible to being damaged by stomach acid. In addition to being infected with *H. pylori*, other factors are associated with the development of peptic ulcers, particularly smoking cigarettes, heavy consumption of alcohol, and use of NSAIDs (nonsteroidal anti-inflammatory drugs) such as aspirin, ibuprofen, and naproxen. Table 4.B lists these and other factors that increase a person's risk of peptic ulcers. Note that stress is still considered a risk factor for ulcer formation. People who have difficulty coping with excess emotional stress are more likely to develop peptic ulcers when compared to people who manage their stress better. Having good stress management skills may explain why some people who are infected with *H. pylori* do not develop these ulcers.

Today, a combination of medical approaches is used for ulcer therapy. People infected with *H. pylori* are given antibiotics as well as medications that reduce stomach acid production. This treatment is highly effective for combating *H. pylori* infections and healing peptic ulcers.

Current dietary approaches to treatment simply recommend avoiding foods that increase ulcer symptoms; often such foods vary individually. For example, a man who has a history of peptic ulcer may find peppery foods irritating to his stomach, while his friend who is being treated for an ulcer may be able to tolerate the same foods. Today, the combination of medical treatment and lifestyle changes has minimized the need for peptic ulcer patients to make drastic dietary changes.

Irritable Bowel Syndrome (IBS)

An estimated 10 to 30% of adult Canadians suffer from irritable bowel syndrome (IBS), a condition characterized by intestinal cramps and abnormal bowel function, particularly diarrhea, constipation, or alternating episodes of both. Loose stools are often accompanied with mucus, and after bowel movements, the affected person feels as though elimination of stools was incomplete. For

TABLE 4.A

Recommendations to Reduce the Risk of Heartburn

1. If you have too much body fat, lose the excess weight.
2. Don't lie down within two hours after eating a meal.
3. Don't overeat at mealtimes.
4. Avoid smoking cigarettes.
5. Elevate the head of your bed 15 cm (6 in.) higher than the foot of the bed.
6. Don't wear tight belts or clothes with tight waistbands.
7. Learn to recognize foods that cause heartburn.
8. Don't consume foods proven to relax the gastroesophageal sphincter.

TABLE 4.B

Factors that Increase the Risk of Peptic Ulcers

Factors
Infection with *H. pylori*
NSAIDs
Alcohol consumption
Genetics
Smoking
Emotional stress
Excess acid production

reasons that are unknown, women are more likely than men to suffer from IBS.[6A,7A]

The cause of IBS is unknown, but many sufferers report a history of anxiety as well as verbal, physical, or sexual abuse. The intestinal tract muscles of people with IBS produce stronger contractions that last longer than the GI muscles of people who do not have this condition.[8A] Researchers are investigating the role of the nervous system in stimulating these abnormal intestinal tract movements.

Therapy is individualized and may include elimination diets that focus on determining which foods are most likely to contribute to IBS symptoms. Foods often eliminated include dairy products, legumes, and certain vegetables, especially cabbage and broccoli. Some fruits, particularly grapes, raisins, cherries, and cantaloupe, may also need to be eliminated from the diet. Treatment often includes learning stress management strategies, obtaining psychological counselling, and taking certain antidepressant and other medications. Although irritable bowel syndrome can be uncomfortable and upsetting, it does not appear to increase the risk of intestinal cancer or other serious digestive problems.[8A]

References for Chapter 4 Highlight

1A. American Gastroenterological Association (AGA): *Constipation*. 2005. www.gastro.org/wmspage.cfm?parml=687. Accessed: August 20, 2005.

2A. Widmaier E and others: *Vander's human physiology*. 10th ed. Boston: McGraw-Hill Publishing Company, 2006.

3A. Cleveland Clinic Information Center: *About nausea and vomiting*. 2004. www.clevelandclinic.org/health/health-info/docs/1800/1810.asp?index=8106. Accessed: September 3, 2005.

4A. AGA: *Heartburn*. www.gastro.org/wmspage.cfm?parm1=848. Accessed: September 4, 2005.

5A. American Society for Gastrointestinal Endoscopy: *Understanding upper endoscopy*. 2004. www.askasge.org/pages/brochures/upper.cfm. Accessed: August 23, 2005.

6A. Irritable Bowel Syndrome Self-help and Support Group. www.ibsgroup.org. Accessed: September 1, 2005.

7A. Canadian Society of Intestinal Research: *Irritable Bowel Syndrome*. www.badgut.com/index.php?contentFile=ibs&title=Irritable%20Bowel%20Syndrome. Accessed: June 4, 2010.

8A. Mayo Clinic.com: Irritable bowel syndrome. 2005. www.mayoclinic.com/invoke.cfm?id=DS00106&. Accessed: September 1, 2005.

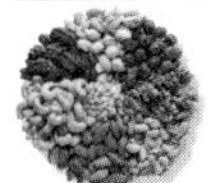

SUMMARY

Matter is composed of chemicals. More than 100 different types of atoms exist, and each type is an element. Atoms of elements may react with each other to form chemical bonds that hold the atoms together in a new arrangement called a molecule. Molecules that contain two or more different elements are called compounds. A solution is an evenly distributed mixture of two compounds. In living things, water is the solvent, the primary compound of a solution.

Ions, acids, and bases play important physiological roles in the body. An ion is an atom or group of atoms that has a positive or negative electrical charge. Electrolytes are ions that can conduct electricity. An acid is a molecule that donates hydrogen ions (H^+); a base is a molecule that accepts H^+. Chemists use the pH scale to describe the H^+ concentration of a watery solution.

Most molecules undergo chemical reactions that change their arrangement of atoms, forming new molecules or compounds. When elements or compounds combine to form new substances, a synthetic reaction has occurred. The new substances often have physical and chemical properties that are quite different than the reactants. Decomposition reactions, such as those occurring during digestion, involve the breaking down of molecules. Enzymes are proteins that facilitate or catalyze chemical reactions. Enzymes do not become part of the products of a reaction and, as a result, can catalyze many reactions.

Anatomy is the scientific study of cells and other body structures; physiology is the scientific study of how cells and body structures function. A cell is the smallest functioning structural unit in a living organism. Cells that have similar characteristics and functions are usually joined together into larger masses called tissues. An organ is composed of various tissues that function in a related fashion. An organ system is a group of organs that work together for a similar purpose.

The cardiovascular system involves the pumping action of the heart to circulate blood in blood vessels throughout the body. Arteries carry blood away from the heart; veins convey blood back to the heart. The thin walls of capillaries allow nutrients and oxygen to move out of the blood and into cells, and carbon dioxide and other waste products to pass from cells and into the blood.

The respiratory system enables the body to obtain oxygen and eliminate carbon dioxide. The lymphatic system helps maintain fluid balance, absorb certain nutrients, and defend the body against infectious disease. The urinary system filters and excretes unneeded substances from blood and maintains proper fluid balance.

The muscular and skeletal systems enable the body to move within its environment and provide support and protection for the body. The nervous system produces intellectual and emotional responses, and controls and regulates many body functions. The endocrine system produces hormones that convey information to target cells; hormones regulate a variety of physiological activities. Hair, nails, and skin are structures of the integumentary system. Skin protects against minor injuries and infectious disease-causing agents, and helps maintain body temperature. The main function of the reproductive organs is to produce children.

To be healthy, all organ systems must work together in a coordinated manner to maintain homeostasis. When homeostasis is disrupted, the body uses various mechanisms to regain its normal internal status, but sickness and even death can result if the abnormality persists.

Your cells do not need food to carry out their metabolic activities—they need nutrients that are in food. The primary roles of the digestive system are the breakdown of large food molecules into smaller components (nutrients) and the absorption of nutrients into the bloodstream.

Digestion is a mechanical and chemical process that breaks down large food components into nutrients that can be absorbed. The mechanical aspects of digestion include the chewing action of teeth as well as involuntary muscular activity, including peristalsis. Chemical digestion includes the actions of enzymes and substances such as hydrochloric acid and bile.

Digestion begins in the mouth with the mechanical action of teeth and some minor chemical action of salivary amylase and lipase. The esophagus conveys food from the mouth to the stomach, where it mixes with gastric juice and is referred to as chyme. The chyme moves from the stomach to the duodenum of the small intestine. In the small intestine, enzymes that are primarily from the pancreas complete the process of digestion. In the small intestine, cells of villi absorb the end products of digestion and transfer them to blood or lymph. Any remaining undigested material, some water, and intestinal bacteria eventually exit the body as feces.

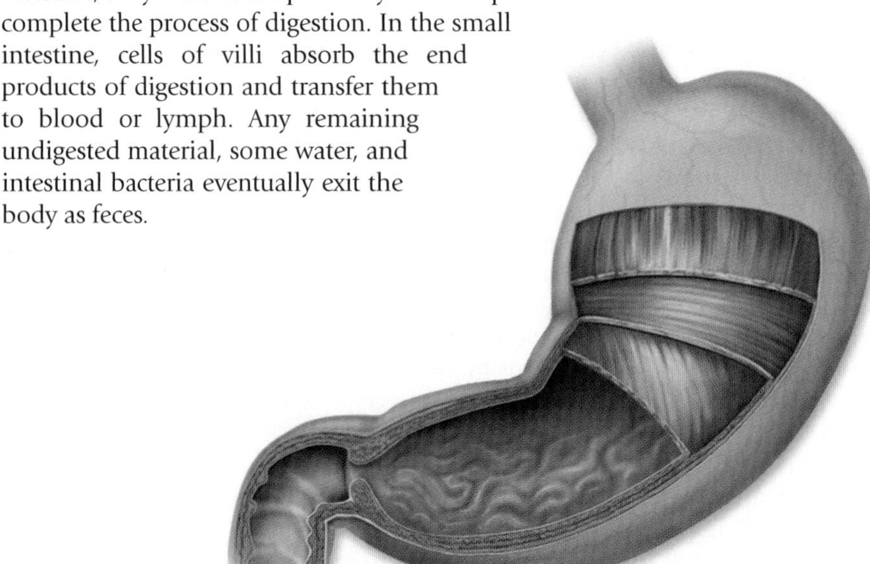

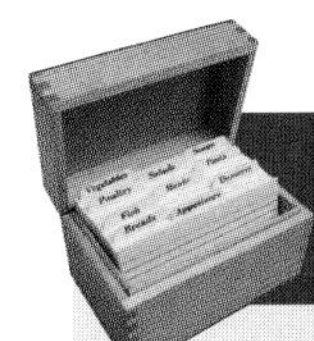

Recipes for Healthy Living

Chopped Chicken Liver Pâté

At some point, you may have sampled calves, beef, or pork liver and decided it would never become one of your favourite foods. You might change your mind when you learn that liver is an excellent source of several vitamins and minerals.

This following recipe for pâté (*pah-tay'*) uses chicken livers, because they are more mild-tasting than beef or other commonly eaten types of liver. Adding onions, hard-cooked eggs, and a sauce made from chili peppers to the liver makes a flavourful and nutritious spread for crackers. Although liver is very nutritious, the organ produces cholesterol and contains high amounts of this lipid. If you are concerned about consuming too much cholesterol, but you still want to try this recipe, eat small amounts of the pâté as a snack or appetizer.

This recipe makes approximately 8 servings. Each serving supplies 150 kcal, 11 g protein, 11 g fat, 250 g cholesterol, 1892 RAE vitamin A, 11 mg vitamin C, 5.5 mg niacin (a B vitamin), 341 mcg folate (a B vitamin), 223 mg sodium, 5.3 mg iron, and 1.6 mg zinc.

INGREDIENTS:

454 g (1 lb.) raw chicken livers
45 mL (3 Tbsp) vegetable oil
125 mL (½ cup) sweet onion, peeled and coarsely chopped
30 mL (2 Tbsp) low-fat mayonnaise
2 hard-cooked eggs,* peeled
2–3 mL (½ tsp) salt
1 mL (¼ tsp) ground black pepper
3 to 5 drops commercially prepared hot pepper sauce (optional)

*** To hard-cook eggs:**

1. Place the eggs in a small saucepan and cover the eggs completely with about 5 cm (2 in.) of water.
2. Heat the saucepan containing the water and eggs to a boil, then cover the saucepan with its lid, and remove it from the heat.
3. Allow the eggs to remain in the hot water for approximately 20 to 25 minutes (large eggs).
4. Remove eggs from the saucepan and cool by immersing in cold water.
5. Prepare a hard-cooked egg for peeling by tapping it on a countertop, cracking the shell as completely as possible.
6. If the shell sticks to the egg white, run cold water over the egg as you peel it. Discard the shells in the garbage.

PREPARATION STEPS:

1. Rinse chicken livers in cool water and drain on paper towels. Cut each liver into thirds.
2. Place oil in a large frying pan and heat at a medium-high temperature for about 45 seconds. Add chopped onion and gently cook in oil (sauté) until translucent.
3. Add liver to the onion mixture. Reduce the heat to medium-low temperature and cook slowly for 7 to 10 minutes, stirring until no pinkness remains within the liver.
4. Drain excess oil from cooked liver and onions, and transfer mixture to the top of a large cutting board.
5. Add peeled eggs. Using a knife, chop the mixture until its texture is coarse. Add salad dressing and seasonings. Mix with a spoon until ingredients are well blended. If you have a food processor or blender, just add the ingredients into the bowl of the machine and blend.
6. Place in a bowl, cover, and refrigerate for several hours.
7. Serve as a spread on whole-grain crackers.

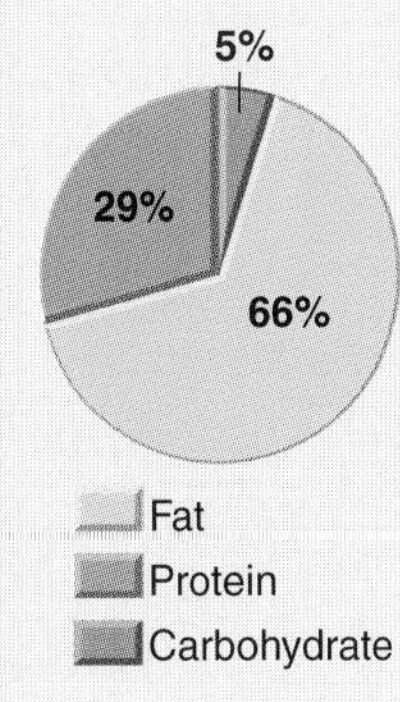

Egg Salad

Like liver, eggs are a nutrient-dense food. Egg salad is an easy-to-make meal or snack. This recipe makes about three ⅓ cup servings. Each serving supplies approximately 131 kcal, 8.5 g protein, 9 g fat, 280 mg cholesterol, 125 mg sodium, and 0.8 mg iron.

INGREDIENTS:

30 mL (2 Tbsp) peeled, finely chopped yellow onion
4 hard-cooked large eggs
30 mL (2 Tbsp) low-fat mayonnaise
5 mL (1 tsp) pickle relish
dash of black pepper

PREPARATION STEPS:

1. Place chopped onion in small mixing bowl.
2. Peel hard-cooked eggs and discard peels. Chop eggs on a cutting board.
3. Add chopped eggs to onions.
4. Add low-fat mayonnaise and pickle relish to the egg and onion mixture. Blend together. Mixture should be moist.
5. Wash a few lettuce leaves. Shake excess water from lettuce and dry by patting with clean paper towels. Arrange lettuce leaves on a plate.
6. Spoon egg salad on lettuce. Serve as a spread on whole-wheat crackers or on rye bread.
7. Egg salad is perishable, so cover any leftover salad and store in the refrigerator for no longer than a day.

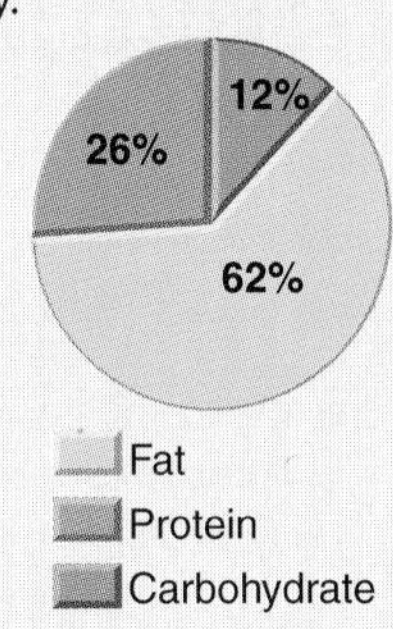

CRITICAL THINKING

1. If you stain your clothes with blueberry juice, what can you do to remove the stain? Explain your answer.
2. Why would a person's stomach feel uncomfortably full several hours after eating a bacon-topped double cheeseburger, large serving of French fries, and a milkshake?
3. Explain why the label for a multivitamin supplement recommends taking the pill with meals, particularly meals that contain some fat.
4. Taylor had a serious condition that required removal of most of his ileum. Based on this information, is Taylor at risk for developing multiple nutrient deficiencies? Explain why or why not.
5. Your mother complains of having persistent heartburn, but she doesn't think her discomfort is serious enough to be investigated by her physician. Do you agree or disagree with her attitude about heartburn? Explain your position.

PRACTICE TEST

Select the best answer.

1. Which of the following substances is insoluble in water?
   a. fat
   b. sugar
   c. calcium
   d. sodium
2. Which of the following substances has the lowest pH?
   a. plain coffee
   b. household ammonia
   c. plain water
   d. gastric juice

3. Cells are joined together into larger masses called
   a. organs.
   b. tissues.
   c. cytoplasms.
   d. systems.

4. Which of the following organs is an accessory organ of the digestive system?
   a. heart
   b. kidney
   c. liver
   d. bladder
5. Which of the following statements is false?
   a. Arteries carry blood away from the heart.
   b. Hemoglobin carries most of the oxygen in the blood.
   c. Cells need oxygen to obtain energy.
   d. All arteries carry deoxygenated blood.

Answers to Chapter 4 Quiz Yourself

1. The atom is the smallest living unit in the body. **False.** (p. 91)
2. The stomach produces hydrochloric acid. **True.** (p. 99)
3. Taste buds can be found in the lining of your mouth. **True.** (p. 97)
4. The human intestinal tract cannot digest certain combinations of foods, such as mixtures of simple carbohydrates and proteins. **False.** (p. 103)
5. Undigested food rots in your stomach, causing toxic materials to build up in your tissues. **False.** (p. 103)

6. Mechanical digestion begins in the
   a. mouth.
   b. stomach.
   c. small intestine.
   d. liver.
7. Two or more atoms that are held together by a chemical bond form a
   a. pH.
   b. molecule.
   c. proton.
   d. nucleus.
8. A salt forms when an ______ combines with a ______ .
   a. electrolyte; proton
   b. acid; base
   c. element; pH
   d. enzyme; mineral
9. Chemical messengers in the body are
   a. enzymes.
   b. cells.
   c. capillaries.
   d. hormones.
10. Tiny fingerlike projections of the small intestine that absorb nutrients are called
    a. lumen.
    b. villi.
    c. duodenum.
    d. calculi.
11. A lacteal is a
    a. lymph vessel within each villus.
    b. form of carbohydrate in milk.
    c. muscular structure that regulates digestion in the large intestine.
    d. none of the above
12. A ______ is a type of lipoprotein.
    a. sodium acetate
    b. cholecystokinin
    c. gastrin
    d. chylomicron
13. The stomach secretes
    a. salivary amylase.
    b. hydrochloric acid.
    c. bile.
    d. all of the above
14. Peristalsis
    a. is a common intestinal infection.
    b. interferes with lipid absorption in the small intestine.
    c. stimulates red blood cell formation in bone marrow.
    d. none of the above
15. Starch digestion begins in the
    a. gastric pouch.
    b. esophagus.
    c. mouth.
    d. gallbladder.

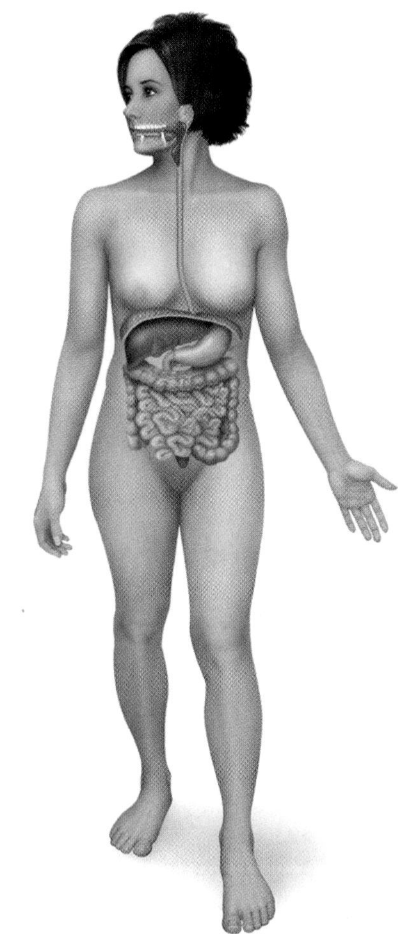

Please visit Connect at

www.mcgrawhillconnect.ca

Chapter **5**

Carbohydrates

Chapter Learning Outcomes

After reading Chapter 5, you should be able to:

1. Identify the major carbohydrates in human diets and their major food sources.
2. Recognize chemical and common names of nutritive sweeteners and identify common alternative sweeteners.
3. List the functions of carbohydrate in the body and the roles of carbohydrates in health.
4. Describe how the body digests carbohydrates and regulates blood glucose.
5. Discuss differences between type 1 and type 2 diabetes and list common signs and symptoms of each disorder.
6. Identify risk factors for type 2 diabetes and measures that may prevent this disease.
7. Explain the health benefits of soluble and insoluble fibre and identify rich food sources of these types of fibre.
8. Define lactose intolerance, explain why the condition occurs, and discuss dietary measures that will reduce signs and symptoms of the disorder.

When you are bored, excited, or in a good or bad mood, do you reach for something sweet to eat? Can you imagine celebrating birthdays, weddings, or holidays without cakes, candies, or cookies? If you are like many Canadians, you enjoy eating sweets and may even describe yourself as having a sweet tooth.

Why do humans, even newborn infants, prefer foods that taste sweet? The pleasant and sometimes irresistible taste of sugar is a clue that the food contains **carbohydrates**, a major source of energy for cells. Without a steady supply of energy, cells cannot function and they die. Plants are rich sources of carbohydrates; they make these substances by using the sun's energy to combine carbon, oxygen, and hydrogen atoms from carbon dioxide and water (Fig. 5.1). Some of the energy from the sun is stored in the bonds that hold the carbon and hydrogen atoms together. Our cells can break down some of those bonds, releasing energy that powers various forms of cellular work, including the energy to contract muscles, make vital compounds, and build bones.

Whether your goals include becoming a computer programmer, health care professional, or world class athlete, carbohydrates play an important role in your health. In Chapter 5, you will learn about the major roles of carbohydrates in the body. Additionally, you will learn which foods are rich sources of carbohydrates, including simple sugars and complex carbohydrates.

Quiz YOURSELF

Do "carbs" cause diabetes or unwanted weight gain? Would sweetening your cereal with honey be a healthier choice than using table sugar? Should you choose foods according to their *glycemic index*? Check your knowledge of carbohydrates by taking the following quiz. The answers are found on page 145.

1. Compared to table sugar, honey is a natural and far more nutritious sweetener. _____T_____F
2. Ounce per ounce, sugar provides more energy than starch. _____T_____F
3. Eating a high-fibre diet can improve the functioning of your large intestine and reduce your blood cholesterol levels. _____T_____F
4. The average Canadian consumes 40 to 50% of his or her energy intake as refined sugars. _____T_____F
5. The results of clinical studies indicate that eating too much sugar makes children hyperactive. _____T_____F

carbohydrates class of nutrients that is a major source of energy for the body

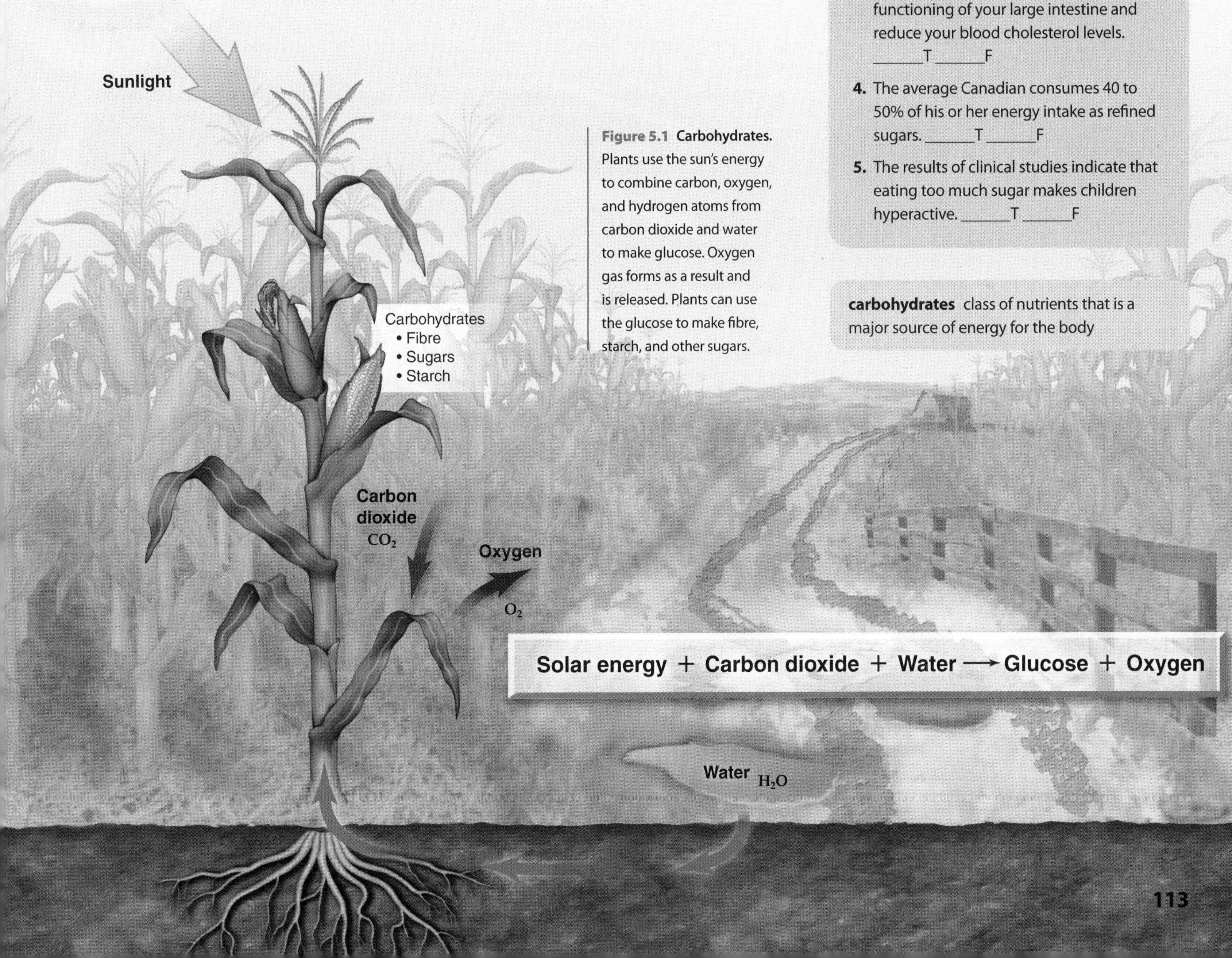

Figure 5.1 Carbohydrates. Plants use the sun's energy to combine carbon, oxygen, and hydrogen atoms from carbon dioxide and water to make glucose. Oxygen gas forms as a result and is released. Plants can use the glucose to make fibre, starch, and other sugars.

monosaccharide simple sugar that is the basic molecule of carbohydrates

disaccharide simple sugar comprised of two monosaccharides

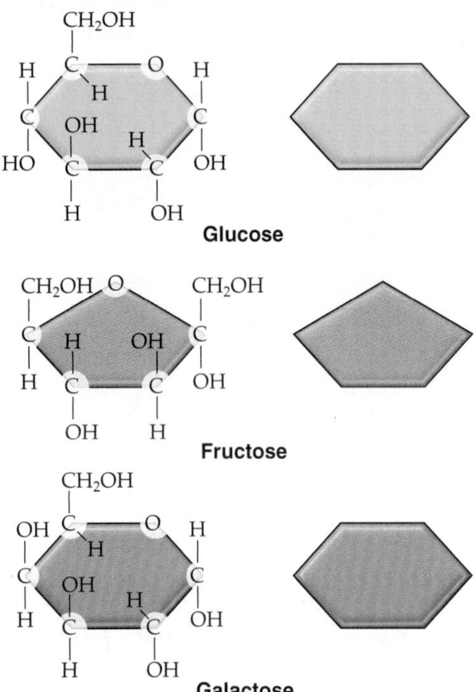

Figure 5.2 Monosaccharides. These chemical symbols for glucose, fructose, and galactose indicate the number and arrangement of carbon, hydrogen, and oxygen atoms. For simplicity, we will omit the atoms and just show the colour symbol for each monosaccharide.

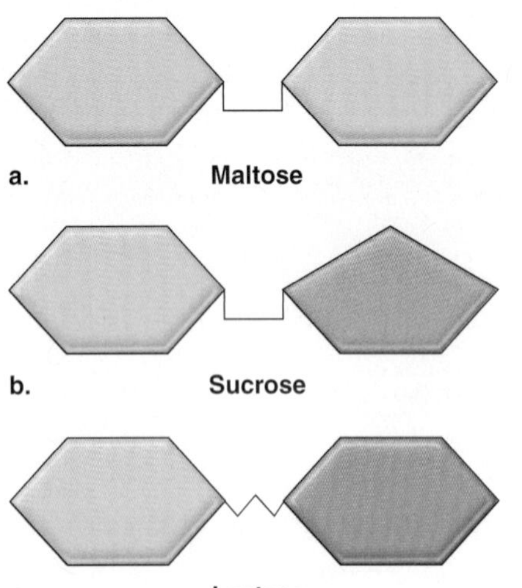

Figure 5.3 Disaccharides. Disaccharides include maltose, sucrose, and lactose. (a) Maltose consists of two glucose molecules. (b) Sucrose consists of a glucose and a fructose molecule. (c) Lactose consists of a galactose and a glucose molecule.

Simple Carbohydrates: Sugars

You probably are familiar with sugar as the sweet, white, granulated crystals often sprinkled on cereal or into iced tea, but table sugar is only one type of sugar. You may be unaware that there are different types of sugars in milk, blood, and DNA, the genetic material in cells. The simplest type of sugar, the **monosaccharide** (*mono* = one; *saccharide* = sugar), is the basic chemical unit of carbohydrates. A **disaccharide** (*di* = two) is a sugar comprised of two monosaccharides. By combining monosaccharides, plants and animals can form more complex carbohydrates.

Monosaccharides

The three most important dietary monosaccharides are glucose, fructose, and galactose. Figure 5.2 shows the chemical structures of glucose, fructose, and galactose as well as the geometric symbols used to represent them in this textbook. The chemical names of carbohydrates, particularly sugars, end in *ose*. Gluc*ose*, fruct*ose*, and sucr*ose* are sugars commonly found in foods.

Fruits and vegetables, especially berries, grapes, corn, and carrots, are good food sources of **glucose**. Glucose is the most important monosaccharide in the human body because it is a primary fuel for muscle and other cells. In fact, red blood cells and nervous system cells, including brain cells, must use glucose for energy under normal conditions. Thus, a healthy body maintains its *blood glucose* levels carefully. Glucose in the blood may be referred to as blood sugar.

Fructose is naturally found in fruit, honey, and a few vegetables, particularly cabbage, green beans, and asparagus. Because fructose tastes much sweeter than glucose and is easily made from corn, food manufacturers use large amounts of high-fructose corn syrup (HFCS) as a food additive to satisfy Canadians' demand for "regular" soft drinks, candies, and baked goods. The body has little need for fructose; therefore, most fructose is converted into glucose or fat.

Unlike glucose and fructose, **galactose** is not commonly found in foods. Galactose is a component of lactose, the form of carbohydrate in milk. After a woman gives birth, special glands in her breasts convert glucose into galactose, which is necessary for production of lactose in breast milk.

Disaccharides

Disaccharides include maltose, sucrose, and lactose. **Maltose** (malt sugar) has two glucose molecules bonded together (Fig. 5.3a). Few foods naturally contain maltose. **Sucrose** (table sugar) consists of a molecule of glucose and one of fructose (Fig. 5.3b). **Lactose** (milk sugar) forms when a galactose molecule bonds to a glucose molecule (Fig. 5.3c). Although most animal foods are not sources of carbohydrate, milk and some products made from milk, such as yogourt and ice cream, contain lactose.

Sucrose

Although sucrose occurs naturally in honey, maple syrup, carrots, and pineapples, much of the sucrose in the Canadian diet is refined from sugar cane and sugar beets. The refining process strips away the small amounts of vitamins and minerals in sugar cane and sugar beets. "Raw sugar," turbinado sugar, and some forms of brown sugar are not as fully processed from sugar cane as white sugar. These sweeteners contain a small amount of molasses, which contributes to their flavour, colour, and nutritional value. Because refined sucrose has the reputation of being a "junk food," some manufacturers use creative names, such as "granulated cane juice," to disguise the presence of table sugar in their product's ingredient list.

TABLE 5.1 *Nutritional Comparison of Selected Sweeteners*

Sugar/Syrup 15 mL (1 Tbsp)	Water %	Kcal	Protein g	Carb g	Vit. C mg	Calcium mg	Folate mcg	Potassium mg	Iron mg	Zinc mg
Honey	17	64	0	17	0.1	1	0	11	0.09	0.05
Raw sugar	2	46	0	12	0	10	0.125	42	0.23	0.03
Brown sugar	<1	36	0	9	0	8	0	33	0.18	0.02
White granulated sugar	0	48	0	13	0	0	0	0	0	0

Some people claim that refined white sugar is poisonous and honey is nutritionally superior to table sugar. However, these claims are not true. Table sugar does not contain toxic substances; in fact, it is almost 100% carbohydrate. Table 5.1 compares the nutritional value of honey with certain forms of sucrose. Note that none of the sweeteners is a good source of protein, vitamins, or minerals. The simple sugars in honey are not superior to those that comprise sucrose, and your body does not distinguish whether glucose or fructose came from sugar or honey.

A tablespoon of white table sugar is almost 100% sucrose; a tablespoon of honey has glucose, fructose, water, and a small amount of sucrose. A tablespoon of honey contains more protein and micronutrients than a tablespoon of white sugar, but the amounts are insignificant. For example, you would have to eat a cup of honey to obtain 1 g of protein, 2 mg of vitamin C, and 1.4 mg of iron. That amount of honey supplies over 1000 kcal! Although honey contains phytochemicals, substances in plant foods that may provide health benefits, the amounts are too small to make the sticky sweetener a valuable source of these compounds.

glucose monosaccharide that is a primary fuel for muscles and other cells; also referred to as blood sugar

fructose monosaccharide in fruits, honey, and certain vegetables

galactose monosaccharide that is a component of lactose

maltose disaccharide comprised of two glucose molecules; also referred to as malt sugar

sucrose disaccharide comprised of a glucose and a fructose molecule; also referred to as table sugar

lactose disaccharide comprised of a glucose and a galactose molecule; also referred to as milk sugar

tip

Honey can contain spores, the inactive life stage, of the deadly bacterium *Clostridium botulinum* that resist being destroyed by food preservation methods.[1,2] These spores can become active within an infant's intestinal tract and produce a poison that is extremely toxic to nerves. According to experts at Health Canada, honey should not be fed to children younger than 12 months of age or used to sweeten infant foods because it may cause botulism poisoning.[2] Older children and adults can eat honey without being concerned about botulism, because the mature stomach produces enough acid to destroy the bacterial spores.

Did You Know?

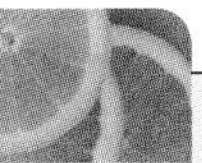

Bees make honey by consuming the sucrose-rich nectar from flowers and digesting most of it into glucose and fructose. The bees regurgitate this material within the beehive, and eventually it's collected by beekeepers for human processing and packaging.

Honey and table sugar have similar nutritional value.

TABLE 5.2 *Names for Sugars*

Sugars Can Be:		
brown sugar	fruit juice concentrate or concentrated fruit juice sweetener	maple syrup
confectioner's or powdered sugar	glucose	molasses
corn sweeteners	granulated cane juice	polydextrose
corn syrup or cultured corn syrup	honey	raw sugar
date sugar	invert sugar	sorbitol*
dextrose	lactose	mannitol*
evaporated cane juice	maltose	xylitol*
fructose (levulose), high-fructose corn syrup (HFCS), or syrup	maltodextrin	table sugar (sucrose)
		turbinado sugar

* Alcohol forms of sugars

Nutritive and Nonnutritive Sweeteners

nutritive sweetener sweetener that contributes energy to foods

added sugars sugars and syrups added to foods during processing or preparation

Sugars, especially sucrose and HFCS, which is chemically similar to sucrose, are widely added to processed foods. In baked cereal products, sugars contribute to the browning and tenderness of the food. Sugar also serves as a preservative, inhibiting the growth of moulds and bacteria that would otherwise cause food spoilage. Additionally, a **nutritive sweetener** contributes energy to foods. Each gram of a mono- or disaccharide supplies 4 kcal. If one of the nutritive sweeteners listed in Table 5.2 is the first or second ingredient listed on a product's label, the food contains a high amount of added sugar. Table 5.3 indicates the amount of added sugars that are in commonly consumed foods and beverages. **Added sugars** are sugars and syrups that are added to foods during processing or preparation. The following section provides information about other kinds of sweeteners.

Alternative Sweeteners

Many people consume artificially sweetened foods and beverages because they want to enjoy the sweet taste of the products while controlling their intake of energy from refined

TABLE 5.3 *How Much Added Sugar Is in that Food?*

Food	Serving Size	Kcal	Approximate Teaspoons Added Sugars
Doughnut, cake, plain	8¼-cm (3¼-in.) diameter	226	2
Chocolate chip cookies, commercial brand	2 medium (50 g)	239	4
Sugar-frosted cornflakes	187 mL (¾ cup)	114	3
Chocolate-flavoured 2% milk	250 mL (1 cup)	158	3
Ice cream, vanilla, light, soft-serve	125 mL (½ cup)	111	2
Chocolate bar with almonds	50 g (1.76 oz.)	235	5
Apple pie, double crust	⅙ of 20¼-cm (8-in.) diameter pie	277	4
Snack sponge cake with cream filling	1 cake (43 g)	157	4
Yogourt, vanilla, low-fat	240 mL (<1 cup)	193	4
Cola, canned	355 mL (12 oz.)	136	8
Fruit punch drink	355 mL (12 oz.)	175	10
Chocolate milkshake, fast food	475 mL (16 oz.)	580	10

Source of data: Krebs-Smith SM: Choose beverages and foods to moderate your intake of sugars: Measurement requires quantification. *Journal of Nutrition* 131:527S, 2006.

TABLE 5.4 *Comparing Artificial Sweeteners*

Sweetener	Comparison to Sugar	Brand Name	Kilocalories/tsp
Aspartame	200 times sweeter	NutraSweet, Equal	Nearly 0
Saccharin	200 to 700 times sweeter	Sweet'N Low, Sweet Twin, Necta Sweet	0
Acesulfame-K	200 times sweeter	Sunett, Sweet One	0
Neotame	7,000 to 13,000 times sweeter	Neotame	0
Sucralose	600 times sweeter	Splenda	0

Source: Artificial sweeteners: No calories…sweet! *FDA Consumer Magazine*. 2006. www.fda.gov/fdac/features/2006/406_sweeteners.html

sugars. **Alternative sweeteners** (also referred to as sugar replacers, sugar substitutes, or artificial sweeteners) are substances added to food that sweeten the item while providing few or no kilocalories. Alternative nutritive sweeteners include the sugar alcohols sorbitol, xylitol, and mannitol. Unlike sugars, sugar alcohols do not promote dental decay.[3] Thus, these compounds are used to replace sucrose and other sugars in products such as sugar-free chewing gums, breath mints, and "dietetic" candies. Sugar alcohols are not fully absorbed by the intestinal tract, and as a result, they supply an average of 2 kcal/g. However, they may cause diarrhea when consumed in large amounts.

alternative sweeteners substances that sweeten foods while providing few or no kilocalories

nonnutritive sweeteners group of synthetic compounds that are intensely sweet tasting compared to sugar

Nonnutritive sweeteners are a group of synthetic compounds that elicit an intensely sweet taste when compared to the same amount of sugar (Table 5.4). Thus, a very small amount of a nonnutritive sweetener is needed to sweeten a food, and they supply no energy per serving. Nonnutritive sweeteners can help people control their energy intake and manage their body weight without increasing their appetite.[4] Consumers, however, need to recognize that most "sugar-free" foods are not calorie free. Unlike sugars, nonnutritive sweeteners do not contribute to dental decay. Health Canada has approved the use of the nonnutritive sweeteners aspartame, acesulfame-K, and sucralose as additives to sweeten foods.

In Canada, the safety of nonnutritive sweeteners has been under public and scientific scrutiny for decades. Although saccharin has been in use for over 100 years, its safety has also been questioned. Despite the concern, most of the scientific evidence indicates that saccharin is safe when consumed in typical amounts.

Aspartame, better known by its trade names NutraSweet or Equal, consists of phenylalanine and aspartic acid, two amino acids, the molecules that comprise proteins. Some people must avoid aspartame and certain protein-rich foods because they have phenylketonuria (PKU) (*fen´-nul-keet´-en-yur´-e-ah*), a rare inherited disorder that results in abnormal phenylalanine metabolism. If an infant with PKU is not treated with a special diet, phenylalanine and its metabolic by-products accumulate in the child's bloodstream and cause severe brain damage. To alert people with PKU about the presence of aspartame in foods, Health Canada requires manufacturers of products containing the nonnutritive sweetener to include a warning on the label grouped together with the ingredient list, warning that aspartame contains phenylalanine (Fig. 5.4).[5] The Real People, Real Stories feature in Chapter 7 is about a young person who has PKU.

Since its approval for use as a food additive in 1981, aspartame has been blamed for causing a variety of health problems including cancer, certain immune system diseases, and chronic headaches. Despite claims to the contrary, no scientifically reliable studies have linked aspartame to any health disorder.[5] In 2006, results of a European study involving rats concluded aspartame increased the risk of cancer in the animals.[6] The European Food Safety Authority challenged the findings of this study when the Authority determined the conclusions were not supported by the data. According to Health Canada, the safety of aspartame has been studied extensively in laboratory animals, and no links to cancer have

Figure 5.4 Warning label for people with PKU. People with PKU need to be concerned about their phenylalanine intake. Artificially sweetened foods that contain aspartame carry this warning on the label because aspartame contains phenylalanine.

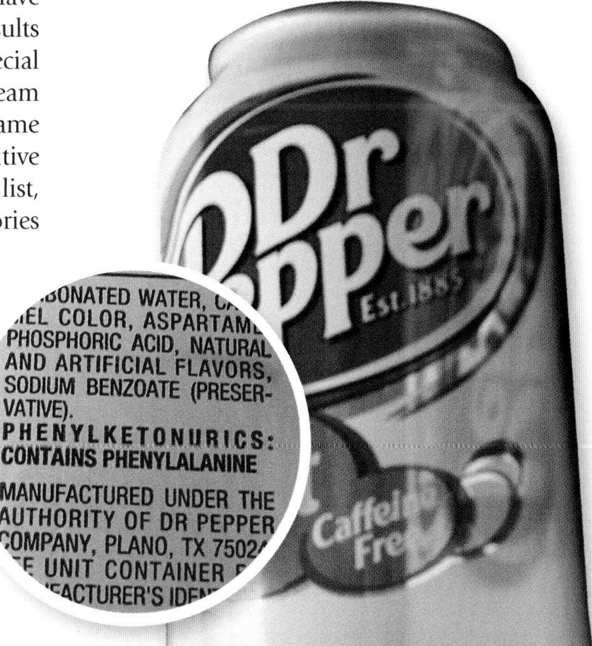

Did You Know?

Stevia is an herbal extract from a South American shrub (*Stevia rebaudiana* Bertoni) that is used to sweeten foods in Japan and South America. Although it can be sold as a dietary supplement in the United States, Health Canada has not approved its use or sale in Canada.

been found.[7] Health Canada, however, continues to review the data from the 2006 European study.

Sucralose, sold under the brand name Splenda, is made from a molecule of sucrose that has been chemically modified to escape digestion and absorption. As a result, sucralose sweetens foods and beverages without increasing their caloric value. Because the sweetener is not digested or absorbed by the intestinal tract, it is excreted in feces unchanged. During normal cooking and storage conditions, sucralose resists destruction by heat, a feature that makes it better for sweetening baked products than aspartame.

Do nonnutritive sweeteners pose a danger to health? According to Health Canada, these food additives are safe when consumed "within acceptable daily intakes, even during pregnancy."[8] Nevertheless, researchers continue to monitor the use of artificial sweeteners, particularly the newer ones, among the Canadian population because their long-term safety remains a public concern.

Concept Checkpoint

1. What is the major function of carbohydrate in the body?
2. Identify the three most important dietary monosaccharides.
3. What are the chemical names for blood sugar, table sugar, milk sugar, and malt sugar? Which monosaccharides comprise each molecule of maltose, lactose, and sucrose?
4. What is the difference between a nutritive sweetener and a nonnutritive sweetener?
5. Parents of a child with PKU can give their child either a beverage sweetened with sucralose or one containing aspartame. Which drink should they choose? Explain your answer.

Complex Carbohydrates

complex carbohydrates (polysaccharides) compounds comprised of ten or more monosaccharides bonded together

starch storage polysaccharide in plants

glycogen storage polysaccharide in animals

dietary fibre (fibre) indigestible plant material; most types are polysaccharides

soluble fibre forms of dietary fibre that dissolve or swell in water

insoluble fibre forms of dietary fibre that generally do not dissolve in water

Complex carbohydrates (polysaccharides) are comprised of ten or more monosaccharides bonded together. Plants and animals use complex carbohydrates to store energy or make certain structural components such as stems and leaves. The most common dietary polysaccharides consist of hundreds of glucose molecules and include digestible and indigestible forms.

Starch and Glycogen

Starch and **glycogen** (animal starch) are polysaccharides that contain hundreds of glucose molecules bound together into large chainlike structures (Fig. 5.5). Plants store glucose as starch, particularly in their seeds, roots, and in fleshy underground stems called tubers. Rich food sources of starch include bread and cereal products made from wheat, rice, barley, and oats; vegetables such as corn, squash, beans, and peas; and tubers such as potatoes, yams, taro, cassava, and jicama. Sports drinks and sports or energy bars often include modified starches such as maltodextrin, dextrin, and glucose polymers. Regardless of its source, each gram of starch supplies 4 kcal.

The human body stores limited amounts of glucose as glycogen (see Fig. 5.5b). Muscles and the liver are the major sites for glycogen formation and storage. Although muscles contain glycogen, most animal foods (for example, meat or the flesh of fish and poultry) are not sources of this complex carbohydrate, because muscle glycogen breaks down soon after an animal dies.

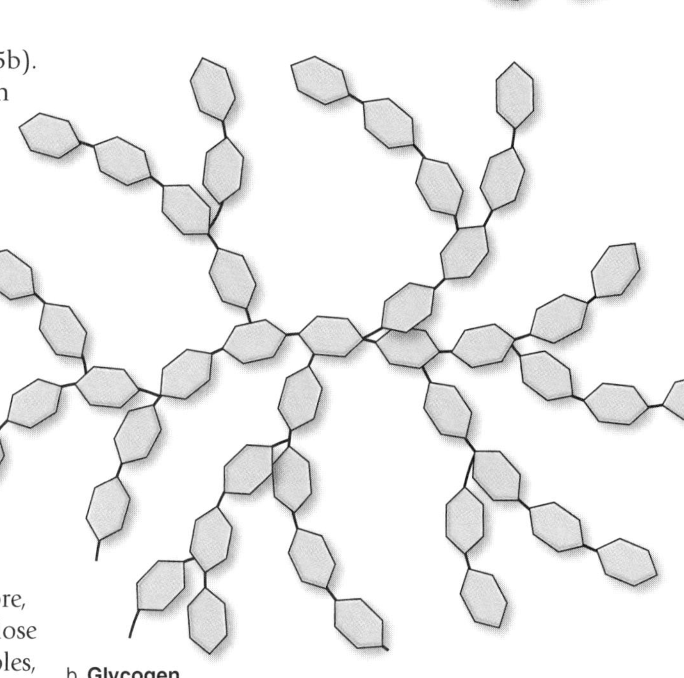

Figure 5.5 Starch (amylose) and glycogen. Polysaccharides, such as starch and glycogen, contain hundreds of glucose molecules bound together into large chainlike structures. Note that the chains of glycogen are more highly branched than those of starch.

Fibre

In addition to storing energy as starch, plants use complex carbohydrates to make supportive structures and protective seed coats that contribute to the fibre content of your diet. Most forms of **dietary fibre** are complex carbohydrates comprised of monosaccharides connected by bonds that humans cannot digest. Cellulose, hemicellulose, pectin, gums, and mucilages are carbohydrate forms of fibre; lignin is the only type of fibre that is not carbohydrate. Because fibre is not digested, it moves through the intestinal tract and contributes to the fecal residue that is eventually eliminated in bowel movements.

There are two types of dietary fibre, **soluble fibre** and **insoluble fibre**. Soluble fibre, such as pectins and gums, dissolve or swell in water. Insoluble fibre, such as cellulose and lignin, generally do not dissolve in water. Oat bran and oatmeal, beans, apples, carrots, oranges and other citrus fruits, and psyllium seeds are rich sources of soluble fibre; whole-grain products, including brown rice, contain high amounts of insoluble fibre. Whole grains are the intact, ground, cracked, or flaked seeds of cereal grains. Such grains may include wheat, buckwheat, oats, corn, rice, wild rice, rye, barley, bulgur, millet, and sorghum. If a "whole grain" product is made from ground, cracked, or flaked cereal grains, the forms must contain the starchy endosperm, oily germ, and fibre-rich bran seed components in the same relative proportions as they exist in the intact grain.[9] Figure 5.6 is an illustration of a whole grain, showing the endosperm, germ, and bran components.

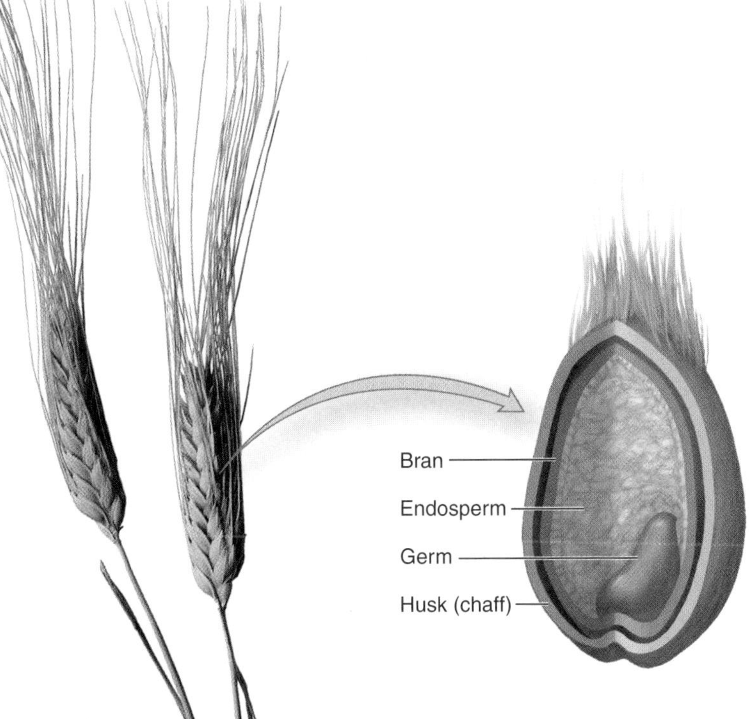

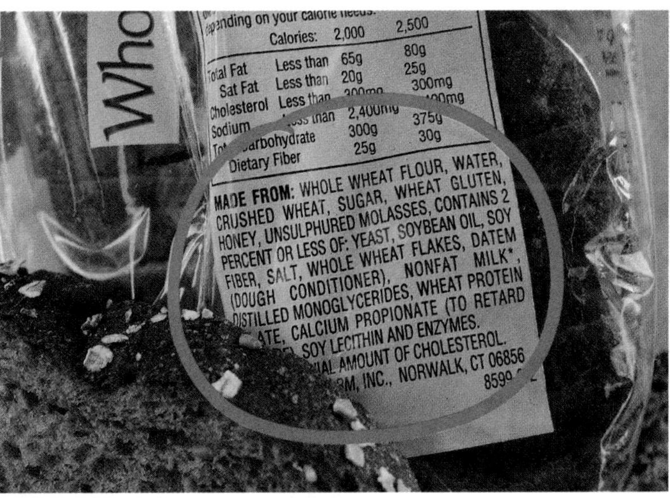

Figure 5.6 Whole grain. Whole grains are the intact, ground, cracked, or flaked seeds of cereal grains.

TABLE 5.5 *Classifying Fibre*

Type	Component(s)	Physiological Effects	Food Sources
Insoluble			
Carbohydrate	Cellulose, hemicelluloses	Increases fecal bulk and speeds fecal passage through GI tract	All plants Wheat, rye, brown rice, vegetables
Noncarbohydrate	Lignin	Increases fecal bulk, may ease bowel movements	Whole grains, wheat bran
Soluble			
Carbohydrate	Pectins, gums, mucilages, some hemicelluloses	Delays stomach emptying; slows glucose absorption; can lower blood cholesterol	Apples, bananas, citrus fruits, carrots, oats, barley, psyllium seeds, beans, and thickeners added to foods

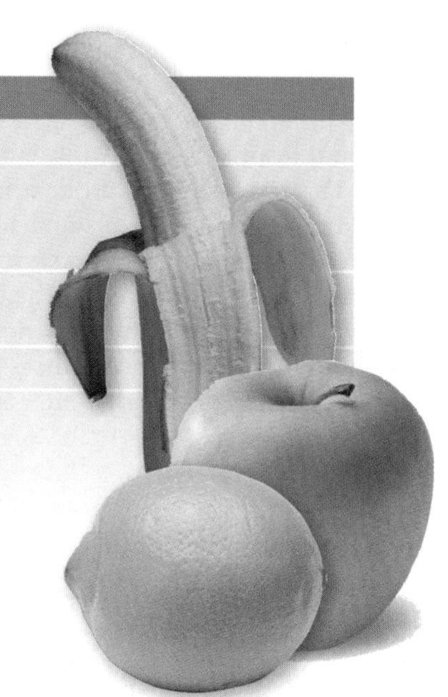

Table 5.5 provides information about the solubility of various types of fibre, the effects of fibre in the body, and major food sources of soluble and insoluble fibre. Although these foods are rich sources of either soluble or insoluble fibre, fruits, vegetables, whole-grain cereals, and other plant foods usually contain both forms (Fig. 5.7). Table 5.6 lists common foods that are sources of dietary fibre. Note that only plant foods provide fibre; animal flesh contains muscle fibres, which are digestible proteins. The "Carbohydrates and Health" section, later in this chapter, provides information about the benefits of adding more fibre to your diet and practical ways to increase your fibre intake.

Concept Checkpoint

6. What is starch? What is glycogen?
7. What is dietary fibre? Identify at least two food sources of soluble and insoluble fibre.

Figure 5.7 Sources of fibre. Most plant foods contain both soluble and insoluble fibre.

TABLE 5.6 *Dietary Fibre Content of Common Foods*

Food	Fibre (g)	Food	Fibre (g)
Kidney beans (250 mL/1 cup)	16.4	Beans, green snap (250 mL/1 cup)	4.0
Split peas, cooked (250 mL/1 cup)	16.3	Banana (250 mL/1 cup)	3.9
Black beans, cooked (250 mL/1 cup)	15.0	Strawberries, raw (250 mL/1 cup)	3.3
Dates, dried (250 mL/1 cup)	14.2	Apple, with skin (approx. 140 g/5 oz.)	3.3
Chickpeas, cooked (250 mL/1 cup)	12.5	Almonds (24 almonds)	3.3
Baked beans, canned (250 mL/1 cup)	10.4	Orange, raw (1 orange)	3.1
Kellogg's All-Bran cereal (125 mL/½ cup)	8.8	Carrots, raw (250 mL/1 cup)	3.1
Frozen peas, cooked (250 mL/1 cup)	8.8	Prunes, dried uncooked (5 prunes)	3.0
Raspberries, raw (250 mL/1 cup)	8.0	Barley, cooked (125 mL/½ cup)	3.0
Blackberries (250 mL/1 cup)	7.6	Whole-grain bread (1 slice)	1.7
Kellogg's Raisin Bran (250 mL/1 cup)	7.3	Romaine lettuce (250 mL/1 cup)	1.2
Oat bran, cooked (250 mL/1 cup)	5.7	Iceberg lettuce (250 mL/1 cup)	0.7
Baked potato, with skin (medium)	4.4	White bread (1 slice)	0.6

Source: Data from the U.S. Department of Agriculture, Agricultural Research Service, *USDA nutrient database for standard reference*, release 18, 2005. www.ars.usda.gov/services/doc.htm?docid+8964.

What Happens to Carbohydrates in Your Body?

If you eat cooked oatmeal made with milk and sweetened with a little brown sugar for breakfast, what happens to the carbohydrates in these foods? The carbohydrates in oats are primarily starch and fibre; mixing milk and brown sugar with the cereal adds lactose and sucrose. The small intestine is the main site for carbohydrate digestion and absorption, but a minor amount of starch digestion begins in the mouth, as **salivary amylase** converts some of the oat starch molecules into maltose (Fig. 5.8). Starch digestion stops soon after the food enters the acid environment of the stomach.[10]

In the small intestine, an amylase secreted by the pancreas (**pancreatic amylase**) breaks down the remaining polysaccharides in oat starch into maltose molecules. The enzyme maltase digests maltose into glucose molecules. The final products of starch digestion, glucose molecules, are absorbed into the intestinal bloodstream and transported to the liver via the portal vein. Under normal conditions, the process is very efficient and nearly all the starch is digested. The complex carbohydrates that remain are primarily forms of fibre.

The molecules of sucrose in brown sugar and lactose in milk are too large to enter the bloodstream directly from the intestinal tract. The small intestinal enzyme **sucrase** splits each sucrose molecule, forming one glucose and one fructose molecule in the process (see Fig. 5.8). Additionally, the enzyme **lactase** breaks down the lactose from milk into glucose

salivary amylase enzyme secreted by salivary glands that begins starch digestion

pancreatic amylase enzyme secreted by pancreas that breaks down starch into maltose molecules

sucrase enzyme that splits sucrose molecule

lactase enzyme that splits lactose molecule

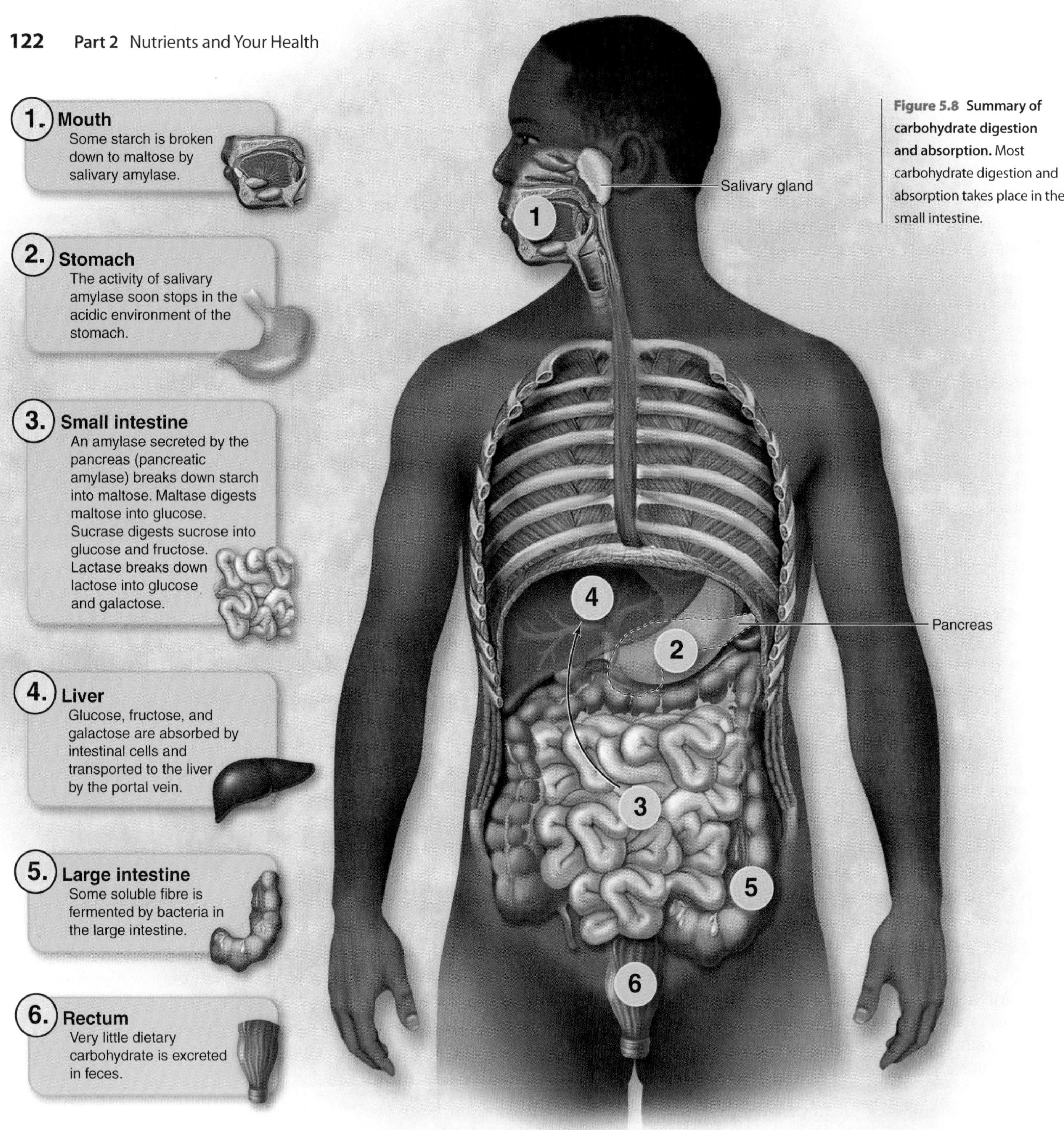

Figure 5.8 Summary of carbohydrate digestion and absorption. Most carbohydrate digestion and absorption takes place in the small intestine.

and galactose molecules. Intestinal cells absorb the monosaccharides, and the portal vein transports them to the liver. The liver can use the simple sugars to make glycogen or fat, but if the body needs energy, the organ releases glucose into the bloodstream.

The fibre in oats is not digested by your small intestine, and it eventually enters the large intestine. The "friendly" intestinal bacteria that reside in the large intestine can break down (ferment) the soluble fibre and metabolize the fermentation products for energy. Soluble fibre is sometimes referred to as *viscous fibre*, because it usually forms a semisolid mass in the intestinal tract that is rapidly fermented by bacterial action. On the other hand, insoluble or fermentation-resistant fibre does not break down completely, and as a result, contributes to softer and easier-to-eliminate bowel movements.[11]

At one time, scientists thought fibre was a nonnutrient because it had no nutritional value. Recent scientific evidence indicates that the body, particularly the cells that line the large intestine, can use by-products produced by the bacterial metabolism of fibre for energy. According to estimates, a gram of fibre adds fewer than 2 kcal to human diets and Health Canada still attributes zero kcal to a gram of dietary fibre.[12] The average Canadian consumes only about 15 to 20 g of fibre daily, therefore fibre would contribute relatively little to a typical person's energy intake.[12,13]

Did You Know?

Dried plums (*Prunus domestica* L.) are commonly called prunes. The fruit contains fibre, the sugar alcohol sorbitol, and other substances that are mild natural laxatives. Prune juice provides the laxative effect of prunes but lacks the whole fruit's fibre content.

Maintaining Blood Glucose Levels

Glucose is such an important cellular fuel, its blood level is carefully maintained by hormones. Hormones are chemicals that convey messages concerning specific responses to target cells. The pancreas, a digestive system organ shown in Figure 4.21 on page 97, contains beta cells, clusters of special cells that produce **insulin**, and groups of alpha cells that produce **glucagon**. These two hormones play key roles in regulating blood glucose levels. Figure 5.9 illustrates the effects of insulin and glucagon on blood glucose levels.

If you are healthy, your body maintains your blood glucose level between 3.9 and 6.0 millimoles per litre (mmol/L) of blood. If you have not eaten for a while, your blood glucose level begins to fall, you start to feel hungry, and your stomach growls. You may grab an apple or a cheese sandwich to eat, and as the carbohydrates in these foods are digested, the glucose from these foods is absorbed into your bloodstream and transported to the liver. As your blood glucose level begins to rise, your pancreas responds by secreting insulin into the bloodstream (see Fig. 5.9). Insulin helps regulate blood glucose levels because the hormone enables glucose to enter most cells.[14]

Insulin also influences fat and protein metabolism. The hormone enhances energy storage by promoting fat, glycogen, and protein production. Another effect of insulin's action is that you feel satisfied with your snack or meal and are no longer hungry.

If you ignore the hunger signals and do not eat, the alpha cells in your pancreas secrete glucagon. Glucagon opposes insulin's effects by promoting the breakdown of glycogen. This process, called **glycogenolysis** (*lysis* = break down), releases glucose into the bloodstream and as a result, boosts your blood glucose level back to normal (see Fig. 5.9). Glucagon also stimulates liver and kidney cells to produce glucose from certain *amino acids*, the basic molecules that make up proteins. Furthermore, glucagon stimulates **lipolysis** (*lipo* = fat), the breakdown of triglyceride (fat) into *glycerol* and *fatty acids*. As a result, glycerol and fatty acids rapidly enter into the bloodstream. The liver uses glycerol

insulin hormone that helps regulate blood glucose levels

glucagon hormone that helps regulate blood glucose levels

glycogenolysis glycogen breakdown

lipolysis fat breakdown

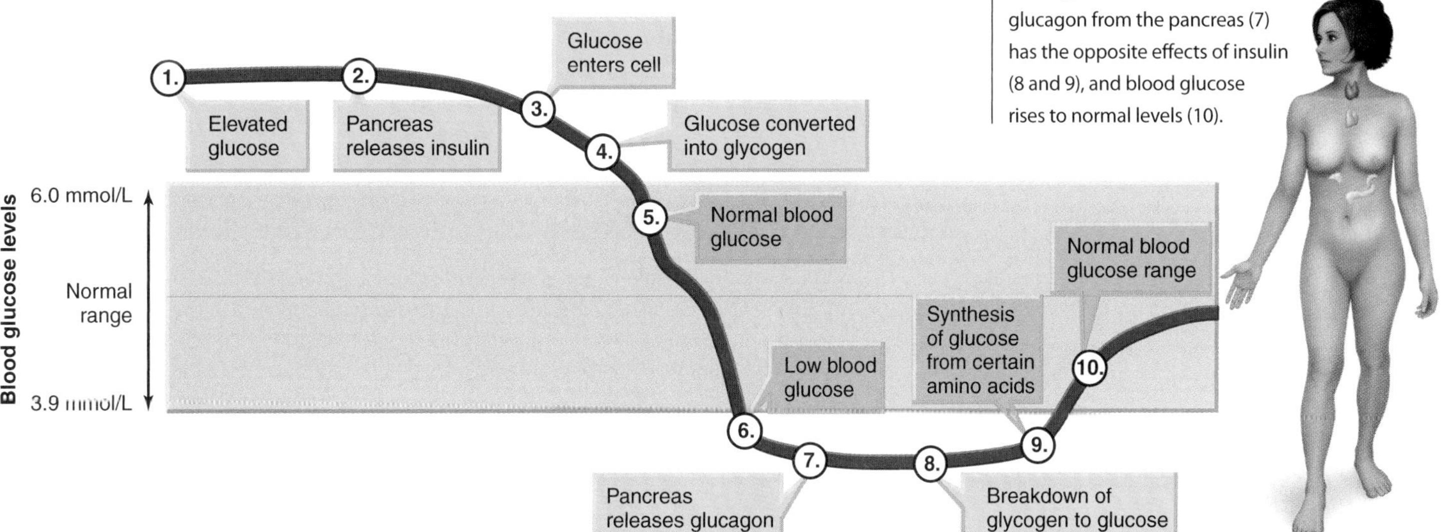

Figure 5.9 Regulating blood glucose. Insulin and glucagon are key hormones in maintaining normal blood glucose concentration. When blood glucose rises above the normal range (1), insulin from the pancreas (2) acts to lower the level (3 and 4), and blood glucose level becomes normal (5). When blood glucose falls below normal (6), glucagon from the pancreas (7) has the opposite effects of insulin (8 and 9), and blood glucose rises to normal levels (10).

to produce glucose, and most cells, including muscle cells, can metabolize fatty acids for energy. Although the body can convert certain amino acids into glucose, it cannot use fatty acids to make glucose.

What happens to glucose? Its fate depends on the state of your body. If your muscles are working vigorously and need more energy to continue contracting, glucose enters the muscle cells quickly and is metabolized for energy. When you are well fed and resting, your body stores the extra glucose as glycogen. When glycogen storage reaches maximum capacity, your liver converts excess glucose into fat and releases it into the bloodstream. Adipose (*ad´-eh-pose*) (fat) cells remove and store the fat.

Glucose for Energy

Cells metabolize glucose to release the energy stored in the molecule's chemical bonds. As a result of this process, cells form carbon dioxide and water (Fig. 5.10). Glucose is a primary fuel for the body's cells. Furthermore, red blood cells as well as brain and other nervous system cells burn mostly glucose for energy.[15]

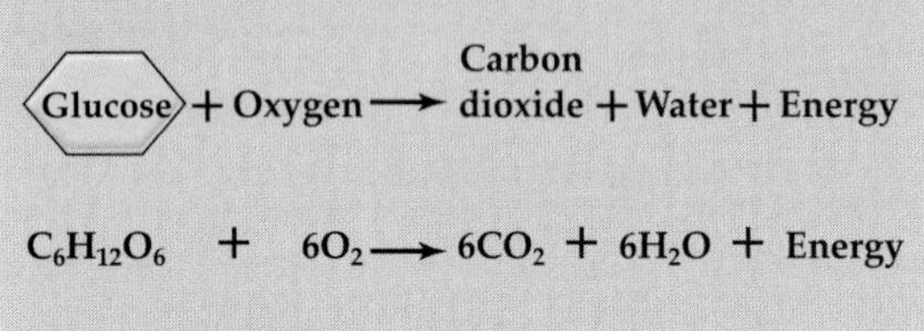

Figure 5.10 Releasing energy from glucose. Cells use oxygen to release the energy stored in glucose. As a result of this process, cells produce carbon dioxide and water.

Cells need a small amount of glucose to metabolize fat for energy properly. When a person has poorly controlled diabetes, is fasting or starving, or follows a very low-carbohydrate/high-protein diet (the Atkins diet, for example), his or her cells must use greater than normal amounts of fat for energy. Under these conditions, there is not enough glucose available for cells to metabolize the fat efficiently, and excessive amounts of ketones form as a result. **Ketones** are chemicals that result from the incomplete breakdown of fat. Muscle and brain cells can use ketones for energy, but a condition called ketosis occurs when these compounds accumulate in the blood. If not treated, severe ketosis can disrupt the body's ability to maintain normal blood chemistry, resulting in loss of consciousness and even death.

ketones chemicals that result from incomplete fat breakdown

The Recommended Dietary Allowance (RDA) for carbohydrate is 130 grams per day.[12] This amount of carbohydrate is enough to prevent ketosis. (The RDAs and other Dietary Reference Intakes [DRIs] were discussed in Chapter 3.) To estimate your daily carbohydrate intake, complete the Personal Dietary Analysis near the end of this chapter. Recall also from Chapter 3 that the Acceptable Macronutrient Distribution Range (AMDR) for carbohydrate is 45 to 65% of total energy intake.

Under normal conditions, human cells obtain a small proportion of their energy needs by converting certain amino acids from proteins into glucose. Starvation, however, dramatically alters the body's energy metabolism. Starvation diets lack sources of energy such as glucose and amino acids. The body, however, desperately needs glucose to fuel vital activities such as breathing, transmitting nervous impulses, and pumping blood. To meet the body's energy needs, the starving person's skeletal muscles sacrifice amino acids from their proteins for glucose production. Using muscle proteins for energy extends the starving person's survival time, but results in muscle wasting, weakness, and eventually, death. Chapter 7 provides information about amino acids and proteins.

Concept Checkpoint

8. Sherita ate some whole-wheat crackers with grape jelly for a snack. As this snack passed through her digestive tract, discuss what happened to the starch, sucrose, and fibre in the food.
9. What is the difference between viscous and fermentation-resistant forms of dietary fibre?
10. What is a ketone? Under what conditions does the body form excessive ketones?
11. What effects do insulin and glucagon have on blood glucose levels?

Carbohydrate Consumption Patterns

In developing nations, millions of people rely on diets that supply 70% or more of energy from relatively unprocessed carbohydrates, especially complex carbohydrates from whole grains, beans, potatoes, corn, and other starchy vegetables. In industrialized nations, people tend to eat more highly refined starches and added sugars. The typical Canadian's diet, for example, supplies about 51% of calories from carbohydrates. Nutritionally adequate diets should provide 45 to 65% of total energy from carbohydrates.[16] The graph in Figure 5.11 shows the average Canadian's intake of carbohydrates and other macronutrients.

According to the *Eating Well with Canada's Food Guide* recommendations discussed in Chapter 3, added sugars are grouped with solid fats in the "other foods" group. It is important to limit intake from the *other foods* group as these foods are typically nutritionally poor and provide empty calories. A 355-mL (12-oz.) serving of 100% orange juice supplies about the same amount of sugar as 355 mL (12 oz.) of a sugar-sweetened cola. Because they both contain simple sugars, should you drink regular soft drinks instead of fruit juices? Unlike colas and other soft drinks, 100% fruit juices, such as orange, grapefruit, and cranberry juice, contribute water-soluble vitamins and antioxidant phytochemicals to your diet. According to the *Eating Well with Canada's Food Guide* recommendations, adults should consume seven to ten servings of fruit or vegetables each day depending on gender.

Percent of Kilocalories per Day

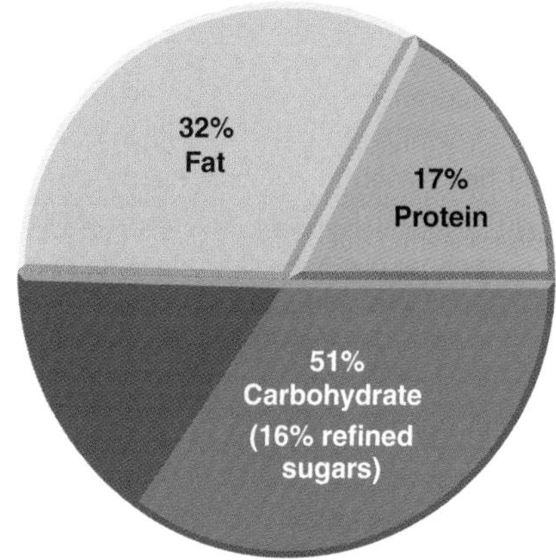

Figure 5.11 Average macronutrient intakes as percentage of total energy. This graph shows the average Canadian's intake of macronutrients as percentages of kilocalories per day. Percentage of total energy from alcohol is not shown.

Source: Adapted from Statistics Canada: Overview of Canadians' eating habits, 2004 (Nutrition: Findings from the Canadian Community Health Survey), 82-620-MIE2006002, January 29, 2010 (http://www.statcan.gc.ca/pub/82-620-m/82-620-m2006002-eng.pdf).

Reducing Your Intake of Refined Carbohydrates

Regular soft drinks, cookies, chips, and other processed foods that contain large amounts of refined carbohydrates can satisfy your hunger, but they may be crowding out more nutritious items from your diet. If you frequently purchase foods and beverages from vending machines, convenience stores, or fast food restaurants, you are probably eating unhealthy amounts of refined carbohydrates. Some fast food restaurants and university and college cafeterias sell yogourt, fresh fruit, and fat-free or low-fat milk as well as unsweetened fruit juices. With a little advance planning, you can prepare your own portable, nutritious snacks. For example, place whole fresh fruit or small plastic containers filled with chunks of fresh fruit and pieces of vegetables into your purse or book bag to eat during the day. At home, keep a bowl of fresh grapes, apples, bananas, or other easy-to-eat fruit available for handy snacks—eat fresh fruit for dessert. Most fruits contain a variety of antioxidants, and they have less fat and more fibre, vitamins, and minerals than pastries or chips.

Understanding Nutrient Labelling: Carbohydrates and Fibre

You can learn how much total carbohydrate, sugars, and dietary fibre are in packaged foods and beverages by reading the Nutrition Facts table of a food label. As you can see in Figure 5.12, total grams of carbohydrate in a slice (one serving) of whole-wheat bread is listed, and under it, grams of fibre and sugar. Food labels for high-fibre products, such as whole-grain cereals, may indicate amounts of soluble and insoluble fibre in a serving of the product. However, information about a product's sugar content does not distinguish between added sugars and sugars naturally present in the food.

According to the label shown in Figure 5.12, 17 g of carbohydrate are in one serving (a slice) of the bread; of this amount, sugar contributes 3 g and fibre supplies 2 g. How can you estimate the grams of starch in the serving of bread? In this example, add the number of grams of sugar with that of fibre and subtract this amount from grams of total carbohydrates, and you will find that starch comprises 12 g of carbohydrate in the slice

of whole-wheat bread. If you are interested in the types of sugars used to make a product, read the ingredient list at the bottom of the panel. In this product, there are three sources of sugar. Can you identify them? Check the nutritive sweeteners listed in Table 5.2 to see if your answers are correct.

Figure 5.12 Using the Nutrition Facts table. This Nutrition Facts table from a package of whole-wheat bread displays carbohydrate content, including amounts of dietary fibre and sugars.

Food & Nutrition *tips*

- Replace soft drinks with a naturally calorie-free thirst-quencher—plain water.
- Make plain water more interesting to drink by adding a slice of lemon, lime, or a few fresh or frozen berries to the beverage.
- Add 1 part club soda to 1 part orange or other 100% fruit juice to make a refreshing carbonated beverage.
- Read the label for information about juice content when selecting a fruit juice product. Compared to fruit juices, fruit "drinks," "punches," "blends," "cocktails," or "ades" may contain several grams of added sugars and only 10% fruit juice.
- In addition to water, manufacturers often use apple or grape juice to dilute more expensive fruit juices, such as cranberry juice. Therefore, beverage descriptors such as "100% juice" can be misleading. Read the ingredient list on the label to determine the types of juices used to prepare the product.
- You can save some money and reduce your caloric intake by drinking water instead of sugary soft drinks with your meals.

Concept Checkpoint

12. What is the AMDR for carbohydrates?

13. Instead of drinking orange juice, should you choose a beverage called "Orange-Ade"? Explain why or why not.

14. According to the Nutrition Facts table, a serving of ready-to-eat cereal contains 44 g of total carbohydrate, 5 g of dietary fibre, and 10 g of sugar. Estimate the grams of starch in the serving of the cereal.

Carbohydrates and Health

Carbohydrates, especially sugar and white flour, get a lot of bad press. Promoters of low-carbohydrate/high-protein diets often blame sugars and starches for causing obesity and diabetes. Many Canadians think consuming sugary foods causes depression and hyperactive behaviour. On the other hand, "carbs" are welcomed by athletes as an inexpensive and efficient source of energy. What have scientists learned about the roles of carbohydrates in health?

Are Carbohydrates Fattening?

If you are one of millions of overweight Canadians who has tried to lose weight recently, you may have followed a low-carbohydrate fad diet, such as the Atkins, the low glycemic index, or Zone diet to shed the extra fat. A fad is a practice that gains widespread popularity rapidly and then loses its appeal quickly when people tire of the behaviour or follow a newer trend. Despite all the hype, overweight Canadians appeared to lose interest in low-carbohydrate diets by 2006. Canadians are fatter now than they were 20 years ago. Are carbohydrates responsible for the epidemic of excess body fat in Canada?

"Calories do count," because you will gain body fat if your intake of food energy from macronutrients and the nonnutrient alcohol exceeds your output of energy for metabolic, physical-activity, and other physiological needs. Regardless of whether you eat a high-carbohydrate, high-fat, or high-protein diet, you will maintain your weight as long as your energy intake matches your energy output. Foods that contain large amounts of refined carbohydrates, however, do not satisfy hunger as well as those that contain more protein or fat. As a result, you may become hungrier sooner after eating a meal or snack that contains a lot of added sugars and refined starches than if you ate a high-protein, high-fat meal or snack. Thus, a person following a high-protein, high-fat diet can lose weight in the short term, because the diet keeps his or her appetite under control by reducing hunger. On the other hand, diets in which carbohydrates supply more than 70% of a person's energy needs also result in weight loss, particularly when the diets include foods that are rich in fibre and contain plenty of unrefined starches.[17] People following such high-carbohydrate diets generally eat less, because fibre-rich foods tend to be more filling than similar amounts of food that contain a lot of refined carbohydrates.[18]

People often consume more energy than needed when they have unlimited access to fatty rather than high-carbohydrate foods.[18,19,20] Why? Fats supply 9 kcal per gram compared to only 4 kcal per gram of carbohydrates; therefore, adding even small amounts of fat to food can dramatically increase its energy content. Nevertheless, people tend to blame carbohydrates for their unwanted weight gain because starches and sugars are often combined with hidden fats such as butter, oil, or shortening (a solid fat) in processed foods. Fats make foods taste rich, creamy, and difficult to resist. Moreover, the sweet taste of sugar masks the bland taste of fat. Although you would not consider eating spoonfuls of plain sugar, flour, shortening, or butter, your mouth waters at the sight of candy bars, fruit pies, doughnuts, and other baked or fried foods, and like many people, you probably find it is difficult to resist eating these foods.

Many people find it difficult to resist foods that contain a lot of sugar and fat, such as cheesecake.

During the past 35 years, the percentage of overweight and obese Canadians rose dramatically. During this same period, Canadians substantially increased their consumption of fructose in HFCS. Some nutrition scientists think North Americans' love of foods and beverages sweetened with HFCS is largely responsible for the population's rising rate of obesity.[21,22,23] The rising prevalence of obesity among children is a major public health concern; regular soft drinks are a leading source of added sugar in the diets of Canadian children.[24] School boards in some communities are so concerned about the epidemic of childhood obesity, they have banned empty-calorie foods, including soft drinks, from school vending machines. Is there a connection between consumption of regular soft drinks and excess body fat?

Findings from scientific studies suggest that people who drink regular soft drinks do not reduce their energy intake from solid food accordingly. The reasons are unclear, but the fructose in these beverages may not reduce the urge to eat as does solid food. As a result, consumers of regular soft drinks ("liquid candy") are likely to overeat and have excessive energy intakes. If, for example, you begin to drink three 355-mL (12-oz.) cans of a cola-flavoured sugar-sweetened soft drink per day, you will obtain about 410 extra kilocalories daily.[25] Unless you increase your daily physical activity level to metabolize the 410 kcal or cut back your food intake by 410 kcal each day, you are likely to gain over 1 kg (nearly 3 lbs.) of fat in 4 weeks! By contributing to unwanted weight gain, consumption of regular soft drinks may increase the risk of type 2 diabetes.[22]

Although consumption of regular soft drinks has increased over the past few decades, other dietary changes have occurred during this period.

What Is Diabetes?

Diabetes mellitus (diabetes) is actually a group of serious chronic diseases characterized by abnormal glucose, fat, and protein metabolism.[27] There are two major types of diabetes mellitus—type 1 and type 2 diabetes. About 5 to 10% of people with diabetes have type 1; in the past, this form of diabetes was called *juvenile diabetes* because it was diagnosed more often in children and young adults. Type 1 diabetes, however, can strike at any age.[27] The majority of people with diabetes have type 2, which used to be called *adult-onset diabetes*. As in the case of type 1 diabetes, type 2 can affect any person, regardless of age.

The primary sign of diabetes is **hyperglycemia** (*hyper* = excess; *glycemia* = blood glucose), abnormally elevated blood glucose levels. A person's blood glucose levels are usually measured after he or she has not eaten (fasted) for about 12 hours. Normal fasting blood glucose levels are between 3.9 mmol/L and 6.0 mmol/L (Table 5.7). People with blood glucose levels of 11.1 mmol/L or more within 2 hours of consuming carbohydrate or individuals who have fasting blood glucose levels of 7.0 mmol/L or more have diabetes.

Some people with diabetes suffer from hyperglycemia because their beta cells do not produce any insulin or do not produce enough to meet their needs. In other cases, the affected person produces some insulin, but his or her body does not respond properly to the hormone, and hyperglycemia results. Major signs and symptoms of hyperglycemia include excessive thirst, frequent urination, blurred vision, and poor wound healing (Table 5.8). Over time, untreated or poorly controlled hyperglycemia damages nerves, organs, and blood vessels. In fact, diabetes is a major cause of heart disease, kidney failure, blindness, and lower limb amputations.

In Canada in 2005, there were 1.8 million individuals with diabetes, representing 5.5% of the Canadian population. This is up from 4.8% in 1998, and it is expected that 2.4 million Canadians will have diabetes in the year 2016.[28] It is also estimated that in 2006, 10% of all admissions to Canadian acute care facilities was related to diabetes or complications associated with diabetes, making the disease a significant burden to the health care system in Canada. However, with proper prevention and management, diabetes can be well controlled and the complications associated with the disorder minimized or even prevented. Nevertheless, public health officials are very concerned about the increasing number of children and adolescents who have diabetes, particularly type 2 diabetes.

Type 1 Diabetes

In most cases, type 1 diabetes is an autoimmune disease that occurs when certain immune system cells malfunction and do not recognize the body's own beta cells.[29] As a result, the immune system cells attack and destroy the beta cells, and the affected person must obtain insulin regularly. It is not clear why the immune cells of some individuals malfunction, but genetic susceptibility and environmental factors, particularly exposure to certain viral intestinal infections, are associated with the development of type 1 diabetes.[30,31,32] Breast-fed infants are less likely to contract intestinal infections than infants who drink cow's milk–based formulas or cow's milk.[30,32] Breast-feeding an infant for the first several months of life may protect the child from developing type 1 diabetes later in life. Nevertheless, the association between type 1 diabetes and consuming cow's milk or infant formulas made from cow's milk is controversial. The role of dietary factors in the development of type 1 diabetes continues to undergo scientific study.

Did You Know?

Many people think sucrose is addictive. Addiction is characterized by an uncontrolled need (compulsion) to take a substance and the development of withdrawal signs and symptoms when the substance is not taken.[26] Many people, especially women, report an extreme preference for sweet fatty foods, such as cakes and pastries. However, there is no scientific evidence that people can become addicted to sugar as cigarette smokers become addicted to nicotine.

diabetes mellitus (diabetes) group of serious chronic diseases characterized by abnormal glucose, fat, and protein metabolism

hyperglycemia abnormally high blood glucose level

glycemic index (GI); glycemic load (GL) standards that indicate the body's insulin response to a carbohydrate-containing food

satiety feeling that enough food has been eaten to delay the next eating episode and/or reduce subsequent food intake

TABLE 5.7
Classifying Diabetes Mellitus

Blood Glucose Level	Classification
4.0 to 6.0 mmol/L (fasting)	Normal
6.1 to 6.9 mmol/L (fasting)	Prediabetes
≥11.1 mmol/L (casual)	Diabetes
≥7.0 mmol/L (fasting)	Diabetes

Tyler S. has type 1 diabetes. You can learn about him and how he manages his health by reading the Real People, Real Stories feature on page 138.

Type 2 Diabetes

The most common form of diabetes is type 2 diabetes. Beta cells of people with type 2 diabetes usually produce insulin, but the hormone's target cells are insulin-resistant cells, which do not respond properly to the hormone and do not allow glucose to enter them. As a result, the level of glucose in the bloodstream becomes abnormally elevated and the signs of diabetes occur.

Over the past 20 years, the number of adults and children with type 2 diabetes has reached epidemic proportions in Canada.[28] Certain people have greater risk of type 2 diabetes than others. Individuals who are physically inactive (sedentary), overweight, and genetically related to a close family member with type 2 diabetes are more likely to develop the disease than persons who do not have these characteristics. Additionally, Canadians who have Hispanic, Native Canadian, Asian, African, and Pacific Islander ancestry are more likely to develop type 2 diabetes than Canadians who are not members of these racial/ethnic groups.[27] To assess your individual risk of developing type 2 diabetes, you may access a risk checklist on the Canadian Diabetes Association Web site at http://www.diabetes.ca/diabetes-and-you/what/at-risk.

Controlling Diabetes

To avoid or delay serious health complications, people who have diabetes need to achieve and maintain normal or near-normal blood glucose levels. Many people with diabetes rely on daily blood testing to monitor their blood glucose levels (Fig. 5.13). Physicians can measure glycated hemoglobin, also called glycosylated hemoglobin or hemoglobin A1c (HbA1c), to determine their patients' average blood glucose level over longer periods. Hemoglobin is the compound in red blood cells that carries oxygen. A1c is a component of hemoglobin that attracts some glucose that is in blood. Normally, about 5% of a healthy person's hemoglobin is HbA1c. A person with poorly controlled diabetes often has blood glucose levels that are much higher than normal. As a result, this individual's hemoglobin will have a higher percentage of HbA1c. According to the Canadian Diabetes Association (www.diabetes.ca), people with diabetes should strive to maintain their HbA1c level below 7%.[27] This measure of blood sugar (HbA1c) provides an average of the blood sugar values over the past 120 days.

Proper blood glucose management involves monitoring blood glucose levels regularly, carefully following a special diet, and including physical activity in one's daily routine. People with type 2 diabetes who are overweight can often reduce their insulin resistance by losing small amounts of excess body fat. Additionally, exercise increases glucose uptake by muscles, reducing blood glucose levels and improving the body's insulin response. In some instances, however, people with type 2 diabetes need oral medication to stimulate their bodies' insulin production, or they must receive insulin injections.

What Is the Glycemic Index? Different carbohydrates undergo different rates of digestion and absorption, which affect the body's insulin response. The **glycemic index (GI)** and **glycemic load (GL)** are standards that indicate the body's insulin response to a carbohydrate-containing food. Foods that have low GIs (less than 70) may promote **satiety**, the feeling that you have eaten enough during a meal or snack to delay the next eating episode and/or reduce your subsequent food intake.[33] Some individuals may be "carbohydrate-sensitive" because they develop hyperinsulinemia (*insulinemia* = blood insulin) after eating foods that have GIs of 70 or more, such as some of the foods listed in Table 5.A on page 139. Hyperinsulinemia occurs when the pancreas releases an excessive amount of insulin, and as a result, cells remove too much glucose from the bloodstream. Eventually, this condition may overtax the beta cells' ability to produce

TABLE 5.8 *Signs and Symptoms of Diabetes Mellitus*

Elevated blood glucose levels
Excessive thirst
Frequent urination
Blurry vision
Vaginal yeast infections (adult women)
Foot pain, abdominal pain
Numbness
Impotence (male)
Sores that do not heal
Increased appetite with weight loss*
Breath that smells like fruit*
Fatigues easily*
Confusion*

*Typical symptoms of poorly controlled type 1 rather than type 2 diabetes.

Figure 5.13 Testing blood glucose. Regular checking of blood glucose is a key part of diabetes treatment.

The mission of the Canadian Diabetes Association is "to lead the fight against diabetes by helping people with diabetes live healthy lives while we work to find a cure." For more information, visit www.diabetes.ca.

adequate amounts of insulin. Thus, hyperinsulinemia may contribute to the development of type 2 diabetes, particularly in people who are genetically prone to develop the disease.[34] Tumours of the pancreas, the organ that produces insulin, may also cause hyperinsulinemia.

Promoters of certain weight reduction diets claim that people can lose weight or control diabetes by following low glycemic index diets. However, the value of the glycemic index and glycemic load for predicting glycemic responses to foods has been questioned.[35] It is important to recognize that typically carbohydrate-containing foods are consumed as part of a meal or snack that contains other foods. The composition of the entire meal or snack, including fat, protein, and fibre, can impact how quickly food exits the stomach and enters the small intestine, therefore impacting how quickly glucose enters the blood. Therefore, the amount of total carbohydrate consumed is more important for maintaining healthy blood glucose levels.[36] More research is needed to determine the extent to which carbohydrates and other dietary components influence the development of diabetes. To learn more about the glycemic index and glycemic load, read the Chapter 5 Highlight on page 139.

Can Diabetes Be Prevented?

There is no way to prevent type 1 diabetes. However, you may reduce your risk of type 2 diabetes by avoiding excess body fat, exercising daily, and changing your diet. Medical experts refer to these actions as *therapeutic lifestyle changes* (*TLC*).

Certain eating habits may help prevent type 2 diabetes. A recent analysis of the eating practices of more than 40,000 North American men identified two major dietary patterns: Western and prudent diets.[37] The Western diet contains high amounts of red meat, processed meats, french fries, high-fat dairy foods, and refined sugars and starches.

The prudent diet contains more poultry, fish, and fibre-rich whole grains, fruits, and vegetables than the Western diet. The results of this study indicated that men who ate Western diets had almost twice the risk of developing type 2 diabetes than those who followed prudent diets. Results of another study indicated that high red meat intake may increase the risk of type 2 diabetes in women.[38] On the other hand, high-fibre diets, particularly those containing cereal fibre, may protect against diabetes.[39,40] Although sugar is often blamed for causing diabetes, the findings of a large survey of adult North American women suggest that eating moderate amounts of sugar does not increase the risk of diabetes.[41]

Currently, there is no cure for diabetes. Medical researchers, however, are testing promising new treatments such as transplanting beta cells from a donor pancreas into the pancreas of a person with diabetes.[42] Since it may take several years before a safe and effective therapy is available, at this time, the best "cure" for diabetes is prevention, if possible.

What Is Hypoglycemia?

If you are healthy and have not eaten for awhile, your blood glucose levels decline, and you become hungry. Eating a meal or snack raises your blood glucose. **Hypoglycemia** (*hypo* = low) is a condition that occurs when the blood glucose level is too low to provide enough energy for cells.

For a person who is not a diabetic, hypoglycemia may be diagnosed when the fasting blood glucose level is less than 4.0 mmol/L.[27] In response to rapidly declining blood glucose levels, the body responds by secreting **epinephrine**, a hormone that is produced by the adrenal glands (see Fig. 4.18 [endocrine system] on page 95). You may be more familiar with epinephrine's common name, adrenalin. Like glucagon, epinephrine increases the supply of glucose and fatty acids in the bloodstream, but the hormone can also make a person suffering from mild hypoglycemia feel irritable, restless, shaky, and sweaty. If the blood glucose level drops too low (approximately 1.7 mmol/L or lower), the affected person can become confused, and he or she may lose consciousness and die.

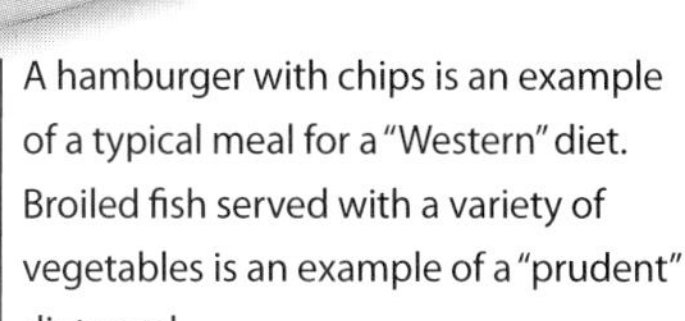

A hamburger with chips is an example of a typical meal for a "Western" diet. Broiled fish served with a variety of vegetables is an example of a "prudent" diet meal.

hypoglycemia condition that occurs when the blood glucose level is abnormally low

epinephrine hormone produced by adrenal glands; also called adrenalin

Several years ago, popular books and magazine articles warned Canadians about the dangers of hypoglycemia and its signs and symptoms. Many people became convinced that they suffered from the condition. Although hypoglycemia is a serious disorder that can affect people with diabetes mellitus and certain tumours of the pancreas, it rarely affects otherwise healthy persons. Some people develop *reactive hypoglycemia* after they eat highly refined carbohydrates because the pancreas responds by releasing too much insulin. However, these individuals generally have normal fasting blood glucose levels. People with reactive hypoglycemia often feel better if they avoid eating large amounts of sugary foods and eat smaller, more frequent meals that contain a mixture of macronutrients.

Metabolic Syndrome

Do you or someone you know have a "spare tire," a "beer belly," "love handles," or an "apple shape?" These popular terms describe a physical condition that has become common among adult Canadians as the prevalence of overweight and obesity increases.

metabolic syndrome condition that increases risk of type 2 diabetes and CVD

syndrome group of signs and symptoms that occur together and indicate a specific health problem

People who are too fat often have excess abdominal fat, which can be dangerous, especially when it is accompanied by hypertension and elevated blood lipid (triglyceride and cholesterol) levels.

Approximately 14.4% of Canadians have **metabolic syndrome**, a condition characterized by three or more of the signs listed in Table 5.9.[43] A **syndrome** is a group of signs and symptoms that occur together and indicate a specific health problem. Compared to people who do not have metabolic syndrome, individuals with this condition have about five times the risk of type 2 diabetes and almost twice the risk of heart and blood vessel (cardiovascular) disease (CVD).[44]

Although genetic factors play a major role in the development of metabolic syndrome, excess abdominal fat and insulin resistance are the primary risk factors for the condition.[44] Poor diet, cigarette smoking, and lack of physical activity also contribute to the development of the syndrome. By exercising more than three times a week, high-risk people may reduce their risk of metabolic syndrome.[44] Furthermore, people may lower their likelihood of developing metabolic syndrome by increasing their intakes of fruits and vegetables and other fibre-rich foods, such as whole-grain cereals.[45]

Individuals who already have metabolic syndrome may reduce their risk of cardiovascular disease by controlling their elevated blood glucose, insulin, and triglyceride levels. Lifestyle changes that help lower high blood glucose, insulin, and triglycerides include losing excess weight, exercising regularly, and reducing intakes of saturated fat, cholesterol, and simple sugars,[44] particularly sucrose and fructose.[46] If such TLC do not alleviate the condition, medication may be necessary to manage blood pressure and blood lipid levels. Chapter 6 provides more information about cardiovascular disease.

Having excess abdominal fat can be dangerous, especially when it is accompanied by hypertension and elevated blood lipid levels.

Tooth Decay

Tooth decay is clearly associated with consuming carbohydrates, particularly complex carbohydrates that adhere (not stick) to teeth. If a person does not follow good dental hygiene practices, the debris becomes food for bacteria that live on teeth. As the bacteria

TABLE 5.9 *Signs of Metabolic Syndrome*

Sign	Defining Value
*Large waist circumference**	≥ 102 cm (40 in.) for men ≥ 88 cm (35 in.) for women
Chronically elevated blood pressure (hypertension)	≥ 130 mm Hg systolic (upper value) or ≥ 85 mm Hg diastolic (lower value) or Drug treatment for hypertension
Chronically elevated fasting blood fats (triglycerides)	≥ 1.7 mmol/L or Drug treatment for elevated triglycerides
Low fasting high-density lipoprotein cholesterol (HDL cholesterol)	< 1.0 mmol/L for men or <1.3 mmol/L for women or Drug treatment for reduced HDL
High fasting blood glucose	≥ 5.6 mmol/L or Drug treatment for elevated glucose

*To measure your waist circumference, remove clothing from the midsection of your body. Locate the top of your hip bones and place a flexible measuring tape around your abdomen at the top of the bones. Exhale normally and take the measurement. (The measuring tape should fit snugly around your waist without pinching the skin and be parallel to floor.)

Source: Canadian Diabetes Association: http://www.diabetes.ca/diabetes-and-you/what/metabolic-syndrome.

metabolize carbohydrate for their energy needs, the acid they produce damages tooth enamel and results in decay.

Infants and young children who drink bedtime bottles of milk, juice, or other beverages that contain sugars are susceptible to "nursing bottle syndrome" (see Fig. 13.10 on page 464). When a sleepy child sucks slowly on the bottle, the carbohydrate-rich solution stays in contact with teeth, increasing the likelihood of dental decay and, eventually, the loss of primary teeth. To reduce the risk of nursing bottle syndrome, offer a young child a bottle of plain water to drink at bedtime.

lactose intolerance inability to digest lactose properly

Lactose Intolerance

An estimated 30 to 50 million North Americans, including 1 million Canadian women and 400,000 Canadian men, suffer from **lactose intolerance** (also referred to as lactose maldigestion), the inability to digest lactose completely.[47] Lactose-intolerant people do not produce enough lactase, the enzyme that breaks lactose into glucose and galactose.[48] Lactose intolerance is not the same as milk allergy, which is an immune system response to cow's milk proteins affecting less than 5% of the population.[49]

When a lactose-intolerant person consumes lactose, the disaccharide is not completely digested and absorbed by the time it enters the large intestine. Bacteria that reside in the large intestine break down lactose and produce irritating gases and acids as metabolic by-products. As a result, a lactose-intolerant person usually experiences intestinal cramps, bloating, gas, and diarrhea within a couple of hours after consuming milk or other lactose-containing products.

Lactose-intolerant people may be able to eat yogourt without experiencing digestive tract discomfort.

Normally, infants produce lactase, but by the time children are 2 years old, their small intestine begins to produce less of the enzyme. Many older children and adults, particularly those with African, Asian, and Eastern European ancestry, are lactose intolerant and experience some degree of abdominal discomfort after drinking milk.

Milk and milk products are excellent sources of protein, many vitamins, and the minerals calcium and phosphorus. What can people with lactose intolerance do to achieve a nutritionally adequate diet without drinking milk? Lactose-intolerant people are often able to eat yogourt and hard cheeses without experiencing any digestive tract discomfort. The bacteria used to make yogourt convert most of the lactose in milk to lactic acid.[44] Additionally, milk loses most of its lactose content when it is processed to make aged cheeses, such as cheddar and Swiss.

Some people with lactose intolerance discover through trial and error that they can consume small amounts of milk without experiencing intestinal discomfort. If you suspect you cannot digest lactose, try consuming a smaller-than-usual size serving of milk and note if you have intestinal discomfort within a few hours. People who cannot tolerate even limited amounts of fresh fluid milk can probably drink milk that has been pretreated with lactase to reduce its lactose content. Most large supermarkets sell fresh lactase-treated milk in the dairy food section (Fig. 5.14). Also, lactase-containing solutions and pills are available without prescription. A lactose-intolerant person simply adds a small amount of the solution to fresh milk before drinking the beverage or takes one of the pills with lactose-containing food.

Figure 5.14 Lactase-treated milk. Fresh lactase-treated milk is often available in the dairy section of supermarkets.

Did You Know?

People who have severe lactose intolerance should read food labels carefully, because lactose-containing substances may be listed as ingredients. Products contain lactose if they include whey, curds, milk by-products, dry milk solids, and nonfat dry milk powder.

Does Sugar Cause Hyperactivity?

If you have ever been in charge of a 7-year-old child's birthday party or observed third graders preparing for their Halloween celebration, you can understand why people often blame sugary foods for causing unruly and "hyperactive" behaviour. Attention deficit hyperactivity disorder (ADHD) is characterized by impulsivity and difficulty controlling behaviour and/or paying attention.[50] Although the cause of ADHD is uncertain, it probably involves genetic and environmental factors. Eating sweets can produce pleasurable sensations, but the results of scientific studies do not indicate that sugar increases children's physical activity levels, causes ADHD, or otherwise negatively affects their behaviour.[51,52] Birthday and school parties are exciting and happy occasions that typically involve a radical change from a child's usual routine. In these situations, a youngster's excitement and more active behaviour is more likely to be the result of the occasion rather than a particular food.

Contrary to popular belief, eating sugary foods does not cause hyperactive behaviour.

Fibre and Health

Technically, fibre is not a nutrient because the human body can live without it. You can live *better*, however, by adding fibre-rich foods to your diet. Eating high-fibre foods may reduce your risk of obesity, diabetes, certain intestinal tract disorders, and cardiovascular disease, which includes heart disease and stroke. The importance of adequate fibre intake to health is so well recognized that information about a food's fibre content can be found on the food label of most packaged foods. The following information discusses some roles of fibre in health.

Fibre and the Digestive Tract

"Bloated, constipated, or irregular? Feeling sluggish? You need a laxative!" According to TV advertisements often targeted at older adults, many Canadians suffer from "irregularity" that can be corrected by taking various over-the-counter remedies. Are serious health problems linked to bowel habits? Can making certain dietary changes improve bowel functioning? What causes intestinal gas?

The frequency and ease of bowel movements influence the health of the large intestine. Constipation (infrequent bowel movements) often results in straining to expel feces during bowel movements. Such straining can increase pressure inside the large intestine and force small portions of tissue to form tiny sacs called colonic **diverticula** (Fig. 5.15). In most people, diverticula do not produce symptoms, but they can become painfully inflamed when bacteria and food particles are trapped within them. When this condition (diverticulitis) occurs, the affected person may need surgery to remove the damaged section of large intestine. Hemorrhoids are clusters of small rectal veins that become swollen, making them likely to bleed and cause discomfort and itching (Fig. 5.16). This condition

diverticula abnormal, tiny sacs that form in wall of colon

commonly affects adults and may be more likely to occur when a person sits for long periods or strains during bowel movements. Although hemorrhoids are generally not a sign of a serious health problem, you should consult a physician if you experience any bleeding during bowel movements, because it may be a sign of colorectal cancer, a major cancer site for Canadians.

Your diet, particularly its fibre content, affects your bowel habits. The insoluble fibre in food attracts water and swells in the digestive tract, forming a large soft mass that applies pressure to the inner muscular walls of the large intestine, stimulating the muscles to push the residue quickly through the tract. People who often eat foods that contain insoluble fibre have softer and more regular bowel movements, and they are less likely to strain while having bowel movements than people whose diets lack fibre. Thus, people generally do not need to rely on over-the-counter laxatives to treat constipation. Eating more fibre-rich foods is the natural way to become "regular."

Fibre and Colorectal Cancer In Canada, the United States, and throughout the world, colon or colorectal cancer (cancer of the large intestine) is one of the most common cancers.[53,54] In the early 1970s, a group of scientists noted that rural African populations who typically ate high-fibre diets rarely developed colorectal cancer. When these populations moved to urban areas and adopted relatively low-fibre Western diets, their risk of colorectal cancer increased. As a result of these observations, the scientists suggested that high-fibre diets were protective against colorectal cancer. By 2005, however, an analysis of the results of several large epidemiological studies indicated diets high in dietary fibre did not reduce the risk of colorectal cancer.[55] Nevertheless, nutrition experts recommend eating high-fibre foods because they provide other important health benefits, such as reducing the risk of cardiovascular disease.[56]

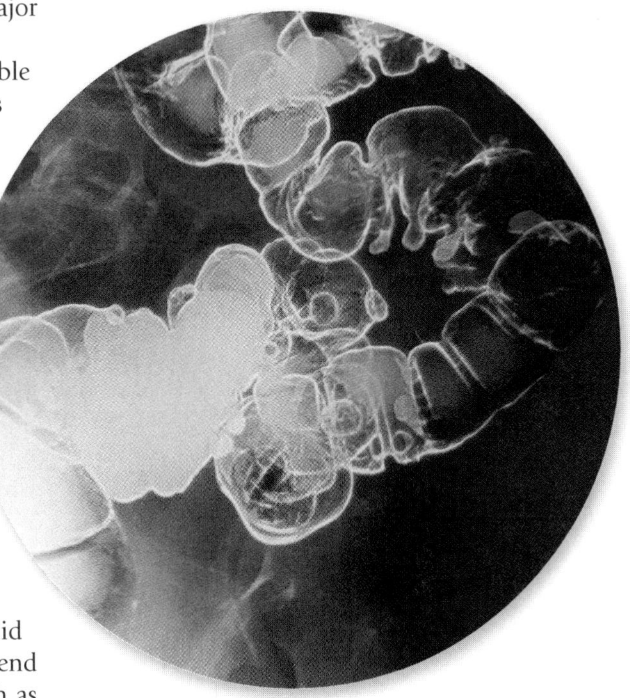

Figure 5.15 Diverticulosis. Constipation can increase the risk of diverticulosis, a condition characterized by the formation of tiny pouches in the lining of the large intestine. In this colour-enhanced x-ray, the blue areas are diverticula.

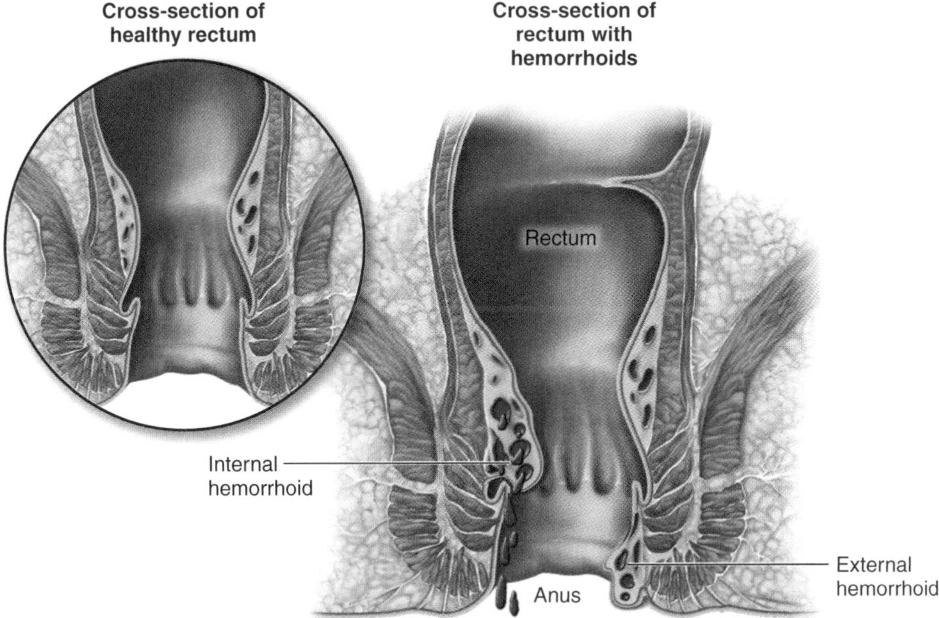

Figure 5.16 Hemorrhoids. Hemorrhoids are clusters of swollen rectal veins that can bleed, cause pain, and become itchy.

Did You Know?

The bacteria that normally reside in the large intestine contribute to the chemical environment of this part of the intestinal tract and help the colon work smoothly. "Colon cleansing" by taking laxatives or using enemas to flush out the "toxic" contents of the large intestine is not necessary for health and can be harmful.

Fibre and Heart Health

Diets rich in fibre, particularly soluble types of fibre, can reduce the risk of cardiovascular disease by reducing blood cholesterol levels.[11] High blood levels of cholesterol are associated with increased risks of cardiovascular disease. The liver uses cholesterol to make bile, a substance that helps digest fats. The gallbladder stores bile and releases the substance into the small intestine during meals. Instead of eliminating bile along with fecal matter in bowel movements, the intestinal tract breaks it down and absorbs its components, which eventually enter the liver. The liver recycles bile components to make new bile. When you eat oat cereal, the soluble fibre in oats interferes with this recycling process because it binds to the bile components in the intestinal tract and prevents them from being absorbed. Thus, the bile components are eliminated in bowel movements. As a result, blood cholesterol levels drop as the liver removes cholesterol from the blood to make new bile.

Fibre and Weight Control

If you are trying to lose excess body fat, you may find it helpful to add more fibre-rich foods to your diet. High-fibre foods tend to be "filling" by increasing the volume of food eaten, which results in satiety. Additionally, a serving of a high-fibre food generally has lower energy content than the same volume of a low-fibre food.[57] As a result, energy intake usually decreases when people switch from consuming low-fibre to high-fibre diets. The following section describes practical ways you can increase the fibre content of your snacks and meals. The Recipes for Healthy Living feature later in this chapter includes high-fibre waffle and oatmeal recipes.

Increasing Your Fibre Intake

The recommended Adequate Intakes (AIs) for fibre are 38 and 25 grams per day for young men and women, respectively, but Health Canada recommends Canadians aim to receive 14 grams of fibre per 1000 kcal consumed each day.[12] The typical Canadian diet supplies less than half of this recommendation. You can estimate your daily fibre intake by completing the Personal Dietary Analysis near the end of this chapter. The Food & Nutrition Tips box on page 137 provides tips for increasing the fibre content of your diet. No Tolerable Upper Intake Level (UL) for fibre has been determined. However, eating excessive amounts of fibre may produce severe intestinal gas and interfere with the intestinal absorption of certain minerals. In rare instances, consuming too much dietary fibre results in intestinal blockage, especially if fluid intake is low.

Intestinal bacteria produce gases when they metabolize fibre; therefore, dietitians recommend that people adjust by gradually increasing their fibre intake. Although having more intestinal gas than usual is a good sign—a sign that the diet contains more fibre—many people would rather experience a different indication of improved digestive health! To reduce the likelihood of having uncomfortable and embarrassing intestinal gas, you can add products such as Beano®, to dishes that contain beans before eating

Food & Nutrition *tips*

- For healthy breakfasts or snacks, eat whole-grain, bran, or oatmeal breads and cereals. Read the ingredient label to find out if a bread or cereal product is whole grain; whole grain or bran should be the first ingredient.
- When comparing bread or cereal products, don't rely on the product's name or appearance. Check the ingredients. Terms such as "100% wheat," "multi-grain," or "stone-ground wheat" are misleading, because the product may contain little or no whole grain.
- Brown rice has more fibre and flavour than white rice. If you are concerned about convenience, instant-cooking brown rice takes less time to cook than regular brown rice.
- Substitute whole-wheat pasta for regular pasta or use half whole-wheat and half regular pasta in pasta dishes.
- Snack on pieces of fresh, frozen, or dried fruit.
- Instead of removing them, eat the edible peels, pulp, and seeds of fruits and vegetables. Eat vegetables as snacks.
- Include more nuts, beans, and seeds in your diet.
- Spread peanut or soy butter on whole-grain crackers for a fibre-filled snack.
- Sprinkle nuts or hulled sunflower seeds on pancakes, waffles, or salads.
- Add frozen, dried, or fresh fruit such as berries, raisins, or bananas instead of sugar or honey to sweeten cereal or plain yogourt.
- Add a small amount of uncooked oatmeal and wheat germ to raw ground meats when making hamburgers or meatloaf.
- Adding bran, wheat germ, and uncooked oatmeal to pancake or waffle batter also enhances the batter's fibre content.
- Good dietary sources of fibre contain at least 2.5 g of fibre per serving.
- You can determine a serving of the food's fibre content by reading the Nutrition Facts table on the product label.

them. Beano® contains natural enzymes that break down undigested complex carbohydrates before they can be fermented by intestinal bacteria. Nevertheless, athletes may choose to avoid notorious gas-forming foods, such as broccoli, cabbage, onions, and beans, 24 to 48 hours before competing. Practices that result in swallowing air such as eating quickly; drinking carbonated beverages, especially with a straw; and chewing gum also contribute to intestinal gas.

Concept Checkpoint

15. What are the signs and symptoms of type 1 and type 2 diabetes?
16. Erika wants to prevent developing type 2 diabetes. What health-related lifestyle practices can she follow to reduce her risk of this serious metabolic disease?
17. Identify at least three signs of metabolic syndrome.
18. What is lactose intolerance?
19. List at least three ways to increase dietary fibre intake.
20. Discuss the health benefits of including soluble and insoluble fibre in diets.
21. How can a person easily determine the carbohydrate and fibre content in a serving of a packaged food?

REAL *people* REAL *stories*

Tyler S.

If you visit Tyler's household, you'll see a wall covered with fascinating photographs—two that are especially attention grabbing. One photo shows a teenage boy holding a large 20-pound Northern pike and another photo is of the same teenager kneeling proudly next to a slain white-tail deer. Tyler S., the teenager in the photos, is only 18 years old, but he's done a lot of amazing things that most 18-year-olds don't even dream about doing. Tyler has taken two fishing trips in northern Alberta. On one of those trips, he caught the huge Northern pike. While on a hunting trip in Cape Breton, Tyler shot the white-tail deer. Closer to home, Tyler enjoys hunting quail and pheasant. Aside from his enthusiasm for hunting, the young man is a high-school athlete and serious NHL hockey fan. Tyler has other interests. Since he was two years old, he has helped raise money for his local branch of the Canadian Diabetes Association. For the past several years, the Association has honoured Tyler for being the top individual fundraiser in his area. The money that's collected by the Canadian Diabetes Association is used to fund research efforts to find a cure for diabetes and support summer camps for children with the disorder. While attending one of those camps as a young child, Tyler learned how to give himself insulin injections. Why? Since he was 14 months old, Tyler has had type 1 diabetes.

As you can tell from Tyler's busy lifestyle, he doesn't let diabetes interfere with his life. Today, he doesn't need to take insulin injections four times a day; he wears an external insulin pump on his belt that is programmed to deliver tiny amounts of the hormone into his body continuously. If Tyler needs extra insulin, he can push a button and the device provides an additional dose of the hormone. Although using an insulin pump has made Tyler's ability to manage diabetes easier, he still watches his diet. He avoids consuming foods that contain high amounts of simple sugars such as candy bars and regular soft drinks. According to Tyler, "Sometimes, when I order a diet soft drink, the restaurant worker asks, 'Why? You don't look like you need a diet drink.'" Tyler responds by informing the person, "I have to; I'm a diabetic."

Tyler's friends don't give him any special treatment, but they're aware of the signs of hyperglycemia and hypoglycemia. According to Tyler, "My friends know when my blood sugar is too high and I need insulin because I'm really thirsty and I have to go to the bathroom [urinate] a lot. When I'm hypoglycemic, I get agitated and shaky, and I have trouble concentrating on what I'm doing. Then my friends know to get me something with sugar in it."

For now, Tyler focuses on school and his part-time job as a service consultant for a small business. As for the future, Tyler is convinced that medical research is close to finding a cure for diabetes. "If transplanting cells that produce insulin into the pancreas works, I would be willing to have the procedure," he says. Until then, Tyler knows he must continue using his insulin pump and taking care of himself. When asked to provide a message to people who do not have diabetes, he replied, "We're [diabetics] just like everyone else. We just have to do something extra for our health."

Chapter 5 Highlight
Glycemic Index and Glycemic Load

In the early 1980s, researchers noted that the body digests carbohydrate-rich foods at different rates, and its insulin response to each food varied. Foods that contained large amounts of refined carbohydrates were digested rapidly, and the rapid flow of glucose into the bloodstream raised blood glucose and insulin levels sharply. Other carbohydrate-rich foods that had high fibre contents were digested slowly and did not cause such a dramatic increase in blood glucose and insulin levels. This observation led to the development of the dietary concepts glycemic index and glycemic load. Currently, the notion that a food's glycemic index could influence health has spurred the publication of popular diet books recommending avoiding foods with high glycemic indices such as potatoes and bread. What is the glycemic index? Should you avoid foods that have high glycemic indices?

The glycemic index (GI) is a way of classifying certain foods by comparing the rise in blood glucose that occurs after eating a portion of food that supplies 50 g of digestible carbohydrate to the rise that occurs after eating a standard source of carbohydrate, either 50 g of glucose or white bread, which have GIs of 100.[1A] A related value, the glycemic load (GL), is the grams of carbohydrate in a serving of food multiplied by the food's GI; this figure is then divided by 100. Compared to the GI, the GL may be a more realistic way of rating foods because the value indicates the relative rise in blood glucose levels after eating a *typical* serving of a carbohydrate-containing food.

Table 5.A lists GIs and GLs of some commonly eaten foods. Note that sucrose and other sugary foods as well as highly refined starchy foods such as cornflakes, baked potatoes, and instant rice have high GIs (70 or more). Milk, fruit, carrots, spaghetti, baked beans, and peanuts have low to moderate GIs (less than 70). It is important to note that the GL of a food is usually lower than its GI. For example, the GI for 30 g of cornflakes is 116, but the GL value for cornflakes is only 21.[2A] Foods with low GLs have values below 15; high GL foods have values of more than 20.

Critics of the GI and GL think the standards have limited usefulness as a menu-planning tool because the values can vary too much. Therefore, the values shown in Table 5.A may vary significantly, depending on where the food was grown, its degree of ripeness, or extent of its processing. Additionally, after eating a particular carbohydrate-rich food, the resulting rise in blood glucose level varies among individuals. Furthermore, the values reflect a single food's effect on blood glucose levels. The effect may be reduced when the food is eaten as part of a meal that contains a mixture of macronutrients and fibre.

TABLE 5.A *Glycemic Index and Load: Selected Carbohydrate-Rich Foods*

Food	GI Glycemic Index*	GL Glycemic Load
Glucose	121	–
Potato (baked)	121	26
Cornflakes cereal	116	21
Jelly beans	112	22
Gatorade	111	12
French fries	107	22
Bagel, white plain	103	25
Popcorn	103	8
White rice, quick cooking	98	29
Snickers candy bar	97	23
Ice cream, vanilla reduced fat	87	8
Sucrose	84	–
Coca-Cola	83	16
Banana	74	12
Orange juice	71	13
Baked beans, canned	69	7
Spaghetti (cooked)	60	20
Peach, raw	60	5
Apple, raw	52	6
Honey	46	7
Fat-free milk	46	4
Fructose	29	–
Carrots, raw	23	1
Peanuts	21	1

* Compared to white bread (GI = 100)

Source: Data from Foster-Powell K and others: International table of glycemic index and glycemic load values. *American Journal of Clinical Nutrition* 76(1):5, 2002.

Despite the criticism directed at the indices, epidemiological studies suggest an association between high GI/GL diets and serious chronic diseases. As people in developing countries abandon traditional diets and eat more high GI/GL foods, they become more likely to develop obesity and type 2 diabetes, as well as cardiovascular disease and certain cancers.[2A] In Canada, results of large studies indicated that as the overall GI/GL of diets increased, blood levels of *high-density lipoprotein* (*HDL*) decreased.[3A,4A,5A] Low HDL levels are a risk factor for heart attacks and strokes. These findings, however, do not mean that eating starch or refined sugars *causes* obesity, type 2 diabetes, and cardiovascular disease. Over the same period of time that populations in developed countries adopted high GI/GL diets, their physical activity levels also declined and their waistlines expanded. Physical inactivity and excessive body fat are risk factors for type 2 diabetes and cardiovascular disease. Results of a recent study involving over 5600 subjects did not indicate an association between eating diets with high GIs or GLs and insulin resistance.[6A] Findings from another study involving over 800 participants suggested a food's glycemic index did not affect blood glucose levels.[7A] Nevertheless, people with diabetes can follow a low GI or low GL diet while monitoring their total carbohydrate intake to control their blood glucose levels.[8A] More long-term research is needed before nutrition experts recommend low GI or GL diets for the general population.[9A]

References for Chapter 5 Highlight

1A. Webb D: Glycemic index: Gateway to good health or grand waste of time? *Environmental Nutrition* 25(1):1, 6, 2002.
2A. Foster-Powell K and others: International table of glycemic index and glycemic load values. *American Journal of Clinical Nutrition* 76(1):5, 2002.
3A. Ford ES, Liu S: Glycemic index and serum high-density lipoprotein cholesterol concentration among U.S. adults. *Archives of Internal Medicine* 161(4):572, 2001.
4A. Liu S and others: A prospective study of dietary glycemic load, carbohydrate intake, and risk of coronary heart disease in U.S. women. *American Journal of Clinical Nutrition* 71(6):1455, 2000.
5A. Kalergis M, De Grandpré E, Andersons C: The role of the glycemic index in the prevention and management of diabetes: A review and discussion. *Canadian Journal of Diabetes* 29(1):27–38, 2005. http://www.diabetes.ca/documents/for-professionals/Kalergis.pdf. Accessed: June 4, 2009.
6A. Lau C and others: Dietary glycemic index, glycemic load, fibre, simple sugars, and insulin resistance. *Diabetes Care* 28(6):1397, 2005.
7A. Mayer-Davis EJ and others: Towards understanding of glycemic index and glycemic load in habitual diet: Associations with measures of glycemia in the Insulin Resistance Atherosclerosis Study. *British Journal of Nutrition* 95(2):397, 2006.
8A. Sheard NF and others: Dietary carbohydrate (amount and type) in the prevention and management of diabetes: A statement by the American Diabetes Association. *Diabetes Care* 27(9):2266, 2004.
9A. Pi-Sunyer FX: Glycemic index and disease. *American Journal of Clinical Nutrition* 76(1):290S, 2002.

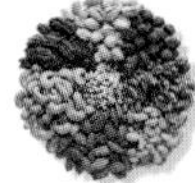

SUMMARY

Carbohydrates are an important source of energy for the body. Plants use energy from the sun to make carbohydrates from water and carbon dioxide. Some of the energy is stored in the bonds that hold the carbon and hydrogen atoms together. Cells break down those bonds, releasing the energy that powers various forms of cellular work.

The three most important dietary monosaccharides are glucose, fructose, and galactose. Glucose is a primary fuel for muscles and other cells; nervous system and red blood cells rely on glucose for energy under normal conditions. Lactose and sucrose are major dietary disaccharides. Starch, glycogen, and most forms of dietary fibre are polysaccharides.

Glucose is the primary end product of carbohydrate digestion. Hormones, particularly insulin and glucagon, maintain normal blood glucose levels. Insulin allows glucose to enter cells, where the sugar is metabolized for energy. Additionally, insulin stimulates glycogen production. Glucagon stimulates the liver to break down glycogen into glucose molecules and release them into the bloodstream.

People in industrialized nations tend to eat less complex carbohydrates and more highly refined sugars than people living in less-developed countries. Healthy Canadians should consume diets that furnish 45 to 65% of energy from carbohydrates, primarily complex carbohydrates. Refined sugar is often blamed for causing obesity, diabetes, and hyperactivity, but tooth decay is the only health problem that is clearly associated with eating carbohydrates. Many adults are lactose intolerant because they do not produce enough lactase, the intestinal enzyme needed to digest the disaccharide.

Diabetes mellitus is characterized by elevated blood glucose levels. Diabetes can result in cardiovascular disease, kidney failure, blindness, and lower limb amputations. There are two major types of diabetes mellitus, type 1 and type 2 diabetes. Type 2 diabetes is the more common form of the disease. In North America, the prevalence of type

2 diabetes has reached epidemic proportions. People who are sedentary, overweight, eat Western diets, and have a close relative with type 2 diabetes are at risk of developing this form of the disease.

Eating fibre-rich foods may reduce your risk of obesity, type 2 diabetes, cardiovascular disease, and certain intestinal tract disorders. High-fibre diets, especially those with ample amounts of insoluble fibre, are associated with lower risk of constipation and hemorrhoids compared to diets that contain little fibre. Additionally, foods that contain soluble fibre may improve cardiovascular health by reducing cholesterol absorption in the intestines. Plant foods generally contain both forms of fibre.

Recipes for Healthy Living

Berry Good Hot Oatmeal Cereal

You don't have time to make or eat breakfast, especially a nutritious, hot breakfast? Think again. This single-serving recipe is a very good source of carbohydrate and provides 7 g of fibre. Furthermore, the recipe takes less than 10 minutes to make. For variety, substitute raisins, frozen or fresh strawberries, or raspberries for the blueberries. A serving of this oatmeal supplies 296 kcal, 14 g protein, 4 g fat, 51 g carbohydrate, 7 g fibre, 295 mg calcium, and 2 mg iron.

19%
12%
69%
Fat
Protein
Carbohydrate

INGREDIENTS:

125 mL (½ cup) frozen or fresh unsweetened blueberries
125 mL (½ cup) quick cooking oats
187 mL (¾ cup) skim fresh fluid milk
5 mL (1 tsp) sugar pinch of ground cinnamon (optional)

PREPARATION STEPS:

1. Place ingredients in a microwaveable bowl and stir.
2. Microwave on "high" for about 2.5 minutes.
3. Stir before eating.

Cleanup tip: After eating, soak cereal bowl in cold water before washing it.

Berry Easy Sauce

This recipe makes about 187 mL (¾ cup) of raspberry berry sauce. Each 60 mL (¼ cup) of sauce supplies about 45 kcal, 11 g carbohydrates, 1.3 g fibre, and 12 mg vitamin C. Berry sauce is a more nutritious choice than maple syrup. A 60-mL (¼-cup) serving of maple-flavoured regular pancake and waffle syrup that contains 2% maple syrup provides about 220 kcal, 55 g sugars, no fibre, and no vitamin C. You can substitute other kinds of frozen fruit, such as strawberries or blueberries, for the raspberries.

100%
Fat
Protein
Carbohydrate

INGREDIENTS:

250 mL (1 cup) thawed unsweetened frozen raspberries
5 mL (1 tsp) white sugar

PREPARATION STEPS:

1. Place thawed berries in a microwave-safe dish, sprinkle sugar over berries, and cover for 30 minutes.
2. Heat berries in microwave oven for about 20 seconds.
3. Stir gently before serving. Sauce will be thick. Place unused portion in a covered container and store in the refrigerator.

Fiber Power Waffles

If you're tired of eating commercial toaster waffles, try this recipe for making your own high-fibre "brand." You can freeze cooked waffles in plastic storage bags; reheat individual waffles in a toaster oven. The recipe makes approximately six 15-cm (6-in.) diameter round waffles; the batter also can be used to make high-fibre pancakes. One waffle provides about 220 kcal, 8 g protein, 7.5 g fat, 5 g fibre, and 2.5 mg iron.

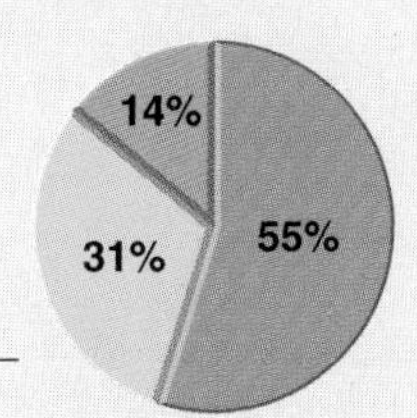

INGREDIENTS:

187 mL (¾ cup) whole-wheat commercial pancake and waffle mix (Do not use "Complete" mixes.)
187 mL (¾ cup) regular commercial pancake and waffle mix (Do not use "Complete" mixes.)
30 mL (2 Tbsp) dry roasted, unsalted, hulled sunflower seeds
30 mL (2 Tbsp) wheat germ
325 mL (1⅓ cup) all-bran ready-to-eat cereal
60 mL (¼ cup) quick cooking instant oats
1 large egg (lightly beaten)
30 mL (2 Tbsp) vegetable oil
375 mL (1½ cup) fat-free fluid milk

PREPARATION STEPS:

1. Mix dry ingredients together.
2. Add egg, oil, and milk to dry ingredients and stir until moistened.
3. Pour 125 mL (½ cup) of the batter into the centre of a heated waffle iron and close iron on batter. Follow the waffle iron manufacturer's directions for making waffles—waffles generally take 1½ to 2 minutes to cook. Top with fresh raspberries or sliced strawberries, or serve with berry sauce (recipe to left).

Personal Dietary Analysis

1. Refer to the three-day food log from the Personal Dietary Analysis feature in Chapter 3. List the total number of kilocalories you consumed for each day of recordkeeping. Add the figures to obtain a total, divide the total by three, and then round the figure to the nearest whole number to obtain your average daily energy intake for the three-day period.

   Sample Calculation:

   Day 1 2500 kcal **Day 2** 3200 kcal **Day 3** 2750 kcal

   Total kcal 8450 ÷ 3 days = **2817** kcal/day

   (average kilocalorie intake, rounded to the nearest whole number)

   Your Calculation:

   Day 1 ____ kcal **Day 2** ____ kcal **Day 3** ____ kcal

   Total kcal ____ ÷ 3 days = ____ kcal/day

   (average kilocalorie intake, rounded to the nearest whole number)

2. Add the number of grams of carbohydrate eaten each day of the period. Divide the total by three and round to the nearest whole number to calculate the average number of grams of carbohydrate consumed daily.

   Sample Calculation:

   Day 1 300 g **Day 2** 495 g **Day 3** 475 g **Total** = 1270 g

   Total g 1270 ÷ 3 days = **423** g/day

   (average, rounded to the nearest whole number)

   Your Calculation:

   Day 1 ____ g **Day 2** ____ g **Day 3** ____ g Total = ____ g

   Total g ____ ÷ 3 days = ____ g of carbohydrate/day

   (average, rounded to the nearest whole number)

3. Each gram of carbohydrate provides about 4 kcal, therefore, you must multiply the average number of grams of carbohydrate obtained in Step 2 by four to obtain the number of kcal from carbohydrates.

   Sample Calculation:

   423 g/day × 4 kcal/g = **1692** kcal from carbohydrates

   Your Calculation:

   ____ g/day × 4 kcal/g = ____ kcal from carbohydrates

4. To calculate the average daily percentage of kilocalories that carbohydrates contributed to your diet, divide the average kilocalories from carbohydrate obtained in Step 3 by the average total daily kilocalorie intake obtained in Step 1, and round figure to the nearest one-hundredth. Multiply the value by 100, drop the decimal point, and add the percent symbol.

Sample Calculation:

1692 kcal ÷ 2817 kcal = 0.60

0.60 × 100 = 60%

Your Calculation:

____ kcal ÷ ____ kcal = ____

____ × 100 = ____%

5. On average, did you consume *at least* the RDA of 130 g of carbohydrate?
Yes ____ No ____

6. Did your average carbohydrate intake meet the recommended 45 to 65% of total energy?
Yes ____ No ____

a. If your average carbohydrate intake was less than 130 g or below 45% of total calories, list five nutrient-dense, carbohydrate-rich foods you could eat that would boost your intake of carbohydrates.
Foods: ____________________

7. Review the log of your three-day food intake. Calculate your average daily intake of fibre by adding the grams of fibre consumed over the three-day period and dividing the total by three.

Your Calculation:

Day 1 ____ g

Day 2 ____ g

Day 3 ____ g

Total = ____ g

Total g ____ ÷ 3 days = ____ g of fibre daily

a. What was your average daily fibre intake? ____ g

b. Did your average daily fibre intake meet the recommended Adequate Intakes of 38 and 25 g/day for young men and women, respectively? Yes ____ No ____

c. If your response is yes, list foods that contributed to your fibre intake.
Foods: ____________________

d. If you did not meet the recommended level of fibre intake, list at least five foods that you would eat to increase your fibre intake to the recommended level.
Foods: ____________________

CRITICAL THINKING

1. One of your friends thinks honey is more nutritious and safer to eat than table sugar. He wants you to avoid table sugar and use only honey as a sweetener. What would you tell this person about the nutritive value and safety of honey compared to sugar?
2. Prepare a pamphlet that describes the health benefits of dietary fibre. In addition to English, you may prepare the pamphlet in French, Spanish, Mandarin, or another modern language.
3. How did you feel about drinking regular soft drinks before reading Chapter 5? Has your opinion changed? If so, explain how.
4. If you were 25 pounds overweight, explain why you would or would not follow a weight loss diet that supplies less than 15% of calories from carbohydrate.
5. Consider the fibre content of your diet. Do you consume enough fibre each day? If your fibre intake is adequate, what foods do you eat regularly that contribute soluble and insoluble fibre to your diet? If your fibre intake is low, list foods you would consume to increase your intake of both types of fibre.

PRACTICE TEST

Select the best answer.

1. Which of the following substances is a disaccharide?
   a. fructose
   b. sucrose
   c. galactose
   d. glycogen
2. ______ is a primary fuel for muscles and other cells.
   a. Protein
   b. Cholesterol
   c. Glucose
   d. HFCS
3. Which of the following substances is a polysaccharide?
   a. glycogen
   b. glucose
   c. lactose
   d. insulin
4. Sugar contributes to
   a. browning of baked cereal products.
   b. food preservation.
   c. a food's energy value.
   d. all of the above
5. Dietary fibre
   a. supplies more energy, gram per gram, than fat.
   b. is not digested by the human intestinal tract.
   c. promotes tooth decay.
   d. all of the above

6. Insoluble fibre
   a. is in beef and pork.
   b. dissolves or swells in water.
   c. is in whole-grain products, including brown rice.
   d. increases the risk of heart disease.
7. ______ is the hormone that enables glucose to enter cells.
   a. Glucagon
   b. Insulin
   c. Glycerol
   d. Ketone
8. ______ are the primary source of added sugars in the typical Canadian diet.
   a. Candies
   b. Regular soft drinks
   c. Refined cereals
   d. Canned fruits
9. Type 2 diabetes is
   a. a disease that primarily affects young children.
   b. characterized by severe hypoglycemia.
   c. often associated with excess body weight.
   d. caused by eating refined sugars.
10. Which of the following signs is associated with metabolic syndrome?
    a. low blood pressure
    b. high fasting blood glucose
    c. low hemoglobin
    d. high fasting HDL cholesterol
11. Which of the following conditions is clearly associated with eating dietary carbohydrates, especially sticky sugars?
    a. tooth decay
    b. type 1 diabetes
    c. attention deficit hyperactivity disorder
    d. hypertension
12. Which of the following substances is an enzyme that breaks down lactose?
    a. galactose
    b. salivary amylase
    c. lactase
    d. lactic acid
13. Which of the following foods is the best source of soluble fibre?
    a. raw fruit
    b. whole-grain oat cereal
    c. sports drink
    d. properly cooked meat

Answers to Chapter 5 Quiz Yourself

1. Compared to table sugar, honey is a natural and far more nutritious sweetener. **False.** (p. 115)
2. Ounce per ounce, sugar provides more energy than starch. **False.** (pp. 116, 119)
3. Eating a high-fibre diet can improve the functioning of your large intestine and reduce your blood cholesterol levels. **True.** (pp. 135–136)
4. The average Canadian consumes 40 to 50% of his or her energy intake as refined sugars. **False.** (p. 125)
5. The results of clinical studies indicate that eating too much sugar makes children hyperactive. **False.** (p. 134)

Chapter **6**

Fats and Other Lipids

Chapter Learning Outcomes

After reading Chapter 6, you should be able to:

1. Distinguish between the various forms of dietary lipid.
2. Identify major food sources of lipids, including trans fatty acids.
3. Explain the process of atherosclerosis and list at least six risk factors of cardiovascular disease.
4. Distinguish the roles of HDL cholesterol and LDL cholesterol.
5. Identify major dietary sources of omega-3 fatty acids.
6. List dietary and other lifestyle actions that can reduce the risk of cardiovascular disease and diabetes.
7. Discuss alcohol's effects on health.

What do you think when you hear the words *fat* or *cholesterol*? Do "bad," "heart attack," or "deadly" enter your mind? If your answer is "yes," are you concerned about the amounts and types of fat in your diet? Do you avoid eating eggs because of their cholesterol content? Does your concern have anything to do with having a family history of heart disease?

Fat and cholesterol are **lipids**, a class of nutrients. You probably know fat is a rich source of energy and ingesting too much energy can result in excess weight gain, which is unhealthy. Additionally, you may know that cholesterol is associated with heart attacks. However, you may not be aware of the many important roles that fat, cholesterol, and other lipids play in the body. Lipids are crucial components of the plasma membrane that surround each human cell. In fact, every cell in the body contains fat as well as other lipids. The layer of fat under your skin (**subcutaneous fat**) stores energy, insulates you against cold temperatures, and protects you against minor bruising. In addition to storing energy, the fat deposits in your abdominal region (**visceral fat**) contribute to your body's contours and cushion your vital organs from jarring movements and damaging blows. However, visceral fat is associated with a greater overall health risk.

In food, lipids enhance intestinal absorption of fat-soluble vitamins and phytochemicals. Furthermore, fatty meals tend to empty more slowly from the stomach than carbohydrate-rich meals. As a result, the fat in foods may contribute to *satiety*, the feeling that you have eaten enough to relieve hunger.

Dietary lipids also provide non-nutritional benefits by contributing to the rich flavour, smooth texture, and appetizing aroma of foods. Whether fat is naturally in food or added to it, the nutrient often makes foods taste more appetizing. For example, if you are used to consuming whole milk that is about 3.25% fat by volume, you will recognize the difference fat makes to "mouth feel" when you drink skim milk that contains less than 0.5% fat. Humans developed a taste for fats presumably due to the relative energy density lipid provided in the diet of our ancestors who had to continually seek out food energy to survive.

It is not surprising that many Canadians are confused about the roles of fat and cholesterol in health. The results from numerous studies conducted over the past 50 years indicate that consuming high amounts of certain lipids may increase the risk of serious health conditions, including obesity,[1,2,3] cancer,[4,5] and cardiovascular disease (CVD), which includes heart disease and stroke.[6] On the other hand, some fat is essential to good health. After reading Chapter 6, you will learn about the roles of lipids in your foods and body as well as their major food sources. Additionally, you will learn how certain lipids may influence your health.

Quiz YOURSELF

What are trans and omega-3 fats, and which foods contain these fats? How much dietary fat is recommended? Should you avoid eating eggs because they contain cholesterol? Test your knowledge of fat and other lipids by taking the following quiz. The answers are found on page 189.

1. To lose weight, use regular, stick margarine instead of butter because it has 25% fewer kilocalories per teaspoon. ______T ______F
2. Egg yolks are a rich source of cholesterol. ______T ______F
3. Taking too many fish oil supplements may be harmful to health. ______T ______F
4. On average, Canadians consume 60% of their calories from fat. ______T ______F
5. Increasing your intake of trans fats can reduce your risk of heart disease. ______T ______F

lipids class of nutrients that do not dissolve in water

subcutaneous fat body fat found under the skin and above the muscles

visceral fat body fat found around abdominal organs

Understanding Lipids

Lipids include fatty acids, triglycerides, phospholipids, and cholesterol. In general, lipids are insoluble in water. Consider what happens when you mix vinegar and olive oil to make a vinaigrette salad dressing. Vinegar is 95% water; oil is 100% lipid. Therefore, the oil does not dissolve in water to make a solution. Additionally, oil is less dense than water, so it rises to the top of the vinegar in small globules when added to vinegar. The globules join others to form an oily layer that floats on the vinegar until you shake the mixture. Shaking the ingredients mixes them temporarily. When left undisturbed, the oil and vinegar soon separate; hence the saying, "Oil and water don't mix." The following sections take a closer look at each major type of lipid.

If left undisturbed, the oil and vinegar used to make vinaigrette salad dressing soon separate.

hydrocarbon chain chain of carbon atoms bonded to each other and to hydrogen atoms

saturated fatty acid fatty acid that has each carbon atom within the chain filled with hydrogen atoms

unsaturated fatty acid a fatty acid that is missing hydrogen atoms and has one or more double bonds within the carbon chain

monounsaturated fatty acid a fatty acid that has one double bond within the carbon chain

polyunsaturated fatty acid a fatty acid that has two or more double bonds within the carbon chain

Fatty Acids

Most lipids have fatty acids in their chemical structures. Fatty acids provide energy for muscles and most other types of cells. As Figure 6.1 illustrates, a fatty acid is comprised of a **hydrocarbon chain**, a chain of carbon atoms bonded to each other and to hydrogen atoms. A methyl group—three hydrogen atoms bonded to a carbon atom—is at one end of the molecule. Chemists call this end of the molecule *omega*. An acid group is at the other end of the fatty acid molecule. An alternative name for the acid group on this end of the fatty acid molecule is a *carboxyl group*.

In nature, common fatty acids typically have even numbers of carbon atoms. Short-chain fatty acids have 2 to 4 carbons; medium-chain fatty acids have 6 to 12 carbons; and long-chain fatty acids have 14 to 24 carbons. Chemists identify a fatty acid by its number of carbon atoms and type of bond between carbon atoms in the hydrocarbon chain. Additionally, these factors influence the physical characteristics of a fatty acid and how various fatty acids can affect your health.

Saturation

Fatty acids can be saturated or unsaturated. The carbons in the fatty acid chain shown in Figure 6.1a have single bonds between them. Note that each carbon in the chain has two hydrogen atoms attached to it. This is a **saturated fatty acid** because each carbon within the chain is saturated, that is, completely filled with hydrogen atoms.

An **unsaturated fatty acid** has two neighbouring carbons within the chain that are missing two hydrogen atoms, and a double bond holds those particular carbons together (Fig. 6.1b). Unsaturated fatty acids can be either monounsaturated or polyunsaturated. The fatty acid illustrated in Figure 6.1b has only one double bond linking two carbon atoms, therefore it is referred to as a ***mono*****unsaturated fatty acid**. The fatty acid shown in Figure 6.1c is also unsaturated, but it has three double bonds within its

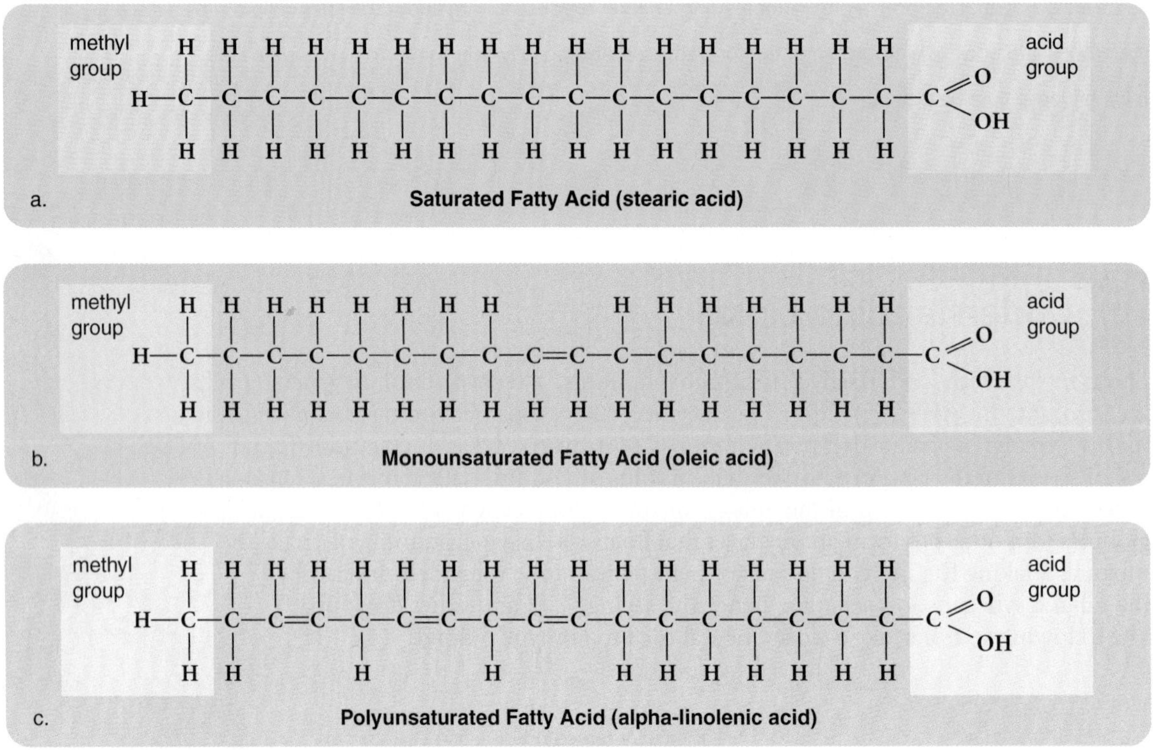

Figure 6.1 Fatty acids. A fatty acid is comprised of a hydrocarbon chain. A methyl group is at one end of the molecule; an acid group is at the other end of the molecule. Note that each of these fatty acids has 18 carbon atoms, but they differ in the number and location of double bonds. (*a*) A saturated fatty acid has single bonds between the carbon atoms in the hydrocarbon chain. (*b*) An unsaturated fatty acid has two neighbouring carbons within the chain that are missing two hydrogen atoms, and a double bond holds those particular carbons together. (*c*) A polyunsaturated fatty acid has two or more double bonds between carbons in the hydrocarbon chain.

hydrocarbon chain. A fatty acid that has two or more double bonds between carbons is a ***poly*unsaturated fatty acid**.

What is the difference between fats and oils? Although both substances contain fatty acids, fats are solid and oils are liquid at room temperature. Compared to foods that contain high amounts of unsaturated fatty acids, foods that are rich sources of long-chain saturated fatty acids tend to be more solid at room temperature. A pat of butter, for example, contains more long-chain saturated fatty acids than a pat of margarine. Thus, butter keeps its shape better than margarine when it is not refrigerated. A later section of this chapter discusses the health effects of eating diets that are rich in saturated or unsaturated fats.

To obtain omega-3 fatty acids, consider including fatty fish such as salmon in your meals at least twice a week.

Essential Fatty Acids

The human body cannot synthesize two polyunsaturated fatty acids: **alpha-linolenic** (*al´-fah lin´-o-len´-ik*) **acid** and **linoleic** (*lin´-o-lay´-ik*) **acid**. These lipids are **essential fatty acids** because they must be supplied by the diet. Alpha-linolenic acid is an **omega-3 fatty acid**. The "3" refers to the position of the first double bond that appears in the fatty acid's carbon chain when you start counting carbons at the omega end of the molecule. Cells use alpha-linolenic acid to synthesize two other omega-3 fatty acids, eicosapentaenoic (*eye´-ko-seh-pen´-tah-e-no´-ik*) acid (EPA) and docosahexaenoic (*doe´-ko-seh-hek´-seh-e´-no´-ik*) acid (DHA). Linoleic acid is an *omega-6 fatty acid*. Cells can convert linoleic acid to arachidonic (*a´-rakeh´-don-ik*) acid (AA). Because the body can only create eicosapentaenoic acid, docosahexaenoic acid, and arachidonic acid when the essential fatty acids are present, these three fatty acids are often referred to as *conditionally essential fatty acids*. The body uses EPA, DHA, and arachidonic acid to make several compounds that have hormone-like functions, including prostaglandins. Prostaglandins produce a variety of important effects on the body such as regulating blood pressure, and promoting the immune system's inflammatory response. Figure 6.2 shows relationships among the essential fatty acids.

A small amount of essential fatty acids is necessary for good health. Infants do not grow properly when their diets lack essential fatty acids. Other signs of essential fatty acid deficiency include scaly skin, hair loss, and poor wound healing. The Adequate Intake (AI) for alpha-linolenic acid is 1.6 grams per day for men and 1.1 grams per day for women. The AI for linoleic acid is 14 to 17 grams per day for men and 11 to 12 grams per day for women who are 19 through 50 years of age.[7] These amounts can be met by eating two to three tablespoons of vegetable fat daily, especially products made with canola and soybean oils, and meals that contain fatty fish at least twice a week.

alpha-linolenic acid an essential fatty acid

linoleic acid an essential fatty acid

essential fatty acids lipids that must be supplied by the diet

omega-3 fatty acid a type of polyunsaturated fatty acid

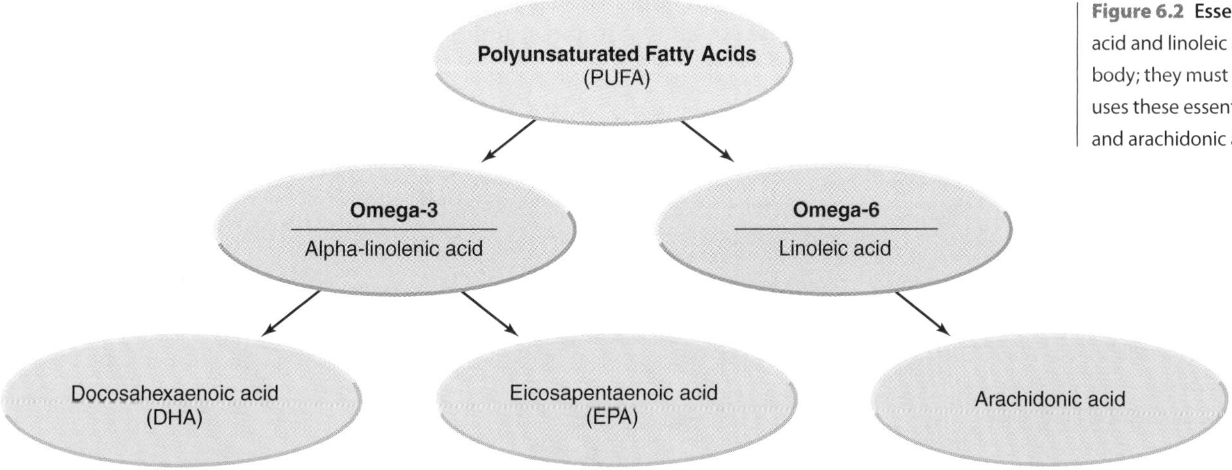

Figure 6.2 Essential fatty acids. Alpha-linolenic acid and linoleic acid are not synthesized by the body; they must be supplied in the diet. The body uses these essential fatty acids to make DHA, EPA, and arachidonic acid.

In Canada, essential fatty acid deficiency is uncommon because most Canadians eat plenty of fat, especially linoleic acid.[8] This omega-6 fatty acid is in vegetable oils often used for frying foods and making margarines and salad dressings. Additionally, whole-grain products contain linoleic acid.

Linoleic acid increases inflammation and blood clotting. Some inflammation is necessary because it attracts immune system cells to disease-causing microorganisms that have entered the body. Inflammation, however, can also damage the inside of arteries. Clotting is also an important function of blood, but consuming too much fat can result in blood that clots too easily. Saturated and trans fats may accelerate blood clotting, increasing atherosclerotic plaque development and the risk of strokes, heart attacks, and other serious blood vessel disorders. Many Canadians eat relatively small amounts of omega-3 fatty acids. A later section of this chapter presents information about the health effects of omega-3 fatty acids.

Trans Fats

trans fats unsaturated fatty acids that have a trans double bond

hydrogenation a food manufacturing process that adds hydrogen atoms to liquid vegetable oil forming trans fats

Trans fats are unsaturated fatty acids that have at least one *trans* double bond in their chemical structure rather than the more common *cis* configuration.[9] The trans double bond enables the hydrocarbon chain to be relatively straight, increasing the stability of the fatty acid. The cis double bond, however, forms a kink in the hydrocarbon chain (Fig. 6.3).

Whole milk and whole milk products, butter, and meat naturally contain very small amounts of trans fats. Most trans fats are the result of *hydrogenation* of plant oils. This process can convert liquid oil to a solid fat at the same temperature, which allows less expensive plant oils to be more effectively utilized in many cooking applications. **Hydrogenation** or partial hydrogenation is a food manufacturing process that adds hydrogen atoms to liquid vegetable oil. The hydrogenation process also converts many of the oil's naturally occurring cis fatty acids into trans fatty acids. Structurally, a trans fatty acid resembles a saturated fatty acid and provides properties of long-chain saturated fatty acids to foods that contain them. As a result of the partial hydrogenation process, vegetable oil can be made into shortening or shaped into sticks of margarine.

Did You Know?

Cooks often use shortening to make pie crust because the partially hydrogenated fat results in a flaky tender crust. When making pie dough, oil can be substituted for shortening, but it produces a crumbly texture that may be undesirable.

Foods made with partially hydrogenated fat can be stored for longer periods of time than foods that contain cis fatty acids. Why? Trans fatty acids are less likely to undergo *oxidation*, a chemical process that alters the compound's structure. When oxidized, the fat in food becomes rancid and develops an unappetizing odour and taste. Unsaturated fatty acids that have the cis double-bond arrangement, especially polyunsaturated fatty acids, are very susceptible to oxidation. Instead of relying on trans fats to extend the shelf life of products, manufacturers can preserve fat and other ingredients in foods by adding antioxidants to them. Certain food additives, vitamins, and plant pigments function as antioxidants (see the Chapter 8 Highlight, "Megadosing on Vitamins").

The body does not require trans fatty acids, and medical researchers have not discovered any positive health effects from consuming them.[10] In the body, trans fats function

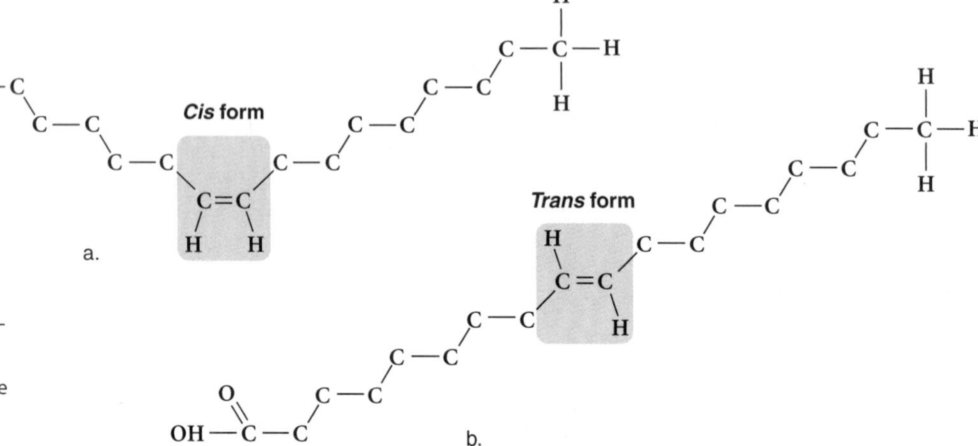

Figure 6.3 Cis and trans double-bond arrangements. Unsaturated fatty acids usually have "kinks" where double bonds are in the carbon chain. (*a*) Oleic acid, a cis fatty acid, has the hydrogen atoms of the double-bonded carbons on the same sides of the molecule, resulting in a kink. (*b*) Elaidic acid, a trans fatty acid, has the hydrogen atoms of the double-bonded carbons on opposite sides, resulting in a straighter arrangement of the fatty acid chain. For simplicity, most of the hydrogen atoms in these molecules are not shown.

like certain saturated fats, raising blood cholesterol levels, which may increase the risk of heart disease.[11,12] In fact, some researchers estimate that trans fat may be up to ten times as damaging as saturated fats with regard to the development of atherosclerosis.[13] In 2007, Health Canada adopted recommendations from the Trans Fat Task Force and asked that food manufacturers achieve new limits for the trans fat found in manufactured foods. The recommendations were to limit the trans fat content of vegetable oils and soft, spreadable margarines to 2% of the total fat content, and limit the trans fat content for all other foods to 5% of the total content, including ingredients sold to restaurants.[14]

Health Canada also announced that if significant progress had not been made toward these goals by 2009, Health Canada would develop regulations to ensure that these recommendations were achieved. The Trans Fat Monitoring Program facilitated via Health Canada indicates that great achievements have been made toward achieving these goals, but some products and manufacturers in Canada are still falling short of these objectives. When these guidelines are met, it is estimated trans fats will represent less than 1% of the total energy intake of Canadians.[14]

Current Canadian nutrition labelling regulations mandate that the quantity of trans fats in packaged foods be listed in combination with saturated fats on the Nutrition Facts table. This amount is reported in grams and is also provided as a percentage of the Daily Value (DV).[12]

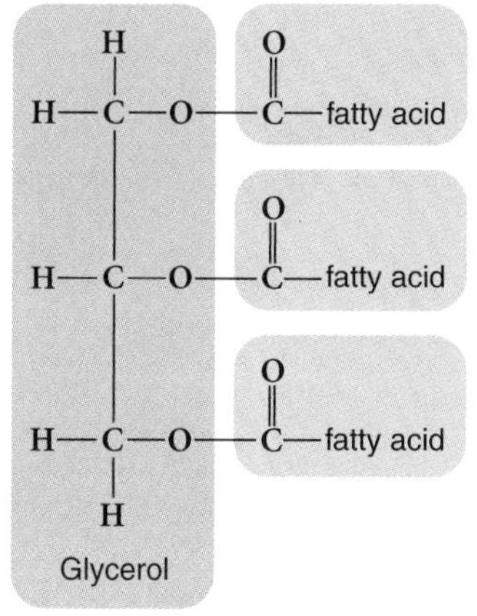

H—C—O—C(=O)—fatty acid
H—C—O—C(=O)—fatty acid
H—C—O—C(=O)—fatty acid
Glycerol

Triglyceride

Figure 6.4 Triglycerides. A triglyceride has three fatty acids attached to a glycerol "backbone."

Triglycerides

A **triglyceride** is comprised of three fatty acids attached to glycerol, a three-carbon compound that is often referred to as the "backbone" of the triglyceride (Fig. 6.4). Triglycerides comprise about 95% of lipids in your body and food. Most triglycerides contain mixtures of unsaturated and saturated fatty acids. In a particular food, such as olives or cheese, the unsaturated and saturated fats occur in different proportions, but one type of fatty acid (saturated, monounsaturated, or polyunsaturated) often predominates. Table 6.1 compares the percentages of saturated, monounsaturated, and polyunsaturated fatty acids in commonly eaten fats. Note that the fat in beef and dairy

triglyceride a lipid that has three fatty acids attached to a three-carbon compound called glycerol. This is the form in which most fat in foods and in our body is found.

TABLE 6.1 *Approximate Percentages of Saturated and Unsaturated Fatty Acids in Common Fats and Oils**

Oil/Fat 15 mL (1 Tbsp)	% Saturated	% Monounsaturated	% Polyunsaturated
Sunflower oil (approx. 65% linoleic)	10.8	20.4	68.8
Safflower oil	6.5	15.1	78.4
Soybean oil	15.1	24.4	60.1
Corn oil	13.6	29.0	57.4
Cottonseed oil	27.1	18.6	54.3
Peanut oil	17.8	48.6	33.6
Canola oil	7.4	61.6	31.0
Margarine, partially hardened corn and soybean oils	19.7	49.5	30.8
Chicken fat	31.2	46.8	21.9
Lard (pork fat)	41.0	47.2	11.7
Olive oil	14.2	75.0	10.8
Palm oil	51.6	38.7	9.7
Beef fat	52.1	43.7	4.2
Butter	66.0	30.0	4.0
Coconut oil	91.9	6.2	2.0

* Values for each fat/oil may not total 100% because of rounding.

Source: Data from U.S. Department of Agriculture, Agricultural Research Service. USDA National Nutrient Database for Standard Reference, Release 19. Nutrient Data Laboratory Home Page, 2006, www.ars.usda.gov/ba/bhnrc/ndl.

Whole eggs or egg yolks are often included as emulsifiers in recipes that involve mixing oily and watery ingredients to form emulsions. Cake batter, for example, is an emulsion.

phospholipids a type of lipid needed to make cell membranes and for proper functioning of nerve cells

Did You Know?

Lard is pork fat. In some parts of Canada, lard is used to make baked goods such as pies and pastries. Lard is high in saturated fat (41%), but it's not as highly saturated as butter (66%).

products contains more saturated than unsaturated fatty acids; olive oil is a rich source of monounsaturated fatty acids; and liquid corn oil contains a greater proportion of unsaturated than saturated fatty acids. Certain animal foods, especially beef and dairy foods such as cheese, cream, and butter, contain higher percentages of saturated fatty acids than most plant fats. Important exceptions are tropical oils such as coconut and palm oils. Tropical oils contain more saturated than unsaturated fatty acids. Fats and oils that contain high amounts of saturated or unsaturated fatty acids are commonly called saturated fats or unsaturated fats.

Why is it important to understand the differences between saturated, unsaturated, and trans fats and identify foods that contain high amounts of these fats? Populations who consume diets rich in saturated fat and trans fat have much higher risk of CVD than populations whose diets contain more unsaturated than saturated fat.[13] The section, "Lipids and Health: Cardiovascular Disease (CVD)," later in this chapter, discusses the role of lipids in CVD.

Phospholipids

A **phospholipid** is chemically similar to a triglyceride, except one of the fatty acids is replaced by chemical groups that contain phosphorus and, often, nitrogen (Fig. 6.5a). Phospholipids are naturally found in plant and animal foods. Lecithin is the major

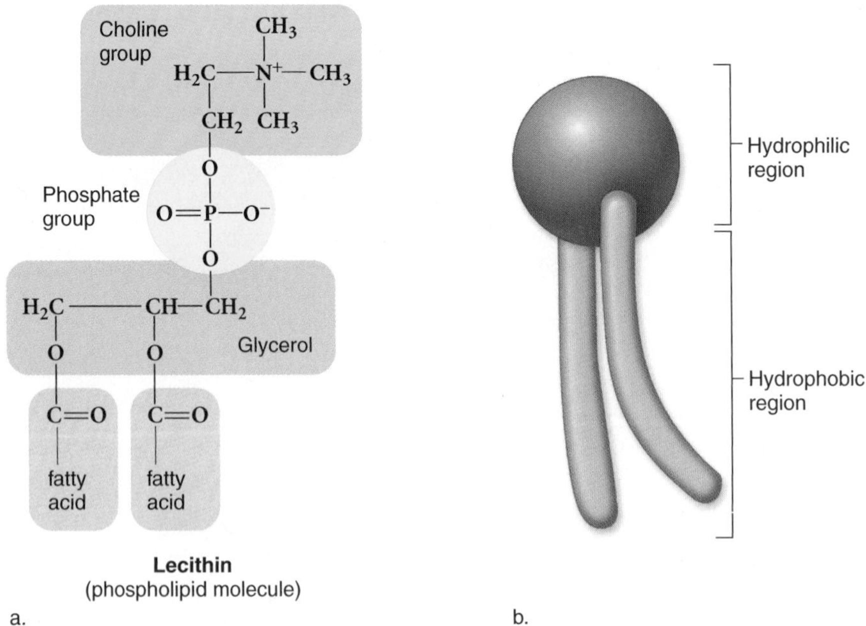

Figure 6.5 (*a*) **Phospholipids.** A phospholipid such as lecithin has a chemical structure that is similar to a triglyceride molecule. The chemical structure of lecithin has a glycerol backbone, phosphorus (P)-containing phosphate group, and nitrogen (N)-containing compound called choline. (*b*) **Hydrophilic/hydrophobic.** Phospholipids have hydrophilic and hydrophobic portions. As a result, a phospholipid can serve as an emulsifier, a substance that keeps water-soluble and water-insoluble compounds mixed together.

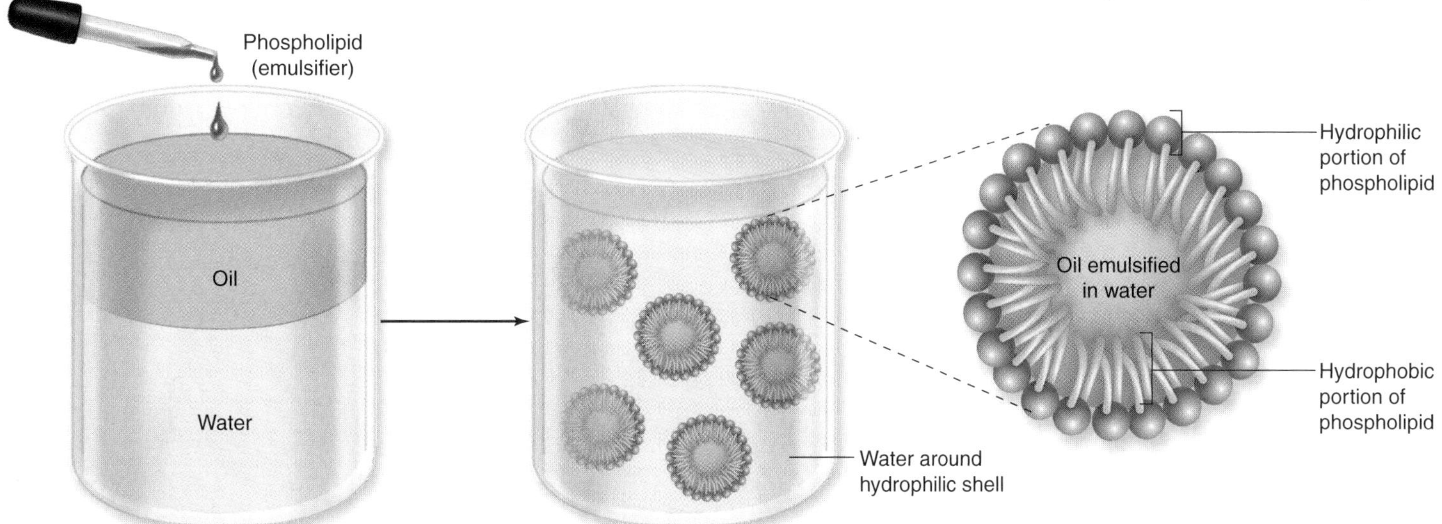

Figure 6.6 Emulsification. Emulsification enhances lipid digestion and absorption by keeping lipids dispersed in small particles, increasing their surface area. As a result, lipases gain greater access to the lipid molecules and can digest them more readily.

phospholipid in food; egg yolks, liver, wheat germ, peanut butter, and soybeans are rich sources of lecithin.

Unlike triglycerides, phospholipids are partially water soluble because the phosphorus-containing portion of the molecule is **hydrophilic** (*hydro* = water; *philo* = loving), that is, it attracts water (Fig. 6.5b). A phospholipid molecule also has a **hydrophobic** (*phobic* = fearing) portion that avoids watery substances and attracts oily ones. By having both hydrophilic and hydrophobic regions, a phospholipid can serve as an **emulsifier**, a substance that keeps water-soluble and water-insoluble compounds mixed together (Fig. 6.6). Manufacturers may add emulsifiers to foods to keep oily and watery ingredients from separating during storage. Processed foods, such as cheese, salad dressing, and ice cream, often have phospholipids added as emulsifying agents. Egg yolk, for example, naturally contains phospholipids and is used to emulsify oil and vinegar when making mayonnaise or oil and milk in cake batters.

In the body, phospholipids are major structural components of cell membranes and are needed for proper functioning of nerve cells, including those in the brain. Lecithin contains **choline**, a water-soluble compound that nerves use to produce the neurotransmitter acetylcholine. A neurotransmitter is a chemical that transmits messages between the nerve cells.

Do healthy people need lecithin, choline, or other phospholipid supplements? No, because phospholipids are widely found in foods and a healthy body synthesizes enough phospholipids to meet its needs.

hydrophilic part of molecule that attracts water

hydrophobic part of molecule that avoids water and attracts lipids

emulsifier substance that helps water-soluble and water-insoluble compounds mix with each other

choline water-soluble compound in lecithin

cholesterol lipid found in animal foods and precursor for steroid hormones, bile, and vitamin D

bile an emulsifier that aids lipid digestion

Cholesterol

Cholesterol is a *sterol*, a more chemically complex type of lipid than a triglyceride or phospholipid (Fig. 6.7). Many people think cholesterol is unhealthy and foods that contain the lipid should be avoided, but it is a very important nutrient. Cholesterol is a component of every cell membrane in your body. Although cholesterol is not metabolized for energy, cells use the lipid to synthesize a variety of substances, including vitamin D, and steroid hormones such as estrogen and testosterone. The liver uses cholesterol to make **bile**, an emulsifier that facilitates lipid digestion in the small intestine. The gallbladder stores bile until it is needed for emulsifying the fatty and watery components of chyme in the small intestine.

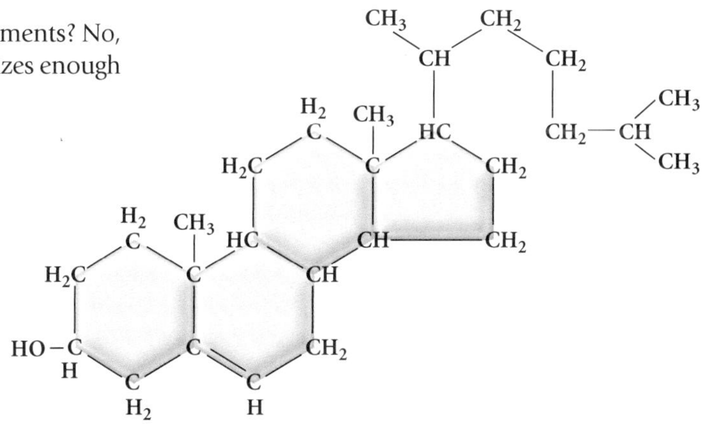

Figure 6.7 Cholesterol. Unlike fatty acids, triglycerides, and phospholipids, cholesterol has carbon, hydrogen, and oxygen atoms arranged in complex ringlike structures.

TABLE 6.2 *Cholesterol Content of Some Common Foods*

Food	Serving Size	Cholesterol mg
Egg	1 large	212
Egg yolk	1	212
Salmon	156 g (5½ oz.)	135
Chicken liver	21 g (¾ oz.)	125
Sardines	85 g (3 oz.)	121
Single-patty cheeseburger	1	111
Beef	85 g (3 oz.)	88
Turkey, ground	85 g (3 oz.)	84
Danish fruit-filled pastry	71 g (2½ oz.)	81
Shrimp	6 large, breaded and fried	80
Ham	85 g (3 oz.)	80
Ice cream, soft-serve	½ cup	78
Ground beef, lean (15% fat)	85 g (3 oz.)	77
Turkey, dark meat	85 g (3 oz.)	71
Egg noodles	1 cup	53
Chicken breast	85 g (3 oz.)	49
Hot dog	1	44
Chocolate milkshake	473 mL (16 oz.)	43
Whole milk	240 mL (1 cup)	34
Cottage cheese	240 mL (1 cup)	32
Cheddar cheese	28 g (1 oz.)	30

Although triglycerides are widespread in foods, cholesterol is only found in animal foods. Egg yolk, liver, meat, poultry, whole milk, cheese, and ice cream are rich sources of cholesterol (Table 6.2). Even if you do not eat animal foods, your body produces cholesterol, primarily in the liver. If you consume too much cholesterol and/or your body makes too much cholesterol, the excess can increase your risk of CVD.

Concept **Checkpoint**

1. What are the major lipids in food and the body?
2. What is the difference between a saturated and unsaturated fatty acid? What is the difference between a monounsaturated and polyunsaturated fatty acid?
3. Identify at least one food that is a rich source of saturated fat, monounsaturated fat, and polyunsaturated fat.
4. Identify the two essential fatty acids.
5. What structural characteristic distinguishes a trans fatty acid from a cis fatty acid? Identify at least two foods that are rich sources of trans fat.
6. What is an omega-3 fatty acid?
7. A recipe mixes 60 mL (¼ cup) of oil with 180 mL (¾ cup) of milk. What common food could you add to keep the oil and milk emulsified?
8. Which foods contain cholesterol? List at least three functions of cholesterol in the body.

What Happens to Lipids in Your Body?

Digesting lipids is a more complicated process than digesting carbohydrates, because the majority of the lipids in food are not water soluble, and the digestion process involves considerable amounts of water. When you eat a meal containing fats, nearly all the lipids in these foods undergo digestion and absorption primarily in your small intestine. Small intestinal cells can absorb cholesterol directly from your food, but triglycerides and phospholipids need to be broken down by lipases before they can be absorbed. **Lipases** are enzymes that digest triglycerides and phospholipids. The pancreas is the primary site of lipase production. After being secreted into the duodenum (the first segment of the small intestine), **pancreatic lipase** digests triglycerides by removing two fatty acids from each triglyceride molecule. This process converts most triglycerides into monoglycerides (Fig. 6.8). A **monoglyceride** has a single fatty acid attached to the glycerol backbone of the molecule. Some triglycerides are completely broken down into glycerol and fatty acid molecules of varying lengths.

The process of digesting phospholipids is similar to that of triglycerides. The enzyme *phospholipase* removes two fatty acids from a phospholipid molecule. The remaining structure contains the lipid's phosphate group (see Fig. 6.5)

As the fatty chyme leaves your stomach, it stimulates small intestinal cells to release the hormone **cholecystokinin** (*kol´-e-sis´-toe-kye´-nin*) (**CCK**). CCK signals the pancreas to secrete digestive enzymes, including pancreatic lipase, into the small intestine. CCK also triggers the gallbladder to contract, forcing bile into the duodenum, where it mixes with chyme. Bile contains *bile salts*, compounds that enhance digestion and absorption by keeping lipids dispersed in small particles, increasing their surface area. As a result, pancreatic lipase gains greater access to the lipid molecules and digests them more readily. If bile is not secreted into the duodenum, lipids clump together in large fatty globules, making lipid digestion less efficient. Glycerol, fatty acids, monoglycerides, cholesterol, and phospholipid fragments are the end products of lipid digestion.

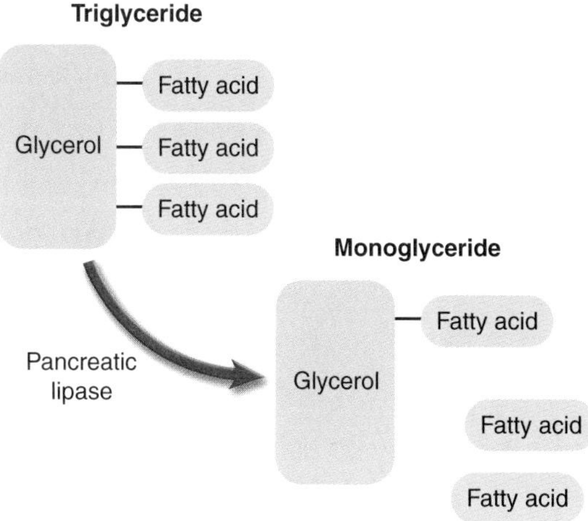

Figure 6.8 Monoglyceride. Pancreatic lipase digests triglycerides by removing two fatty acids from each triglyceride molecule. This process converts most triglycerides into monoglycerides.

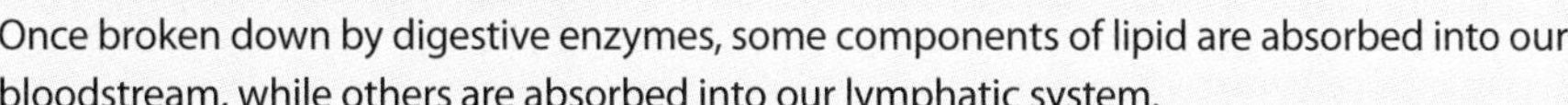

Once broken down by digestive enzymes, some components of lipid are absorbed into our bloodstream, while others are absorbed into our lymphatic system.

lipases enzymes that break down lipids

pancreatic lipase lipase enzymes released from the pancreas to digest lipid

monoglyceride a single fatty acid attached to a glycerol backbone

cholecystokinin (CCK) a hormone that stimulates the gallbladder to release bile and pancreas to secrete digestive enzymes

micelle water-soluble molecules containing bile, phospholipid, free fatty acids, and monoglycerides, which move lipid into the intestinal absorptive cells from the lumen of the GI tract

chylomicron type of lipoprotein produced in absorptive cells of small intestine

lipoprotein water-soluble structure that transports lipids through the bloodstream

Lipoproteins

Under normal conditions, the small intestine digests and absorbs nearly all of the triglycerides and phospholipids in food, but only about 50% of the dietary cholesterol is absorbed. After being absorbed, short- and medium-chain fatty acids and glycerol can enter the bloodstream directly. Most long-chain fatty acids, monoglycerides, and phospholipid fragments are bundled into large molecules called **micelles**, which are absorbed into the intestinal absorptive cells. The majority of the long-chain fatty acids, monoglycerides and phospholipid fragments are reassembled into triglycerides and phospholipids within the absorptive cells of the small intestine. Cholesterol and the reassembled triglycerides are coated with a thin layer of protein, phospholipids, and cholesterol to form chylomicrons (Fig. 6.9). A **chylomicron** (*ky´-low-my´-kron*) is a type of lipoprotein. **Lipoproteins** are water-soluble structures that transport lipids through the bloodstream. Chylomicrons are too large to be absorbed directly into the bloodstream. These lipoproteins must pass through the larger openings of lacteals, lymphatic system vessels in each villus (see Fig. 4.26).

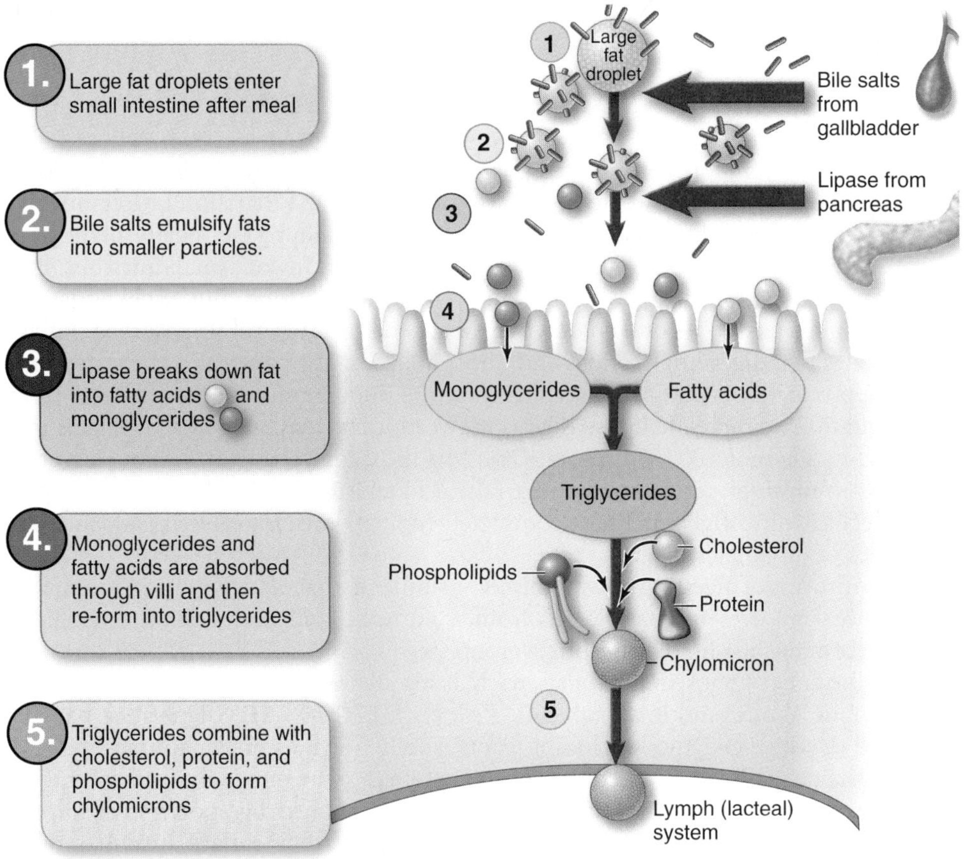

Figure 6.9 Forming chylomicrons. A chylomicron is.a type of lipoprotein, water-soluble structures that transport lipids through the bloodstream. After lipids enter absorptive cells of the small intestine, triglycerides are re-formed. Triglycerides and other lipids are coated with a layer of protein, phospholipids, and cholesterol to form chylomicrons.

1. Large fat droplets enter small intestine after meal
2. Bile salts emulsify fats into smaller particles.
3. Lipase breaks down fat into fatty acids and monoglycerides
4. Monoglycerides and fatty acids are absorbed through villi and then re-form into triglycerides
5. Triglycerides combine with cholesterol, protein, and phospholipids to form chylomicrons

Large fat droplet
Bile salts from gallbladder
Lipase from pancreas
Monoglycerides
Fatty acids
Triglycerides
Cholesterol
Phospholipids
Protein
Chylomicron
Lymph (lacteal) system

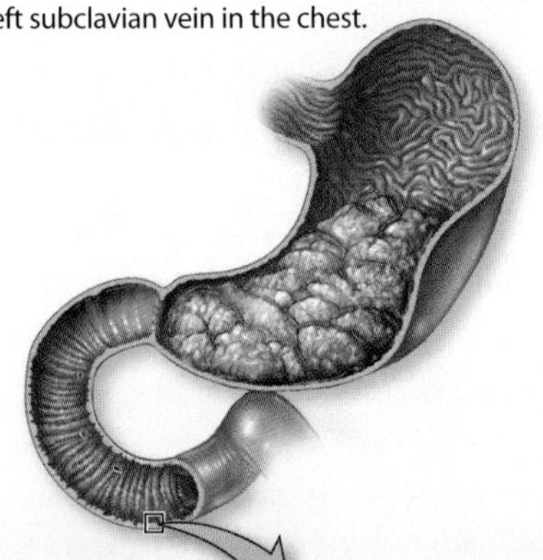

Figure 6.10 Journey into the general circulation. Chylomicrons are too large to be absorbed directly into the bloodstream. These lipoproteins must pass through the larger openings of lacteals, lymphatic system vessels in each villus. The lymphatic system transports chylomicrons to the thoracic duct, where they enter the bloodstream through the left subclavian vein in the chest.

The lymphatic system transports chylomicrons to the thoracic duct, where they enter the bloodstream through the left subclavian vein in the chest (Fig. 6.10). As chylomicrons circulate through the body, **lipoprotein lipase**, an enzyme in the walls of capillaries, breaks down their load of triglycerides into free fatty acids and glycerol. Nearby cells can pick up the fatty acids and glycerol molecules to use for energy. Ten to twelve hours after a meal, most chylomicrons have been reduced to small cholesterol-rich chylomicron

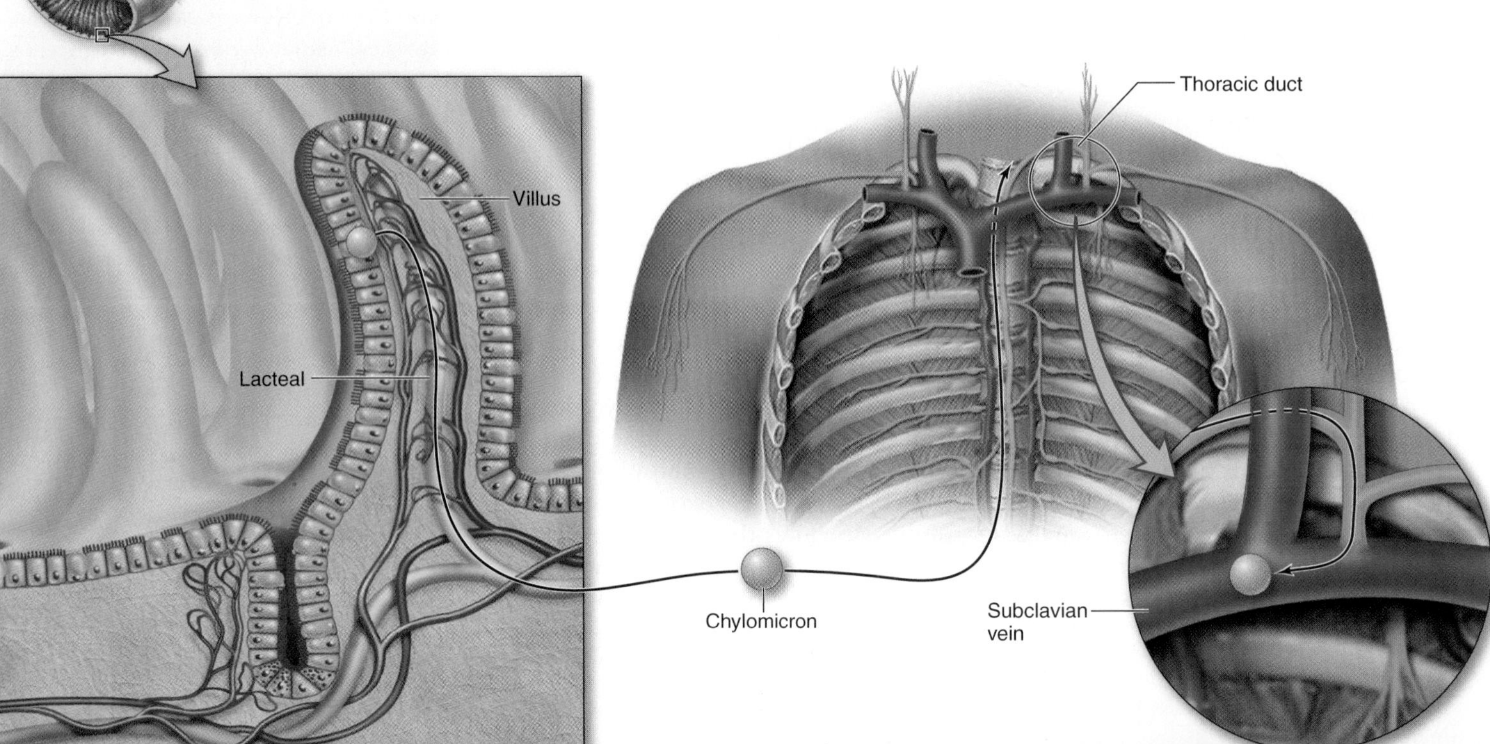

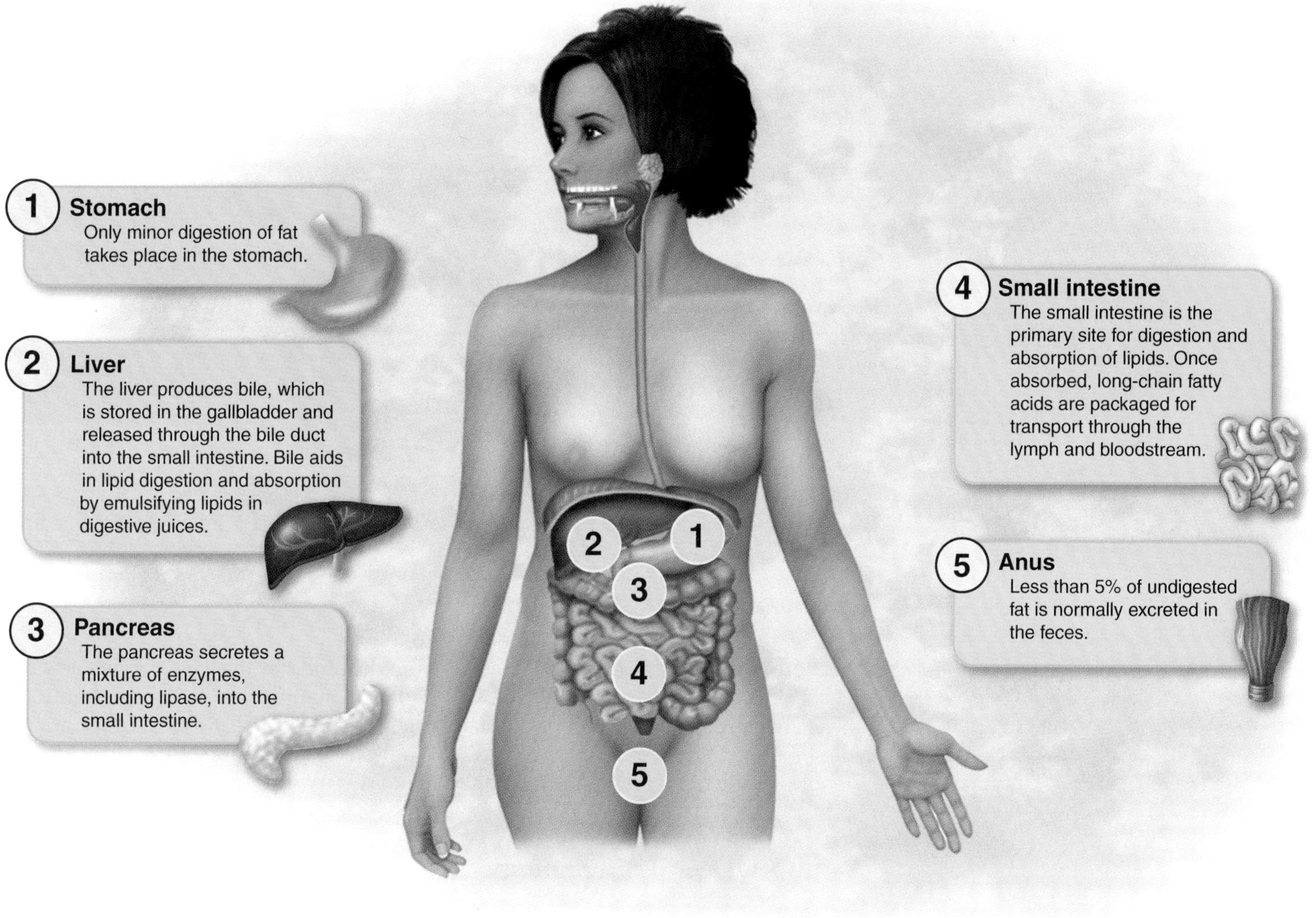

1 Stomach
Only minor digestion of fat takes place in the stomach.

2 Liver
The liver produces bile, which is stored in the gallbladder and released through the bile duct into the small intestine. Bile aids in lipid digestion and absorption by emulsifying lipids in digestive juices.

3 Pancreas
The pancreas secretes a mixture of enzymes, including lipase, into the small intestine.

4 Small intestine
The small intestine is the primary site for digestion and absorption of lipids. Once absorbed, long-chain fatty acids are packaged for transport through the lymph and bloodstream.

5 Anus
Less than 5% of undigested fat is normally excreted in the feces.

Figure 6.11 Lipid digestion and absorption. This illustration summarizes the basic steps of lipid digestion and absorption.

remnants. The liver clears these remnants from the bloodstream and uses their contents to synthesize new lipids and lipoproteins that are released into the general circulation. Figure 6.11 provides a summary of lipid digestion and absorption.

Certain lipoproteins carry lipids from the liver to cells. Other lipoproteins convey lipids from cells to the liver, where they may be converted into new compounds. A later section of this chapter provides more information about lipoproteins and their effects on cardiovascular health.

lipoprotein lipase enzyme in capillary walls that breaks down triglycerides

enterohepatic circulation process that recycles bile salts in the body

Recycling Bile Salts

Most bile salts are absorbed in the ileum, where the compounds enter the bloodstream and travel to the liver. The liver uses the bile salts to make new bile. The process of recycling bile from the intestinal tract is called **enterohepatic** (*ent´-eh-roe-hih-pah´-tik*) **circulation** (Fig. 6.12). Interfering with enterohepatic circulation can reduce blood cholesterol levels, because the liver must use cholesterol to make new bile salts.

Plants contain substances, such as soluble and insoluble fibre, that interfere with cholesterol and bile absorption (see Table 5.5 for foods that contain soluble fibre). Thus, a high-fibre diet can play a valuable role in helping to control blood cholesterol levels by increasing the quantity of bile salts released in the feces. The more bile salts that are lost,

Did You Know?

Abnormalities in normal liver, gallbladder, or pancreas function can impact fat digestion and absorption resulting in elevated levels of fat in the feces. This condition is called *steatorrhea*.

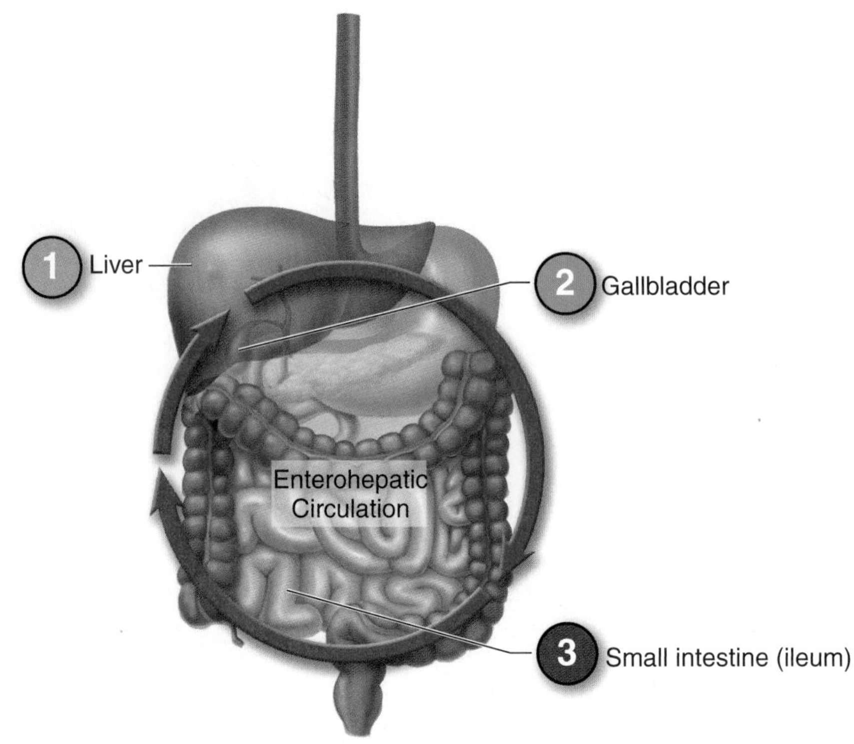

Figure 6.12 Enterohepatic circulation. Enterohepatic circulation is the process of recycling bile salts. (*1*) Liver: The liver secretes bile made from cholesterol, and the gallbladder stores bile. (*2*) Gallbladder: The gallbladder releases bile into the small intestine. (*3*) Small intestine: Most of the bile salts in bile are absorbed in the ileum where they enter the bloodstream and travel to the liver. The liver removes the bile salts and recycles them to make new bile. As a result of this process, the liver conserves cholesterol.

the more cholesterol that must be removed from the blood by the liver to make new bile salts. Plants also make small amounts of **sterols** and **stanols**, lipids that are chemically related to cholesterol. Although plant sterols/stanols are not well absorbed by the human intestinal tract, these substances can reduce cholesterol absorption. Thus, plant sterols/stanols are added to certain foods, beverages, and dietary supplements.

sterols/stanols types of lipids made by plants

adipose cells fat cells that store triglycerides

Using Triglycerides for Energy

Most cells can metabolize fatty acids for energy. Fat is more energy dense than carbohydrate or protein—a gram of fat supplies 9 kcal whereas a gram of carbohydrate or protein provides only 4 kcal. Thus, a high-fat food is a more concentrated source of energy than a high-carbohydrate food. For example, you would need to eat two and a half tablespoons of sugar to obtain the same amount of energy in one tablespoon of oil.

In many instances, your body does not immediately need the energy from the fat in the food you have just eaten. **Adipose cells**, commonly called fat cells, remove fatty acids and glycerol from circulation and reassemble them into triglycerides for storage. Most cells in your body contain triglycerides, but adipose cells are designed to store large amounts of fat (triglycerides). As illustrated in Figure 6.13, a fat droplet comprises most of an adipose cell's volume. When your body needs energy, adipose cells break down some stored triglycerides into fatty acid and glycerol molecules and release these substances into your bloodstream. Muscle and other cells then remove the fatty acids from circulation and metabolize them for energy. The liver may also clear the glycerol molecules from the bloodstream and converts them into glucose molecules that cells can also use for energy.

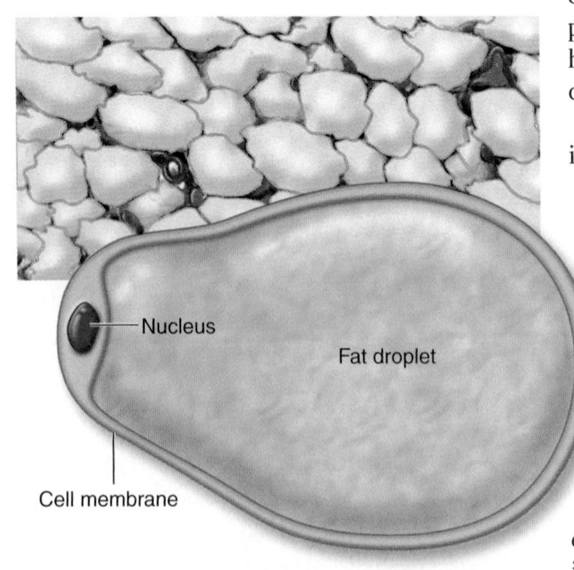

Figure 6.13 Adipose tissue. The primary function of an adipose cell is storing energy in the form of triglyceride.

Eating too much fat contributes to unwanted weight gain, but consuming too much energy from protein and carbohydrates also increases body fat. Why? The body converts excess glucose and amino acids into fatty acids that are used to make triglycerides.[15] Additionally, the nonnutrient alcohol stimulates triglyceride synthesis. Alcohol has many other effects on the body, some of which are beneficial to cardiovascular health. To learn more about alcohol and assess your use of the substance, read the Chapter 6 Highlight, "Drink to Your Health?" later in this chapter. For more information about energy metabolism, see Appendix D at the back of this textbook.

Concept Checkpoint

9. Describe what happens to the fat in a serving of poutine as it undergoes digestion and absorption in your intestinal tract. In your description, include the roles of bile, CCK, pancreatic lipase, villi, and chylomicrons.

Did You Know?

Even with an appropriate level of body fatness, many adults have more than 100 000 kcal worth of stored energy in the form of body fat.

Lipid Consumption Patterns

In the 1960s and 1970s, Canadians consumed approximately 40% of their dietary energy from fats.[16] However, *low-fat* messaging in the closing decades of the twentieth century resulted in Canadians consuming a smaller percentage of their daily caloric intake from fats. In 1998 it was estimated that Canadians received between 29 and 30% of their dietary energy intake from lipids,[17] and data from the Canadian Community Health Survey in 2004 also shows that Canadians received approximately 30% of their dietary energy intake from lipids.[18] A stronger understanding of the valuable role essential fatty acids play in the diet of Canadians has resulted in messaging that directs Canadians toward healthy fats and away from unhealthy fats, such as trans fats, rather than a strategy of strict fat avoidance. Health Canada continues to recommend that no more than 10% of total energy comes from saturated fats and suggests limiting trans fat intake as significantly as possible in an effort to reduce the risk of heart disease.[19]

Lipid Intake Recommendations

The Acceptable Macronutrient Intake Distribution Range (AMDR) for fat in the Canadian diet is 20 to 35% of total energy for those 19 years of age or older.[20,21] However, more important than this guideline is the quality of fats in the diet. Health Canada recommends using vegetable oils such as canola, olive, and soybean, as well as choosing margarines that are low in saturated fats while limiting intake of butter, hard margarine, lard, and shortening. Limiting saturated and trans fats is also a crucial aspect of a healthy lipid intake profile.

The Adequate Intake (AI) for alpha-linolenic acid is 1.6 grams per day for men and 1.1 grams per day for women. The AI for linoleic acid is 14 to 17 grams for men and 11 to 12 grams per day for women.[7]

Other omega-3 fatty acids have also been shown to provide health benefits and should be regularly included in the diet. Although our bodies can convert small amounts of alpha-linolenic acid to EPA and DHA, the preformed forms of these fats are readily available in fish and fish oils. Thus, Health Canada recommends as part of the *Eating Well with Canada's Food Guide* recommendations to consume a minimum of two servings of fatty fish such as salmon, trout, or sardines.[22] Many additional food products are now being marketed in Canada with added EPA and DHA, such as juice, dairy products, and bread.

Over the past 50 years, the percentage of energy derived from fat in the Canadian diet has decreased.

Concept Checkpoint

10. Fat contributes what percentage of total energy in the typical Canadian's diet?

11. What is the AMDR for fat?

12. What are the AI recommendations for alpha-linolenic and linoleic acids?

tip

To lower the fat content of their products, manufacturers of "lite" spreads may have water as the first ingredient. Therefore, replacing the margarine, butter, oil, or shortening in a recipe with a reduced-fat spread could alter the product's taste, texture, and appearance. It's a good idea to read the reduced-fat spread's label to determine whether the product is suitable to use in recipes.

Understanding Nutritional Labelling: Lipids

You can determine how much total fat, saturated fat, trans fat, and cholesterol are in most packaged food products by reading the Nutrition Facts table. Figure 6.14 shows grams of total fat in one serving of bread (a slice), and under it, the number of grams of the different fats that comprise the total amount. The label indicates that there are 2 g of total fat in each slice, and of that amount, 1 g is polyunsaturated fat. According to the label, there are 0 g of saturated, trans, and monounsaturated fats in a slice of the bread. You may be asking yourself, why do the amounts of the various types of fat not add up to 2 g? What happened to the other 1 g of fat? If a food has less than 0.5 g of a specific type of fat, the amount can be reported as 0 g. When the fractions of fat are added together, however, the total amount, in this example, is 2 g. Food manufacturers are not required to provide information about polyunsaturated and monounsaturated fats in their products, but they may choose to disclose the amounts on the Nutrition Facts table.

You can use information from the Nutrition Facts table to determine the percentage of calories that are from fat in a product. In Figure 6.14, the label indicates that a slice of whole-wheat bread provides 100 kcal, 20 of which are from fat. To calculate the percentage of energy from fat, divide the number of kilocalories from fat (20 kcal) by the total number of kilocalories (100 kcal) in the serving. Move the decimal point two places to the right, and then replace the decimal point with a percentage sign (e.g., 20 kcal ÷ 100 kcal = .20; .20 → 20%). In a serving of this type of bread, fat contributes 20% of the energy. By reading the list of ingredients shown at the bottom of the panel, you will note that soybean oil is the main source of fat in this bread.

The Nutrition Facts table also provides information about the cholesterol content of a food. In the table, the amount of cholesterol in a serving is shown below that of total fat. According to information listed on the Nutrition Facts table shown in Figure 6.14, a slice of whole-grain bread provides 0 mg of cholesterol.

Figure 6.14 Nutrition Facts table. This Nutrition Facts table from a package of whole-wheat bread displays the amount of total fat, as well as the amounts of saturated and unsaturated fat, trans fat, and cholesterol in one serving.

Did You Know?

Canada was the first country to make it mandatory for food production companies to list trans fats on food labels.[23]

Concept **Checkpoint**

13. According to the Nutrition Facts table, a serving of potato chips supplies 150 kcal, and fat contributes 100 of the total kcal in the serving of chips. Calculate the percentage of energy from fat in these chips.

Lipids and Health: Cardiovascular Disease (CVD)

Cardiovascular disease (CVD) includes diseases of the heart and blood vessels. Every seven minutes in Canada somebody dies from CVD, and 32% of all deaths in Canada in 2005 were attributed to CVD,[24,25] more than any other disease. Despite these staggering statistics, CVD rates have declined by approximately 50% in the past 20 years.[24] It is estimated that CVD costs the Canadian economy $18 billion each year in direct health care costs and lost productivity.[26]

Figure 6.15 Atherosclerosis. These illustrations depict the progression from a normal arterial lining to an atherosclerotic one. (*a*) Healthy arteries have a smooth lining. (*b*) When the interior of an artery becomes injured and inflamed, certain cells deposit cholesterol and other substances under the artery's lining to repair the damage. This process results in arterial plaque. (*c*) Plaque roughens the normally smooth surface of the arterial lining, which slows blood flow in the area, making clots more likely to form. (*d*) If a blood clot lodges on the plaque, blood flow through the artery can be blocked completely.

From Atherosclerosis to Cardiovascular Disease

Most cases of heart disease and stroke result from **atherosclerosis** (*athero* = lipid containing; *sclerosis* [*skleh-ro´-sis*] = hardening), a chronic process that negatively affects the functioning of arteries. Normal arteries have a smooth lining (Fig. 6.15a). When something in the bloodstream, such as excess cholesterol or glucose, compounds from cigarette smoke, or certain bacteria, irritates the lining of an artery, a cascade of events begin that result in atherosclerosis (Fig. 6.15b). The body's immune system responds to the irritation by producing inflammation within the artery. Inflammation can stimulate healing, but the process can also trigger certain cells within the arterial wall to deposit cholesterol and other substances under the artery's lining. As a result, arterial plaque forms (Fig. 6.15c). Plaque interferes with circulation in the affected area of the artery because it narrows and may even block the opening through which blood flows. Furthermore, plaque roughens the normally smooth surface that lines the artery. The rough lining slows blood flow in the area and makes clots more likely to form (Fig. 6.15d). If a plaque *ruptures* (tears open), repairing the damage also involves clot formation, and such blood clots can be life threatening.

Blood must be able to clot, especially when blood vessels have been injured; otherwise, a person could bleed to death from a minor bruise. In some instances, however, clots form too readily at the injury site. A **thrombus** is a fixed bunch of clots that remains in place and disrupts blood flow. If a thrombus partially closes off an artery that nourishes the heart, the affected section of the heart muscle is unable to receive enough oxygen and nutrients to function properly (Fig. 6.16). As a result, the affected person typically experiences bouts of chest pain, especially when his or her heart beats faster, such as during intense emotional states or physical activities. If a thrombus completely blocks blood flow to a section of the heart muscle, the muscle dies and a **myocardial infarction** (*my´-oh-card-e-al in-farc´-shun*) (heart attack) occurs. Sudden death can result from a severe myocardial infarction. A stroke can happen when a clot blocks an artery in the brain, and brain cells that are nourished by the vessel die. When an artery to a limb is blocked, the tissue in the extremity dies, causing gangrene to occur. If the affected area is large, amputation of the gangrenous limb is often necessary to prevent life-threatening infection. A thrombus or part of a plaque that breaks free from where it formed and travels through the

cardiovascular disease (CVD) a group of diseases that affect the heart and blood vessels

atherosclerosis long-term disease process in which plaques build up inside arterial walls

thrombus a fixed bunch of clots that remains in place

myocardial infarction a heart attack

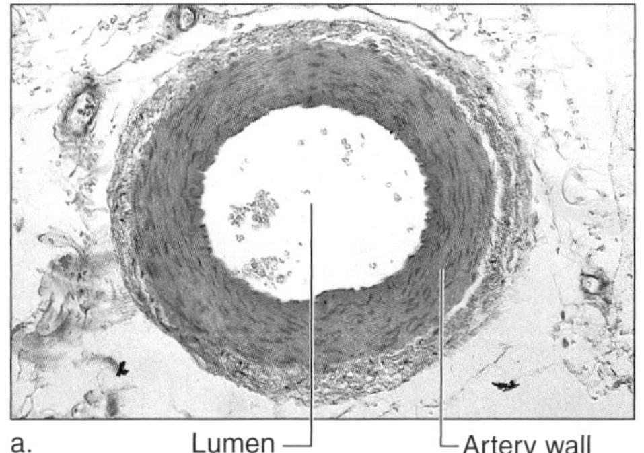

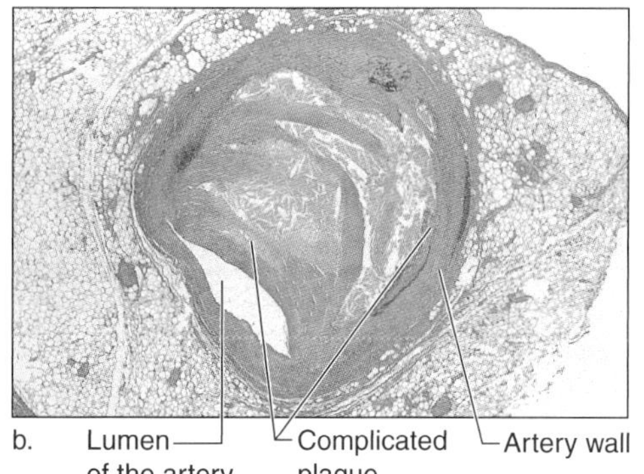

Figure 6.16 Healthy and atherosclerotic arteries. Note the differences between the cross-section of a healthy artery (*a*) and that of an artery nearly completely blocked as a result of atherosclerosis (*b*).

embolus a thrombus or part of a plaque that breaks free and travels through the bloodstream

arteriosclerosis a condition that results from atherosclerosis and is characterized by loss of arterial flexibility

hypertension abnormally high blood pressure levels that persist

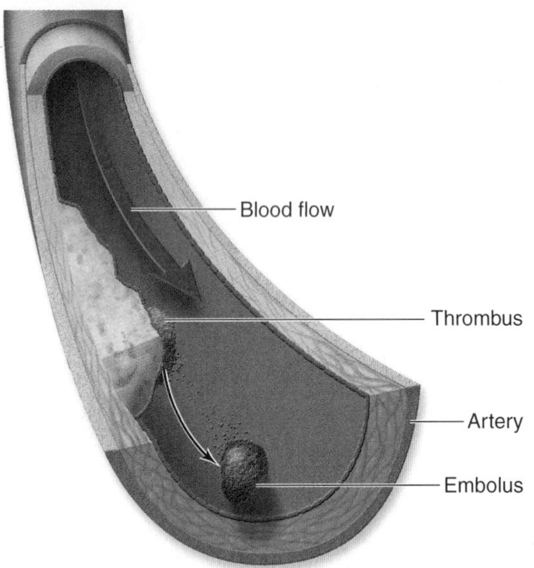

Figure 6.17 Embolus formation. A thrombus or part of a plaque that breaks free from where it formed and travels through the bloodstream is an embolus. If an embolus lodges in an artery, the material can create the same serious consequences as a stationary bunch of clots (thrombus).

Smoking is a major risk factor for cardiovascular disease. If you smoke, simply improving your diet is unlikely to reduce your risk of heart disease; therefore, make every effort to quit using tobacco products.

bloodstream is an **embolus** (Fig. 6.17). An embolus that lodges in an artery can create the same serious consequences as a stationary thrombus.

Certain arteries are more likely to be damaged by atherosclerosis; in addition to the blood vessels of the heart and brain, the blood supply in the kidneys, eyes, and legs are vulnerable. Although atherosclerosis can begin during adolescence and young adulthood, the disease usually does not produce signs or symptoms of CVD until decades later.

Arteriosclerosis

In addition to interfering with blood flow, plaques reduce the flexibility of arteries, causing **arteriosclerosis** (*arterio* = artery), a condition commonly called "hardening of the arteries." Arteriosclerosis contributes to the development of **hypertension**, a chronic condition characterized by abnormally high blood pressure levels that persist even when the person is relaxed. Hypertension is a major risk factor for CVD. The heart of a person with hypertension must work harder to circulate blood through abnormally stiff arteries. Furthermore, elevated blood pressure can cause hardened arteries to tear or burst, causing serious bleeding problems and even sudden death, depending on the artery's size and location.

Major Risk Factors for CVD

The Canadian Heart and Stroke Foundation has identified major risk factors for CVD.[27] The more risk factors a person has, the greater his or her likelihood of CVD. Table 6.3 lists these major CVD risk factors and indicates which are risk factors you can do something about or risk factors you can't control. It is estimated that eight in ten Canadians have at least one risk factor for CVD, such as smoking, physical inactivity, obesity, hypertension, hypercholesterolemia, or diabetes.[24]

Increasing age, male sex, race/ethnic background, and family history are risk factors you can't control. The risk of CVD, including heart disease, increases as people grow older, and men are more likely to have heart attacks than women, though mortality from CVD in Canada remains slightly higher for women.[28] Although a woman's risk of heart attack increases after menopause, her risk is still less than a man's risk. Another trait people cannot change is their family history. For example, if your father had his first heart attack when he was 42 years old, you have a greater risk of developing heart disease than someone whose father had his first heart attack at 75 years of age.

TABLE 6.3 *Cardiovascular Disease: Major Risk Factors*

Risk Factors You Can Control
Hypertension
Diabetes mellitus
Elevated blood cholesterol (especially LDL cholesterol)
Excess body fat
Physical inactivity
Tobacco use
Risk Factors You Can't Control
Family history of CVD
Increasing age
Race or ethnic background
Male sex

Modifiable Risk Factors

Major CVD risk factors, such as hypertension, diabetes mellitus, excess body fat, physical inactivity, and elevated blood cholesterol, involve lifestyle choices that can be modified. Hypertension, diabetes, excess body fat, and elevated blood cholesterol are risk factors that can be influenced by diet. Many people, for example, can reduce their chances of developing CVD by limiting their intake of saturated fat and maintaining a healthy body weight.

Nearly one in five adult Canadians has hypertension.[24] Hypertension is often referred to as a "silent disease," because people with the condition frequently feel healthy and do not have obvious symptoms that indicate trouble within their circulatory system. The condition, however, is quite serious because it damages arterial walls and increases the risk of stroke, heart failure, and kidney disease. Chapter 9 presents information about hypertension, including healthy blood pressure values. Chapter 9 also discusses ways to reduce the likelihood of developing the condition.

Diabetes is another modifiable risk factor for CVD. Adults who have diabetes are two to four times more likely to die of heart disease than adults without diabetes.[29] Chapter 5 discusses diabetes in detail. Excess body fat, especially in the abdominal region, increases the risk of type 2 diabetes and hypertension; Chapter 10 focuses on sensible ways to lose body fat. Physical inactivity also contributes to excess body fat. Chapter 11 provides suggestions for becoming more physically active. Elevated blood lipids, particularly certain lipoproteins, are a risk factor for CVD. The section, "Reducing Your Risk of Atherosclerosis: Dietary Changes," later in this chapter, presents ways people can modify their diets to reduce their chances of developing atherosclerosis and CVD.

Tobacco use is another major risk factor for atherosclerosis that is modifiable. Compared to non-smokers, smokers have two to four times the likelihood of developing heart disease.[30,31,32] If you smoke, simply improving your diet is unlikely to reduce your risk of heart disease; therefore, if you smoke, make every effort to quit using tobacco products.

Emotional stress also plays a role in the development of CVD.[32] Although individuals respond to stress differently, chronic stress generally causes physical changes in the body that can damage arteries and contribute to atherosclerosis. Additionally, people who are "stressed out" may make unhealthy food choices, drink too much alcohol, and get inadequate exercise.

It is important to understand that a risk factor is not the same as a *cause* of disease. AIDS, for example, is caused by human immunodeficiency virus (HIV); a person cannot develop AIDS without being infected with HIV. Atherosclerosis, however, is an extremely complex disease process. In most cases, no single cause for the condition can be identified. Instead, having one or more risk factors increases a person's chances of developing the condition.

You may not be able to prevent having a heart attack or stroke some day, but there is plenty of scientific evidence that suggests you can forestall CVD and live a longer, more satisfying life by reducing or eliminating modifiable risk factors for atherosclerosis. Diet, for example, influences the likelihood of atherosclerosis and is highly modifiable. The following sections of this chapter focus on the role of lipids in the development of atherosclerosis.

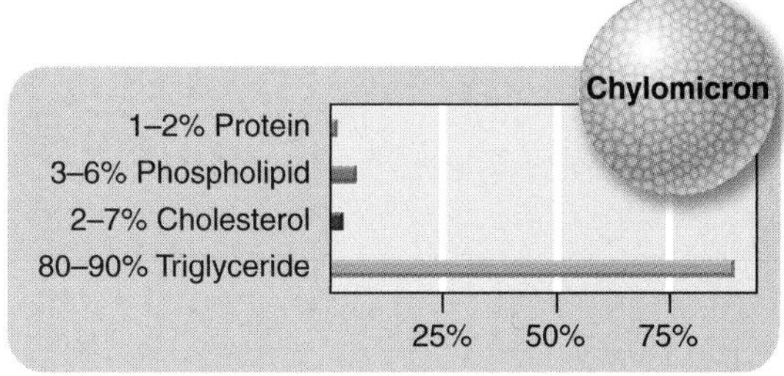

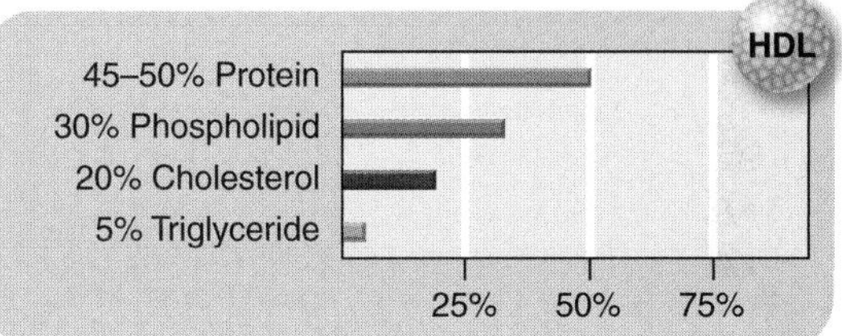

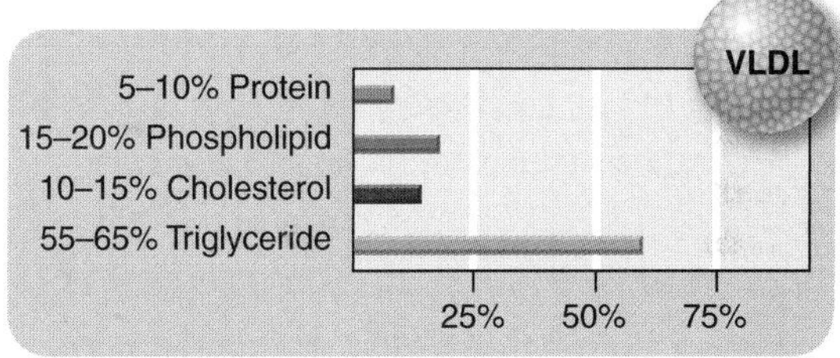

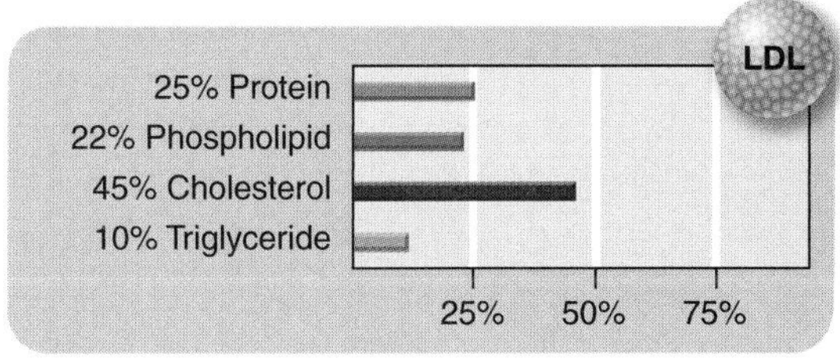

Figure 6.18 Major lipoproteins. Lipoproteins contain different percentages of lipid and protein. Low-density lipoprotein (LDL) carries more cholesterol in the bloodstream than do the other lipoproteins.

Lipids and Atherosclerosis

In addition to chylomicrons, there are three major types of lipoproteins. Each lipoprotein carries different proportions of protein, cholesterol, triglycerides, and phospholipids (Fig. 6.18). **High-density lipoprotein (HDL)** carries about 25 to 40% of cholesterol in the bloodstream. HDL transports lipids away from tissues and to the liver, where they can be processed and eliminated. Thus, the cholesterol carried by HDL (*HDL cholesterol*) is often called "good" cholesterol because it does not contribute to plaque formation.

high-density lipoprotein (HDL) lipoprotein that transports cholesterol away from tissues and to the liver, where it can be eliminated

low-density lipoprotein (LDL) lipoprotein that carries cholesterol into tissues

very-low-density lipoprotein (VLDL) lipoprotein that carries much of the triglycerides in the bloodstream

Low-density lipoprotein (LDL) transports about 60% of the cholesterol in the bloodstream. The cholesterol carried by LDL (*LDL cholesterol*) is often referred to as "bad" cholesterol, because LDL conveys the lipid to tissues, including cells in the arterial walls that make atherosclerotic plaques. However, not all LDL is unhealthy. Some LDL is needed to transport lipids to tissues, where the nutrients are used to make cell structures and vital compounds. In some instances, chemically unstable substances (radicals) damage LDL, forming *oxidized LDL*. This particular form of LDL is not beneficial because it is taken up by arterial cells, and over time, the cholesterol that was in the LDL contributes to atherosclerosis. Figure 6.19 illustrates the roles of HDL, LDL, and oxidized LDL.

A third major class of lipoproteins, **very-low-density lipoprotein (VLDL),** may also contribute to atherosclerosis. This particular lipoprotein contains only about 20% of the cholesterol in the bloodstream; VLDL carries a larger share of triglycerides than cholesterol. As blood triglyceride levels increase, concentrations of HDL cholesterol tend to decrease. [6] Some medical researchers think elevated triglyceride levels play a role in the development of CVD, but the mechanisms are unclear at this point.

Assessing Your Risk of Atherosclerosis

To determine your risk of atherosclerosis, it is a good idea to have a *lipid profile*, a blood test for assessing total cholesterol, HDL cholesterol, LDL cholesterol, and triglyceride levels. Although this textbook generally refers to "blood cholesterol" or "blood lipids," the amount of lipids in serum or plasma rather than whole blood is usually measured. Serum is the liquid portion of blood; plasma is similar to serum except it contains clotting factors.

Table 6.4 presents classifications for healthy and unhealthy blood lipid levels. The desirable range for total cholesterol is less than 5.2 mmol/L.[33] It is estimated that 40% of Canadians have elevated blood cholesterol.[24] Do you know what your blood cholesterol level is? Although knowing the concentration of cholesterol carried by all lipoproteins is important, the amounts of certain lipoproteins in your blood, particularly LDL and HDL, are more critical risk factors. As mentioned earlier, LDL carries cholesterol to cells

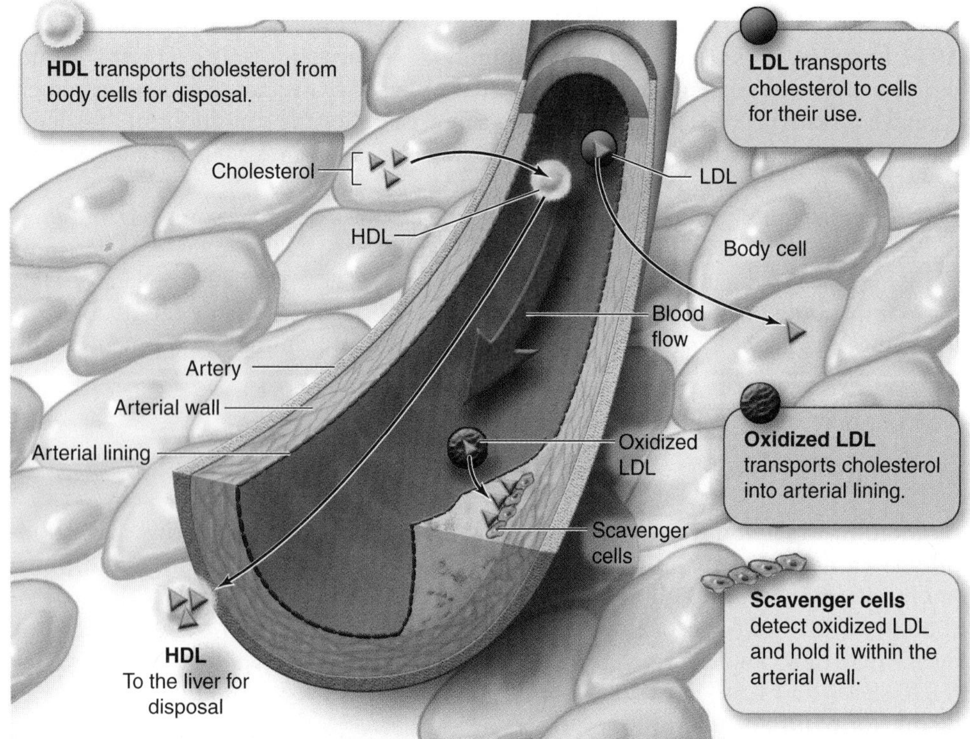

Figure 6.19 HDL, LDL, and oxidized LDL. HDL transports cholesterol away from tissues and to the liver, where it can be processed and eliminated. LDL conveys cholesterol to tissues where the lipid is used to make cell structures and vital compounds. A particular form of LDL, oxidized LDL, is not healthy. Oxidized LDL is taken up by certain arterial cells, and over time, the cholesterol that was in the LDL builds up and contributes to atherosclerosis.

TABLE 6.4 *Blood Lipid Profile Targets*

Total Cholesterol (mmol/L)	HDL Cholesterol (mmol/L)	LDL Cholesterol (mmol/L)	Triglycerides (mmol/L)
<5.20	>1.0 for men >1.3 for women	<3.3	<1.7

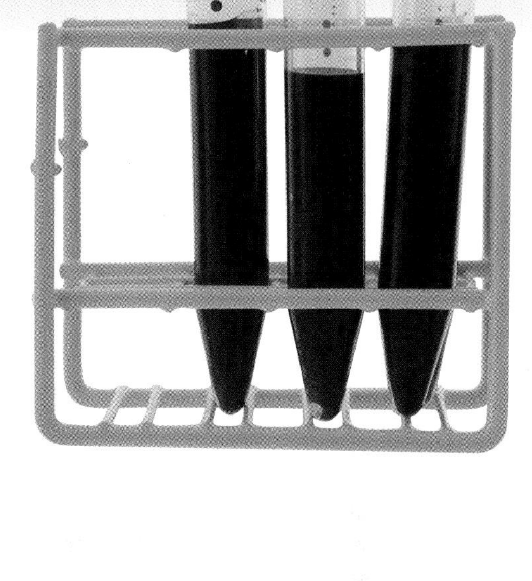

and HDL transports cholesterol away from cells. Simply put, it is healthier to have higher levels of HDL cholesterol than LDL cholesterol.

The LDL cholesterol component of your total blood cholesterol level should be less than 3.3 mmol/L and the HDL cholesterol component should be above 1.0 mmol/L for men and above 1.3 mmol/L for women (see Table 6.4).

C-reactive Protein

Chronic inflammation is involved in the development of CVD.[34] The liver responds to infection and inflammation by producing and releasing **high-sensitivity C-reactive protein (hs-CRP)**, simply referred to as *C-reactive protein* or *CRP*, into the bloodstream. People with elevated CRP are more likely to have CVD and hypertension than people who have low blood levels of the compound.[34,35,36] Thus, elevated CRP is a *marker* for atherosclerosis, which means it is an early warning sign for the condition. If you have a family history of premature CVD, consider having your hs-CRP level measured.

Reducing Your Risk of Atherosclerosis: Dietary Changes

According to epidemiological studies, populations that consume diets rich in saturated fats generally have higher rates of heart disease than populations that eat less saturated fat. Saturated fat alters the structure of liver cell membranes so that they no longer function properly. As a result, the liver removes less cholesterol from the bloodstream.[37]

Most saturated fatty acids increase blood cholesterol levels, by raising concentrations of both LDL and HDL cholesterol. Trans fats also raise blood cholesterol levels, almost as much as saturated fat.[9] However, trans fats raise LDL cholesterol while reducing beneficial HDL cholesterol. High intakes of cholesterol can also raise LDL cholesterol levels.

Specific recommendations for consumption of various types of fat are based on the results of studies that examined the effects of dietary lipids on blood lipids and risk of CVD. Monounsaturated fatty acids generally lower LDL cholesterol without reducing HDL cholesterol levels. Foods rich in monounsaturated fat include peanuts and peanut oil, canola oil, olives and olive oil, almonds, and avocados. The Recipes for Healthy Living feature later in this chapter includes an easy-to-prepare snack made with almonds and cashews, nuts that are rich sources of monounsaturated fat.

Diets containing high amounts of polyunsaturated fatty acids, especially linoleic acid, tend to reduce total cholesterol and LDL cholesterol.[37] In some individuals, however, polyunsaturated fat also reduces HDL cholesterol. Foods rich in polyunsaturated fat include safflower, corn, soybean, and cottonseed oils, as well as some types of sunflower seed oil (see Table 6.1).

Other Dietary Modifications

In addition to modifying your fat intake, you can reduce your risk of CVD by making other dietary changes.[24] Eating foods that are rich sources of fibre, particularly soluble fibre (see Chapter 5), can reduce LDL cholesterol levels without lowering beneficial HDL cholesterol levels.[43] If your blood triglyceride level is too high (>1.7 mmol/L), consider cutting back on your intake of refined carbohydrates by eating less candy and pastries and

high-sensitivity C-reactive protein (hs-CRP) protein produced primarily by the liver in response to inflammation; a marker for CVD

drinking fewer sugar-sweetened soft drinks. Furthermore, consuming less alcohol and losing excess body fat can help reduce elevated triglyceride levels.

Drinking small amounts of alcohol (1 to 2 drinks/day) can raise beneficial HDL cholesterol levels. Consuming too much alcohol, however, contributes to hypertension and damages every organ of the body. Furthermore, excess alcohol consumption has devastating effects on society as well as personal safety and relationships. If you consume several alcoholic beverages regularly, consider reducing your intake to no more than one serving per day. The Chapter 6 Highlight later in this chapter discusses alcohol.

Dietitians and other nutrition experts often promote the traditional Mediterranean diet for healthy eating as well as reducing elevated blood lipid levels and the risk of CVD. The Mediterranean diet (Fig. 6.20) recommends eating small amounts of red meat and using heart-healthy monounsaturated fatty acids, primarily from olive oil; engaging in regular physical activity; and drinking a glass of wine daily. Table 6.5 summarizes ways certain actions, such as dietary manipulations and other therapeutic lifestyle changes, may alter a person's blood lipid levels.

What about Omega-3 Fats? Animal fats and vegetable oils generally contain more omega-6 than omega-3 fatty acids—and the typical Canadian eats far more omega-6 foods. Medical experts think the imbalance between these two types of omega fatty acids increases Canadians' risk of heart disease, worsens arthritis, and may contribute to psychological problems, particularly depression.[38,39] Eating omega-3 fatty acid–rich fatty fish can lower blood triglycerides while increasing HDL cholesterol levels.[13] Moreover, the body uses omega-3 fatty acids to make compounds that can reduce inflammation, blood pressure, and blood clotting. Therefore, dietitians and other health experts recommend that Canadians eat cold-water fish, such as salmon and tuna, a couple times each week. Table 6.6 lists foods that are rich sources of omega-3 fatty acids. Although flaxseeds, soybeans, and walnuts are rich sources of alpha-linolenic acid, plant sources of this omega-3 fatty acid are not as effective as fish oil in reducing deaths from heart disease.[40]

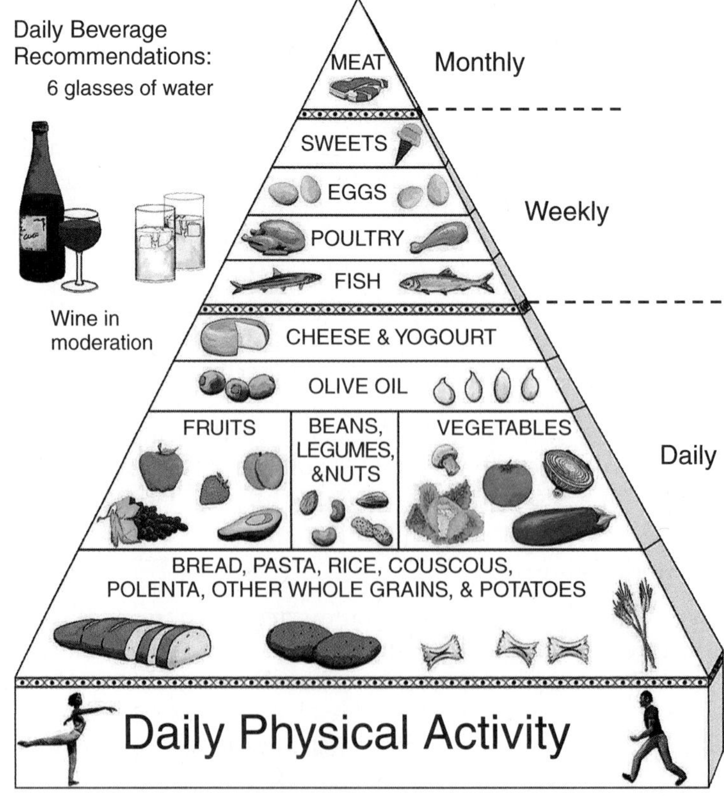

Figure 6.20 Mediterranean Diet Pyramid. Nutrition experts often promote the traditional Mediterranean diet for healthy eating as well as reducing elevated blood lipid levels and the risk of CVD. Breads and other grain products, legumes, nuts, fruits, and vegetables form the foundation of this food guide pyramid. Note that fish and poultry are emphasized instead of red meats, fat is primarily from olive oil, a daily glass of wine may be consumed, and regular physical activity is recommended.

Source: Oldways Presentation & Exchange Trust, 2000.

TABLE 6.5 *Ways to Lower Your Risk of CVD*

Action	Potential Benefits
Increase physical activity level.	Raises HDL levels
Lose excess body fat.	Lowers elevated triglycerides, blood pressure, and risk of type 2 diabetes May increase HDL
Quit smoking.	May raise HDL and lower LDL levels
Make specific dietary changes:	
Reduce intake of saturated and trans fats.	Raises HDL and lowers LDL
Replace saturated fats with unsaturated fats.	Lowers total cholesterol and LDL
Replace some fat with omega-3 fat.	Reduces triglycerides and raises HDL; may reduce blood pressure
Replace margarine or butter with spread made from plant sterols/stanols.	Reduces LDL
Eat more whole-grain, fibre-rich foods, especially those containing soluble fibre.	Reduces total cholesterol and LDL without altering HDL
Consume foods that contain antioxidant nutrients and certain phytochemicals, such as red wine (see Table 1.3). Dietary supplements of these compounds are not recommended.	Reduces risk of heart disease, but the mechanism is unclear
Reduce alcohol and sugar intake.	Lowers triglyceride levels

Because large species of fish can contain high amounts of the toxic metal mercury, young children, pregnant and breast-feeding women, as well as women who are likely to become pregnant should not eat shark, king mackerel, tilefish, and swordfish.[41,42] The second Recipes for Healthy Living feature of this chapter includes an easy recipe made with salmon.

What if you do not like to eat fish? Are fish oil supplements safe? Taking dietary supplements that contain omega-3 fatty acids, such as fish oil supplements, is not generally recommended. Such supplements can increase the risk of bleeding and having a certain type of stroke, therefore, check with your physician before you embark on a campaign to increase the omega-3 fatty acid content of your diet. The Food & Nutrition Tips box below provides some ideas for increasing your intake of omega-3 fatty acids from dietary sources.

Should You Avoid Eggs? Although eggs are a relatively economical source of protein and many micronutrients, egg yolks are the most concentrated source of cholesterol in

TABLE 6.6 *Rich Food Sources of Omega-3 Fats*

Fish/Shellfish
Herring, salmon, sablefish, anchovies, tuna, bluefish, sardines, tilefish, striped bass, mackerel, trout, shark, swordfish, flounder, shrimp
Oils
Flaxseed, walnut, canola, soybean
Nuts and Seeds
Walnuts, flaxseeds

Food & Nutrition *tips*

- Eat seafood, especially fatty cold-water fish, two times a week. Before cooking, marinate fresh fish in olive or canola oil that has been seasoned with a small amount of garlic, pepper, and lemon juice. The light coating of oil on fish can help keep the food from drying out during cooking.
- Bake, grill, or broil fish.
- Add water-packed tuna to salads, or mix tuna with a little olive oil and spread on toast.
- If you don't want the flavour of olive oil in a food, use canola, soybean oil, or soft margarines made from these oils for frying or sautéing.
- Sprinkle chopped walnuts on salads, yogourt, or cereal, or simply eat the nuts as a snack.

Did You Know?

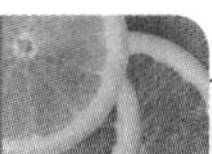

Chicken eggs normally contain very little omega-3 fatty acids. By feeding hens ground flaxseed, farmers can increase the amount of omega-3 fatty acids in eggs. In supermarkets, such omega-3 enriched eggs are often sold beside cartons of regular eggs.

the typical Canadian's diet. One yolk contains 5 g of fat and about 210 mg of cholesterol; egg whites have no fat or cholesterol (see Table 6.2).

coronary artery disease (CAD) a major form of CVD

Does eating egg yolks and other cholesterol-rich animal foods raise blood cholesterol levels? In a study involving almost 38 000 adult Americans, researchers found that eating up to one egg per day did not increase the risk of **coronary artery disease (CAD)** or stroke in healthy subjects.[50,51] Surprisingly, the cholesterol in food does not have as much effect on blood cholesterol levels as the saturated fat does. Why? In a healthy person, the liver produces less cholesterol when large amounts of cholesterol are eaten. On the other hand, eating large amounts of saturated fat increases the liver's cholesterol production. Because foods that are high in cholesterol are often rich sources of saturated fat, dietary cholesterol was blamed for raising blood cholesterol levels.

For those who must limit their cholesterol intake, egg whites can often be used in recipes that call for whole eggs, and egg substitutes are available in supermarkets. By feeding hens a naturally occurring cholesterol-lowering substance, farmers can produce eggs that contain up to 14% less cholesterol than eggs laid by hens that were not fed the substance.[52] You may be able to find these eggs in supermarkets, but be prepared to pay a higher price than for "regular" eggs.

Is It Safe to Eat Butter? Over the past 60 years, many Canadians switched from using butter to partially hardened vegetable oil margarines because of concern over butter's cholesterol and saturated fat content. By the late 1990s, however, news reports alerted Canadians that eating trans fat in margarine was more harmful than consuming the natural lipids in butter.[53] If you use margarine, should you be concerned about its trans fat content, and switch to using butter?

Although margarine made from partially hydrogenated vegetable oil contains small amounts of trans fat, margarine contains more unsaturated fat and less saturated fat than butter.[54] One way to reduce your intake of trans fats is to use soft (tub) or liquid margarine instead of stick margarine. These products contain little or no saturated and trans fats. The results of clinical studies suggest that people who use soft or liquid margarine can lower their LDL cholesterol more than those who use butter.[55,56] If you enjoy butter, occasionally having some is unlikely to clog your arteries. The following Food & Nutrition Tips suggest ways to reduce your trans fat intake.

Food & Nutrition *tips*

- Read the Nutrition Facts table and the ingredient list on the label when choosing processed foods, especially margarine. Compare margarines to find the product with 0 g of trans fat. Margarines that have "liquid" vegetable oil as the first ingredient generally have less trans fat than stick margarines.
- Avoid products that include hydrogenated oil, partially hydrogenated oil, or shortening in the ingredient list.
- Eat fewer commercially prepared baked goods, snack foods, and fried fast-food items.
- Purchase brands of microwave popcorn that have little added fat or no trans fats. Buy plain popcorn, and to pop the kernels use a small amount of hot oil in a covered sauce pan or use a hot-air machine.
- Commercial frostings that are made with vegetable shortenings are likely to be high in hydrogenated oils.
- Pastry dough may be made with shortening. Replace shortening with oil or soft margarine to make your own pastry dough "from scratch."

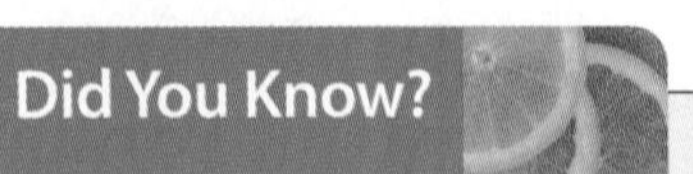

Did You Know?

Garlic, onions, and chives are sources of sulphur-containing compounds, such as allicin, that have antioxidant properties. Fresh garlic and garlic supplements have been promoted to lower blood cholesterol levels. However, results of a study involving more than 190 adults who had moderately elevated cholesterol levels did not support the usefulness of consuming fresh garlic or garlic supplements to reduce elevated blood lipids.[48]

Did You Know?

Eggs with brown shells are not more nutritious than eggs with white shells; the colour of an egg shell is determined by the breed of hen that laid it. Also, grading does not reflect the nutritional content of an egg.

Will Weight Loss and Exercise Help? Having a healthy body weight often reduces the risk of CVD. Excess body fat, especially around the midsection of the body, is associated with unhealthy LDL cholesterol and triglyceride levels. Physical inactivity and excess energy consumption contribute to unwanted weight gain. Performing moderate-intensity physical activity nearly every day and balancing energy intake with energy expenditure each day can help people achieve and maintain healthy body weights. Taking such steps can also reduce elevated LDL cholesterol and triglyceride levels.

When foods such as chicken or fish are breaded and fried, the breading soaks up fat, greatly increasing the food's energy value.

Food Selection and Preparation

You can change your food selection and preparation practices to reduce the amount of fat in your diet. Fatty meats such as rib steaks are often more tender and expensive than leaner cuts such as chuck roasts. Certain cooking methods, however, can increase the tenderness of lean cuts of meat. Moist cooking methods, such as pot roasting or tightly covering the baking dish with foil, help tenderize meats without adding fat. In addition to using a moist cooking method, reduce the oven temperature from 350 °F to less than 325 °F. The meat will take longer to cook, but it is less likely to toughen and dry out. After cooking, avoid eating the visible fat that remains. For example, trim away much of the fat from the meat and do not use pan drippings to make sauces or gravies. Steaming meats and vegetables is a cooking method that does not require adding fat during preparation. Stir-frying pieces of raw vegetables, meat, fish, shellfish, and poultry in small amounts of hot vegetable oil cooks them quickly and preserves micronutrients. Additionally, when you brown ground beef in a pan, drain much of the fat before you add other ingredients to the meat. Dipping raw foods in batter and deep-fat frying them adds considerable amounts of fat to your diet, because breading serves as a sponge that soaks up oil. Furthermore, some fatty acids in vegetable oil are converted to unhealthy trans fats when the oil is heated.[11] If you prepare breaded fried foods, place the items on paper towels after cooking them to soak up as much excess fat as possible. Some people think the breading is the "best part" of a fried food, but removing some or all of the breading before eating the item can reduce your overall fat intake.

Although it is easy to peel greasy breading from fried fish, much of the fat that you eat is hidden in foods and beverages. For example, do you drink 2% milk? Fat comprises only 2% of the milk's volume, but the lipid contributes 37% of the beverage's calories. Skim milk actually contains less than 0.5% fat by volume, and fat contributes essentially no energy to the beverage. What about the fat content of the cream cheese, margarine, or butter that you spread on a piece of toast? About 90% of the calories in cream cheese and about 100% of the calories in butter and margarine are from fat. Vegetable oils are almost 100% fat, so fat contributes all the energy in most salad dressings. Fried foods, chips, and salad dressings are high in fat; bacon, sausage, hot dogs, luncheon meats, and hard cheeses are also fatty foods. Nuts, including peanuts and almonds, have high fat contents, but they generally contain high amounts of healthy monounsaturated fats. Table 6.7 lists some high-fat foods and indicates their fat contents.

Did You Know?

About 80% of stick margarine is fat—the same percentage of fat as in butter. A pat of stick margarine (approximately a teaspoon) also supplies about the same amount of energy as a pat of butter—35 kcal.

TABLE 6.7 *Common Foods: Percentage of Energy from Fat*

80 to 90% of Energy from Fat
Macadamia nuts
English walnuts
Cream cheese
Sour cream
Olives
Avocados
Hot dog
Sausage
Bologna
Processed cheese
60 to 79% of Energy from Fat
Peanut butter
Salami
Bacon (cooked)
Mayonnaise
Cashews
Swiss cheese
Cheesecake
Chicken wings with skin
Ground beef, reg.
40 to 59% of Energy from Fat
Parmesan cheese
Semisweet chocolate chips
Corn or potato chips
Tofu
Fried chicken, extra crispy
Corned beef
French fries
Vanilla ice cream, reg.
Whole milk
20 to 39% of Energy from Fat
2% milk
Chicken breast, roasted with skin
Brownie with nuts and frosting

Instead of striving to eliminate all fatty foods from your diet, try reducing your intake of them. For example, if you drink 2% or whole milk, switch to 1% or skim milk. Nearly all the lipids in skim milk have been removed, which is why it tastes watery to people who are not accustomed to drinking it. Except for energy and lipid content, the nutritional value of skim milk is basically the same as that of whole and 2% milks. Instead of eating a large order of french-fried potatoes, have a baked potato topped with a teaspoon of soft margarine. By eating the baked potato instead of french fries, you will consume about 300 fewer kilocalories and 21 fewer grams of fat. The Food & Nutrition Tips on page 171 provide more practical suggestions for reducing your fat and cholesterol intake.

Fat Replacers In response to consumer demand for more fat-reduced and fat-free foods, manufacturers can use several synthetic fat replacers to substitute for some or all of the fat in their products. Fat replacers used in Canada are typically carbohydrate based or protein based.[57] These additives are typically included during food production to mimic functional qualities provided by lipid in foods, such as moisture and mouth feel. The ideal synthetic fat is safe, provides little or no energy, mimics natural fat's contribution to the taste and texture of food, and withstands typical cooking temperatures. Olestra, for example, is used to make snack foods such as potato chips. Olestra is not approved for use as a food additive in Canada and thus is not found in foods available in Canada. This particular fat replacer contains fatty acids arranged in an unnatural configuration that is not digested. As a result, Olestra passes through the intestinal tract unchanged and unabsorbed. Some people, however, report experiencing diarrhea when they eat large amounts of food made with Olestra. Additionally, Olestra can attract fat-soluble vitamins and interfere with their absorption; therefore, products containing Olestra are fortified with these vitamins.

People who are concerned about their energy intake should recognize that fat-reduced and fat-free foods are not "calorie-free." Moreover, food manufacturers often increase the amount of simple sugars in these products to improve taste and compensate for reduced-fat content. Nevertheless, fat replacers can help people reduce their total fat intake.[58,59]

Genetic Factors

Until recently, much of the research examining the role of diet in the development of atherosclerosis focused on the association between lipids and CVD. Nevertheless, some people with normal cholesterol levels and no other major CVD risk factors still had heart attacks, strokes, and related blood vessel diseases. In many cases, affected individuals were under 40 years of age. This puzzling observation led to the discovery that the amino acid **homocysteine** is a risk factor for CVD.[44,45] Amino acids are the chemical units that comprise proteins. Cells use two vitamins, B-6 and folate, to convert homocysteine into a safer compound. Some people, however, have a genetic abnormality that causes the amino acid to accumulate in their bloodstream, particularly when their intake of folate is low.[46,47] Such persons have high risk of CVD. Medical researchers think elevated blood levels of homocysteine may injure arterial walls and contribute to atherosclerosis. Eating foods that are rich sources of folate and B-6, as well as taking a multivitamin supplement that contains these vitamins, can reduce elevated blood homocysteine. At this point, however, results of research do not indicate that vitamin therapy to lower homocysteine levels reduces the risk of CVD.[43] More studies are needed to determine whether people with elevated blood homocysteine can benefit from taking certain vitamins.

Scientists have identified a gene that increases a person's susceptibility to atherosclerosis, particularly when this individual eats a high-fat diet.[49] As a result of this research, scientists may be able to locate more genes that are involved in the process of atherosclerosis and develop a blood test that identifies protein markers produced by the abnormal genes. Thus, young people could undergo testing to determine their risk of

Food & Nutrition *tips*

Plain yogourt is a low-fat substitute for sour cream.

- Reduce your intake of fried foods, including fried fish, chicken, and french-fried potatoes.
- Purchase lean meats and trim visible fat from meat before cooking. Before eating cooked meat, trim and discard any remaining visible fat.
- Try replacing some fatty foods with reduced-fat or fat-free alternatives. For example, substitute plain, fat-free yogourt in recipes that call for sour cream. Place a spoonful of the yogourt, instead of butter or sour cream, on a baked potato.
- Because most nuts are rich sources of healthy unsaturated fats, replace foods that contain saturated fat with nuts. For example, use peanut or soy nut butters instead of cheese or luncheon meat in sandwiches.
- Remove and discard the skin before eating poultry, because a layer of fat is under the skin.
- Pretzels, air-popped popcorn, and most fruits and vegetables are low in fat and generally more nutrient dense than chips, cookies, pastries, and candy bars.
- Patronize fast food restaurants that offer low-fat menu items such as meatless salads, baked or broiled chicken and fish, low-fat yogourt, and bean burritos.
- Use less salad dressing on salads. When in restaurants, order salad dressings "on the side" so that you can control the amount that is added.
- Use ¼ less butter, oil, or margarine than is indicated in recipes. Use olive or canola oils in recipes that call for vegetable "oil."

atherosclerosis well before the signs and symptoms of the condition appear. Until then, it is wise to have regular health checkups that include blood pressure, lipid profile, and homocysteine testing to assess your risk of atherosclerosis, especially if you have a family history of premature CVD. Ask your physician for a copy of the laboratory results, and keep them along with others in your personal medical file for future reference.

homocysteine amino acid that plays a role in the development of atherosclerosis

What if Lifestyle Changes Don't Work?

Some people are unable to lower their risk of CVD significantly by making dietary changes, exercising regularly, and losing excess body fat. If your blood lipids are too high and the levels have remained elevated even after you made these lifestyle modifications, it is important to discuss additional treatment options with your physician and dietitian. Millions of Canadians take a class of prescription drugs called *statins* to reduce their elevated blood lipid levels.[33] Statins interfere with the liver's metabolism of cholesterol, effectively reducing LDL cholesterol and triglyceride levels as a result. Statins are relatively safe when taken as directed. In addition, strategies that aim to increase the total dietary fibre intake of the diet may help Canadians control blood lipid levels. This concept is discussed further in Chapter 5.

Concept **Checkpoint**

14. Define atherosclerosis, arteriosclerosis, arterial plaque, thrombus, and embolus. Discuss the series of physiological changes that occur in arteries and contribute to the development of CVD.
15. What are Health Canada's recommendations concerning the maximum amount of cholesterol per day and percentages of total calories from fat, saturated fat, and trans fat?
16. List at least three major risk factors for CVD that are non-modifiable, and at least five that are modifiable.
17. Bernard's total blood cholesterol level is 7.1 mmol/L, and his HDL cholesterol level is 0.85 mmol/L. Based on this information, does Bernard have a high risk or low risk of CVD? Explain your answer.
18. What is hs-CRP? What can you learn about your risk of CVD from having a lipid profile performed on your blood?
19. Suggest at least four ways people can reduce their intakes of saturated and trans fats and increase their intakes of unsaturated fats.
20. Identify at least two foods that are rich sources of omega-3 fatty acids.
21. What role does homocysteine play in the development of heart disease?
22. List at least three foods in which fat contributes 80 to 90% of the energy in the items.
23. What is a statin?

Chapter 6 Highlight
Drink to Your Health?

What do beer, wine, vodka, whiskey, sake (*sak´-e*), koumiss (*koo´-mis*), and kefir (*keh-feer´*) have in common? These beverages contain *ethanol*, a two-carbon compound that chemists classify as an alcohol. Alcohols such as ethanol, glycerol, and cholesterol are organic molecules that have one or more hydroxyl (OH) groups in their chemical structures (Fig. 6.A). This textbook refers to ethanol simply as "alcohol."

Offering wine in religious ceremonies, toasting the bride and groom with champagne at a wedding, or barhopping with friends on their 19th birthdays—for many Canadians, alcohol consumption is a part of celebrating religious rites and life's milestones. When consumed in moderation, alcoholic beverages can make social situations more enjoyable. Many people, however, experience serious problems as a result

Figure 6.A Ethanol. Alcohol (ethanol) is a simple two-carbon compound.

$CH_3—CH_2—OH$

Ethanol

of their drinking habits. This Chapter 6 Highlight focuses on alcohol production and metabolism as well as the chemical's effects on the body.

Alcohol Production

Throughout the world, people have been producing and drinking alcoholic beverages for thousands of years. The chemical process that results in alcohol is not complicated and occurs naturally. The process requires certain microbes, warm conditions, and a source of simple sugars. Although some types of bacteria produce alcohol, commercial alcoholic beverage production relies on *yeast*, one-celled fungi (*fun´-ji*) that break down (*ferment*) simple sugars in the absence of oxygen to obtain energy and the metabolic waste product, alcohol. Grains, fruit, and potatoes—just about anything that contains simple sugars—will ferment under the proper conditions. Yeast will even ferment lactose in milk. In arid parts of southeastern Europe, central Asia, and the Middle East, the climate and land are generally not suitable for growing grains, fruit, or other fermentable plant foods. The nomadic populations who live in these regions drink fermented mare's milk (*koumiss*) or camel's milk (*kefir*).

Alcohol is soluble in water, and alcoholic beverages generally contain a considerable amount of water. Beers are typically 3 to 6% alcohol, wines contain about 8 to 14% alcohol, and wine coolers are about 10% alcohol by volume. Alcohol is poisonous (*toxic*), and yeast dies when the concentration of alcohol in the fermenting solution reaches 14 to 16%. The distilling process increases the alcohol concentration of an alcoholic beverage. Distilled spirits (hard liquors) such as whiskey, bourbon, and vodka are generally 40 to 50% alcohol. You can determine the percentage of alcohol in hard liquor by dividing the "proof" declaration on the label by two. Tequila, for example, is "80 proof," or 40% alcohol.

Although each gram of alcohol provides 7 kcal, alcohol is not a nutrient; it is a mind-altering drug that is often classified as a food. Beer and wine contain simple carbohydrates and small amounts of certain minerals and B vitamins. Distilled spirits have essentially no nutritional value other than water. Mixing distilled spirits with juices, cocktail mixes, or other flavourings increases the alcoholic beverage's energy content and may add some nutrients, particularly simple sugars, depending on the ingredients in the mixer. Table 6.A indicates the grams of alcohol and carbohydrates in certain alcoholic drinks as well as their caloric content. A standard drink (approximately 355 mL [12 oz.] of beer or wine cooler, 150 mL [5 oz.] of wine, or 45 mL [1.5 oz.] of liquor) contains 13 to 14 g of alcohol (Fig. 6.B).

How the Body Processes Alcohol

Alcohol requires no digestion and readily passes through the tissues lining the inside of the mouth, esophagus, stomach, and small intestine. When alcohol is consumed with meals, food delays its absorption from the stomach and slows the rate in which alcohol enters the bloodstream. To reduce alcohol's harmful effects, the body detoxifies the simple chemical by converting it into less damaging compounds. Detoxification begins in the stomach where the enzyme gastric alcohol dehydrogenase metabolizes up to 20% of the alcohol. Most of the remaining alcohol passes through the small intestinal wall and travels to the liver, the primary site for metabolizing alcohol. Because alcohol is a poison, the liver shifts its metabolic focus from macronutrient metabolism to alcohol detoxification when the compound enters its tissues.

TABLE 6.A *Approximate Alcohol, Carbohydrate, and Energy Contents of Alcoholic Beverages**

Beverage	Amount	Kcal	Alcohol (g)	Carbohydrates (g)
Beer				
Regular	355 mL (12.0 fl. oz.)	139	13	11
Light	355 mL (12.0 fl. oz.)	103	11	5
Table Wines	150 mL (5.0 fl. oz.)	114	14	5
Distilled Spirits	45 mL (1.5 fl. oz.)	96	14	0
Gin, rum, vodka, whiskey				

* Protein and fat contribute little or nothing to the caloric content.

Source: Health Canada, Nutrient Value of Some Common Foods, Beverages, http://www.hc-sc.gc.ca/fn-an/nutrition/fiche-nutri-data/nutrient_value-valeurs_nutritives-table17-eng.php.

Figure 6.B What's a standard drink? A standard drink is approximately 355 mL (12 oz.) of beer or wine cooler, 150 mL (5 oz.) of wine, or 45 mL (1.5 oz.) of liquor. Each standard drink contains 13 to 14 g of alcohol.

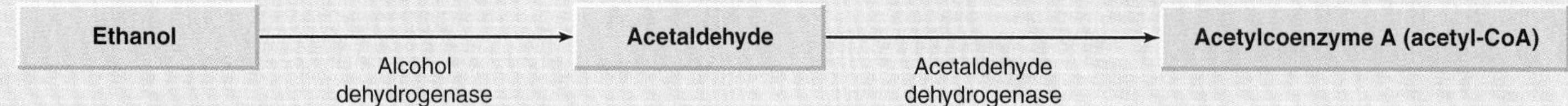

Figure 6.C Alcohol metabolism: Major metabolic steps. This diagram simplifies the major chemical steps involved in the metabolism of low doses of alcohol to less toxic compounds. Acetyl-CoA is an important by-product of ethanol metabolism, because the molecule can be further metabolized to carbon dioxide (CO_2) and water (H_2O), or used to form fatty acids.

The liver relies on two biochemical pathways to metabolize alcohol. When relatively low doses are consumed, the enzyme alcohol dehydrogenase converts most of the alcohol to acetaldehyde, a substance that is more toxic than alcohol. Another enzyme, acetaldehyde dehydrogenase, reacts with acetaldehyde to form acetyl-coenzyme A (acetyl-CoA), an important molecule in energy metabolism. Acetyl-CoA may be further metabolized to carbon dioxide (CO_2) and water (H_2O), or the molecule can be used to synthesize fatty acids (Fig. 6.C).

If a person consumes excessive amounts of alcohol, such as during a drinking binge, the alcohol overwhelms the liver's ability to metabolize the drug using the dehydrogenase pathway. When this occurs, the second method of processing alcohol, the microsomal ethanol oxidizing system (MEOS), takes over. Unlike the alcohol dehydrogenase pathway, MEOS wastes energy in the form of body heat that dissipates into the environment. Thus, alcoholics typically gain little weight from their energy intake when alcohol supplies most of their energy.

Factors that Influence Alcohol Metabolism

You may have noticed that a few of your friends who drink can "hold their liquor" better than others. Why are some people able to drink more alcohol at one time than others? Several physiological factors account for the variability. In addition to the amount and timing of alcohol consumption, personal characteristics such as sex, ethnicity, body size and composition, age, and prior drinking history affect his or her body's detoxification rate. For example, a healthy person who weighs 70 kg (154 lbs.) metabolizes about one alcoholic drink per hour. Drinking caffeinated beverages, exercising, or taking vitamins does not increase this rate. To sober up, the drinker must stop consuming alcohol and give his or her liver time to metabolize the alcohol.

Alcohol is not stored in the body. Until the liver can detoxify the toxic chemical, it circulates in the bloodstream and diffuses into the watery fluids within and surrounding cells. The lungs and perspiration eliminate some of the alcohol; that's why you can smell alcohol when you're around someone who's been drinking. The kidneys also filter some of the drug from the bloodstream and eliminate it in urine. To determine whether someone is legally intoxicated as a result of drinking alcohol, law enforcement officials use special devices to analyze the alcohol in blood, urine, or expired air to estimate the person's blood alcohol concentration (BAC). BAC is reported as a percentage that indicates the amount of alcohol in the blood. In most of Canada, a BAC of 0.08% is the legal limit for intoxication for automobile operators who are 19 years of age or older. However, beginning in August 2010, Ontario became the first province to institute a zero-tolerance policy for drivers aged 21 and under. Drivers who are 21 and under and who are caught with any alcohol in their blood face a fine and licence suspension.[1A]

Men and women have different physical responses to alcohol. Men produce more gastric alcohol dehydrogenase than women, and the alcohol that escapes being metabolized exits their stomachs faster.[2A] As a result, men have less alcohol available for intestinal absorption and their BACs will be lower after they drink the same amount of alcohol as women (Fig. 6.D). Compared to men who drink heavily, women have a higher risk of serious health problems, especially damage to their liver, brain, and heart, when they abuse the same amounts of alcohol.[3A]

The reasons for these sexual differences are unclear, but they probably involve physiological factors including body size and composition. The average man is larger than the average woman, and larger people can often drink more alcohol than smaller individuals, because they have bigger livers that detoxify more alcohol at a time. Additionally, a healthy 68-kg (150-lb.) man typically has more body water than a healthy 68-kg (150-lb.) woman. After the man drinks a beer, the alcohol diffuses out of his bloodstream and into the water compartments of his body. Because the woman's body has less water, more alcohol remains in her bloodstream after she drinks a beer. As a result, her BAC rises faster and she becomes more intoxicated after drinking the same amount of alcohol as her male counterpart.

Prior alcohol exposure also influences the rate of alcohol metabolism. People who drink regularly develop tolerance. Tolerance occurs as the levels of liver enzymes needed to metabolize alcohol increase, and as a result, the rate of alcohol metabolism increases. As a result, the regular drinker needs to consume more alcohol at a time to achieve the same mind-altering effects as a person who drinks infrequently. Tolerance can lead to alcohol dependence (alcoholism).

Classifying Drinkers

According to the National Survey of Canadians' Use of Alcohol and Other Drugs survey in 2004, 79% of Canadian women and

Figure 6.D Alcohol consumption and BAC. This table shows the relationship between the number of alcoholic drinks consumed within the same period and BACs for healthy men and women. For example, a 77-kg (170-lb.) man will have his BAC reach 0.05 after he has three drinks, whereas a 62-kg (137-lb.) woman will have her BAC reach 0.05 after drinking only two drinks. However, alcohol's effects on individuals can vary. In the United States and Canada, a person is legally intoxicated when his/her BAC is 0.08 or higher.

82% of Canadian men over the age of 15 years had consumed alcohol within the past 12 months. Three-quarters of the respondent women and half of the respondent men reported being moderate drinkers (one to two drinks per day). However, it is estimated that 4 to 5 million Canadians participate in high-risk drinking behaviour each year, including binge drinking and driving while impaired.[4A]

As a college or university student, you may have observed binge drinking or engaged in the practice; almost one in five university and college students binge drinks regularly.[5A] Regardless of their backgrounds, binge drinking is a common practice among Canadians. According to results of a survey conducted in 2001, binge drinking rates were highest among people who were 18 to 25 years old.[4A] Youthful binge drinking is a serious public health concern because the behaviour may increase a person's later risk of alcoholism. Furthermore, the practice can result in death.

Binge drinking has become an expected "rite of passage" for Canadian youth celebrating their 19th birthday. On March 15, while celebrating his birthday with friends in a bar, Jason rapidly drank 16 shots of alcohol. Although he managed to return home and go to bed, his lifeless body was discovered a few hours later. The young man's blood alcohol concentration was 0.361, well within the deadly range. Jason's death was not an isolated incident. What makes binge drinking so dangerous?

Binge drinking increases a person's BAC rapidly and to a point at which signs of alcohol poisoning occur. An individual suffering from alcohol poisoning is confused, "passes out" and cannot be aroused (*comatose*), breathes slowly and irregularly, and has pale or bluish skin. Alcohol poisoning can cause the heartbeat to slow down and lungs to stop functioning, resulting in death. Additionally, if a comatose person vomits, his or her stomach contents can enter the lungs, causing the person to choke to death. Jason died in his sleep from alcohol poisoning. His breathing rate slowed, his heartbeat became irregular, and his organs gradually shut down while he slept. Thus, it is important

TABLE 6.B *Classifying Drinkers*

Level	Amount of Alcohol Consumed (Standard Drinks)
Abstainer	None or fewer than 12 drinks/year
Light	1 to 13 drinks/month
Moderate	4 to 14 drinks/week
Heavy	3 or more drinks/day
Binge drinker	5 or more drinks/occasion (males)
Binge drinker	4 or more drinks/occasion (females)

Source: Modified from Dufour MC: What is moderate drinking? Defining "drinks" and drinking levels. *Alcohol Research & Health*, 23(1):5, 1999.

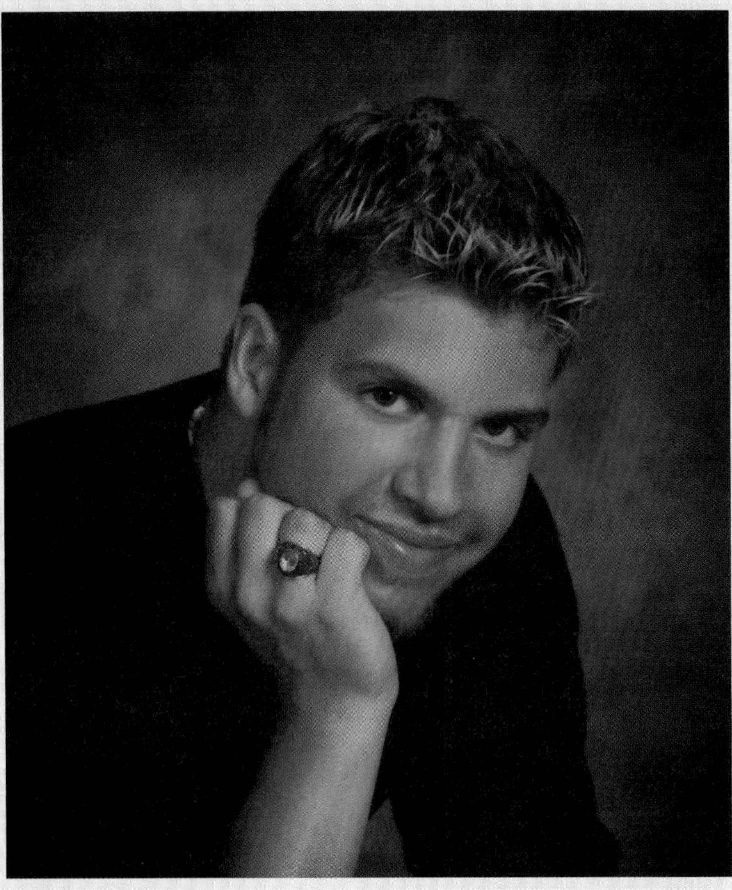

Jason Reinhardt tragically died after binge drinking with friends in celebration of his birthday.

to recognize that alcohol poisoning is a life-threatening condition—if you suspect someone has consumed a deadly amount of alcohol, don't waste time trying to estimate how many drinks that person has drunk, call 911 immediately.

Alcohol Abuse and Dependence

A person who is dependent on alcohol (an alcoholic) has an uncontrollable need to drink; is unable to limit his or her alcohol consumption; suffers withdrawal symptoms, such as shakiness and anxiety, when alcohol is unavailable after a period of heavy drinking; and experiences tolerance to the drug.

Unlike an alcohol-dependent person, someone who abuses alcohol has control over his or her intake and does not have a powerful craving for the drug.[6A] Additionally, the abuser does not experience withdrawal symptoms when he or she stops drinking as do alcoholics. The alcohol abuser, however, experiences problems at home, work, and school that are associated with his or her drinking habits. Furthermore, both abusers and alcoholics engage in behaviours that place themselves and others in danger, such as drinking and driving. Table 6.C lists signs of alcohol abuse, which often lead to alcoholism. If your drinking behaviours correspond to any of those listed in this table, you may be abusing alcohol. Some individuals should avoid alcohol because of their responses to the drug.

Alcohol and Health

Alcohol is a central nervous system depressant. Mild alcohol intoxication often produces pleasant sensations and relaxed inhibitions. Consuming large amounts, however, depresses normal motor functioning, including breathing, and death can result.

The potentially harmful physiological effects of abusing the drug vary from person to person, primarily because of differences in overall health, drinking habits, and genetic background. Alcohol affects every cell in the body, and when consumed in excess, the drug damages every system in the body, particularly the gastrointestinal, nervous, and cardiovascular systems. Figure 6.E summarizes major damaging physiological effects of alcohol.

Alcohol and the Gastrointestinal Tract

If you've consumed distilled spirits without adding mixers, you probably felt a burning sensation as the alcohol entered your throat and stomach. This sensation is an indication of alcohol's irritating effects on the lining of your gastrointestinal tract. Not surprisingly, chronic drinking contributes to intestinal ulcer formation, particularly in the esophagus and stomach. An ulcer is a sore. Intestinal ulcers can cause chronic bleeding and may

The three teenagers who died in this automobile had consumed alcohol before the accident.

TABLE 6.C *Signs of Alcohol Abuse*

Not everyone who drinks alcohol regularly abuses the drug, but you might be abusing alcohol if you:
Drink to relax, forget your worries, or improve mood.
Lose interest in food as a result of your drinking habits.
Consume drinks in a few quick gulps.
Lie about your drinking habits or try to hide them.
Drink alone more often that you did in the past.
Hurt yourself, or someone else, while drinking.
Were drunk more than three or four times last year.
Need to drink more alcohol than you used to drink to get "high."
Feel irritable and resentful when you are not drinking.
Have medical, social, or financial problems caused by drinking habits.
Have been cited for driving while intoxicated (DWI) or driving under the influence of alcohol (DUI).

Source: National Institute of Alcohol Abuse and Alcoholism. www.niaaa.nih.gov/publications/agep-age.htm.

penetrate through the intestinal wall. When this occurs, intestinal contents leak into the pelvic cavity, causing serious and often deadly infections. Although the reasons are unclear, chronic alcohol consumption increases the risk of *alcoholic pancreatitis*, a painful and sometimes fatal condition characterized by inflammation and destruction of the pancreas.

Alcohol and the Brain

Alcohol's effects on the central nervous system, especially the brain, appear within a few minutes of having a drink. Alcohol acts as a depressant, slowing the transmission of messages between nerve cells. At low BACs (<0.06%), the drinker is relaxed and less inhibited socially as regions of the brain that control decision making and reasoning ability are depressed. If the person continues to drink and his or her BAC increases to between 0.08 and 0.15%, the person loses control over voluntary muscles, particularly muscles that move the lips, eyes, and limbs. As a result, the drinker's speech is slurred, his or her eyes have difficulty focusing on objects, and the person's ability to drive or operate any heavy equipment is seriously compromised. When the drinker's BAC reaches 0.20 to 0.30%, his or her brain is unable to process information. Higher BACs (0.30 to 0.50%) usually result in loss of consciousness ("passing out"). Moreover,

Figure 6.E Some of alcohol's effects on the body. Chronic alcohol abuse seriously damages various organs and increases the risk of various cancers.

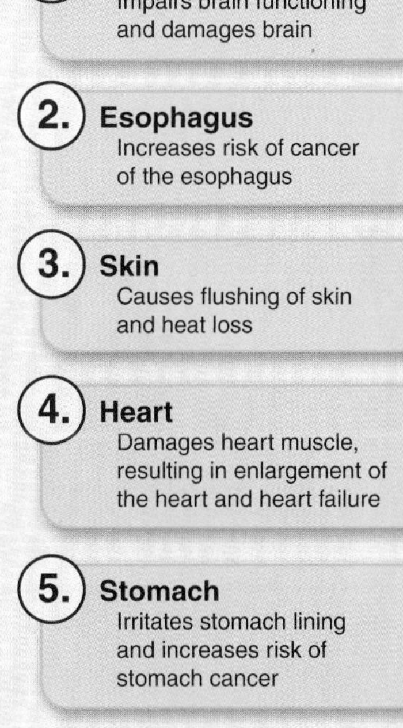

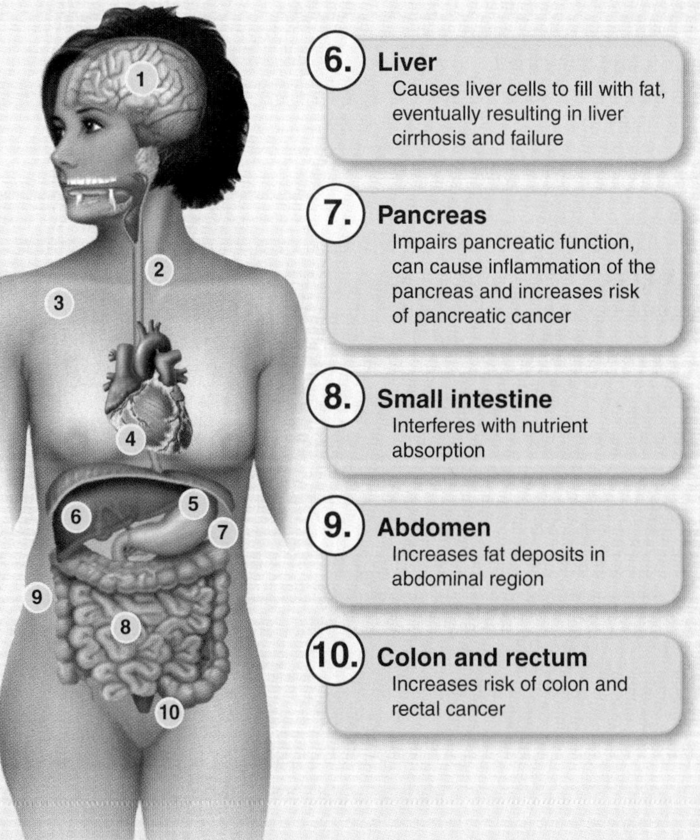

TABLE 6.D
Typical Effects of Alcohol at Various BAC Levels (Adults)

BAC	Typical Effects *
0.02 to 0.06	Positive mood; less inhibited; relaxed
0.06 to 0.08	Slight speech and vision impairment; elevated mood; impaired decision making
0.08 to 0.15	Reduction in motor skills; loss of emotional control; rapid eye movements; slurred speech; aggressive behaviour in some individuals
0.20 to 0.30	Loss of motor and cognitive skills; decreased level of consciousness
0.30 to 0.35	Severe intoxication; barely aware of environment
> 0.35	Loss of consciousness; death

* Effects vary among adults.

Sources: Doty CI, Shah BR: Toxicity, ethanol. Last Updated: March 30, 2006. www.emedicine.com/PED/topic2715.htm; Miller WR: *Characteristic effects of various BAC levels: Alcohol and its effects on behavior*. Center on Alcoholism, Substance Abuse, and Addictions. Last modified: July 25, 2005.

coma and even death can occur as the brain loses control over lung and heart functioning. Table 6.D lists BAC levels and typical nervous system effects at each level.

Alcohol can kill nerve cells (neurons) in the brain, and the organ is unable to replace many types of neurons. The brain of a chronic alcoholic has lost so many neurons, major regions shrink and the organ develops other structural abnormalities. Confusion and memory loss are common signs of the extensive brain damage that occurs in a chronic heavy drinker.

Alcohol and the Liver

In addition to harming the brain, alcohol can damage the liver. Some acetyl-CoA that forms when alcohol is metabolized enters the complex series of biochemical pathways that eventually produce carbon dioxide, water, and ATP, the primary energy storage molecule for cells. The liver, however, uses most of the acetyl-CoA to make fatty acids for synthesizing triglycerides (see Fig. 6.C). Even after a single bout of heavy drinking, fat accumulates in liver cells and causes a condition called "fatty liver." Fatty liver is reversible; if the affected person avoids alcohol for an extended period, the liver metabolizes the fat, and the organ eventually heals itself. If the person continues to drink, the buildup of fat destroys his or her liver cells, and tough scar tissue replaces them. This irreversible condition is called liver cirrhosis or hardening of the liver (Fig. 6.F). Alcoholics are prone to develop hepatitis, inflammation of the liver. Hepatitis can cause cirrhosis and increases the risk of liver cancer.

The scarred regions of an alcoholic's liver have no function other than holding the organ together. Under normal conditions, a healthy liver can regenerate sections of itself, but when destruction of liver cells is extensive, the organ begins to fail. In this situation, the affected person will die unless he or she undergoes liver transplantation. Chronic alcohol abuse is a major cause of liver failure among adult Canadians.

Alcohol and the Cardiovascular System

When consumed in low to moderate intakes (1 to 2 drinks per day), alcohol reduces the risk of heart disease. Excess consumption, however, can damage heart muscle and elevate blood pressure to dangerous levels. As a result, chronic alcoholics often have enlarged but weakened hearts and suffer strokes.

Alcohol and Cancer

Compared to people who do not consume alcohol, chronic drinkers are more likely to develop certain cancers. Alcohol causes changes to intestinal cells that increase the drinker's risk of oral cavity, esophageal, stomach, liver, pancreatic, and colorectal cancer. Women who consume two or more drinks daily have a higher risk of breast cancer than women who abstain from alcohol or drink less than two drinks per day. Heavy drinkers who smoke tobacco products have a much greater risk of developing cancers of the oral cavity and esophagus than people who drink less and do not smoke.

Alcohol and Drug Interactions

People who drink alcohol while taking other drugs, including prescription medications and over-the-counter remedies, need to recognize that alcohol's harmful effects may be amplified by the medications. Additionally, alcohol may interact with other drugs, causing serious side effects that do not occur when the drug is consumed alone. For example, combining alcohol with products that contain the pain-reliever acetaminophen can cause severe liver damage and even death.

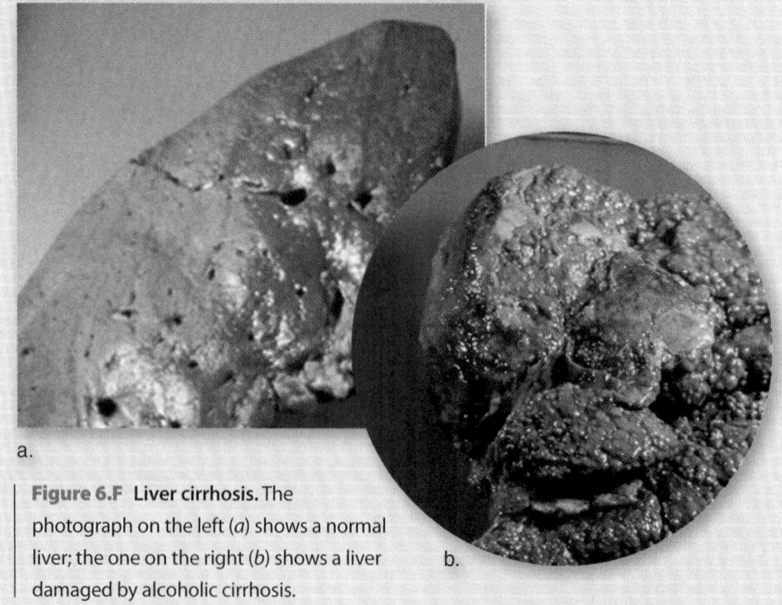

a. b.

Figure 6.F Liver cirrhosis. The photograph on the left (*a*) shows a normal liver; the one on the right (*b*) shows a liver damaged by alcoholic cirrhosis.

Effects of Alcohol on Nutritional Status

When consumed in moderation, alcohol stimulates the appetite. Alcohol, however, lowers blood glucose levels and raises blood triglycerides. Chronic, excessive alcohol intake can have adverse effects on the drinker's nutritional intake and status. Many alcoholics consume a considerable portion of their energy as alcohol, which often displaces nutrient-dense foods from their diets and increases their risk of malnutrition. Even when an alcoholic consumes nutritious meals while drinking, the alcohol interferes with the absorption, metabolism, and storage of various vitamins and increases the excretion of certain nutrients, particularly fat and the mineral magnesium.

Poor diets contribute to deficiencies of vitamin A, C, and the B vitamins thiamin and folate among alcoholics. It is not unusual for chronic alcoholics to become thiamin deficient and develop Wernicke-Korsakoff syndrome, a brain disorder characterized by mental confusion, memory loss, and uncoordinated muscular movements. The person with this condition typically staggers when trying to walk. Taking thiamin supplements can resolve some of the signs of the syndrome, but the person must avoid drinking alcohol while being treated.

Although chronic alcohol abuse is associated with an increased risk of bone loss and fractures, light to moderate alcohol drinkers tend to have stronger bones and lower risk of fractures than nondrinkers, especially among women who are past child-bearing age. More research, however, is needed to determine the role of alcohol on bone health.

Figure 6.G Fetal alcohol syndrome. Physical deformities and developmental delays are characteristics of fetal alcohol syndrome (FAS).

Alcohol and Body Water

Billboard and commercial advertisements for alcoholic beverages often show sweaty physically active young adults gulping down beer or liquor to relieve their thirst. These ads are misleading. Alcohol is not a good "thirst-quencher" because it's a diuretic that suppresses the production of antidiuretic hormone (ADH) by the pituitary gland. Without ADH's action, the kidneys produce more urine, and the body loses water and certain vitamins and minerals along with it. If a dehydrated drinker consumes even more alcohol to relieve thirst, this response only increases his or her water losses. Drinking water and other nonalcoholic drinks is the best way to keep the body well hydrated.

Fetal Alcohol Syndrome

When a pregnant woman drinks alcohol, her embryo/fetus also "drinks" alcohol, because the drug passes freely from the mother's bloodstream into the embryo/fetus's bloodstream. Alcohol is most devastating when it affects an embryo because organs develop during the first two months after conception. Unfortunately, many women are not aware that they are pregnant during this early stage of their child's prenatal (before birth) development, and they may drink socially or binge drink. Alcohol is toxic to cells, including rapidly dividing embryonic cells. An infant born with fetal alcohol syndrome (FAS) has certain facial and heart defects as well as extensive, irreversible damage to its nervous system that causes mental retardation (Fig. 6.G). Children with FAS also experience delayed and abnormal physical development.

The amount of alcohol that can be safely consumed by a pregnant woman has not been determined. Therefore, if you or someone you know is trying to conceive or is pregnant, you or that person should play it safe and avoid alcohol. The risks are too high to justify even one drink. Table 6.E identifies people, including pregnant women, who should not drink alcohol.

Health Benefits of Alcohol

Drinking light to moderate amounts of alcohol can protect against cardiovascular disease. Consuming this amount of alcohol raises HDL cholesterol levels; reduces blood levels of fibrinogen, an important blood-clotting factor; and decreases platelet stickiness. Platelets are cell fragments involved in the blood-clotting process. Reducing the likelihood of blood clot formation lowers the risk of heart attack and certain types of strokes.

Some medical researchers think drinking beer and red wine is healthier than consuming white wines or spirits. Although the alcohol in beer is the same as that in wine and distilled spirits, red wine and beer have higher levels of certain antioxidants and

TABLE 6.E *Who Should Avoid Alcohol?*

Who Should Avoid Alcohol?
Women who suspect they are pregnant, know they are pregnant, or are trying to become pregnant
People who plan to drive or use heavy machinery
People taking certain over-the-counter or prescription medications
People with medical conditions that alcohol can aggravate
Recovering alcoholics
People younger than 21 years of age

Source: Adapted from National Institute on Alcohol Abuse and Alcoholism. Q #13 in: FAQ's on alcohol and alcohol abuse. www.niaaa.nih.gov/faq/q-a.htm#question13. Accessed: February 12, 2005.

B vitamins than other alcoholic beverages, which may explain their health benefits. Other researchers point to studies that suggest all alcoholic beverages confer the same heart-healthy benefits when a person consumes one to two drinks daily.[7A] Purple grape juice, which is used to make red wine, contains the same antioxidants as the wine and appears to protect against heart disease as well.[8A]

The role of moderate alcohol consumption in coronary artery disease prevention is controversial. Drinking small amounts of alcohol seems to reduce the risk of heart disease, but consuming moderate to excessive amounts of alcohol are associated with increased risks of addiction, hypertension, heart failure, cancer, liver cirrhosis, and automobile accidents. More research is needed to determine if alcohol alone or other compounds present in certain alcoholic beverages provide beneficial effects on health when consumed in moderation.

Alcohol and Physical Performance

Although some athletes may think consuming a small amount of alcohol before a competitive event might help relieve anxiety, alcohol reduces eye-hand coordination and slows reaction times even when BACs are relatively low (0.02 to 0.05%). Studies indicate conflicting findings concerning the effects of low to moderate amounts of alcohol on strength and endurance. In some instances, low to moderate intakes of alcohol reduce endurance and have negative effects on strength, but in other cases, this level of alcohol consumption produces no detrimental effects on strength and endurance. Alcohol can contribute to dehydration, which impairs muscular performance and causes heat injuries such as heat exhaustion and heat stroke. Chronic alcohol abuse causes muscular wasting that affects skeletal as well as heart muscle. Obviously, such effects will have negative effects on muscular mass, strength, and endurance.

According to the American College of Sports Medicine, athletes should learn about alcohol's effects on health, and avoid consuming excess alcohol during the 48 hours before an event. After exercise, and until his or her body recovers its normal fluid status, the athlete should focus on consuming nonalcoholic beverages.

Where to Get Help for Alcohol Abuse or Dependence

If you think you are abusing alcohol or dependent on the drug, seek help from your personal physician. For information about alcohol abuse, you can contact the Centre for Addiction and Mental Health at 1-800-463-6273. You can also visit the Canadian Web site of Alcoholics Anonymous (www.aacanada.com), the Canadian Centre on Substance Abuse (www.ccsa.ca), or Al-Anon/Alateen (www.al-anon.alateen.org).

References for Chapter 6 Highlight

1A. Ministry of Transportation: Impaired driving fact sheet, blood alcohol concentration (BAC). www.mto.gov.on.ca/english/safety/impaired/fact-sheet.shtml. Accessed: June 4, 2010; Consequences of drinking and driving. www.mto.gov.on.ca/english/safety/impaired/index.shtml. Accessed: October 8, 2010.

2A. Baraona E and others: Gender differences in pharmokinetics of alcohol. *Alcohol and Clinical Experimental Research* 25(4):502, 2001.

3A. Gordis E: Are women more vulnerable to alcohol's effects? In: *Alcohol alert. National Institute on Alcohol Abuse and Alcoholism, No. 46.* 1999. www.niaaa.nih.gov/publications/aa46.htm. Accessed: February 5, 2005.

4A. Canadian Centre on Substance Abuse: *Canadian Addiction Survey 2004.* www.ccsa.ca/eng/priorities/research/canadianaddiction/pages/default.aspx. Accessed: June 4, 2010.

5A. Wechsler H and others: College alcohol use: A full or empty glass? *Journal of American College Health* 47(6):247, 1999.

6A. National Institute on Alcohol Abuse and Alcoholism: *Alcohol Alert, No. 30.* PH 359, October 1995. pubs.niaaa.nih.gov/publications/aa30.htm. Accessed: April 13, 2007.

7A. Mukamal KJ, Rimm EB: Alcohol's effects on the risk for coronary heart disease. *Alcohol Research & Health* 25(4):255, 2001.

8A. Folts JD: Potential health benefits from the flavonoids in grape products on vascular disease. *Advances in Experimental Medicine and Biology* 505:95, 2002.

SUMMARY

Lipids are needed for energy, proper growth and development, nerve functioning, maintenance of healthy skin and hair, and the production of bile and several hormones. Major lipids are triglycerides, phospholipids, and sterols. In addition to being a source of fuel, body fat contributes to body contours, insulates the body against cold temperatures, and protects against damaging blows.

Triglycerides, an important fuel for the body, comprise most of the lipid content of your food and body. Lipids can be sources of the essential fatty acids. Furthermore, the fat in food enhances absorption of fat-soluble vitamins and phytochemicals. Dietary lipids also contribute to the appealing flavour, texture, and aroma of foods. Although consuming some lipids are essential for health, high amounts may increase your risk of serious health conditions, including obesity, certain cancers, and CVD.

Most lipids have fatty acids in their chemical structures. Fatty acids can be saturated or unsaturated, and unsaturated fatty acids can be either monounsaturated or polyunsaturated. The body cannot synthesize the omega-6 fatty acid linoleic acid and the omega-3 fatty acid alpha-linolenic acid; these essential fatty acids must be supplied by the diet. The typical Canadian eats too much omega-6 fats and not enough omega-3 fat. Fatty cold-water fish, canola and soybean oils, walnuts, and flaxseed are rich sources of the omega-3 fats.

Trans fatty acid molecules have a different configuration than cis fatty acid molecules. This difference enables fats that contain a high proportion of trans fatty acids to be more solid at room temperature than fats with a high proportion of cis fatty acids. Most of the trans fat in food results from the hydrogenation process. Partial hydrogenation partially hardens the oil so that it can be made into shortening or shaped into sticks of margarine. Diets that contain high amounts of trans fats are associated with an increased risk of heart disease and stroke.

A triglyceride has three fatty acids attached to glycerol. Triglycerides comprise about 95% of lipids in the body and food. Triglycerides usually contain mixtures of unsaturated and saturated fatty acids, but one type of fatty acid (saturated, monounsaturated, or polyunsaturated) tends to predominate. In general, animal fats contain higher percentages of saturated fatty acids than plant fats. Important exceptions are the highly saturated coconut, palm, and palm kernel oils.

Phospholipids have both hydrophilic and hydrophobic regions, and as a result, they are partially soluble in water and can serve as emulsifiers. Phospholipids are the major structural component of cell membranes and are needed for proper functioning of nerve cells, including those in the brain. Lecithin is the major phospholipid in food; egg yolks, liver, wheat germ, peanut butter, and soybeans are rich sources of this compound.

The sterol cholesterol is a component of every cell membrane. Cells use cholesterol to make a variety of substances, including vitamin D, bile, and steroid hormones such as estrogen and testosterone. Cholesterol is only found in animal foods. Plants synthesize sterols and stanols that are not well absorbed by humans. Plant sterols and stanols, however, may be beneficial to health because they interfere with cholesterol absorption.

The triglycerides and phospholipids in food undergo digestion primarily in the upper part of the small intestine. Cholesterol is not broken down and is absorbed through the intestinal wall. Before leaving the small intestine, triglycerides, cholesterol, and other lipids are coated with a layer that contains protein to form chylomicrons. Chylomicrons enter the lymphatic system of the small intestine and eventually reach the bloodstream. The liver uses lipids from chylomicrons to make various lipoproteins, substances that transport lipids in the bloodstream. Enterohepatic circulation enables the liver to recycle bile salts to make new bile.

Triglycerides and carbohydrates are major sources of cellular energy. If energy is not needed, adipose cells remove fatty acids and glycerol from circulation and use them to synthesize triglycerides for storage. When energy is needed, adipose cells break down some stored triglycerides and release glycerol and fatty acids into the bloodstream.

During the last 50 years, the amount of fat eaten by Canadians decreased. Today fat contributes about 30% of the average Canadian's daily energy intake. Recommended diets for healthy people generally limit fat to 30% of total energy intake; the AMDR for fat is 20 to 35% of total calories. Consumers can use nutrient labels to determine how much fat, saturated fat, trans fat, and cholesterol are in packaged food.

CVD affects the heart and blood vessels. In Canada, heart disease is the leading cause of death. Atherosclerosis is a long-term process that can result in CVD. Numerous risk factors are associated with atherosclerosis; some risk factors are inherited and difficult to modify, but many are related to lifestyle practices that can be altered. Smoking cigarettes, eating certain fats, and being physically inactive are lifestyle practices that increase a person's risk of atherosclerosis and CVD.

Your blood lipid levels can have a major influence on your risk of CVD. Lipoproteins transport much of the lipids in the bloodstream. Having high blood levels of HDL cholesterol is healthier than having high LDL cholesterol levels, because elevated LDL cholesterol contributes to atherosclerosis, whereas elevated HDL cholesterol reduces the risk of this condition.

Exercising and replacing saturated fats with monounsaturated fats may reduce LDL levels and increase HDL levels. On the other hand, physical inactivity and eating high amounts of saturated fat can raise LDL and blood triglyceride levels, increasing one's risk of CVD. Many people, however, do not experience an increase in their blood cholesterol levels when they eat cholesterol in foods. In the body, trans fats function like certain saturated fats, raising blood cholesterol levels.

Although oils, fatty spreads, and salad dressings are obvious sources of dietary fat, much of the fat we eat is not visible. High-fat foods include fried foods, chips, luncheon meats, sausage, hot dogs, hard cheeses, and whole milk. If people make dietary modifications, lose excess weight, and exercise regularly, and their blood lipid levels remain elevated, they should discuss additional treatment options with their physicians and dietitians. Millions of Canadians take prescription medications to reduce their elevated blood lipid levels.

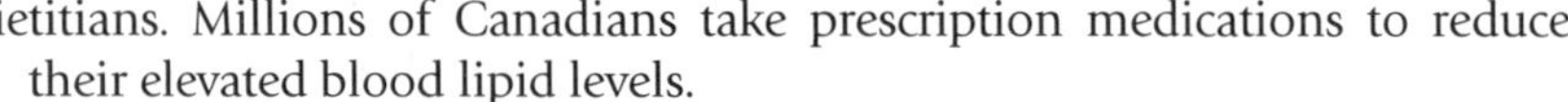

Recipes for Healthy Living

Nutty Stuff

Looking for a snack that's more nutritious and tasty than chips? It's easy to make your own heart-healthy high-fibre portable snack. The basic recipe is provided, and you can use it as the foundation for your own combinations of nuts and dried fruit. For example, you can replace the dried cranberries with raisins, chopped dates, or dried apricots; and use walnuts or peanuts instead of cashews. Adding some dark chocolate chips to the mixture is another option. This particular recipe makes about four ½-cup servings. Although the fats in most nuts are healthy fats, you may want to limit your serving size to less than ½ cup because of the caloric load—unless you have higher than average energy needs. Each ½-cup serving of this snack supplies 185 kcal, 3.8 g protein, 8.5 g fat, 2.5 g fibre, 5 mg iron, 145 mg potassium, 4 mg zinc, 100 mcg folate (a vitamin), 5 mg niacin (a vitamin), and 36 mg vitamin E.

INGREDIENTS

¼ cup unsalted almonds
¼ cup unsalted cashews
½ cup dried cranberries
1 cup multigrain ready-to-eat oat cereal

8%
42%
50%
Fat
Protein
Carbohydrate

PREPARATION STEPS

1. Mix nuts, cereal, and dried fruit together.
2. Measure ½-cup servings, place in plastic sandwich bags, and seal the bags.
3. Store in a dry place. Mixture tastes best if eaten fresh or within a day or two.

Salmon Salad Sandwiches

Are you tired of eating burgers? Try something different that's easy to prepare and a rich source of omega-3 fatty acids—salmon salad sandwiches. You can use canned salmon or leftover baked salmon to make the salad. This recipe makes enough salad for two sandwiches. Each sandwich provides approximately 350 kcal, 12 g fat, 28 g protein, 3.7 g fibre, and 290 mg calcium.

INGREDIENTS

1 cup canned or cooked salmon
2 Tbsp pickle relish
2 Tbsp minced (finely chopped) sweet onion
1½ Tbsp lite mayonnaise
4 slices whole-wheat bread
1 slice fresh tomato (optional)
1 piece leaf lettuce (optional)

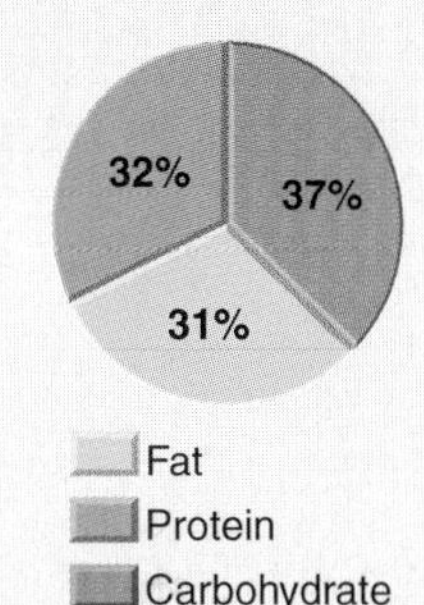

PREPARATION STEPS

1. If using canned salmon, drain fluid from salmon. In a bowl, break up salmon with a fork, including the small bones. Add other ingredients to the salmon and mix until well-blended.
2. Toast slices of whole-wheat bread.
3. Spread ½ cup of salad on one slice of the toasted bread. Add a fresh tomato slice or piece of leaf lettuce, if desired.

Personal Dietary Analysis

1. Refer to the three-day food log from the Personal Dietary Analysis feature in Chapter 3. List the total number of kilocalories you consumed for each day of recordkeeping. Add the figures to obtain a total, divide the total by three, and then round the figure to the nearest whole number to obtain your average daily energy intake for the three-day period.

   Sample Calculation:

   Day 1 2000 kcal

   Day 2 1700 kcal

   Day 3 2350 kcal

   Total kcal 6050 ÷ 3 days = **2017** kcal/day

   (average kilocalorie intake, rounded to the nearest whole number)

   Your Calculation:

   Day 1 ______ kcal

   Day 2 ______ kcal

   Day 3 ______ kcal

   Total kcal ______ ÷ 3 days = ______ kcal/day

   (average kilocalorie intake, rounded to the nearest whole number)

2. Add the number of grams of fat eaten each day of the period. Divide the total by three and round to the nearest whole number to calculate the average number of grams of fat consumed daily.

   Sample Calculation

   Day 1 50 g

   Day 2 57 g

   Day 3 42 g

   Total = 149 g

   Total grams 149 ÷ 3 days = 50 g/day (average)

   Your Calculation

   Day 1 ______ g

   Day 2 ______ g

   Day 3 ______ g

   Total = ______ g

   Total grams ______ ÷ 3 days = ______ g of fat/day

   (average, rounded to the nearest whole number)

3. Each gram of fat provides about 9 kcal, therefore, you must multiply the average number of grams of fat that you ate daily (Step 2) by nine to obtain the average number of kilocalories from fat.

Sample Calculation

50 g/day × 9 kcal/g = 450 kcal from fat

Your Calculation

______ g/day × 9 kcal/g = ______ kcal from fat

4. To calculate the average percentage of kilocalories that fat contributed to your diet, divide the average number of kilocalories from fat obtained in Step 3 by the average total daily kilocalorie intake obtained in Step 1, and round to the nearest one-hundredth. Multiply the value by 100, drop the decimal point, and add the percent symbol.

Sample Calculation

450 kcal ÷ 2017 kcal = 0.22

0.22 × 100 = 22 %

Your Calculation

______ kcal ÷ ______ kcal = ______

______ × 100 = ______ %

5. Did your average daily fat intake meet the recommended 20 to 35% of total energy?
Yes ______ No ______
   a. If your average fat intake was more than 35% of your total energy intake, which foods contributed to your intake of fats?
   Foods: ____________________

6. Review the log of your three-day food intake. Calculate your average daily intake of cholesterol by adding the milligrams of cholesterol consumed over the three-day period and dividing the total by three.

Your Calculation

Day 1 ______ mg

Day 2 ______ mg

Day 3 ______ mg

Total = ______ mg

Total g ______ ÷ 3 days = ______ mg of cholesterol daily

   a. What was your average daily cholesterol intake? ______ grams
   b. If your average cholesterol intake was greater than 200 mg, list foods that contributed to your cholesterol intake.

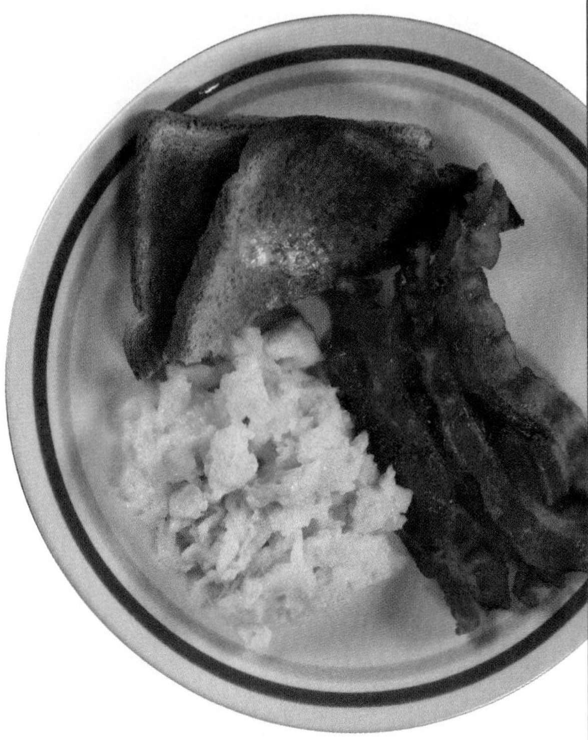

Using Nutrient Labels: Fats and Cholesterol

1. Remove the labels from three different packaged foods. Using information from each of the product's Nutrition Facts table, answer the following questions.
   - a. Name of food: ______
   - b. A serving is ______. How many servings are in the package? ______
   - c. How many grams of fat, saturated fat, trans fat, and cholesterol are in a serving of each product?

     Product 1

     ______ grams of fat

     ______ grams of trans fat

     ______ grams of saturated fat

     ______ milligrams of cholesterol

     Product 2

     ______ grams of fat

     ______ grams of trans fat

     ______ grams of saturated fat

     ______ milligrams of cholesterol

     Product 3

     ______ grams of fat

     ______ grams of trans fat

     ______ grams of saturated fat

     ______ milligrams of cholesterol
   - d. Calculate the percentage of kilocalories from fat in each product by dividing the number of kilocalories from fat by total number of kilocalories per serving. (The Nutrition Facts table uses the term "calories" for kilocalories.)

     Product 1 is ______ % fat

     Product 2 is ______ % fat

     Product 3 is ______ % fat
   - e. Read the list of ingredients for each product. If the food contains fat and cholesterol, identify ingredients that contributed fat and cholesterol to the product.

     Fat ingredients in Product 1 ______

     Cholesterol ingredients in Product 1 ______

     Fat ingredients in Product 2 ______

     Cholesterol ingredients in Product 2 ______

     Fat ingredients in Product 3 ______

     Cholesterol ingredients in Product 3 ______

Assessment: Evaluating Your Fat Intake

Do You Consume:	Rarely or Never	1 to 2 Times/ Week	3 to 5 Times/ Week	Daily
1. Bacon, hot dogs, sausage, salami, bologna, or other fatty luncheon meat?	0	1	2	3
2. Whole milk?	0	1	2	3
3. 2% milk?	0	1	2	3
4. Ice cream or milkshakes?	0	1	2	3
5. Sour cream or cream cheese?	0	1	2	3
6. Fatty cuts of pork or beef?	0	1	2	3
7. Hard cheeses, such as cheddar or Swiss?	0	1	2	3
8. Breaded and fried meat, fish, seafood, or poultry?	0	1	2	3
9. French fries, home fries, hash browns?	0	1	2	3
10. Gravy, cheese sauce, or cream-based sauce?	0	1	2	3
11. Chips, buttered popcorn, or other greasy snack foods?	0	1	2	3
12. Biscuits, croissants, doughnuts, Danish pastries, pies, cakes, or cookies?	0	1	2	3
13. Regular salad dressing or mayonnaise?	0	1	2	3
14. Cream in your coffee or tea?	0	1	2	3
15. Pizza or egg rolls?	0	1	2	3
16. Creamed soups such as cream of potato soup or clam chowder?	0	1	2	3
TOTAL	______	______	______	______

Scoring: Add points in each column and then add those figures together. (The higher the total points, the higher your fatty food intake.)

My "Fat Score" is ______

If your score is 30 or more: Your fat intake is probably too high. Note which high-fat foods you eat more than three times per week. Consider reducing your intake of these items and replacing them with low-fat foods.

CRITICAL THINKING

1. Think about your risk of atherosclerosis and CVD. Are you concerned about your risk? Explain why or why not. If you are concerned, discuss steps you can take to reduce your risk of atherosclerosis and CVD.
2. Do you avoid fried foods and look for "light" and "fat-reduced" foods when shopping for groceries? If your answer is "no," explain why?
3. Plan a meal that supplies 20 to 35% of energy from fat. The meal should include foods from the major food groups and provide 700 to 900 kcal.
4. Prepare a pamphlet that provides information about risk factors for CVD. In addition to English, you may prepare the pamphlet in French, Hindi, Mandarin, or another modern language.
5. Develop a lesson for older school-aged children that describes atherosclerosis and the role that personal choices (lifestyles) play in the development of the disease.
6. If you drink alcohol, assess your alcohol consumption habits. After reading the information in the Chapter 6 Highlight, are you abusing alcohol? If your answer is yes, what aspects of your behaviour make you an alcohol abuser? What can you do to obtain help?

PRACTICE TEST

Select the best answer.

1. Fats in foods
   a. add taste and contribute to satiety.
   b. are rapidly digested and absorbed.
   c. carry water-soluble nutrients.
   d. need to be eliminated to have a healthful diet.
2. Solid fats generally have a high proportion of ______ fatty acids.
   a. unsaturated
   b. saturated
   c. polyunsaturated
   d. monounsaturated
3. A saturated fatty acid has
   a. one double bond within the hydrocarbon chain.
   b. two double bonds within the hydrocarbon chain.
   c. no double bonds within the hydrocarbon chain.
   d. none of the above
4. Which of the following statements is true?
   a. Certain fish are rich sources of omega-3 fatty acids.
   b. Omega-3 fatty acids increase the risk of cardiovascular disease.
   c. Trans fats are rich sources of omega-3 fatty acids.
   d. The human body converts dietary fibre into omega-3 fatty acids.

5. Trans fatty acids are
   a. naturally in many foods.
   b. a by-product of the hydrogenation process.
   c. essential to good health.
   d. all of the above
6. Phospholipids
   a. do not have fatty acids in their chemical structures.
   b. lack glycerol in their chemical structures.
   c. do not occur naturally.
   d. are partially water soluble.
7. Cholesterol is
   a. metabolized for energy.
   b. found only in animal foods.
   c. not made by the human body.
   d. harmful to health.
8. The primary site of triglyceride digestion and absorption is the
   a. stomach.
   b. liver.
   c. small intestine.
   d. gallbladder.
9. Lipoproteins
   a. are water insoluble.
   b. transport lipids in the bloodstream.
   c. contain glucose.
   d. none of the above
10. Controllable risk factors for cardiovascular disease include
    a. family history.
    b. age.
    c. tobacco use.
    d. all of the above
11. Homocysteine is a(n)
    a. form of folate.
    b. lipid.
    c. risk factor for cardiovascular disease.
    d. essential amino acid.
12. Alcohol metabolism is not influenced by a person's
    a. sex.
    b. body size and composition.
    c. prior history of alcohol use.
    d. level of caffeine consumption.

Answers to Chapter 6 Quiz Yourself

1. To lose weight, use regular, stick margarine instead of butter because it has 25% fewer calories per teaspoon. **False.** (p. 168)
2. Egg yolks are a rich dietary source of cholesterol. **True.** (p. 167)
3. Taking too many fish oil supplements can be harmful to health. **True.** (p. 167)
4. On average, Canadians consume 60% of their energy from fat. **False.** (p. 159)
5. Increasing your intake of trans fats will reduce your risk of heart disease. **False.** (p. 150)

Please visit Connect at

www.mcgrawhillconnect.ca

Chapter **7**

Proteins

Chapter Learning Outcomes

After reading Chapter 7, you should be able to:

1. List the primary functions of proteins in the body.
2. Identify the basic structural unit of proteins.
3. Distinguish between essential and nonessential amino acids.
4. Explain the basic steps of protein synthesis and digestion.
5. Discuss conditions that contribute to positive nitrogen balance, negative nitrogen balance, and nitrogen balance.
6. Identify food sources of protein and foods that provide high- and low-quality proteins.
7. Plan meals and snacks that reduce animal protein intakes.
8. Discuss the pros and cons of vegetarian diets.
9. Describe how protein-energy malnutrition (PEM) can affect the body.

Since ancient times, many people have believed that eating animal foods, particularly meat, was necessary for good health and optimal physical performance. Milo of Croton, an ancient Greek Olympian wrestler with extraordinary strength, reportedly consumed about 20 pounds of meat daily. Although accounts of Milo's superhuman capacity for eating meat are unreliable, modern athletes often make protein-rich foods and protein supplements the foundation of their diets.

Furthermore, it is not unusual for non-athletes to associate meat with protein and a lack of protein with physical weakness.

Protein is an important nutrient, but it is not more valuable to your health than other nutrients. Nutrients work together in your body like members of a well-trained basketball team on the playing court. Making one player the star while neglecting to develop the other athletes' skills can have disastrous effects on the team's success. Similarly, overemphasizing one class of nutrients in your diet, such as protein, while ignoring other nutrients, can lead to nutritional imbalances that result in health problems and poor functioning.

Quiz YOURSELF

How much protein is recommended for optimal health? Can people obtain enough protein by eating only plant foods? What happens if you eat more protein than your body needs? After reading Chapter 7, you will learn to identify good food sources of protein and understand the nutrient's roles in the body. You will also learn how the amount and quality of the protein in your diet can affect your health. Before reading this chapter, take the following quiz to test your knowledge of protein. The answers are on page 223.

1. Animal foods such as meat and eggs are almost 100% protein. ____T ____F
2. Foods made from processed soybeans can be sources of high-quality protein. ____T ____F
3. An adult bodybuilder should consume about five times more protein than a healthy adult who is not a bodybuilder. ____T ____F
4. Registered dietitians generally recommend that vegetarians take amino acid supplements to increase their protein intake. ____T ____F
5. People can nourish their hair by using shampoo that contains protein. ____T ____F

What Are Proteins?

Proteins are complex organic molecules that are chemically similar to lipids and carbohydrates because they contain carbon, hydrogen, and oxygen atoms. Proteins, however, contain nitrogen, the element cells need to make a wide array of important biological compounds. Plants, animals, bacteria, and even viruses contain hundreds of proteins.

Proteins are necessary for muscle development and maintenance, but the estimated 100 000 proteins in your body have a wide variety of functions. Skin, blood, nerve, bone—all cells in your body—contain proteins. Structural proteins such as *collagen* are in your cartilage, ligament, and bone tissue. *Keratin* is another structural protein; it is in your hair, nails, and skin. Contractile proteins in your muscles enable you to move, and the pigment protein *melanin* determines the colour of your eyes, hair, and skin. Proteins are also necessary for your blood to clot properly.

Certain hormones, such as insulin and glucagon, are proteins. **Hormones** are chemical messengers that regulate body processes and responses, such as growth, metabolism, and hunger. Nearly all **enzymes** are proteins. Enzymes speed up the rate (catalyze) of chemical reactions without becoming a part of the products (see Fig. 4.8 on p. 90). Additionally, infection-fighting **antibodies** are proteins. Although cells can use proteins for energy, normally they metabolize very little for energy, conserving the nutrient for other important functions that carbohydrates and lipids are unable to perform.

In the bloodstream, proteins transport nutrients and oxygen. Proteins in blood, such as *albumin*, also help maintain the proper distribution of fluids in blood and body tissues (Fig. 7.1). The force of blood pressure moves watery fluid out of the bloodstream and into tissues. Blood proteins help counteract the effects of blood pressure by

proteins large complex organic molecules made up of amino acids

hormones chemical messengers that regulate body processes and responses

enzymes compounds that speed up chemical reactions

antibodies infection-fighting proteins

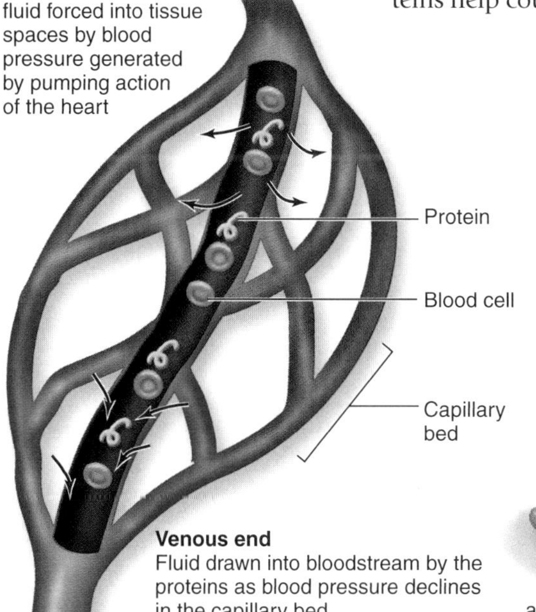

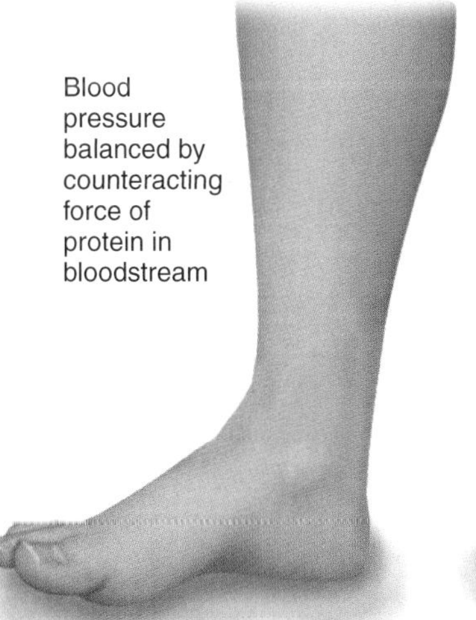

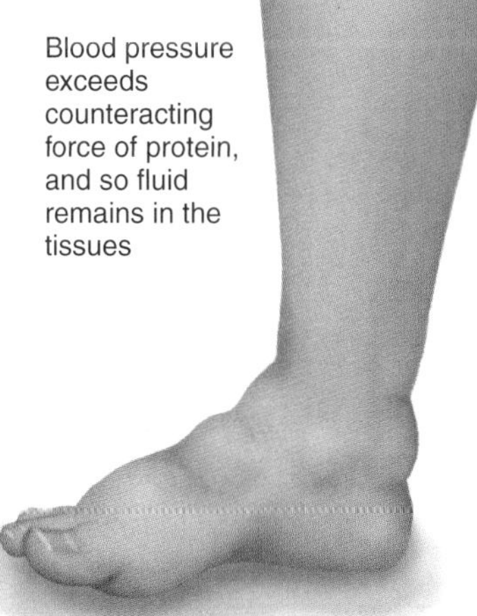

Figure 7.1 Fluid balance. (*a*) Proteins in blood, such as albumin, help maintain the proper distribution of fluids in blood and body tissues. (*b*) When blood pressure exceeds counteracting force of blood proteins, fluid remains in tissues, causing edema.

colloidal osmotic pressure role of blood proteins attracting and holding fluid in the bloodstream

edema accumulation of fluid in tissues

acid–base balance maintaining the proper pH of body fluids

buffer solution that resists changes in pH under certain conditions

amino acids nitrogen-containing chemical units that comprise proteins

amino- or nitrogen-containing group portion of an amino acid that contains nitrogen

R group (side chain) part of amino acid that determines the molecule's physical and chemical properties

acid group acid portion of a compound

nonessential amino acids group of amino acids that the body can make

essential amino acids amino acids the body cannot make or make enough to meet its needs

attracting the fluid, returning it to the bloodstream. The role of blood proteins attracting and holding fluid in the bloodstream is called **colloidal osmotic pressure**. During starvation, the level of protein in blood decreases, and as a result, some water leaks out of the bloodstream and enters spaces between cells. The resulting accumulation of fluid in tissues is called **edema** (*eh-dee´mah*).

Proteins also help maintain **acid–base balance**, the proper pH of body fluids. To function properly, blood and tissue fluids need to maintain a pH of 7.35 to 7.45, which is slightly basic.[1] (To review the concept of pH, see Chapter 4.) Metabolic processes can produce acid or basic by-products. If a particular body fluid becomes too acidic or too basic, cells may die. A **buffer** is a solution that resists changes in pH under certain conditions. Proteins can act as buffers, because they have acidic and basic components. For example, if cells form an excess of hydrogen ions (H), the pH of tissues decreases. To help restore the pH level to within the normal range, the basic portions of protein molecules bind to the excess H, neutralizing the excess ions and raising the pH.

Amino Acids

Proteins are comprised of smaller chemical units called **amino acids**. The human body contains proteins made from 20 different amino acids (see Appendix E, "Amino Acids," which can be found on Connect at www.mcgrawhillconnect.ca). To understand how the body uses amino acids, it is necessary to learn some basic chemistry that relates to these compounds.

Each amino acid has a carbon atom that anchors a hydrogen atom and three different groups of atoms: the **amino- or nitrogen-containing group**, the **R group** (sometimes called the **side chain**), and the **acid group**. The chemical structure of the amino acid *alanine* shown in Figure 7.2 indicates these three groups. Note that the nitrogen atom is in the amino group. The R group identifies the molecule as a particular amino acid, such as *serine* or *lysine*. When the nitrogen-containing group is removed, the R group, acid group, and anchoring carbon atom form the "carbon skeleton" of an amino acid (see Fig. 7.2). The carbon skeleton is an important component of an amino acid, because the body can convert the carbon skeletons of certain amino acids to glucose and use the simple sugar for energy. Carbon skeletons from many amino acids can be used for a myriad of different functions within the body. It is important to recognize that the human body has no storage capacity for extra amino acids, and all amino acids not incorporated into body proteins will be disassembled and the carbon fragments used to create another metabolic intermediate, including fatty acids, which can be stored as body fat.

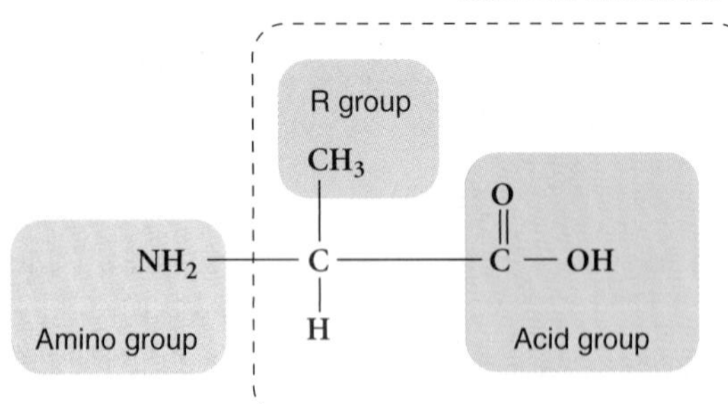

Figure 7.2 Amino acid: Basic chemical structure. Alanine has the typical chemical features of an amino acid—the amino group, R group, and acid group. When the nitrogen-containing component is removed from an amino acid, the "carbon skeleton" remains.

Classifying Amino Acids

Dietitians classify amino acids as either nonessential or essential according to the body's ability to make them. A healthy human body can make 11 of the 20 amino acids. These compounds are the **nonessential amino acids**. The remaining nine amino acids are

TABLE 7.1 *Amino Acids*

Essential		Nonessential	
Histidine	Threonine	Alanine	Cysteine*
Isoleucine	Tryptophan	Aspartic acid	Glutamine*
Leucine	Valine	Asparagine	Glycine*
Lysine		Glutamic acid	Proline*
Methionine		Serine	Tyrosine*
Phenylalanine		Arginine*	

* Under certain conditions, this amino acid can become essential.

essential amino acids that must be supplied by foods, because the body cannot synthesize them or make enough to meet its needs. Sometimes, nonessential and essential amino acids are referred to as "dispensable" and "indispensable" amino acids, respectively. Table 7.1 lists amino acids according to their classification as essential and nonessential.

Concept **Checkpoint**

1. What is the chemical unit that makes up a protein?
2. List at least four different functions of proteins in the body.
3. Identify the three groups of atoms that make up a typical amino acid.
4. What is the "carbon skeleton" of an amino acid?
5. How many different kinds of amino acids are needed to make human proteins? How many of these amino acids are essential?

Proteins in Foods

People often associate animal foods with protein, but beans, nuts, seeds, grains, and certain vegetables are good sources of protein too. In fact, nearly all foods contain protein, but no naturally occurring food is 100% protein. Protein comprises only about 20 to 30% of the weight of a piece of beef; 25% of the weight of drained, water-packed tuna fish; and only 12% of an egg's weight. Nevertheless, animal foods generally provide higher amounts of protein than similar quantities of plant foods. A 75-g (2.5-oz.) serving of broiled lean ground beef supplies approximately 19 g of protein; a 125-mL (½-cup) serving of steamed broccoli or cooked carrots provides only about 1 g of protein. In general, most plant foods provide less than 3 g of protein per serving. Table 7.2 lists some commonly eaten foods and their approximate protein content per serving.

TABLE 7.2 *Protein Content of Some Commonly Eaten Foods*

Food	Serving Size	Protein g/serving
Steak, rib eye, lean, broiled	75 g (2.5 oz.)	20
Chicken, ½ breast, roasted, meat only	75 g (2.5 oz.)	22
Ham, lean	75 g (2.5 oz.)	18
Pepperoni pizza, regular crust, 14" pie	2 slices (200 g)	25
Tuna, canned, water-packed, drained	75 g (2.5 oz.)	12
Tofu, regular	175 mL (¾ cup)	12
Processed cheese	50 g (1.5 oz.)	10
Baked beans	175 mL (¾ cup)	9
Bagel, plain	½ bagel (45 g)	4
Egg, hard cooked	1	6
White rice	125 mL (½ cup)	2
Peas, green	125 mL (½ cup)	4
Banana	1	1

legumes plants that produce pods with a single row of seeds

high-quality (complete) protein protein that contains all nine essential amino acids in amounts that support the growth

low-quality (incomplete) protein protein that lacks or has inadequate amounts of one or more of the essential amino acids

Food & Nutrition *tip*

Canned beans often have considerable amounts of salt added to them. Dried beans do not have salt added to them, but they take a long time to cook, unless you soak them for several hours before cooking. The soaking process softens the beans, reducing cooking time, and making them more digestible and less likely to contribute to intestinal gas. (See Recipes for Healthy Living later in this chapter for a black bean recipe.)

Figure 7.3 Legumes. Legumes are plants that produce pods that have a single row of seeds.

Certain parts of plants contain more protein than other parts. Seeds, tree nuts, and legumes supply more protein per serving than servings of fruit or the edible leaves, roots, flowers, and stems of vegetables. Tree nuts include walnuts, cashews, and almonds; **legumes** are plants that produce pods that have a single row of seeds, such as soybeans, peas, peanuts, lentils, and beans (Fig. 7.3). A 60-mL (¼-cup) serving of almonds, dry roasted peanuts, or sunflower seed kernels supplies about 8 g of protein. Many seeds and nuts, however, pack a lot of calories from fat. Snack on just 60 mL of almonds, dry roasted peanuts, or sunflower seed kernels and you will add approximately 200 kcal to your diet!

Peas, lentils, and most kinds of beans contain more protein and complex carbohydrate than fat. Eating a 125-mL (½-cup) serving of vegetarian baked beans, for example, adds about 6 g of protein, 27 g of carbohydrate, and less than 1 g of fat to your diet. Although soybeans contain more fat than carbohydrate, soy fat is high in unsaturated fatty acids. The health benefits of unsaturated fatty acids are discussed in Chapter 6.

Protein Quality

Foods differ not only in the amount of protein they contain but also in their protein quality. A **high-quality** or **complete protein** contains all essential amino acids in amounts that will support protein deposition in muscles and other tissues, as well as a young child's growth.[2] High-quality proteins are well digested and absorbed by the body. Meat, fish, poultry, eggs, and milk and milk products contain high-quality proteins. Egg protein generally rates very high for protein quality because it is easy to digest and has a pattern of essential amino acids that closely resembles that needed by humans.

A **low-quality** or **incomplete protein** lacks or contains inadequate amounts of one or more of the essential amino acids. Furthermore, the human digestive tract does not digest low-quality protein sources as efficiently as foods containing high-quality protein. The essential amino acids that are in relatively low amounts are referred to as *limiting* amino acids, because they reduce the protein's ability to support growth, repair, and maintenance of tissues. In most instances, tryptophan, threonine, lysine, and the

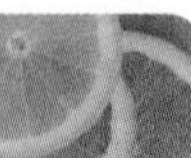

Did You Know?

Gelatin is made from *collagen*, a protein derived from the connective tissue of animals, but it's not a complete source of protein.

sulphur-containing amino acids methionine and cysteine are the limiting amino acids in foods.[3]

Most plant foods are not sources of high-quality proteins. Soy protein is an exception. After being processed, the quality of soy protein is comparable to that of most animal proteins.[4,5] Processed soybeans are used to make a variety of nutritious foods, including soy milk, infant formula, and meat substitutes. Furthermore, eating foods made from soybeans may reduce the risk of osteoporosis, cardiovascular disease, and certain cancers.[6,7] More research, however, is needed to determine the health benefits of eating diets that contain soy products.

Understanding the concept of protein quality is important. Regardless of how much protein is eaten, a child will fail to grow properly if his or her diet lacks essential amino acids. The section, "Vegetarianism," later in this chapter, explains how you can obtain these and other essential nutrients by eating only plant foods.

After being processed, the quality of soy protein is comparable to that of most animal proteins.

Concept Checkpoint

6. Explain the difference between a high-quality protein and a low-quality protein.
7. Identify at least three dietary sources of high-quality protein and three dietary sources of low-quality protein.
8. List at least three essential amino acids that are most likely to be limiting amino acids.

What Happens to Proteins in Your Body?

In a television crime series, police in a major city are investigating what could be a homicide. A man has been reported missing by his parents, who suspect foul play and their daughter-in-law's involvement in their son's disappearance. While knocking on the door of the missing man's house, police notice some dried blood on the front porch. The man's wife, who lives in the house, tells police that the blood is from her injured dog. How can police know she is telling the truth? The blood holds important clues. Every organism synthesizes proteins—including those in blood—that are unique. Samples of the blood can be analyzed to determine whether it contains proteins from a dog or another animal, such as a human. We will leave it to your imagination to finish this story, but we will examine a real life story—how human cells make proteins.

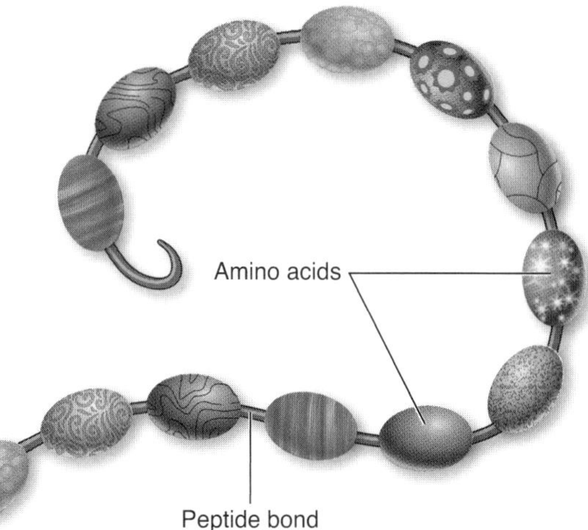

Figure 7.4 Amino acids form proteins. Each type of bead represents a specific amino acid in human proteins. The "hook" that connects the beads represents a peptide bond, a chemical attraction between the acid group of one amino acid and the amino group of another amino acid.

How Your Body Synthesizes Proteins

Your body makes proteins by following information coded in your **DNA** or deoxyribonucleic (*de-ox´-e-rye´-bow-new-klay´-ik*) acid, the hereditary material in a cell's nucleus. To make proteins, cells assemble the 20 amino acids in specific sequences according to the information provided by DNA. To understand this process, imagine proteins as various chains made from 20 different amino acid "beads." Figure 7.4 illustrates some of these beads and how they can be assembled into chains. Note that each bead has two metal wires that are used to link it with another bead. To make a copy of a particular beaded chain, you would follow directions for connecting the beads in a specific order and length by hooking the metal wires of each bead together. Consider the vast variety of beaded chains comprised of different bead sequences and chain lengths that you could make from just 20 different beads.

DNA hereditary material that provides instructions for making proteins

peptide bond chemical attraction that connects two amino acids together

peptides small chains of amino acids

polypeptides proteins comprised of 50 or more amino acids

gene portion of DNA

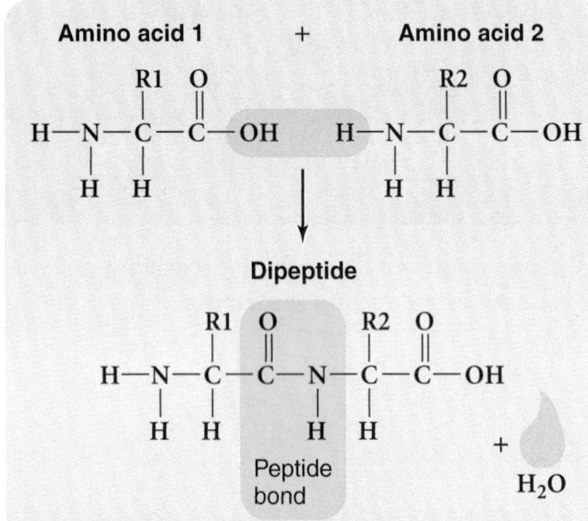

Figure 7.5 Peptide bond. A peptide bond is a chemical attraction between the acid group of one amino acid and the amino group of another amino acid. A dipeptide forms when two amino acids bond and a molecule of water is released in the process.

In living things, the beaded chains are proteins that contain amino acids. DNA supplies the directions for synthesizing each protein and the "hook" on each bead is a **peptide bond**, a chemical attraction between the acid group of one amino acid and the amino group of another amino acid (Fig. 7.5). A dipeptide forms when two amino acids bond and a molecule of water is released in the process. **Peptides** usually contain fewer than 15 amino acids. Most naturally occurring proteins are **polypeptides** (*poly* = many; *peptides* = amino acids) comprised of 50 or more amino acids.

Figure 7.6 summarizes the basic steps of protein synthesis. Protein synthesis begins with DNA in the cell's nucleus. DNA is a twisted two-stranded molecule referred to as a double helix. To begin the process, a section of the DNA double helix unwinds, exposing a gene. A **gene** is a portion of DNA that contains information concerning the order of amino acids that comprise a specific protein. *Messenger ribonucleic acid* (*mRNA*), a compound that is chemically similar to DNA, "reads" or transcribes the gene. The actual production of a protein occurs in the cytoplasm, so mRNA leaves the nucleus and moves to ribosomes—protein manufacturing sites in the cytoplasm. Ribosomes translate the gene's coded instructions for adding amino acids to the polypeptide chain. During this translation process, *transfer ribonucleic acid* (*tRNA*) conveys specific amino acids, one at a time, to the ribosomes. At ribosomes, the amino acid from tRNA is added to the last amino acid, causing the peptide chain to grow longer. After the mRNA is read completely, the ribosome releases the polypeptide, and then the new protein generally undergoes further processing at other sites within the cytoplasm.

Diets that contain low-quality protein can result in poor growth, slowed recovery from illness, and even death. These situations occur because protein synthesis in cells cannot proceed when the supply or "pool" of amino acids does not have one or more of the essential amino acids needed for constructing the polypeptide chain. When this happens, production of the protein stops. The partially made polypeptide chain is dismantled, and its amino acids are returned to the pool.

Figure 7.6 Protein synthesis. This illustration summarizes the basic steps of protein synthesis.

1. Protein synthesis begins with DNA in the cell's nucleus. A section of DNA unwinds, exposing a single portion (a gene) that contains coded information concerning the order of amino acids that comprise a specific protein.

2. The gene undergoes transcription, that is, its code is used to form messenger RNA (mRNA).

3. mRNA transfers the information concerning the amino acid sequence from the gene to ribosomes, protein manufacturing sites in the cytoplasm.

4. Ribosomes "read" the gene's coded instructions for adding amino acids to the polypeptide chain.

5. During this translation process, transfer RNA (tRNA) conveys specific amino acids to the ribosomes. Each amino acid bonds to the peptide chain, lengthening it. When the translation process is complete, the ribosome releases the polypeptide, and then the new protein generally undergoes further processing at other sites within the cytoplasm.

TRANSCRIPTION
DNA
mRNA
Cell nucleus
mRNA
Ribosome
TRANSLATION
tRNA
Peptide chain
Amino acid
Cytoplasm

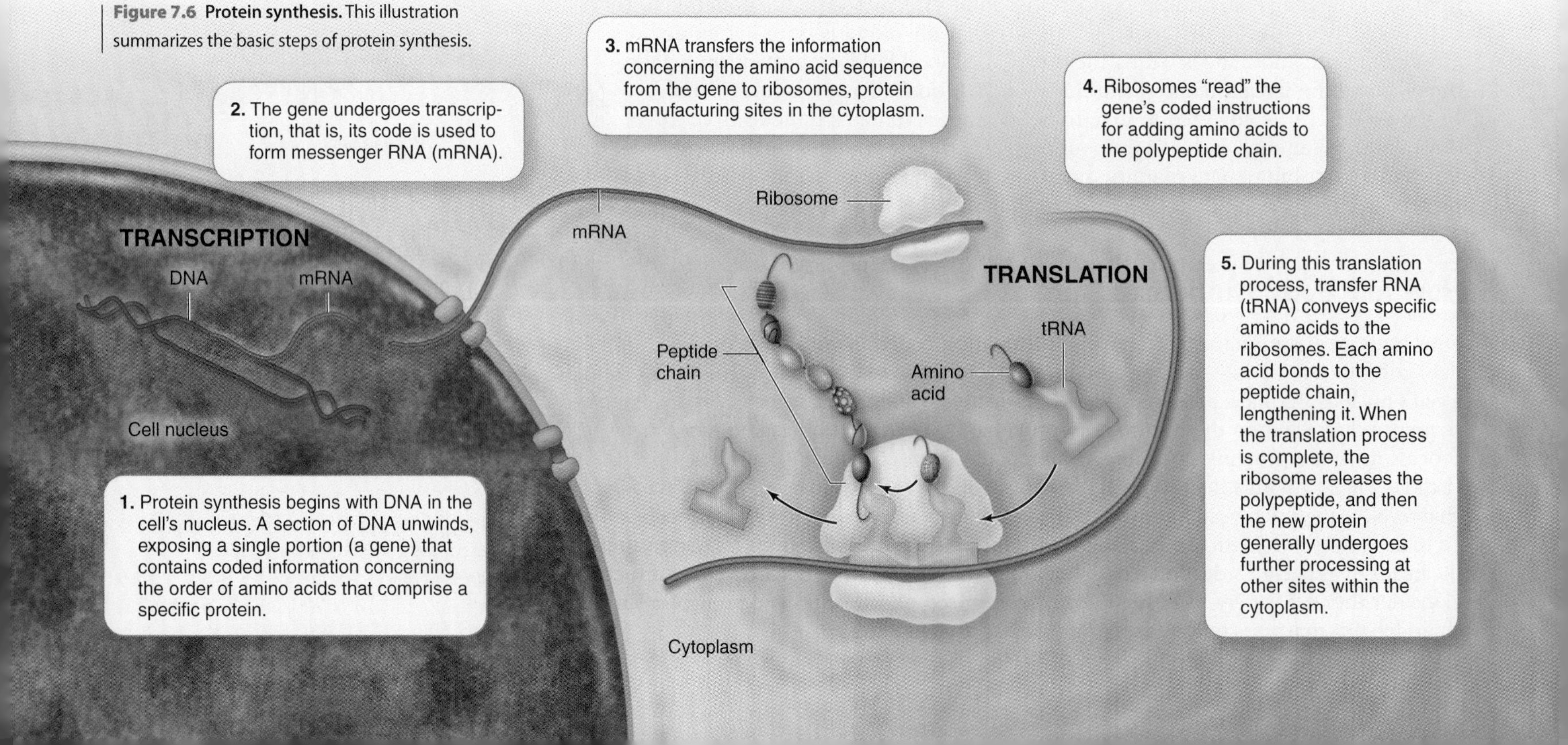

When assembly of the new protein has been completed, the polypeptide acid chain coils and folds into three-dimensional shapes that are characteristic of that particular protein. In some instances, more than one polypeptide chain curls around each other to form large protein complexes. For example, *hemoglobin*, a protein in red blood cells, is comprised of four polypeptide chains coiled together (Fig. 7.7). The shape of a protein is important because it influences the compound's activity in the body.

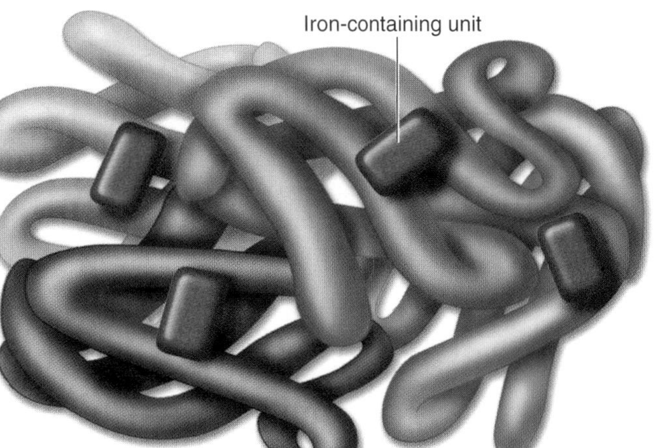

Figure 7.7 Shaping of a protein. A polypeptide chain can fold and coil into characteristic three-dimensional shapes, such as the four polypeptide chains of a hemoglobin molecule. In a hemoglobin molecule, each chain is associated with an iron-containing unit.

Occasionally, the wrong amino acid is introduced into the amino acid chain during the protein synthesis process. Cells usually check for such errors and replace the amino acid with the correct one. If the DNA code is faulty, however, the wrong amino acid will be inserted into the chain consistently, forming an abnormal polypeptide. Such errors often cause genetic defects that have devastating, even deadly effects, on the organism. *Sickle cell anemia*, for example, is an inherited condition characterized by abnormal hemoglobin. Cells in red bone marrow synthesize hemoglobin by following DNA's instructions concerning proper amino acid sequencing. If the DNA codes for the insertion of the wrong amino acid in two of hemoglobin's four polypeptide chains, the resulting protein is defective and does not function correctly. Figure 7.8a shows a red blood cell that contains normal hemoglobin; the red blood cells shown in Figure 7.8b have the defective hemoglobin associated with sickle cell anemia. The crescent-shaped red blood cells cannot transport oxygen efficiently. As a result, the abnormal cells can clog small blood vessels, causing pain, organ damage, and premature death. Sickle cell anemia is a common genetic disorder that generally affects people with African, Caribbean, or Mediterranean ancestry.

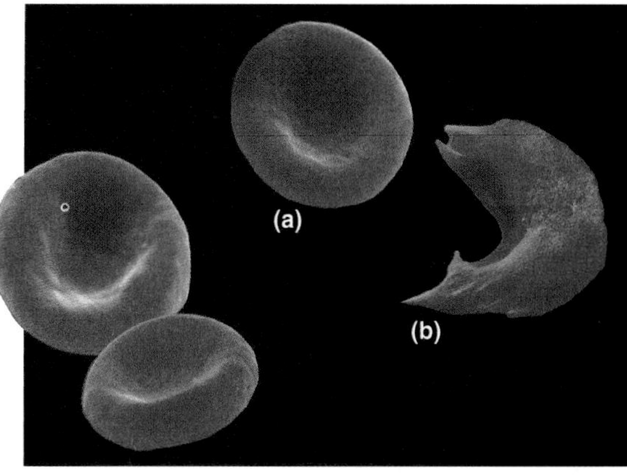

Figure 7.8 Sickle cell anemia. This microscopic view of red blood cells shows (a) normal disk-shaped cells and (b) a sickle cell that contains abnormal hemoglobin.

Protein Denaturation

A protein undergoes **denaturation** when it is exposed to various conditions that alter the macronutrient's natural folded and coiled shape (Fig. 7.9). We often cook protein-rich foods to make them more digestible and safe to eat, but heat also causes the proteins in foods to unfold. The protein in raw egg white, for example, is almost clear and has a jelly-like consistency. When you cook egg white, it becomes white and firm as its proteins become denatured. This process is irreversible; we can't "unboil" an egg. Other treatments often used during food preparation also denature proteins, including whipping or exposing them to alcohol or acid. Wine, for example, is often used in marinades, because the alcohol it contains denatures proteins in meat, helping tenderize it. Adding acidic lemon juice to milk denatures ("curdles") the proteins in milk. In your stomach, hydrochloric acid denatures food proteins, making them easier to digest. Denaturation does not "kill" a protein (because proteins are not living) but the process usually permanently alters the protein's shape and functions. Once an egg white has been cooked or milk has curdled, the food cannot return to its original state.

denaturation altering a protein's natural shape and function by exposing it to conditions such as heat, acids, and physical agitation

protein turnover cellular process of breaking down proteins and recycling their amino acids

Protein Turnover

Not all protein must be supplied by the diet. **Protein turnover**, the process of breaking down old or unneeded proteins into their component amino acids and recycling them to make new proteins, occurs constantly within cells. Amino acids that are not incorporated into proteins become part of a small amino acid pool, a readily available supply of amino acids that cells can use for future

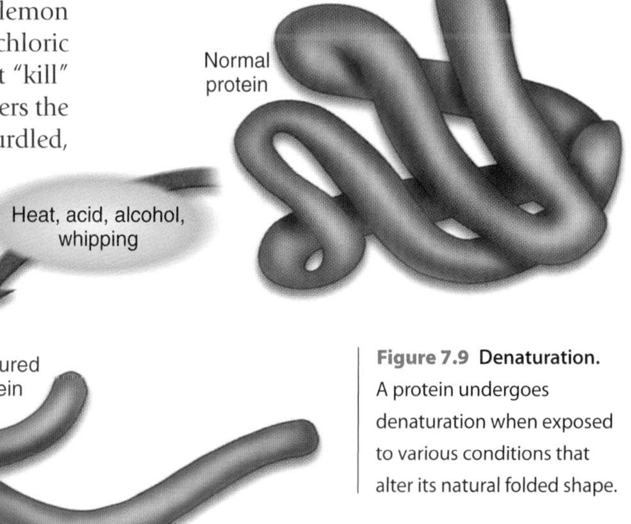

Figure 7.9 Denaturation. A protein undergoes denaturation when exposed to various conditions that alter its natural folded shape.

deamination removal of the nitrogen-containing group from an amino acid

transamination transfer of the nitrogen-containing group from an unneeded amino acid to a carbon skeleton to form an amino acid

urea waste product of amino acid metabolism

nitrogen balance (equilibrium) balancing nitrogen intake with nitrogen losses

positive nitrogen balance state in which the body retains more nitrogen than it loses

negative nitrogen balance state in which the body loses more nitrogen than it retains

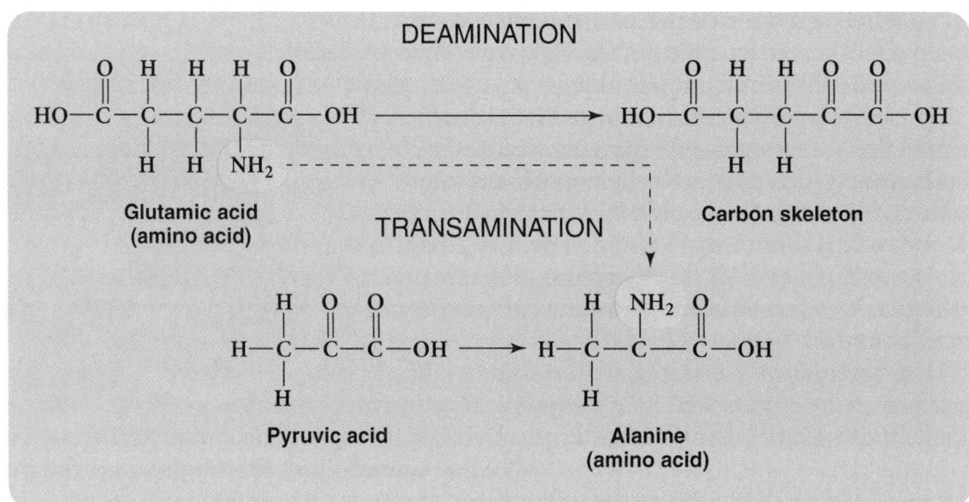

Figure 7.10 Deamination and transamination. Deamination is the process of removing the nitrogen-containing group from an unneeded amino acid. In this example, glutamic acid loses its amino group and becomes a carbon skeleton. Transamination occurs when the nitrogen-containing group is transferred to another substance to make an amino acid. In this example, pyruvic acid receives the amino group from glutamic acid, forming alanine, a nonessential amino acid.

protein synthesis. The amino acid pool is an *endogenous,* or internal, source of nitrogen. Your body obtains about two-thirds of its amino acid supply from endogenous sources and the remainder from *exogenous* (dietary) sources.

Transamination and Deamination

A healthy human body can make 11 of the 20 amino acids. The liver is the main site of nonessential amino acid production. Chemical reactions called deamination and transamination are involved in the synthesis of amino acids. **Deamination** is the process of removing the nitrogen-containing group (usually NH_2) from an unneeded amino acid. As a result of deamination, the amino acid that gives up its amino group becomes a carbon skeleton (Fig. 7.10). **Transamination** occurs when the nitrogen-containing group is transferred to another substance to make an amino acid. To make the amino acid alanine, for example, liver cells remove the amino group (NH_2) from glutamic acid and transfer it to pyruvic acid (see Fig. 7.10). Transamination reactions are reversible.

Deamination occurs primarily in the liver. Liver cells remove NH_2 from glutamic acid, forming ammonia (NH_3), a highly poisonous waste product (Fig. 7.11). The liver can use the ammonia to make **urea**, a metabolic waste product that is released into your bloodstream. The kidneys filter urea, small amounts of ammonia, and *creatinine* (a nitrogen-containing waste produced by muscles) from blood and eliminate the compounds in urine. After an amino acid undergoes deamination, the carbon skeleton that remains can be used for energy or converted to other compounds, such as glucose. Muscle cells can deaminate certain amino acids and use their carbon skeletons for energy.

If you consume more protein than you need, what happens to the extra amino acids? The body does not store excess amino acids in muscle or other tissues. The unnecessary amino acids undergo deamination, and cells convert the carbon skeletons into glucose or fat, or metabolize them for energy.

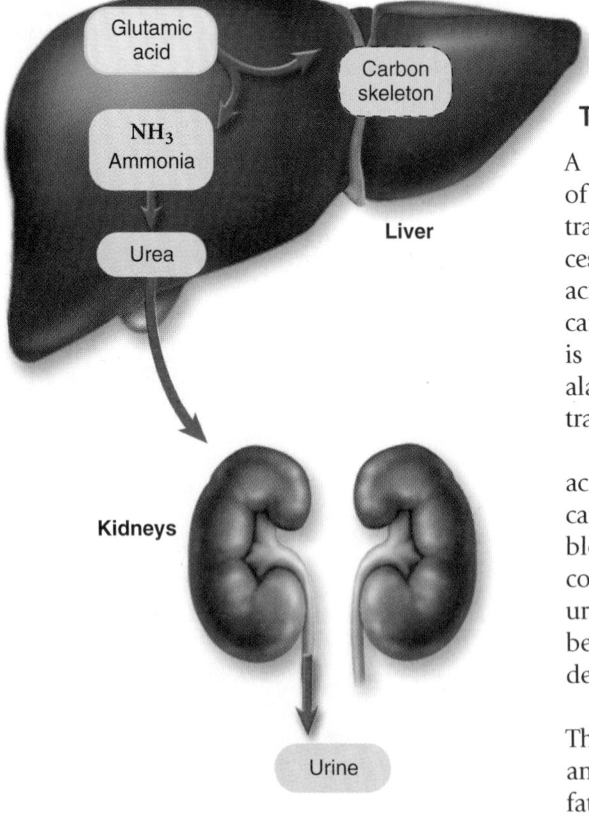

Glutamic acid
Carbon skeleton
NH_3 Ammonia
Liver
Urea
Kidneys
Urine

Figure 7.11 Deamination. This diagram illustrates the process of deamination and the production of the highly toxic compound ammonia in the liver. The liver converts ammonia to urea and releases it into the blood. Kidneys pick up urea and other nitrogen-containing wastes and eliminate them in urine.

Nitrogen Balance

Although your body conserves nitrogen by recycling amino acids, each day you lose some protein and nitrogen from your body. Urinary elimination of urea and creatinine accounts

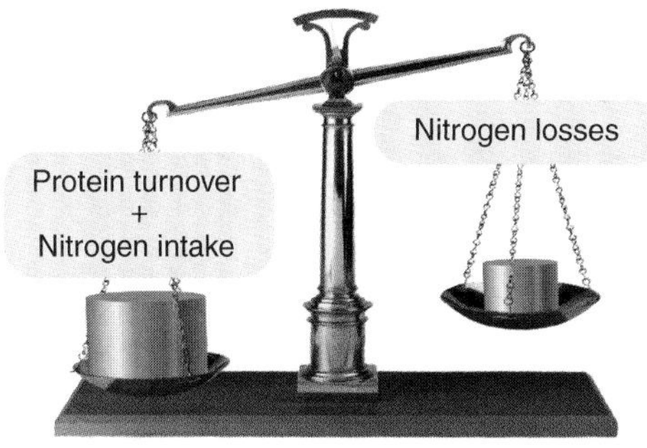

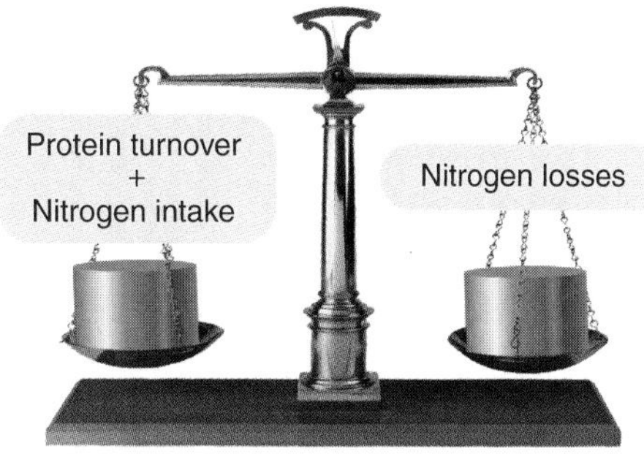

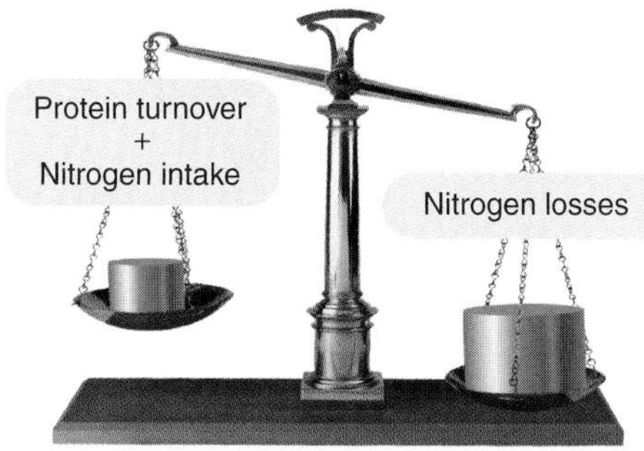

Positive Nitrogen Balance	Nitrogen Equilibrium	Negative Nitrogen Balance
• Growth • Pregnancy • Recovery from illness/injury • Increased levels of the hormones insulin, testosterone, and growth hormone • Resistance exercise	• Healthy adult meets protein and energy needs	• Inadequate protein intake or digestive tract diseases that interfere with protein absorption • Increased protein losses resulting from certain kidney diseases or blood loss • Bed rest • Fever, injuries, or burns • Increased secretion of thyroid hormone or cortisol (a "stress hormone")

Figure 7.12 Nitrogen balance. This diagram illustrates the concept of nitrogen balance and lists conditions that result in positive and negative nitrogen balance. Note that nitrogen balance occurs when nitrogen intake and turnover equals nitrogen losses.

for most of the lost nitrogen.[8] Daily nitrogen losses also occur as your nails and hair grow, and when you shed the outermost layer of your skin and cells from your intestinal tract. Your body uses amino acids from foods to replace the lost nitrogen.

Normally, an adult's body maintains its protein content by maintaining **nitrogen balance** or **nitrogen equilibrium**, that is, balancing nitrogen intake and protein turnover with losses. During certain stages of life or physical conditions, however, nitrogen intake and retention do not equal nitrogen losses. When the body is in a state of **positive nitrogen balance**, it retains more nitrogen than it loses as proteins are added to various tissues. In this case, a person must eat more protein to satisfy the increased need for the nutrient. Positive balance occurs during periods of rapid growth such as pregnancy, infancy, and puberty, and when people are recovering from illness or injury. Hormones such as insulin, growth hormone, and testosterone stimulate positive nitrogen balance. Performing weight (resistance) training also leads to nitrogen retention.[9,10] When the body is in a state of **negative nitrogen balance**, the body loses more nitrogen than it retains and protein intake is less than what the body needs. Negative balance occurs during starvation, serious illnesses, and severe injuries. Recovery from the illness or injury and refeeding protein results in positive nitrogen balance until nitrogen equilibrium is restored. Figure 7.12 illustrates the concept of nitrogen balance and lists conditions that result in positive and negative nitrogen balance.

How Much Protein Do You Need?

The Estimated Average Requirement (EAR) for protein is 0.66 g of protein/kg of body weight.[11] The EAR for protein increases during pregnancy, breast-feeding, periods of rapid growth, and recovery from serious illnesses, blood losses, and burns. Recall from Chapter 3 that scientists use EARs to establish Recommended Dietary Allowances (RDAs). A healthy adult's RDA for protein is 0.8 g/kg of body weight.[11] By reviewing DRI tables (inside back cover of this book), you will note that the RDAs for protein vary during certain ages and conditions.

Did You Know?

Despite information provided in commercials or advertisements, you cannot "feed" your hair, nails, or skin by using shampoos, conditioners, or lotions containing proteins or other nutrients. Hair, nails, and the outermost layer of skin are not living. By eating a nutritious diet, you'll provide your body with the nutrients it needs to make healthy hair, nails, and skin.

To determine your RDA for protein, multiply your weight in kilograms by 0.8 grams. If you are underweight or overweight, use a healthy weight for your height when making this calculation (see Fig. 10.14 on p. 353). For example, a healthy man who is 5′ 10″ tall and weighs 75 kilograms (his weight in pounds divided by 2.2) should consume 60 grams of protein daily (75 kg × 0.8 g) to meet his RDA for the nutrient. The Personal Dietary Analysis at the end of this chapter can help you estimate your daily protein intake.

Protein Digestion and Absorption

pepsin gastric enzyme that breaks down proteins into smaller polypeptides

When you eat oatmeal mixed with milk for breakfast, the large proteins in these foods must be digested before undergoing absorption. Protein digestion begins in the stomach where hydrochloric acid denatures food proteins and **pepsin**, an enzyme, digests proteins into smaller polypeptides. Soon after the polypeptides enter the small intestine, the pancreas secretes protein-splitting enzymes, including trypsin (*trip´-sin*) and chymotrypsin (*ki´-mo-trip´-sin*). *Trypsin* and *chymotrypsin* break down polypeptides into shorter peptides and amino acids. Enzymes released by the absorptive cells of the small intestine break down most of the shortened peptides into individual amino acids. The absorptive cells pick up the amino acids and any remaining dipeptides and tripeptides, compounds that consist of two and three amino acids, respectively. Within the absorptive cells, di- and tripeptides are broken down into amino acids. Thus, amino acids are the end products of protein digestion. After being absorbed, the amino acids enter the portal vein and travel to the liver where they may enter the general circulation. Protein digestion and absorption is very efficient—very little dietary protein escapes digestion and is eliminated in feces. Figure 7.13 summarizes protein digestion and absorption.

The liver keeps some amino acids for its needs and releases the rest into the general circulation. By the time cells obtain amino acids from blood, they cannot distinguish the ones that were originally in oat proteins from those that were in milk proteins. The cells, however, now have all the amino acids they need to make *your* body's proteins.

Disorders Related to Certain Food Proteins

Have you ever experienced an allergic reaction after eating certain foods or drinks? A food allergy is an inflammatory response that results when the body's immune system reacts inappropriately to one or more harmless substances (*allergens*) in the food. In most instances, the allergen is a protein. For reasons that are unclear, some protein in a food that is eaten does not undergo digestion, and the small intestine absorbs the whole molecule. Immune system cells in the small intestine recognize the food protein as a foreign substance and try to protect the body by mounting a defensive response. As a result of the immune response, the person who is allergic to that food experiences typical signs and symptoms. Common signs and symptoms of food allergies include *hives*, red raised bumps that usually appear on the skin; swollen or itchy lips; skin flushing; a scaly skin rash (eczema); difficulty swallowing; wheezing and difficulty breathing; and

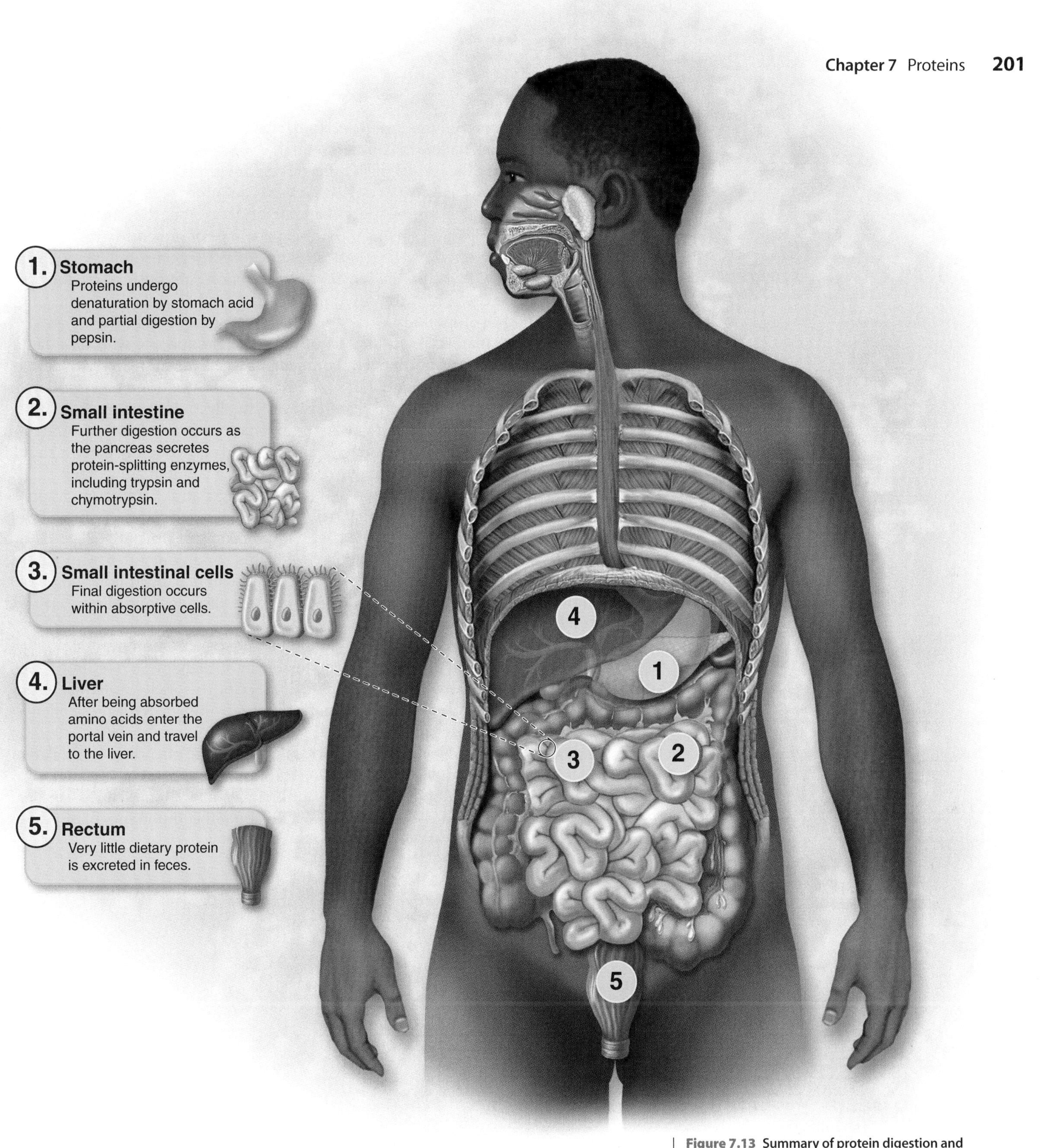

Figure 7.13 Summary of protein digestion and absorption. This illustration summarizes protein digestion and absorption.

abdominal pain, vomiting, and diarrhea. Allergic reactions generally occur within a few minutes to a couple of hours after eating the offending food. In severe cases, sensitive people who are exposed to food allergens can develop anaphylactic shock, a serious drop in blood pressure that affects the whole body. Anaphylaxis (*an-a-pha-lax´-is*) can be fatal, unless emergency treatment is provided.

Although any food protein has the potential to cause an allergic reaction in a susceptible person, the most allergenic proteins are in cow's milk, eggs, peanuts and other nuts, wheat, soybeans, fish, and shellfish. Allergic responses to non-protein food dyes or other food additives such as *sulphites* can also occur.[12] Sulphites are a group of sulphur-containing compounds that can be found naturally in foods, but they are often added to wines, fruits, vegetables, and shellfish to prevent spoilage or preserve flavours. People who suffer from asthma often develop breathing difficulties after consuming food treated with the compounds. Other sulphite-sensitive people report skin flushing (redness and warmth), hives, difficulty swallowing, vomiting, diarrhea, and dizziness after consuming foods that contain the compounds.

Genetics play a major role in the risk of food allergies; people who have family histories of allergies to foods or other environmental triggers are more likely to develop food allergies. Most children outgrow their food allergies by the time they are 5 years old. Allergies to nuts, seafood, and wheat, however, usually are not outgrown. Thus, it is important that parents realize that children, who have mild reactions to some food products early in life, may overcome these as they age, and consequently parents should speak to a dietitian about reintroducing these foods as their children grow older.

Gluten, a protein in wheat, barley, and rye, can trigger an inflammatory response in the small intestine, damaging intestinal cells and causing celiac disease. (Gluten forms elastic strands of protein that provide the chewy texture and stiff structure of breads and other products made from dough.) Children with this condition suffer from chronic diarrhea, severe weight loss, and poor growth due to nutrient malabsorption and protein malnutrition. A gluten-free diet is necessary to treat the disorder, and the special diet must be followed for a lifetime.

Accurate diagnosis of a food allergy should be undertaken by an immunologist, a physician who specializes in the diagnosis and treatment of allergies. Skin testing is a reliable way to identify allergens. Although hair analysis, cytotoxic or electrodermal testing, and kinesiology are promoted by alternative medical practitioners to diagnose allergies, these are unproven diagnostic methods.[13]

Treatment of food allergies involves strict avoidance of the offending foods. Parents or caregivers of young children with food allergies should read food labels carefully to check for allergens listed among ingredients. Additionally, they should educate teachers and other adults who associate with the allergic child about the importance of not exposing the youngster to specific foods.

Emergency treatment for anaphylaxis often involves injecting a medication that prevents or blunts the allergic response. This child is using an *autoinjector pen*, a special syringe, to inject herself with a dose of the medication.

Skin testing is a reliable way to identify allergens.

Concept **Checkpoint**

9. Explain the basic steps involved in protein synthesis.
10. Define denaturation, deamination, and transamination.
11. Describe conditions that can cause the body to be in negative nitrogen balance. Describe conditions in which the body is in positive nitrogen balance.
12. A healthy young woman weighs 65 kg (143 lbs.). Calculate her RDA for protein.
13. Explain what happens to proteins in beans as they undergo digestion and absorption in the human digestive tract.
14. List three common signs or symptoms of food allergy.
15. Discuss what parents of infants with PKU can do to help their children grow and develop normally.

REAL *people* REAL *stories*

Dallas C.

Dallas C. is an energetic teenager who loves mountain bike and road bike racing, downhill skiing, wrestling, and climbing ropes and trees. Not only is he athletic, he is also smart—his marks place him at the top of his class. According to his proud parents, Dallas is the perfect son—"a nice boy." Dallas *is* a special young man, but he also needs a special diet. Dallas was born with phenylketonuria (PKU).

A few days after birth, Dallas underwent standard newborn blood testing. The results of the test indicated that the level of phenylalanine in his blood was about 40 times higher than the normal amount, a sign of the inherited disorder PKU. To avoid developing severe brain damage and other physiological effects of PKU, the infant needed to receive the care of a physician who specializes in treating children with the disorder. The primary treatment for PKU is a low-phenylalanine diet.

Most foods that are rich sources of protein, especially high-quality animal proteins, contain more phenylalanine than people with PKU can tolerate. Thus, from the time Dallas was a week old, he has consumed a formula that does not contain the amino acid. In addition to the formula, Dallas eats special foods that resemble "regular" foods but are not available in supermarkets. To obtain low-phenylalanine foods, his parents order them from companies that manufacture such products. Dallas can eat limited amounts of grain products and most fruits and vegetables. To determine whether the diet is working, Dallas must have the level of phenylalanine in his blood checked weekly.

Dallas' parents and his two younger sisters do not have PKU. At home, he eats the low-phenylalanine foods, while the other members of his family consume regular foods. Foods that are eaten away from home can present problems for people with PKU. In Dallas' case, his mother provides his school with a supply of low-phenylalanine foods for the teen's lunches. When the family visits restaurants, Dallas usually orders french fries, which are allowed in his diet. Dallas is so accustomed to his special diet that he thinks meat looks "gross."

In the past, children with PKU were often allowed to eat regular foods after they were about 6 years of age. However, the importance of continuing the low-phenylalanine diet became evident when many of the children experienced learning and behavioural problems as they matured. Dallas is aware of the consequences that can occur if he does not limit his phenylalanine intake, and he accepts the need to follow the special diet for the rest of his life. According to Dallas, "Being on a strict diet has not only made me disciplined, it has taught me to do whatever is needed to always take good care of myself. I have learned that we are all different, anyway. So, accept who you are!"

Protein Consumption Patterns

The Canadian Community Health Survey (CCHS) Cycle 2.2 revealed that Canadian adults receive approximately 17% of their energy intake from protein.[14] For healthy adults, this level of consumption is within the Acceptable Macronutrient Distribution Range (AMDR), which is 10 to 35% of energy from protein.[3] Canadians, however, now consume more protein from meat, fish, and poultry than from plant foods (Fig. 7.14). This poses a health risk for Canadians as many animal sources of protein contain high levels of total fat and saturated fat. Plant-based protein sources, while often incomplete protein sources, are typically high in polyunsaturated and monounsaturated fats that are associated with improved blood lipid profiles.

Eating Well with Canada's Food Guide: Recommendations for Protein Intake

Animal sources of protein are often rich sources of saturated fat and cholesterol. According to Health Canada and the *Eating Well with Canada's Food Guide* recommendations, Canadians should choose fish or lean or low-fat cuts of meat and poultry.[15] The leanest cuts of beef include round steaks, top round, loin, and top sirloin, as well as chuck and arm roasts. Before cooking a piece of beef, you can reduce its fat content by trimming the visible fat away from the meat. When buying ground beef, consider choosing "extra lean" products. The label on a package of extra lean ground beef should state that the meat is at least 90% lean. When cooked, extra lean ground beef can taste "dry." You can improve the taste of the beef by adding a small amount of "heart healthy" olive oil to the raw meat before shaping it into hamburger patties. The leanest cuts of pork include pork loin, tenderloin, and centre loin. *Eating Well with Canada's Food Guide* recommends two servings of fish per week.

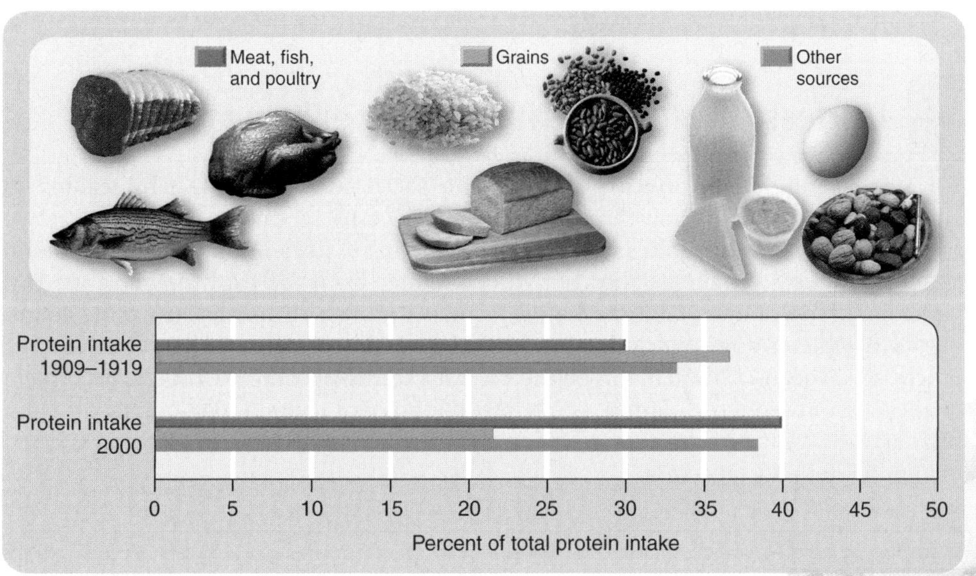

Figure 7.14 Protein consumption patterns. Canadians today eat slightly more protein than they did in the early 1900s. Much of this increase reflects the population's greater consumption of protein from meat, fish, and poultry.

Ham, bacon, sausage, frankfurters, and deli meats, such as salami and bologna, generally contain high amounts of fat and sodium.

Did You Know?

There is nothing inherently "bad" about eating small portions of red meat. Red meat is a good source of zinc and iron, minerals that are often less available from plant foods.

The *Eating Well with Canada's Food Guide* recommendations suggest consumers use lean turkey, roast beef, or low-fat luncheon meats for sandwiches, instead of processed meat products.[15] Processed meat products, such as ham, bacon, sausage, hot dogs, and bologna and salami, generally contain a lot of fat and also have high amounts of added sodium. Excessive sodium intakes are associated with increased risk of hypertension. If you decide to purchase processed meats, check the Nutrition Facts table on products' labels to compare fat as well as sodium contents.

Eating Well with Canada's Food Guide also recommends varying your protein choices.[15] For example, consider eating fish that are rich sources of beneficial omega-3 fatty acids, such as salmon, trout, and herring. You can also replace main menu items that contain meat with dishes made with dry beans, peas, or foods made from soybeans. Additionally, consider snacking on nuts, such as peanuts, almonds, cashews, walnuts, and pecans, instead of pieces of meat or cheese.

Concept Checkpoint

16. What is the AMDR for adult protein intake?

17. Describe how Canadians' food sources of protein have changed since the early 1900s.

18. Consider your usual food choices. Using the recommendations of the *Eating Well with Canada's Food Guide*, discuss ways you can reduce your intake of protein from animal foods.

Understanding Nutritional Labelling: Proteins

You can determine how much protein is in a packaged food product by reading its Nutrition Facts table. As you can see in Figure 7.15, one serving of maple and brown sugar instant oatmeal contains 4 g of protein. The panel does not provide information about a product's protein quality, but you can judge from the list of ingredients. This particular brand of oatmeal, for example, contains proteins from various whole grains, but its ingredients do not include sources of high-quality proteins such as eggs, milk, or processed soybeans. Although this oatmeal is not a source of complete protein, its protein quality is improved if the oatmeal is eaten with foods that contain high-quality proteins, such as with milk. The following section explains how you can use plant proteins to obtain high-quality protein.

Figure 7.15 Nutrition Facts table. The Nutrition Facts table provides information about a product's protein content.

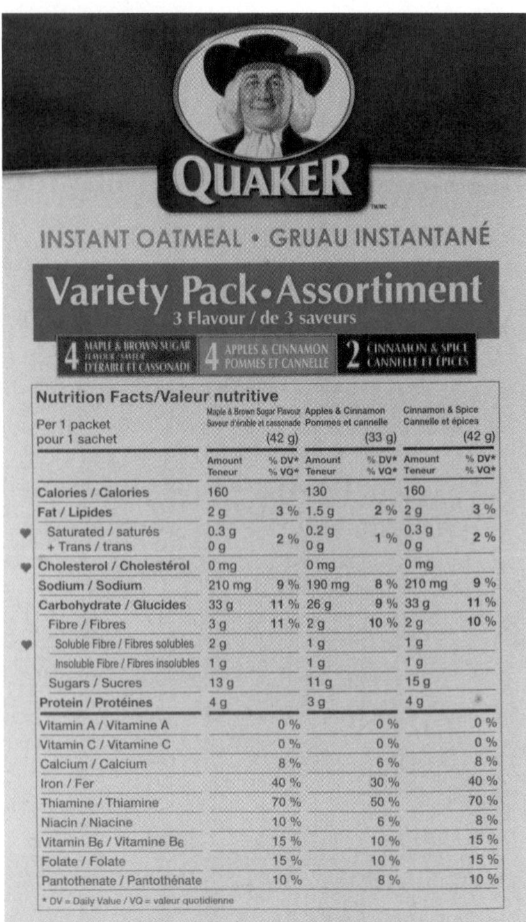

Nutrition Facts/Valeur nutritive

Per 1 packet / pour 1 sachet	Maple & Brown Sugar Flavour / Saveur d'érable et cassonade (42 g)		Apples & Cinnamon / Pommes et cannelle (33 g)		Cinnamon & Spice / Cannelle et épices (42 g)	
	Amount / Teneur	% DV* / % VQ*	Amount / Teneur	% DV* / % VQ*	Amount / Teneur	% DV* / % VQ*
Calories / Calories	160		130		160	
Fat / Lipides	2 g	3 %	1.5 g	2 %	2 g	3 %
Saturated / saturés + Trans / trans	0.3 g 0 g	2 %	0.2 g 0 g	1 %	0.3 g 0 g	2 %
Cholesterol / Cholestérol	0 mg		0 mg		0 mg	
Sodium / Sodium	210 mg	9 %	190 mg	8 %	210 mg	9 %
Carbohydrate / Glucides	33 g	11 %	26 g	9 %	33 g	11 %
Fibre / Fibres	3 g	11 %	2 g	10 %	2 g	10 %
Soluble Fibre / Fibres solubles	2 g		1 g		1 g	
Insoluble Fibre / Fibres insolubles	1 g		1 g		1 g	
Sugars / Sucres	13 g		11 g		15 g	
Protein / Protéines	4 g		3 g		4 g	
Vitamin A / Vitamine A		0 %		0 %		0 %
Vitamin C / Vitamine C		0 %		0 %		0 %
Calcium / Calcium		8 %		6 %		8 %
Iron / Fer		40 %		30 %		40 %
Thiamine / Thiamine		70 %		50 %		70 %
Niacin / Niacine		10 %		6 %		8 %
Vitamin B_6 / Vitamine B_6		15 %		10 %		15 %
Folate / Folate		15 %		10 %		15 %
Pantothenate / Pantothénate		10 %		8 %		10 %

* DV = Daily Value / VQ = valeur quotidienne

Concept Checkpoint

19. Discuss how you can use information on a food product's label to determine whether the food is a source of high-quality protein.

Eating Well for Less

Does your favourite breakfast include some slices of ham or bacon, two fried eggs, a slice of toast, and a glass of milk? For lunch, would you enjoy eating a submarine sandwich made with three different types of cold cuts and two kinds of cheese? Perhaps your mouth waters at the thought of a dinner eating "surf and turf"—lobster tail accompanied by a steak. If you are a typical Canadian, animal foods contribute the largest share of the protein in your diet.[16] Some of these foods, however, are among the most expensive items on our grocery lists, and you may be able to reduce your food costs if you eat less of them.

Because animal foods are among the best dietary sources of essential amino acids, is it safe to eat less animal protein? Yes! One way you can lower your intake is to include only one animal source of protein in a meal and reduce its serving size. For example, if your breakfast is a 170-g (6-oz.) slice of ham with two large poached eggs, you are obtaining approximately 500 kcal and almost 60 g of high-quality protein. That is enough protein in one meal to meet the RDA for a person who weighs 60 kg (132 lbs.). Instead of eating such a large serving of ham with the poached eggs, have 75 g (2.5 oz.) of ham without the eggs, or skip the ham and just eat the eggs. Two poached eggs supply 12.5 g of high-quality protein and only 180 kcal.

Many commonly eaten menu items provide the proper amounts and mixtures of essential amino acids without relying heavily on animal products. The following sections describe ways you can eat less meat and save money without sacrificing the nutritional quality of your diet.

Animal foods contribute the largest share of the protein in the typical Canadian's diet. Some of these foods, however, are among the most expensive items on our grocery lists.

Did You Know?

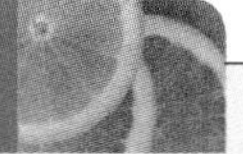

Humans use nearly every part of an animal for food. *Meat* is muscle tissue; *tripe* is from the stomach of cattle; *prairie* or *Rocky Mountain oysters*, *lamb* or *calf fries*, and *huevos del toro* are testicles of male sheep or cattle; and *sweetbreads* are the thymus glands of calves and lambs. In some cultures, people even consume the tongues, brains, and blood of certain animals.

protein complementation the process of combining incomplete plant-based protein sources to provide all the essential amino acids

Combining Complementary Proteins

Although research findings indicate that it is not necessary to consume all essential amino acids during a meal for the body to utilize them for growth, certain plant-based recipes ensure that these compounds are consumed at one time. **Protein complementation** is the process of mixing incomplete plant-based protein sources to provide all essential amino acids without adding animal proteins. However, to make dishes that contain complementary amino acid combinations, you must know which plant foods are good protein sources and which essential amino acids are limiting or low in those plant foods. In general, plant foods are poor sources of one or more essential amino acids, particularly tryptophan, threonine, lysine, and methionine. Green peas, for example, are good sources of lysine, but they contain low amounts of tryptophan and methionine. Cereal grains such as wheat, rice, and corn are good sources of tryptophan and methionine, but they tend to be low in lysine. Wheat germ, however, is a rich source of lysine. Legumes are generally low in methionine. Although most fruits and some kinds of vegetables are poor sources of protein, they add appealing colours and textures as well as vitamins, minerals, and phytochemicals to plant-based meals.

Many cultures have traditional foods that combine complementary plant proteins. For example, a peanut butter sandwich combines two foods that supply complementary plant proteins. Peanuts are a fair source of lysine. Bread contains some methionine, but the grain product is very low in lysine. Serving the two foods together as a peanut butter sandwich provides adequate amounts of these essential amino acids. Table 7.3

A taco or burrito combines a relatively large amount of a grain product with smaller amounts of lysine-rich meat, seafood, chicken, or cheese. The proteins in the animal foods enhance the quality of the wheat or corn proteins.

Peanut butter on bread is an example of a popular food made from complementary plant proteins.

TABLE 7.3 *Complementary Protein Dishes*

Red beans and rice
Peanut or soy nut butter on bagel, sprinkled with wheat germ
Hummus (mashed chickpeas/garbanzo beans) with sesame seeds*
Hummus on whole-grain pita bread
Black beans and cornmeal tortilla*
Split pea soup with toasted whole-wheat bread
Meatless kidney bean chili with macaroni
Cornmeal tortilla with black bean salsa
Peanut butter on whole-grain crackers, sprinkled with wheat germ
Green beans with brown rice and cashews

* See the Recipes for Healthy Living feature for hummus and black bean recipes.

lists some other foods that are examples of complementary protein combinations. When menu planning, you can combine a variety of legumes, tree nuts, seeds, and grains with vegetables to prepare dishes that provide adequate mixtures of the essential amino acids. Figure 7.16 shows three categories of plant proteins (legumes, grains, tree nuts, and seeds) that make complementary combinations when one or more foods from at least two different groups are mixed together.

Not every mixture of plant foods creates a complementary combination. For example, making a fruit salad by combining apples, grapes, and oranges will not provide a complementary mixture of essential amino acids. Fruits are nutritious foods, but they are generally poor sources of protein. Combining Boston, iceberg, and romaine varieties of lettuce with carrots and onions makes a tasty salad, but simply mixing leafy greens with other vegetables does not make a complementary combination, because vegetables have small amounts of protein that tend to contain low amounts of essential amino acids. However, adding sunflower seed kernels, kidney or black beans, cashews, and bread cubes to the salad boosts the amount of protein and provides a complete mix of amino acids. To increase the essential amino acid content of the salad even further, you can add a small amount of hard-cooked egg, shredded cheese, or bits of tofu, a soybean product, to it. Processed soybean foods are good sources of essential amino acids. If you are interested in trying foods made from soybeans, the Food & Nutrition Tips on page 209 provide information about some of the more popular foods made from soybeans.

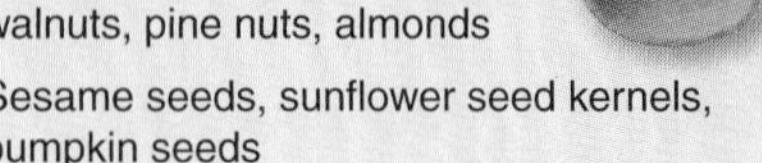

Figure 7.16 Complementary combinations. Combining certain plant foods can result in complementary combinations of essential amino acids. To assure an adequate mix of proteins, combine one or more foods from at least two different food groups (legumes, grains, tree nuts and seeds).

Food & Nutrition *tips*

The following information describes popular soybean foods and tips for how to use them in menu planning.

- Tofu is made from pureed soybeans and has the consistency of thick jelly. Plain tofu has little flavour, so it can be added to a variety of foods including stir-fried vegetables and scrambled eggs.
- Tempeh is a fermented soybean and grain mixture that can substitute for meat in sandwiches and casseroles.
- Miso is also made from fermented soybeans. Miso can be used to boost the protein content and add flavour to other foods.
- Soy nuts are roasted soybeans that are often eaten as a snack. Ground soy nuts form a spread that is used like peanut butter.
- Soy milk is made from crushed soybeans. Soy milk is usually fortified with calcium and vitamins A, D, B-12, and riboflavin. Regular soy milk can substitute for cow's milk as a beverage or in recipes. Soy milk cheeses and yogourt are also available.
- Texturized soy protein (TSP) is made from soybean flour. TSP is often processed to imitate the texture, taste, and appearance of meat or poultry. A TSP product that resembles ground beef can be used to replace half or all of the ground beef in meatloaf, meatball, chili, taco, or meat sauce recipes.
- Soy protein concentrate is a high-protein, high-fibre refined soybean product that is used to boost the protein content of foods.

Concept Checkpoint

20. Explain the difference between substituting high-quality proteins and extending high-quality proteins. Give examples of common foods that are high-quality substitutes for meat and foods that extend a source of high-quality protein.

21. Does a recipe that combines apples and oranges with peanuts provide a complementary mixture of proteins? Explain why or why not.

22. A recipe mixes cereals made from wheat, rice, and corn. What plant foods could you add to this combination of cereals to make the recipe a source of high quality protein?

Vegetarianism

Are you or anyone you know vegetarian? If you are vegetarian, do you eat any animal foods? A growing number of Canadians are adopting vegetarian diets, and it is estimated that 4% of Canadian adults have adopted vegetarian lifestyles.[17] **Vegetarians** rely heavily on plant foods and may or may not include some animal foods in their diets. There are many different types of vegetarian diets, including some that contain animal foods. A semi-vegetarian, for example, avoids red meat but consumes other animal foods including fish, poultry, eggs, and dairy products. Other vegetarians have more restrictive diets, particularly when choosing whether to eat animal foods. A **lactovegetarian** (*lacto* = milk) consumes milk and milk products, including yogourt, cheese, and ice cream, to obtain

vegetarians people who eat plant-based diets

lactovegetarian vegetarian who consumes milk and milk products for animal protein

ovovegetarian vegetarian who eats eggs for animal protein

lactoovovegetarian vegetarian who consumes milk products and eggs for animal protein

vegan vegetarian who eats only plant foods

animal protein. An **ovovegetarian** (*ovo* = egg) eats eggs, and a **lactoovovegetarian** consumes milk products and eggs. A **vegan**, or total vegetarian, eats only plant-based foods.

Vegetarians have various reasons for eating little or no animal products. Many vegetarians have religious, ethical, and other philosophical beliefs that do not support the practice of killing and eating animals. For others, vegetarianism is a matter of economics; plant foods are generally less expensive than animal foods. Some vegetarians believe that humans are not physically able to digest animal foods. This is not true. The omnivore's intestinal tract is able to obtain nutrients from both plants and animals, and humans are omnivores. Nevertheless, eating more plant than animal sources of protein may provide important health benefits.

Is Vegetarianism a Healthy Lifestyle?

Vegetarians are generally healthier than people who eat "Western diets" that contain animal foods, particularly plenty of red meat.[17,18,19] Vegetarians tend to weigh less and are less likely to die of heart disease than non-vegetarians.[17,20] It is difficult to pinpoint diet responsible for vegetarians' health status. Why? Vegetarians often adopt other healthy lifestyle practices such as exercising regularly; practising relaxation activities, such as meditation; and avoiding tobacco products and excess alcohol. Causes of death for non-vegetarians who are also health conscious are similar to causes of death for vegetarians.[17,20]

Compared to the typical North American diet, vegetarian diets provide more fibre, folate (a B vitamin), vitamin C, and the minerals magnesium and copper.[17,21] Furthermore, vegetarian diets often supply less saturated fat and cholesterol than diets that include animal foods. If poorly planned, however, plant-based diets may not contain enough energy, high-quality protein, omega-3 fatty acids, vitamins B-12 and D, and minerals zinc, iron, and calcium to meet a person's nutritional needs. In general, plant foods have low energy density—they add bulk to the diet without adding a lot of calories. Thus, vegetarians may feel "full" soon after eating a meal of plant foods, and they may not consume as much energy, vitamins, and minerals as they need. When compared to people who eat large amounts of animal foods, total vegetarians are less likely to be overweight.

A vegan or total vegetarian might enjoy this dish—couscous with vegetables and chickpeas. Couscous is a grain product.

Although animal foods are excellent sources of high-quality protein, total vegetarians, including vegan athletes, can obtain adequate amounts of the essential amino acids by eating foods that combine complementary plant proteins.[17] Plant foods, however, do not contain vitamin B-12, and there are few dietary sources of vitamin D other than fortified cow's milk. Furthermore, mineral nutrients such as calcium and iron are more available from animal than from plant foods. Plants often contain phytochemicals that interfere with the body's absorption of minerals, particularly iron, zinc, and calcium. Nevertheless, vegans can obtain vitamin B-12, vitamin D, iron, zinc, and many other micronutrients by consuming fortified foods such as soy milk, nutritional yeast, and breakfast cereals. Vegetarians can also take a multiple vitamin/mineral supplement to provide dietary "insurance."

Children have higher protein and energy needs per kilogram of body weight than an adult. Because plant foods add bulk to the diet, vegan children are more likely to eat far less food than adult vegans as they become full sooner during meals. Thus, very young vegans may be unable to eat enough plant foods to meet their protein and energy needs. Therefore, it is very important for parents or other caretakers to plan nutritionally adequate diets for vegetarian children and monitor the youngsters' growth rates.

Vegan women who breast-feed their infants may produce milk that is deficient in vitamin B-12, particularly if the mothers' diets lack the vitamin. These infants of vegan mothers have a high risk of developing severe developmental delays associated with neurological damage, especially when breast milk is their only source of vitamin B-12.[22]

Pregnant vegan women should consult with their physicians about the need to take a vitamin B-12 supplement to reduce the likelihood of having a baby who is deficient in this nutrient. Additionally, vegan mothers who breast-feed their infants may need to provide the babies with a source of vitamin B-12 as well.

Many Canadian teenagers and young adults are adopting vegetarian diets. Switching from the typical Western diet to vegetarianism can be a healthy practice for teens; vegetarian youth often eat more fruits and vegetables and fewer fast foods than their non-vegetarian peers.[17] On the other hand, vegetarian teenagers may have a higher risk of eating disorders, such as *anorexia nervosa,* than young people who eat meat.[17] Anorexia nervosa ("anorexia") is a serious psychological disorder that can result in starvation and suicide. The Chapter 10 Highlight provides more information about anorexia nervosa and other eating disorders.

Commercially prepared vegetarian foods are often available in the frozen food section of supermarkets.

How to Decrease Your Intake of Animal Foods

An easy way to reduce your meat consumption is to replace meat with other high-quality protein sources. Eggs, milk, cheese, and yogourt are animal sources of high-quality protein that you can substitute for meat, fish, or poultry items in your diet. For example, simply have a cheese sandwich instead of eating a submarine sandwich made with various luncheon meats and cheeses. If you are interested in eating less fat, a serving of low-fat cottage cheese or low-fat yogourt makes a protein-rich substitute for the "sub" or cheese sandwich.

Another way to reduce the amount of animal food in your diet and your food costs is to make meals that contain less animal protein and more plant protein. In many parts of the world, people with limited access to meat and other animal foods rely heavily on recipes that combine small amounts of animal protein with larger portions of certain plant proteins. Proteins in animal foods contain enough essential amino acids to extend or "beef up" the lower quality plant proteins in peas, beans, cereals, and other grain products. Pasta made from white flour, for example, contains cereal (wheat) proteins that have limiting amounts of lysine. By mixing large amounts of cooked pasta with smaller amounts of lysine-rich meat, seafood, chicken, or cheese, the proteins in the animal foods enhance the quality of the wheat proteins. As a result, the body can use the amino acids in pasta for growth, repair, and maintenance of tissues.

Pancakes, waffles, crepes, and cornflakes with milk are examples of breakfast foods that extend egg and milk proteins with large amounts of cereal proteins. Many popular Asian dishes mix small amounts of chicken, beef, or seafood with large portions of rice; Italian dishes often combine pasta with small amounts of cheese or meat sauce. Serving meals that extend the high-quality protein in animal foods is an economical way to feed large numbers of people. For example, you can use 454 g (1 lb.) of ground meat to make a single hamburger for each of your four friends. However, you will have enough chili con carne to feed six or more friends if you combine that 454 g (1 lb.) of ground meat with three cans of kidney beans and a couple of large cans of tomatoes. The ground meat has plenty of cysteine and methionine, the essential amino acids that are low in kidney beans. By mixing plant and animal sources of protein together in chili con carne, the beef protein extends the quality of the protein in the kidney beans. Although the chili recipe calls for adding tomatoes to the meat and beans, tomatoes are botanically classified as fruit, so they add very little protein to the dish. (Imagine eating chili con carne without tomatoes!) If you want to extend the chili even more, add cooked macaroni to the mixture. Macaroni is made from wheat, so it contains cereal proteins that are enhanced by the proteins in the meat and beans.

Traditional Asian dishes, such as beef stir-fry, combine small amounts of animal protein with larger amounts of cereal and vegetable proteins.

Meatless Menu Planning

Many common menu items can be converted into vegetarian foods by removing the meat, fish, or poultry. For example, pizza and lasagna can be prepared without meat and still provide plenty of protein from the cheese as well as the crust or pasta. Stir-fried foods can also be a reliable source of protein without adding meat, fish, or poultry. To stir-fry, heat a small amount of peanut or canola oil in a frying pan and add cooked rice and pieces of raw vegetables. While the mixture is heating, add a beaten egg to it and stir so that the egg cooks thoroughly. Before serving the dish, sprinkle cashews or sunflower seed kernels over the hot rice and vegetable mixture. Table 7.4 presents more meatless menu suggestions.

Commercially prepared vegetarian foods that substitute for meat, fish, and poultry items are often available in the frozen food section of supermarkets. These vegetarian products can look and taste like their non-vegetarian counterparts, but they generally do not contain cholesterol and may be lower in saturated fat. Such foods include soy-based sausage patties or links, soy hot dogs, "veggie" burgers, and soy "crumbles" that look like bits of cooked ground beef. Asian restaurants usually offer vegetarian dishes. Some "Western-style" restaurants offer vegetarian menu items, or their cooks can modify menu items by substituting meatless sauces, omitting meat from stir-fries, and adding vegetables or pasta in place of meat.

With careful planning, vegetarians can overcome the nutritional limitations of a plant-based diet and consume adequate diets.[17,18] If you are interested in learning more specific details about vegetarian cookery and menu planning, contact a registered dietitian in your area. It is easy to locate a dietitian through the find a dietitian service on the Dietitians of Canada Web site at www.dietitians.ca/public/content/find_a_nutrition_professional/find_a_dietitian.asp.

TABLE 7.4 *Meatless Menu Ideas*

• Cooked pasta with marinara sauce and grated Parmesan or part-skim mozzarella cheese
• Vegetable lasagna with layers of thinly sliced zucchini, mushrooms, and bell peppers
• Vegetable stir-fry with bits of tofu and cheese
• Grilled vegetable kabobs served over cooked rice and black beans
• Black or red bean burritos
• Bean tacos

Concept Checkpoint

23. Describe how the diets of semi-vegetarians differ from other vegetarian diets.
24. Identify nutrients that are most likely lacking in a vegan's diet.
25. Explain why vegans must be careful when planning vegan meals for children.

Protein Adequacy

If some protein is necessary for proper growth and good health, can eating extra amounts of the nutrient make you *extra* healthy or physically fit? Intuitively, the idea of eating more protein to improve your health seems logical, but protein is no different than the other nutrients. If your diet contains adequate amounts of protein, then eating "more is not better." You may, however, be able to reap substantial health benefits by reducing your animal protein intake and increasing your consumption of plant foods.

In many parts of the world, the lack of foods containing high-quality proteins is a serious problem, particularly for young children. Protein deficiency interferes with a child's normal growth and development, and contributes to many childhood deaths. The following sections examine protein malnutrition.

Excessive Protein Intake

Heart disease and cancer are the leading causes of death in developed countries, including Canada and the United States. In these nations, the typical Western diet that contains high amounts of animal proteins may increase the risk of certain chronic diseases, particularly heart disease,[23,24,25] colorectal cancer,[26, 27] and probably prostate cancer.[27] Consumption of red meats and processed meats, such as ham and sausage, are associated with increased risk of pancreatic cancer [28] as well as stomach cancer.[29] Furthermore, high intakes of red meat may increase the risk of certain breast cancers among women of child-bearing age.[30]

Healthy individuals may adapt to protein intakes that are higher than the AMDR for the macronutrient, and they do not experience health problems as a result. However, bodybuilders and other athletes often consume amino acid or protein supplements along with dietary sources of protein. Taking amino acid supplements can cause imbalances that interfere with the body's absorption and use of these nutrients. Additionally, high-protein diets can lead to higher than normal urinary losses of the mineral nutrient calcium.[31] Excessive loss of urinary calcium may be more likely to occur when people, particularly elderly women, consume diets that contain more animal than vegetable proteins.[32] Some nutrition experts suspect that high-protein diets are associated with *osteoporosis*, a condition characterized by thin bones that fracture easily, though the literature in this area is mixed. Chapter 9 discusses dietary and other factors that contribute to osteoporosis.

In addition to increasing urinary losses of calcium, excess amino acid or protein intake can lead to *dehydration*, because the kidneys need more water to dilute and eliminate the toxic waste products of amino acid metabolism in urine. Dehydration is a potentially life-threatening condition in which the body's water level is too low. People with liver or kidney diseases may need to avoid protein-rich diets and amino acid supplements because metabolizing the excess amino acids is a burden to their bodies. The Chapter 7 Highlight provides more information about the use of amino acid and protein supplements.

What about High-Protein Weight-Loss Diets?

Certain popular weight-loss diets, such as the Atkins, Protein Power, and Sugar Busters diets, promote high intakes of protein. While following high-protein diets to lose weight, people often report decreased feelings of hunger and increased sense of fullness (satiety) after meals.[33] However, results of one study indicated subjects following high-protein/low-carbohydrate, low-fat, or moderate-calorie controlled diets for a year lost similar amounts of weight.[34] It is also important to differentiate diets that provide a protein intake towards the higher end of the AMDR for protein, which can be achieved without carbohydrate restriction and high-protein, low-carbohydrate diets which may inadvertently be high in

protein-energy malnutrition (PEM) condition that results from chronic lack of food or poor food choices

kwashiorkor form of PEM that results from consuming adequate energy but incomplete protein

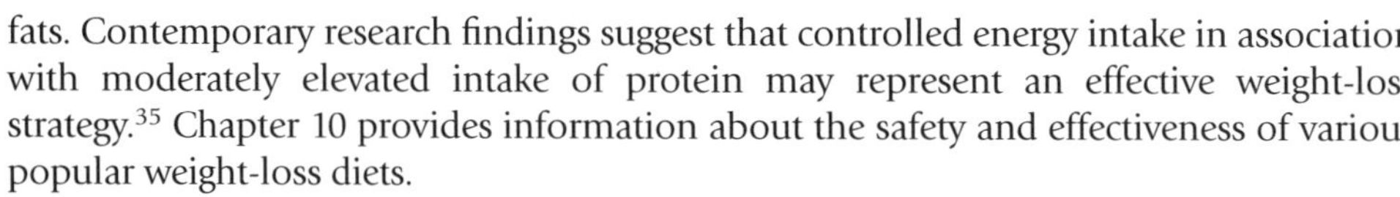

fats. Contemporary research findings suggest that controlled energy intake in association with moderately elevated intake of protein may represent an effective weight-loss strategy.[35] Chapter 10 provides information about the safety and effectiveness of various popular weight-loss diets.

Protein Deficiency

Although food insecurity exists in Canada, protein deficiency is uncommon. (See the Chapter 1 Highlight for information about food insecurity.) People suffering from alcoholism, anorexia nervosa, or certain intestinal tract disorders are at risk of protein malnutrition. People with low incomes, especially elderly, are also at risk of protein deficiency. Many elderly Canadians have limited incomes and must make difficult choices concerning their expenses. If you were 80 years old and needed to take several medicines daily to treat heart disease, abnormally high fluid pressure in your eyes, and breathing problems, what would you think is more important—purchasing costly prescription medications or nutritious foods?

As discussed in the Chapter 1 Highlight, *undernutrition*, the lack of food, is often widespread in poor nations in which populations endure frequent famine resulting from crop failures, political unrest, or civil wars. In these countries, **protein-energy malnutrition (PEM)** affects people whose diets lack sufficient protein as well as energy. The failure to consume nourishing food also results in vitamin and mineral deficiencies.

When food is limited, it is often more difficult for children to obtain nutritionally adequate diets than adults. Why? Adults may be able to consume enough plant proteins to meet their protein and energy needs, but children have smaller stomachs and higher energy and protein needs per kilogram of body weight than adults. They are unable to eat enough plant foods to meet their relatively high protein and other nutrient requirements.

According to the World Health Organization (WHO), PEM affects one of every four children and results in almost 11 million childhood deaths each year.[36] Impoverished children in Asia and Africa are most likely to develop PEM, and the effects of PEM are especially devastating for the very young. Children with PEM do not grow and are very weak, irritable, and vulnerable to dehydration and infections, such as measles, that can kill them. If these children survive, their growth may be permanently stunted and their intelligence may be lower than normal because malnutrition during early childhood can cause permanent brain damage.

Figure 7.17 Mild to moderate protein-energy malnutrition. This Nigerian child is suffering from marasmic kwashiorkor. Note the edema in the child's abdomen, lower legs, and feet. These photos were taken during the late 1960s.

Kwashiorkor and Marasmus

At one time, nutritionists thought there were only two types of PEM, kwashiorkor and marasmus. The distinctions between these conditions, however, are often blurred, because protein deficiency is unlikely when a person's energy intake is adequate. Nevertheless, the World Health Organization identifies *kwashiorkor*, *marasmic kwashiorkor*, and *marasmus* as forms of PEM.[37]

Kwashiorkor (*qwash´-e-or´-kor*) primarily occurs in developing countries where mothers commonly breast-feed their infants until they give birth to another child. The older youngster, who is usually a toddler, is fairly healthy until abruptly weaned from its mother's milk to make way for the younger sibling. Although the toddler may obtain adequate energy by consuming a traditional diet of cereal grains, the diet lacks enough complete protein to meet the youngster's high needs, and he or she soon develops signs of protein deficiency. Children affected by kwashiorkor have stunted growth (see Fig. 1.C, p. 21); unnaturally blond, sparse, and brittle hair; and patches of skin that have lost its normal coloration. Children with kwashiorkor have some subcutaneous (under the skin) fat and swollen cheeks, arms, legs, and bellies that make them look well fed, but their appearance is misleading. An important function of certain proteins in blood is to maintain proper fluid balance within cells and blood vessels as well as between cells. During starvation, levels of these proteins decline, resulting in edema, which makes the protein-deficient child look plump and overfed instead of thin and undernourished. In many cases, the child suffering from kwashiorkor does not obtain enough energy and eventually develops marasmic kwashiorkor, a condition characterized by edema and wasting (Fig. 7.17). Wasting is the loss of organ and muscle proteins as the body tears down these tissues to obtain amino acids for energy metabolism.

Severe PEM causes extreme weight loss and a condition called **marasmus** (*mahraz´-mus*), which is commonly referred to as starvation (Fig. 7.18). Obvious signs of marasmus are weakness and wasting. The body of a starving person loses most of its subcutaneous fat and deeper fat stores. The marasmic person is so thin, his or her ribs, hip, and spinal bones are visible through the skin. People suffering from marasmus avoid physical activity to conserve energy, and they are often irritable.

marasmus starvation

The World Health Organization has guidelines for identifying and treating children with PEM.[38] According to these guidelines, treatments for kwashiorkor, marasmic kwashiorkor, and marasmus are similar. The sickest children need hospitalization, carefully controlled refeedings, and frequent health assessments to recover from PEM.

Concept Checkpoint

26. In North America, which groups of people are most likely to suffer from protein malnutrition?

27. Define protein-energy malnutrition.

28. Police bring a 2-year-old child into a clinic; the child has a swollen belly and feet, but the arms and upper legs are so thin, the skin hangs from them. The police report indicates the child was severely neglected by the parents. According to this information, is this child suffering from PKU, marasmic kwashiorkor, marasmus, sickle cell anemia, or anorexia nervosa? Choose one of these conditions and explain why you selected it.

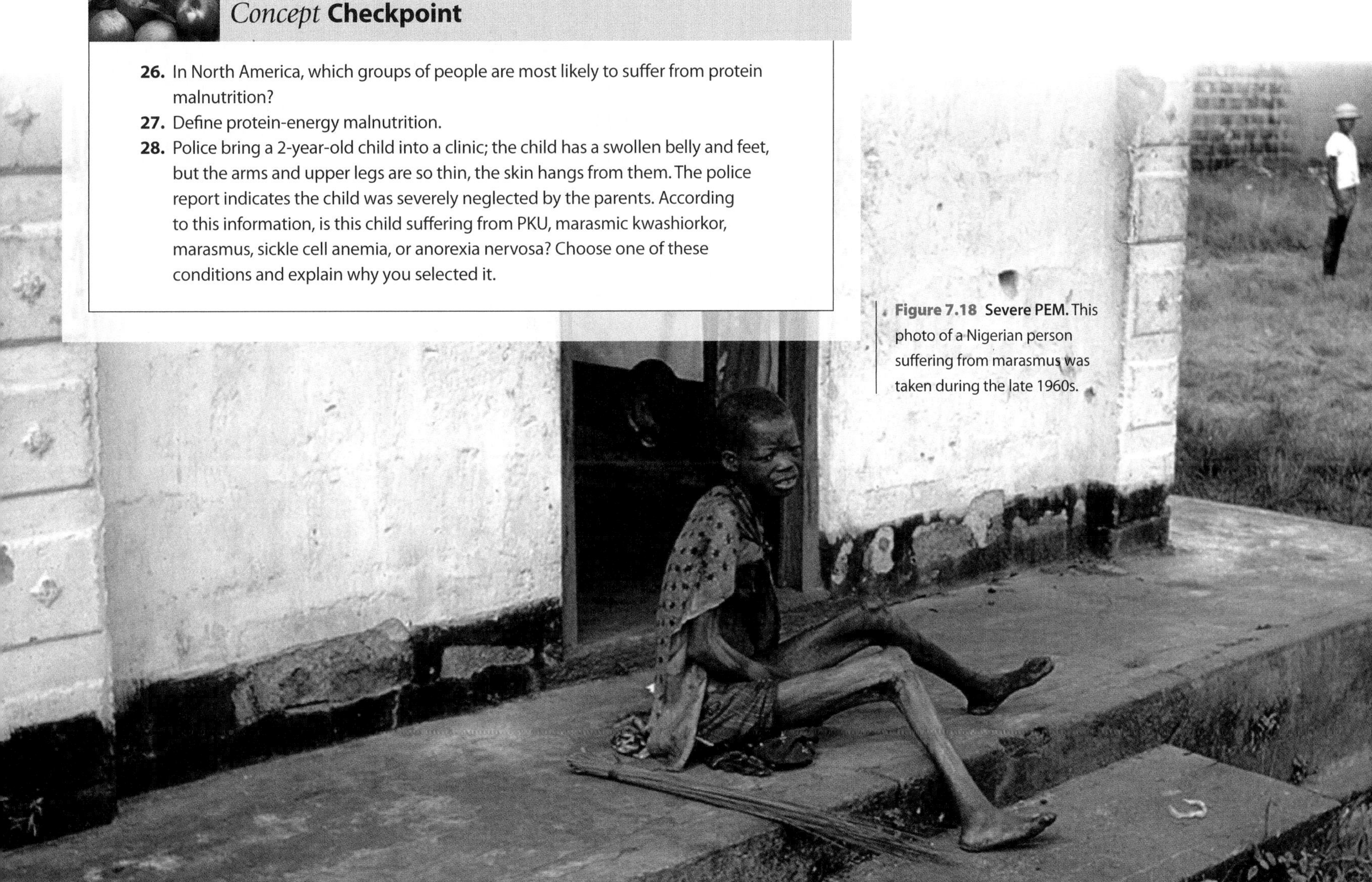

Figure 7.18 Severe PEM. This photo of a Nigerian person suffering from marasmus was taken during the late 1960s.

Chapter 7 Highlight
Building a Bulkier Body

It's not surprising that people associate protein with muscle. Skeletal muscle mass comprises the largest share (approximately 43%) of protein in your body. Although many athletes and bodybuilders consume large quantities of protein-rich animal foods and supplements to increase their muscle mass, this practice does not build bigger stronger muscles.[1A] A fitness program that includes resistance training is the only safe and reliable way to increase muscle mass.

During resistance exercise, proteins in working muscles break down, but protein synthesis occurs during the recovery period that follows and lasts about 24 to 48 hours.[2A] As a result, muscles grow larger, particularly when amino acids are available. Over time, resistance training induces a state of positive nitrogen balance. It should be noted, however, that 70% of muscle tissue is water and only about 22% is protein.[2A] Thus, resistance training adds a considerable amount of water to muscle tissue.

To gain a 454 g (1 lb.) of muscle in a week, a healthy young person undergoing resistance training needs to increase the RDA level of his or her protein intake only by about 14 g/day.[2A] For example, a 22-year-old woman who weighs 70 kg has an RDA for protein of 56 g (70 kg × 0.8 g of protein/kg). While undergoing resistance training, she'll need to consume 70 g of protein daily (14 g + 56 g) to gain 454 g (1 lb.) of muscle in a week. Because the average Canadian eats more than 100 g of protein a day, registered dietitians generally do not recommend adding protein or amino acid supplements to the diets of athletes.[3A,4A]

Proteins: General Advice for Athletes

Carbohydrate spares protein for muscle maintenance and growth; therefore, athletes should not overly focus on their protein intake. Eating a snack that supplies both protein and carbohydrate before or after exercise is recommended.[2A] Nutritious choices include a bowl of cereal and fat-free milk, low-fat cottage cheese and a whole-wheat bagel, or a sandwich made with lean meat or poultry. If you don't have time to prepare these foods, energy drinks and bars are convenient ways to obtain carbohydrate and protein. Chapter 11 provides more information about nutrition for athletes and other physically active people.

The results of studies indicate that injecting various amino acids into the blood can stimulate the pituitary gland in the brain to release *human growth hormone* (*HGH*). Although HGH fosters muscle tissue growth, the results of studies examining the effects of *consuming* individual amino acids on HGH release do not support the use of these nutrients for stimulating muscle growth. Nevertheless, supplements that contain the amino acids arginine, lysine, and ornithine are popular among resistance athletes.

Taking protein supplements is not recommended for healthy persons, especially if the products supply individual amino acids. Why? The human digestive system is designed to digest large protein molecules from the mixture of proteins that naturally occurs in foods. Consuming supplements that supply large amounts of individual amino acids can upset intestinal cells' ability to absorb other amino acids. Moreover, excessive intakes of certain amino acids, particularly methionine and tyrosine, can be toxic.

For thousands of years, humans have obtained amino acids directly by eating plants and animals. The use of amino acid and protein supplements as sources of the nutrient is a relatively recent development, and little is known about the long-term safety of using these products. Chapter 11 examines the evidence concerning the value and safety of using certain foods and dietary supplements to enhance physical performance.

High-protein diets are not recommended for athletes. Eating generous portions of animal foods, especially red meats, can contribute excessive amounts of cholesterol and saturated fat to diets. Although physically active people may be able to tolerate high-protein, high-fat, and high-cholesterol diets, the only effective way to increase muscle mass safely is to combine a nutritionally adequate diet with a program of muscle-strengthening exercises. An athlete's diet should supply enough calories from carbohydrate and fat to support energy needs for increased physical activity and spare the use of protein for growth, repair, and maintenance of muscle tissue.

References for Chapter 7 Highlight

1A. Lemon PW and others: Protein requirements and muscle mass/strength changes during intensive training in novice bodybuilders. *Journal of Applied Physiology* 73(2):767, 1992.

2A. Williams MH: *Nutrition for health, fitness, & sport*, 8th ed. New York: McGraw-Hill, 2007.

3A. Gerrior S, Bente L: *Nutrient content of the U.S. food supply, 1909–1999: A summary report*. U.S. Department of Agriculture, Center for Nutrition Policy and Promotion. Home Economics Research Report, No. 55. 2002.

4A. Position of Dietitians of Canada, the American Dietetic Association, and the American College of Sports Medicine: endorsed by the Coaching Association of Canada Nutrition and Athletic: Performance: Nutrition and Athletic Performance. http://www.dietitians.ca/news/downloads/sports_nutrition_position2000.pdf. Accessed: June 7, 2010.

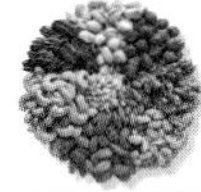

SUMMARY

Proteins are organic compounds that contain nitrogen, the element that cells need to make a wide array of important biological compounds with structural or metabolic functions in the body. Proteins, for example, participate in muscular movement, catalyze chemical reactions, transport nutrients, and help maintain proper fluid and acid–base balance. Additionally, a relatively small amount of protein contributes to the body's energy needs. Numerous vital functions as well as physical growth and development would not be possible without specific proteins.

The typical amino acid has amino, acid, and R groups. The diet must supply nine of the amino acids, because the body cannot make them or make enough of them to meet its needs. Cells can synthesize the remaining amino acids if the raw materials are available.

Human proteins are comprised of 20 different amino acids arranged in various combinations. Cells produce proteins by linking amino acids together in specific sequences that are dictated by instructions coded in DNA. Faulty DNA results in the wrong amino acids being inserted into peptide chains, causing genetic defects. If an essential amino acid is not available when protein synthesis occurs, proteins in muscles and organs can provide the essential amino acids. Otherwise, protein synthesis halts, and the amino acids in the unfinished peptide are removed and returned to the amino acid pool. Excess amino acids are metabolized for energy or converted into body fat.

Protein turnover is the process of breaking down old or unneeded proteins into their component amino acids and recycling them to make new proteins. The body conserves nitrogen by recycling amino acids, but each day it loses some protein and nitrogen primarily in urine, nails, hair, feces, and skin. Amino acids from food replace the lost nitrogen. An adult's body maintains its protein content by carefully balancing nitrogen intake and losses. In positive nitrogen balance, the body retains more nitrogen than it loses; in negative nitrogen balance, the body loses more nitrogen than it retains.

A healthy adult requires only about 0.5 g of protein/kg of body weight daily. The protein requirement increases during pregnancy, breast-feeding, periods of growth, and recovery from serious illnesses, blood losses, and burns. The adult RDA for protein is 0.8 g/kg of body weight daily.

Protein digestion begins in the stomach where hydrochloric acid denatures food proteins and pepsin breaks proteins into polypeptides. In the small intestine, enzymes secreted by the pancreas and absorptive cells digest polypeptides into amino acids and di- and tripeptides. The absorptive cells pick up these compounds and break the remaining peptides into amino acids. The end-products of protein digestion, amino acids, travel to the liver. The liver uses the amino acids or releases them into the general circulation.

The AMDR for adults is 10 to 35% of energy intake from protein. Although total meat consumption increased over the past century, Canadians ate less red meat and more poultry, fish, nuts, and legumes in 2000 than they did in the 1970s. People can reduce their intake of animal protein without sacrificing the protein quality of their diets.

The average Canadian consumes over 100 g of protein daily, well over the RDA. Protein-rich diets that contain animal products generally contain high amounts of saturated fat and cholesterol, and such diets are associated with increased risk of certain chronic diseases, particularly heart disease and certain cancers. High-protein diets may result in amino acid imbalances, high urinary losses of calcium, and dehydration.

Animal foods generally provide more protein than similar quantities of plant foods. High-quality or complete protein is well digested and contains all essential amino acids in amounts that will support protein deposition and a young child's growth. Low-quality or incomplete protein is low in one or more of the essential amino acids and often is poorly digested. In general, meat, fish, poultry, eggs, milk, and milk products contain high-quality proteins. When compared to animal foods, plant foods provide low-quality protein, except for foods made from processed soybeans.

Vegetarian diets are based on plant foods and limit animal foods to some extent. Although vegetarians are generally healthier than people who eat Western diets, it is difficult to pinpoint diet responsible for vegetarians' better health. If not properly planned, plant-based diets may not contain enough energy, high-quality protein, omega-3 fatty acids, vitamins B-12 and D, and minerals zinc, iron, and calcium to meet a person's nutritional needs, especially children's needs.

PEM affects people whose diets lack sufficient protein as well as energy; children are more likely to be affected by PEM than adults. In impoverished developing countries, PEM is a major cause of childhood deaths. Severely undernourished children do not grow and are very weak, irritable, and vulnerable to dehydration and life-threatening infections. Undernutrition during early childhood can cause permanent brain damage.

Recipes for Healthy Living

Trendy Black Beans

You've probably eaten ordinary canned baked beans as an accompaniment to hot dogs and hamburgers. If you're interested in eating a more trendy kind of bean, try this recipe for black beans. Although canned black beans are more convenient to use in recipes than dried black beans, the canned products generally contain a lot of salt.

This black bean recipe makes about four ½-cup servings. Each serving supplies approximately 120 kcal, 8 g protein, less than 1 g fat, 7.5 g fibre, 2 mg iron, 340 mg potassium, 70 mg sodium, and 130 mcg folate (a B vitamin). To make the beans a complementary protein source, serve them wrapped in a soft burrito or on cooked rice.

INGREDIENTS:

- 1 cup dried black beans
- ¼ cup coarsely chopped green pepper
- ¼ cup peeled, chopped yellow onion
- 1 large clove garlic, peeled and minced
- ⅛ tsp ground black pepper
- ⅛ tsp salt
- 3–5 drops hot pepper sauce (optional)

PREPARATION STEPS:

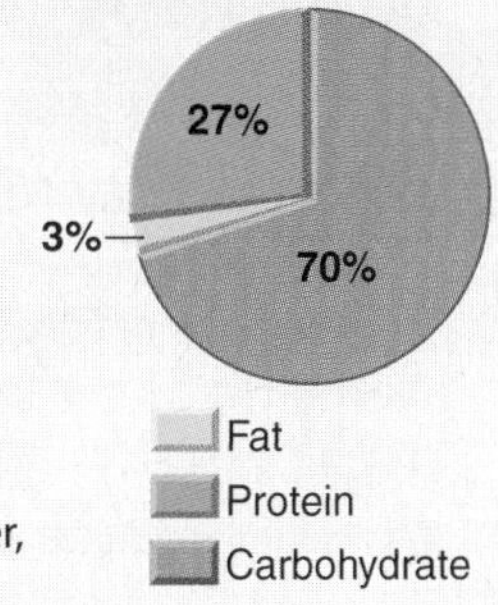

1. Rinse dried beans in cold water, draining excess water.
2. Place the beans in a saucepan and add 1¾ cups of water.
3. Heat beans and water on high heat until mixture boils. Boil for 2 minutes, then turn off heat, and remove saucepan from the burner. Cover saucepan and allow beans to remain in the hot water for 1 hour. While beans are soaking, prepare green pepper, onion, and garlic.
4. Do not drain water from beans. Simmer beans on low heat, in the covered saucepan, for 45 minutes. Stir occasionally.
5. Add green pepper, onion, garlic, black pepper, and salt. Simmer for an additional 15 minutes.
6. Serve hot. Cooked beans can be frozen.

Hummus

Hummus may have originated in the Middle East, but it's become popular in this country as a dip for vegetables or bread. Hummus is a good source of protein, monounsaturated fat, fibre, the minerals potassium and iron, and the B vitamin folate.

This hummus recipe makes about eight ¼-cup servings. If you don't have a blender, you can mash the chickpeas and garlic with a fork before you add the other ingredients. To make hummus a complementary protein source, serve it with whole-grain crackers, tortilla chips, or pita bread. Each serving (with no added salt) supplies about 130 kcal, 3 g protein, 8 g fat, 3 g fibre, 0.8 mg iron, 120 mg potassium, 4 mg sodium, and 70 mcg folate.

INGREDIENTS:

- 2 cups unsalted, cooked garbanzo beans (chickpeas)
- 1 Tbsp lemon juice
- 1 medium clove garlic, peeled
- ¼ cup cold water
- ¼ cup olive oil pinch salt and paprika (optional)

35%
55%
10%
Fat
Protein
Carbohydrate

PREPARATION STEPS:

1. Drain beans. Place the beans, lemon juice, garlic clove, oil, and water in a blender. Blend until the mixture is smooth.
2. Serve in a bowl. If desired, sprinkle paprika on top of hummus.

Personal Dietary Analysis

1. Refer to the three-day food log from the Personal Dietary Analysis feature in Chapter 3. Calculate your average protein intake by adding the grams of protein eaten each day, dividing the total by three, and rounding the figure to the nearest whole number.

Sample Calculation:

Day 1 76 g

Day 2 55 g

Day 3 103 g

Total grams 234 g ÷ 3 days = **78** g of protein/day

Your Calculation:

Day 1 ______ g

Day 2 ______ g

Day 3 ______ g

Total grams ______ ÷ 3 days = ______ g/day

My average daily protein intake was ______ g.

2. The RDA for protein is based on body weight. Using the RDA of 0.8 g of protein/kg of body weight, calculate the amount of protein that you need to consume daily to meet the recommendation. To determine your body weight in kilograms, divide your weight (pounds) by 2.2, multiply this number by 0.8 to obtain your RDA for protein, and then round the figure to the nearest whole number.

My weight in pounds ______ ÷ 2.2 = ______ kg

My weight in kg ______ × 0.8 = ______ g

My RDA for protein = ______ g

   a. Did your average intake of protein meet or exceed your RDA level that was calculated in step 1? ______ yes ______ no

   b. If your answer to 2a is "yes," which foods contributed the most to your protein intake?

3. Review the log of your 3-day food intake. Calculate the average number of kilocalories that protein contributed to your diet each day during the 3-day period.

   a. Each gram of protein provides about 4 kcal, therefore you must multiply the average number of grams of protein obtained in Step 1 by 4 kcal to obtain the average number of kcal from protein.

   Sample Calculation:

   78 g/day × 4 kcal/g = 312 kcal from protein

   Your Calculation:

   ______ g/day × 4 kcal/g = ______ average number of kcal from protein

4. Determine your average energy intake over the three-day period by adding the kilocalories for each day and dividing the sum by three, and then rounding to the nearest whole number.

Sample Calculation:

Day 1 2500 kcal

Day 2 3200 kcal

Day 3 2750 kcal

Total kcal 8450 ÷ 3 days = **2817** kcal/day (average caloric intake)

Your Calculation:

Day 1 ______ kcal

Day 2 ______ kcal

Day 3 ______ kcal

Total kcal ______ ÷ 3 days = ______ kcal/day (average)

5. Determine the average percentage of energy that protein contributed to your diet by dividing the average kilocalories from protein obtained in Step 3 by the average total daily energy intake obtained in Step 4. Then round this figure to the nearest one-hundredth. Multiply this value by 100, move the decimal point two places to the right, drop the decimal point, and add a percent symbol.

Sample Calculation:

312 kcal from protein ÷ 2817 kcal intake = 0.11 (rounded)

0.11 × 100 = 11%

Your Calculation:

______ kcal from protein ÷ ______ kcal intake = ______

______ × 100 = ______ %

6. Did your average intake of protein meet the recommendation of 10 to 35% of total calories? If your average protein intake was below 10%, list at least five foods you could eat that would boost your intake.

CRITICAL THINKING

1. Are you a vegetarian? If so, describe your dietary practices (e.g., vegan or semivegetarian) and explain why you decided to become vegetarian. If you are not a vegetarian, explain why you would or would not consider this lifestyle.
2. Have you used or are you currently using protein or amino acid supplements? ______ yes ______ no

   If you answered "yes," explain why you use these supplements.
3. Plan a day's meals and snacks for a healthy 60 kg (132-lb.) adult female who is not pregnant or breast-feeding. The menu should contain all essential amino acids but contain no animal foods other than eggs and foods from the milk group. Your meal plan can range from 1800 to 2200 kcal, and it should include foods from the major food groups and follow the recommendations of the *Eating Well with Canada's Food Guide*.
4. Using only plant foods, plan a day's meals and snacks for a healthy 70 kg (154-lb.) adult male. The menu should supply at least 2200 kcal, follow the recommendations of the *Eating Well with Canada's Food Guide*, and include foods from the major food groups (except for the milk foods group).
5. A recipe for bean salad has the following main ingredients:

   1 cup kidney beans

   1 cup green beans

   1 cup butter beans

   1 cup black beans

   1½ cups wine vinegar

   ⅓ cup canola oil

   ¼ cup chopped onion

   Explain why this recipe is not a complementary mixture of plant proteins. What plant foods could you add to the recipe to make it a complementary mixture?

PRACTICE TEST

Select the best answer.

1. A protein
   a. is comprised of glucose molecules.
   b. has nitrogen in its chemical structure.
   c. provides more energy per gram than carbohydrate.
   d. is a complex inorganic molecule.
2. Which of the following statements is false?
   a. Certain hormones are proteins.
   b. Nearly all enzymes are proteins.
   c. Proteins are part of triglycerides.
   d. The body uses protein to make antibodies.

3. Which of the following foods generally provides the least amount of protein per serving?
   a. fruits
   b. milk
   c. nuts
   d. seeds
4. Which of the following foods is not a source of complete protein?
   a. peanut butter
   b. cheese
   c. fish
   d. eggs
5. In cells, ______ controls the assembly of amino acids into proteins.
   a. food
   b. DNA
   c. insulin
   d. the nervous system
6. ______ is the process of removing nitrogen from an amino acid.
   a. Transamination
   b. Denaturation
   c. Hydrogenation
   d. Deamination
7. Which of the following physical states are characterized by positive nitrogen balance?
   a. starvation
   b. illness
   c. puberty
   d. all of the above
8. What is the RDA for protein of a healthy adult woman who weighs 62 kg?
   a. 49.6 g
   b. 59.6 g
   c. 69.6 g
   d. 79.6 g
9. Which of the following foods is not a source of complementary protein?
   a. red beans and rice
   b. hummus on pita bread
   c. peanut butter on toast
   d. whole-wheat bread with fruit spread
10. A person following a vegan diet would eat
    a. eggs.
    b. cheese.
    c. nuts.
    d. fish.
11. By eating more protein than needed, a person can
    a. build bigger muscles.
    b. lose weight.
    c. absorb more calcium.
    d. become dehydrated.
12. Strength and endurance athletes
    a. should take amino acid supplements.
    b. need about double the RDA for protein.
    c. do not need more protein than the RDA.
    d. should eliminate protein from plant sources.

Answers to Chapter 7 Quiz Yourself

1. Animal foods such as meat and eggs are almost 100% protein. **False.** (p. 191)
2. Foods made from processed soybeans can be sources of high-quality protein. **True.** (p. 195)
3. An adult bodybuilder should consume about five times more protein than a healthy adult who is not a bodybuilder. **False.** (p. 216)
4. Registered dietitians generally recommend that vegetarians take amino acid supplements to increase their protein intake. **False.** (p. 210)
5. People can nourish their hair by using shampoo that contains protein. **False.** (p. 200)

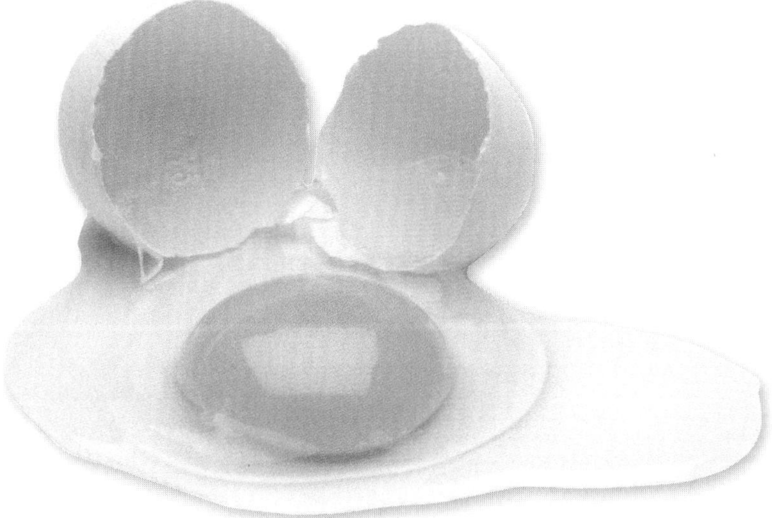

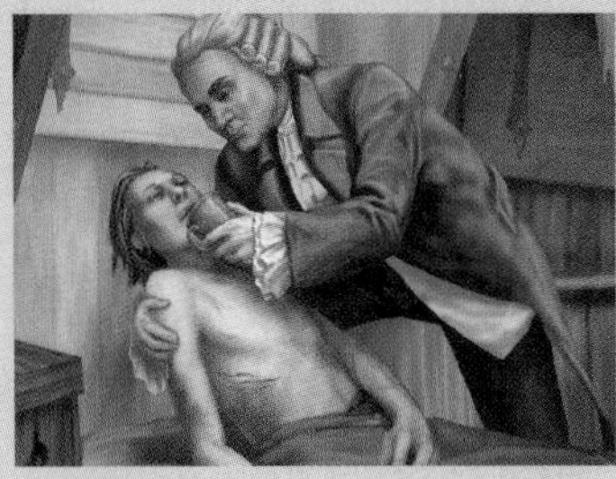

Chapter **8**

Vitamins

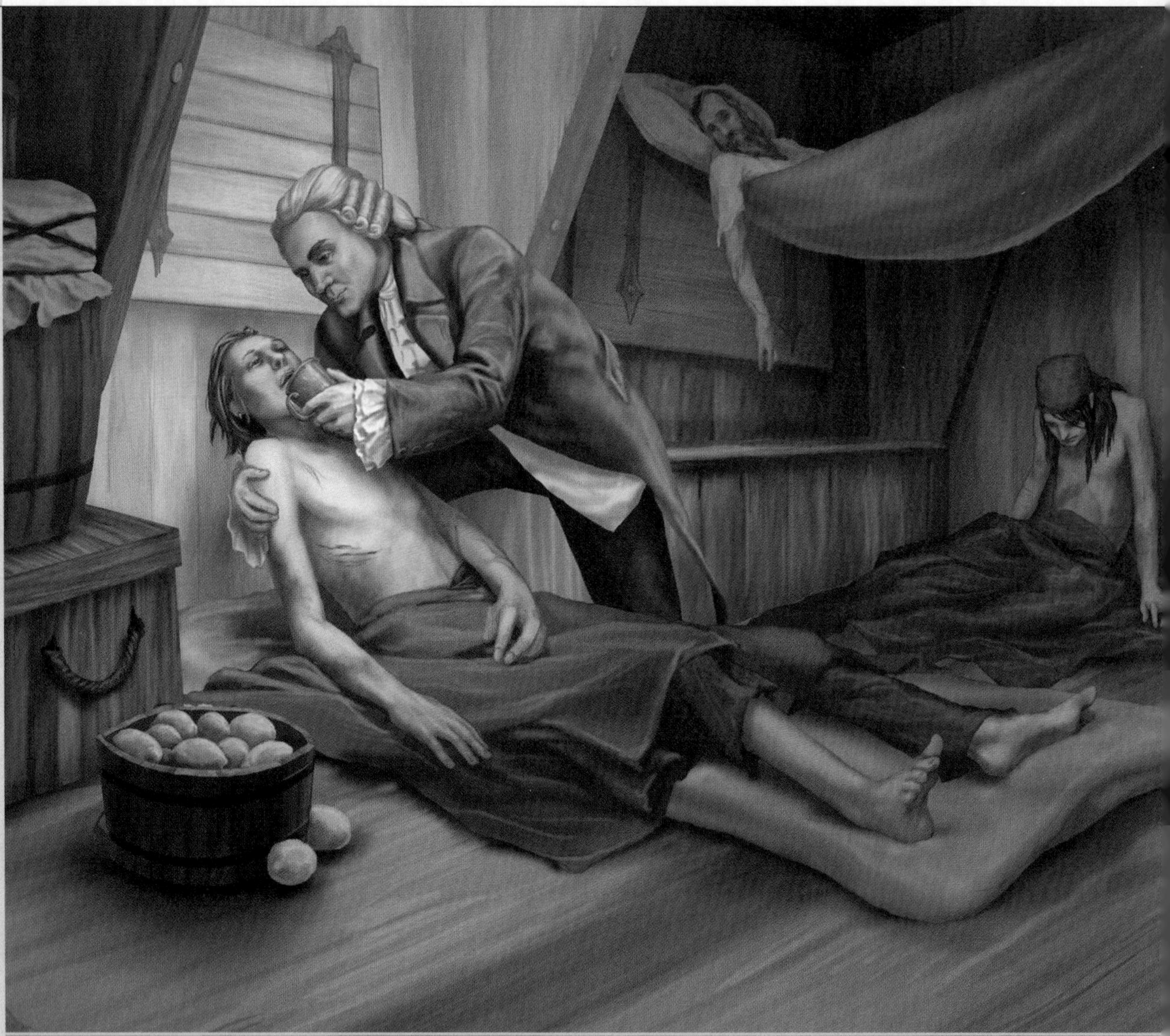

Chapter Learning Outcomes

After reading Chapter 8, you should be able to:

1. Classify vitamins according to whether they are fat soluble or water soluble.
2. List major functions and sources for each vitamin.
3. Describe deficiency and/or toxicity signs and symptoms for certain vitamins, including A, D, thiamin, folate, and C.
4. Discuss ways to conserve the vitamin content of foods.
5. Evaluate the use of vitamin supplements with respect to their potential health benefits and hazards.

For centuries, taking lengthy ocean voyages was a dangerous venture, not just because of the threat of severe storms and pillaging pirates, but also because of a terrifying and deadly disease called **scurvy**. The first signs and symptoms of scurvy, fatigue and petechiae (*peh-tee'-key-eye*), pinpoint hemorrhages in skin, occurred about 20 to 40 days after setting sail. As the disease progressed, the affected person's skin bruised easily;

gums swelled, became spongy, and bled after being barely touched; teeth loosened and fell out. Not surprisingly, the person suffering from scurvy also became irritable and depressed. A particularly devastating sign of the disease was the opening up of old scars, exposing wounds that could become infected. Scurvy victims eventually died, generally from infections, brain hemorrhages, or heart complications.

In 1753, British physician James Lind published an article describing an experiment he performed on 12 sailors suffering from scurvy. Lind divided the sick sailors into six pairs, and each pair received a different treatment. The six treatments were cider, vinegar, sulphuric acid, sea water, nutmeg, and oranges and lemons. Lind observed that the pair of sailors given the citrus fruit were the only ones to recover from scurvy. By today's standards, Lind's experiment was primitive, but as a result of his testing, Lind found the cure for scurvy—eating oranges and lemons. Eventually, food rations for British sailors included lemon juice to prevent the disease. The sailors earned the nickname "limeys" because at that time, people often referred to citrus fruits collectively as "limes."

Today we know that scurvy results from a deficiency of vitamin C and citrus fruits are among the richest dietary sources of the vitamin. Although Lind is often credited with having discovered the cure for scurvy, he did not suspect the disease resulted from the lack of something in the typical seafarer's diet. At that time, scientists were unaware that food contained vitamins. Lind thought scurvy was a digestive system disorder that could be treated with substances associated with warm climates.[1] In his experiment, Lind happened to administer citrus fruits to a pair of the sailors with scurvy because these fruits were associated with such climates.

In 1911, Polish chemist Casimir Funk discovered a substance in an extract made from rice bran that he thought would cure the disease beriberi. Funk called the compound a "vitamine" (*vita* = necessary for life; *amine* = a type of nitrogen-containing substance) because of its chemical structure. The term *vitamine* was later modified to *vitamin*, when scientists determined that there were several kinds of these substances in foods, and not all were amines. By the end of the twentieth century, scientists had added riboflavin, niacin, biotin, B-6, B-12, pantothenic acid, folate, ascorbic acid, choline, A, D, E, and K to the list of vitamins.

It is unlikely that any vitamins still need to be discovered. Why? Babies grow and thrive on infant formulas, synthetic liquid diets containing vitamins and other nutrients known to be essential for health. Additionally, very ill people who cannot eat solid food can be kept alive for years on liquid synthetic feedings that contain all known nutrients, including vitamins. If a vitamin remained undiscovered, infants and people who are unable to consume solid foods would not be able to survive on formula diets.

Chapter 8 presents information about the 14 vitamins, including physiological roles and major food sources. After reading this chapter, you will understand what can happen to the body when too little or too much of certain vitamins are consumed. Many Canadians take vitamin supplements to prevent disease; the Chapter 8 Highlight examines current scientific evidence concerning the usefulness of taking megadoses of certain vitamins. In general, a **megadose** is an amount that is at least ten times the Recommended Dietary Allowance (RDA) of the micronutrient.[2]

Quiz YOURSELF

Can vitamins give you more energy and reduce your chances of developing heart disease and cancer? Which cooking methods can increase the loss of vitamins from foods? Which vitamins are added to cereal grains during enrichment? Test your knowledge of vitamins by taking the following quiz. The answers are on page 273.

1. Natural vitamins are better for you because they have more biological activity than synthetic vitamins. ______T______F
2. Certain vitamins are toxic. ______T______F
3. Vitamin E is an antioxidant. ______T______F
4. Vitamins are a source of "quick" energy. ______T______F
5. According to scientific research, taking large doses of vitamin C daily prevents the common cold. ______T______F

scurvy vitamin C deficiency disease

megadose amount of a micronutrient that is at least ten times the Recommended Dietary Allowance (RDA)

Vitamins: Basic Concepts

vitamin complex organic molecule that regulates a variety of responses in the body

What is a vitamin? A **vitamin** is a complex organic compound that meets the following criteria:

- The body cannot synthesize the compound or make enough to maintain good health.
- The compound naturally occurs in commonly eaten foods.
- Signs and symptoms of an illness (deficiency disease or disorder) eventually occur when the substance is missing from the diet.
- Good health is restored, if the deficiency disorder is treated early by supplying the missing substance.

Although vitamins are organic molecules in foods, they are distinctly different than carbohydrates, fats, and proteins. Foods generally contain much smaller amounts of vitamins than macronutrients. A slice of whole-wheat bread, for example, weighs 28 g. Of that weight, only about 0.005% (1.48 mg) is comprised of vitamins; carbohydrate, water, protein, fat, and minerals make up the remaining weight of the bread. Furthermore, the body requires vitamins in milligram or microgram amounts, but it needs grams of macronutrients.

To estimate the vitamin contents of packaged foods, you can check the Nutrition Facts tables on food packaging. Food manufacturers are required to indicate amounts of vitamins A and C in a serving of food as percentages of these micronutrients' Daily Values (%DVs). Daily Values have been established for most vitamins (see Appendix C).

In the past, amounts of most vitamins in foods, particularly fat-soluble vitamins, were often expressed in International Units (IUs). Today IUs have largely been replaced by more precise milligram or microgram measures. One microgram of vitamin D, for example, equals 40 IUs of the vitamin. Food composition tables and the information panel on food and supplement labels often still list IU values for fat-soluble vitamins.

A slice of bread weighs about 28 g (1 oz.). Vitamins comprise only about 0.005% (1.48 mg) of the weight of the bread.

Roles of Vitamins

Vitamins play numerous roles in the body, and each vitamin generally has more than one function (Fig. 8.1). Some vitamins, such as vitamin D, act as hormones; other vitamins, such as vitamin C and thiamin, participate in chemical reactions by accepting or donating electrons. In general, vitamins regulate a variety of body processes, including those involved in cell division and development as well as the growth and maintenance of tissues.

Advertisements for vitamins often promote the notion that the micronutrients can "give" you energy. Vitamins, however, are not a source of energy, because cells do not metabolize them for energy. Although the body does not use vitamins directly for energy, many vitamins participate in the chemical reactions that release energy from glucose, fatty acids, and certain amino acids. The diagram in Appendix G (available on *Connect* at www.mcgrawhillconnect.ca) presents a simplified view of energy metabolism and indicates vitamins that are involved in the various steps of the process.

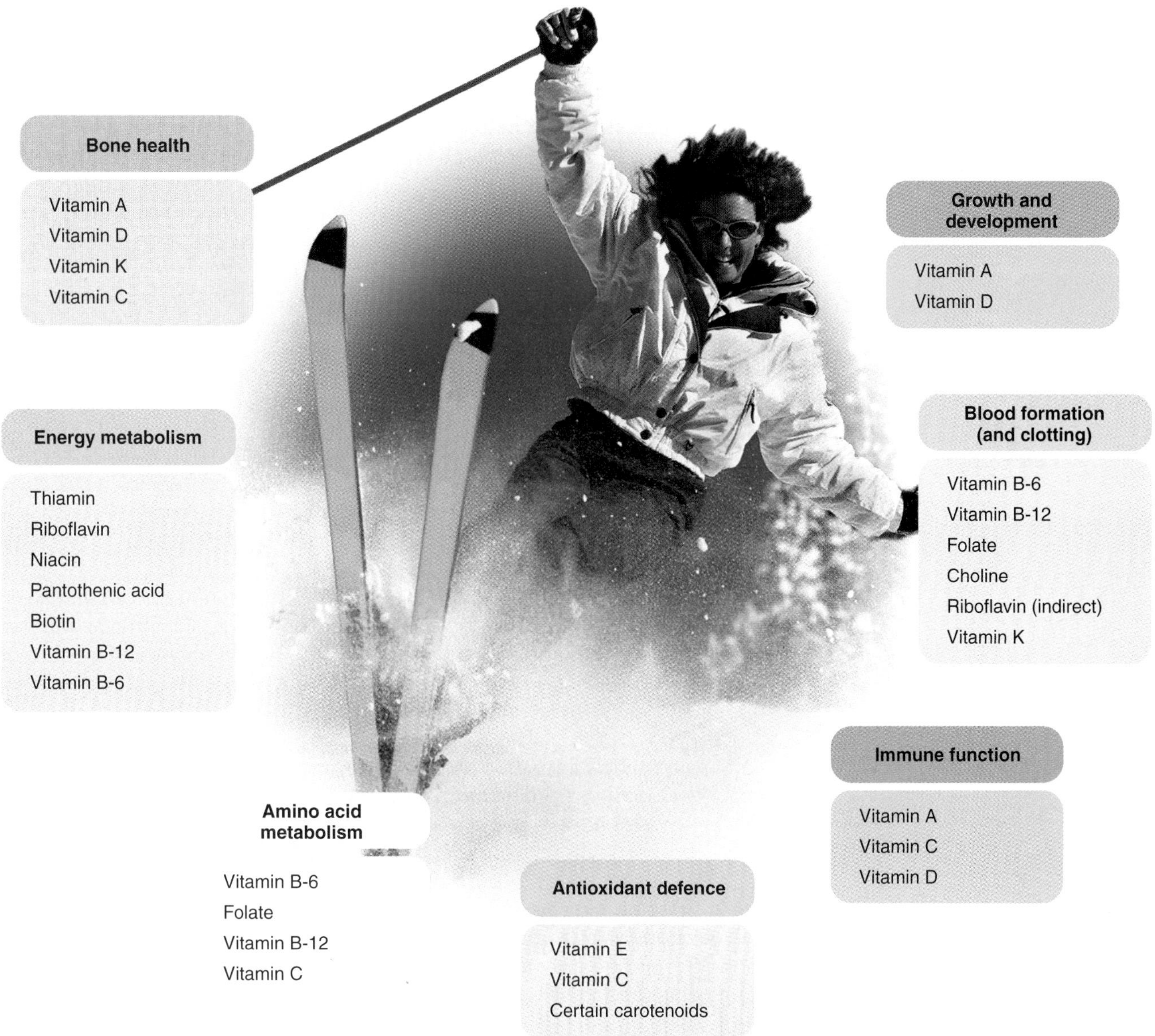

Figure 8.1 Vitamins and their functions. Groups of vitamins and related compounds (e.g., certain carotenoids) work together to maintain good health.

Most vitamins have more than one chemical form that functions in the body. For example, retinol, retinal, and retinoic acid are chemically related types of vitamin A that have roles in the body. Additionally some vitamins have precursors or **provitamins** that do not function as vitamins until the body converts them into active forms. For example, the plant pigment beta-carotene is a precursor for vitamin A, and the amino acid tryptophan is a precursor for the B-vitamin niacin.

What Is an Antioxidant?

When many biochemical reactions take place, the compounds participating in the reactions lose or gain electrons. When an atom or molecule gains one or more electrons, it has been *reduced*. When an atom or molecule loses one or more electrons, it has been *oxidized*. An **oxidizing agent** or **oxidant** is a substance that removes electrons from atoms or molecules. An oxidation reaction can form a **radical** (commonly referred to as free radical), a substance with an unpaired electron. Radicals are highly reactive (chemically unstable), and they remove electrons from more stable molecules, such

provitamins vitamin precursors that do not function in the body until converted to active forms

oxidizing agent or **oxidant** substance that removes electrons from atoms or molecules

radical substance with an unpaired electron

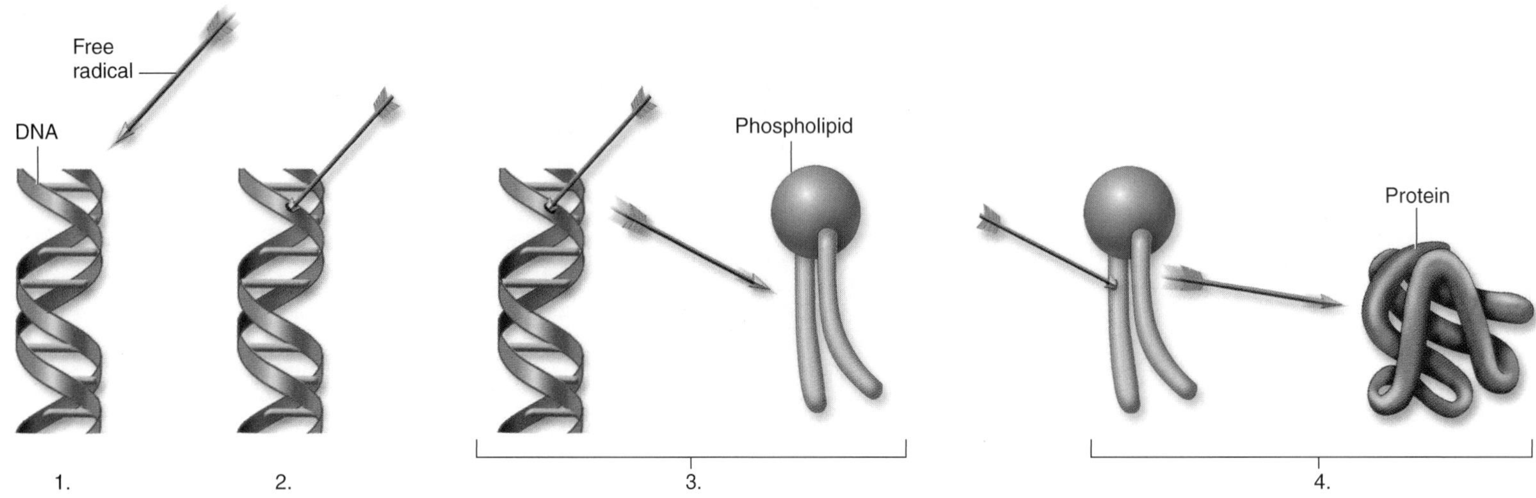

Figure 8.2 What is a radical? A radical is a highly reactive substance because it has an unpaired electron. Radicals remove electrons from more stable molecules, such as DNA in the cell's nucleus. A radical acts as an "arrow" by hitting a vulnerable molecule (1, 2). The damaged molecule becomes a radical that "strikes" another vulnerable molecule, in this case, a phospholipid (3). The reaction repeats itself as another radical forms and attacks another vulnerable molecule, such as a protein (4).

as proteins, fatty acids, and DNA (Fig. 8.2). As a result, radicals can damage or destroy these molecules. If the loss of electrons is uncontrolled, a chain reaction can occur in which excessive oxidation takes place and affects many cells. Many medical researchers suspect excess oxidation is responsible for promoting chemical changes in cells that ultimately lead to heart attack, stroke, cancer, Alzheimer's disease, and even the aging process.

Some radical formation in the body is necessary and provides some benefits.[3] Radicals, for example, stimulate normal cell growth and division. Additionally, white blood cells generate radicals as part of their activities that destroy infectious agents. Under normal conditions, cells regulate oxidation reactions by using antioxidants such as vitamin E. **Antioxidants** protect cells by giving up electrons to radicals. When a chemically unstable substance accepts an electron, it can form a more stable structure that does not pull electrons away from other compounds. By sacrificing electrons, antioxidants protect molecules such as polyunsaturated fatty acids in the membrane or DNA in the nucleus from being oxidized (Fig. 8.3).

Did You Know?

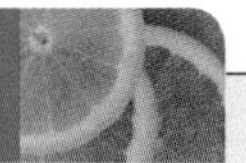

Rancidity results when fat in food, particularly the unsaturated fat, undergoes oxidation. Rancid fat makes the food smell and taste bad, and people usually refuse to eat it. To inhibit oxidation of fatty acids and increase a food's shelf life, manufacturers add antioxidants such as BHT and BHA to the food during production.

antioxidant substance that gives up electrons to radicals to protect cells

fat-soluble vitamins vitamins A, D, E, and K

water-soluble vitamins thiamin, riboflavin, niacin, vitamin B-6, pantothenic acid, folate, biotin, vitamin B-12, choline, and vitamin C

Classifying Vitamins

Vitamins A, D, E, and K are **fat-soluble vitamins**. These vitamins are in the lipid portions of food and tend to associate with lipids in the body. Thiamin, riboflavin, niacin, vitamin B-6, pantothenic acid, folate, biotin, vitamin B-12 (collectively known as the B vitamins), choline, and vitamin C are **water-soluble vitamins**. Water-soluble vitamins dissolve in the watery components of food and the body. Table 8.1 presents the vitamins and provides some other names that may be used to identify them.

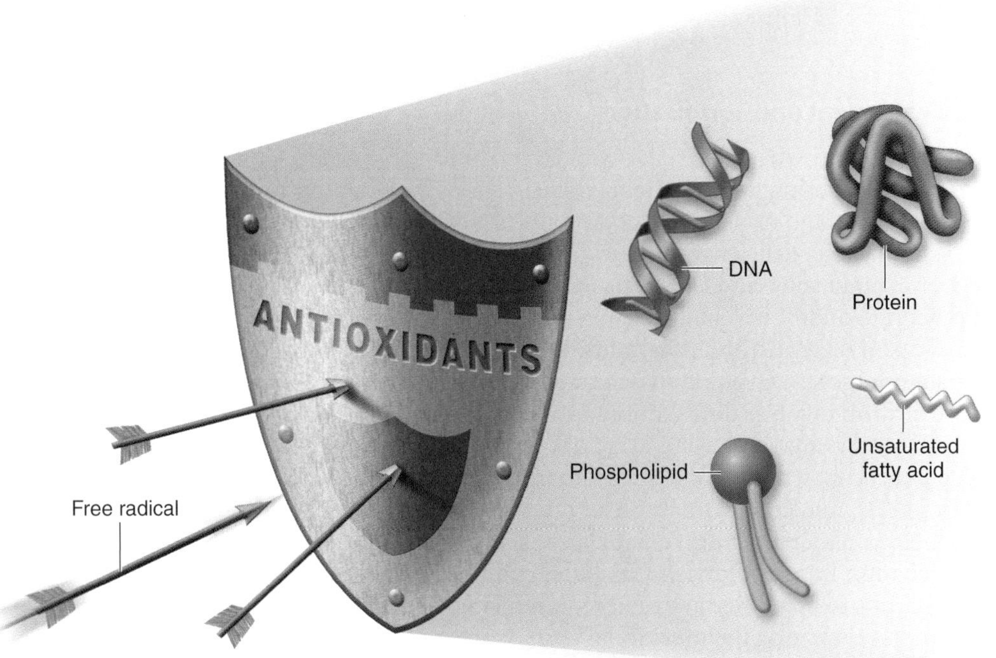

Figure 8.3 Antioxidant action. Beta-carotene and vitamins C and E are antioxidants that can protect the cell's plasma membrane and DNA from radicals. By sacrificing electrons, antioxidants protect molecules such as polyunsaturated fatty acids in the plasma membrane or DNA in the nucleus from being oxidized.

Why is it important to know the difference between fat- and water-soluble vitamins? The body generally has more difficulty eliminating excess fat-soluble vitamins because these nutrients do not dissolve in water substances such as urine. As a result, the body stores extra fat-soluble vitamins primarily in the liver and body fat. Over time, these vitamins can accumulate and cause toxicity. On the other hand, the body stores only limited amounts of most water-soluble vitamins—vitamin B-12 is an exception. Furthermore, kidneys can filter excesses of water-soluble vitamins from the bloodstream and eliminate them in urine. Thus, water-soluble vitamins are generally not as toxic as fat-soluble vitamins.

biological activity describes vitamin's degree of potency or effects in the body

Sources of Vitamins

Plants, animals, fungi, and even bacteria supply natural forms of vitamins in our diets. In addition to foods, vitamin supplements are another source of these micronutrients. Although chemists can synthesize vitamins, certain types of bacteria and algae produce vitamins. These organisms can be grown in laboratory settings for the purpose of "harvesting" their vitamins to use in supplement production.[4]

Regardless of whether a particular vitamin is naturally in foods or synthesized in a laboratory, it generally has the same chemical structure and works equally well in the body—but there are exceptions. The natural form of vitamin E has more **biological activity**, that is, it produces more effects in the body, than synthetic vitamin E. On the other hand, *synthetic folic acid*, the type of folate that is added to flour and many ready-to-eat and cooked cereals, has almost twice the biological activity as the natural form of the vitamin.

Many Canadians take vitamin supplements. According to the Canadian Community Health Survey 2.2, over 40% of Canadian adults reported taking a multivitamin in the month preceding the interview. For adults of all ages, women were more likely than men to be taking a multivitamin.[5]

It is not necessary to consume 100% of every vitamin each day. If you are healthy and usually follow a nutritionally adequate diet, your cells should contain a supply of vitamins that can last for several days and possibly even years, depending on the vitamin. Furthermore, bacteria that reside in your lower intestinal tract produce certain vitamins, particularly biotin and vitamin K, and you can absorb these micronutrients, to some extent. Additionally, your body can synthesize vitamins D and niacin under certain conditions.

TABLE 8.1 *Classifying Vitamins*

Fat-Soluble Vitamins
A
D
E (alpha-tocopherol, other tocopherols)
K
Water-Soluble Vitamins
Thiamin (thiamine, B-1)
Riboflavin (B-2)
Niacin (B-3, nicotinamide, nicotinic acid)
B-6 (pyridoxine)
B-12 (cobalamin, cobalamine)
Biotin (H)
Pantothenic acid (B-5)
Folate (folic acid, folacin)
C (ascorbic acid)
Choline

enrichment addition of specific amounts of vitamins and minerals to foods such as cereal grains

fortification addition of one or more nutrients to a wide array of commonly eaten foods during their manufacturing process

bioavailability the percentage of an ingested nutrient that is absorbed into the body

Vitamin Enrichment and Fortification

Cereal grains such as wheat, rice, and corn lose considerable amounts of their natural vitamin contents during milling (refinement). Enrichment is the process of adding additional vitamins and minerals to food products. **Enrichment** helps protect Canadians from developing the deficiency diseases associated with the lack of these nutrients. However, enrichment does not replace the vitamin E, vitamin B-6, potassium, magnesium, several other micronutrients, and fibre that were naturally in the unrefined grains. This is the major reason dietitians and other nutrition experts promote regular consumption of whole-grain products, such as whole-wheat bread and brown rice.

Fortification involves the addition during manufacturing of one or more vitamins (and/or other nutrients) to a wide array of commonly eaten foods. The vitamins that are added may or may not be in the food naturally. For example, milk is often fortified with vitamins A and D, and many ready-to-eat cereals are sprayed with additional vitamins before packaging.[6] In Canada, fortification and enrichment of foods have improved vitamin intakes of many Canadian children and adults by giving consumers more alternatives to meet their nutrient requirements. One example of how mandatory fortification has improved the nutritional quality of the food supply is the requirement for milk to be fortified with vitamin D, which has virtually eliminated childhood rickets (softening of bones).[7]

In summary, enrichment typically replaces nutrients lost during processing, while fortification typically adds additional nutrients to food products which may not have been found in the product originally.

Vitamin Absorption

The small intestine is the primary site of vitamin absorption. However, the intestine does not absorb 100% of the vitamins in food. Vitamin absorption tends to increase when the body's needs for the micronutrients are also higher than usual. The body's requirements for vitamins generally increase during periods of growth, such as infancy and adolescence, and during pregnancy and breast-feeding. The percentage of an ingested vitamin or mineral that is absorbed into the body is referred to as **bioavailability**. Typically, when the body is in need of a nutrient, the bioavailability of that nutrient increases to meet the body's need.

Fat-soluble vitamins are chemically similar to lipids, and the vitamins are in fatty portions of food. Thus, processes that normally occur during fat digestion facilitate the absorption of fat-soluble vitamins. For example, bile enhances lipid as well as fat-soluble vitamin absorption. In the small intestine, the presence of fat stimulates the secretion of a hormone that causes the gallbladder to release bile. Therefore, adding a small amount of fat to low-fat foods, such as tossing raw vegetables with some salad dressing, adding a pat of soft margarine to steamed carrots, or stir-frying green beans in peanut oil, can enhance your intestinal tract's ability to absorb the fat-soluble vitamins in these foods. To review lipid digestion, see Chapter 6.

Diseases or conditions that affect the GI tract can reduce vitamin absorption and result in deficiencies of these micronutrients. People with the inherited disease cystic fibrosis (*sis´-tik fie-broe´-sis*) are unable to digest fat properly, because the disease causes blockages to form in ducts that convey pancreatic enzymes to the small intestine. As a result, cystic fibrosis reduces fat absorption, and people suffering from the disease often develop deficiencies of fat-soluble vitamins. People who are unable to absorb vitamins may need to take large oral doses of vitamin supplements just to enable small amounts of the vitamins to be absorbed. In other cases, physicians inject vitamins into their patients' bodies, completely bypassing the need for the intestine to absorb the micronutrients.

Vitamin Deficiency and Toxicity Disorders

A diet that contains adequate amounts of a wide variety of foods, including minimally processed fruits, vegetables, and whole-grain breads and cereals, can help supply the vitamin needs of most healthy people. Vitamin deficiency disorders generally result from inadequate diets or conditions that increase the body's requirements for vitamins, such as reduced intestinal absorption or higher than normal excretion of the micronutrients. Today, severe vitamin deficiencies are uncommon in Canada and the United States, thanks in part to modern food preservation practices, food enrichment and fortification, and the year-round, widespread availability of fresh fruits and vegetables from other countries. Nevertheless, results of dietary surveys conducted in Canada suggest that a small percentage of some segments of the Canadian population consumes inadequate amounts of certain vitamins, such as vitamin C.[8]

Certain segments of the population are at risk of vitamin deficiencies. These vulnerable people include alcoholics, elderly persons, and patients who are hospitalized for lengthy periods. Additionally, people who suffer from anorexia nervosa, have intestinal conditions that interfere with vitamin absorption, or have rare metabolic defects that increase their vitamin requirements are more likely to develop vitamin deficiency disorders than people who do not have these conditions.

If your usual diet is nutritionally adequate but you occasionally have low intakes of vitamins, you are unlikely to develop vitamin deficiency diseases, because your cells store these micronutrients to some extent. The likelihood of developing a deficiency disease increases when a person's diet consistently lacks the vitamin. When this happens, the person's body stores or tissue levels of the vitamin become depleted, and the signs and symptoms of the nutrient's deficiency disease begin to occur. A person, for example, can become thiamin deficient after 14 days of consuming a diet that lacks the vitamin.[9]

If you are considering taking vitamin supplements or are taking them already, you need to recognize that "more" is not necessarily better. When cells are saturated with a vitamin, they contain all they need and cannot accept additional amounts of the micronutrient. When this situation occurs, continuing to take the vitamin can produce a toxicity disorder, because exposure to the excess micronutrient or its by-products can damage cells.

Do you need to be concerned about developing a vitamin toxicity disorder? Probably not, unless you are taking megadoses of vitamin supplements or consuming large amounts of vitamin-fortified foods regularly. In their natural states, most commonly eaten foods do not contain toxic levels of vitamins. A "one-a-day" type of multiple vitamin and mineral supplement usually contains less than two times the Daily Values of each micronutrient component, therefore regular use of these products is unlikely to cause toxic effects in adults.

Did You Know?

A plant's vitamin content is largely determined by its genetic makeup; growing conditions, including soil composition and sunlight exposure; and maturity when harvested.

Preserving the Vitamin Content of Foods

Are fresh fruits and raw vegetables better sources of vitamins than canned or frozen versions? Sometimes they are. Regardless of whether you pick fruits and vegetables from your own garden or buy them from a farmer's market or supermarket, many kinds of produce, especially berries and leafy vegetables, are highly perishable. Therefore, these foods should be eaten as soon as they are harvested or purchased to ensure maximum vitamin retention. In many instances, unpackaged ("bulk") fresh fruits or vegetables that are sold in supermarkets do not have dates indicating when they should be used, and consumers have no way of knowing when the produce was harvested.

A farmer's market can be a source of locally grown fresh produce during the growing season.

Did You Know?

Have you ever wondered why a freshly peeled apple, eggplant, potato, or banana eventually turns brown? Damaged plant cells release an enzyme that results in the production of brown pigments when it is exposed to air. The action of this enzyme can be reduced by sprinkling salt or sugar on cut pieces of raw food; coating the pieces with an acidic solution, such as lemon juice; or covering them with an airtight plastic wrapper and chilling the food. Because heat destroys the enzyme, the unappetizing discolouring won't occur if you cook the fruit or vegetable immediately after peeling.

Fresh fruits and vegetables can lose substantial amounts of vitamins as a result of improper handling or lengthy storage conditions. Therefore, select fresh produce carefully when buying them in grocery stores. Avoid produce that is bruised, wilted, or shrivelled, or that shows signs of decay such as mould. If you are uncertain how to choose ripe fruits and vegetables, ask the person who manages the produce section of the supermarket for advice.

Some vitamins, such as niacin and D, resist destruction by usual food storage conditions or preparation methods. Other vitamins—particularly vitamin C, thiamin, and folate—are easily destroyed or lost by improper food storage and cooking methods. Fresh produce is more likely to retain its natural vitamin content when stored at temperatures near freezing, in high humidity, and away from air. Therefore, you should keep most fresh fruits and vegetables in plastic packaging and chilled until you are ready to use them. Tomatoes, bananas, and garlic should be stored at room temperature. Although precut, packaged salad greens and other vegetables may be convenient to use, they are highly perishable and should be used soon after purchasing.

Figure 8.4 Conserving vitamins. Steaming vegetables can conserve much of the vitamin content of the produce.

Exposure to excessive heat, alkaline substances, light, and air can destroy certain vitamins, especially vitamin C. To reduce such losses, trim, peel, and cut raw fruits and vegetables just before eating or serving them. The darker leaves of vegetable greens generally contain more vitamins than the inner, paler colour leaves or stems. Therefore, lightly trim away the outer leaves of lettuce and cabbage, and keep edible peels intact—just remove rotten or shrivelled parts.

Water-soluble vitamins can leach out of food and dissolve in the cooking water, which is often discarded. By cooking vegetables in small amounts of water and reusing that water for soups or sauces, you are likely to consume those water-soluble nutrients. When preparing produce for cooking, cut the food into large pieces to reduce the amount of surface area that will be exposed to heat, water, and other conditions that can increase vitamin losses. Whenever possible, cook fruits and vegetables in their skins, and if the skins are edible, eat them too.

Quick-cooking methods that involve little contact between produce and water, such as microwaving, steaming, and stir-frying, can conserve much of the vitamin content of the food. Microwave cooking does not reduce the nutrient content of foods any more than do conventional cooking methods.[10,11] Microwave cooking may help conserve more vitamins in food because the method cooks quickly and without the need to add much water.

Food & Nutrition *tip*

To avoid having to discard old or mouldy produce, plan a few days' menus and then prepare a shopping list that includes only those fresh fruits and vegetables that you'll need to purchase for that brief period's meals and snacks.

To steam vegetables, place them in a steamer basket that fits inside a pot, add enough water to touch the bottom of the basket, cover the pot, and then heat the water until it boils (Fig. 8.4). As the steam gently cooks the vegetables, add more water, if necessary. To stir-fry vegetables, heat a small amount of oil in a wok or pan that has deep sides, add small pieces of fresh vegetables, and stir the mixture, lightly coating the vegetables with oil (Fig. 8.5). Stir-fried vegetables should be cooked until they are barely tender, to retain their nutrients as well as appealing textures, flavours, and colours. The Recipes for Healthy Living feature, later in this chapter, has a recipe for stir-fried vegetables.

Freezing food is an excellent preservation method that also helps retain vitamins. Frozen fruits and vegetables are often economical alternatives to fresh produce, but they need to be cooked without thawing to conserve much of their vitamin content. The thawing process causes some of the water that was naturally in the produce to drip out, taking water-soluble vitamins with it. If this water is discarded, vitamins in the fluid are lost. The following Food & Nutrition Tips feature provides practical ways to preserve the vitamin content of food.

Figure 8.5 Conserving vitamins. Stir-frying conserves vitamins by cooking vegetables quickly without adding water.

Food & Nutrition *tips*

- Eat fresh fruits and vegetables along with their edible peels or skins whenever possible.
- Cook fresh vegetables by microwaving, steaming, or stir-frying. Vegetables generally have high water content, therefore add no water or just a small amount when microwaving vegetables.
- Do not overcook vegetables, and minimize reheating, because prolonged heating reduces vitamin content.
- Do not add margarine or butter to vegetables during cooking, because fat-soluble vitamins and phytochemicals may enter the fat and be discarded, when the fat is drained before serving. Fat in foods can enhance the body's absorption of fat-soluble vitamins; therefore, you can add some olive oil, soft margarine, or butter to vegetables after they are cooked.
- Store canned foods in a cool place. Canned foods can vary in the amount of nutrients they contain, largely because of differences in storage times and temperatures. Commercially canned food is safe to eat, even after many months or years.[12] However, if the can has been on the shelf for an extended period of time, the food's vitamin content may have deteriorated and its taste and texture may be less than desirable. To get maximal nutritive value from canned vegetables, drain the liquid that is packed with the food and use it as a base for soups, sauces, or gravies. If the liquid is too salty, discard it.

Concept Checkpoint

1. List at least three criteria used to designate a substance as a vitamin.
2. List three factors that distinguish vitamins from macronutrients.
3. Define the following terms: provitamin, antioxidant, and radical.
4. Explain the difference between enrichment and fortification.
5. Discuss at least five ways to preserve the vitamin content of fruits and vegetables during food preparation and storage.

retinol (preformed vitamin A) most active form of vitamin A in the body

carotenoids yellow-orange pigments in fruits and vegetables

Fat-Soluble Vitamins

This section focuses on three fat-soluble vitamins: A, D, and E. Table 8.2 presents a summary of general information about all fat-soluble vitamins, including K.

Vitamin A

Do you associate vitamin A with eating carrots and good vision? It is true that vitamin A is involved in the visual process and carrots contain vitamin A precursors. However, vitamin A can multitask—it has numerous functions in the body. Furthermore, carrots are not the only source of vitamin A precursors; many fruits and vegetables are rich sources of these compounds.

Vitamin A is actually a family of compounds that includes retinol. **Retinol (preformed vitamin A)** is the most active form of the vitamin in the body. Although retinol and the other forms of vitamin A are only in animal foods, plants contain hundreds of yellow-orange pigments called **carotenoids**. A few carotenoids are vitamin A precursors, because the body can use them to make some retinol.

All cells in the body need vitamin A to develop and function properly. Vitamin A participates in the processes of cell production, growth and development, function, and

TABLE 8.2 *Summary of Fat-Soluble Vitamins*

Vitamin	Major Functions in the Body	Adult RDA/AI	Major Dietary Sources	Major Deficiency Signs and Symptoms	Major Toxicity Signs and Symptoms
Vitamin A (preformed and provitamin A)	Normal vision and reproduction, cellular growth, and immune system function	700–900 mcg RAE	Preformed: liver, milk, fortified cereals Provitamin: yellow-orange and dark green fruits and vegetables	Night blindness, xerophthalmia, poor growth, dry skin, reduced immune system functioning	Nausea and vomiting, headaches, bone pain and fractures, hair loss, liver damage
Vitamin D	Absorption of calcium and phosphorus, maintenance of normal blood calcium, calcification of bone, maintenance of immune function	5–15 mcg	Vitamin D–fortified milk, fortified cereals, fish oils, fatty fish	Rickets in children, osteomalacia in adults: soft bones, depressed growth, and reduced immune system functioning	Poor growth, calcium deposits in soft tissues
Vitamin E	Antioxidant	15 mg (alpha-tocopherol)	Vegetable oils and products made from these oils, certain fruits and vegetables, nuts and seeds, fortified cereals	Hemolysis of red blood cells resulting in anemia	Excessive bleeding as a result of interfering with vitamin K metabolism
Vitamin K	Production of active blood-clotting factors	90–120 mcg	Green leafy vegetables, canola and soybean oils, and products made from these oils	Excessive bleeding	Unknown

- **Eat at least one dark green and one orange vegetable each day.**
  - Go for dark green vegetables such as broccoli, romaine lettuce and spinach.
  - Go for orange vegetables such as carrots, sweet potatoes and winter squash.
- **Choose vegetables and fruit prepared with little or no added fat, sugar or salt.**
  - Enjoy vegetables steamed, baked or stir-fried instead of deep-fried.
- **Have vegetables and fruit more often than juice.**

Figure 8.6 Dark green vegetables as well as yellow and orange fruits and vegetables are rich sources of the provitamin beta-carotene.

maintenance. For example, the vitamin is necessary for the production and maintenance of **epithelial cells**, cells that form protective tissues that line the body, including skin, tissues covering the eyeball, and linings of the digestive, respiratory, and reproductive tracts. Certain epithelial cells secrete *mucus*, a sticky fluid that keeps the tissue moist and forms a barrier against many environmental pollutants and infectious agents. When the mucus-secreting epithelial cells do not have vitamin A, they deteriorate and no longer produce mucus. A lack of vitamin A can also reduce fertility, because the vitamin is required for maintaining the epithelial cells that line the reproductive tracts of men and women.

Certain white blood cells produce antibodies, proteins that participate in the body's immune response. Antibodies help destroy infectious agents such as bacteria. Vitamin A plays a role in the production and activity of white blood cells.[13] Thus, vitamin A-deficient people are at greater risk of infections than those with adequate levels of the vitamin in their bodies.

Normal bone growth and development also require vitamin A. Although your bones do not appear to change their shape, they are constantly remodelled by processes that involve tearing down and rebuilding the tissues to meet the physical demands that you place on them each day. Vitamin A participates with other vitamins and minerals in the bone remodelling process.

Be wary of claims that taking vitamin A supplements will improve your vision so that you won't need to wear eyeglasses or contact lenses. Vitamin A deficiency does not cause the kinds of visual defects that are correctable with glasses or contacts. Furthermore, large doses of vitamin A are toxic.

What Is Night Blindness? Have you ever walked from a brightly lit theatre lobby into the darkened movie auditorium and felt blinded for a few seconds? This is a normal visual response to the sudden and dramatic reduction in light intensity. The *retina*, the light-sensitive area inside each eye, contains rods and cones, specialized nerve cells that are essential for vision (Fig. 8.7). Rods enable you to adapt to poorly lit environments and see objects as shades of black. Cones are responsible for colour vision and function in well-lit environments. Rods and cones need vitamin A to function properly.

Night blindness, the inability to see in dim light, occurs if vitamin A is unavailable. Night blindness is an early sign of vitamin A deficiency. Although cone cells also need vitamin A to function, the inability to see certain colours (colour blindness) is a genetic defect and not the result of vitamin A deficiency.

epithelial cells cells that form protective tissues that line the body

beta-carotene carotenoid that the body can convert to vitamin A

Food Sources of Vitamin A

Animal foods such as liver, butter, fish, fish oils, and eggs are good sources of preformed vitamin A. Some foods are fortified with the vitamin during processing. Vitamin A-fortified dairy products, margarine, and cereals are important sources of the nutrient for Canadians. Carrots, spinach and other leafy greens, pumpkin, sweet potatoes, broccoli, mangoes, and cantaloupe are rich sources of **beta-carotene**, a carotenoid that the body can convert to vitamin A. However, the body only obtains 1 mcg of retinol from every 12 mcg of beta-carotene in a food. Furthermore, vitamin A precursors in plant foods are not as well absorbed as retinol in animal foods.[14]

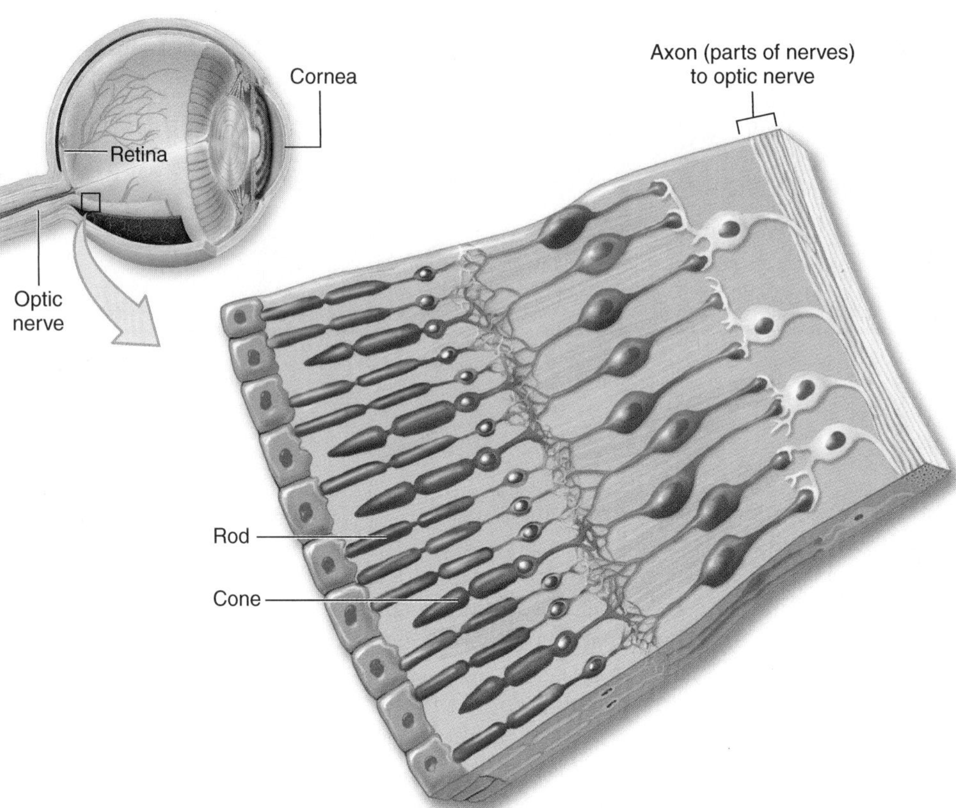

Figure 8.7 Vitamin A and vision. The retina, the light-sensitive area inside each eye, contains rods and cones, specialized nerve cells that are essential for vision. Rods and cones need vitamin A to function properly.

Fruits and vegetables generally are good sources of antioxidants, including carotenoids such as beta-carotene and lycopene.

In addition to beta-carotene, common carotenoids include lutein (*loo′-tee-en*), zeaxanthin (*zee-ah-zan′-thin*), and lycopene (*lie′-ko-peen*). Green, leafy vegetables, such as spinach and kale, have high concentrations of lutein and zeaxanthin. Tomato juice and other tomato products, including pizza sauce, contain considerable amounts of lycopene. Although lutein, zeaxanthin, and lycopene are carotenoids, the body does not convert them to vitamin A. Nevertheless, these plant pigments function as beneficial antioxidants in the human body.

Darkly pigmented fruits and vegetables usually contain more beta-carotene and other provitamin A carotenoids than lightly coloured produce. For example, carrots, sweet potatoes, mangoes, and peaches contain more beta-carotene than celery, white potatoes, apples, and bananas. Dark green fruits and vegetables also contain carotenoids, but their green pigment chlorophyll contents hide the yellow-orange pigments.

Food & Nutrition *tips*

When preparing salads or meals, don't discard the edible dark green leaves of lettuce, cabbage, or broccoli. These darkly pigmented parts of the plants contribute more provitamin A carotenoids to your diet than the lighter coloured parts. Use them in salads or on sandwiches. In addition to carotenoids, many fruits and vegetables contain hundreds of other phytochemicals that may benefit your health. To obtain a variety of these compounds, include colourful vegetables and fruits in your meals and snacks.

Figure 8.8 lists some foods that are sources of vitamin A and its precursors. Amounts of vitamin A in food are often reported as micrograms of retinol activity equivalents (RAE). One RAE is approximately 1 mcg of retinol.

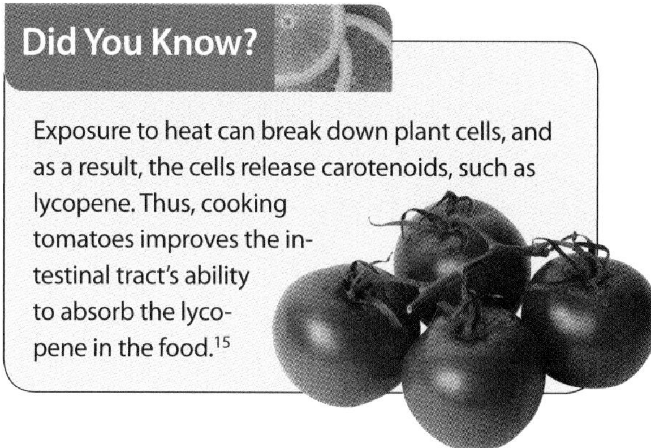

Did You Know?

Exposure to heat can break down plant cells, and as a result, the cells release carotenoids, such as lycopene. Thus, cooking tomatoes improves the intestinal tract's ability to absorb the lycopene in the food.[15]

Dietary Adequacy

For adults, the RDA for vitamin A is 700 to 900 mcg RAE.[16,17] According to the Canadian Community Health Survey, Cycle 2.2, in 2004, adult Canadian men had a mean vitamin A intake of just over 700 mcg and adult women just below 700 mcg.[18] Thus, the average adult Canadian consumes approximately enough vitamin A and its precursors to meet the RDA. Therefore, Canadian adults generally do not need to take vitamin A supplements. Preschool children who do not eat enough vegetables, urban poor, older adults, and people with severe alcoholism, fat malabsorption, or liver diseases are at risk for vitamin A deficiency.

Vitamin A Deficiency Epithelial cells are among the first to become affected by a deficiency of vitamin A. In skin, vitamin A–deficient epithelial cells produce too much **keratin**, a tough protein found in hair, nails, and the outermost layers of skin. Keratin accumulates within the skin and makes the tissue rough and bumpy. Keratin also forms in tissues that do not normally contain the protein, such as the cornea, the clear covering over the coloured portion of the eye (iris) that enables light to enter the organ (see Fig. 8.7). The epithelial cells that line the inner eyelids secrete mucus that helps keep the cornea moist and clean. In a person suffering from chronic vitamin A deficiency,

keratin tough protein found in hair, nails, and the outermost layers of skin

Figure 8.8 Vitamin A Content of Selected Foods.

Source: Data from U.S. Department of Agriculture, Agricultural Research Service, USDA Nutrient Data Laboratory: Vitamin A, RAE (μg) content of selected foods by common measure, sorted by nutrient content. *USDA national nutrient database for standard reference, release 18*. 2004.

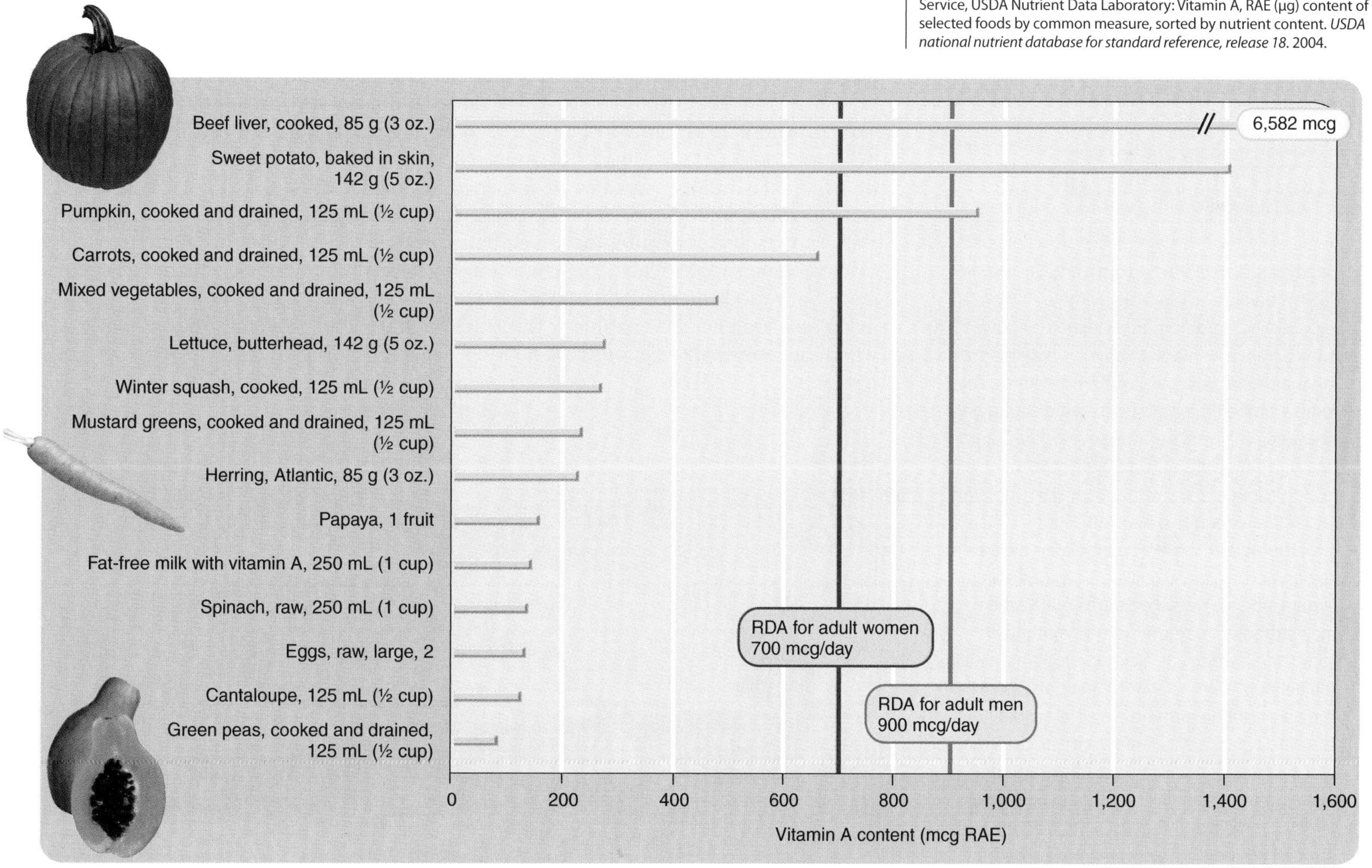

Beef liver, cooked, 85 g (3 oz.)
6,582 mcg
Sweet potato, baked in skin, 142 g (5 oz.)
Pumpkin, cooked and drained, 125 mL (½ cup)
Carrots, cooked and drained, 125 mL (½ cup)
Mixed vegetables, cooked and drained, 125 mL (½ cup)
Lettuce, butterhead, 142 g (5 oz.)
Winter squash, cooked, 125 mL (½ cup)
Mustard greens, cooked and drained, 125 mL (½ cup)
Herring, Atlantic, 85 g (3 oz.)
Papaya, 1 fruit
Fat-free milk with vitamin A, 250 mL (1 cup)
Spinach, raw, 250 mL (1 cup)
Eggs, raw, large, 2
Cantaloupe, 125 mL (½ cup)
Green peas, cooked and drained, 125 mL (½ cup)
RDA for adult women 700 mcg/day
RDA for adult men 900 mcg/day
0 200 400 600 800 1,000 1,200 1,400 1,600
Vitamin A content (mcg RAE)

xerophthalmia condition affecting the eyes that results from vitamin A deficiency

teratogen an agent that causes birth defects

carotenemia yellowing of the skin that results from excess beta-carotene in the body

these cells become hardened and stop producing mucus. This condition is called **xerophthalmia** (*zir-op-thal'-me-a*) or "dry eye." Corneas affected by xerophthalmia can be damaged easily by dirt and bacteria. Unless a person with xerophthalmia receives vitamin A, the condition eventually leads to blindness (Fig. 8.9).

Each year, thousands of children in developing nations, especially in Africa and Southeast Asia, become blind because of severe vitamin A deficiency. Vitamin A deficiency also reduces the effectiveness of the immune system, and many children suffering from vitamin A deficiency die from infections, such as measles. In countries where vitamin A deficiency is widespread, public health efforts are being taken to reduce the prevalence of the condition. Such efforts include educating people about the need to eat regionally grown foods that are rich in beta-carotene and giving vitamin A injections twice yearly to vulnerable populations. In some countries, governments encourage food manufacturers to fortify commonly eaten foods, such as sugar and margarine, with vitamin A. According to a report by the World Health Organization, public health programs to reduce the prevalence of vitamin A deficiency have been largely successful.[19]

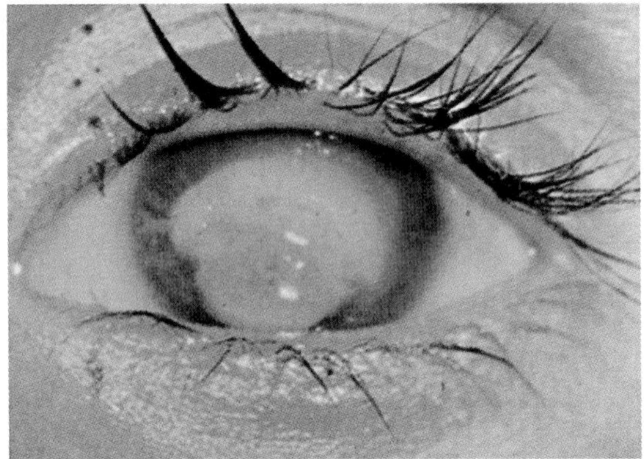

Figure 8.9 Xerophthalmia. Unless a person with xerophthalmia is treated with vitamin A, the condition will eventually lead to blindness.

The results of animal studies suggest that women who are vitamin A deficient during pregnancy may give birth to infants with circulatory, urinary, skeletal, and nervous systems defects.[20] However, pregnant women should not take vitamin A supplements to prevent birth defects without consulting with their physicians. When taken during pregnancy, excess vitamin A is a **teratogen**, an agent that causes birth defects.

Vitamin A Toxicity The Upper Limit (UL) for vitamin A intake is 3000 mcg per day of preformed vitamin A for adults.[16,17] Excessive consumption of vitamin A can damage the liver, because the organ is the main site for vitamin A storage. Toxicity signs and symptoms include headache, nausea, vomiting, visual disturbances, hair loss, bone pain, and bone fractures.

Miscarriage and birth defects may result when excessive amounts of vitamin A are taken early in pregnancy. Women of child-bearing age should limit their overall intake of vitamin A to about 100% of the Daily Value (1000 mcg RAE or 5000 IU). In addition, women who may become pregnant or who are pregnant should restrict their intakes of rich food sources of vitamin A, such as liver and fish liver oils. Specific recommendations for fish intake during pregnancy are provided in Chapter 13.

Carotenemia (*kar'-et-eh-ne'-me-ah*), a condition characterized by yellowing of the skin, can result from eating too much beta-carotene-rich produce or taking too many beta-carotene supplements. This condition occasionally develops in infants who eat a lot of baby foods that contain carrots, apricots, winter squash, or green beans.[21] In most instances, carotenemia is harmless. The skin's natural colour eventually returns to normal when the carotenoid-rich foods are no longer eaten.

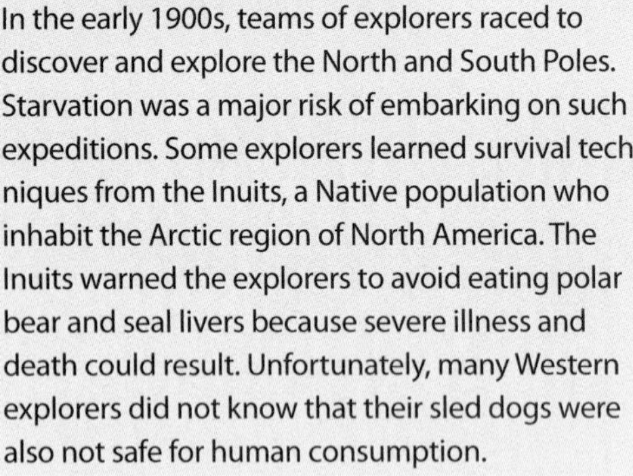

Did You Know?

In the early 1900s, teams of explorers raced to discover and explore the North and South Poles. Starvation was a major risk of embarking on such expeditions. Some explorers learned survival techniques from the Inuits, a Native population who inhabit the Arctic region of North America. The Inuits warned the explorers to avoid eating polar bear and seal livers because severe illness and death could result. Unfortunately, many Western explorers did not know that their sled dogs were also not safe for human consumption.

During 1911 to 1913, Douglas Mawson and Xavier Mertz were on an ill-fated expedition to explore an area near the South Pole. As the two men struggled to return to their winter base camp, they had to eat their sled dogs, particularly the animals' livers, to avoid starvation. Both men suffered terribly from the diet—Mertz did not survive. Over 50 years later, scientists determined that sled dogs can accumulate large amounts of vitamin A in their livers without showing ill effects. However, eating just 50 to 60 grams (a few ounces) of sled dog liver can be toxic for humans.

Physicians may prescribe medications derived from vitamin A to treat severe acne and other skin disorders. Although these medications are less toxic than natural vitamin A, ingesting excessive amounts can produce harmful symptoms. Furthermore, vitamin A derivatives can cause miscarriage or severe birth defects in the offspring of women who use them during pregnancy. Therefore, women of child-bearing age should avoid pregnancy while using these medications.

Vitamin D

By the 1700s, some people in parts of northern Europe had learned that exposing children to sunlight or giving the youngsters fish liver oil could prevent or treat **rickets**. Children with rickets have bones that are soft and can become misshapen. Leg bones, for example, bow under the weight of carrying the upper part of the body. Additionally the affected child's joints, rib cage, and hips (pelvis) also become deformed (Fig. 8.10). In 1922, scientists discovered a fat-soluble factor in cod liver oil that they thought was a vitamin needed for proper bone health and preventing rickets. The fat-soluble factor in the fish oil that was necessary for healthy bones was actually a hormone. The body can make this hormone when skin cells are exposed to the sun's ultraviolet (UV) radiation, which explains why vitamin D is often called the "sunshine vitamin." The radiation converts a substance in skin that is derived from cholesterol into *prohormone vitamin* D_3. The liver metabolizes vitamin D_3 to the inactive compound 25-OH vitamin D. Eventually, the kidneys convert 25-OH vitamin D into the active form we call "vitamin D" (Fig. 8.11).[22] Vitamin D is also classified as a vitamin, because rickets can be prevented and treated by taking vitamin D supplements or eating vitamin D–rich foods.

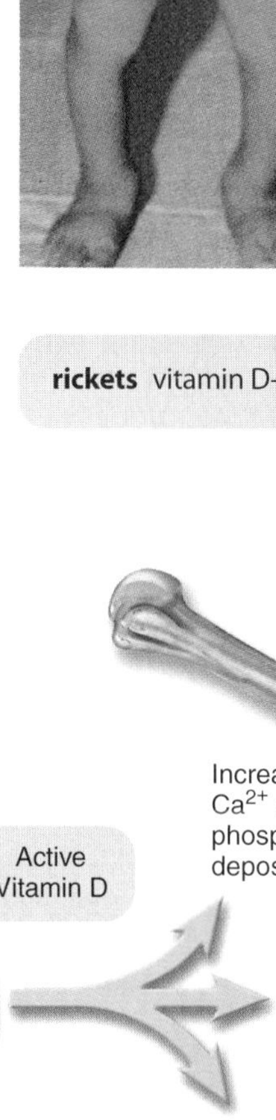

Figure 8.10 Rickets. A child suffering from rickets has soft bones that do not grow properly. The youngster's leg bones bow under the weight of carrying the upper part of the body, and his or her joints, rib cage, and hips (pelvis) also become deformed.

rickets vitamin D–deficiency disorder in children

Why Is Vitamin D Necessary?

Vitamin D is necessary for the metabolism of the minerals calcium and phosphorus, and the production and maintenance of healthy bones. Vitamin D stimulates small intestinal cells to absorb calcium and phosphorus from food. When vitamin D is lacking, the intestine absorbs only 10 to 15% of the calcium in foods; with the vitamin, intestinal absorption of dietary calcium increases to 30 to 80%.[23] Vitamin D also stimulates bone cells to form *calcium phosphate*, the major mineral compound in bone. Without adequate vitamin D, bone cells cannot deposit enough calcium and phosphorus to produce strong bone tissue (see Fig. 8.10). The vitamin also stimulates kidneys to reduce the elimination of calcium in urine. These actions help conserve calcium in the body.

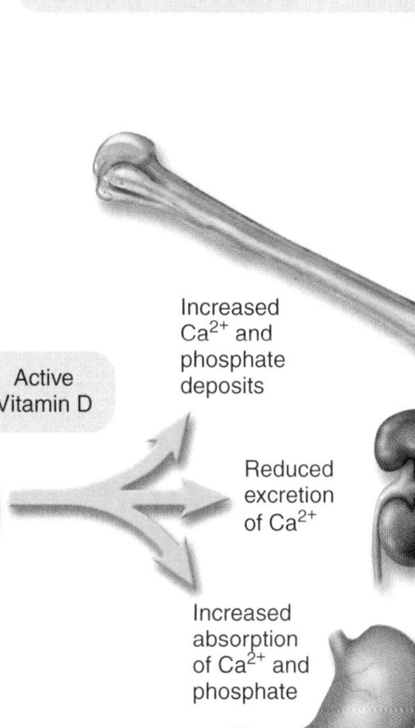

Figure 8.11 Vitamin D. After skin synthesizes vitamin D_3, the compound undergoes changes in the liver and kidneys to become the active form of the vitamin, increases calcium and phosphorus deposits in bone, increases intestinal absorption of calcium and phosphorus, and reduces excretion of calcium by kidneys.

Salmon is a good source of vitamin D.

When blood calcium levels drop, vitamin D works with *parathyroid hormone (PTH)* to signal bones to release calcium. PTH also stimulates the kidneys to increase vitamin D production and decrease the elimination of calcium in urine. These actions help raise the level of calcium in blood to normal (Fig. 8.12). Removing too much calcium from bones can weaken them, but calcium is essential for normal heartbeat and other muscle contractions. If bones did not supply calcium for such vital functions, a person could experience serious, even fatal consequences.[24]

Vitamin D has other roles in the body. Cancerous cells exhibit uncontrolled growth and division. Vitamin D is involved in controlling cell growth, and as a result, it may reduce the risk of certain cancers, particularly colon cancer.[25,26] Additionally vitamin D regulates the function of certain immune system cells, but more research is needed to clarify the vitamin's role in disease prevention.[27]

Sources of Vitamin D

Fish liver oils and fatty fish, especially salmon and herring, are among the few foods that naturally contain vitamin D. Milk is routinely fortified with vitamin D, and some brands of ready-to-eat cereals, orange juice, and margarine have the vitamin added to them as well. Figure 8.13 lists some food sources of vitamin D. Food composition tables often list the vitamin D content of foods in International Units; 1 mcg of vitamin D equals 40 IU.

Vitamin D and Sunlight Vitamin D is not widespread in food, therefore your body depends on sun exposure to synthesize the vitamin. The amount of time you should

Figure 8.12 Maintaining normal blood calcium levels. When the level of calcium in blood drops below normal (1), a variety of complex physiological responses help raise the level to normal. (2) The drop in blood calcium signals the parathyroid glands to secrete PTH. (3) PTH acts on the kidneys to decrease calcium excretion in urine and increase vitamin D production. (4) PTH also stimulates bone tissue to remove calcium, so the mineral can enter the blood. (5) Vitamin D stimulates the removal of calcium from bones and (6) absorption of calcium (and phosphorus) in the small intestine. (7) These complex actions help raise blood calcium levels to normal.

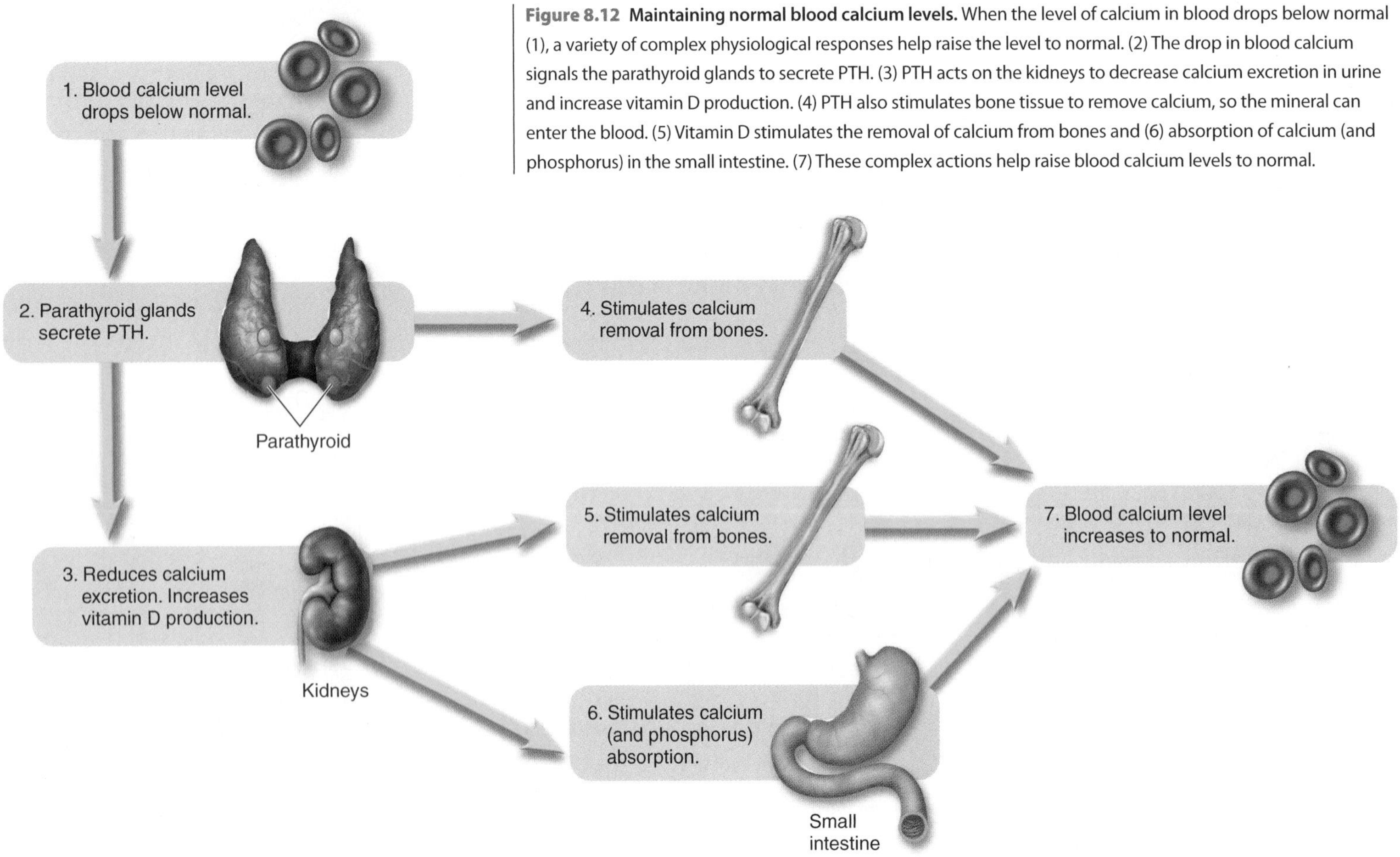

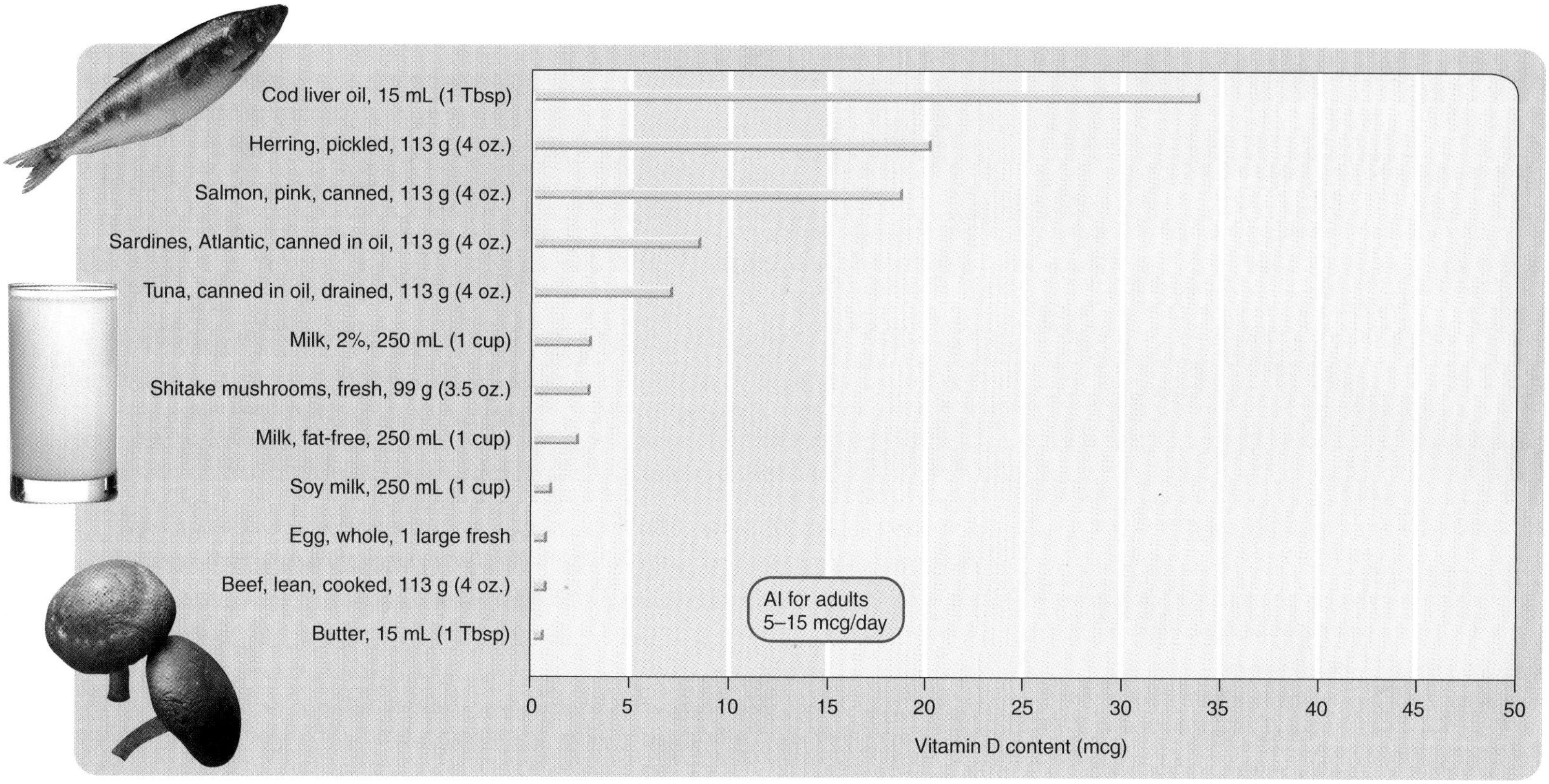

Cod liver oil, 15 mL (1 Tbsp)
Herring, pickled, 113 g (4 oz.)
Salmon, pink, canned, 113 g (4 oz.)
Sardines, Atlantic, canned in oil, 113 g (4 oz.)
Tuna, canned in oil, drained, 113 g (4 oz.)
Milk, 2%, 250 mL (1 cup)
Shitake mushrooms, fresh, 99 g (3.5 oz.)
Milk, fat-free, 250 mL (1 cup)
Soy milk, 250 mL (1 cup)
Egg, whole, 1 large fresh
Beef, lean, cooked, 113 g (4 oz.)
Butter, 15 mL (1 Tbsp)
AI for adults
5–15 mcg/day
0 5 10 15 20 25 30 35 40 45 50
Vitamin D content (mcg)

Figure 8.13 Vitamin D Content of Selected Foods.

Source: Data from U.S. Department of Agriculture, Human Nutrition Information Service: *Provisional table on the vitamin D content of foods.* HNIS/PT-108, 1991, Revised 1999.

spend in the sun to form vitamin D depends primarily on your location, the time of day and year, and your age and skin colour.

If you live south of the 37th parallel and are outdoors between 10 a.m. and 3 p.m. when sunlight is most intense, you probably will obtain enough sun exposure to synthesize vitamin D most of the year. In North America, the 37th parallel extends from about southern Virginia through southern Missouri to San Francisco, California (Fig. 8.14).

Earth's atmosphere blocks UV radiation. If you live north of the 37th parallel, the angle of the winter sun is such that the sun's rays must pass through more of the atmosphere than at other times of the year (Fig. 8.15). As a result, your skin cannot make sufficient amounts of provitamin vitamin D during the winter, and you may not have adequate vitamin D stored in your body to last until spring.[22] In addition, typically from fall through spring, Canadians wear long-sleeved shirts and long pants to stay warm, which limits the amount of direct sunlight which reaches the skin. Most Canadians get enough vitamin D in their diet through the winter, but if you have a poor dietary intake you may need to take a supplement that contains 100% of the adult Daily Value for vitamin D (10 mcg or 400 IU), especially from October through April. Clouds, shade, and air pollution also limit the amount of UV radiation that reaches your skin. The Dietitians of Canada organization is concerned that Canadians are at risk for inadequate intakes of vitamin D because the current recommendations may be too low. Ongoing research on vitamin D requirements may cause the recommendations to change in the future.[28]

Skin contains *melanin*, the brown pigment that can prevent skin from absorbing too much solar radiation and forming toxic amounts of vitamin D. Darker skin contains more melanin than lighter skin. If your skin is fair or has a medium degree of pigmentation,

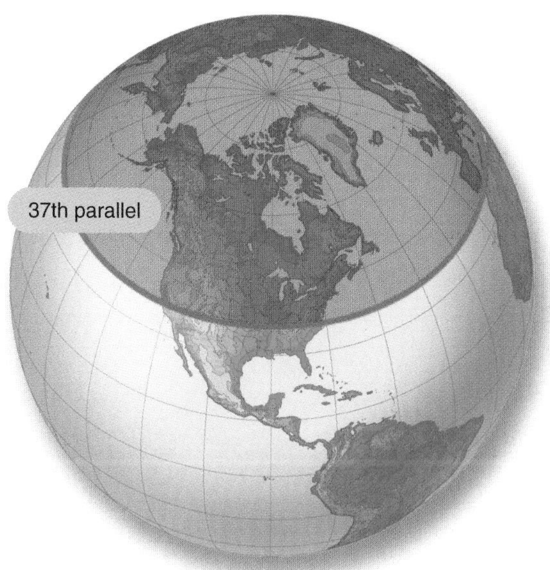

Figure 8.14 Where you live can affect your vitamin D status. In North America, the 37th parallel extends from about southern Virginia through southern Missouri to San Francisco, California. If you live in North America, south of the 37th parallel and are outdoors when sunlight is most intense during the day, you are likely to obtain enough sun exposure to synthesize vitamin D most of the year. However, because Canada exists above the 37th parallel, it is important that Canadians receive dietary sources of vitamin D in the winter to ensure optimal health throughout the year.

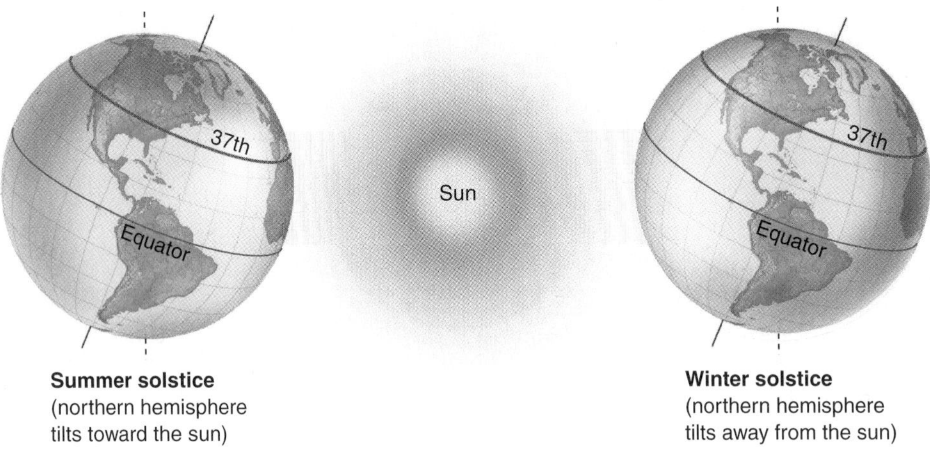

Figure 8.15 Seasonal variations in sunlight intensity. If you live north of the 37th parallel, the angle of the winter sun is such that the sun's rays must pass through more of the atmosphere than at other times of the year. As a result, skin forms less prohormone vitamin D in the winter.

Did You Know?

Information provided by tanning parlours may include claims that the tanning process is safe. Nevertheless, the ultraviolet radiation emitted by tanning beds increases the risk of wrinkles and skin cancer. Therefore, the excess use of tanning beds should be avoided.

exposing your hands, face, and arms at least two to three times a week for five to ten minutes may enable your body to synthesize enough vitamin D. If you have dark skin, you will need to spend at least 15 minutes and maybe even more time in the sun to form adequate amounts of the vitamin.

In response to increased UV light, skin becomes tanned as it produces more melanin. Although you may think tanned skin is attractive, tanning and severe sunburn increase the risk of developing wrinkles and skin cancer. In Canada, skin cancer is the most common cancer,[29] and sunburn during childhood is a major risk factor for melanoma, the most deadly form of skin cancer.[30] Dermatologists often advise people to apply sunscreens consistently before going outdoors. Using a sunscreen, however, limits skin's ability to synthesize prohormone vitamin D. When properly applied, a sunscreen with a sun protection factor (SPF) of 15 almost completely blocks prohormone vitamin D formation.[22] To allow your body to synthesize vitamin D, you can expose your skin to the sun for 5 to 10 minutes *before* applying a commercial sunscreen.

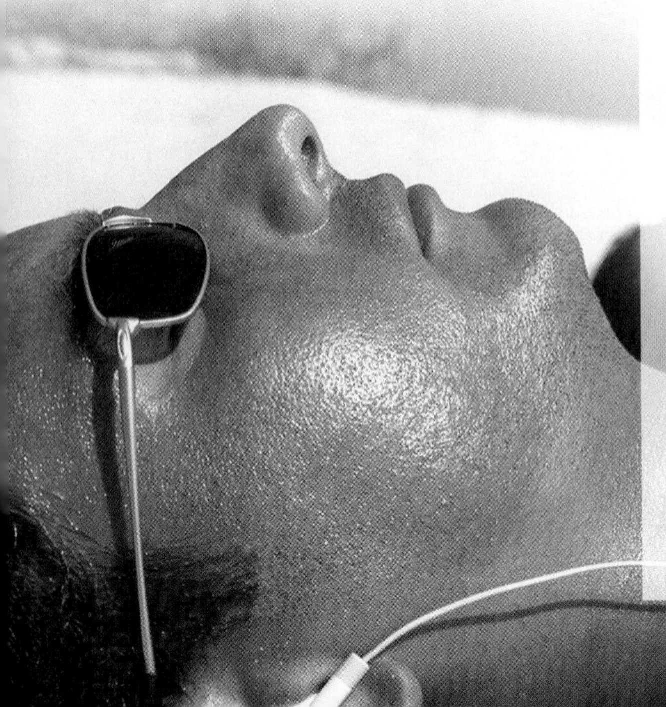

Exposure to ultraviolet radiation from the sun can increase the risk of wrinkles and skin cancer.

Vitamin D Deficiency Rickets is a major public health concern in many developing countries.[31] In Canada, milk producers fortify milk with vitamin D, and as a result, rickets is rare in this country.[7] Breast milk contains insufficient amounts of vitamin D to prevent rickets. Children who are most likely to develop rickets are exclusively breast-fed, and they have dark skin, minimal sunlight exposure, and little or no vitamin D intake.[32] Exposing breast-fed infants to sunlight reduces their risk of the disease, but medical experts do not know how much sun exposure is necessary. According to guidelines established by the Canadian Paediatric Society, breast-fed infants should consume a minimum of 400 IU of vitamin D per day, and 800 IU per day if they live above the 55° latitude (approximately at the point of Edmonton, Alberta) or have dark skin, between the months of October and April when there is less sunlight.[33] Healthy children should consume 5 mcg (200 IU) of vitamin D per day through adolescence and into adulthood.[16,17] Health Canada also now recommends that all Canadians over the age of 50 years consume 10 mcg or 400 IU of supplemental vitamin D per day.[34]

The adult form of rickets is called **osteomalacia** (*ahs'-tee-o-mah-lay'-she-a*). The bones of people with osteomalacia contain less than normal amounts of calcium, and they are weak and break easily as a result. Adults who are confined indoors or almost fully covered during the day, such as for religious reasons,[35] are at risk for severe vitamin D deficiency (osteomalacia) (Fig. 8.16). Adults who have kidney, liver, or intestinal diseases may develop osteomalacia, because these conditions may reduce both vitamin D production and calcium absorption. In Canada, mild to moderate cases of vitamin D deficiency among adults may be common.[36] The results of a recent American survey indicated that about 42% of African-American women and 4% of white women had low blood levels of vitamin D.[37] Exposing skin to sunlight, eating vitamin D–rich foods, or taking vitamin D supplements will help to avoid vitamin D deficiency.

As a person ages, production of prohormone vitamin D in skin declines and conversion of the prohormone to active vitamin D in kidneys also decreases.[25] As a result of these age-related changes, older adults have a higher risk of developing vitamin D deficiency than younger persons. Additionally, elderly persons are at risk for bone fractures. An analysis of several studies indicated elderly subjects who took 700 to 800 IUs of vitamin D per day had a lower risk of hip fractures than elderly persons who took 400 IUs of vitamin D per day.[38] Thus, people over 50 years of age may benefit from using a daily vitamin D supplement.[34]

Vitamin D Toxicity The UL for vitamin D is 50 mcg per day (2000 IU per day).[16,17] When excess vitamin D is consumed, the small intestine absorbs too much calcium from foods and the mineral is deposited in soft tissues, including the kidneys, heart, and blood vessels. The calcium deposits can interfere with cells' ability to function and cause cellular death. Other signs and symptoms of vitamin D toxicity include muscular weakness, loss of appetite, diarrhea, vomiting, and mental confusion. Long-term ingestion of vitamin D supplements that supply 250 to 1250 mcg per day (10 000 to 50 000 IU per day) can produce toxicity.[39] You do not have to be concerned about your body making toxic levels of vitamin D, because skin is able to limit its production of prohormone vitamin D.

Figure 8.16 Clothing and vitamin D status. Adults who are almost fully covered during the day, such as for cold Canadian winters, are at risk for osteomalacia.

osteomalacia adult rickets

alpha-tocopherol vitamin E

Vitamin E

Vitamin E (**alpha-tocopherol**) is the major fat-soluble antioxidant found in cells. The vitamin protects polyunsaturated fatty acids in cell membranes from being damaged by radicals. Such oxidative damage may be associated with the development of atherosclerosis, the process that occurs within arteries and contributes to heart attack and stroke; cancer; and premature cellular aging and death. Other roles for vitamin E include improving vitamin A absorption and maintaining nervous tissue and immune system function.

Food Sources of Vitamin E

Rich food sources of vitamin E include sunflower seeds, almonds, and plant oils, especially sunflower, safflower, canola, and olive oils. Products made from vitamin E-rich plant oils—margarine and salad dressings—also supply the micronutrient. Other important dietary sources of the vitamin include fish, whole grains, nuts, seeds, and certain vegetables. Meats, processed grain products, and dairy products generally do not contain much vitamin E. Figure 8.17 lists some common foods that are sources of the micronutrient.

Harvesting, processing, storage, and cooking methods influence the amount of vitamin E retained in food. During the milling process, most of the vitamin E that is in whole grains is lost, and it is not restored by enrichment. Furthermore, vitamin E is highly susceptible to destruction by exposure to oxygen, metals, and light, as well as high temperatures that occur when heating oil for deep-fat frying.

Dietary Adequacy

For adults, the RDA for vitamin E is 15 mg per day of alpha-tocopherol (*al'-fah toe-koff '-e-roll*).[16,17] Although adults can benefit by eating more vitamin E–rich foods, if necessary, people can take a multivitamin supplement that contains the vitamin.

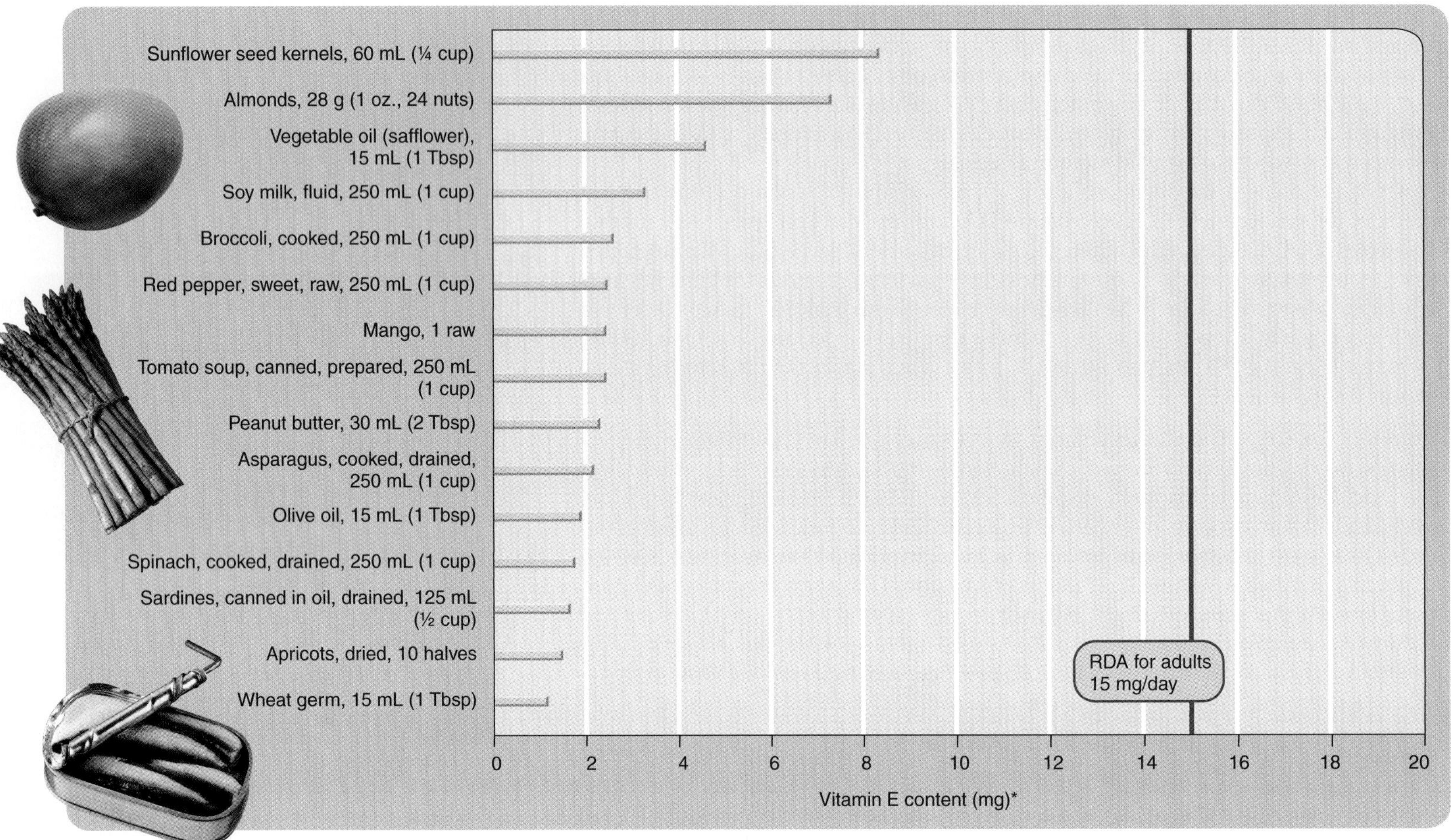

Figure 8.17 Vitamin E Content of Selected Foods.

*As alpha-tocopherol.

Source: Data from U.S. Department of Agriculture, Agricultural Research Service, USDA Nutrient Data Laboratory: Vitamin E (alpha-tocopherol) (mg) content of selected foods by common measure, sorted by nutrient content. *USDA national nutrient database for standard reference, release 18.* 2004.

hemolysis disintegration of red blood cells

anemia disorder characterized by too few red blood cells

coenzyme small molecule that interacts with enzymes, enabling the enzymes to function

Amounts of vitamin E may be reported as a number of IUs. One IU of vitamin E equals 1.5 mg of natural forms of the vitamin.[3] Synthetic vitamin E is used to fortify foods and produce supplements that supply the vitamin. One milligram of synthetic vitamin E equals one IU of the vitamin.

Vitamin E Deficiency In cases of vitamin E deficiency, unsaturated fatty acids in red blood cell (RBC) membranes are vulnerable to damage by oxidizing agents. When damaged, RBC membranes break easily, and the cells undergo **hemolysis** (*hemo = blood; lysis = disintegrate*), that is, they break apart and die. Hemolysis can cause **anemia**, a disorder characterized by too few RBCs. In addition to anemia, vitamin E deficiency may also damage the nervous system and reduce the functioning of the immune system.[3]

Cases of vitamin E deficiency are rare,[40] probably because a healthy body stores the vitamin in body fat, skeletal muscle, and the liver. Smokers are at risk of the deficiency because smoking destroys vitamin E in the lungs, reducing the total amount of the micronutrient in the body.[41] Infants who are born too early (premature infants) tend to have low vitamin E stores, because the vitamin is transferred from mother to fetus late in pregnancy. If premature infants develop hemolysis, they can be given special infant formulas and supplements that provide vitamin E.

Vitamin E Toxicity For healthy adults, the UL for vitamin E is 1000 mg per day of alpha-tocopherol.[16,17] Excessive amounts of vitamin E can interfere with vitamin K's role in blood clotting, leading to uncontrolled bleeding (hemorrhage). Therefore, people who are taking medications that interfere with blood clotting ("blood thinners") should check with their physicians before using vitamin E supplements.

Concept **Checkpoint**

6. Prepare a table for fat-soluble vitamins. For each vitamin, indicate its major function in the body, major food sources, deficiency disorder (if it has a specific name), and major signs and symptoms of the deficiency disorder. If the vitamin is known to be toxic, also indicate major toxicity signs and symptoms. Check your table against the information provided in Table 8.2.

Water-Soluble Vitamins

In the body, most water-soluble vitamins function as components of specific coenzymes. A **coenzyme** is a *cofactor*, an ion or small molecule that regulates a chemical reaction. To synthesize a coenzyme, cells combine one of the B vitamins with a nitrogen-containing, non-protein compound (Fig. 8.18). When activated by the coenzyme, the enzyme enables the reaction to occur (Fig. 8.19).

Many of the chemical reactions involved in the metabolism of carbohydrates, fats, and amino acids involve coenzymes that contain B vitamins. Thiamin, riboflavin, niacin, vitamin B-6, and pantothenic acid function as part of coenzymes involved in energy metabolism.[42] Coenzymes containing these vitamins are also necessary for synthesizing glucose, amino acids, and certain lipids. Biotin, folate, vitamin B-12, and choline function as part of coenzymes needed for reactions that transfer single carbon units, such as methyl (CH_3) groups.[42]

Foods contain B vitamins in their coenzyme forms. Health-food stores often sell supplements that contain coenzymes, but buying these products is a waste of money. In the small intestine, coenzymes in food or supplements are not absorbed intact. The compounds undergo digestion to release their B vitamin components. The small intestine absorbs much of the B vitamins that were in foods and supplements, and the micronutrients eventually enter the general circulation. Cells then remove the free vitamins from the bloodstream and use them to rebuild coenzymes.

This section of Chapter 8 focuses on seven water-soluble vitamins: thiamin, riboflavin, niacin, B-6, folate, B-12, and C. Table 8.3 provides a summary of general information about all the water-soluble vitamins.

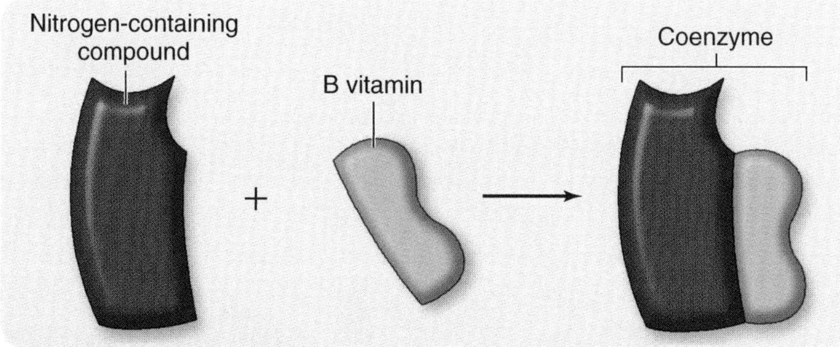

Figure 8.18 What is a coenzyme? A coenzyme is a small molecule that regulates a chemical reaction. To synthesize a coenzyme, cells combine a B vitamin with a nitrogen-containing, non-protein compound.

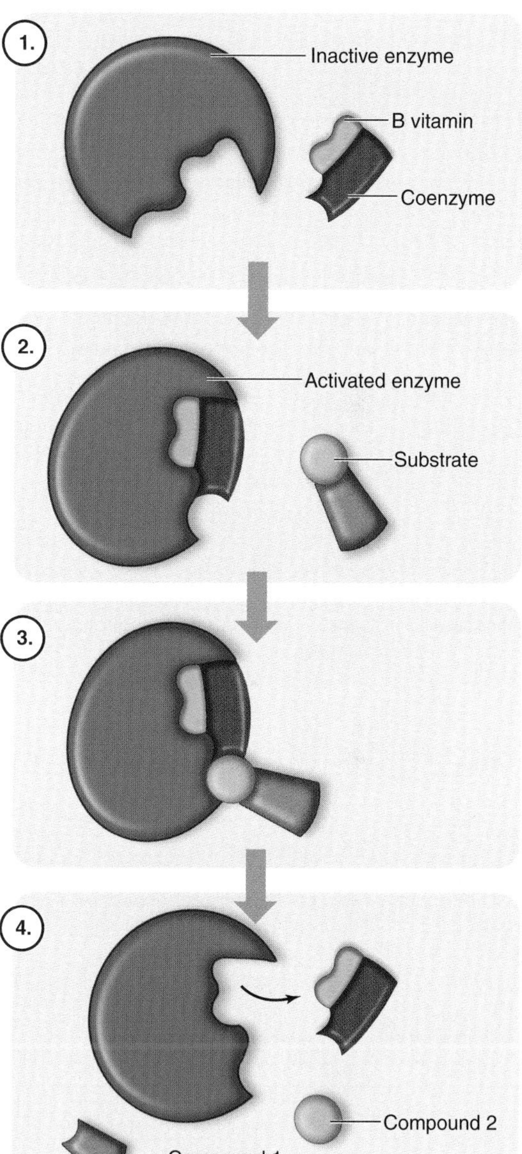

Figure 8.19 Coenzyme action. Many enzymes need coenzymes to convert substrates to other compounds. (1) This enzyme is unable to function (inactive) without its coenzyme in place. (2) By combining with the coenzyme, the enzyme is activated and able to bind to the substrate (3). The enzyme-coenzyme complex enables the reaction to occur. In this case, the substrate is split into its two components (4).

TABLE 8.3 *Summary of Water-Soluble Vitamins*

Vitamin	Major Functions in the Body	Adult RDA/AI	Major Dietary Sources	Major Deficiency Signs and Symptoms	Major Toxicity Signs and Symptoms
Thiamin	Part of coenzyme needed for carbohydrate metabolism and the metabolism of certain amino acids; may help produce neurotransmitters	1.1–1.2 mg	Pork, wheat germ, enriched breads and cereals, brewer's yeast	Beriberi and Wernicke-Korsakoff syndrome: Weakness, abnormal nervous system functioning	None
Riboflavin	Part of coenzymes needed for carbohydrate, amino acid, and lipid metabolism	1.1–1.3 mg	Milk, yogourt, and other milk products; enriched breads and cereals; liver	Inflammation of the mouth and tongue, eye disorders	None
Niacin	Part of coenzymes needed for energy metabolism	14–16 mg	Enriched breads and cereals, beef, liver, tuna, salmon, poultry, pork, mushrooms	Pellagra: • Diarrhea • Dermatitis • Dementia • Death	Flushing of facial skin, itchy skin, nausea and vomiting, liver damage
Pantothenic acid	Part of the coenzyme that is needed for synthesizing fat and releasing energy from macronutrients	5 mg	Cereals that have been fortified with the vitamin, beef and chicken liver, sunflower seeds, mushrooms, peas, soy milk	Rarely occurs	Unknown
Biotin	Cofactor needed for synthesizing glucose and fatty acids	30 mcg	Liver, eggs, peanuts, salmon, pork, mushrooms, sunflower seeds	Rarely occurs: Skin rash, hair loss, convulsions, and other neurological disorders; developmental delays in infants	Unknown
Vitamin B-6	Part of coenzyme needed for amino acid metabolism, involved in neurotransmitter and hemoglobin synthesis	1.3–1.7 mg	Meat, fish, and poultry; potatoes, bananas, spinach, sweet red peppers, broccoli	Dermatitis, anemia, depression, confusion, and neurological disorders such as convulsions	Nerve destruction
Folate	Part of coenzyme needed for DNA synthesis and conversion of cysteine to methionine, preventing homocysteine accumulation	400 mcg DFE	Dark green, leafy vegetables, liver, legumes, asparagus, broccoli, orange juice, enriched breads and cereals	Megaloblastic anemia, diarrhea, neural tube defects in embryos	Unknown
Vitamin B-12	Part of coenzymes needed for various cellular processes, including folate metabolism; maintenance of myelin sheaths	2.4 mcg	Animal foods, fortified cereals, fortified soy milk	Pernicious anemia: megaloblastic anemia and nerve damage resulting in paralysis and death	None
Ascorbic acid (vitamin C)	Connective tissue synthesis and maintenance; antioxidant; synthesis of neurotransmitters and certain hormones; immune system functioning	75–90 mg (non-smokers)	Peppers, citrus fruits, papaya, broccoli, cabbage, berries	Scurvy: Poor wound healing, pinpoint hemorrhages, bleeding gums, bruises, depression	Diarrhea and GI tract discomfort
Choline	Neurotransmitter and phospholipid synthesis; methionine metabolism	425–550 mg	Widely distributed in foods and human biosynthesis	Liver damage	Fishy body odour and reduced blood pressure

Thiamin

In the body, thiamin is used to make a coenzyme that participates in chemical reactions involved in the release of energy from carbohydrates. Additionally, the thiamin-containing coenzyme plays a role in the metabolism of certain amino acids, and the coenzyme may be necessary for the synthesis of neurotransmitters. A neurotransmitter is a chemical produced by a nerve cell that enables the cell to communicate to other nerve cells.

Food Sources of Thiamin

Foods that contribute thiamin to Canadian diets include whole-grain and enriched breads and cereals, pork, legumes, and orange juice. Brewer's yeast is a rich source of thiamin, but most Canadians do not eat the product. Figure 8.21 lists some common foods that are good sources of thiamin. Overcooking and cooking food in alkaline solutions can destroy thiamin.

Figure 8.20 Fruits and vegetables are excellent sources of many water-soluble vitamins including vitamin C and folate.

Dietary Adequacy

The adult RDA for thiamin is 1.2 mg per day and 1.1 mg per day, for men and women, respectively.[16,17] According to the Canadian Community Health Survey, Cycle 2.2, in 2004, the mean daily intake of thiamin for Canadian adult men and women is 1.99 mg and 1.46 mg, respectively.[18] There are no reports of toxicity from consuming high amounts of thiamin from food or supplements, probably because the excess vitamin is readily excreted in urine.[42] Thus, no UL has been established for thiamin.

The body stores very little thiamin, so deficiency symptoms can occur within a few days of consuming a thiamin-deficient diet. The thiamin-deficiency disease is called **beriberi**. People suffering from beriberi are very weak and have poor muscular

beriberi thiamin-deficiency disease

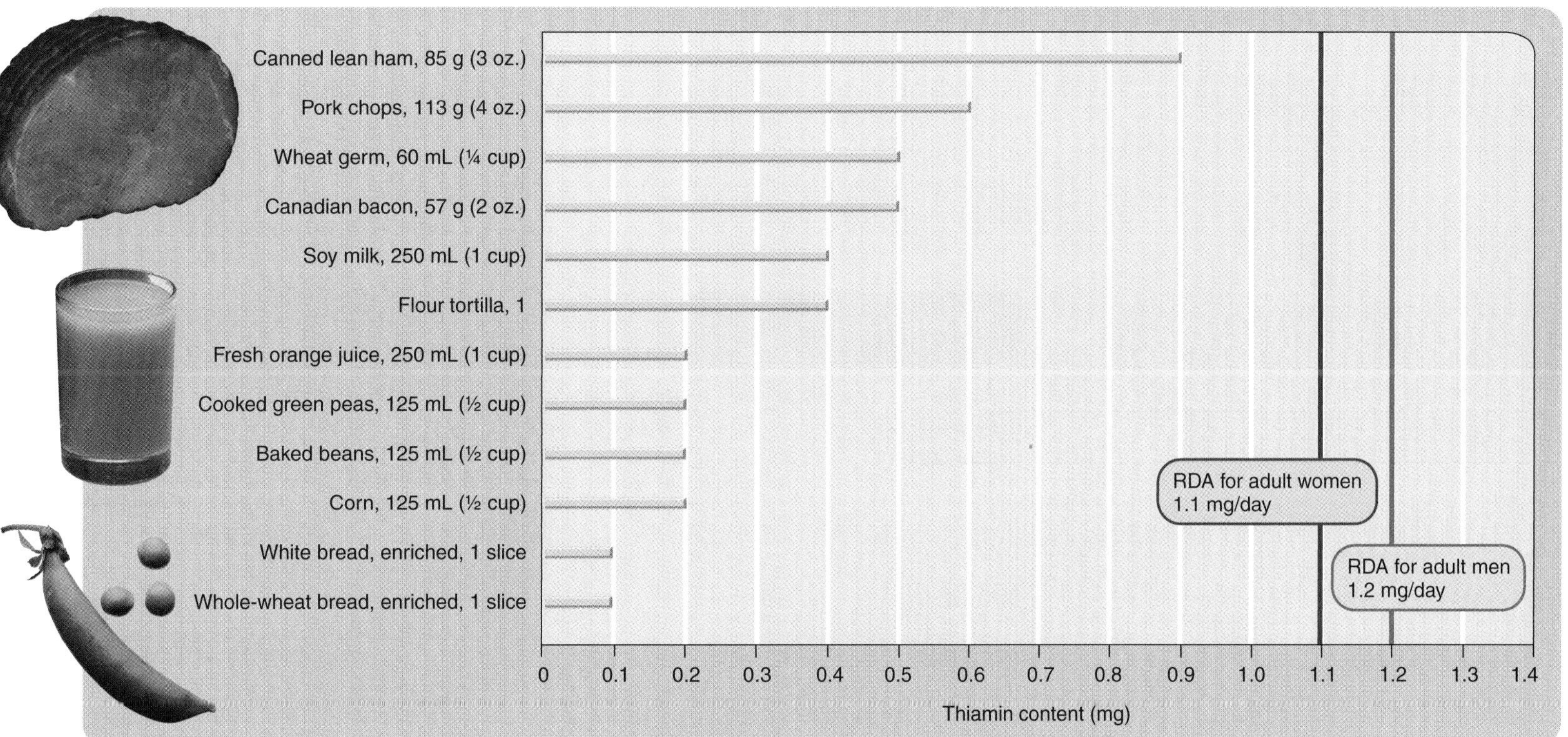

Figure 8.21 **Thiamin Content of Selected Foods.**

Source: Data from U.S. Department of Agriculture, Agricultural Research Service, USDA Nutrient Data Laboratory: Thiamin (mg) content of selected foods by common measure, sorted by nutrient content. *USDA national nutrient database for standard reference, release 18.* 2004.

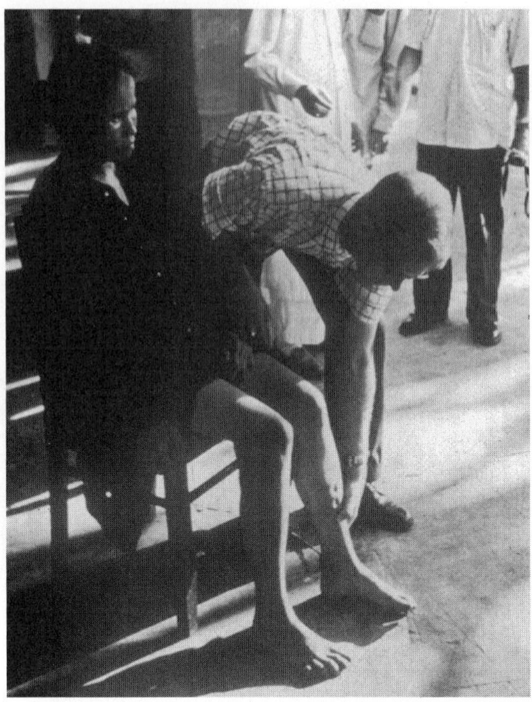

Figure 8.22 Beriberi. The woman sitting in the chair has a form of beriberi called "wet beriberi." In addition to suffering from fatigue and nervous system disorders, she has cardiovascular abnormalities that result in severe "pitting" edema in her lower legs.

coordination (Fig. 8.22). The severe lack of thiamin also negatively affects the functioning of the cardiovascular, digestive, and nervous systems.

The degenerative brain disorder associated with thiamin deficiency is called **Wernicke-Korsakoff syndrome** (*vear'-nih-key kor'-sah-koff*). Most cases of Wernicke-Korsakoff syndrome occur in alcoholics, because alcohol reduces thiamin absorption and increases the vitamin's excretion. People with alcoholism also tend to have poor eating habits that contribute to deficiencies of thiamin and other vitamins. Signs of Wernicke-Korsakoff syndrome include abnormal eye movements, staggering gait, and distorted thought processes. Treatment involves avoiding alcohol and obtaining thiamin injections. Without prompt treatment, people with Wernicke-Korsakoff syndrome can become disabled permanently or die.

Wernicke-Korsakoff syndrome degenerative brain disorder resulting from thiamin deficiency that primarily occurs among alcoholics

Riboflavin

Riboflavin is a component of two coenzymes that play key roles in metabolism of carbohydrates, lipids, and amino acids. Milk, yogourt, and other milk products; enriched cereals; and liver are among the best sources of riboflavin. Mushrooms, broccoli, asparagus, and spinach and other green leafy vegetables also contain substantial amounts of the vitamin. Figure 8.23 lists these and other food sources of riboflavin. Riboflavin's chemical structure is fairly stable, but exposure to light causes the vitamin to break down rapidly. Therefore, riboflavin-rich foods, such as milk and milk products, should not be packaged or stored in clear glass containers.

Dietary Adequacy

The RDA for riboflavin is 1.1 mg per day for women and 1.3 mg per day for men.[16,17] The typical riboflavin intake of North Americans is about 1.5 mg per day for women and 2.1 mg per day for men.[42] According to the Canadian Community Health Survey, Cycle 2.2, in 2004, adult Canadian men and women had mean daily intake of riboflavin of 2.18 mg and 1.68 mg, respectively.[18] Riboflavin deficiency is rare in Canada because many commonly eaten foods contain riboflavin (see Figure 8.23).[43] However, people who do not consume milk, milk products, or enriched breads and cereals may develop mild cases of riboflavin deficiency. A symptom of mild riboflavin deficiency is to become fatigued easily. Riboflavin is rapidly eliminated in urine, so consuming large amounts of the vitamin does not appear to cause side effects.[42] Thus, no UL has been established for riboflavin.

Did You Know?

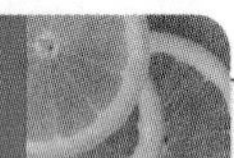

Riboflavin is naturally yellow. If you take a dietary supplement that contains high amounts of riboflavin, your kidneys will excrete the excess, and you may notice the bright yellow colour of your urine.

Niacin

The body uses niacin to synthesize two coenzymes that participate in at least 200 reactions, including those involved in the release of energy from macronutrients. Major food sources of niacin include enriched cereals, beef liver, tuna, salmon, poultry, pork, and mushrooms (Figure 8.24). The chemical structure of niacin is very heat stable, so food retains much of its niacin content during usual preparation and cooking methods.

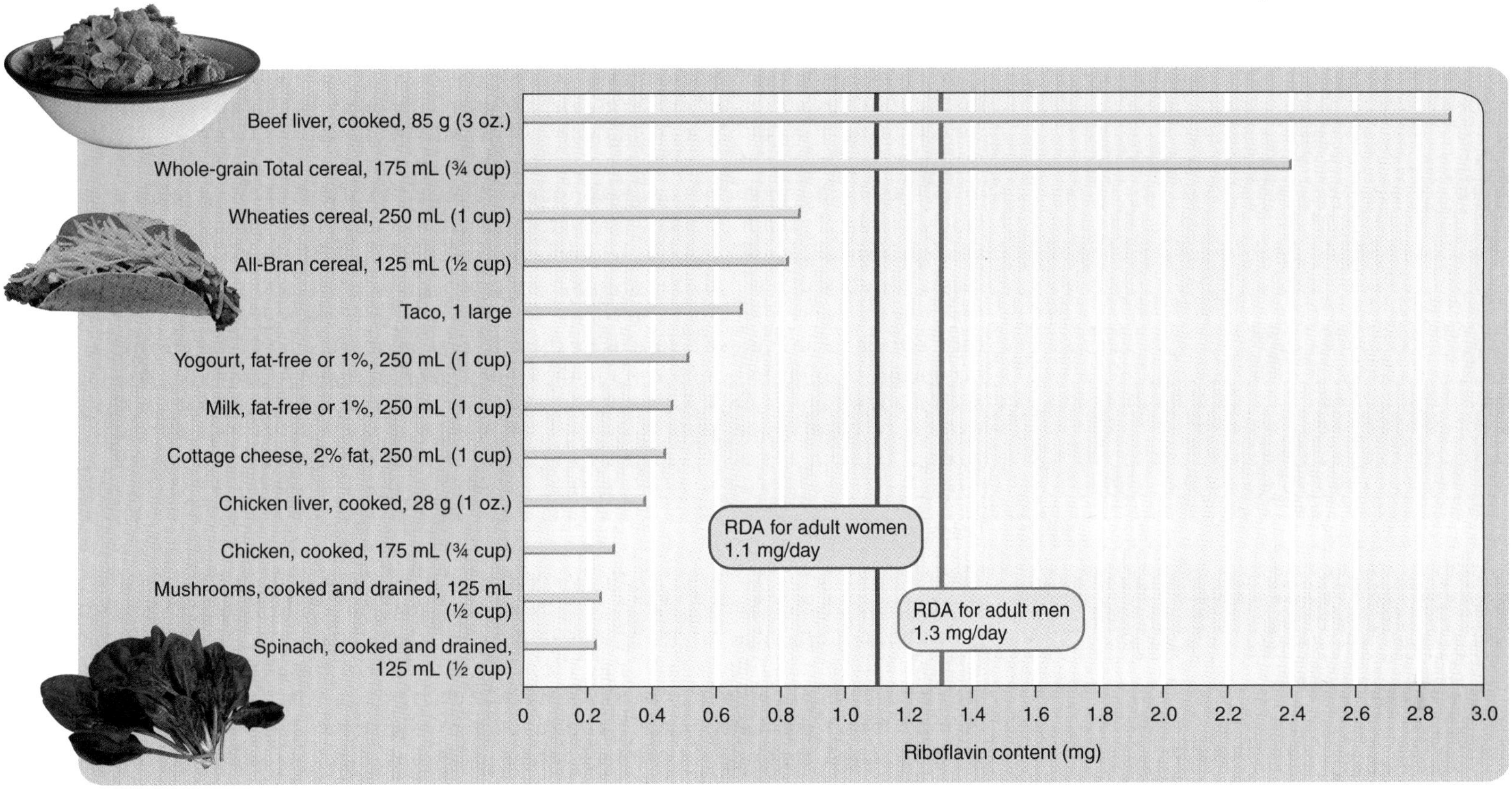

Beef liver, cooked, 85 g (3 oz.)
Whole-grain Total cereal, 175 mL (¾ cup)
Wheaties cereal, 250 mL (1 cup)
All-Bran cereal, 125 mL (½ cup)
Taco, 1 large
Yogourt, fat-free or 1%, 250 mL (1 cup)
Milk, fat-free or 1%, 250 mL (1 cup)
Cottage cheese, 2% fat, 250 mL (1 cup)
Chicken liver, cooked, 28 g (1 oz.)
Chicken, cooked, 175 mL (¾ cup)
Mushrooms, cooked and drained, 125 mL (½ cup)
Spinach, cooked and drained, 125 mL (½ cup)
RDA for adult women 1.1 mg/day
RDA for adult men 1.3 mg/day
0 0.2 0.4 0.6 0.8 1.0 1.2 1.4 1.6 1.8 2.0 2.2 2.4 2.6 2.8 3.0
Riboflavin content (mg)

Figure 8.23 **Riboflavin Content of Selected Foods.**

Source: Data from U.S. Department of Agriculture, Agricultural Research Service, USDA Nutrient Data Laboratory: Riboflavin (mg) content of selected foods by common measure, sorted by nutrient content. *USDA national nutrient database for standard reference, release 18.* 2004.

Whole-grain Total, ready-to-eat cereal, 175 mL (¾ cup)
Raisin bran, ready-to-eat cereal, 250 mL (1 cup)
Beef liver, cooked, 85 g (3 oz.)
Chicken, ½ breast, 85 g (3 oz.)
Tuna, canned in water, 85 g (3 oz.)
Wheaties, ready-to-eat cereal, 250 mL (1 cup)
Turkey roast, cooked, 85 g (3 oz.)
Peanuts, oil roasted, 28 g (1 oz.)
Mushrooms, cooked, drained, 125 mL (½ cup)
Potato, baked with skin, 184 g (6.5 oz.)
White rice, enriched, cooked, 125 mL (½ cup)
Macaroni, enriched, cooked, 125 mL (½ cup)
RDA for adult women 14 mg/day
RDA for adult men 16 mg/day
0 2 4 6 8 10 12 14 16 18 20 22 24 26 28 30
Niacin content (mg)

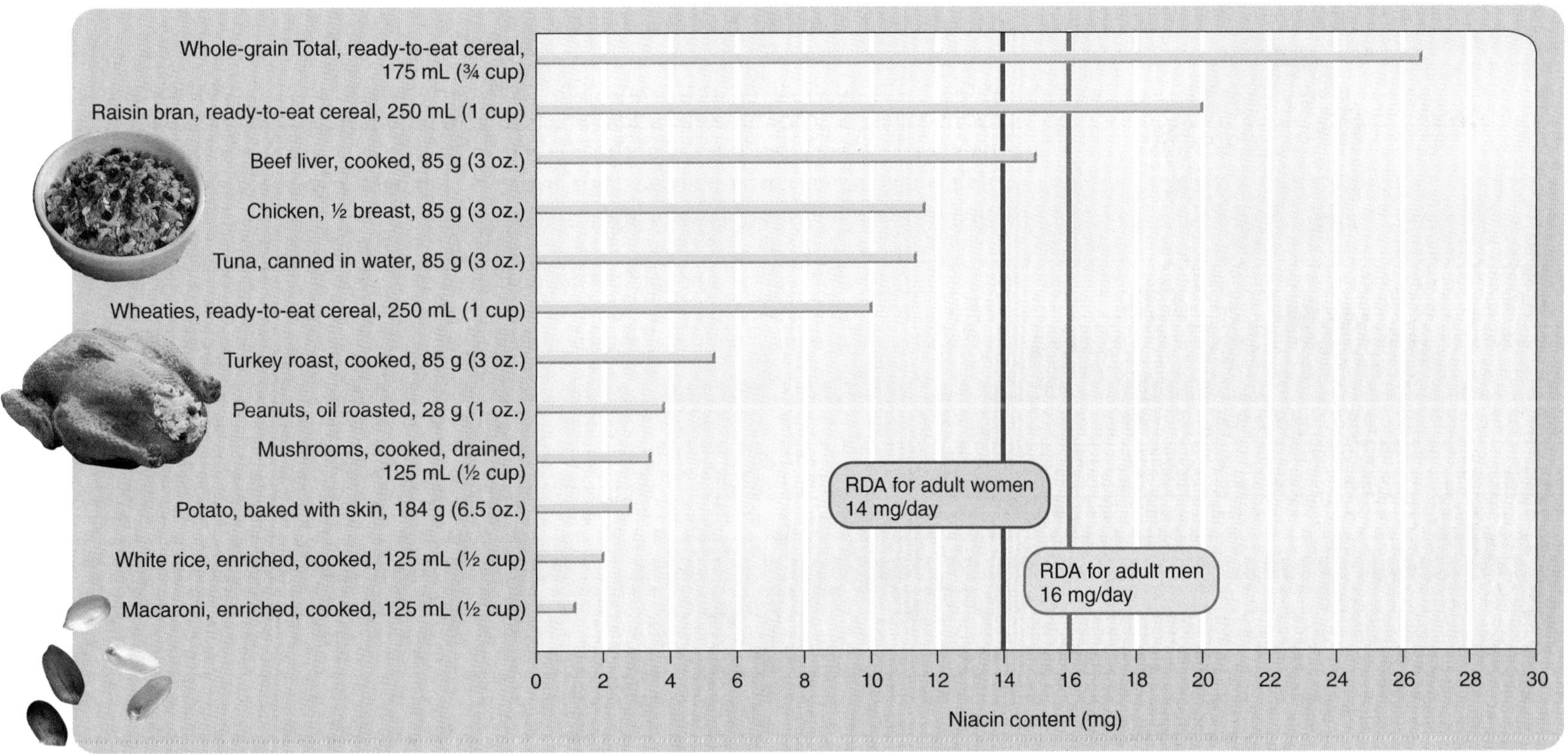

Figure 8.24 **Niacin Content of Selected Foods.**

Source: Data from U.S. Department of Agriculture, Agricultural Research Service, USDA Nutrient Data Laboratory: Niacin (mg) content of selected foods by common measure, sorted by nutrient content. *USDA national nutrient database for standard reference, release 18.* 2004.

When diets supply plenty of protein-rich foods, the human body can synthesize niacin from a precursor, the amino acid tryptophan. It takes about 60 mg of tryptophan to yield about 1 mg of niacin. For example, eggs and milk lack niacin, but they are rich sources of tryptophan that can be converted to the B vitamin.

The niacin content of corn is considerably higher than that of most other vegetables, but the B vitamin is tightly bound to a protein that resists digestion. Thus, people who eat corn as their staple food are prone to develop pellagra. The traditional Mexican diet is corn-based, but pellagra was not a widespread disease in Mexico when it was a major health concern in other parts of the world. Why? The Mexican practice of soaking corn kernels in lime water before using them to prepare tortillas helps free the niacin, enhancing its ability to be absorbed. In the United States, corn products such as hominy and grits are sources of niacin because they have been treated with lime before cooking. Some sources still report niacin intakes in *niacin equivalents* (NE) per day. One NE is equal to 1 mg of niacin.

Dietary Adequacy

pellagra niacin deficiency disease

The adult RDA for niacin is 14 to 16 mg per day.[16,17] According to the Canadian Community Health Survey, Cycle 2.2, in 2004, Canadian adult men and women consumed a mean intake of 46 mg and 34 mg of niacin per day, respectively.[18] People with alcoholism and those with rare disorders that disrupt tryptophan metabolism are generally the only groups at risk of niacin deficiency. Early signs and symptoms of mild niacin deficiency include poor appetite, weight loss, and weakness. If the affected person continues to consume a niacin-deficient diet, the condition worsens and **pellagra** (*peh-lah'-gra* or *peh-lay'-gra*) develops. The classic signs and symptoms of pellagra are dermatitis, diarrhea, dementia, and death—the 4 Ds of pellagra (Fig. 8.25). In the early twentieth century, pellagra was widespread in the southeastern United States (see the introduction of Chapter 2). Today, the disease is rare in Western societies, but it still occurs among impoverished populations in developing countries, particularly in regions of Africa, India, and China.[42]

There have been no reports indicating that the niacin naturally in foods can cause toxicity.[42] The adult UL for niacin (nicotinic acid) is 35 mg per day.[16,17] Physicians may prescribe megadoses of nicotinic acid to treat elevated blood cholesterol levels. However, patients taking such high doses of the vitamin may experience side effects such as facial flushing and even liver damage. The Chapter 8 Highlight discusses the use of niacin supplements to reduce cholesterol levels.

The Mexican practice of soaking corn kernels in lime water before using them to prepare tortillas helps free the niacin, enhancing its ability to be absorbed.

Vitamin B-6

The body requires vitamin B-6 to make a coenzyme needed for amino acid metabolism, including transamination reactions that form nonessential amino acids, and the conversion of the amino acid tryptophan to niacin (see Fig. 7.10 on p. 198). The coenzyme that contains B-6 also helps convert a toxic amino acid, **homocysteine**, to cysteine, a nonessential amino acid (Fig 8.26). If the body lacks vitamin B-6, homocysteine can accumulate in blood and may contribute to cardiovascular disease (see Chapter 6). Folate and vitamin B-12 also participate in homocysteine metabolism.

During red blood cell (RBC) production, the coenzyme participates in the synthesis of heme. *Heme* is the iron-containing portion of **hemoglobin**, the protein in RBCs that transports oxygen. If vitamin B-6 is unavailable for heme synthesis, a type of anemia develops. Vitamin B-6 is also involved in the synthesis of *neurotransmitters*, chemicals that nerves produce to transmit messages.

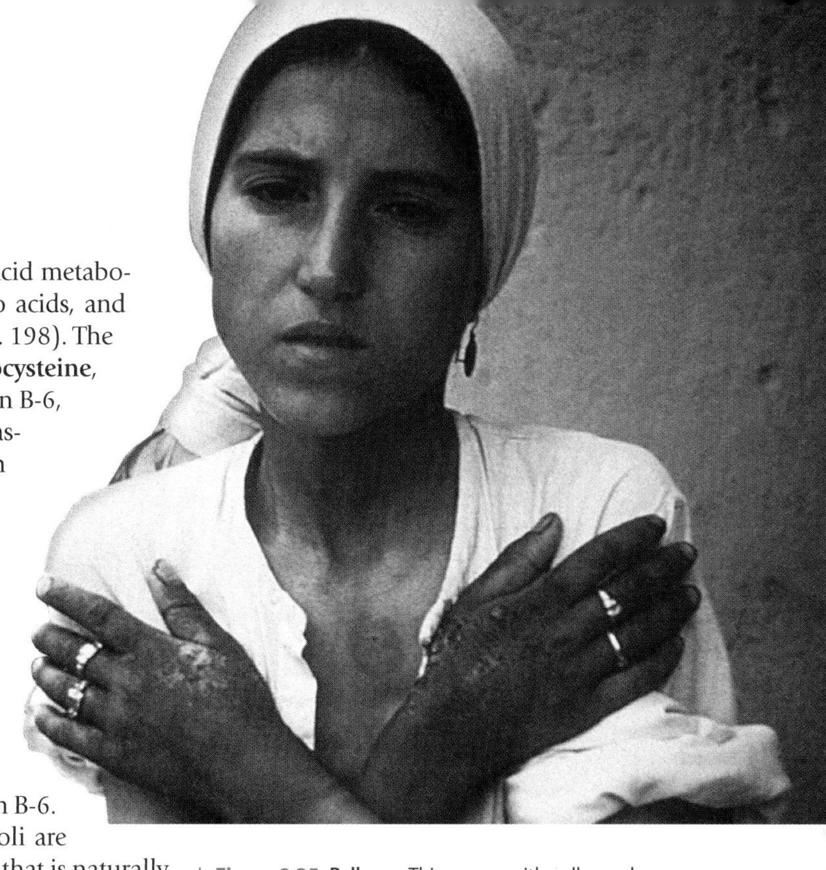

Figure 8.25 Pellagra. This person with pellagra shows one of the classic signs of the niacin deficiency disease—dermatitis, particularly on parts of the body exposed to sun.

Food Sources of Vitamin B-6

Liver, meat, fish, and poultry are among the best dietary sources of vitamin B-6. Additionally, potatoes, bananas, spinach, sweet red peppers, and broccoli are good sources of vitamin B-6. During the refining process, the vitamin B-6 that is naturally in grains is lost, and the nutrient is not added back to the grain products during enrichment. However, many ready-to-eat and cooked cereals have been fortified with the vitamin. Figure 8.27 lists some foods that are major sources of vitamin B-6. During cooking, excessive heat can cause major losses of the vitamin.

Dietary Adequacy

The adult RDAs for vitamin B-6 range from 1.3 to 1.7 mg per day.[16,17] In Canada, the average adult consumes more than the RDA of the vitamin. According to the Canadian Community Health Survey, Cycle 2.2, in 2004, mean daily vitamin B-6 intake for adult Canadian men and women are 2.17 mg and 1.63 mg, respectively.[18] Therefore, cases of vitamin B-6 deficiency are rare, but they can result from alcoholism or genetic conditions that affect vitamin B-6 metabolism. Signs and symptoms of vitamin B-6 deficiency include dermatitis, anemia, convulsions, depression, and confusion.

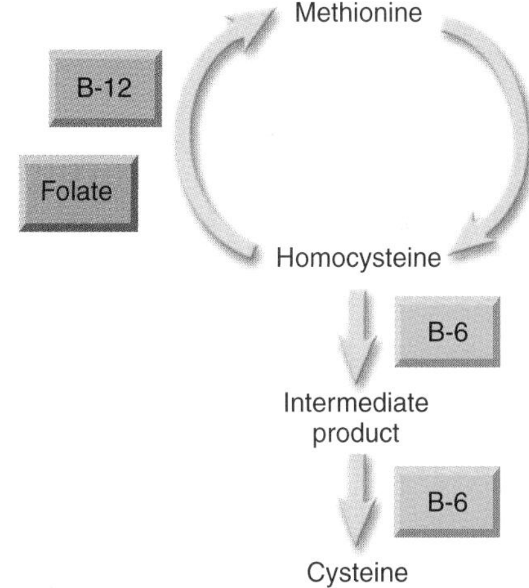

Figure 8.26 Converting homocysteine. Homocysteine can be converted to cysteine, a nonessential amino acid, in reactions that depend on B-6-containing coenzymes. The conversion of homocysteine to the essential amino acid methionine involves vitamins B-12 and folate.

Did You Know?

In the early 1950s, some infants became unusually irritable and developed convulsions after being fed a commercial formula. It was determined that the vitamin B-6 in the formula had been destroyed by excessive heating during the manufacturing process. The convulsions may have resulted from a lack of neurotransmitters in the infants' brains. The babies were effectively treated with vitamin B-6.

homocysteine amino acid that is a toxic by-product of methionine metabolism

hemoglobin iron-containing protein in red blood cells that transports oxygen

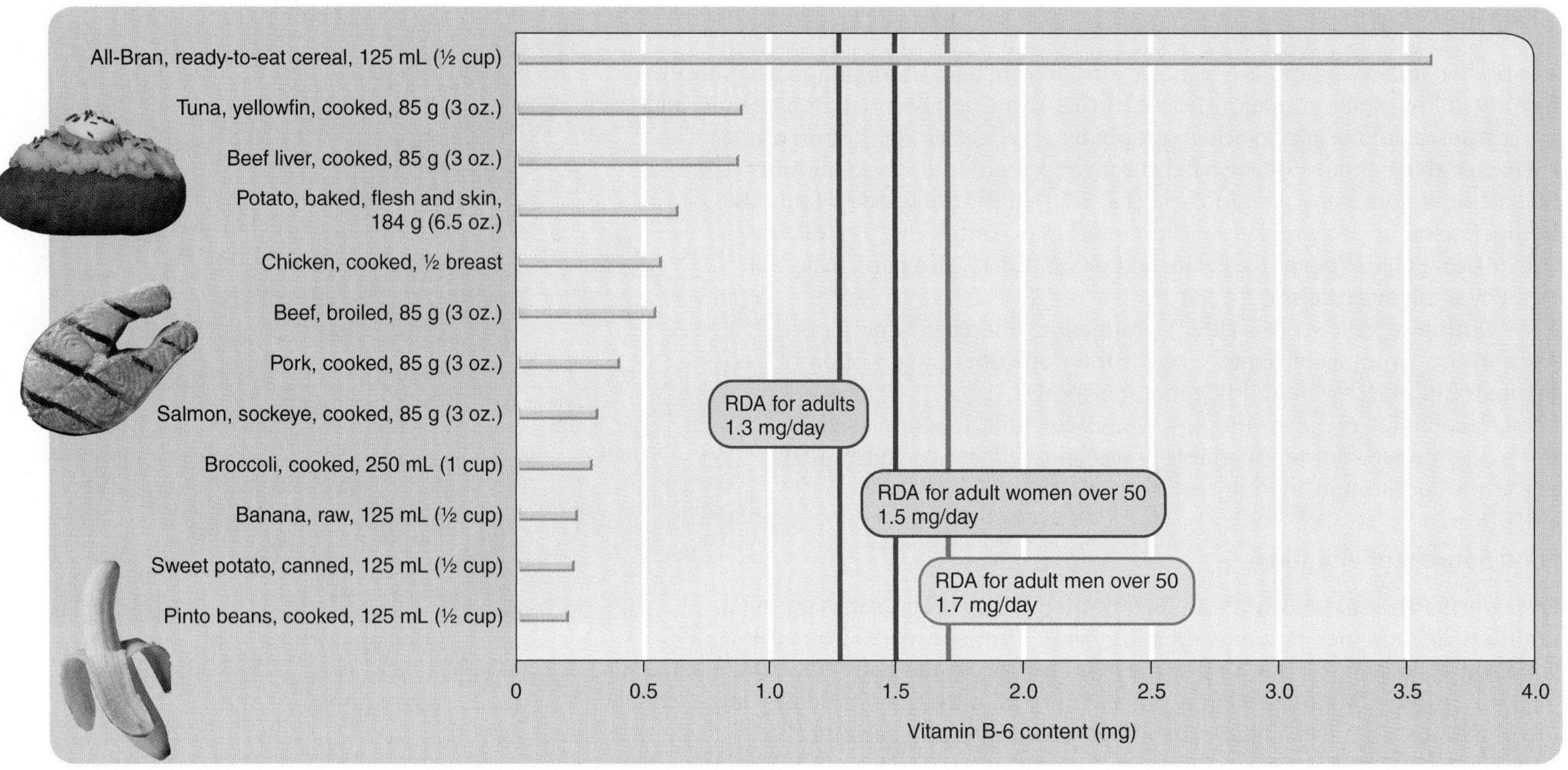

Figure 8.27 Vitamin B-6 Content of Selected Foods.

Source: Data from U.S. Department of Agriculture, Agricultural Research Service, USDA Nutrient Data Laboratory: Vitamin B-6 (mg) content of selected foods by common measure, sorted by nutrient content. *USDA national nutrient database for standard reference, release 18.* 2004.

Meat, fish, and poultry are among the best dietary sources of vitamin B-6.

The adult UL for vitamin B-6 is 100 mg per day.[16,17] Unlike most B vitamins, megadoses of vitamin B-6 are toxic. The Chapter 8 Highlight provides information about vitamin B-6 toxicity.

Folate

Folate is the name for a group of related compounds that includes **folic acid** and **folacin**. Folic acid refers specifically to the synthetic form of the vitamin found in supplements and added to fortify foods. In the body, cells convert all forms of folate to a group of folate-containing coenzymes collectively called **tetrahydrofolic** (*the'-tra-hi-drow-foe-lik*) **acid** or simply **THFA**. THFA participates in many chemical reactions involved in DNA and amino acid metabolism. As cells prepare to divide, they need THFA to synthesize DNA. THFA can also play a role in the conversion of homocysteine to the essential amino acid methionine. Certain roles of folate and vitamin B-12 are interrelated; a deficiency of vitamin B-12 can block the metabolism of folate, resulting in folate deficiency.

Food Sources of Folate

Leafy vegetables, liver, legumes, asparagus, broccoli, and orange juice are naturally good sources of folate. The synthetic folic acid that is used to fortify or enrich food is better absorbed than naturally occurring forms of folate. Thus, enriched grain products, dark green leafy vegetables and fortified cereals are among the richest sources of folate in the Canadian diet.[44]

The folate content of foods may be reported as micrograms of dietary folate equivalents (DFEs). DFE units account for differences in the body's ability to absorb folic acid and natural forms of folate. Figure 8.28 lists the folate content of selected foods in micrograms of DFE.

Folate is extremely susceptible to destruction by heat, oxidation, and ultraviolet light. Food processing and preparation can destroy 50 to 90% of the folate in food. By eating fresh fruits and raw or lightly cooked vegetables, you are likely to obtain most of the foods' folate content.

These foods are naturally good sources of folate.

folic acid and **folacin** forms of folate

tetrahydrofolic acid (THFA) folate coenzyme

Dietary Adequacy

The adult RDA for folate is 400 mcg (DFE) per day.[16,17] Folate deficiency usually results from nutritionally inadequate diets, but excess alcohol consumption and use of certain medications can negatively affect the body's ability to absorb and use folate, resulting in deficiencies of the vitamin. Furthermore, the risk of folate deficiency increases with age, but reasons for the increase are unclear.[45] According to the Canadian Community Health Survey, Cycle 2.2, in 2004, Canadian adult men and women had mean daily folate intakes of 520 mcg and 405 mcg, respectively.[18] This is a significant finding as it suggests that a significant number of adult Canadian women may be consuming below the RDA for folate, putting them at an increased risk of complication during pregnancy.

Initially folate deficiency affects cells that rapidly divide, such as red blood cells (RBCs). Mature RBCs do not have nuclei, and they only live for about four months. Thus, the body must replace old or worn-out RBCs constantly. To keep up with their rapid rate of cell division, the precursor cells that mature into RBCs must actively synthesize DNA. Without folate, RBC precursor cells that reside in bone marrow enlarge, but they cannot divide normally, because they are unable to form new DNA. Bone marrow releases some of the abnormal RBCs (*megaloblasts*) into the bloodstream (Fig. 8.29). This condition, called megaloblastic or macrocytic anemia, is characterized by large, immature RBCs that still have nuclei and do not carry normal amounts of oxygen.

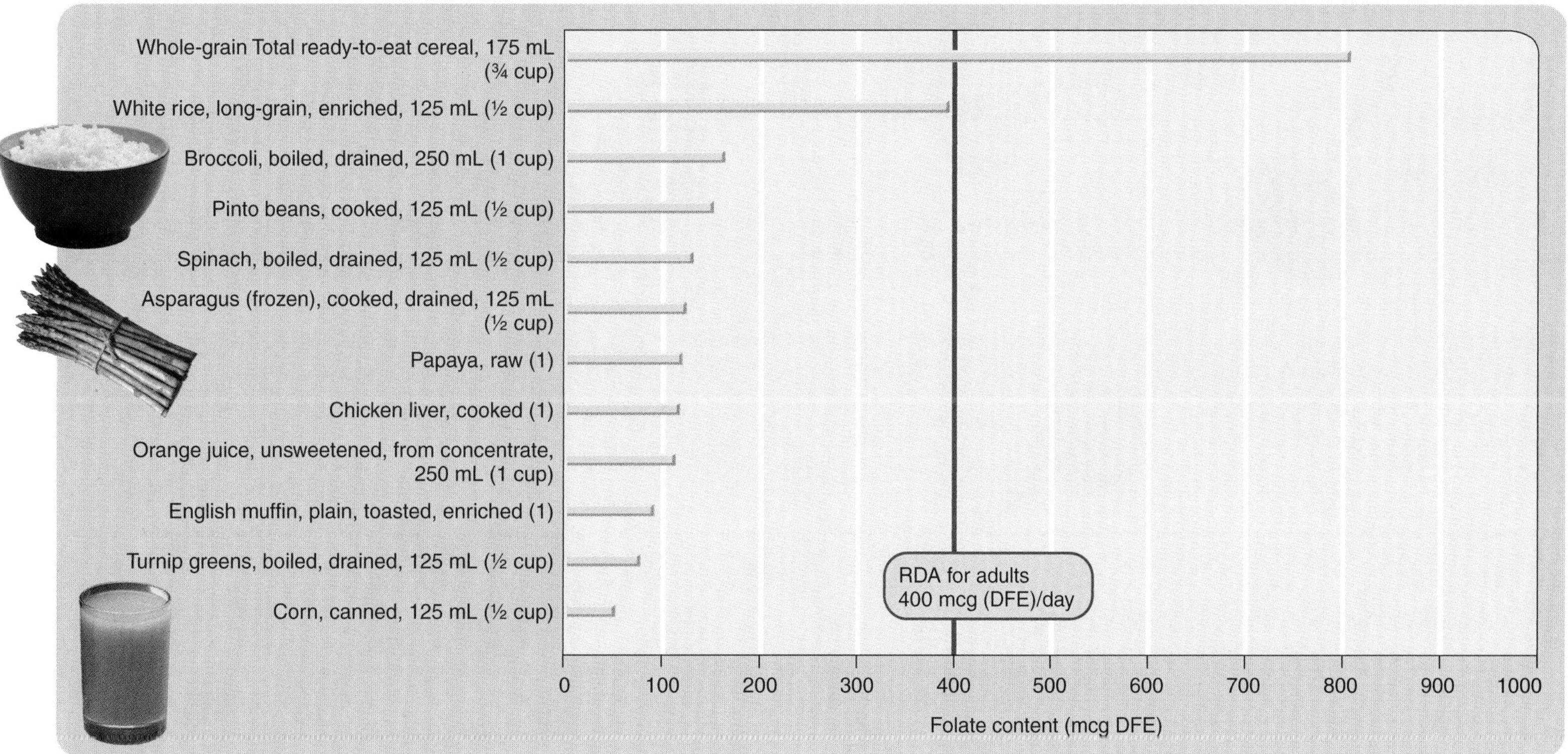

Figure 8.28 **Folate Content of Selected Foods.**

Source: Data from U.S. Department of Agriculture, Agricultural Research Service, USDA Nutrient Data Laboratory: Folate, DFE (μg) content of selected foods by common measure, sorted by nutrient content. *USDA national nutrient database for standard reference, release 18.* 2004.

neural tube embryonic structure that eventually develops into the brain and spinal cord

spina bifida type of neural tube defect in which the spine does not form properly before birth, and it fails to enclose the spinal cord

anencephaly type of neural tube defect in which the brain does not form properly or is missing

intrinsic factor (IF) substance produced in the stomach that facilitates intestinal absorption of vitamin B-12

Because many of folate's metabolic roles are related to those of vitamin B-12, diets that lack either vitamin produce a number of identical deficiency signs and symptoms. For example, being deficient in folate or vitamin B-12 can cause megaloblastic anemia. Therefore, a person with this type of anemia needs further analysis of his or her blood to determine which vitamin is lacking. It is also important to note that folate supplementation may mask vitamin B-12 deficiency, and thus those at risk of vitamin B-12 deficiency should speak with a physician regarding proper vitamin B-12 status testing.

Although the folate naturally in foods does not appear to be toxic, the UL for the synthetic form of the vitamin (folic acid) is 1000 mcg per day.[16,17] The UL was established because taking folic acid supplements can cure not only the anemia that occurs in folate deficiency but also the anemia that is a sign of vitamin B-12 deficiency. Folic acid supplementation, however, does not prevent the serious nervous system damage that accompanies the B-12 deficiency.

Neural Tube Defects A woman's diet before and during pregnancy provides the raw materials for her developing offspring's needs as well as her body's needs. Recommendations for intakes of many nutrients increase during pregnancy. A pregnant woman has an increased requirement for folate because DNA synthesis and cell division take place at a rapid pace during embryonic development.

During the first few weeks after conception, the **neural tube** forms in the human embryo (Fig. 8.30a). This tube eventually develops into the brain and spinal cord. Pregnant women who suffer from folate deficiency have high risk of giving birth to infants with neural tube defects. The two most common neural tube defects are **spina bifida** (*spy′-na bif′-eh-dah*) and **anencephaly** (*an-en-sef′-ah-lee*). Spina bifida occurs when the embryo's spine does not form properly, and it fails to enclose the cord completely. As you

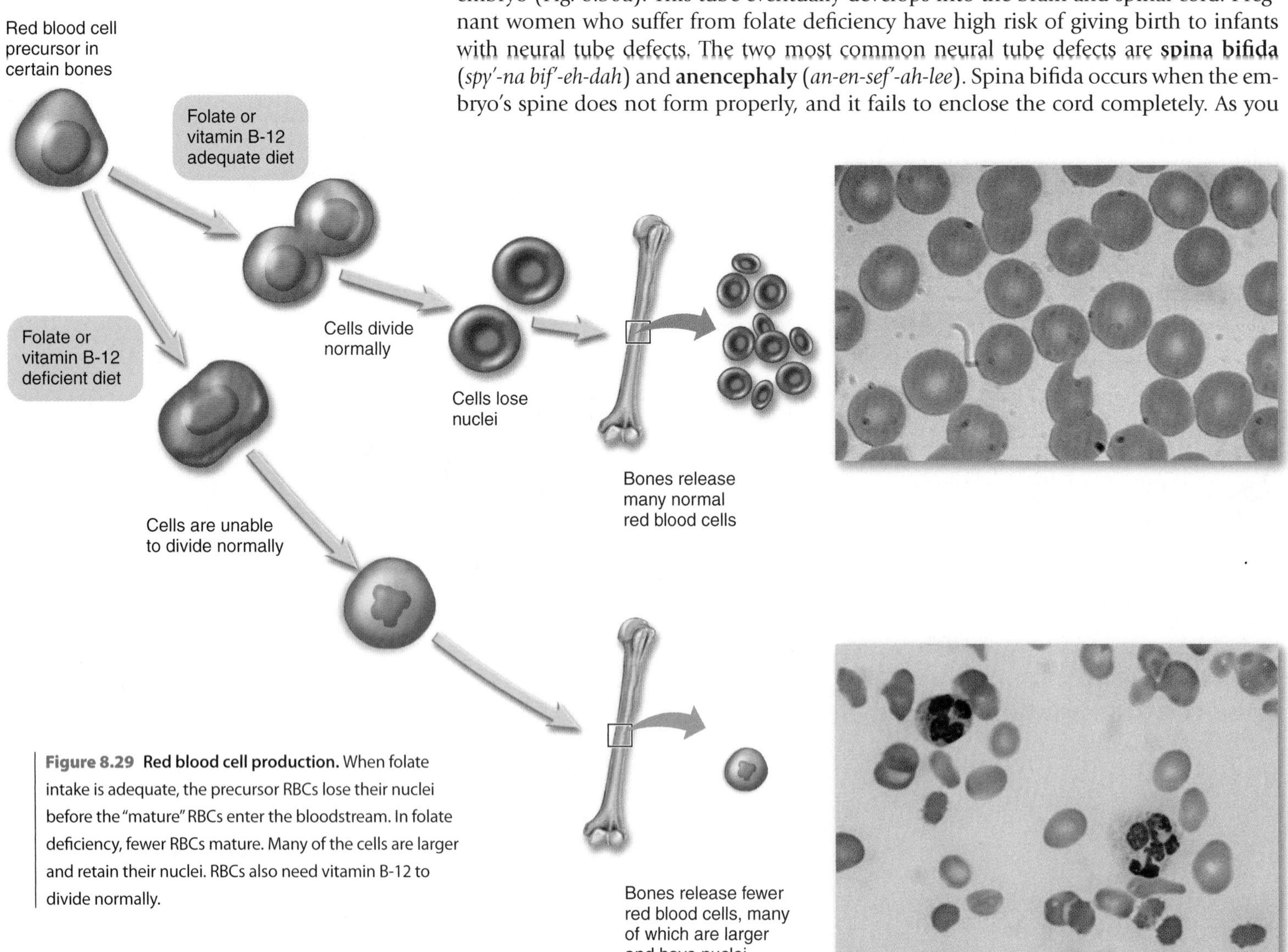

Figure 8.29 Red blood cell production. When folate intake is adequate, the precursor RBCs lose their nuclei before the "mature" RBCs enter the bloodstream. In folate deficiency, fewer RBCs mature. Many of the cells are larger and retain their nuclei. RBCs also need vitamin B-12 to divide normally.

can see in Figure 8.30b, infants with severe spina bifida have a section of their spinal cord or a sac containing some spinal fluid bulging through an opening in their backs. Often, people with spina bifida are unable to use muscles in the lower part of their bodies, and as a result, they cannot walk independently. Infants born with anencephaly have much of their brain malformed or missing, and they usually die shortly after birth.

Because of the importance of folate for optimal embryonic development and growth, in Canada, all wheat flour must be fortified with folic acid. Thus, bread products in Canada are generally good sources of folic acid. For pregnant women, adequate folate status is critical early in pregnancy because the neural tube begins to form about 21 days after conception. This developmental milestone occurs when many women are not even aware they are pregnant.[46]

Because women of child-bearing age may become pregnant at some point, they need to be aware of the association between the lack of folate and neural tube defects. In addition to including folate-rich foods in their diets, young women can prepare for pregnancy by taking a daily multivitamin supplement that contains 400 mcg of synthetic folic acid.[46] Although folic acid intakes have increased among Canadians since the enrichment program began, women of child-bearing age are recommended to consume a folic acid supplement that supplies at least 400 mcg per day.[47]

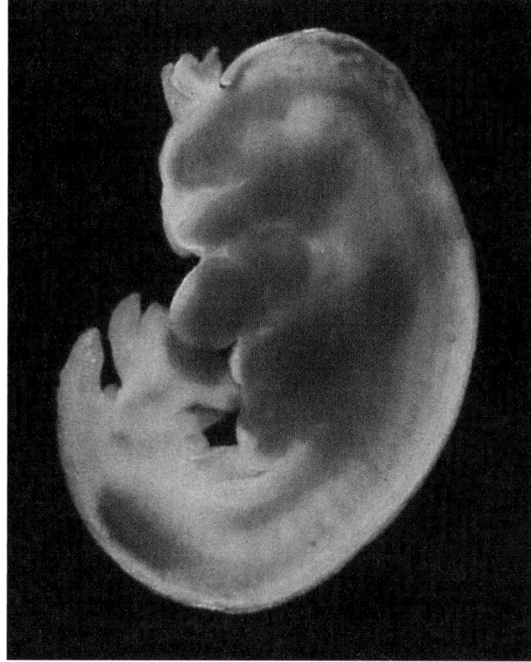

a.

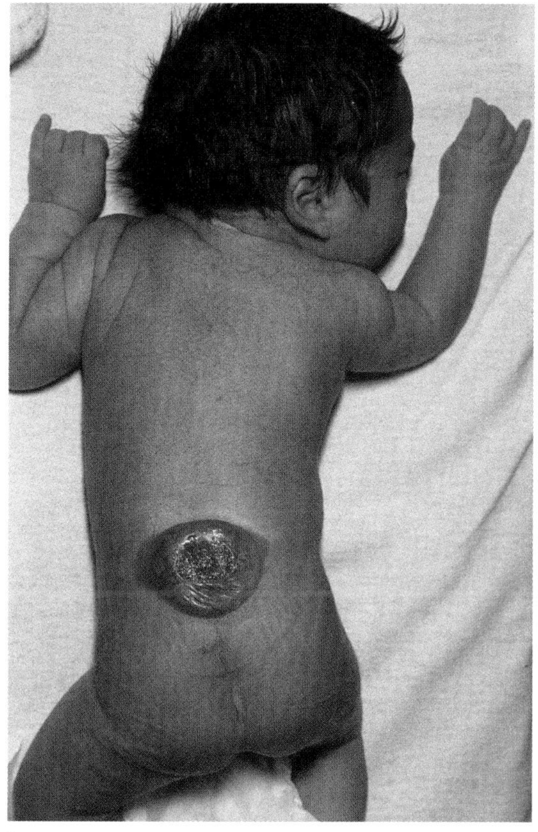

b.

Figure 8.30 Neural tube defect. (*a*) During the first few weeks after conception, the neural tube forms in the human embryo. (*b*) Infants born with severe spina bifida have a section of their spinal cord or a sac containing some spinal fluid bulging through their backs.

Vitamin B-12

Cells require vitamin B-12 to make coenzymes that participate in a variety of cellular processes, including the transfer of CH_3 groups in the metabolism of folate. Vitamin B-12 is also needed to convert folate to coenzyme forms that are needed for metabolic reactions, including DNA synthesis. Vitamin B-12 also participates in homocysteine metabolism.

There is one vital function of vitamin B-12 that does not involve folate—maintaining the *myelin sheaths* that insulate parts of certain nerve cells. Myelin enables the nerves to communicate effectively. Without vitamin B-12, segments of myelin sheath gradually undergo destruction that can lead to paralysis. If a person who is vitamin B-12 deficient does not obtain treatment with the vitamin, he or she can die as a result of the deficiency.

Absorbing the vitamin B-12 that is naturally in food requires a complex series of steps that are unique for a vitamin (Fig. 8.31). The natural vitamin B-12 in food is bound to proteins that prevent its absorption. When the food enters the stomach, the vitamin is released, primarily by the actions of hydrochloric acid and pepsin in gastric juice. Synthetic vitamin B-12 in dietary supplements or fortified foods is not bound to proteins, so it does not need stomach acid and pepsin to release it from foods. Thus, synthetic vitamin B-12 is more readily absorbed than the natural form of the micronutrient.

In the small intestine, vitamin B-12 binds with **intrinsic factor (IF)**, a compound produced by certain stomach cells. Eventually, the vitamin B-12/intrinsic factor complex reaches the ileum of the small intestine where the vitamin is absorbed. After vitamin B-12 enters the bloodstream, the liver removes about 50% of the vitamin and stores much of this amount. A healthy liver has enough vitamin B-12 reserves to last up to 5 years.[48] Therefore, a healthy person who decides to follow a diet that completely lacks vitamin B-12 is not likely to experience signs and symptoms of the vitamin's deficiency disorder for about five years.

Food Sources of Vitamin B-12

Only bacteria, fungi (for example, mushrooms and molds), and algae can synthesize vitamin B-12. Plants do not make vitamin B-12; therefore, we rely almost entirely on animal foods to supply the vitamin naturally. Major sources of vitamin B-12 in the typical Canadian's diet are animal products such as meat, milk and milk products, poultry, fish, shellfish, and eggs.[49] Although liver is not a popular food, it is one of the richest sources of

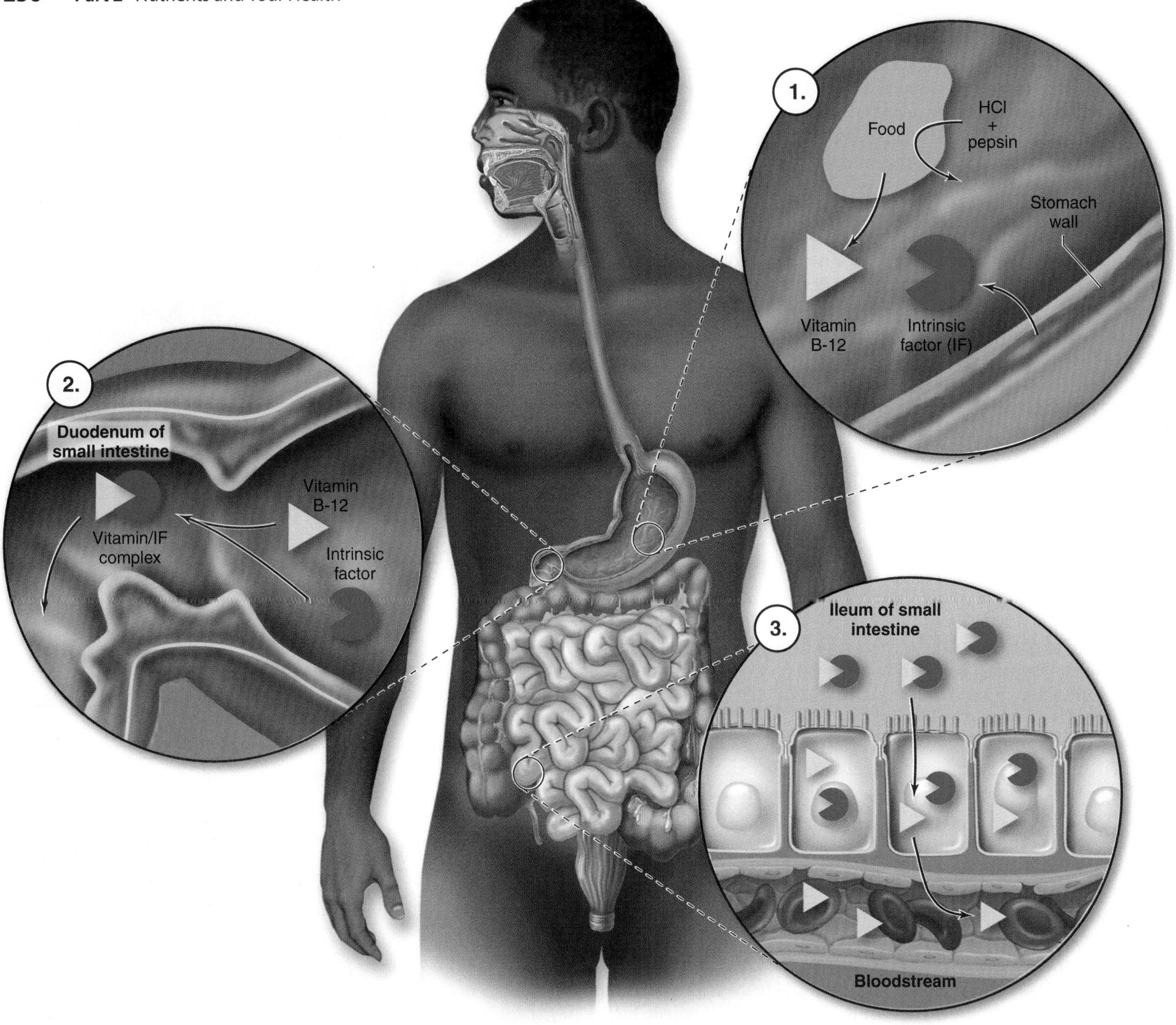

Figure 8.31 Natural vitamin B-12 absorption. Absorbing natural vitamin B-12 from food requires a complex series of steps. The vitamin B-12 in food is bound to proteins that prevent its absorption. When the food enters the stomach, the vitamin is released (1). In the small intestine, vitamin B-12 binds with intrinsic factor (IF), a substance made by the stomach (2). Eventually, the vitamin B-12/intrinsic factor complex reaches the ileum of the small intestine where the vitamin can be absorbed (3).

vitamin B-12. Many soy products, such as soy milk, and ready-to-eat cereals are fortified with synthetic vitamin B-12. Figure 8.32 lists some foods that provide vitamin B-12.

Dietary Adequacy

The adult RDA for vitamin B-12 is 2.4 mcg per day.[16,17] Most Canadians who eat animal products consume more than the RDA.[42] According to the Canadian Community Health Survey, Cycle 2.2, in 2004, Canadian adult men and women had mean daily vitamin B-12 intakes of 5.1 mcg and 3.8 mcg, respectively.[18] No UL has been established for vitamin B-12, because no adverse effects have been observed with excess intake from food or dietary supplements.

Pernicious Anemia Some people have a genetic defect that reduces their stomach's ability to produce intrinsic factor. In these cases, diets may supply adequate amounts of

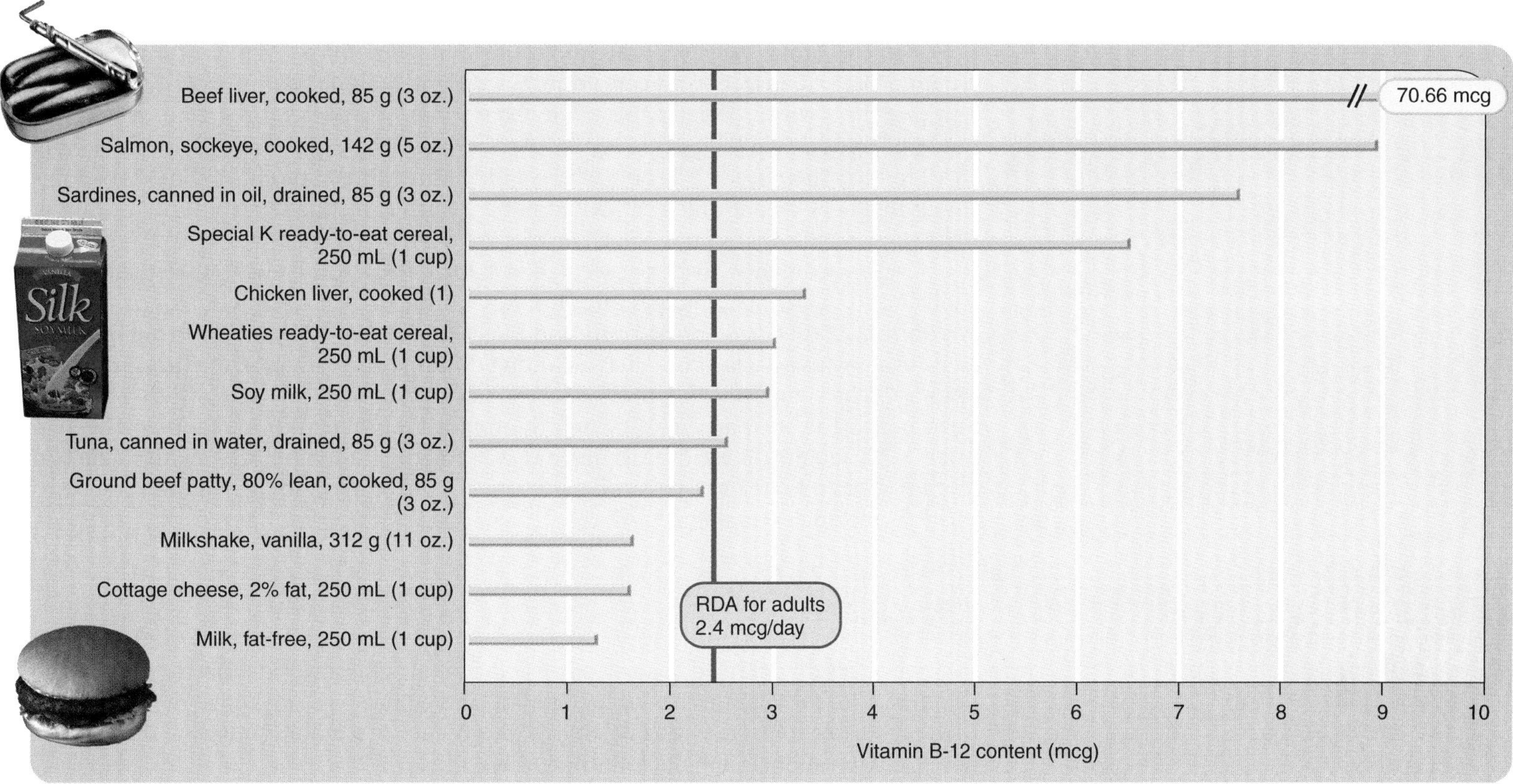

Figure 8.32 **Vitamin B-12 Content of Selected Foods.**

Source: Data from U.S. Department of Agriculture, Agricultural Research Service, USDA Nutrient Data Laboratory: Vitamin B-12 (μg) content of selected foods by common measure, sorted by nutrient content. *USDA national nutrient database for standard reference, release 18.* 2004.

vitamin B-12, but the lack of intrinsic factor prevents most of the micronutrient from being absorbed. Eventually, people who lack intrinsic factor develop a condition called **pernicious** ("deadly") **anemia**. This condition is characterized by nerve damage and megaloblastic RBCs. Other signs and symptoms of pernicious anemia include muscle weakness, sore tongue, memory loss, confusion, difficulty walking and maintaining balance, and numbness and tingling sensations, particularly in the lower extremities. As its name implies, pernicious anemia can lead to death.

pernicious anemia condition associated with vitamin B-12 deficiency that is characterized by nerve damage and megaloblastic RBCs

Intrinsic factor and hydrochloric acid production decline with aging. As a result of these age-related changes, approximately 15% of people who are 60 years of age or older are vitamin B-12 deficient.[50] In addition to advanced age, family history is a risk factor for pernicious anemia.[48] In addition, folate can mask vitamin B-12 deficiency by facilitating the production of healthy red blood cells. Therefore, it is a good idea to have your blood tested to assess vitamin B-12 status as you grow older, and especially if you have a close relative with the disorder.

In most instances, dietitians and other nutrition experts recommend healthy people obtain vitamins by eating a well-balanced, varied diet. However, nearly all cases of pernicious anemia result from defective vitamin B-12 absorption, rather than from inadequate intakes. Therapy usually involves bypassing the need for intestinal absorption by providing monthly vitamin B-12 injections or regular use of nasal gels that contain the micronutrient. In some instances, patients with mild vitamin B-12 deficiencies can take megadoses of dietary supplements that contain the nutrient. According to the results of one study, oral doses that supplied at least 200 times the RDA for vitamin B-12 were effective for treating mild deficiencies of the nutrient.[51] Ingesting such large doses floods the intestinal tract with the vitamin and enables a small amount to be absorbed without the need for intrinsic factor.

ascorbic acid vitamin C

collagen fibrous protein that gives strength to connective tissue

Vegans ("total" vegetarians) avoid eating animal products. Plant foods supply little vitamin B-12, therefore, vegans need to be concerned about their intakes of the nutrient (see the section, "Vegetarianism," in Chapter 7). Even vegetarians who include egg and milk products in their diets (lactoovovegetarians) may not consume enough vitamin B-12 to meet their needs.[48] People who eat little or no animal products should consume foods that have been fortified with vitamin B-12, such as fortified soy milk and cereals, or take supplements that supply the vitamin.

Vegan women who breast-feed their babies need to be aware that their breast milk may contain inadequate amounts of vitamin B-12. Babies who consume only vitamin B-12–deficient breast milk are likely to develop megaloblastic anemia and serious nervous system problems, including diminished brain growth and spinal cord damage. The signs and symptoms of the deficiency are likely to occur during the first few months of life, particularly when the infants' mothers did not supplement their diets with vitamin B-12 during pregnancy. Providing vitamin B-12 to the deficient babies effectively treats the anemia, but some of the damage to the children's nervous systems may be permanent.[52]

Vitamin C

Most animals do not need dietary sources of vitamin C (**ascorbic acid**) because they can synthesize all the vitamin they need. Humans and guinea pigs are among the few species that are unable to make vitamin C due to the absence of a required enzyme in the body, and for these animals, the micronutrient is essential.

Vitamin C absorption occurs in the small intestine. As intakes of the vitamin increase, the amount absorbed decreases. The intestine, for example, absorbs 50% or less of the vitamin when intakes are 1 g or more per day. Additionally, the kidneys increase their excretion of the vitamin in response to high intakes. Therefore, taking megadoses of vitamin C may be wasteful, because such high amounts of the vitamin are not well absorbed and excesses are eliminated in urine.

Functions of Vitamin C

Vitamin C does not function as part of a coenzyme as do B vitamins, but the vitamin serves as a nutrient cofactor that facilitates certain chemical reactions.[3] Vitamin C performs a variety of important cellular functions, primarily by donating electrons to other compounds. In the body, vitamin C has widespread physiological roles; the following sections describe some of the micronutrient's most well-understood functions.

Collagen Synthesis Vitamin C participates in reactions that form and maintain collagen.[54] **Collagen** is a fibrous protein that gives strength to *connective tissue*. Connective tissues, such as bone, cartilage, and tendons, connect and support other structures in the body. During collagen formation, vitamin C helps create numerous cross-connections between the amino acids in collagen that greatly strengthens the connective tissue (Fig. 8.33). If vitamin C is unavailable, the body forms weak connective tissue and is unable to maintain existing collagen. Some of the more obvious signs of scurvy, such

Vitamin C supplements that contain "ester" forms of the vitamin do not provide any advantage over "regular" vitamin C supplements. The ester forms of the supplements are usually more expensive, too.

Did You Know?

Vitamin C plays a role in the absorption of the mineral iron (Fe). Plants are major sources of *non-heme* iron (Fe^{+++}). The small intestine, however, absorbs Fe^{++} more readily than Fe^{+++}. Vitamin C promotes iron absorption by donating an electron to Fe^{+++}, forming Fe^{++} as a result.[53] The vitamin may also form a complex with iron that enhances the body's ability to absorb the mineral. Therefore, adding citrus fruits, broccoli, peppers, or other vitamin C–rich foods to meals can increase absorption of nonheme iron.

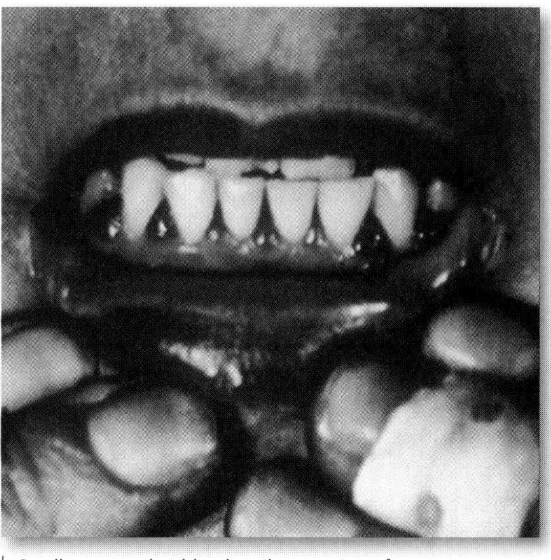

Swollen gums that bleed easily are a sign of scurvy.

as swollen gums that bleed easily, teeth that loosen and fall out of their sockets, skin that bruises easily, and old scars that open, are primarily the result of poorly formed and maintained collagen.

Antioxidant Activity Results of some experiments indicate vitamin C can act as an antioxidant by donating electrons to radicals. Vitamin C also may donate electrons to another antioxidant—vitamin E. Thus, vitamin C recycles vitamin E so that it can regain its antioxidant function. Scientists, however, do not know the extent of vitamin C's antioxidant abilities in the human body. Taking excessive amounts of vitamin C may be harmful, because in high doses, the vitamin has **prooxidant** effects. A prooxidant promotes radical production.

prooxidant substance that promotes free radical production

Other Roles of Vitamin C in the Body Vitamin C plays a role in the body's immune function, and the vitamin is necessary for the synthesis of bile and certain neurotransmitters. Vitamin C is also involved in the production of various hormones, including the "stress hormone" cortisol; adolsterone, a hormone involved in blood pressure regulation; and thyroxin, the thyroid hormone that regulates energy metabolism.

Food Sources of Vitamin C

Plant foods are the best dietary sources of vitamin C. Peppers, citrus fruit, papaya, broccoli, cabbage, and berries contain relatively high amounts of the micronutrient (Figure 8.34). Potatoes and vitamin C–fortified fruit drinks and ready-to-eat cereals also supply vitamin C. Most animal foods are not sources of the micronutrient.

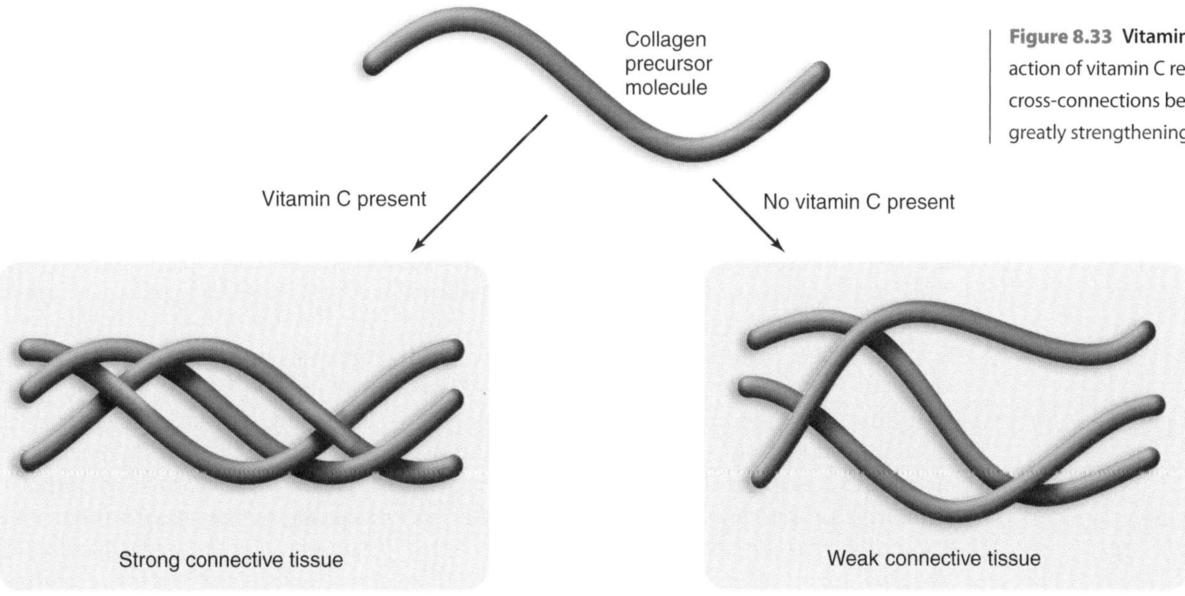

Figure 8.33 Vitamin C and collagen formation. The action of vitamin C results in the formation of numerous cross-connections between the amino acids in collagen, greatly strengthening the connective tissue.

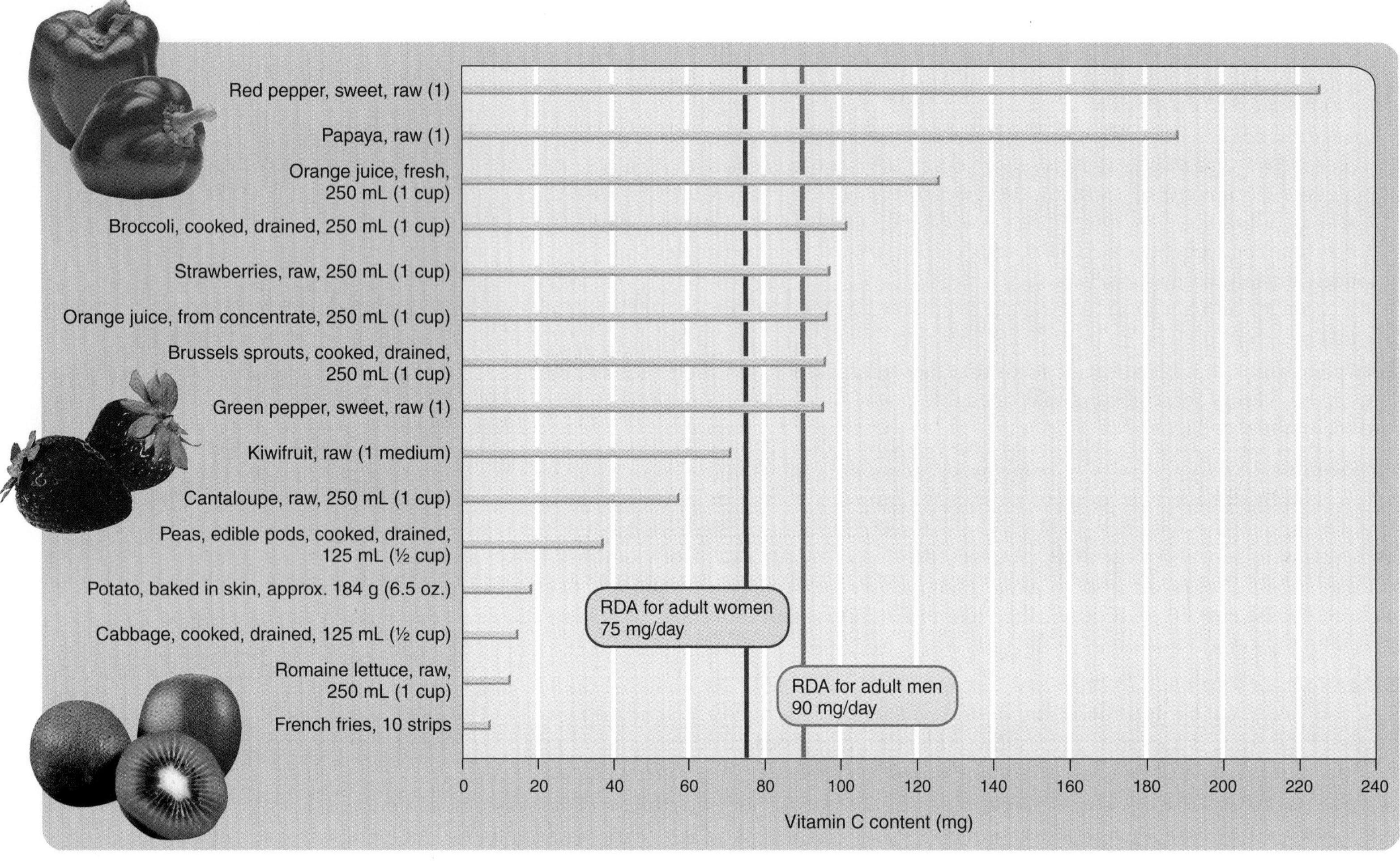

Figure 8.34 Vitamin C Content of Selected Foods.

Source: Data from U.S. Department of Agriculture, Agricultural Research Service, USDA Nutrient Data Laboratory: Vitamin C, total ascorbic acid (mg) content of selected foods by common measure, sorted by nutrient content. *USDA national nutrient database for standard reference, release 18.* 2004.

Vitamin C is very unstable in the presence of heat, oxygen, light, alkaline conditions, and the minerals iron and copper. Storing vitamin C–rich foods in cool conditions, such as in the refrigerator, will help preserve the micronutrient. Because vitamin C is easily lost during cooking, eat raw fruits and vegetables whenever possible.

Dietary Adequacy

The adult RDA for vitamin C is 75 to 90 mg per day, for women and men, respectively.[16,17] Cigarette smokers need to add an extra 35 mg per day to their RDA, because exposure to cigarette smoke increases radical formation in their lungs.[3] According to recommendations of the *Eating Well with Canada's Food Guide*, Canadian adults should consume seven to ten servings from the Vegetables and Fruit group daily.[55] By choosing vitamin C–rich fruits and vegetables, such as those presented in Figure 8.34, healthy people can obtain adequate amounts of vitamin C.

According to the Canadian Community Health Survey, Cycle 2.2, in 2004, Canadian men and women had mean daily vitamin C intakes of 133 mg and 120 mg, respectively.[18] The adult UL for vitamin C is 2000 mg per day.[16,17] When people exceed this amount of the vitamin, gastrointestinal upsets, including diarrhea, often occur.[3] Taking megadoses of vitamin C supplements is wasteful, because the small intestine reduces absorption of the micronutrient when intakes of the vitamin exceed 200 mg per day. Furthermore, when cells are saturated with vitamin C, the excess vitamin and *oxalate*, a by-product of breaking down vitamin C, circulate in the bloodstream. The kidneys filter and eliminate these unnecessary substances in urine. Excess oxalate excretion raises the risk of kidney stones.[56] Therefore, people who are susceptible to develop such stones should avoid consuming vitamin C supplements. The Chapter 8 Highlight provides more information about the value of taking megadoses of vitamin C to prevent or treat colds and other disorders.

Even if you do not regularly eat foods that naturally contain the vitamin or take a vitamin C supplement, you are unlikely to develop a vitamin C deficiency, because most people require less than 10 mg of the vitamin daily to prevent scurvy. A 175-mL (6-oz.) serving of fresh orange juice provides about 60 mg of vitamin C. Additionally, Canadians rarely develop scurvy because vitamin C is added to many processed foods, including fruit and sports drinks and nutrition or power bars. If you would still like to take a vitamin C supplement daily, consider choosing a product that provides 50 to 100 mg of the vitamin in each tablet.

Many kinds of fruits and vegetables are rich sources of vitamin C.

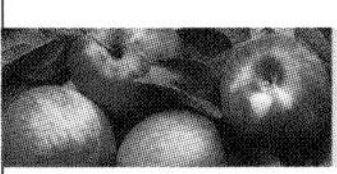

Concept Checkpoint

7. Prepare a table for water-soluble vitamins. For each of these micronutients, indicate its major function in the body, major food sources, deficiency disorder (if it has a specific name), and major signs and symptoms of the deficiency disorder. If the micronutrient is known to be toxic, also indicate major toxicity signs and symptoms. Check your table against the information provided in Table 8.3.

Chapter 8 Highlight
Megadosing on Vitamins

Are you among the millions of Canadians who take vitamin supplements? If your answer is "Yes," why do you use them? Many people take multiple vitamin/mineral supplements as an "insurance policy" in case their diets are not nutritionally adequate. Other people use specific vitamin supplements because they think the practice will result in optimal health. Vitamin supplements are effective for treating people with specific vitamin deficiency diseases, metabolic defects that increase vitamin requirements, and a few other medical conditions. However, scientific evidence generally does not support claims that megadoses of vitamins can prevent or treat everything from grey hair to lung cancer.

How did vitamins earn the reputation of being cure-alls? The fact that a very small amount of a vitamin can prevent or cure the vitamin's deficiency disease provides the foundation for beliefs that these micronutrients are useful for preventing or treating serious chronic diseases. Furthermore, many people think that vitamins are helpful and safe in any amount. When ingested in high doses, however, vitamins and related compounds such as carotenoids often have druglike effects in the body. In some cases, these physiological responses are beneficial, but in other instances, vitamin excesses cause unpleasant and even dangerous side effects. Therefore, people should be just as cautious about using megadoses of vitamins as they need to be when taking medications. This Chapter 8 Highlight focuses on some current scientific evidence regarding the usefulness and safety of using large doses of certain vitamins and related compounds as medications.

Niacin As Medicine?

In Chapter 6, we discussed the association between elevated blood levels of LDL cholesterol and increased risk of cardiovascular disease (CVD), the number one killer of Canadians. Heart disease and stroke are the major forms of CVD. Megadoses of dietary supplements containing nicotinic acid, a form of niacin, can reduce elevated LDL cholesterol levels and increase beneficial HDL cholesterol levels in blood. However, such therapy may have unpleasant side effects, including flushing of the skin, usually on the face and chest; itchy skin; and GI tract upsets, such as nausea and vomiting. High doses of nicotinic acid can also cause liver damage. Some people experience these side effects while taking only 50 mg per day. (The adult RDA for niacin ranges from 14 to 16 mg.) Therefore a physician should supervise the use of niacin megadoses to treat elevated LDL cholesterol levels.

Vitamin B-6 As Medicine?

Popular sources of nutrition information often recommend large doses of vitamin B-6 to treat *premenstrual syndrome (PMS)*, a condition that many women experience a few days before their menstrual period begins, and *carpal tunnel syndrome*, a nerve disorder that affects the wrist. A few studies have been conducted to determine whether taking vitamin B-6 supplements can improve PMS symptoms. Although results of some studies indicated the vitamin can alleviate the discomfort of PMS, the findings have limited value because they were based on poorly designed experiments.[1A] Studies investigating the value of vitamin B-6 supplementation for relieving carpal tunnel syndrome have provided inconsistent results, but generally do not support the use of the micronutrient to treat the disorder.[2A]

Unlike most other B vitamins, vitamin B-6 is toxic in high doses. In the early 1980s, a group of medical researchers described seven adults who developed severe sensory nerve damage after taking high doses of vitamin B-6 daily for extended periods.[3A] Signs and symptoms of vitamin B-6 toxicity included walking difficulties and numbness of the hands and feet. The indications of nerve damage resolved when the affected people stopped using the supplements. Not long after this finding was published, more reports of neurological problems resulting from excessive vitamin B-6 intakes appeared in the medical literature. In most instances, the individuals who developed nerve damage had ingested 500 mg or more of the vitamin daily for two years, or higher doses for shorter periods.[4A] Thus, vitamin B-6 is not recommended for treating PMS, and nutrition experts caution about taking amounts of the vitamin that exceed the UL.

Folic Acid As Medicine?

Earlier in this chapter, we provided evidence supporting the use of folic supplements before and during pregnancy to reduce the risk of neural tube defects in newborns. The following section discusses the use of large doses of folic acid to reduce the risk of cardiovascular disease (CVD) and the decline in cognitive functioning associated with aging and Alzheimer's disease.

Folic Acid and Homocysteine A step in the biochemical pathway that converts methionine to cysteine produces homocysteine, an amino acid that is not used for protein synthesis. Elevated blood homocysteine levels may be a biochemical marker (an indicator in the body) or a risk factor for CVD. After conducting a review of research, a group of scientists concluded folic acid and vitamin B-12 supplementation reduces blood homocysteine levels, slightly lowering the risk of heart disease and stroke, the most common forms of CVD.[5A] Two recent studies to determine whether B vitamin supplementation benefits patients with heart disease had disappointing results. Although taking folic acid along with vitamins B-6 and B-12 lowered the patients' blood homocysteine levels, the practice did not reduce their risk of having another heart attack.[6A,7A] More research is needed to determine whether *healthy* people can reduce their risk of heart disease and other forms of CVD by taking folic acid supplements for long periods.

Elevated blood homocysteine levels may also be a marker or risk factor for Alzheimer's disease.[8A,9A] Alzheimer's disease is characterized by a gradual progressive decline in cognitive functioning, including memory and decision-making skills. There is no cure or effective treatment for the disease. The results of one study suggested a relationship between mild cognitive impairment (an early sign of Alzheimer's disease) and both folate deficiency and high blood levels of homocysteine.[8A] In another study, low intakes of folate, vitamin B-12, and vitamin B-6 were associated with high blood levels of homocysteine and reduced cognitive functioning in aging men.[9A] The results of a pilot study indicated that a combination of folic acid, vitamin B-6, and vitamin B-12 supplements lowers homocysteine levels in blood.[10A] However, more research is needed to determine whether taking supplements that contain these micronutrients can reduce the risk of cognitive decline or slow the progression of Alzheimer's disease.

Vitamin C As Medicine?

In 1970, Nobel prize-winning chemist Dr. Linus Pauling (1901–1994) published *Vitamin C and the Common Cold*. This bestselling book established the popular belief that megadoses of vitamin C could prevent colds. As a result of Pauling's claim, many North Americans take megadoses of the micronutrient when they notice the first cold symptoms.

In the years that followed the publication of *Vitamin C and the Common Cold*, Pauling became more convinced of vitamin C's health benefits. He claimed large doses of vitamin C could battle a variety of diseases including influenza, cancer, and CVD. He even believed the vitamin could slow the aging process. Despite Pauling's impressive credentials in chemistry, conventional nutrition scientists have approached his ideas about vitamin C's health benefits with caution and skepticism.

Can taking vitamin C protect you against infection by cold viruses? The evidence collected from several scientific studies indicates that routine vitamin C supplementation (200 mg or more of the vitamin daily) does not prevent colds in the general population.[11A] However, taking such large doses of the vitamin may reduce the duration of cold symptoms by a day or so. Additionally, vitamin C may reduce the severity of cold symptoms because the micronutrient acts like an antihistamine when taken in very large doses.[12A]

Beyond the Common Cold When LDL cholesterol is oxidized, it is more likely to contribute to atherosclerosis than nonoxidized LDL cholesterol (see Chapter 6). As an antioxidant, vitamin C may reduce the oxidation of LDL cholesterol, lowering the risk of CVD. Well-designed large-scale studies to determine whether vitamin C can help prevent CVD have not provided convincing evidence that the micronutrient reduces the risk of CVD or deaths from the condition.[13A] On the other hand, when scientists analyzed results from nine prospective studies of people using antioxidant supplements (see Chapter 2), they determined that taking 700 mg or more of vitamin C daily may lower the risk of *coronary artery disease (CAD)*, a major form of CVD.[14A] Atherosclerosis takes years and probably decades to result in heart attack, strokes, and other forms of CVD. More research is needed to determine whether long-term vitamin C supplementation can reduce the risk of these serious diseases.

Findings of some observational studies suggest high intake of vitamin C–rich foods may reduce the risk of Alzheimer's disease.[15A] Several studies have examined the benefits of using combinations of antioxidant vitamin supplements, particularly vitamins C and E, to lower the risk of this dreaded disease. In a large study of more than 4500 elderly people, taking vitamin C supplements did not protect against Alzheimer's disease, but using a combination of vitamins C and E reduced the risk of the disease.[16A] Other researchers, however, determined that total dietary or supplemental intakes of vitamin C and/or vitamin E did not delay the development of Alzheimer's disease.[17A,18A]

According to findings of epidemiological studies, people who consume diets containing high amounts of vitamin C-rich fruits and vegetables have lower risk of cancer than people who do not eat much of these foods. However, results of some recent experiments suggest that taking megadoses of vitamin C can damage DNA, which may actually *increase* the likelihood of cancer.[19A]

There is some encouraging scientific evidence that vitamin C and other antioxidants may be useful in treating cancer.[20A] The results of *in vitro* studies indicate that exposing cancerous cells to extremely high amounts of vitamin C can kill many of them while sparing healthy cells.[21A] Because the intestinal tract tightly controls the amount of vitamin C it absorbs, the only way to expose cells to such high amounts of the vitamin is to administer the doses *intravenously* (*intra* = within; *venous* = vein). A review of three cases that involved treating terminally ill cancer patients with intravenous megadoses of vitamin C (15 to 65 g twice/week) presented encouraging findings.[22A] The patients, however, took various herbal and dietary supplements while receiving the experimental vitamin C treatment, so the scientists could not conclude the vitamin was responsible for the improved outcomes.

It is important to note that complex chronic diseases such as CVD, Alzheimer's disease, and cancer do not have simple causes. Therefore, it is unlikely that a particular practice, such as taking vitamin C or any other dietary supplement, will prevent or treat these conditions. Other lifestyle practices besides diet—smoking, obesity, and lack of physical activity—contribute to the development of these diseases. Nevertheless, more research is needed to determine whether vitamin C and other dietary supplements are useful for the prevention and treatment of serious chronic diseases.

Carotenoids As Medicine?

Findings of observational studies suggest an association between eating diets rich in fruits and vegetables and lower risk of certain cancers, heart disease, and *age-related macular degeneration*, a leading cause of blindness in North America. Such diets provide plenty of beta-carotene and other antioxidant carotenoids. Scientists have conducted numerous large-scale studies to determine whether carotenoid supplements provide health benefits. The following sections review some recent research findings regarding the health effects of taking these supplements.

Carotenoid Supplements and Cancer Since the 1970s, results of several epidemiological studies have indicated that diets supplying beta-carotene and other carotenoid-rich fruits and vegetables reduce the risk of cancer, including lung cancer.[23A] However, findings of a large-scale study designed to determine whether beta-carotene supplements could reduce the risk of lung cancer in men failed to show any benefit.[24A] Moreover, researchers halted the study when they determined that taking the supplements actually increased the risk of lung cancer among the participants who were smokers. Beta-carotene supplements are not recommended for the prevention of cancer.[25A] Furthermore, it is not advisable for the general population to supplement their diets with beta-carotene.[12A]

Other carotenoids may hold more promise for reducing the risk of cancer than beta-carotene. For example, data collected from observational studies suggest an association between regular consumption of foods rich in beta-cryptoxanthin and reduced risk of lung cancer.[26A] Additionally, diets that supply high amounts of *lycopene*, the red pigment in watermelon, tomatoes, and other fruits, may reduce the risk of prostate cancer. (The prostate is a male reproductive system organ.) Results of a large-scale study, however, were disappointing—eating lycopene-rich diets did not reduce the risk of prostate cancer.[27A] As is often the case, more research is needed to determine if consuming a particular carotenoid, other than beta-carotene, or a mixture of these compounds can lower the risk of certain cancers.

Carotenoid Supplements and CVD Findings from observational studies suggest that high intakes of fresh fruits and vegetables reduce the risk of CVD. Results of clinical studies, however, do not provide support for taking beta-carotene supplements to reduce the risk of heart disease and stroke, major forms of CVD.[28A] Nevertheless, more research is needed to determine whether other carotenoids, such as lycopene and betacryptoxanthin, protect against CVD.[29A]

Carotenoid Supplements and AMD Age-related macular degeneration (AMD) is a leading cause of vision loss among North American adults over 60 years of age.[30A] The disease is associated with changes in the *macula*, the region within the eye that provides the most detailed central vision (Fig. 8.A). When the macula is damaged, objects appear to be distorted as in the grid shown in Figure 8.B. Major risk factors for AMD are genetics, smoking, and advanced age, but diet also plays a role in the development of the condition.

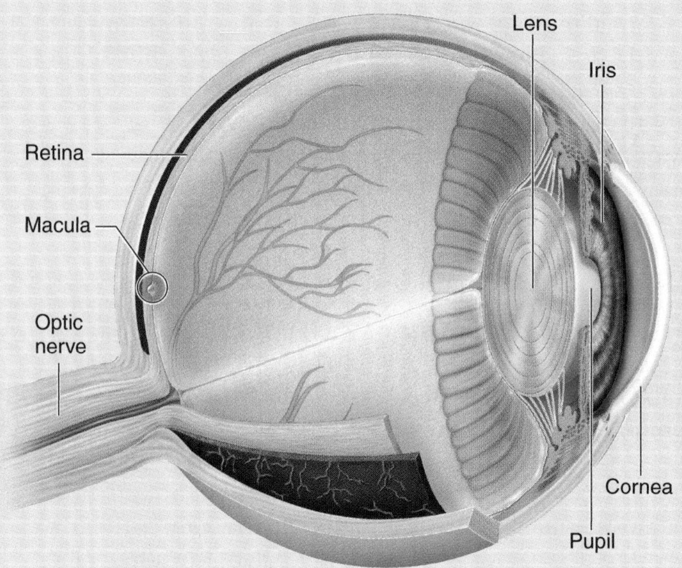

Figure 8.A The macula. The macula is the region within the eye that provides the most detailed central vision.

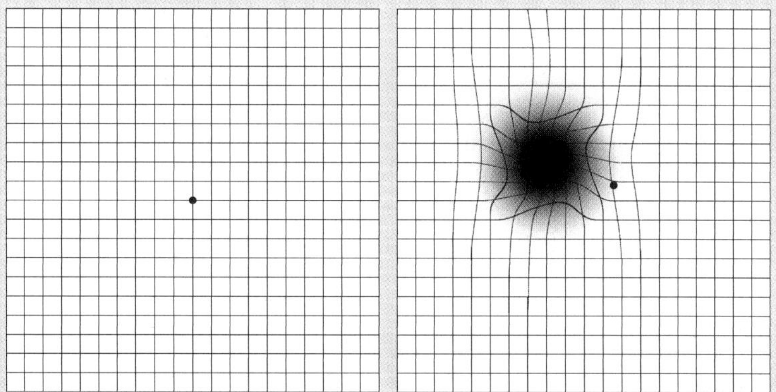

Figure 8.B Visual effect of macular degeneration. The appearance of this grid illustrates the visual distortion that results from macular degeneration. (*left*) Appearance of grid when a person has normal vision. (*right*) How the grid appears to a person with age-related macular degeneration (AMD).

The macula contains the carotenoids lutein and zeaxanthin. According to data from epidemiological studies, diets supplying high amounts of carotenoids (beta-carotene, lutein, and zeaxanthin) may lower the risk of AMD.[31A,32A,33A] In the Age-Related Eye Disease Study (AREDS), patients who already had AMD benefited from taking dietary supplements that contained vitamins C and E, beta-carotene, and the mineral zinc.[33A] However, there is no clear scientific evidence that taking antioxidant supplements prevents healthy people from developing AMD.[34A] Additionally, the long-term use of these supplements could be harmful.

Vitamin E as Medicine?

In the early 1980s, epidemiological reports indicated that populations who ate vitamin E–rich diets had lower risk of heart disease than groups who ate diets that did not contain high amounts of the micronutrient. Additionally, results of other studies suggested that vitamin E might reduce the risk of cancer, particularly lung cancer in smokers. Soon more good news about vitamin E appeared in the medical literature. Some researchers promoted the use of vitamin E megadoses to slow the decline in mental functioning that is associated with Alzheimer's disease. Not surprisingly, sales of vitamin E supplements increased dramatically between 1987 and 2000.[35A]

Over the past few years, the scientific community's enthusiasm for using high doses of vitamin E supplements has subsided considerably. Major long-term trials have failed to show that high intakes of vitamin E can reduce the risk of heart attacks.[14A,36A,37A] Additionally, an analysis of results collected from several studies found that large doses of vitamin E did not reduce the risk of cancer,[37A] including lung cancer;[38A] or macular degeneration.[39A,40A] Vitamin E supplementation was not useful for treating people with signs of *mild cognitive impairment*, a condition characterized by declining cognitive abilities that can progress to Alzheimer's disease.[16A] Moreover, taking dietary supplements containing the alpha-tocopherol form of the vitamin did not lower the likelihood of developing Alzheimer's disease.[41A]

Did scientists *prove* vitamin E supplements are useless or "bad"? No. Vitamin E has several forms, and it is possible that the alpha-tocopherol form of vitamin E that is typically in supplements does not provide druglike effects on the body. More research is needed to determine whether taking supplements containing mixed tocopherols can be recommended to prevent or treat certain chronic diseases.

Some Final Thoughts

According to many dietitians and physicians, people do not need to be discouraged from taking vitamin supplements unless there is strong evidence to indicate the practice is harmful, such as smokers who use beta-carotene supplements.[42A] However, for healthy Canadian adults who eat a balanced diet, these products are frequently an unnecessary cost and likely provide no additional health benefit. Although the health benefits of vitamin supplementation remain uncertain, there is more consistent evidence that a diet high in fruits, vegetables, and legumes has important benefits; other constituents besides vitamins may account for the benefits of such diets.

Consuming a wide variety of vitamins, antioxidants, and phytochemicals in their natural states and concentrations (in foods) may be the most effective way to lower your risk of CVD, cancer, and many other serious chronic diseases. Why? These substances probably work together to enhance health, and isolating them from their natural sources or synthesizing and concentrating them into supplements may reduce their usefulness and increase their risks.[43A] Therefore, dietitians recommend that you consume seven to ten servings of various vegetables and fruit per day rather than take antioxidant or phytochemical supplements.

Nutrition experts tend to emphasize the importance of combining a nutritious diet with regular exercise for achieving and maintaining good health. However, an overwhelming amount of scientific evidence links tobacco use to several forms of cancer, heart disease, AMD, and other serious chronic conditions. If you smoke tobacco, quitting may have a greater beneficial impact on your long-term health than improving your diet or increasing your physical activity level while still continuing tobacco use.

References for Chapter 8 Highlight

1A. Dickerson LM and others: Premenstrual syndrome. *American Family Physician* 67:1743, 2003.

2A. Aufiero E and others: Pyridoxine hydrochloride treatment of carpal tunnel syndrome: A review. *Nutrition Reviews* 62:96, 2004.

3A. Schaumburg H and others: Sensory neuropathy from pyridoxine abuse. A new megavitamin syndrome. *New England Journal of Medicine* 309:445, 1983.

4A. Bendich A: The potential for dietary supplements to reduce premenstrual syndrome (PMS) symptoms. *Journal of the American College of Nutrition* 19:3, 2000.

5A. B-Vitamin Treatment Trialists' Collaboration: Homocysteinelowering trials for prevention of cardiovascular events: A review of the design and power of the large randomized trials. *American Heart Journal* 151:282, 2006.

6A. The Heart Outcomes Prevention Evaluation (HOPE) 2 Investigators: Homocysteine lowering with folic acid and B vitamins in vascular disease. *The New England Journal of Medicine* 345: March 12 [E-pub ahead of print], 2006.

7A. Bønaa KH and others: Homocysteine lowering and cardiovascular events after acute myocardial infarction. *The New England Journal of Medicine* 345: March 12 [E-pub ahead of print], 2006.

8A. Quadri P and others: Homocysteine, folate, and vitamin B-12 in mild cognitive impairment, Alzheimer disease, and vascular dementia. *American Journal of Clinical Nutrition* 80:114, 2004.

9A. Tucker KL and others: High homocysteine and low B vitamins predict cognitive decline in aging men: The Veterans Affairs Normative Aging Study. *American Journal of Clinical Nutrition* 82:627, 2005.

10A. Aisen PS and others: A pilot study of vitamins to lower plasma homocysteine levels in Alzheimer disease. *American Journal of Geriatric Psychiatry* 11:246, 2003.

11A. Douglas RM and others: Vitamin C for preventing and treating the common cold. *Cochrane Database Systematic Review* 18:CD000980, 2004.

12A. Food and Nutrition Board: Dietary Reference Intakes for vitamin C, vitamin E, selenium, and carotenoids. Washington, DC: National Academy Press, 2000.

13A. Duvall WL: Endothelial dysfunction and antioxidants. *The Mount Sinai Journal of Medicine* 72:71, 2005.

14A. Knekt T and others: Antioxidant vitamins and coronary heart disease risk: A pooled analysis of 9 cohorts. *American Journal of Clinical Nutrition* 80:1508, 2004.

15A. Engelhart MJ and others: Dietary intake of antioxidants and risk of Alzheimer disease. *Journal of the American Medical Association* 287:3223, 2002.

16A. Zandi PP and others: Reduced risk of Alzheimer disease in users of antioxidant vitamin supplements: The Cache County Study. *Archives of Neurology* 61:82, 2004.

17A. Fillenbaum GG and others: Dementia and Alzheimer's disease in community-dwelling elders taking vitamin C and/or vitamin E. *Annals of Pharmacotherapy* 39:2009, 2005.

18A. Luchsinger JA and others: Antioxidant vitamin intake and risk of Alzheimer disease. *Archives of Neurology* 60(2):203, 2003.

19A. Lee KW and others: Vitamin C and cancer chemoprevention: Reappraisal. *American Journal of Clinical Nutrition* 78:1074, 2003.

20A. Golde DW: Vitamin C in cancer. *Integrative Cancer Therapies* 2:158, 2003.

21A. Chen Q and others: Pharmacologic ascorbic acid concentrations selectively kill cancer cells: Action as a pro-drug to deliver hydrogen peroxide to tissues. *Proceedings of the National Academy of Sciences of the United States* 102:13604, 2005.

22A. Padayatty SJ and others: Intravenously administered vitamin C as cancer therapy: Three cases. *Canadian Medical Association Journal* 174:937, 2006.

23A. Holick CN and others: Dietary carotenoids, serum betacarotene, and retinol and the risk of lung cancer in the alphatocopherol, beta-carotene cohort study. *American Journal of Epidemiology* 156:536, 2002.

24A. The ATBC Study Group: Incidence of cancer and mortality following α–tocopherol and β–carotene supplementation. *Journal of the American Medical Association* 290:476, 2003.

25A. The Alpha-Tocopherol, Beta-Carotene Cancer Prevention Study Group: The effect of vitamin E and beta-carotene on the incidence of lung cancer and other cancers in male smokers. *The New England Journal of Medicine* 330:1029, 1994.

26A. Yuan J-M and others: Dietary cryptoxanthin and reduced risk of lung cancer: The Singapore Chinese Health Study. *Cancer Epidemiology, Biomarkers, & Prevention* 12:890, 2003.

27A. Kirsh VA and others: A prospective study of lycopene and tomato product intake and risk of prostate cancer. *Cancer Epidemiology, Biomarkers, & Prevention* 15:92, 2006.

28A. Asplund K: Antioxidant vitamins in the prevention of cardiovascular disease: A systematic review. *Journal of Internal Medicine* 251:372, 2002.

29A. Sesso HD: Carotenoids and cardiovascular disease: What research gaps remain? *Current Opinion in Lipidology* 17:11, 2006.

30A. National Eye Institute, National Institutes of Health: *Agerelated macular degeneration: What you should know.* Updated 2005. www.nei.nih.gov/health/maculardegen/armd_facts.asp Accessed: April 23, 2006

31A. Gale CR and others: Lutein and zeaxanthin status and risk of age-related macular degeneration. *Investigative Ophthalmology & Visual Science* 44:2461, 2003.

32A. van Leeuwen R and others: Dietary intake of antioxidants and risk of age-related macular degeneration. *Journal of the American Medical Association* 294:3101, 2005.

33A. Bylsma GW, Guymer RH: Treatment of age-related macular degeneration. *Clinical and Experimental Optometry* 88:322, 2005.

34A. A feast for the eyes: Nutrition for good vision. *University of California, Berkeley Wellness Letter*, p. 1, December 2005.

35A. Ford ES and others: Brief communication: The prevalence of high intakes of vitamin E and the use of supplements among U.S. adults. *Annals of Internal Medicine* 143:116, 2005.

36A. Eidelman RS and others: Randomized trials of vitamin E in the treatment and prevention of cardiovascular disease. *Archives of Internal Medicine* 164:1552, 2004.

37A. Lee IM and others: Vitamin E in the primary prevention of cardiovascular disease and cancer: The Women's Health Study: A randomized controlled trial. *Journal of the American Medical Association* 294:56, 2005.

38A. Cho E and others: Intakes of vitamins A, C, and E and folate and multivitamins and lung cancer: A pooled analysis of 8 prospective studies. *International Cancer Journal* 118:970, 2006.

39A. Vitamin E gets an F. Research linking high doses of vitamin E to heart failure is causing new worries about the AREDS vitamins for macular degeneration. *Harvard Health Letter*, p. 6, June 2005.

40A. Taylor HR and others: Vitamin E supplementation and macular degeneration: Randomized controlled trial. *British Medical Journal* 325:11, 2002.

41A. Morris MC and others: Relation of the tocopherol forms to incident Alzheimer disease and to cognitive change. *American Journal of Clinical Nutrition* 81:508, 2005.

42A. U.S. Preventive Services Task Force: *Routine vitamin supplementation to prevent cancer and cardiovascular disease: Recommendations and rationale*. Agency for Healthcare Research and Quality, Rockville, MD, June 2003. www.ahrq.gov/clinic/uspstf/uspsvita.htm. Accessed: April 9, 2006.

43A. Liu RH: Health benefits of fruit and vegetables are from additive and synergistic combinations of phytochemicals. *American Journal of Clinical Nutrition* 78:517S, 2003.

SUMMARY

Vitamins are organic compounds that the body cannot synthesize or make enough of to maintain good health, naturally occur in commonly eaten foods, cause deficiency disease when they are missing from diets, and restore good health when added back to the diet. Foods generally contain much smaller amounts of vitamins than macronutrients.

Vitamins play numerous roles in the body, and each vitamin generally has more than one function. In general, vitamins regulate a variety of body processes, including those involved in cell division and development as well as the growth and maintenance of tissues. Vitamins, however, are not a source of energy, because cells do not metabolize them for energy. Most vitamins have more than one chemical form that functions in the body. Additionally some vitamins have precursors or provitamins that do not function as vitamins until the body converts them into active forms.

Oxidation reactions can form a radical, a substance with an unpaired electron. Radicals are highly reactive, and they damage or destroy molecules by removing electrons from them. Many medical researchers suspect excess oxidation is responsible for promoting chemical changes in cells that ultimately lead to heart attack, stroke, cancer, Alzheimer's disease, and even the aging process. Cells normally regulate oxidation reactions by using antioxidants such as vitamin E.

Vitamins A, D, E, and K are fat-soluble vitamins; thiamin, riboflavin, niacin, vitamin B-6, pantothenic acid, folate, biotin, vitamin B-12, choline, and vitamin C are water-soluble vitamins. The body generally has more difficulty eliminating excess of fat-soluble vitamins than water-soluble vitamins. As a result, the body stores extra fat-soluble vitamins. Over time, these vitamins can accumulate and cause toxicity. Water-soluble vitamins are generally not as toxic as fat-soluble vitamins.

The enrichment program specifies amounts of thiamin, riboflavin, niacin, and folic acid and the mineral iron that manufacturers must add to their refined flour and other milled grain products. However, enrichment does not replace the vitamin E, vitamin B-6, potassium, magnesium, several other micronutrients, and fibre that were naturally in the unrefined grains. Fortification involves the addition of one or more vitamins (and/or other nutrients) to a wide array of commonly eaten foods during manufacturing. The vitamins that are added may or may not be in the food naturally.

Vitamin deficiency disorders generally result from inadequate diets or conditions that increase the body's requirements for vitamins, such as reduced intestinal absorption or higher than normal excretion of the micronutrients. Although severe vitamin deficiencies are uncommon in Canada, certain segments of the population, particularly alcoholics, elderly persons, and patients who are hospitalized for lengthy periods, are at risk of vitamin deficiencies. The chances of developing a vitamin deficiency disease increases when the diet consistently lacks the micronutrient and levels of the nutrient in the body become depleted.

Most commonly eaten foods do not contain toxic levels of vitamins. Vitamin toxicity is most likely to occur in people who take megadoses of vitamin supplements or consume large amounts of vitamin-fortified foods regularly. A diet that contains adequate amounts of a wide variety of foods, including minimally processed fruits, vegetables, and whole-grain breads and cereals, can help supply the vitamin needs of overall healthy people.

Vitamin A is involved in vision, immune function, and cell development. The vitamin A precursor, beta-carotene, functions as an antioxidant. Dietary sources of preformed vitamin A include liver, fish, and fish oils; provitamin A carotenoids are especially plentiful in dark green and orange fruits and vegetables. Excess vitamin A can be quite toxic and cause birth defects when taken during pregnancy.

Vitamin D is both a hormone and a vitamin. Exposure to sunlight enables human skin to synthesize a precursor of the vitamin from a cholesterol-like substance. A few foods, including fatty fish and fortified milk, are dietary sources of the vitamin. Vitamin D helps regulate the level of blood calcium by increasing calcium absorption from the intestine. Infants and children who do not obtain enough vitamin D may develop rickets, and adults with inadequate amounts of the vitamin in their bodies develop osteomalacia. Older people and breast-fed infants often need a supplemental source of the vitamin. Excess intakes of vitamin D can cause the body to deposit calcium in soft tissues.

Vitamin E functions primarily as an antioxidant. By donating electrons to electron-seeking compounds, vitamin E neutralizes them. This effect shields cell membranes and red blood cells from breakdown. Plant oils and products made from these oils are generally rich sources of vitamin E.

Thiamin, riboflavin, and niacin play key roles as part of coenzymes in energy-yielding reactions. These water-soluble vitamins help cells metabolize carbohydrates, fats, and proteins. Enriched grain products are common sources of all three of the vitamins. Beriberi is the severe thiamin deficiency disease; pellagra results from a severe lack of niacin. Excess intakes of niacin can cause toxicity.

Vitamin B-6 is involved in protein metabolism, especially in synthesizing nonessential amino acids. The vitamin also participates in the synthesis of neurotransmitters and the metabolism of homocysteine. Healthy people can obtain enough vitamin B-6 by eating a varied diet that contains animal foods and rich plant sources of the micronutrient. High doses of vitamin B-6 should be avoided because the vitamin can cause nervous system damage.

Folate plays important roles in DNA synthesis and homocysteine metabolism. Rich food sources of folate are leafy vegetables, organ meats, and orange juice. Signs of folate deficiency include megaloblastic anemia. Pregnancy increases the body's needs for folate; a deficiency during the first month of pregnancy can result in neural tube defects in offspring. Women of child-bearing age can meet the RDA for the vitamin by taking dietary supplements that contain synthetic folic acid. Excess folate in the diet can mask a vitamin B-12 deficiency.

The body needs vitamin B-12 to metabolize folate and homocysteine, and maintain the insulation surrounding nerves. Although vitamin B-12 does not occur naturally in plant foods, the vitamin is in animal foods and products that have been fortified with the micro-nutrient. A deficiency of vitamin B-12 results in pernicious anemia.

The body uses vitamin C to synthesize and maintain collagen, a major protein in connective tissue. Vitamin C also functions as an antioxidant. Fresh fruits and vegetables, especially citrus fruits, are generally good sources of the micronutrient. Because vitamin C is readily lost in cooking, diets should emphasize fresh or lightly cooked fruits and vegetables. Smoking increases the body's requirement for vitamin C. Scurvy is the vitamin C deficiency disease. Excess vitamin C may cause diarrhea and increase the risk of kidney stones in some people.

Recipe for Healthy Living

Stir-Fried Vegetable Medley

"Eat your vegetables!" Does this order bring back some not-so-fond dinnertime memories? If you're like many Canadians, cooked vegetables were not high on your list of favourite foods when you were a child. Corn on the cob was fun to eat, but you may have picked at your peas and carrots, and refused to eat broccoli unless it was smothered in a gooey cheese sauce, and you probably drew a "line in the sand" when offered brussels sprouts. Now that you've read Chapter 8, you should appreciate the nutritional contribution that a wide variety of colourful vegetables can make to your diet. Your parents told the truth when they said, "Vegetables are good for you."

This vegetable medley can be the foundation of a vegetarian meal or colourful accompaniment to main dishes. If you use fresh vegetables, wash them in cool water and drain on paper towels before cutting them into bite-size pieces. If you use frozen vegetables, add them directly to the hot oil, without thawing them first. Be careful because ice from the vegetables can cause hot oil to spatter.

Your goal is to heat the vegetables in a small amount of hot oil only until they are still colourful and crisp—about four to eight minutes. Add the quicker cooking vegetables (for example, zucchini) last, so they don't overcook. Use a slotted spoon to drain oil from vegetables and serve immediately.

This recipe (without rice or noodles) makes about four ½-cup servings. Each serving supplies approximately 123 kcal, 3 g protein, 7 g fat, 3 g fibre, 50 mg vitamin C, 53 mcg folate, 173 RAE vitamin A, and 4 mg vitamin E.

INGREDIENTS:

15 mL (1 Tbsp) soy sauce
30 mL (2 Tbsp) water
15 mL (1 Tbsp) brown sugar
⅛ tsp ground black pepper
30 mL (2 Tbsp) vegetable oil
1 large garlic clove, minced
125 mL (½ cup) onions, sliced
250 mL (1 cup) asparagus, cut into 2" long pieces
125 mL (½ cup) broccoli, small pieces
125 mL (½ cup) carrots, sliced into "coins"
½ medium green pepper, cut in 2" strips, about ¼" wide
½ medium sweet red pepper, cut in 2" strips, about ¼" wide
6 button mushrooms, cross-cut into quarters
250 mL (1 cup) zucchini, cut into ½" thick "coins"

10%
39%
51%
Fat
Protein
Carbohydrate

PREPARATION STEPS

1. In a small dish, prepare mixture of soy sauce, water, and brown sugar. Set aside.
2. Heat oil in a wok or large deep frying pan over medium-high heat. Add garlic and onions. Stir.
3. When onions and garlic are translucent, add asparagus, broccoli, carrots, peppers, and mushrooms. Stir mixture constantly to coat vegetables with oil.
4. Add soy sauce, water, and brown sugar mixture.
5. Add zucchini. Sprinkle black pepper over vegetables.
6. Do not overcook. If the mixture seems too dry, add another tablespoon of water.
7. Serve immediately over cooked rice or noodles.

Personal Dietary Analysis

Using the DRIs

1. Refer to your one- or three-day food log from the Personal Dietary Analysis feature in Chapter 3.

   a. Find the RDA/AI values for vitamins under your life stage/gender group category in the DRI tables (see the inside front cover of this book). Write those values under the "My RDA/AI" column in the table below.

   b. Review your personal dietary assessment. Find your three-day average intakes of vitamins A, E, C, D, folate, B-12, thiamin, riboflavin, and niacin. Write those values under the "My Average Intake" column of the table.

   c. Calculate the percentage of the RDA/AI you consumed for each vitamin by dividing your intake by the RDA/AI amount and multiplying the figure you obtain by 100. For example, if your average intake of vitamin C was 100 mg per day, and your RDA for the vitamin is 75 mg per day, you would divide 100 mg by 75 mg to obtain 1.25. To multiply this figure by 100, simply move the decimal point two places to the right, and replace the decimal point with a percentage sign (125%). Thus, your average daily intake of vitamin C was 125% of the RDA. Place the percentages for each vitamin under the "% of My RDA/AI" column.

   d. Under the ">, <, = " column, indicate whether your average daily intake was greater than (>), less than (<), or equal to (=) the RDA/AI.

2. Use the information you calculated in the first part of this activity to answer the following questions:

   a. Which of your average vitamin intakes equaled or exceeded the RDA/AI value?

   b. Which of your average vitamin intakes was below the RDA/AI value?

   c. What foods would you eat to increase your intake of the vitamins that were less than the RDA/AI levels? (Review sources of certain vitamins in Chapter 8.)

   d. Turn in your completed table and answers to your instructor.

Personal Dietary Analysis: Vitamins

Vitamin	My RDA/AI	My Average Intake	% of My RDA/AI	>, <, or =
A				
E				
C				
D				
Folate				
B-12				
Thiamin				
Riboflavin				
Niacin				

CRITICAL THINKING

1. Choose a vitamin and type the nutrient's name in the search box of an Internet browser. Locate three sites that sell products containing the vitamin. Review the pages of each site, making notes about claims, prices, and the kinds of links provided. Then write a three- to five-page report that describes and compares the information you found at the sites. In your paper, discuss any claims made on behalf of these products that you consider false or misleading. Include the URLs for the sites in your report.
2. Choose three different Web sites that sell vitamin supplements. Choose three different products and compare prices for the same product at the different Web sites. Then compare price of the vitamins from these sites with the price you would pay at a local supermarket, discount department store, or drugstore. Make sure to compare products with the same chemical composition (alpha-tocopherol, for example) and that have the same amount of the vitamin or vitamin-like compound in each dose. Write a one-page report about your findings.
3. While watching an infomercial on TV, you hear a so-called nutrition expert make claims for a substance that he or she claims to be a vitamin. What questions would you ask the expert to ascertain whether the substance truly is a vitamin?
4. One of your friends takes megadoses of vitamin A, C, B-6, and E because she thinks it helps her stay healthy. What would you tell her about taking such large doses of these vitamins?
5. According to the *Eating Well with Canada's Food Guide* recommendations, a 25-year-old female should consume seven to eight servings of fruit and vegetables daily. Plan a day's meals and snacks that provide these amounts of fruits and vegetables. In your plan, incorporate foods you like to eat.

PRACTICE TEST

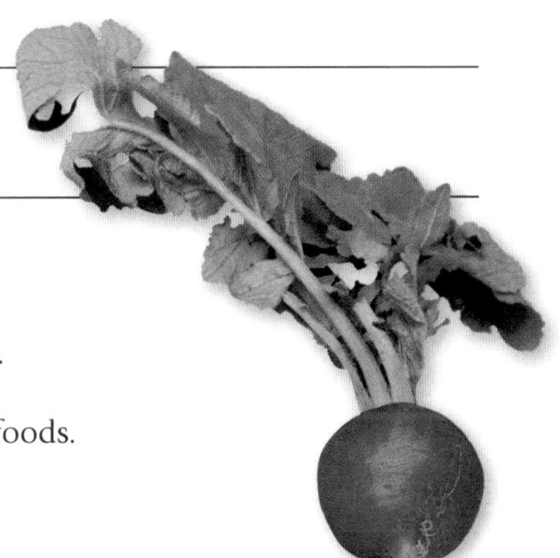

Select the best answer.

1. Megadoses of vitamins
   a. are safe to take, if the vitamin is water soluble.
   b. can prevent chronic diseases.
   c. are available naturally from a wide variety of foods.
   d. none of the above
2. Vitamins
   a. are metabolized to yield energy.
   b. occur in gram amounts in foods.
   c. are organic molecules.
   d. are macronutrients.
3. People who are unable to absorb fat are likely to develop a ______ deficiency.
   a. vitamin A
   b. folate
   c. vitamin B-12
   d. calcium

4. Enriched grain products have specific amounts of ______ added during processing.
   a. vitamin C
   b. vitamin A
   c. vitamin B-12
   d. thiamin
5. The vitamin content of a plant can be affected by
   a. soil composition.
   b. the plant's maturity when harvested.
   c. sunlight exposure.
   d. all of the above
6. Which of the following foods is not a rich source of provitamin A?
   a. beef
   b. carrots
   c. squash
   d. sweet potato
7. Children who lack vitamin D can develop
   a. pellagra.
   b. rickets.
   c. beriberi.
   d. scurvy.
8. During pregnancy, excess ______ intake is known to be teratogenic.
   a. vitamin A
   b. biotin
   c. vitamin K
   d. folate
9. Lack of vitamin ______ causes scurvy.
   a. A
   b. C
   c. D
   d. K

10. Which of the following vitamins is toxic in high doses?
    a. C
    b. thiamin
    c. B-6
    d. riboflavin
11. Diets that lack niacin can lead to
    a. rickets.
    b. beriberi.
    c. pellagra.
    d. pernicious anemia.

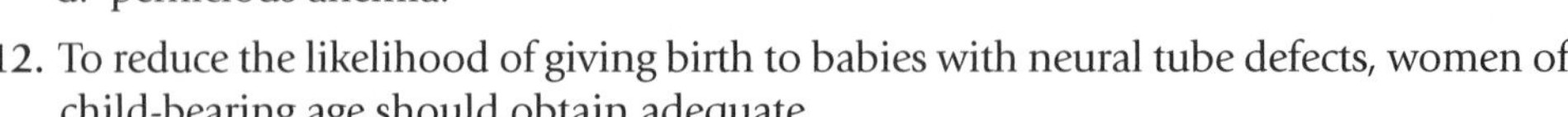

12. To reduce the likelihood of giving birth to babies with neural tube defects, women of child-bearing age should obtain adequate
    a. folate.
    b. biotin.
    c. choline.
    d. niacin.

13. Major food sources of vitamin B-12 include
    a. enriched grain products.
    b. meat and milk products.
    c. fruit and vegetables.
    d. nuts and seeds.
14. Which of the following statements is false?
    a. Intrinsic factor is need for vitamin B-12 absorption.
    b. Vitamin B-12 deficiency is common among elderly persons.
    c. Patients with pernicious anemia are treated with high doses of folic acid.
    d. If untreated, pernicious anemia can be deadly.
15. Which of the following foods is a rich source of vitamin C?
    a. whole milk
    b. egg white
    c. hamburger patty
    d. green pepper

Answers to Chapter 8 Quiz Yourself

1. Natural vitamins are better for you because they have more biological activity than synthetic vitamins. **False.** (p. 229)
2. Certain vitamins are toxic. **True.** (p. 229)
3. Vitamin E is an antioxidant. **True.** (p. 243)
4. Vitamins are a source of "quick" energy. **False.** (p. 226)
5. According to scientific research, taking large doses of vitamin C daily prevents the common cold. **False.** (p. 262)

Please visit Connect at

www.mcgrawhillconnect.ca

Chapter **9**

Water and Minerals

Chapter Learning Outcomes

After reading Chapter 9, you should be able to:

1. Discuss the functions of water in the body as well as typical sources of intakes and losses.
2. Discuss how the body maintains its water balance.
3. List major signs and symptoms of heat-related illnesses.
4. Classify mineral nutrients as major, trace, or ultratrace minerals.
5. Describe factors that can affect the absorption, retention, and availability of mineral nutrients.
6. List key functions and major food sources of mineral nutrients.
7. Identify signs and symptoms associated with deficiencies as well as excesses of mineral nutrients.
8. Describe the roles of minerals in achieving and maintaining good health.
9. Identify major risk factors for hypertension and osteoporosis.

In late August 1997, a 19-year-old student wrestler who weighed 106 kg (233 lbs.) attended a university in North Carolina. The young man was anxious to lose enough weight to qualify for the 89-kg (195-lb.) weight class when the wrestling season began later that semester. By November 6, the wrestler had lost about 10 kg (23 lbs.), but the first tournament was to be held in two days and he was still about 7 kg (15 lbs.) too heavy. To cut the extra weight, he engaged in an intense, almost nonstop training session.

In a 12-hour period that spanned November 6 and 7, the wrestler restricted his water and food intake severely. Additionally, he wore a special suit made from a rubberized material that was *vapour impermeable*, and he even covered it with a cotton warm-up outfit. By wearing this combination of clothing, the young man perspired profusely. Sweating can cause the body to lose a significant amount of water weight; however, sweating can also cause **dehydration** (body water depletion), especially when a person restricts his or her fluid intake. Severe dehydration is a life-threatening condition that requires urgent medical care.

At 3 p.m. on November 6, the student wrestler began exercising vigorously in a hot environment. By 11:30 p.m. that night, he had lost about 4 kg (9 lbs.). After resting for about 2 hours, the young man resumed his exercise regimen in a desperate effort to lose the remaining 3 kg (about 6 lbs.). Around 2:45 a.m. on November 7, he had to discontinue exercising—he was extremely fatigued and unable to communicate. An hour later, he stopped breathing and his heart ceased beating. Attempts to revive him were unsuccessful.[1]

During the 33 days that followed this young man's death, two more young male wrestlers died under similar circumstances at two other universities. As in the first wrestler's case, the two student athletes were trying to lose approximately 15% of their preseason body weights in a relatively short period of time. At the time of their deaths, all three wrestlers suffered from dehydration. Furthermore, the young men presented signs of **hyperthermia** (very high body temperature) that may have contributed to their deaths.[1]

The rapid weight loss practices that resulted in the deaths of these young wrestlers were prohibited by National Collegiate Athletic Association (NCAA) regulations. However, the NCAA's guidelines concerning weight management practices for wrestlers were often ignored by the athletes. Why? At that time, many wrestlers were determined to lose enough weight prior to a meet so that they could compete in weight categories that were lower than their preseason weights. By competing in a lower weight class, the wrestlers hoped to increase their competitive edge over opponents. After weighing in for an event, the dehydrated athletes counted on having enough time to restore their body's normal water status before the start of their match.

After the deaths of these athletes, the NCAA instituted sweeping changes establishing new guidelines concerning weight certification, weight classification, and weighing-in procedures for student wrestlers.[2] NCAA rules prohibit the athletes from losing weight rapidly by restricting food and fluid intakes excessively; staying in hot boxes, saunas, or other rooms designed to produce sweating; wearing vapour-impermeable suits to cause sweating; and using laxatives, self-induced vomiting, or medications that increase urine production. Failure to follow the NCAA's wrestling guidelines can result in suspension from competition. Since these rules were established, no dehydration-related deaths among student wrestlers have been reported.

The tragic and preventable deaths of the three young wrestlers emphasize the importance of water and the consequences of dehydration. Many of water's functions involve certain minerals. The mineral nutrients are key components of body structures and play vital roles in metabolism, water balance, muscle movement, and various physiological processes. Mineral deficiencies can cause serious health problems, and in severe cases, death. In this chapter, we will focus on water first, and then discuss some of the essential minerals that are of major concern for public health officials in Canada, the United States, and other parts of the world.

Quiz YOURSELF

Can water be toxic when consumed in excess? What is osteoporosis? Which foods are rich sources of iron? Test your knowledge of water and minerals by taking the following quiz. The answers are on page 329.

1. Your body constantly loses water through insensible perspiration, a form of water loss that is not the same as sweat. ______T______F
2. Gram per gram, cottage cheese contains more calcium than plain yogourt. ______T______F
3. Potassium, sodium, and chloride ions are involved in fluid balance. ______T______F
4. Arsenic is an ultratrace mineral. ______T______F
5. In general, plants are good dietary sources of iron because the plant pigment chlorophyll contains iron. ______T______F

dehydration body water depletion
hyperthermia very high body temperature

Perspiring helps maintain normal body temperature because water can hold a lot of heat. As sweat evaporates from skin, it takes some heat along with it, cooling the body.

Water

Compared to other nutrients, water is so unusual, it is in a class by itself. Water is a simple compound; a molecule of water is comprised of two hydrogen atoms and one oxygen atom (H_2O). Water does not need to be digested, and it is easily absorbed by the intestinal tract.

Depending on a person's age, sex, and body composition, about 45 to 75% of his or her body is water weight.[3] Lean muscle tissue contains more water (about 73%) than fat tissue (about 20%). On average, young adult men have more lean tissue than young women. Approximately 55 to 60% of an average young man's body weight is water; the average young adult woman's body has more fat and, therefore, slightly less water than an average young man's body. A person's percentage of body water declines from birth to old age. A newborn's weight may be 75% water, whereas an elderly person's body may be only 45% water weight.[3]

Water is a major solvent; many substances, including glucose, dissolve in water. Water often participates directly in chemical reactions, such as those involved in digesting food. Water's other physiological roles include transporting substances, removing waste products, lubricating tissues, and regulating body temperature and acid-base balance (proper blood pH). Furthermore, water is a major component of blood, saliva, sweat, tears, mucus, and the fluid in joints. Although water has numerous functions in the body, this unique nutrient does not provide energy.

We often take water for granted, but this simple molecule is highly essential. You can survive for weeks, even months, if your diet lacks carbohydrates, lipids, proteins, and vitamins. But if you do not have any water, your life will end within a week or two. Fortunately, your body makes small amounts of water through normal physiological and metabolic chemical reactions and obtains the nutrient from many foods, such as fruits, vegetables, and meats.

Body Temperature Regulation

Metabolism generates heat in the body. Much of this heat simply radiates from the skin into the surrounding air. The remaining body heat helps maintain the narrow

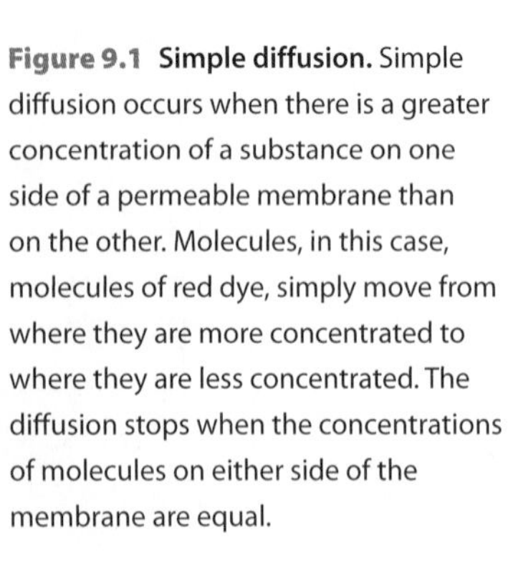

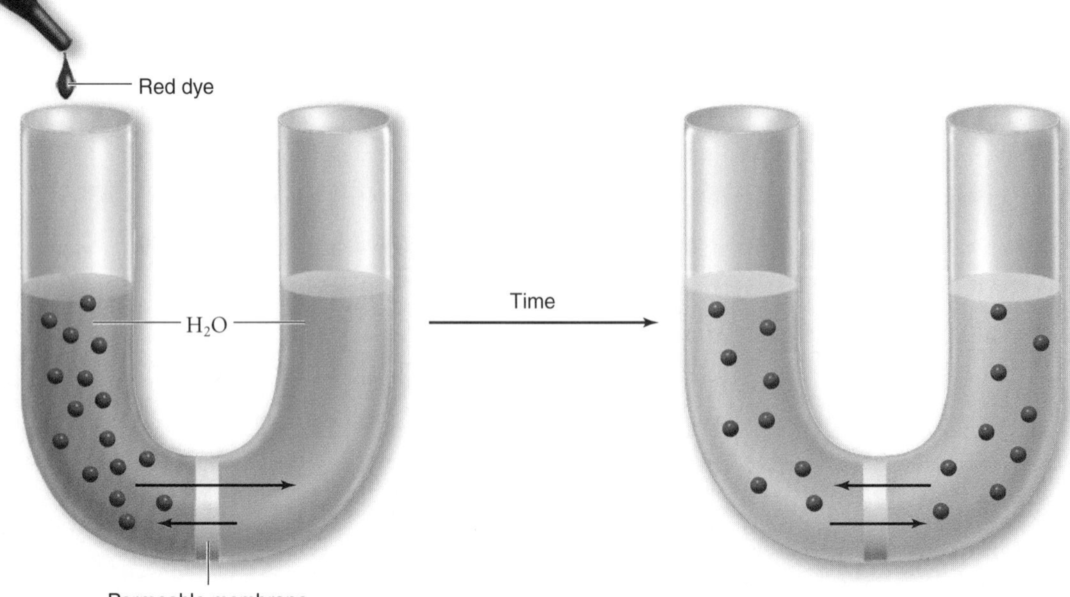

Figure 9.1 Simple diffusion. Simple diffusion occurs when there is a greater concentration of a substance on one side of a permeable membrane than on the other. Molecules, in this case, molecules of red dye, simply move from where they are more concentrated to where they are less concentrated. The diffusion stops when the concentrations of molecules on either side of the membrane are equal.

range of temperature that is necessary for enzymes to function. If body temperature increases to 41 °C (106 °F) or more, the excessive heat denatures enzymes, damages tissues, and can cause death.[3] To avoid overheating, the body must dissipate the excess heat into the environment, primarily by the help of sweat glands that secrete water (perspiration).

Perspiring (sweating) helps maintain normal body temperature because water can hold large amounts of heat. As water evaporates from skin, it takes some heat along with it, cooling the body. Each litre of perspiration that evaporates represents 500 kcal of energy removed from the skin and surrounding tissues.[3] However, the body cooling effect of perspiration only works when the sweat evaporates from the skin. Sweat that drips from the body doesn't draw body heat with it. Thus, exercising in a hot, humid environment can result in increased body temperature more quickly than in hot, dry conditions. This is because in very humid conditions, the air already contains a high level of moisture and thus sweat does not evaporate as readily.

simple diffusion molecular movement from a region of higher to lower concentration

selectively permeable membrane barrier that allows the passage of certain substances and prevents the movement of other substances

osmosis movement of water through a selectively permeable membrane

Body Water Distribution

Cells can use a variety of methods to obtain materials from their environment and eliminate wastes. Some materials, such as oxygen and carbon dioxide, easily pass through the plasma membrane by **simple diffusion**. Simple diffusion occurs when there is a greater concentration of molecules on one side of a permeable membrane than on the other. The material simply moves from where it is more concentrated to where it is less concentrated. The diffusion stops when the concentrations of material on either side of the membrane are equal (Fig. 9.1).

The plasma membrane of a human cell is **selectively permeable**, which means the membrane controls the passage of substances in and out of the cell. **Osmosis** is the diffusion of water through a selectively permeable membrane. The concentration of substances dissolved in the water, such as sodium ions or glucose, influences osmosis. Water moves from a region that has less material dissolved in it (dilute) to a region that has more material dissolved in it (Fig. 9.2).

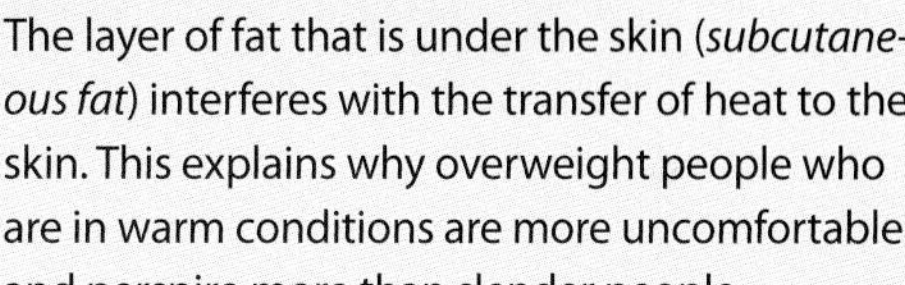

The layer of fat that is under the skin (*subcutaneous fat*) interferes with the transfer of heat to the skin. This explains why overweight people who are in warm conditions are more uncomfortable and perspire more than slender people.

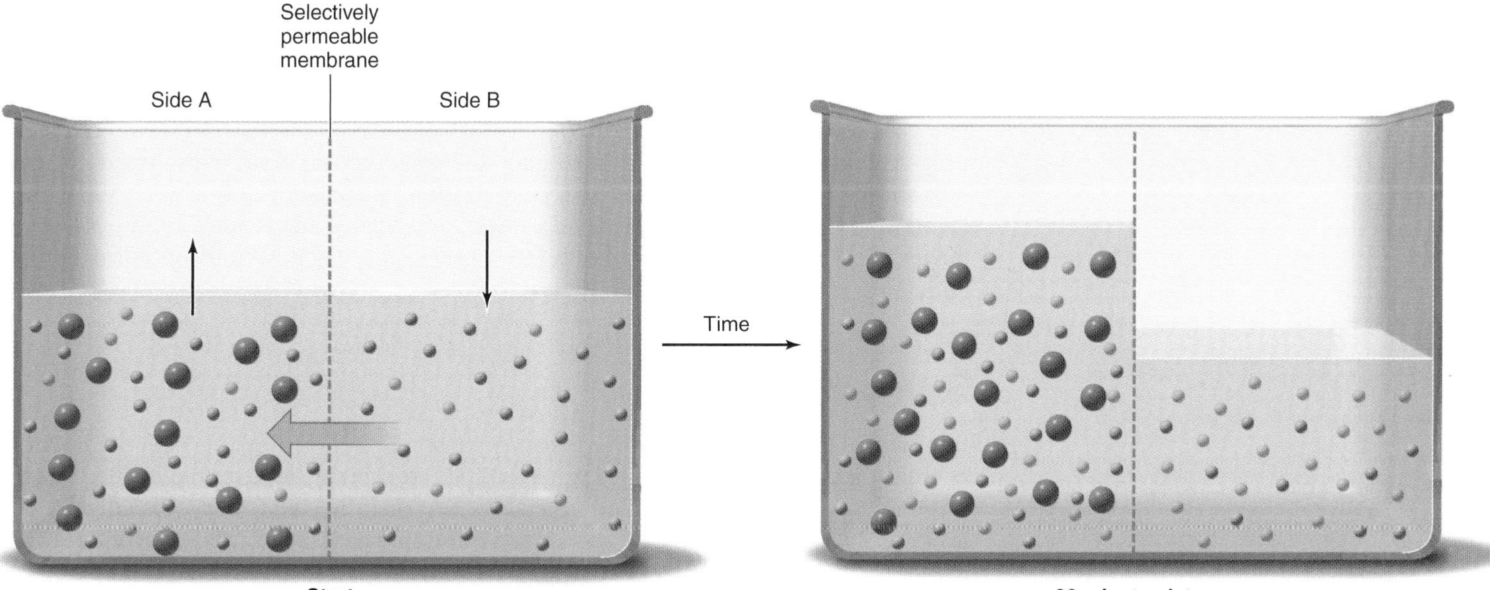

Figure 9.2 Osmosis. Osmosis is the diffusion of water through a selectively permeable membrane. Water moves from a compartment that is less concentrated to a compartment that has more material dissolved in it.

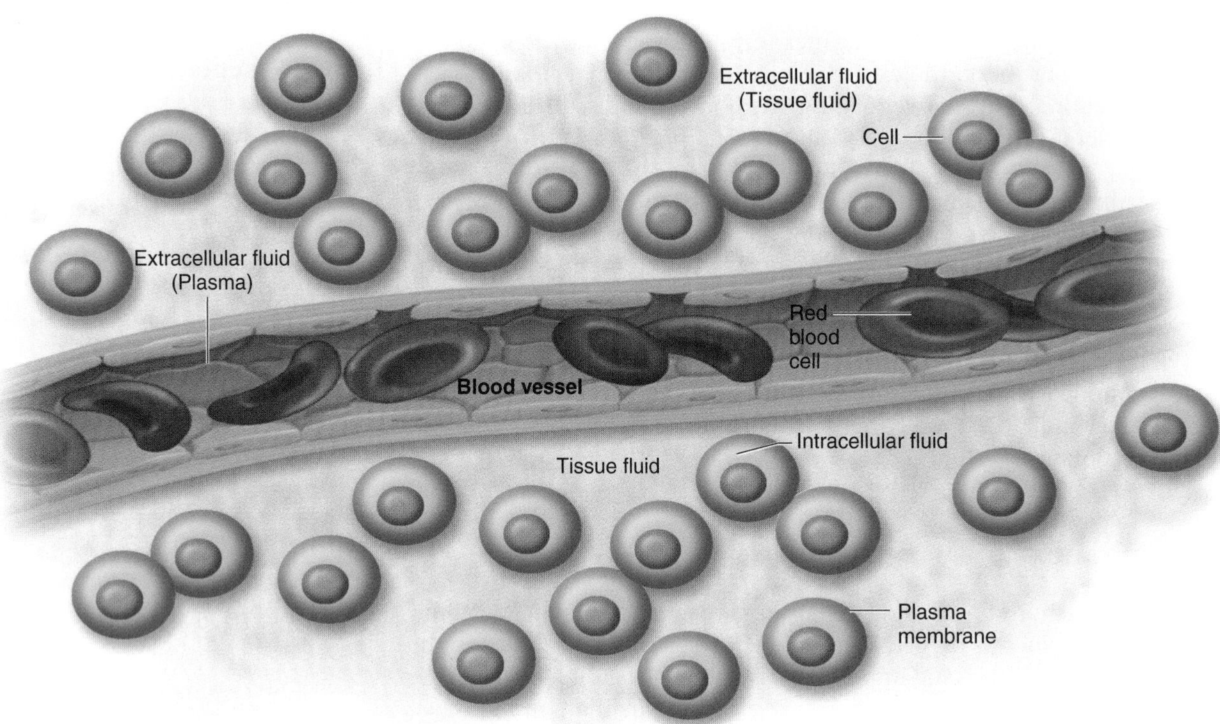

Figure 9.3 Fluid compartments in the body. Intracellular water is inside cells; extracellular water surrounds cells (tissue fluid) or is the fluid in blood (*plasma*). The cell's plasma membrane is selectively permeable, because it allows the passage of certain substances and prevents the movement of other substances through it.

The body has two major fluid compartments—intracellular water and extracellular water (Fig. 9.3). **Intracellular water** is inside cells. **Extracellular water** surrounds cells (tissue fluid) or is the fluid portion of blood (*plasma*). About two-thirds of the body's water is in the intracellular compartment.

The body maintains the balance of compartmental fluids and proper **hydration**, adequate water status, primarily by controlling concentrations of ions in each compartment. Ions are elements or small molecules that have electrical charges (electrolytes). Water is attracted to ions, such as sodium, potassium, phosphate, and chloride ions. Overall, where ions go, water follows.

Maintenance of intracellular water volume depends to a large extent on the intracellular concentration of potassium and phosphate ions. On the other hand, maintenance of extracellular water volume depends primarily on the extracellular concentration of sodium and chloride ions. Changes in the normal concentrations of these ions can cause water to shift out of one compartment and move into the other. For example, if extracellular fluid has fewer than normal sodium ions, water moves from the extracellular compartment into cells. When this occurs, the cells swell and can burst (Fig. 9.4a). On the other hand, if extracellular fluid has an excess of sodium ions, water moves out of cells. As a result, the cells shrink and die because they lack enough intracellular fluid to function (Fig. 9.4b). Recall from Chapter 7 that edema (*eh-dee'-mah*) occurs when an excessive amount of water moves into the space surrounding cells (see Fig. 7.1 on p. 191). To function normally, the body must maintain intracellular and extracellular water volumes within certain limits.

intracellular water water that is inside cells

extracellular water water that surrounds cells or is in blood

hydration water status

total water intake water in beverages and foods

metabolic water water formed by cells as a metabolic by-product

Sources of Water

In addition to plain tap water, we consume water in the form of various liquids, such as fruit juice, milk, soup, coffee, tea, soft drinks, and plain or flavoured bottled water. Although foods such as fruits and vegetables appear to be solid, they generally are 60 to 95% water weight. Table 9.1 lists some commonly consumed foods and their water content by weight. **Total water intake** refers to water in beverages and foods. About 80% of our total water intake is from water and other beverages; food supplies the remaining amount of our water intake.[4]

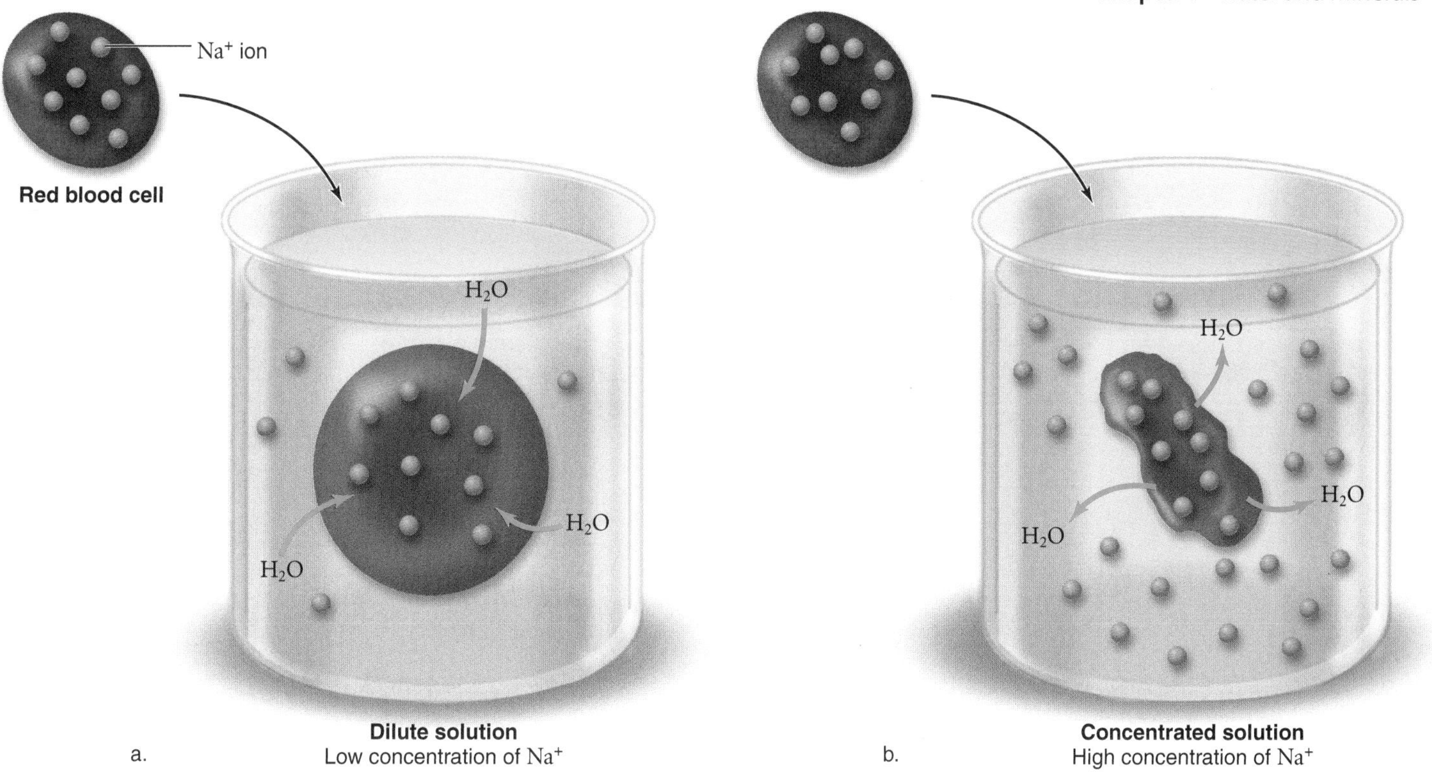

Figure 9.4 Maintaining proper hydration. Cells, such as red blood cells, need to maintain their fluid balance. Changes in the normal concentrations of ions can cause water to shift out of one compartment and move into the other. The cell in beaker A is placed in a solution that contains few sodium ions (Na^+) in relation to the concentration of Na^+ in the cell. As a result, water moves from the solution and into the red blood cell. The cell can swell and burst. The solution in beaker B has an excess of sodium ions (Na^+) compared to the concentration of Na^+ inside the cell. Water moves out of the red blood cell placed in beaker B. As a result, the cell shrinks, and can die as a result.

In addition to the water in beverages and foods, a considerable amount of water enters the digestive tract daily through secretions from the mouth, stomach, intestine, pancreas, and gallbladder. The intestinal tract absorbs most of this water too. Each day, only about 100 to 200 mL of the water that enters the digestive tract is not absorbed. The body eventually eliminates the unabsorbed water in feces.

Cells also form some water as a metabolic by-product of metabolism. Physically inactive people typically form about 250 to 350 mL of water per day; very active people can produce about 500 mL to 600 mL of water daily.[4] This source of water is referred to as **metabolic water**. Metabolic water also contributes to the body's fluid balance.

TABLE 9.1 *How Much Water Is in That Food or Beverage?*

Food	Water % by Weight
Lettuce	95
Tomato	95
Milk, 1% fat	90
Apple, with skin	86
Avocado	79
Potato, white, baked with skin	75
Banana	75
Chicken, white meat, roasted	65
Ground meat, 80% lean	56
Bread, whole wheat	38
Margarine, stick	16
Crackers, saltines	5
Vegetable oil	0

Source: Data from U.S. Department of Agriculture, Agricultural Research Service, USDA Nutrient Data Laboratory: *USDA national nutrient database for standard reference, release 19.* 2006.

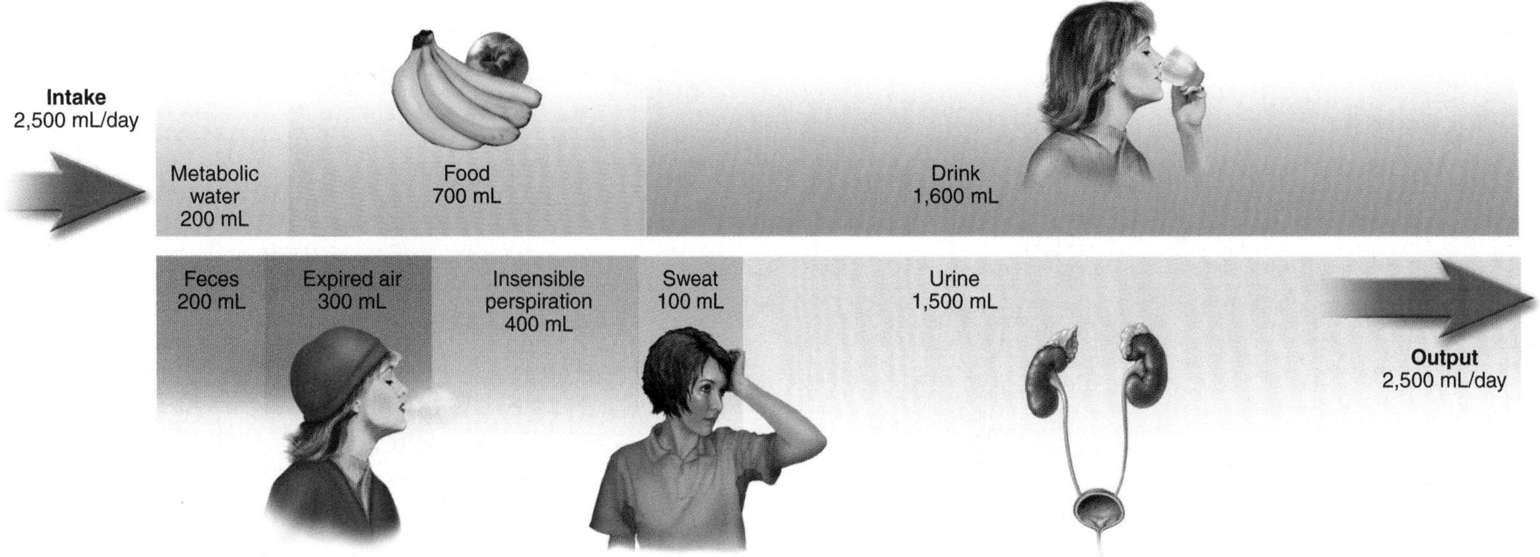

Figure 9.5 Daily water balance. An average healthy adult consumes and produces approximately 2500 mL of water and eliminates about 2500 mL of water daily. A healthy person's average daily water input equals his or her average daily losses.

The Essential Balancing Act

The body loses water in urine, perspiration, exhaled air, feces, and insensible perspiration (Fig. 9.5). **Insensible perspiration** or insensible water loss is body water that diffuses through the layers of skin instead of being secreted by sweat glands.[3] When insensible perspiration reaches the skin's surface, it evaporates into the air or condenses on a cooler surface. People are usually unaware that their bodies are constantly losing water in this manner, hence the term "insensible" perspiration.

An average healthy adult consumes and produces approximately 2.5 L (2500 mL) of water and eliminates about 2.5 L of water daily (see Fig. 9.5).[3] Thus, a healthy person's average daily water input equals his or her average daily losses (output). Various factors, however, influence a person's fluid input and output. Environmental factors such as temperature, humidity, and altitude can affect body water losses. Physiological conditions, especially fever, vomiting, and diarrhea, and lifestyle practices, such as exercise habits and sodium and alcohol intakes, can also alter the body's fluid balance.

Figure 9.6 Kidney stones. Some people form kidney stones. Although small enough to fit on a fingertip, such stones can be quite painful when they move from the kidneys and are eliminated in urine.

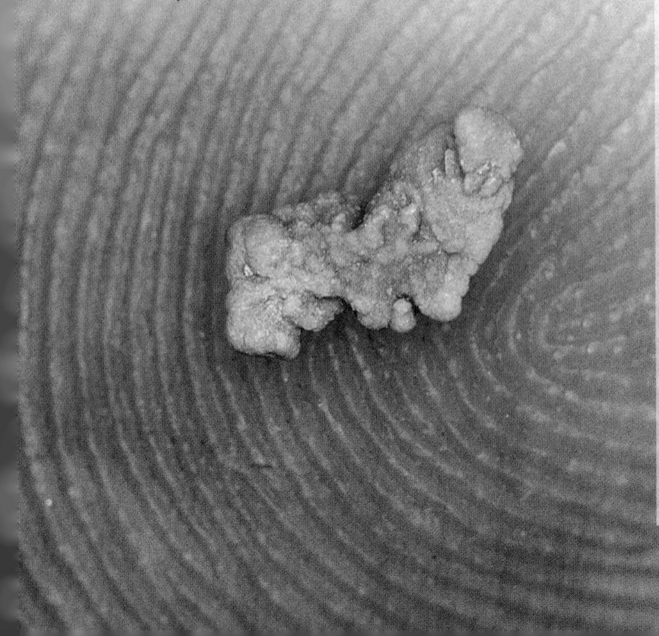

Kidneys and Hydration

The kidneys are the major regulator of the body's water content and ion concentrations. In a healthy person, the kidneys maintain proper hydration by filtering excess ions from blood as it flows through the kidney's tissues. When the kidneys remove ions such as sodium, water follows and becomes the main component of urine. If you drink more watery fluids than your body needs, your kidneys excrete the excess water in urine.

Kidneys also remove drugs and metabolic waste products, such as urea, from the bloodstream. Sometimes, minerals and waste products settle out of urine and collect into crystals. If the crystals enlarge and form a hard mass, the object is called a kidney stone (Fig. 9.6). As a kidney stone moves out of the kidney and enters the tube leading to the bladder, it can cause considerable pain and bloody urine until it passes out of the body. The majority of kidney stones contain the minerals calcium and phosphorus.[5,6]

The amount of urine a person produces is determined primarily by his or her total water intake. A healthy person produces about 1 to 2 L of urine per day.[6] Healthy kidneys can form more urine, but they become less efficient at urine production when fluid intakes are less than about 500 mL (2 cups) per day.

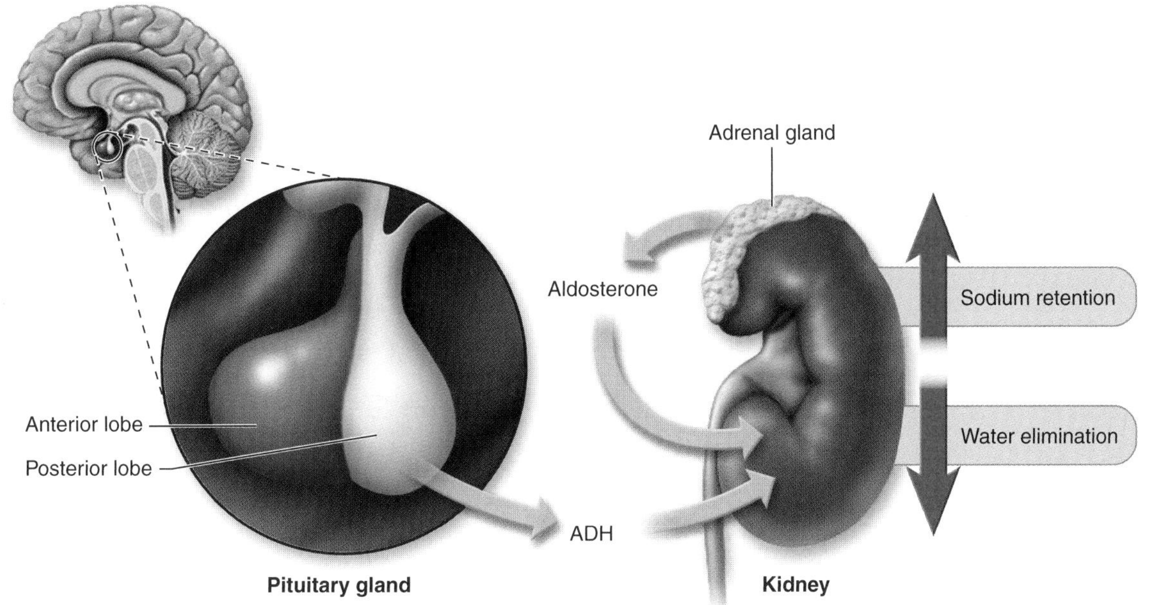

Figure 9.7 Effects of antidiuretic hormone and adolsterone on kidneys. In response to dehydration, the posterior pituitary gland in the brain secretes antidiuretic hormone (ADH), which signals the kidneys to conserve water. Additionally, the adrenal glands secrete the hormone aldosterone. Aldosterone reduces urinary excretion of sodium. When the kidneys retain sodium, they return the mineral to the general circulation. Because water follows sodium, it is conserved as well.

Water Conservation

When you are hot and perspiring heavily, your kidneys try to conserve as much water as possible. **Antidiuretic hormone (ADH)** and **aldosterone** are two hormones that participate in the body's efforts to maintain fluid balance. In response to dehydration, the posterior pituitary gland in the brain releases antidiuretic hormone. Antidiuretic hormone stimulates the kidneys to conserve water. Additionally, the adrenal glands secrete aldosterone. Aldosterone signals kidneys to reduce the elimination of sodium in urine and, as a result, the kidneys return the mineral to the general circulation. Because water follows sodium, it is conserved as well. The diagram in Figure 9.7 summarizes the effects of antidiuretic hormone and aldosterone on the kidneys.

Contrary to popular belief, there is no "rule of thumb" recommendation that specifies how many glasses of water to drink each day.[7] The Adequate Intake (AI) for *total* water intake is approximately 2.7 L (11 cups) for young women and approximately 3.7 L (15 cups) for young men.[8] These amounts do not need to be consumed in the form of fluids, because most solid foods contain some water.

The simplest way to determine if you are consuming enough water is to observe the volume and colour of your urine. When your fluid intake is adequate, your kidneys will produce enough urine to maintain fluid balance. If you consume more fluid than needed, your kidneys will eliminate the excess, and you will produce plenty of urine. On the other hand, if you limit your fluid intake or have high fluid losses such as in sweat, you will produce small amounts of urine. People often refer to the colour of urine as an indicator of hydration status. Observing the colour of urine may not be a reliable guide for judging a person's hydration status.[7] It is important to recognize that having urinary tract infections, or ingesting certain medications, foods, and dietary supplements, especially those containing the B-vitamin riboflavin, can alter urine's colour. However, for most people, under normal circumstances, urine should be nearly clear.

insensible perspiration body water that passes through the skin and not from sweat glands

antidiuretic hormone (ADH) hormone that participates in water conservation

aldosterone hormone that participates in water conservation

Did You Know?

Under normal conditions, nearly 1200 mL (5 cups) of blood flows through your kidneys each minute, resulting in the formation of 1 mL of urine per minute.[5] A cup holds 250 mL (8 oz.), so you can produce about 60 mL (¼ cup) of urine in an hour.

diuretic substance that increases urine production

water intoxication condition that occurs when too much water is consumed in a short time period or the kidneys have difficulty filtering water from blood

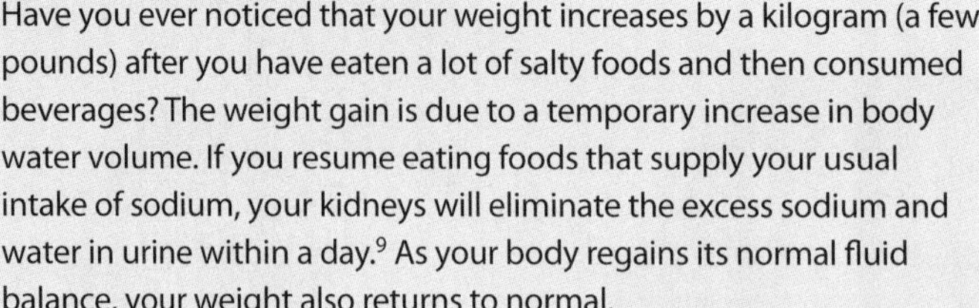

Did You Know?

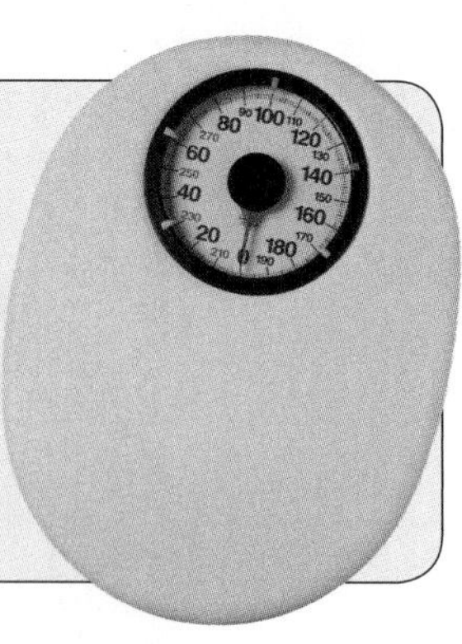

Have you ever noticed that your weight increases by a kilogram (a few pounds) after you have eaten a lot of salty foods and then consumed beverages? The weight gain is due to a temporary increase in body water volume. If you resume eating foods that supply your usual intake of sodium, your kidneys will eliminate the excess sodium and water in urine within a day.[9] As your body regains its normal fluid balance, your weight also returns to normal.

What Is a Diuretic? Caffeine is a **diuretic**, a substance that increases water excretion and urine production. Coffee, tea, "energy" drinks, and soft drinks often contain caffeine or caffeine-related compounds. However, the water consumed in caffeinated beverages is not completely lost in urine, so drinking these fluids can still contribute to your water needs.[4]

Alcohol is also a diuretic. Normally, antidiuretic hormone signals the kidneys to conserve water. Alcohol, however, inhibits ADH secretion from the pituitary gland in the brain, enabling the kidneys to eliminate more urine than normal.[3] Alcohol consumption actually results in urinary water losses that are greater than the volume of fluid consumed.[10] Therefore, alcohol contributes to dehydration. A *hangover*, the headache and overall discomfort that occurs a few hours after drinking too much alcohol, may be the effects of dehydration on brain cells.

People who work or exercise outdoors, especially in hot conditions, need to stay hydrated to avoid dehydration and heat-related illnesses.

Dehydration

Despite the body's mechanisms to balance its water content, some fluid is constantly being lost, primarily via the skin and lungs. If a person does not consume enough fluids to replace that water, dehydration can occur. Weight loss is a sign of dehydration. Every 500 mL of water that the body loses represents 454 g (1 lb.) of body weight. If you lose 1 to 2% of your usual body weight in fluids, you will feel fatigued and thirsty. If you weigh 68 kg (150 lbs.), for example, and your weight drops approximately a kilogram (23 lbs.) after exercising in hot conditions, you have lost 2% of your body weight, primarily as water weight.

As the loss of body water approaches 4% of body weight, muscles lose considerable amounts of strength and endurance. By the time body weight is reduced by 7 to 10% as a result of body fluid losses, severe weakness results. At a 20% reduction of body weight, coma and death are likely.

Thirst is the primary regulator of fluid intake.[3] The thirst response alerts you to the need to replenish water that was lost by sweating and other means. The majority of healthy people, even older adults, meet their AI for water by letting thirst be their guide.[4] Thirst stimulates people to drink fluids *before* dehydration occurs.[7] However, elderly people who live or exercise in warm environments or are deprived of fluids do not sense thirst as quickly as younger people.[11] Furthermore, elderly individuals may be more susceptible to develop dehydration than young adults, because as kidneys age, they become less able to conserve water when fluid intakes are low. Therefore, it may be necessary to remind older adults to drink water, especially when they are physically active or in warm conditions. Nevertheless, the results of studies indicate that most healthy elderly persons who live independently are able to maintain adequate hydration.[11,12,13]

People who are sick, especially children with fever, vomiting, diarrhea, and increased perspiration, may need to be given special solutions of water and electrolytes to prevent dehydration. Athletes and other people who work or exercise outdoors, especially in hot

Did You Know?

A massive earthquake struck northwestern Pakistan on October 8, 2005. Four days later, a team of rescuers found a five-year-old girl who was buried alive underneath the ruins of her home. People can survive for a few days in such conditions before dehydration contributes to their deaths. After being lifted from the rubble, the little girl uttered, "I want to drink."

Rescue teams, including members of the U.S. military, assisted people affected by the October 2005 earthquake in Pakistan. To maintain her fluid balance, this injured girl is receiving fluid.

conditions, also need to stay hydrated to avoid dehydration and heat-related illnesses such as heat exhaustion. Chapter 11 provides information about heat-related illnesses.

Can Too Much Water Be Toxic?

There is no Upper Limit (UL) for water.[4] **Water intoxication**, however rare, can occur when an excessive amount of water is consumed in a short time period or when the kidneys have difficulty filtering water from blood. The excess water dilutes the sodium concentration of blood, disrupting water balance. As a result of the imbalance, too much water moves into cells, including brain cells. Signs and symptoms of water intoxication may include dizziness, headache, confusion, inability to coordinate muscular movements, bizarre behaviour, and seizures.[14] If the condition is not detected early and treated effectively, coma and death can result.

Healthy people rarely drink enough water to become intoxicated. However, water intoxication can develop in people with disorders that interfere with the kidney's ability to excrete water normally. Marathon runners who consume large amounts of plain water in an effort to keep hydrated during competition may be at risk of water intoxication. Chapter 11 discusses the importance of proper hydration for athletes.

Did You Know?

Extreme thirst and reduced urine production are side effects of the illegal drug Ecstasy.[7] As a result of taking Ecstasy, people can rapidly develop water intoxication that may result in death.[15,16]

Concept Checkpoint

1. List at least five different functions of water in the body.
2. Define osmosis.
3. Which ions are found primarily in extracellular water? Which ions are found primarily in intracellular water?
4. Discuss ways the body obtains and loses water.
5. What can happen to cells if the body is unable to regulate its water balance?
6. How do antidiuretic hormone and aldosterone help maintain fluid balance in the body?
7. How much water do healthy young men and women need to consume daily (AI values)?
8. What is a diuretic? Identify two diuretics commonly consumed by North Americans.
9. List at least three signs and symptoms of dehydration.
10. List at least three signs and symptoms of water intoxication.

Marathon runners who consume large amounts of plain water in an effort to keep hydrated during competition may be at risk of water intoxication.

major minerals essential mineral elements required in amounts of 100 mg or more per day

trace minerals essential mineral elements required in amounts that are less than 100 mg per day

ultratrace minerals mineral elements not classified as essential nutrients but that may have physiological functions

cofactor ion or molecule that catalyzes chemical reactions

Minerals: Basic Concepts

Minerals, such as iron and calcium, are a group of elements in Earth's rocks, soils, and natural water sources. Plants, animals, and other living things cannot synthesize minerals. Plants obtain the minerals they need from soil or fertilizer; animals generally obtain minerals when they consume plants and other animals or substances that contain these elements.

About 15 mineral elements have known functions in the body and are necessary for human health. The body requires these particular micronutrients in milligram or microgram amounts. The essential minerals are classified into two groups—**major minerals** and **trace minerals** (Tables 9.2 and 9.3). If we require 100 mg or more of a mineral per day, the mineral is classified as a major mineral; otherwise, the micronutrient is a trace mineral. The body also contains very small amounts of **ultratrace minerals**. The essential nature of this particular group of minerals has not been fully determined.

Several minerals, including lead and mercury, are often found in the human body, but they are environmental contaminants that have no known functions. The body can eliminate most minerals in urine. However, exposure to excessive amounts of minerals can cause toxicity.

Unlike vitamins, minerals are indestructible. Because minerals cannot be destroyed, heating a food or exposing it to most other environmental conditions will not affect the food's mineral content. However, minerals are water soluble, and they can leach out of a food and into cooking water. By using the cooking water to make soups or sauces, you can obtain minerals from the food that would otherwise be discarded.

Why Are Minerals Necessary?

Essential minerals have diverse roles in the body (Fig. 9.8). Some minerals form inorganic structural components of tissues, such as calcium and phosphorus in bones and teeth. Minerals may also function as inorganic ions, substances that have negative or positive charges (see Chapter 4). For example, calcium ions (Ca^{++}) participate in blood clotting, and sodium ions (Na^{+}) help maintain fluid balance. Sodium, potassium, and chloride ions are among the ions that participate in acid-base balance. Some ions, such as magnesium (Mg^{++}) and copper (Cu^{++}), are cofactors. A **cofactor** is an ion or molecule that catalyzes chemical reactions. Many minerals are components of various enzymes, hormones, or other organic molecules, such as cobalt in vitamin B-12, iron in hemoglobin, and sulphur in the amino acids methionine and cysteine. Although cells cannot

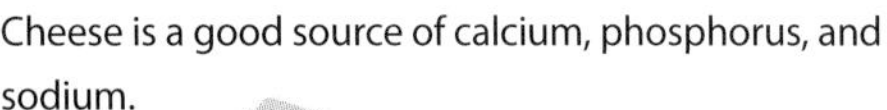

Cheese is a good source of calcium, phosphorus, and sodium.

TABLE 9.2 *Minerals with Known or Possible Roles in the Body**

Major Mineral	Trace Mineral	Ultratrace Mineral
Calcium (Ca)	Chromium (Cr)	Arsenic (As)
Chloride (Cl)	Fluoride (F)‡	Boron (B)
Magnesium (Mg)	Copper (Cu)	Lithium (Li)
Phosphorus (P)	Iodide (I)	Nickel (Ni)
Potassium (K)	Iron (Fe)	Silicon (Si)
Sodium (Na)	Manganese (Mn)	Vanadium (V)
Sulphur (S)	Molybdenum (Mo)	
	Selenium (Se)	
	Zinc (Zn)	

*Chemical symbol is shown in parentheses next to mineral's name.

‡Although fluoride is not essential, the mineral plays an important role in strengthening teeth and bones.

TABLE 9.3 *Summary of Major Minerals*

Mineral	Major Functions in the Body	Adult RDA or AI	Major Dietary Sources	Major Deficiency Signs and Symptoms	Major Toxicity Signs and Symptoms
Calcium (Ca)	• Structural component of bones and teeth • Blood clotting • Transmission of nerve impulses • Muscle contraction • Regulation of metabolism	1000–1200 mg	Milk and milk products, canned fish, tofu made with calcium sulphate, leafy vegetables, calcium-fortified foods such as orange juice	• Increased risk of osteoporosis • May increase risk of hypertension	• Intakes >2.5 g/day may cause kidney stones and interfere with absorption of other minerals.
Sodium (Na)	• Maintenance of proper fluid balance • Transmission of nerve impulses • Maintenance of acid-base balance	AI for young adults: 1500 mg	Table salt; luncheon meats; processed foods; pretzels, chips, and other snack foods; condiments; sauces	• Muscle cramps	• Contributes to hypertension in susceptible individuals • Increases urinary calcium losses
Potassium (K)	• Maintenance of proper fluid balance • Transmission of nerve impulses • Maintenance of acid-base balance	4700 mg	Fruits, vegetables, milk, meat, legumes, whole grains	• Irregular heartbeat • Muscle cramps	• Slowing of heart rate that can result in death
Magnesium (Mg)	• Strengthens bone • Cofactor for certain enzymes • Heart and nerve functioning	Men: 400–420 mg Women: 310–320 mg	Wheat bran, green vegetables, nuts, chocolate, legumes	• Muscle weakness and pain • Poor heart function	• Diarrhea
Phosphorus (P)	• Structural component of bones and teeth • Maintenance of acid-base balance • Component of DNA, phospholipids, and other organic compounds	700 mg	Dairy products, processed foods, soft drinks, fish, baked goods, meat	• None reported	• Poor bone mineralization
Chloride (Cl)	• Maintenance of proper fluid balance • Production of stomach acid • Transmission of nerve impulses • Maintenance of acid-base balance	AI for young adults: 2300 mg	Table salt, certain vegetables, processed foods	• Convulsions (observed in infants)	• Hypertension (because of the association with sodium in table salt)
Sulphur (S)	• Component of organic compounds such as certain amino acids and vitamins	None	Protein-rich foods	• None reported	• Unlikely from dietary sources

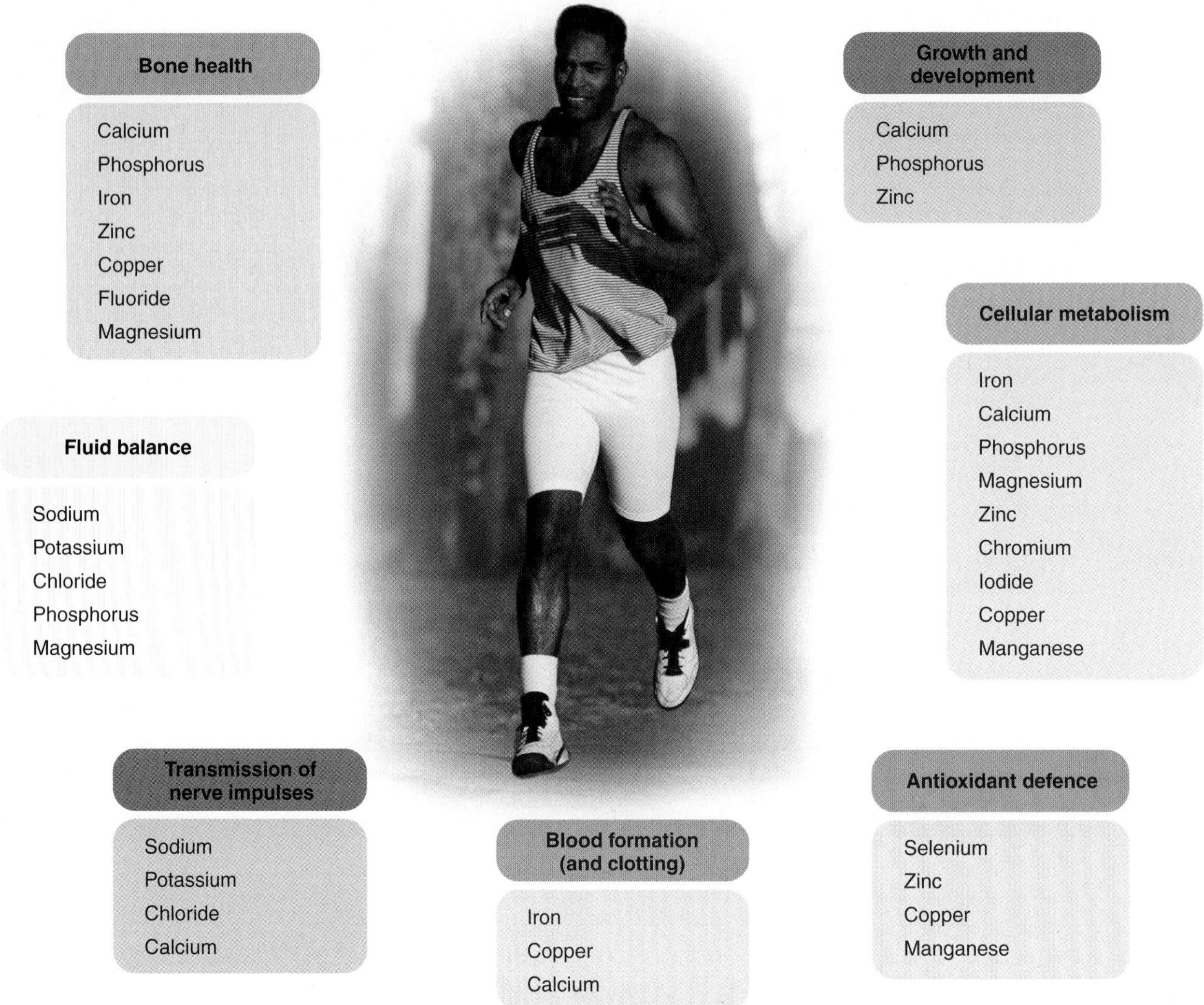

Figure 9.8 Minerals and their functions. Groups of minerals work together to maintain good health.

metabolize minerals for energy, certain minerals are involved in chemical reactions that release energy from macronutrients.

In some instances, the digestive tract absorbs more minerals than the body needs, but the excess is excreted, primarily in urine or feces. In other instances, the body stores the extra minerals in the liver, bones, or other tissues. Toxicity signs and symptoms occur when minerals accumulate in the body to such an extent that they interfere with the functioning of cells. Under normal conditions, the human body does not store large quantities of most minerals, and it loses small amounts of these essential elements every day. Therefore, people should choose their diets carefully so that their bodies can maintain an adequate supply of minerals.

Sources of Minerals

Most foods contain small amounts of minerals. However, the digestive tract does not absorb 100% of the minerals in food or dietary supplements. The body's ability to absorb and use minerals (bioavailability) depends on many factors. A major factor is the body's need for the micronutrient. In general, mineral requirements increase during periods of growth, such as infancy and puberty, and during pregnancy and breast-feeding. During these critical life stages, the bioavailability of minerals also tends to increase to help meet the body's demand.

Compared to plant foods, animal foods tend to be more reliable sources of minerals such as calcium, zinc, and iron. Why? Animal products generally have higher concentrations of these particular minerals. Additionally, the bioavailability of minerals from animal foods is often higher than that of plant foods. For example, 250 mL (one cup) of skim milk supplies almost 300 mg of calcium, and about 30% of the calcium in milk is bioavailable;[17] 250 mL (1 cup) of raw spinach supplies 30 mg of calcium, but only about 13% of that amount is bioavailable. On the other hand, plants supply more magnesium and manganese than animal foods.

In general, the more processing a plant food undergoes, the lower its mineral content. Cereal grains, for example, naturally contain selenium, zinc, copper, and some other minerals, but these micronutrients are lost during refinement. Iron is the only mineral added to grains during enrichment. To obtain a variety of minerals, include some whole-grain products in your diet each day. By following the recommendations of the *Eating Well with Canada's Food Guide* (see Chapter 3) and eating a variety of plant and animal foods, you are likely to obtain adequate amounts of all essential minerals.

To estimate the mineral contents of packaged foods, you can check the Nutrition Facts tables on food packaging. Food manufacturers are required to indicate amounts of iron and calcium in a serving of food as percentages of these micronutrients' Daily Values (%DVs). Daily Values have been established for several mineral nutrients (see Appendix C).

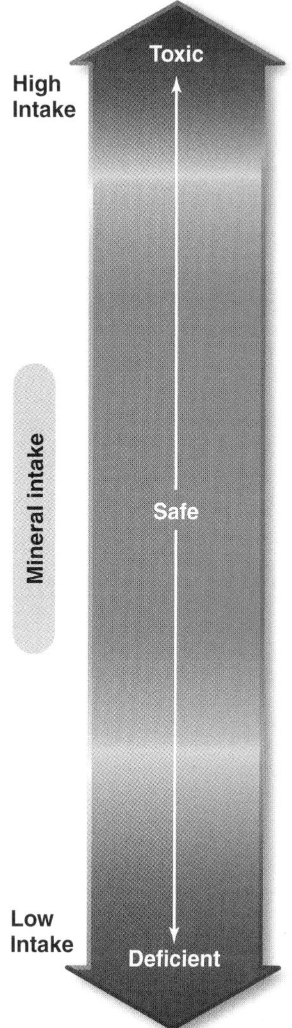

Figure 9.9 Mineral intakes. Many minerals have a narrow range of safe intake. As a result, it is relatively easy to consume a toxic amount, especially by taking supplements that only contain a particular mineral.

Other Sources of Minerals

The tap water in your community may be a source of minerals that you may have overlooked. "Hard" water naturally contains a variety of minerals, including calcium, sulphur, copper, iron, and zinc. Additionally, fluoride is often added to public water supplies. Although fluoride is not essential for life, the mineral strengthens bones and teeth. Individuals who live in rural areas and obtain their water from a well typically have lower fluoride levels in their water than those served by municipal water supplies.

Water with high mineral content often tastes and smells unpleasant. Many people drink bottled water as a substitute for tap water because they think bottled water tastes better and it is safer. To learn more about bottled water, read the Chapter 9 Highlight.

Dietary supplements are another source of minerals. A daily multiple vitamin and mineral supplement is generally safe for healthy people, because a dose of this type of supplement does not provide high amounts of minerals. However, people need to be careful when taking dietary supplements that contain individual minerals, such as iron or selenium. Many minerals have a narrow range of safe intake, therefore it is easy to consume a toxic amount, especially by taking supplements that only contain a particular mineral (Fig. 9.9). Additionally, an excess of one mineral can interfere with the absorption or metabolism of other minerals. For example, the presence of a large amount of zinc in the intestinal tract decreases copper absorption. Single mineral supplements are usually unnecessary and unsafe unless they are prescribed to treat a specific medical condition, such as iron deficiency.

Concept Checkpoint

11. List at least three different functions of minerals in the body and provide an example of a mineral that performs each function.

12. What is the primary difference between a major mineral and a trace mineral? List three major minerals and three trace minerals.

13. Explain how minerals that are naturally in foods can be lost during food processing, including preparation.

14. Discuss factors that influence mineral absorption in the digestive tract.

Major Minerals

Table 9.3 summarizes nutrition-related information about the major minerals. This section focuses on calcium, sodium, potassium, and magnesium because North Americans tend to consume too much or too little of them. For more information about Dietary Reference Intake (DRI) values for minerals, see the inside cover of this textbook.

Calcium (Ca)

Calcium is the most plentiful mineral element in the human body. All cells need calcium, but more than 99% of the body's calcium is in an inorganic compound that forms the structural component of bones and teeth. The remaining calcium is in extracellular fluid.

Healthy adults absorb about 25% of the calcium in foods.[18] However, during stages of life when the body needs extra calcium—such as infancy and pregnancy—absorption can be as high as 60%. Older people, especially aging women, do not absorb calcium as well as younger people. In addition to advanced age, other factors that reduce calcium absorption include vitamin D deficiency, diarrhea, and foods that contain large amounts of phosphorus, oxalic acid, and phytic acid, a compound in whole grains.[18]

Why Is Calcium Necessary?

The body needs calcium to form and maintain bones. Calcium is also a structural component of teeth, and the mineral is involved in muscle contraction, blood clot formation, nerve impulse transmission, and cell metabolism. Additionally, calcium may play important roles in maintaining healthy blood pressure and functioning of the immune system.

Bone Development and Maintenance Although your bones do not appear to change shape, they are being remodelled continually in response to the physical stresses placed on them. The remodelling process involves breaking down bone where there is little

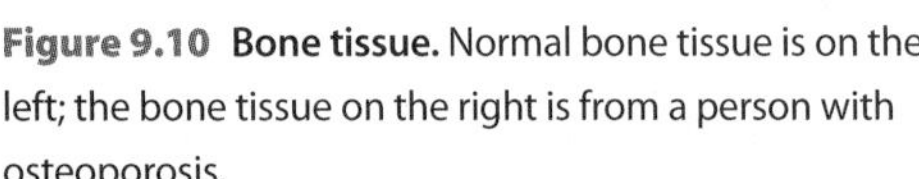

Figure 9.10 Bone tissue. Normal bone tissue is on the left; the bone tissue on the right is from a person with osteoporosis.

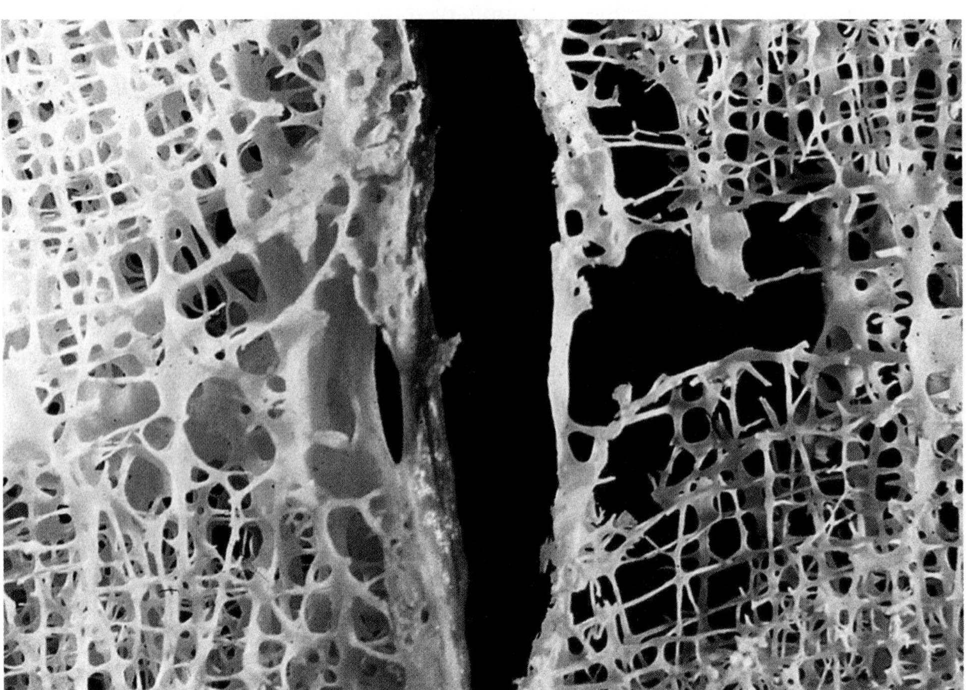

Did You Know?

Bone remodelling occurs throughout life, and as a result of this process, most of your skeleton is replaced about every 10 years.[19]

stress and building bone where it is needed. Special bone cells called **osteoclasts** tear down bone tissue where it is not necessary; **osteoblasts** are bone cells that add bone tissue where it is needed. For example, if you play tennis regularly and hold the racquet in your right hand, the bones in your right arm are denser and, therefore, stronger than the bones in your left arm. Bones that are denser have greater bone mass, and they are less likely to fracture than less dense bones. Figure 9.10 shows X-rays of bone tissue. By just looking at the photos, can you tell which bone is denser and has greater mass?

A supply of calcium is vital to all cells, not just to bone cells. The body stores calcium primarily in bone tissue. Osteoclasts become very active and release calcium from bone, when the diet lacks calcium. The mineral enters the blood and becomes available to all cells that need it.

The body has complex hormonal systems to maintain calcium homeostasis (see Fig. 8.11 on p. 239). The thyroid and parathyroid glands help regulate blood calcium levels (Fig. 9.11). In response to falling blood calcium levels, the parathyroid glands secrete **parathyroid hormone (PTH)** that signals osteoclasts to release calcium from bones so that the mineral can enter the bloodstream. PTH also works with vitamin D to increase intestinal calcium absorption and reduce calcium excretion in urine. The thyroid gland secretes the hormone **calcitonin** when the level of calcium in blood is too high. Calcitonin signals osteoblasts to remove excess calcium from blood for storage in bone. All these physiological responses help maintain your blood calcium level within the normal range (see Fig. 8.11).

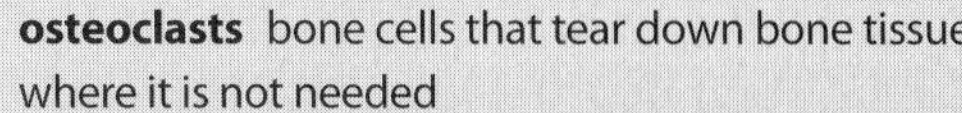

osteoclasts bone cells that tear down bone tissue where it is not needed

osteoblasts bone cells that add bone to where the tissue is needed

parathyroid hormone (PTH) hormone secreted by parathyroid glands when blood calcium levels are too low

calcitonin hormone secreted by the thyroid gland when blood calcium levels are too high

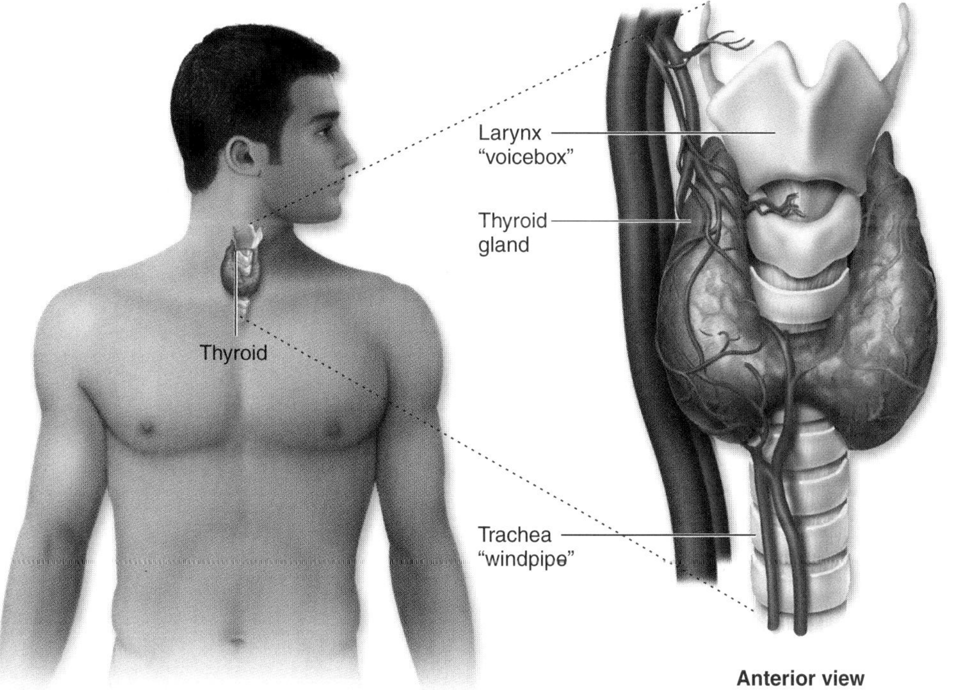

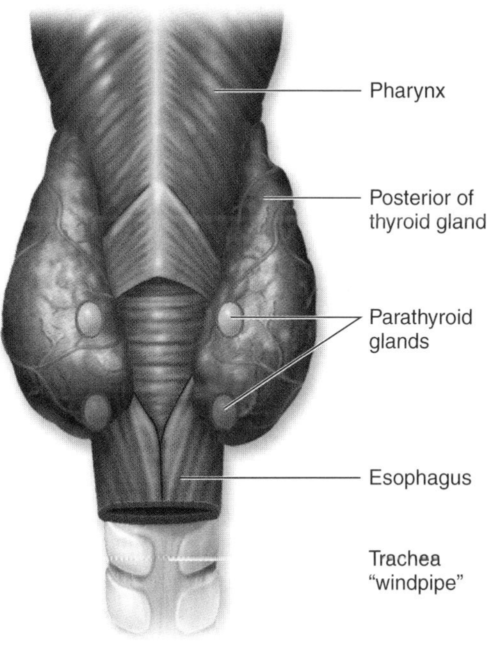

Figure 9.11 Thyroid and parathyroid glands. The thyroid gland has the four parathyroid glands imbedded in the back (posterior) of the organ. Hormones secreted by the thyroid and parathyroid glands help regulate blood calcium levels.

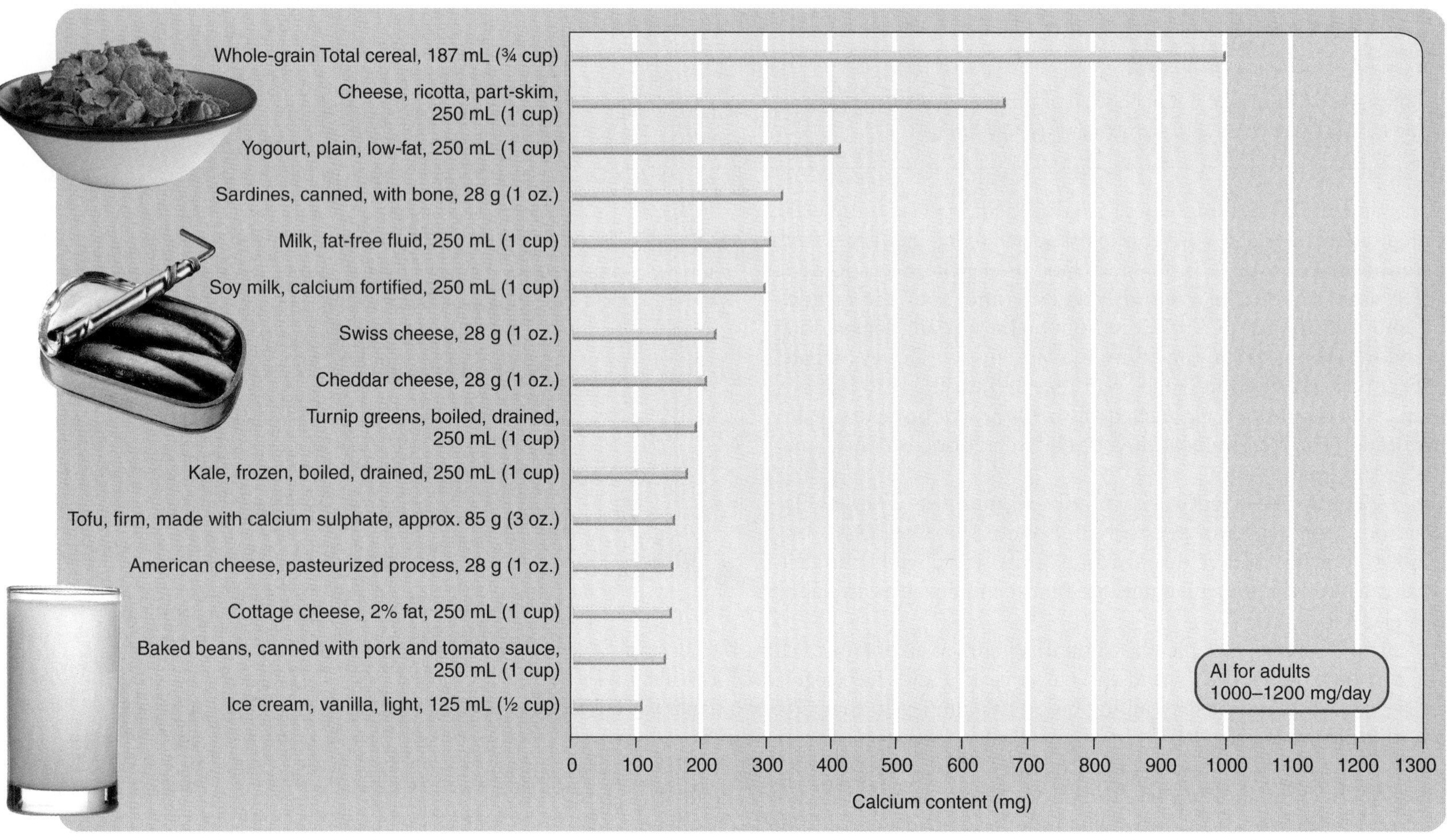

Figure 9.12 **Calcium content of selected foods.**

Figure 9.13 **Calcium-rich greens.** Leafy vegetables, such as bok choy and collard greens, are rich sources of calcium.

Sources of Calcium

Figure 9.12 includes some foods that are among the richest sources of calcium. Milk products, such as fluid milk, yogourt, and cheese, provide about 75% of the calcium in North American diets.[20] Moreover, the calcium in milk products is well absorbed and used by the body. Cottage cheese, however, does not supply as much calcium as the milk from which it is made (see Fig. 9.12). Milk loses about half of its calcium content when it is processed to make cottage cheese. Although butter, sour cream, and cream cheese are made from whole milk, people generally do not eat enough of these energy-dense foods to contribute much calcium to their diets. Furthermore, butter, sour cream, and cream cheese contain relatively high amounts of saturated fat that can be a risk factor for cardiovascular disease. Leafy greens, especially kale, collard, turnip, bok choy, and mustard greens; broccoli; and breads and rolls made with milk or calcium-containing additives are good plant sources of calcium (Fig. 9.13).

Calcium is added to a variety of foods, including fortified orange juice, soy milk, cereals, and breakfast bars. Another source of calcium is soybean curd (tofu) that is made with calcium sulphate. You can read labels to learn about the calcium content of

Did You Know?

Canned fish with edible soft bones such as sardines and salmon are good calcium sources. When making salmon patties using canned fish, mash up the bones along with the salmon. The bones are so soft, you won't notice them in the cooked product.

Vegetables and Fruit	Grain Products	Milk and Alternatives	Meat and Alternatives
Greens	Calcium-fortified snack foods	Milk	Tofu
Spinach	Calcium-fortified flour tortillas	Yogourt	Almonds
Broccoli	Calcium-fortified ready-to-eat cereals	Cheese	Shrimp
Green beans			Sardines
Calcium-fortified orange juice			Canned salmon

Figure 9.14 Good sources of calcium. Certain foods from these groups are good sources of calcium.

packaged foods; the information is a mandatory component of the Nutrition Facts table. Figure 9.14 indicates food groups from the *Eating Well with Canada's Food Guide* that are naturally good sources of calcium.

Calcium Supplements Many adults find it difficult to consume enough milk products and other calcium-rich foods to achieve adequate intakes of the mineral. Thus, taking calcium supplements has become a common practice, especially among older adults. Dietary supplements containing calcium carbonate are the most commonly used calcium supplement. Supplements made with calcium citrate are also available. The body absorbs both forms of calcium to about the same extent.

Each of the following foods contains about the same amount of calcium (approximately 300 mg) that's in 250 mL (1 cup) of skim milk:

- 500 mL (2 cups) low-fat (2% milk) cottage cheese
- 65 g (2.3 oz.) processed cheese
- 158 mL (⅔ cup) plain, low-fat yogourt
- 42 g (1.5 oz.) natural cheese (e.g., cheddar or Swiss)
- 250 mL (1 cup) calcium-fortified soy milk

Did You Know?

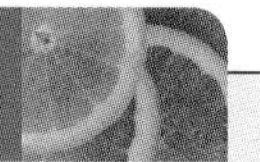

Certain brands of antacids contain calcium carbonate. These products can be an inexpensive way of obtaining some calcium. An antacid pill that contains 750 mg of calcium carbonate provides 300 mg of elemental calcium. However, using calcium carbonate–containing antacids as a source of calcium can increase the likelihood of calcium toxicity. Therefore, consumers should avoid taking too many antacids or other calcium supplements. The UL for calcium is 2500 mg per day.

Figure 9.15 Osteoporosis. In many people with severe osteoporosis, bones in the upper back fracture and then heal in an abnormally curved position.

Dietary Adequacy

The adult Adequate Intake (AI) for calcium ranges from 1000 to 1200 mg per day.[18,21] For children and adolescents between the ages of 9 and 18, the AI is higher (1300 mg/day) to allow for increases in bone mass during growth and development.

Calcium Deficiency Women tend to consume less than the AI for calcium, whereas most men have intakes that are roughly equivalent to the AI. Total vegetarians (vegans) and people who are lactose intolerant are at risk of calcium deficiency, because they often avoid consuming milk and milk products, the most reliable dietary sources of calcium.[22]

What Is Osteoporosis? **Osteoporosis** is a chronic disease characterized by low bone mass and reduced bone structure (see Fig. 9.10).[19,23] People with osteoporosis have weak bones that are susceptible to fractures. In severe cases, spinal bones in the upper back fracture and then heal in an abnormally curved position, giving the obvious "widow's hump" appearance associated with osteoporosis (Fig. 9.15).

In Canada, as many as 2 million people suffer from osteoporosis. It is estimated that, in Canada, 1 in 4 women over 50 years of age and 1 in 8 men over the age of 50 have osteoporosis, though it can occur at any age.[23] Each year, an estimated $1.3 billion are spent treating osteoporosis in Canada.[23] Osteoporosis-related fractures often involve the hip, wrist, or ankle bones, and they can be devastating events for the elderly. For example, about 20% of older North Americans who experience a broken hip die within one year of the injury.[19,23] Most deaths resulted from complications after surgery to repair the broken hip. Results of a study involving nearly 2450 patients who had surgery to repair hip

TABLE 9.4 *Risk Factors for Osteoporosis*

Factors You Can't Change:
Being a woman
Growing older
Having white or Asian ancestry
Having a family history of osteoporosis
Having a small body frame
Factors You Can Change:
Having low estrogen levels in women; low testosterone levels in men
Following diets that contain inadequate amounts of calcium and vitamin D
Using medications such as steroids or some types of anticonvulsants
Being physically inactive
Smoking cigarettes
Consuming excessive alcohol
Consuming excess protein, sodium, and caffeine, especially when calcium intake is low

Modified from: Bennett B: The low-down on osteoporosis: What we know and what we don't. *Word on health: Consumer health information based on research from the National Institutes of Health*. 2003. www.nih.gov/news/WordonHealth/dec2003/osteo.htm. Accessed: June 11, 2006.

osteoporosis chronic disease characterized by bones with low mass and reduced structure

estrogen hormone needed for normal bone development and maintenance

peak bone mass level of maximum bone density achieved in early adulthood

fractures indicated that heart failure and chest infection were the most common surgical complications that led to death.[24]

Several factors contribute to bone loss and osteoporosis. Consuming a high-protein diet may increase urinary calcium excretion, particularly when calcium intake is low. Additionally, family history of osteoporosis, cigarette smoking, and excessive alcohol consumption are also associated with increased risk of the disease. Other factors that contribute to low bone mass include small body-frame size, irregular or absent menstrual cycles, prolonged bed rest, and use of certain medications. Table 9.4 lists these and other risk factors for osteoporosis. Note that some of these factors cannot be modified, but other factors can be changed to prevent or delay the development of the disease.

Regardless of one's sex, loss of bone tissue begins in mid-adulthood. In men, bone loss is slow and steady beginning around age 30. In women, however, the rate of bone loss increases significantly after menopause, that is, after menstrual cycles have ceased. At this time of life, women have the highest risk of osteoporosis.[25,26] Why? The hormone **estrogen** is needed for normal bone development and maintenance. In women of child-bearing age, ovaries are the primary source of estrogen. After menopause, a woman's ovaries no longer produce estrogen, and as a result, her rate of bone loss exceeds the rate of bone replacement. Because estrogen is so important to maintaining strong bones, women should see a physician if they have signs of estrogen deficiency such as irregular menstrual cycles.

Efforts to reduce the risk of osteoporosis should begin early in life. Proper diet and regular exercise are especially important from early childhood through late adolescence, because the body actively builds bone during these life stages. In late adolescence and early adulthood, most Canadians achieve **peak bone mass** (or peak bone density).[27] The best way to prevent osteoporosis as we age is to maximize peak bone mass in early adulthood. By following the recommendations of the *Eating Well with Canada's Food Guide*, most Canadians can obtain adequate amounts of calcium from foods.[28] Exposing skin to sunlight can stimulate the body's ability to form vitamin D, but some people will need to take calcium and vitamin D supplements.

Exercise training, especially performing weight-bearing activities, increases bone mass, because contracting muscles keep tension (physical stress) on bones.[29] Table 9.5 lists examples of weight-bearing activities. Regardless of one's age, regular physical activity provides numerous benefits to health, such as improving balance and reducing the likeli-

Regular physical activity provides numerous benefits to health, including strengthening bones. These older adults are performing tai chi, an activity that can improve balance and reduce the likelihood of falling.

TABLE 9.5 *Examples of Weight-Bearing Activities*

Examples of Weight-Bearing Activities
Low-impact aerobics
Basketball
Running or jogging
Walking
Dancing
Hiking
Stair climbing
Strength training with weights
Tennis and other racquet sports

hood of falling. Among the elderly, falls often result in fractures and the need for costly long-term medical care.

A simple way to monitor bone mass is by tracking height. Losing an inch or more of adult height may be the first sign that a person has experienced spinal fractures due to osteoporosis.[30] If osteoporosis is suspected, a person can undergo special painless X-ray testing to determine the extent of bone loss. Individuals with a family history of osteoporosis, men who have low testosterone levels, and women who are postmenopausal should ask their physician if testing to determine bone mineral density is necessary. People who are high risk for or who already have osteoporosis may require medication to reduce their rate of bone loss. For postmenopausal women, taking calcium and vitamin D supplements may not reduce the risk of hip fractures.[31] In this life stage, it may be too late to benefit from simply taking dietary supplements to prevent osteoporosis.

Everyone needs to be concerned about their risk of osteoporosis and focus on maximizing their peak bone mass while they are young. The "60 Second Osteoporosis Risk Quiz" on the Osteoporosis Canada Web site (www.osteoporosis.ca) can help you determine whether you or someone you know is at risk for the disease.

Food & Nutrition *tips*

The following suggestions can add more calcium to your diet:

- Sprinkle grated low-fat cheeses on top of salads, bean or pasta dishes, and cooked vegetables.
- If you don't like the taste of plain skim milk, try adding a small amount of flavoured syrup to the beverage. Two teaspoons of "lite" chocolate syrup add 50 kcal and some trace minerals to the milk.
- For a snack, melt a slice of low-fat cheese on half a whole-wheat bagel, whole-wheat crackers, or a slice of rye bread.
- If a recipe calls for water, substitute skim milk for water, if it's appropriate. For example, use fat-free milk when making cooked oatmeal or pancake batter.
- Add 60 mL (¼ cup) skim milk powder to 454 g (1 lb.) of raw ground meat when preparing hamburgers, meatballs, or meatloaf.
- Make homemade smoothies by blending plain low-fat yogourt with fresh or frozen fruit and fat-reduced ice cream or sherbet (see the Recipes for Healthy Living feature near the end of this chapter).
- If you use a calcium supplement, take only 500 mg at a time and ingest the supplement with meals to enhance the mineral's absorption.

Calcium Toxicity The Upper Level (UL) for calcium is 2500 mg per day.[21] Normally, the small intestine prevents too much calcium from being absorbed. However, taking too many calcium-containing antacids or supplements, or drinking too much vitamin D–fortified milk can result in excessive calcium absorption and hypercalcemia. **Hypercalcemia** (*hyper* = excess; *calcemia* = calcium in the blood) is a condition characterized by a higher than normal concentration of calcium in blood. Signs and symptoms of hypercalcemia include kidney stones, bone pain, muscle weakness, fatigue, and hypertension.[32] Treatment for hypercalcemia may include avoiding vitamin D and calcium supplements to reduce calcium absorption.

hypercalcemia condition characterized by higher than normal concentration of calcium in blood

Sodium (Na)

Table salt is the primary source of sodium in Canadian diets.[33] The chemical commonly called "table salt" or simply "salt" is actually sodium chloride, a compound comprised of two minerals, sodium and chloride. A teaspoon of table salt supplies 2325 mg of sodium. (Unless otherwise noted, we will refer to sodium chloride simply as "salt" or "table salt.") The human digestive tract absorbs almost all of the sodium that is in foods and beverages.

Why Is Sodium Necessary?

Sodium is the major positively charged ion in extracellular fluid. Sodium plays a major role in maintaining normal fluid balance and conducting nerve impulses. The mineral also participates in certain transport mechanisms that help small substances such as glucose and amino acids to enter cells.

Sources of Sodium

Most vegetables, meats, and grain products are naturally low in sodium. Thus, most of the sodium Canadians consume is from the salt that is added to food during processing, preparation, or at the table.[33] As a food additive, salt enhances flavours and can prevent the growth of microorganisms responsible for food spoilage. Other food additives that contain sodium include sodium nitrate, sodium citrate, and *monosodium glutamate (MSG)*, a seasoning that is frequently added to foods served in Chinese restaurants.

Salted snack foods, French fries, canned soups, sauces and gravies, hot dogs and "deli" meats, cheeses, and pickled foods are high in sodium (Figure 9.16). If you frequently eat these foods, your sodium intake is probably higher than recommended. Although sodium is an essential mineral, diets that contain high amounts of sodium are associated with increased risk of hypertension.

Dietary Adequacy

Humans require only about 180 mg of sodium per day, but the AI for adults under 51 years of age is 1500 mg per day.[4,21] The AI for sodium does not apply for people who perspire heavily, such as marathon runners, or people who work in extremely hot conditions.[4] Sweat contains small amounts of sodium, chloride, and some other minerals. People who perspire extensively can lose large amounts of these minerals in their sweat.

The Canadian Community Health Survey revealed that for Canadians aged 9 to 70 years, 85% of males and 60 to 80% of females had sodium intakes in excess of the UL.[33] Health Canada encourages Canadians to use the Nutrition Facts table on food products to try to moderate sodium intake.[34] In October 2007, Health Canada announced that it was establishing a multi-stakeholder working group to develop and oversee the implementation of a strategy for reducing sodium intake among Canadians, which may include regulation to control the amount of sodium Canadian food production companies add to food products.[34]

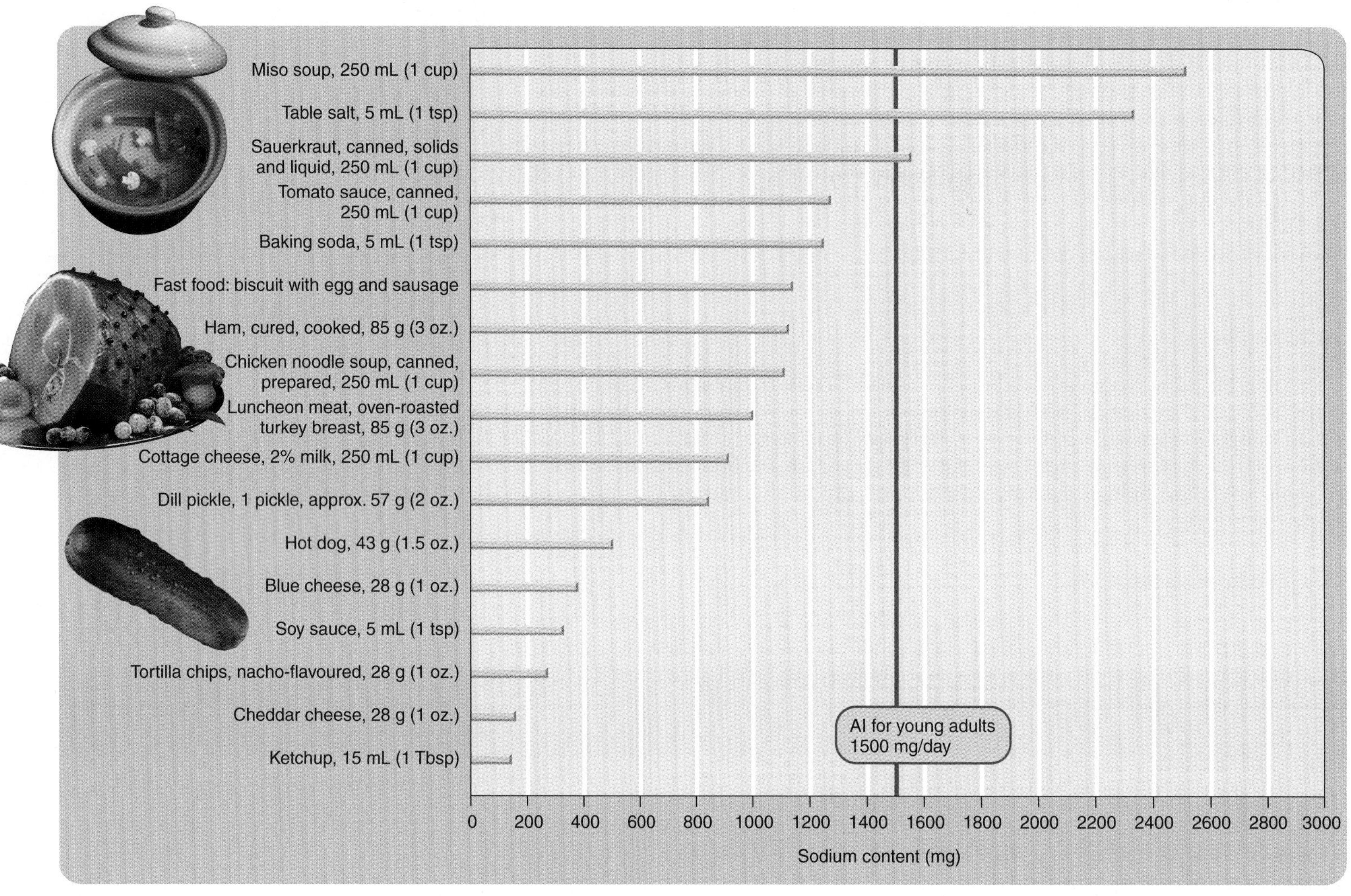

Figure 9.16 Sodium content of selected foods and food additives.

Sodium Deficiency The typical North American's diet supplies far more sodium than the AI amount, and as a result, the average person is unlikely to become sodium deficient. A healthy body is able to regulate its sodium concentration effectively, but sodium depletion can occur in certain situations. A person who loses more than 2 to 3% of body weight as a result of excessive sweating is at risk of sodium depletion. In most cases, drinking fluids and simply eating some salty foods or adding salt to foods is usually effective for restoring the body's sodium content. Endurance athletes may need to consume sports drinks during competition to avoid dehydration and sodium depletion. Salt tablets, however, are generally not recommended for sodium replacement. Sodium depletion also can result from diarrhea or vomiting, especially in infants. In these cases, it is necessary to obtain medical care promptly to replace the lost fluids and electrolytes, because infants can develop dehydration rapidly.

Sodium Toxicity The adult UL for sodium is 2300 mg per day.[4,21] The average adult Canadian, however, consumes more than 2500 mg of sodium daily.[35] According to the results of numerous studies, high sodium intakes are associated with increased risk of hypertension.[36] Thus, health experts generally recommend that Canadians limit their sodium consumption. To evaluate your sodium intake, take the "Sodium Intake Assessment" below.

Sodium and Hypertension **Hypertension**, a condition characterized by persistently elevated blood pressure, is a serious public health problem in Canada and the United States. Compared to people with normal blood pressure, hypertensive individuals have greater risk of cardiovascular disease (CVD), especially heart disease and stroke, as well as kidney failure and damage to other organs. According to data from recent surveys, an estimated 22% of adult Canadians have hypertension.[37] Children can also develop hypertension. A study of ethnically diverse 14-year-old children in Texas, California, and North Carolina indicated that nearly one-fourth of the adolescents had hypertension.[38] Hypertension is often called the "silent killer," because high blood pressure generally does not cause symptoms until the affected person's organs and blood vessels have been damaged.

The best way to detect hypertension is to have regular blood pressure screenings. When you have your blood pressure determined, two measurements are actually taken. The first measurement is the **systolic pressure**, which is the maximum blood pressure within an artery. This value occurs when the ventricles, the heart's pumping chambers, contract. The second measurement is the diastolic pressure, which measures the pressure in an artery when the ventricles relax between contractions. The systolic value is always higher than the **diastolic value**. For adults, healthy blood pressure readings are less than 120/80 millimetres of mercury (mm Hg). After having your blood pressure measured, ask the clinician for your systolic and diastolic readings and keep a record of the values.

A person who is under physical or emotional stress can expect his or her blood pressure to rise temporarily. However, persistent systolic blood pressure readings of 120 mm Hg to 139 mm Hg and diastolic readings of 80 mm Hg to 89 mm Hg are signs of **prehypertension**.[39] People with prehypertension are more likely to develop hypertension than people with normal blood pressure. If a person's blood pressure persists at systolic values that are greater than or equal to (≥) 140 mm Hg and diastolic values that are ≥ 90 mm Hg, he or she has hypertension. Table 9.6 presents categories for blood pressure levels in adults.

Most cases of hypertension do not have simple causes, but advanced age, African ancestry, obesity, physical inactivity, smoking cigarettes, and excess alcohol and sodium

hypertension condition characterized by persistently elevated blood pressure

systolic pressure maximum blood pressure within an artery that occurs when the ventricles contract

diastolic pressure pressure in an artery that occurs when the ventricles relax between contractions

prehypertension persistent systolic blood pressure readings of 120 mm Hg to 139 mm Hg and diastolic readings of 80 mm Hg to 89 mm Hg

Sodium Intake Assessment ✓

For each question, place a check in the column that best describes your sodium intake habits.

How Often Do You...	Rarely	Occasionally	Often	Daily
1. Eat cured or processed meats ("deli" meats), such as bacon, sausage, hot dogs, ham, and other luncheon meats?				
2. Eat canned or frozen vegetables with sauce?				
3. Eat commercially prepared meals, main dishes, or canned or dehydrated soups?				
4. Eat processed cheeses, such as cheese spreads?				
5. Eat salted nuts, popcorn, pretzels, corn chips, or potato chips?				
6. Add salt to cooking water for vegetables, rice, or pasta?				
7. Add salt, seasoning mixes, salad dressings, or condiments—such as soy sauce, steak sauce, pickles, and ketchup—to foods during preparation or at the table?				
8. Salt your food before tasting it?				
9. Ignore reading the Nutrition Facts table for sodium content when buying foods?				
10. Choose restaurant menu items that are salty or with sauces, when dining out?				

Scoring: The more checks you put in the "often" or "daily" columns, the higher your dietary sodium intake is. To reduce your sodium intake, choose low-sodium foods from each food group more often and balance high-sodium food choices with high-potassium ones.

Adapted from: USDA: *Home and Garden Bulletin*, No. 232–6, April 1986.

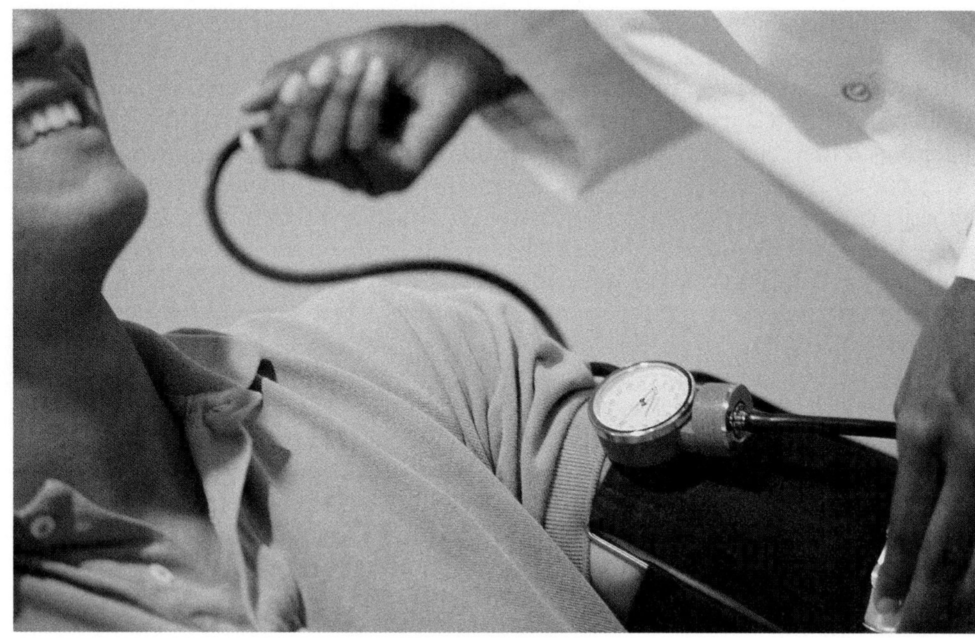

The best way to detect hypertension is to have regular blood pressure screenings.

Did You Know?

Some homeowners install water-softening machines, because "hard water" interferes with the cleansing ability of soap and laundry detergent. Water softeners usually replace calcium and magnesium ions with sodium ions. Therefore, drinking softened water or using the treated water for preparing foods is not recommended because of its high sodium content.

TABLE 9.6 *Categories for Blood Pressure Levels in Adults (Ages 18 Years and Older)*

Category*	Blood Pressure Level (mm Hg)	
	Systolic	**Diastolic**
Normal	< 120 and	< 80
Prehypertension	120 to 139 or	80 to 89
Hypertension	≥ 140 or	≥ 90

* When systolic and diastolic blood pressures fall into different categories, the higher category should be used to classify blood pressure level. For example, a person with a blood pressure of 160/80 mm Hg would be classified as having hypertension. In people who are older than 50 years, elevated systolic values are a more significant risk factor for heart disease and stroke than elevated diastolic readings.

Source: National Heart, Lung, and Blood Institute: *Seventh report of the Joint National Committee on prevention, detection, evaluation, and treatment of high blood pressure.* (JNC 7) Express, 2003. www.nhlbi.nih.gov/guidelines/hypertension/express.pdf. Accessed: May 8, 2006.

TABLE 9.7 *Major Risk Factors for Hypertension*

Family history
Advanced age
African ancestry
Obesity
Physical inactivity
Consuming excess sodium
Cigarette smoking
Consuming excess alcohol
Type 2 diabetes

intakes are among the major risk factors for the condition (Table 9.7). Blood pressure usually increases as a person ages, probably in part because plaque builds up in arteries (atherosclerosis) and interferes with the normal functioning of the blood vessels. Healthy arteries are flexible tubes that expand with each heartbeat and recoil in between beats. Atherosclerotic arteries are less flexible and cannot expand as much as healthy arteries. As a result, the heart must work harder to pump blood through the stiff arteries and blood pressure becomes chronically elevated.

For reasons that are unclear, non-Hispanic North Americans of African descent are more likely than non-Hispanic white North Americans to develop hypertension, especially early in life. Recent studies show diets that limit sodium but contain adequate amounts of calcium, potassium, and magnesium may decrease high blood pressure, especially among North Americans of African descent.[36,40]

Obesity, a condition characterized by excessive amounts of body fat, is a major risk factor for hypertension.[36,40] Physical inactivity is another leading risk factor related to hypertension. Obesity and physical inactivity are modifiable risk factors. By exercising and losing some excess fat, obese people who have hypertension often experience reductions in their blood pressure.[36,40]

Excessive alcohol intake increases the risk of hypertension. To reduce their chances of developing high blood pressure, people should avoid alcohol or limit their consumption to two or fewer drinks per day (men) and only one drink per day (women and older adults). Other important risk factors for hypertension include having diabetes and using tobacco.

Finally, a high-sodium diet is associated with increased risk of hypertension, and in some cases, such diets can be a cause of hypertension.[36,41] Many medical researchers think some people are genetically "sodium sensitive." A person who is sodium sensitive is more likely to develop hypertension as a result of consuming a high-sodium diet than an individual who lacks this sensitivity. The kidneys of a sodium-sensitive person may be unable to eliminate excess sodium as effectively as the kidneys of a healthy person. The excess sodium causes the body to retain water, and blood volume and pressure increase as a result.

Health Canada recommends less than 1500 mg of sodium daily.[21] People with high blood pressure may need to consume even less sodium. According to Health Canada recommendations, people can lower their blood pressure by limiting their sodium intake to no more than 1500 mg per day.[21,34]

If you want to lower your sodium intake, try gradually reducing your use of salt and consumption of salty foods. By doing so, you will eventually become accustomed to the taste of less salty food. To replace salt as a seasoning, try using garlic, citrus juice, and herbs and spices to enhance the taste of foods. Furthermore, avoid buying seasonings with added salt, such as "garlic salt" or "onion salt," and purchase seasonings without added salt (garlic *powder* or onion *powder*) instead.

Information about a packaged food's sodium content is a mandatory component of the Nutrition Facts table. If you take the time to read labels, you can find foods that have little or no salt added to them during processing. For example, 28 g (1 oz.) of salted peanuts provide 230 mg of sodium; the same amount of unsalted peanuts has only 2 mg of sodium. The following Food & Nutrition Tips provide some suggestions for reducing your salt (sodium) intake.

Even if your blood pressure is normal now, it is important to have regular blood pressure checks as you grow older, because the risk of hypertension increases with age. In Canada, the majority of individuals with hypertension are 45 years of age or older, and 43% of those with hypertension do not know that they have it.[42] Young people, however, are not immune to hypertension. Justin S., the university student featured in the Real People, Real Stories feature on page 300, was 18 when he found out he had hypertension. When was the last time you had your blood pressure measured? What were the systolic and diastolic values?

By reading the label, you can find foods that have high amounts of added sodium. A serving of these chips provides nearly 10% of the recommended amount of sodium for a day.

To reduce your sodium intake:

- Prepare homemade meals and snacks as much as possible so that you have control over your salt intake.
- Do not add salt while preparing foods, even though instructions tell you to "add salt."
- Taste your food *before* salting it. Adjust to eating foods with less salt in them.
- Do not keep a salt shaker on your table.
- Read the Nutrition Facts tables before purchasing packaged foods to determine sodium contents of the items.

REAL *people*

REAL *stories*

Justin S.

If you were to meet 23-year-old Justin S., your first impression would be that he is the "picture" of good health. At 6'1", Justin weighs 77 kg (170 lbs.) and appears to be in great physical condition. Justin enjoys bicycling; he also runs three to five miles a day and weight trains three days a week to maintain his muscle mass. In addition to being very physically active, Justin has other healthy habits—he doesn't smoke, he doesn't consume caffeine or alcohol, and he keeps his salt intake low.

In the spring of his senior year of high school, Justin decided to join the Canadian military after graduation. As part of military enlistment activities, Justin underwent thorough physical screening. Much to his surprise, his blood pressure was elevated to such an extent that the Canadian military denied his entrance into the service. "It was a huge shock," said Justin. "I had no signs or symptoms of hypertension. I didn't even know what 'hypertension' was."

After being evaluated by his family doctor, Justin was eventually accepted into the Canadian military, but he had to see a cardiologist, a physician who specializes in diseases of the heart and blood vessels. To treat his condition, Justin was given medication. He also learned to avoid salty foods and monitor his blood pressure at least three times daily.

It is unusual for physically active young adults who have healthy lifestyles and body weights to develop chronic high blood pressure. However, Justin now realizes that he was at risk for hypertension because of his family history of the disease. His mother, mother's sister, and maternal grandmother have the condition.

Justin has some excellent advice for university students: "As a young person, you may think you are invincible. But even if you don't think there's anything wrong with you, have your blood pressure tested. I thought I was the healthiest person ever! For people who are struggling with hypertension like me, be sure to exercise regularly, watch your diet, and remember to take your medication. We may not be able to cure hypertension, but we can do our best to control it. For those individuals fortunate enough to be healthier than I am, go to the doctor anyway and get your blood pressure checked a couple times per year. You may be surprised to discover you're hypertensive, just as I was. They don't call it 'the silent killer' for nothing."

Treatment for hypertension usually includes taking certain medications, following dietary modifications, and making some other lifestyle changes (Table 9.8). The Dietary Approaches to Stop Hypertension (DASH) diet is low in sodium, total fat, saturated fat, and cholesterol, and high in fruits, vegetables, and low-fat dairy products.[36] Research indicates that people can lower their blood pressure and reduce their risk of CVD by following the DASH diet, losing excess body fat, and increasing their physical activity level.[36] To obtain more information about this diet and some low-sodium recipes, visit the Heart and Stroke Foundation of Canada's Web site: www.heartandstroke.com/site/c.ikIQLcMWJtE/b.3862329/k.4F4/Healthy_living__The_DASH_Diet_to_lower_blood_pressure.htm.

TABLE 9.8 *Practical Steps to Reduce Your Risk of Hypertension*

1. Follow the dietary recommendations of the *Eating Well with Canada's Food Guide* concerning fruit, vegetable, and low-fat milk intakes. Furthermore, consider using fresh fruit to replace some empty calories in your daily meals and snacks. (See Chapter 3 for more information about empty calories.)
2. Reduce your consumption of salty foods and have your blood pressure checked regularly.
3. Attain and maintain a healthy body weight.
4. Incorporate more physical activity into your daily schedule. For example, walk more often and climb stairs instead of riding elevators or escalators.
5. If you drink alcohol, consume alcoholic beverages in moderation—no more than two drinks per day for men and one drink per day for women and older adults.
6. Avoid using tobacco products.

Potassium (K)

Potassium is the primary positively charged ion in the intracellular fluid. In fact, most of the body's potassium is in cells. All cells need potassium, but nerve and muscle cells contain high amounts of the mineral.

Why Is Potassium Necessary?

Like sodium, potassium plays a key role in maintaining proper fluid balance. Unlike sodium, potassium is associated with lower, rather than higher, blood pressure values. Potassium is also necessary for transmitting nerve impulses, contracting muscles, and maintaining normal kidney function. Potassium-rich diets may lower blood pressure, reduce the risk of developing kidney stones, and possibly decrease bone loss.[4] A natural way to counteract high sodium intakes is to consume foods naturally rich in potassium and low in sodium, such as fruits.[40]

Sources of Potassium

Overall, fresh fruits, fruit juice, and vegetables are good dietary sources of potassium. Milk, whole grains, dried beans, and meats are also major contributors of potassium to Canadian diets. Figure 9.17 lists foods that are among the richest sources of this mineral. Figure 9.18 indicates food groups that are naturally good sources of potassium.

Did You Know?

Salt substitutes often contain a type of salt called potassium chloride. People who have severe kidney diseases may accumulate toxic levels of potassium in their blood. Therefore, kidney disease patients should consult their physicians before using salt substitutes made with potassium chloride. Fruits and vegetables are recommended sources of potassium instead of potassium chloride.[43]

Dietary Adequacy

The adult AI for potassium is 4700 mg per day.[21] On average, Canadians consume only about 3100 mg of potassium per day.[44] People can raise their potassium intakes by increasing their consumption of fruits, vegetables, whole-grain breads and cereals, and low-fat and skim milk and milk products.[4]

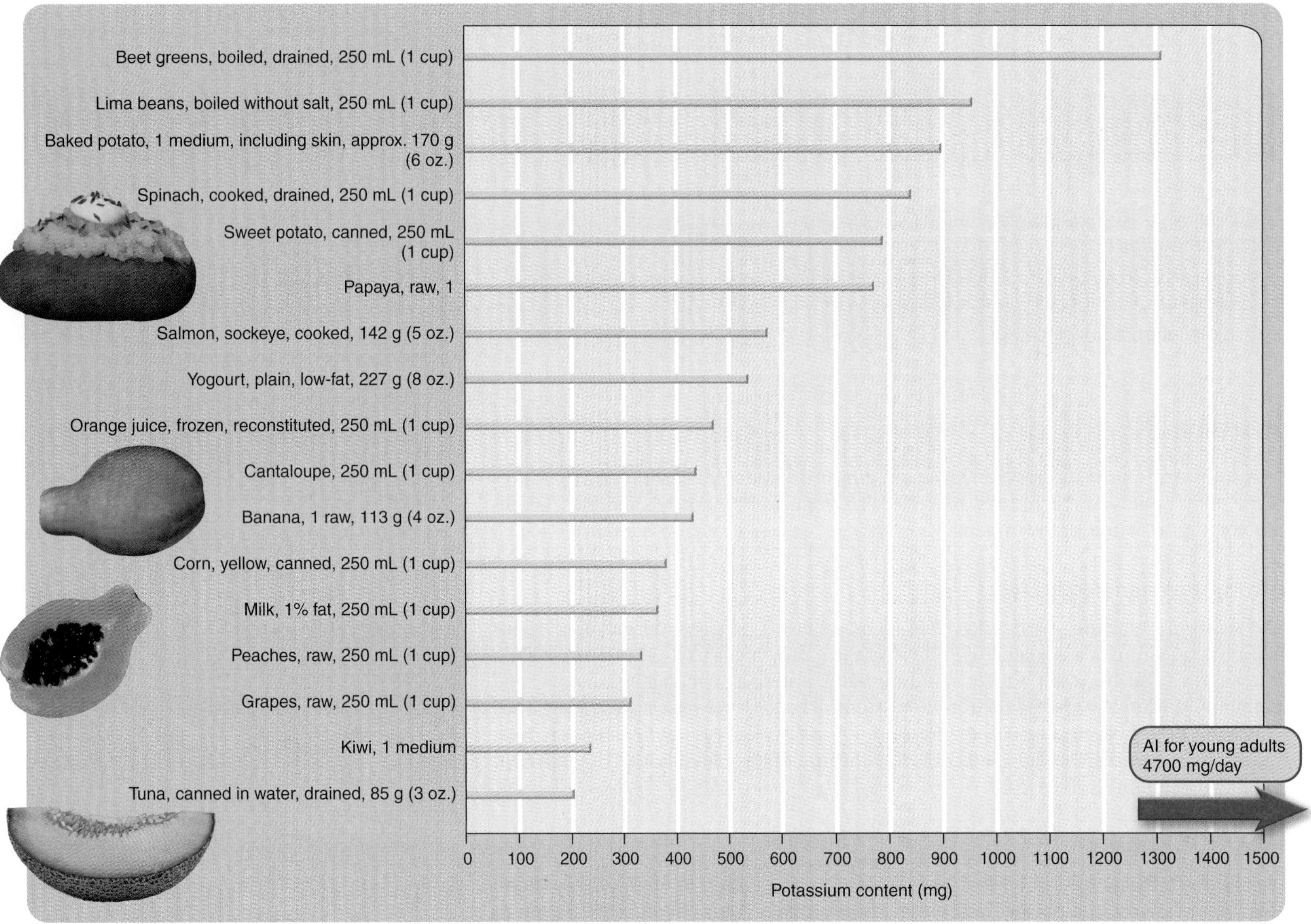

Figure 9.17 Potassium content of selected foods.

Source: Data from U.S. Department of Agriculture, Agricultural Research Service, USDA Nutrient Data Laboratory: Potassium K (mg) content of selected foods per common measure, sorted by nutrient content. *USDA national nutrient database for standard reference, release 19.* 2006.

The body is unable to conserve potassium as well as sodium, therefore the risk of potassium deficiency is greater than that of sodium. Individuals suffering from excessive sweating, vomiting, diarrhea, or kidney diseases that increase potassium excretion are at risk for potassium depletion. Symptoms of the condition generally include loss of appetite, muscle cramps, confusion, constipation, and increased urinary calcium excretion.

Although there is no UL for potassium, taking potassium supplements can upset the GI tract. Moreover, if a person's kidneys are not able to eliminate the excess potassium, the mineral accumulates in the blood and can cause the heart to stop beating. To avoid toxicity, do not take potassium supplements unless you are under a physician's care.

Magnesium (Mg)

Magnesium participates in more than 300 chemical reactions in the body.[45,46] The essential mineral also helps regulate normal muscle and nerve function as well as blood

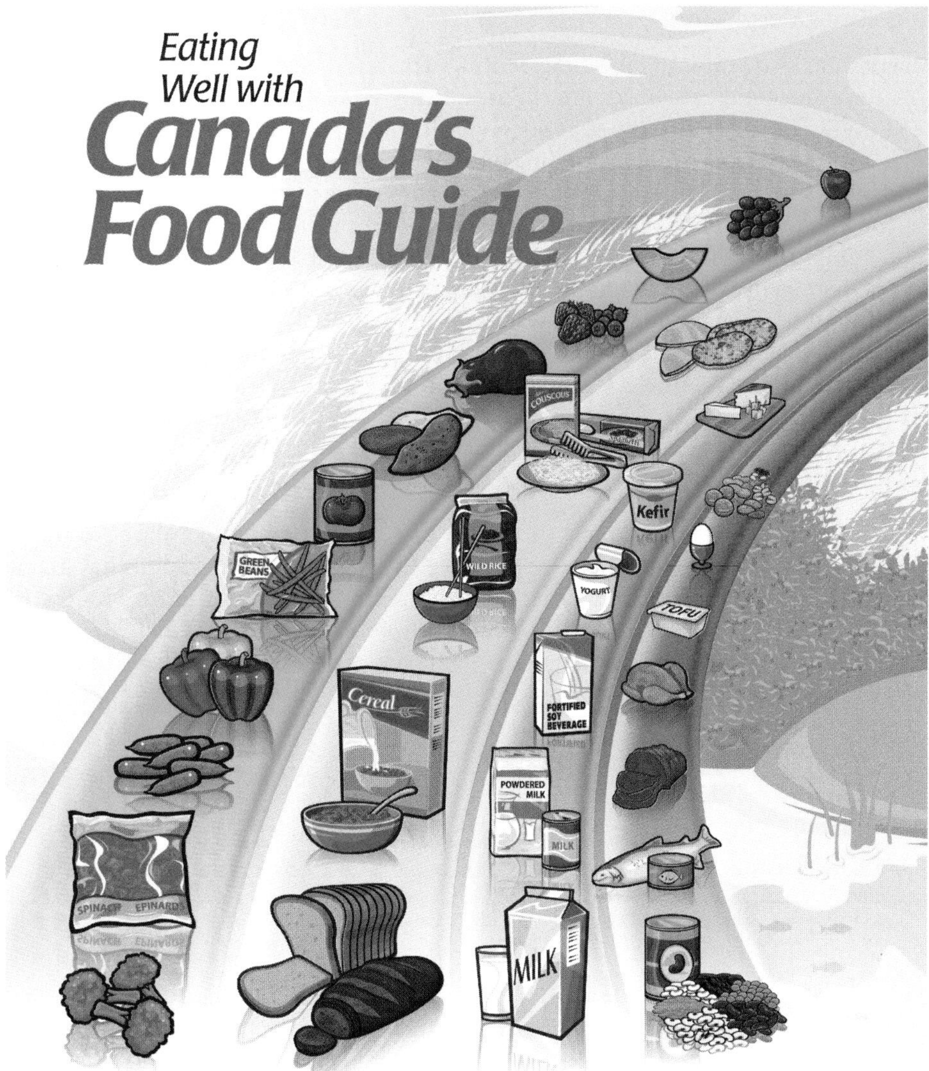

Vegetables and Fruit		Grain Products	Milk and Alternatives	Meat and Alternatives
Spinach	Pears	Whole-wheat bread	Milk	Meat
Squash	Prunes	Whole-grain products	Yogourt	Chicken
Potatoes	Peaches		Cottage cheese	Fish
Tomatoes	Avocados		Ricotta cheese	Shrimp
Lettuce	Cantaloupes			Beans
Lima beans	Bananas			

Figure 9.18 Good sources of potassium. Certain foods in these groups are good sources of potassium.

pressure and blood glucose levels. Additionally, the body needs magnesium to maintain strong bones and a healthy immune system. Magnesium may help prevent diabetes, hypertension, and CVD. However, more research is needed to clarify the mineral's role in these diseases.

Normally, humans absorb about 40 to 60% of the magnesium in their diets, but as much as 80% of the magnesium in food may be absorbed, when the body lacks the mineral. The kidneys regulate blood concentrations of magnesium and can reduce urinary losses of the mineral, when the body's level of magnesium is low.

Sources of Magnesium

Magnesium is in chlorophyll, the green pigment in plants. Therefore, it is not surprising that plant foods, such as spinach, green leafy vegetables, whole grains, beans, nuts, seeds, and chocolate, are the richest sources of magnesium. Animal products, such as milk and meats, also supply some magnesium. Figure 9.19 lists some commonly eaten foods that supply magnesium. Refined grains are generally low in magnesium, because the magnesium-rich bran and germ are removed during processing. Figure 9.20 indicates food groups that are naturally good sources of magnesium.

Other sources of magnesium are "hard" tap water and dietary supplements. However, amounts of magnesium in tap water can vary considerably. Moreover, the body does not absorb the form of magnesium (magnesium oxide) in multivitamin/mineral supplements very well. Nevertheless, hard water and magnesium oxide supplements can still contribute to a person's magnesium needs.

Dietary Adequacy

Adult RDAs for magnesium range from 310 to 420 mg per day.[21] Data from the 2004 Canadian Community Health Survey (CCHS 2.2) suggest that many adults in Canada do not consume recommended amounts of magnesium.[44] Among adult men and women, white Canadians tend to consume significantly more magnesium than Canadians of African descent. Nevertheless, magnesium intake is lower among older adults in every racial and ethnic group.

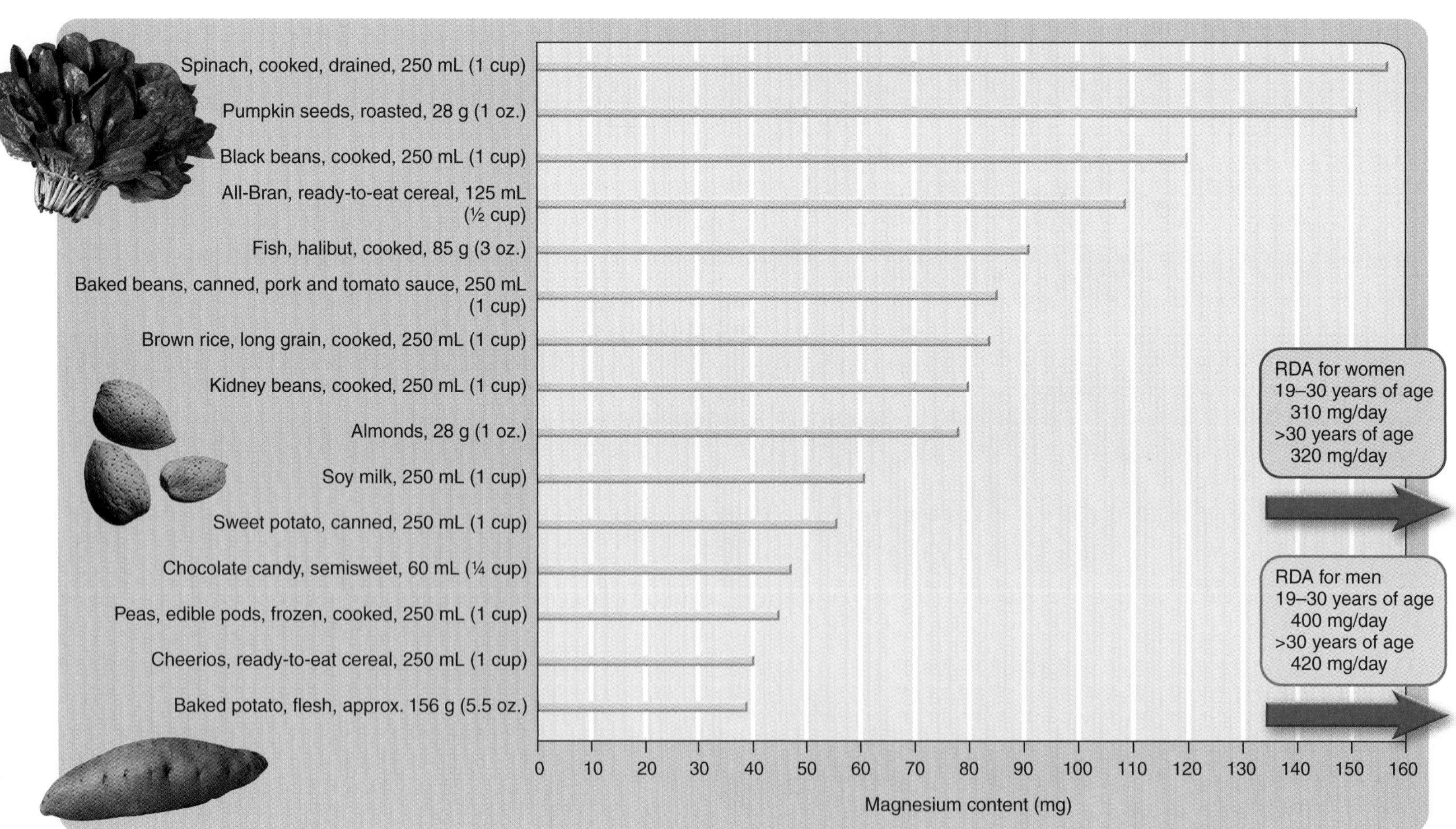

Figure 9.19 Magnesium content of selected foods.

Source: Data from U.S. Department of Agriculture, Agricultural Research Service, USDA Nutrient Data Laboratory: Magnesium, Mg (mg) content of selected foods per common measure, sorted by nutrient content. *USDA national nutrient database for standard reference, release 19.* 2006.

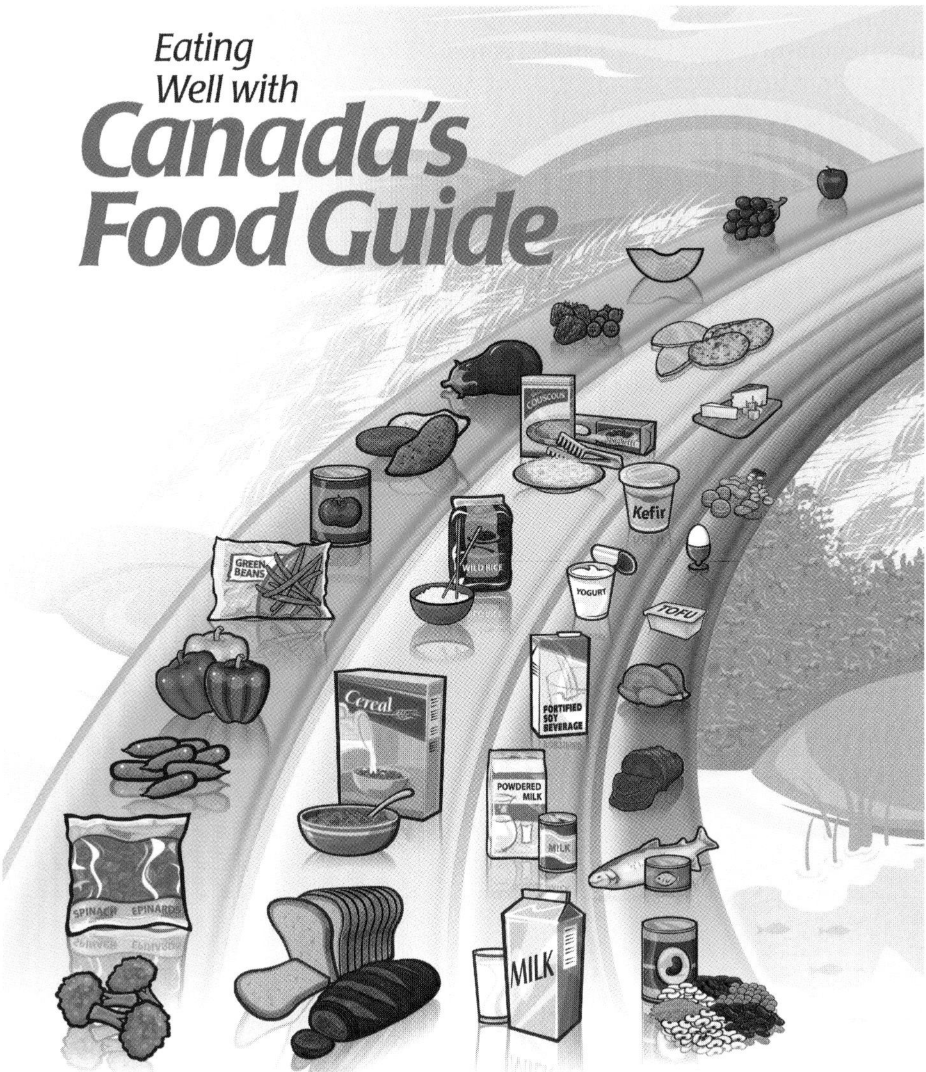

Figure 9.20 **Good sources of magnesium.** Certain foods in these groups are good sources of magnesium.

Vegetables and Fruit		Grain Products	Milk and Alternatives	Meat and Alternatives
Spinach	Figs	Wheat bran	Milk	Tofu
Greens	Peaches	Wheat germ	Yogourt	Nuts
Broccoli	Avocados	Whole-grain products		Shrimp
Lima beans	Bananas			Kidney beans
Potatoes	Berries			Sunflower seeds
Squash				

Magnesium Deficiency Although many Canadians consume less than recommended amounts of magnesium, cases of magnesium deficiency rarely occur among healthy members of the population.[45,46] Nevertheless, alcoholics or people who use certain medications (diuretics) that increase urinary excretion of magnesium have high risk of magnesium deficiency. In humans, mild magnesium deficiency can cause irritability, weakness, loss of appetite, and muscle twitching. Signs and symptoms of severe magnesium deficiency often include rapid heartbeat, inability to relax muscles, disorientation, and hallucinations. Chronic magnesium deficiency may increase the risk of osteoporosis, because the deficiency lowers the level of calcium in blood.

Magnesium Toxicity Magnesium toxicity rarely occurs from eating too much magnesium-rich foods.[45,46] Toxicity is more likely to occur from ingesting excessive magnesium from laxatives, antacids, or dietary supplements that contain the mineral. Thus, the UL for the micronutrient (350 mg/day) is for magnesium-containing medications and not food sources.[18] A person who consumes too much magnesium often develops diarrhea.[18]

Patients suffering from kidney failure and elderly persons have high risk of magnesium toxicity, because their kidneys do not excrete the mineral as effectively as the kidneys of younger, healthier individuals. In cases of kidney failure, the high concentration of magnesium in blood causes weakness, nausea, slowed breathing, coma, and death.

Concept **Checkpoint**

15. What is osteoporosis, and why is it a major public health concern in Canada?
16. Identify at least four major risk factors for osteoporosis. Which risk factors can be modified to reduce the risk of osteoporosis?
17. What is prehypertension? What is hypertension? What are major risk factors for hypertension?
18. What is the DASH diet? Aside from making dietary modifications, what other lifestyle changes can people with hypertension make to lower their blood pressure?
19. Prepare a table for the major minerals that includes information about each mineral's major roles in the body, primary food sources, and signs and symptoms of the mineral's deficiency as well as toxicity disorders. Check your table against the information provided in Table 9.3.

hemoglobin iron-containing protein in red blood cells that transports oxygen to tissues and some carbon dioxide away from tissues

Trace Minerals

Before 1960, nutritionists knew little about the importance of most trace minerals to human nutrition. Today, many nutrition scientists are focusing their attention on this group of minerals. As a result of the researchers' efforts, we are learning more about the roles of trace minerals in human nutrition and the effects these elements can have on health. This section of Chapter 9 discusses iron, zinc, iodine, selenium, and chromium in detail. Table 9.9 summarizes nutrition-related information about these and the other trace minerals.

| Whole grains are good sources of several trace minerals.

Iron (Fe)

Iron is one of Earth's most plentiful metals, but the total amount of iron in the human body is quite small, averaging only about 0.006% of a person's body weight.[3] Under normal conditions, the body regulates iron absorption carefully. The digestive tract absorbs only 5 to 15% of the iron in foods. However, the intestinal tract can absorb more iron, when the body's need for the trace mineral increases. The liver, the body's main site for iron storage, incorporates the trace mineral into the protein ferritin (*fer´-ih-tin*) until it is needed.[9]

Why Is Iron Necessary?

Do you think of "iron," when you think of "strength"? Associating iron with strength makes sense, because muscular strength and endurance are reduced when the body lacks iron. Iron is a component of hemoglobin and myoglobin. **Hemoglobin** is the iron-containing protein in red blood cells that transports oxygen to tissues and some

TABLE 9.9 *Summary of Trace Minerals*

Mineral	Major Functions in the Body	Adult RDA or AI	Major Dietary Sources	Major Deficiency Signs and Symptoms	Major Toxicity Signs and Symptoms
Iron (Fe)	• Component of hemoglobin and myoglobin that carries oxygen • Energy generation • Immune system function	Women (ages 19–50 years): 18 mg Men: 8 mg	Meat and other animal foods, except milk; whole-grain and enriched breads and cereals; fortified cereals	• Fatigue upon exertion • Small, pale red blood cells • Low hemoglobin levels • Poor immune system function • Growth and developmental retardation in infants	• Intestinal upset • Organ damage • Death
Zinc (Zn)	• Component of numerous enzymes	Women: 8 mg Men: 11 mg	Seafood, meat, whole grains	• Skin rash • Diarrhea • Depressed sense of taste and smell • Hair loss • Poor growth and physical development	• Intestinal upset • Depressed immune system function • Supplement use can reduce copper absorption
Copper (Cu)	• Promotes iron metabolism • Component of antioxidant enzymes • Component of enzymes involved in connective tissue synthesis	900 mcg	Liver, cocoa, legumes, whole grains, shellfish	• Anemia • Reduced immune system function • Poor growth and development	• Vomiting • Abnormal nervous system function • Liver damage
Selenium (Se)	• Component of an antioxidant system	55 mcg	Meat, eggs, fish, seafood, whole grains	• Muscle pain and weakness • Form of heart disease	• Nausea • Vomiting • Hair loss • Weakness • Liver damage
Iodide (I)	• Component of thyroid hormones	150 mcg	Iodized salt, saltwater fish, dairy products	• Goiter • Cretinism (intellectual impairment and poor growth in infants of women who were iodine deficient during pregnancy)	• Reduced thyroid gland function
Fluoride (F)	• Increases resistance of tooth enamel to cavity formation • Stimulates bone formation	Men: 4 mg Women: 3 mg	Fluoridated water, tea, seaweed	• No true deficiency, but increased risk of tooth decay	• Stomach upset • Staining of teeth (mottling) during development • Bone deterioration
Chromium (Cr)	• Enhances insulin action	Men: 30–35 mcg Women: 20–25 mcg	Egg yolks, whole grains, pork, nuts, mushrooms	• Blood glucose level remains elevated after meals	• Unknown but currently under scientific investigation • May interact with certain medications
Manganese (Mn)	• Cofactor for certain enzymes, including some involved in carbohydrate metabolism	Men: 2.3 mg Women: 1.8 mg	Nuts, oats, beans, tea	• None in humans	• Abnormal nervous system function
Molybdenum (Mo)	• Component of certain coenzymes	45 mcg	Liver, peas, beans, cereal products, leafy vegetables, low-fat milk	• None in healthy humans	• Rarely occurs from usual dietary sources • Overdoses of dietary supplements containing molybdenum may cause joint pain; side, lower back, or stomach pain; swelling of feet or lower legs

myoglobin iron-containing protein in muscle cells that controls oxygen uptake from red blood cells

cytochromes group of proteins involved in the release of energy from macronutrients

heme iron form of iron in hemoglobin and myoglobin

nonheme iron form of iron in vegetables, grains, meats, and supplements

carbon dioxide away from tissues. Hemoglobin is also responsible for the red colour of oxygenated blood. **Myoglobin** is the iron-containing protein in muscle cells that controls oxygen uptake from red blood cells. Oxygen is critical for energy metabolism. Cells also contain iron in **cytochromes**, a group of proteins that carry electrons during certain chemical reactions involved in the release of energy from macronutrients. If the body does not have enough iron to make the cytochromes and the oxygen carriers hemoglobin and myoglobin, cells cannot obtain the energy they need to perform work. Thus, fatigue is a major symptom of iron deficiency. Iron also plays roles in immune system function and brain development.

After red blood cells die, the body breaks them down and conserves most of the iron that was in hemoglobin. By doing so, the body can recycle the trace mineral to make hemoglobin for new red blood cells. Nonetheless, some iron is lost each day via the GI tract, urine, and skin. Any form of bleeding, including menstruation, also contributes to iron losses. Replacing the iron is essential to good health.

Dietary Sources

Beef, fish, and poultry ("meat") contain more iron than most plant foods. Some of the iron in meat is present as hemoglobin and myoglobin. These forms of iron are collectively referred to as **heme iron** because the iron is found associated with heme protein. The remaining iron in meat, as well as all the iron in vegetables, grains, and supplements, is **nonheme iron**.

The intestinal tract absorbs more of the heme iron than nonheme iron in foods.[47] Some plant foods, such as spinach, contain nonheme iron, but oxalic acid in spinach binds to the mineral, reducing its absorption. Other naturally occurring compounds that

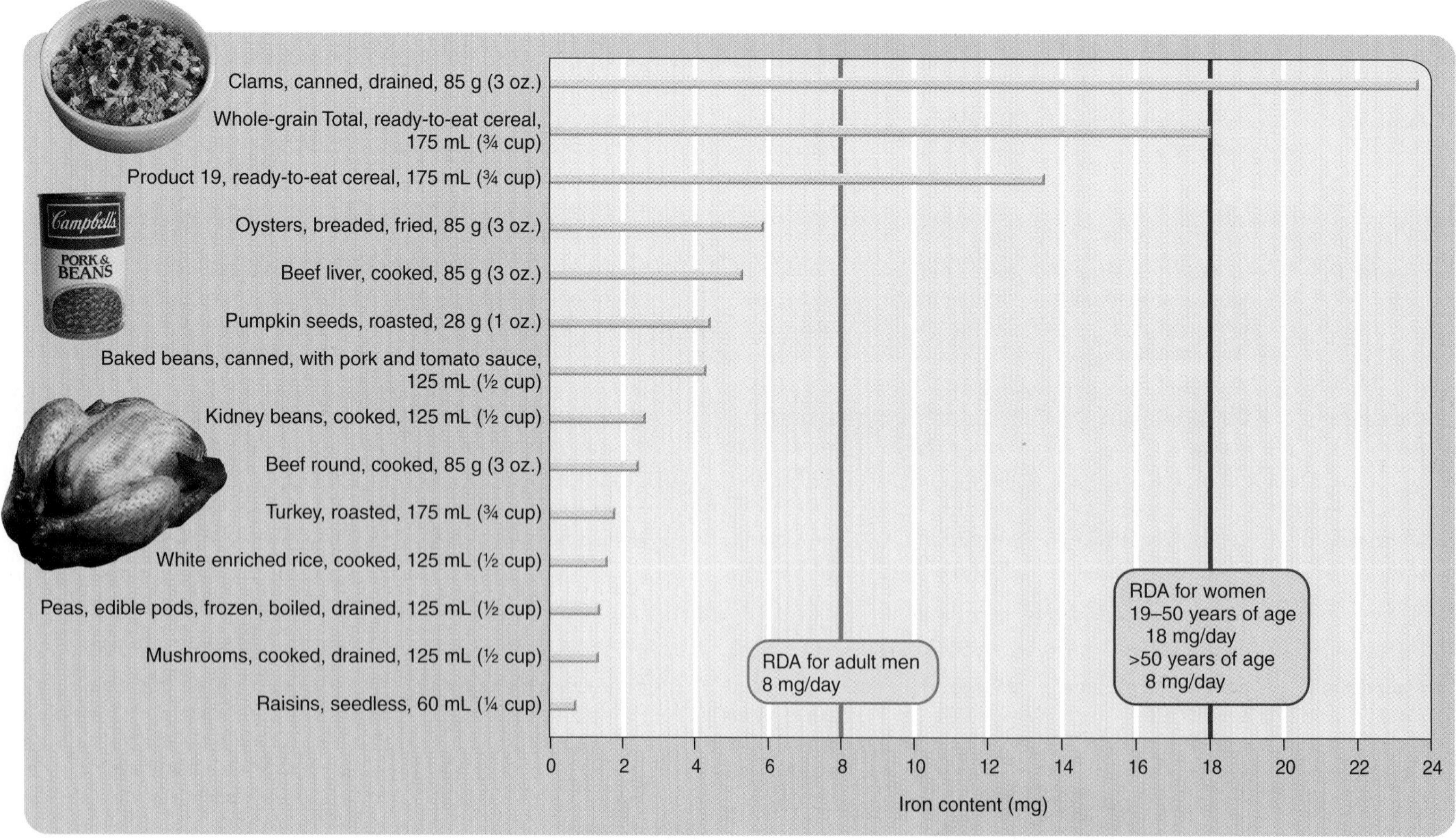

Figure 9.21 Iron content of selected foods.

Source: Data from U.S. Department of Agriculture, Agricultural Research Service, USDA Nutrient Data Laboratory: Iron, Fe (mg) content of selected foods per common measure, sorted by nutrient content. *USDA national nutrient database for standard reference, release 19.* 2006.

reduce iron absorption include phytic acid in whole grains, tannins in tea, and substances that are chemically related to tannins in coffee.[47]

Meat is the major source of iron in the typical Canadian diet.[48] Other important sources of iron are fortified cereals and products made from enriched flour, such as breads and rolls. Despite iron enrichment and fortification, only about 5% of the iron added to grain products is absorbed.[47] Dairy products are poor sources of iron. Figure 9.21 lists some foods that are among the richest sources of iron. Figure 9.22 indicates food groups that are good sources of iron.

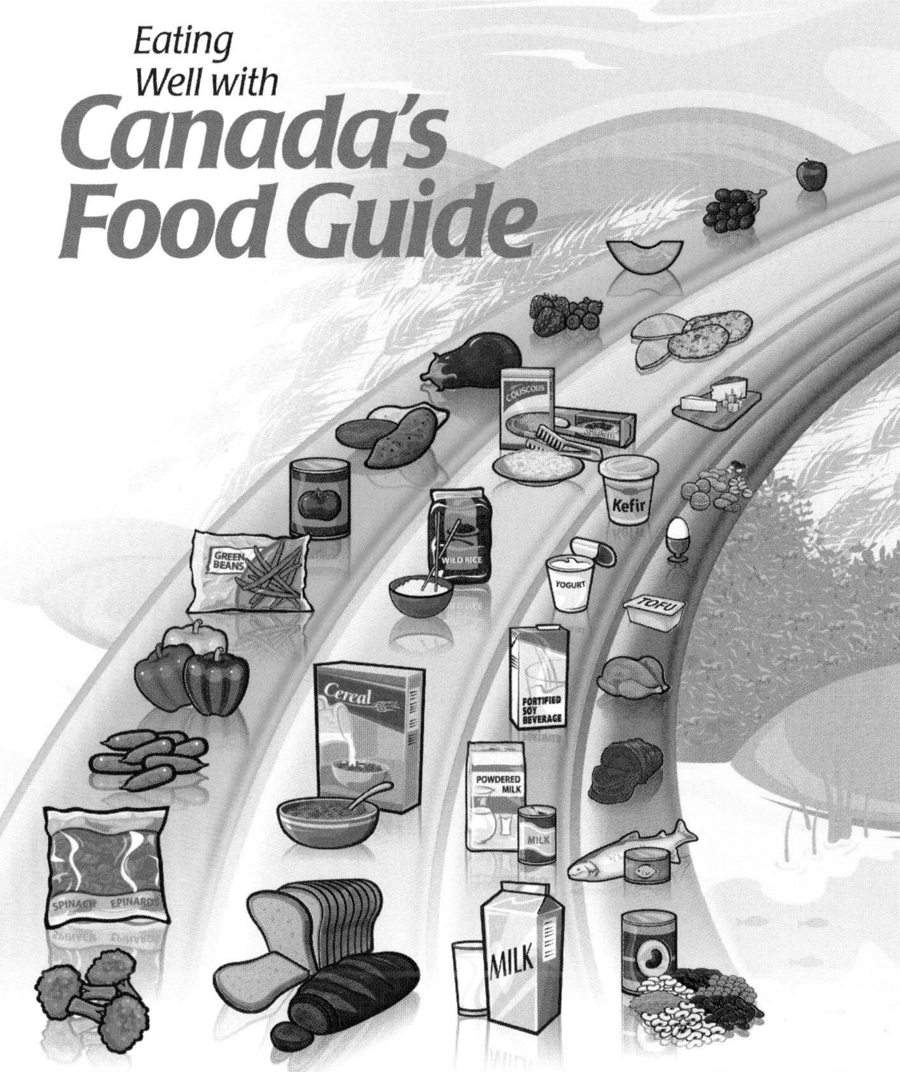

Vegetables and Fruit		Grain Products	Milk and Alternatives	Meat and Alternatives
Spinach	Peaches	Whole grains		Beef
Peas	Prune juice	Enriched grains		Tofu
Potatoes	Dried apricots	Wheat germ		Beans
Green beans		Oatmeal		Seafood
Broccoli				Organ meats

Figure 9.22 Good sources of iron. Certain foods in these groups are good sources of iron.

Did You Know?

Cooking utensils may be a source of dietary iron. When acidic foods, such as tomato sauce, are cooked in cast-iron cookware, some iron migrates from the cookware and enters the food. Replacing the heavy iron cookware with lighter stainless steel and aluminum pots and pans can reduce the amount of iron in diets.

iron deficiency condition characterized by low body stores of iron

anemia condition characterized by poor oxygen transport in blood

pica practice of eating nonfood items

Dietary Adequacy

For adult women, the RDA for iron is 18 mg per day; for adult men, the RDA is 8 mg of iron per day.[21] The average daily intake for North American women is 12 mg, whereas the intake for men is about 17 mg.

Iron Deficiency–Related Disorders Throughout the world, **iron deficiency** is the most common dietary deficiency disorder.[49] Low blood iron levels can result from consuming diets that lack iron or the body's inability to absorb dietary iron. In cases of iron deficiency, the body's iron stores are low, but not low enough to result in severe health problems. Nevertheless, iron deficiency can still have widespread negative effects on the body, including interfering with normal growth, behaviour, immune system function, cardiac function, and energy metabolism.[48,50] Furthermore, iron deficiency can lead to iron deficiency anemia.

Anemia occurs when oxygen transport in blood is impaired, generally because there are not enough red blood cells to carry the oxygen or red blood cells do not contain enough hemoglobin (Fig. 9.23). If oxygen is lacking, cells cannot release considerable amounts of energy from macronutrients, so symptoms of iron deficiency anemia include lack of energy and difficulty concentrating on mental activities. Furthermore, the heart of a person suffering from anemia has to work harder to circulate oxygen-poor blood throughout the body. Over time, anemia can cause rapid or irregular heartbeat, chest pain, an enlarged heart, and even heart failure. Table 9.10 lists common signs and symptoms of iron deficiency anemia.

There are many different kinds of anemia, but iron deficiency anemia is the most common form. According to the World Health Organization (WHO), over 30% of the world's population suffers from anemia, primarily due to iron deficiency.[49] Substantial blood loss is the most common cause of iron deficiency anemia.[51] Such losses of blood often result from serious intestinal diseases, severe physical injuries, and excessive menstrual bleeding. Diseases that reduce red blood cell formation or increase red blood cell

TABLE 9.10 *Signs and Symptoms of Iron Deficiency Anemia*

Pale skin and pale mucous membrane
Fatigue and weakness
Irritability
Shortness of breath
Brittle nails
Unusual food cravings (pica)
Decreased appetite (especially in children)
Headache

Source: U.S. Library of Medicine (Medline), National Institutes of Health: Iron deficiency anemia. *Medline plus.* www.nlm.nih.gov/medlineplus/ency/article/000584.htm. Accessed: March 12, 2007.

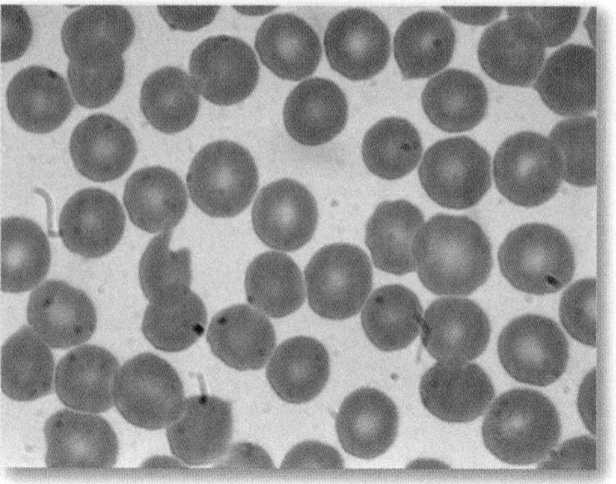

a.

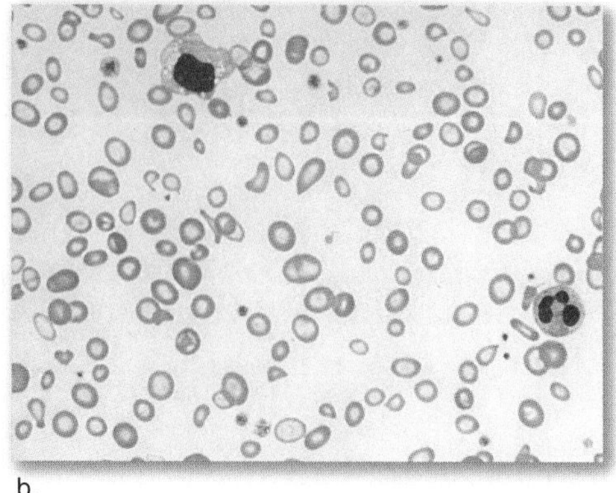

b.

Figure 9.23 Iron-deficient red blood cells. (*a*) Normal red blood cells; (*b*) red blood cells in a person with iron deficiency.

destruction also cause anemia. It is important to note that some types of anemia are the result of genetic defects and not dietary deficiencies. Blood testing can determine which kind of anemia a person has developed, so the condition can be treated properly.

Young women are at risk for iron deficiency–related disorders because they often exclude meat and enriched bread and cereal products from their diets. Additionally, women of child-bearing age generally lose some iron during menstruation. Women with heavy menstrual blood losses are especially prone to iron deficiency anemia. Although pregnant women do not have to contend with menstrual blood losses, they still need to be concerned about their iron intake.

During pregnancy, a woman's need for iron increases as her blood supply expands and new tissues are added to both her body and that of her fetus. Pregnant women who suffer from iron deficiency anemia have higher risk of dying during pregnancy than healthy pregnant women. Anemic pregnant women are also more likely to give birth to premature or low-birth-weight infants. Premature babies are born before the 37th week of pregnancy—normally, pregnancies last about 40 weeks from the date of the mother's last menstrual period. A low-birth-weight baby weighs less than 2500 g (5½ lbs.) at birth. Compared to healthy newborns, premature or low-birth-weight infants are more likely to die during their first year of life.

Iron appears to be necessary for normal nervous system functioning, including brain development. According to the results of studies, iron-deficient infants tend to score lower on mental and motor function tests than infants who are not iron deficient.[48,52,53] Iron deficiency during the preschool years may affect intellectual development negatively.[48,52]

Consuming too much milk may play a role in the development of iron deficiency in children. Milk is a poor source of iron. Thus, children who drink excessive amounts of milk may not have the appetite to eat foods that are more reliable iron sources. The calcium that is in milk also interferes with iron absorption when the beverage is consumed with foods that contain the mineral.[54,55] Children should be encouraged to eat more iron-rich foods, such as products made from soybeans and iron-fortified cereals.

Total vegetarians have a higher risk of iron deficiency–related disorders than people who eat meat, because meat provides heme iron. Combining a small amount of meat with plant foods improves the bioavailability of the plant's nonheme iron. Vegetarians, however, may reject recipes that include any meat, especially red meats. Some plant foods contain high amounts of oxalic acid and phytic acid, substances that can depress iron absorption. On the other hand, vegetarian diets usually are rich in vitamin C, a factor that increases nonheme iron absorption. Thus, vegetarians should consume vitamin C–rich foods along with plant foods, especially those that contain appreciable amounts of iron, such as spinach, lentils, and soybeans. Eating iron-fortified ready-to-eat cereals can also be helpful for vegetarians, even though the form of iron used to fortify cereals is not as well absorbed as heme iron. Finally, vegetarians can take a multivitamin and mineral supplement that contains iron to ensure their iron and other mineral intakes are adequate.

Treatment for iron deficiency anemia generally includes iron supplements and the addition of iron-rich foods to the diet. It is also important to find and treat factors that may be causing the deficiency, such as intestinal bleeding.

Did You Know?

Iron-deficient people occasionally eat dirt or clay.[56] Some medical researchers think they crave clay or dirt in response to being iron deficient. Other researchers think eating these nonfood items is acceptable in some cultures, and the practice causes iron deficiency. Why? Substances in clay and dirt can interfere with iron absorption in the digestive tract. The practice of eating nonfood items is called **pica** (*pié-kah*).

Did You Know?

Donating 1 pint (approximately 0.5 L) of blood represents a loss of 200 to 250 mg of iron. Even when a person consumes adequate amounts of iron, his or her body generally needs several months to replace the iron that was in the donated blood. Most healthy people can give blood two to four times a year without harmful consequences. Women, however, may need to donate blood less often, especially if they lose iron via menstruation.

Food & Nutrition *tip*

- Always treat iron and other dietary supplements as medicinal drugs and store these products in places that are inaccessible to children.

Excess milk consumption contributes to iron deficiency in toddlers and preschool-age children.

Canadian researcher Dr. Stanley Zlotkin developed *Sprinkles*, a dry, tasteless, single-serve packet containing a mixture of iron; vitamins C, D, and A; and zinc.

hereditary hemochromatosis (HHC) common inherited disorder characterized by excess iron absorption

A Canadian doctor and researcher, Dr. Stanley Zlotkin, has made a tremendous contribution to the amelioration of iron deficiency anemia around the world with his development of *Sprinkles*, a dry, tasteless, single-serve packet containing a mixture of iron; vitamins C, D, and A; and zinc. This product can be added to foods such as breakfast cereal without changing the colour of the food or altering the taste. This allows individuals, including the ultra-poor in many underprivileged countries, to receive these vital nutrients. Dr. Zlotkin has been recognized nationally and internationally for this tremendous contribution to the improvement of global dietary intakes.[57]

Iron Toxicity The UL for iron is 45 mg per day.[21] Although not having enough iron in the body interferes with normal growth, development, and functioning, ingesting too much iron poses the risk of toxicity. Children under 6 years of age are more likely than older children to poison themselves accidentally by taking too many iron-containing dietary supplements.[58] The number of iron tablets that a child must consume to produce toxicity varies, depending on the form and amount of iron in the supplements. Early signs of acute iron poisoning include vomiting and diarrhea that may progress to coma and death. In Canada, iron supplement labels must carry a warning about the risk of iron toxicity.

Hereditary Hemochromatosis **Hereditary hemochromatosis** (*he´-mo-crow´-ma-toe-sis*) is one of the most common inherited disorders in Canada, and one in nine Canadians are carriers for the disorder.[59] People who have hereditary hemochromatosis (HHC) absorb too much iron. The excess iron accumulates in tissues and can cause joint pain, abnormal bronze skin colour, and damage to the liver, heart, adrenal glands, and pancreas.

HHC most often affects people who have northern European ancestors. In Canada, about 1 in every 300 Canadians of northern European descent are affected.[59] Men are more likely to be diagnosed with HHC than women. Additionally, men tend to develop health problems from the excess iron at a younger age than women with the condition.

Joint pain is the most common complaint of people suffering from HHC. Other common signs and symptoms of the disorder include fatigue, lack of energy, abdominal pain, loss of sex drive, and heart problems. Even though people with HHC begin accumulating iron early in life, they often do not report any signs and symptoms of the disease until they are over 30 years of age. Testing is available to determine the presence of the genes that are responsible for the disease.

Many people who have HHC experience vague symptoms or no symptoms at all. If the disease is not detected early and treated effectively, the organ damage resulting from the condition can be deadly. Treatment usually includes visiting a clinic periodically to have blood removed. This process stimulates the tissues that produce red blood cells to use storage iron for hemoglobin production. People with HHC should avoid taking dietary supplements that contain iron.

Zinc (Zn)

In 1958, physician Ananda Prasad was working in Iran when he examined a 21-year-old man with dwarfism, mental retardation, iron deficiency anemia, and underdeveloped sexual organs (Fig. 9.24).[60] Prasad noted that the young man ate unleavened ("flat") bread almost exclusively. After examining other patients in Iran and Egypt with similar health problems and dietary practices, Prasad hypothesized that diet was responsible for the condition. Eventually, medical researchers determined that Prasad's patients had severe zinc deficiencies. After these patients were given zinc supplements, they began to grow and develop normally. Prasad later determined that girls also experienced stunted growth and delays in sexual maturation as a result of zinc deficiency.[61]

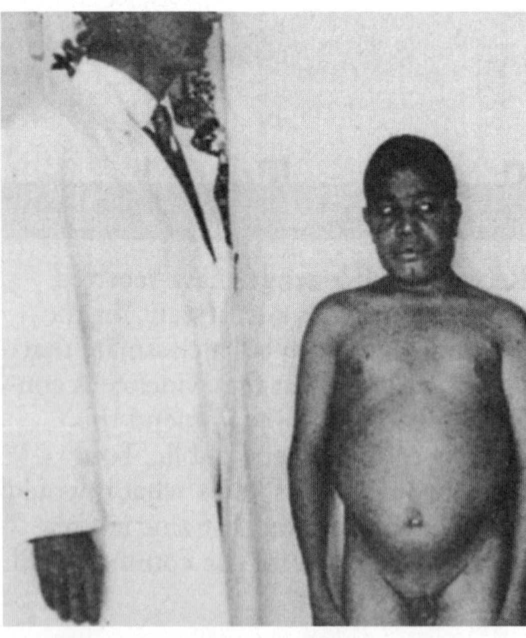

Figure 9.24 Zinc deficiency in young men. Zinc is necessary for normal physical growth and sexual development. This 16-year-old Egyptian boy experienced stunted growth and impaired sexual maturation as a result of a zinc-deficient diet.

In the regions where the men who were zinc deficient lived, the typical diet was comprised primarily of unleavened whole-wheat bread and little animal protein. Unleavened whole-wheat bread is naturally high in phytic acid and fibre, substances that decrease zinc bioavailability. In places where people use yeast to leaven (raise) bread dough, severe zinc deficiency is less likely to occur. Yeast reduces the binding effects of phytic acid and fibre, making zinc more bioavailable. Consuming zinc-rich sources of animal protein, such as meat and milk, also reduces the likelihood of zinc deficiency.

Other factors that influence the bioavailability of zinc include the body's need for the mineral and the presence of large amounts of certain other metals. During times when a healthy body needs zinc, the small intestine absorbs more. However, the presence of excess copper or iron in the small intestine interferes with zinc absorption. Thus, iron supplements should be taken between meals instead of with them.[62] After being absorbed, zinc binds to proteins in blood and is transported to the liver. The liver stores zinc and releases the trace mineral into the blood, when it is needed.

Did You Know?

Zinc lozenges are often promoted for treating the common cold. Results of studies, however, do not provide consistent scientific evidence that the lozenges reduce the severity or duration of cold symptoms.[62]

Why Is Zinc Necessary?

Zinc is a component of hundreds of enzymes and other proteins.[60] Zinc is necessary for wound healing, the sense of taste and smell, DNA synthesis, and proper functioning of the immune system. Zinc is also essential for growth and development during pregnancy, childhood, and adolescence.

Sources of Zinc

Zinc is widespread in foods. Although oysters are the most concentrated food source of zinc, red meat and poultry products supply most of the zinc in the typical Canadian's diet.[63] Beans, nuts, whole grains, fortified ready-to-eat cereals, and dairy products are also common sources of zinc (Fig. 9.25). Figure 9.26 indicates food groups that are good sources of zinc.

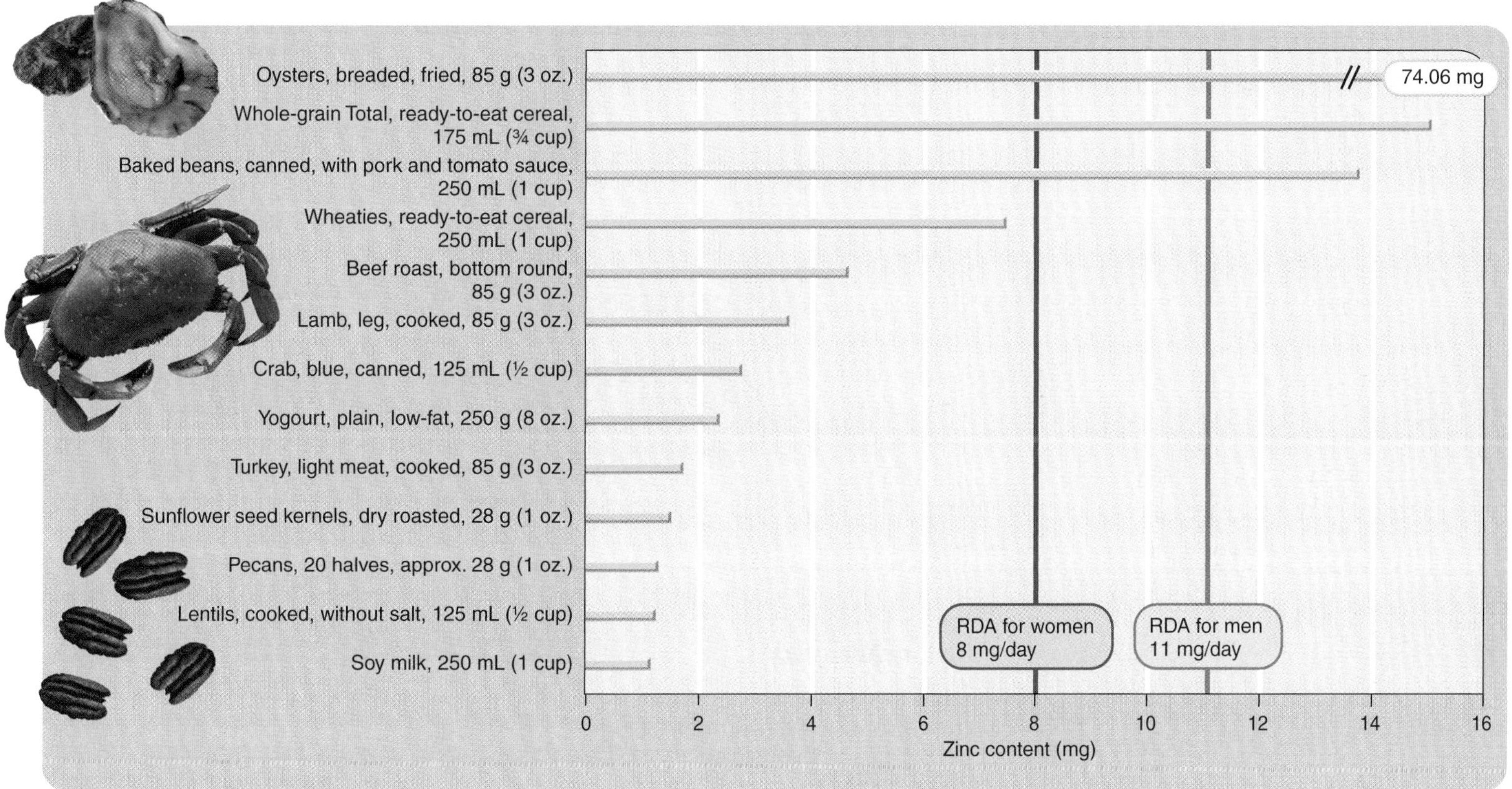

Figure 9.25 Zinc content of selected foods.

Source: Data from U.S. Department of Agriculture, Agricultural Research Service, USDA Nutrient Data Laboratory: Zinc, Zn (mg) content of selected foods per common measure, sorted by nutrient content. *USDA national nutrient database for standard reference, release 19.* 2006.

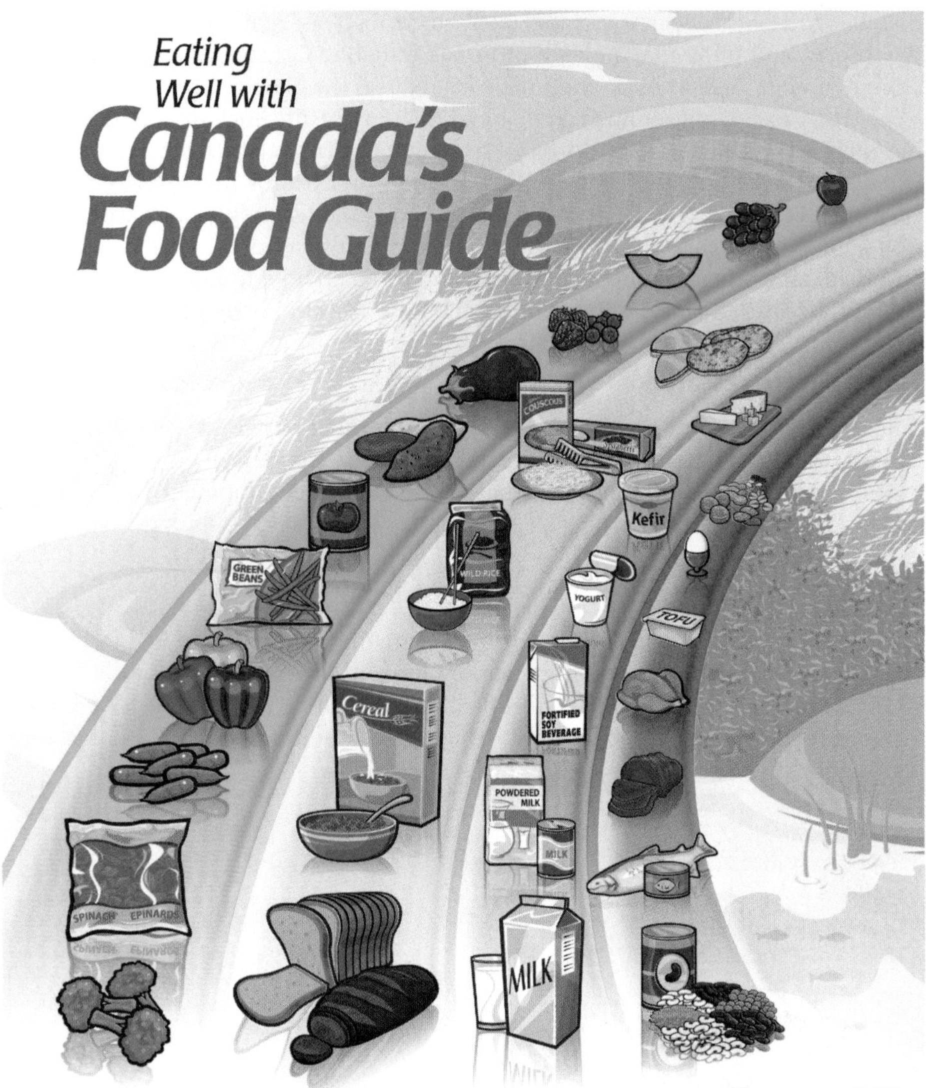

Figure 9.26 Good sources of zinc. Certain foods in these groups are good sources of zinc.

Vegetables and Fruit	Grain Products	Milk and Alternatives	Meat and Alternatives
Spinach Peas Asparagus Avocados Dried fruit	Whole-grain breads and cereals Fortified ready-to-eat cereals	Milk Yogourt Cheese	Beef Eggs Beans Nuts Shellfish Poultry

Dietary Adequacy

Adult RDAs for zinc range from 8 mg to 13 mg per day.[21] In Canada, the average adult consumes adequate amounts of zinc.[63]

Zinc Deficiency Zinc deficiency is not a widespread problem in Canada.[63] However, alcoholics have high risk of zinc deficiency, because alcohol reduces zinc absorption and increases excretion of the mineral in urine. Making matters worse, many people who suffer from alcoholism do not consume nutritious diets. People with chronic diarrhea or digestive tract diseases can also develop zinc deficiency. Furthermore, vegetarians need more zinc than people who eat meat, because the GI tract does not absorb zinc from plant foods as well as from animal foods.[62,64]

Breast-fed babies can be at risk of zinc deficiency. Although breast milk contains zinc, the milk does not supply enough of the trace mineral for infants who are older than 6 months of age. To increase the likelihood that their diets contain enough zinc, breast-fed babies who are between 6 and 12 months of age need to consume foods that contain the trace mineral, such as zinc-fortified infant cereal.

In children and adolescents, zinc deficiency can cause growth retardation and delayed sexual maturation. Adult men who are zinc deficient may experience sexual dysfunction, particularly the inability to attain an erection. Other signs of zinc deficiency include diarrhea, hair loss, dermatitis, poor wound healing, impaired sense of taste, and mental slowness.[62]

Zinc Toxicity The UL for zinc is 40 mg per day.[21] Zinc intakes that exceed the UL can reduce beneficial HDL cholesterol levels in blood. Ingesting more than 100 mg of zinc per day can also result in diarrhea, cramps, nausea, vomiting, and depressed immune system function. Additionally, megadoses of zinc may interfere with copper absorption and metabolism. Therefore, people should avoid high intakes of zinc, unless they are under a physician's supervision.

thyroid hormone hormone that controls the metabolic rate

Iodide (I)

During World War I, physicians noted that men drafted into the U.S. military from the Great Lakes region were far more likely to have goiter (*goy'-ter*) than men from some other areas of the country. Goiter is enlargement of the thyroid gland that is not the result of cancer (Fig. 9.27). Goiters often occur among populations living in areas that have iodine-depleted soil. In general, these regions are inland and far from an ocean. If people in these communities limit their diets to locally produced foods, they might not have enough iodine in their diets.

Iodine (I_2) is poisonous, but most ingested iodine loses an electron to become the iodide ion (I^-) in the digestive tract.[47] Iodide is the form of iodine that the body uses. Most of the iodide in an adult's body is located in the thyroid gland. Under normal conditions, the kidneys filter and eliminate excess iodide from blood.

From 1917 to 1922, researchers in Ohio conducted an experiment on a group of girls in which one group of the children received doses of iodide whereas the other group (the control group) did not receive the trace mineral. The results of the study indicated iodide was nearly 100% effective in preventing goiter in the healthy children. Moreover, the majority of the girls who already had goiters when they received the iodide experienced a reduction in the size of their thyroid glands by the end of the study.[65] The addition of iodine to table salt in Canada is controlled under the regulatory provisions first declared in 1964, and as a result, cases of goiter caused by iodide deficiency rarely occur in this country.[66] Today, use of iodized salt is the major method of preventing iodide deficiencies around the globe, but inadequate iodide intake and goiters are still common in central Asia and central Africa.

Figure 9.27 Goiter and cretinism in Bolivia, South America. The woman on the left is the mother of the woman on the right. Note that both women have goiters. Additionally, the daughter has cretinism.

Why Is Iodide Necessary?

People require iodide for normal thyroid function and for the production of thyroid hormones, collectively referred to as **thyroid hormone**. Thyroid hormone controls the rate of cell metabolism, that is, the rate at which cells obtain energy. The thyroid gland traps iodide from the bloodstream and accumulates the trace mineral for thyroid hormone synthesis. If a person's iodide intake is too low, the thyroid gland enlarges as it attempts to remove as much iodide as possible from the bloodstream. It is important to note that an enlarged thyroid gland can also be a sign of some diseases and conditions that are not related to iodide intake.

Did You Know?

The sea salt that is usually sold in supermarkets is not a good source of iodide and other minerals because it has undergone processing. Some stores sell "unrefined" or "natural" sea salt that contains much of its natural mineral content, including iodide.[69] Consumers, however, need to avoid excess sodium from all sources, including sea salt.

Sources of Iodide

Major sources of iodide include saltwater fish; seafood; seaweed; some plants, especially the leaves of plants grown near oceans; and iodized salt. A half teaspoon of iodine-fortified salt supplies the adult RDA for iodide. Iodide fortification of salt is voluntary in the United States, so not all salt has the trace mineral added to it. In Canada, however, table salt must be fortified with iodide.[67] The iodide content of fruits, vegetables, and grains is dependent on the iodide levels of the soil, and many parts of the world, such as part of Africa and Asia, have soil conditions that are nearly void of iodide. Other dietary sources of iodide include food additives that contain the mineral, such as certain dough conditioners and food dyes. Figure 9.28 lists some foods that are good sources of iodide.

Dietary Adequacy

The adult RDA for iodide is 150 mcg per day.[21] Due to the mandatory fortification of table salt with iodide in Canada, approximately 2 mL (½ tsp) will meet the RDA for Canadian adults.[68]

Iodide Deficiency In cases of iodide deficiency, the thyroid gland produces insufficient amounts of thyroid hormone, and goiter develops. As a result of the lack of thyroid hormone, iodide-deficient people generally have low metabolic rates and elevated blood cholesterol levels. Other signs and symptoms of iodide deficiency include fatigue, difficulty concentrating on mental tasks, weight gain, intolerance of cold temperatures, constipation, and dry skin.

Throughout the world, millions of people, particularly pregnant women and preschool children, are at risk of iodide deficiency and goiter.[70] Pregnant women who are iodide deficient have high risk of stillbirths (giving birth to a dead infant) or low-birth-weight babies. During fetal life, thyroid hormone is crucial for normal brain development. Thus, infants of iodide-deficient women are likely to be born with

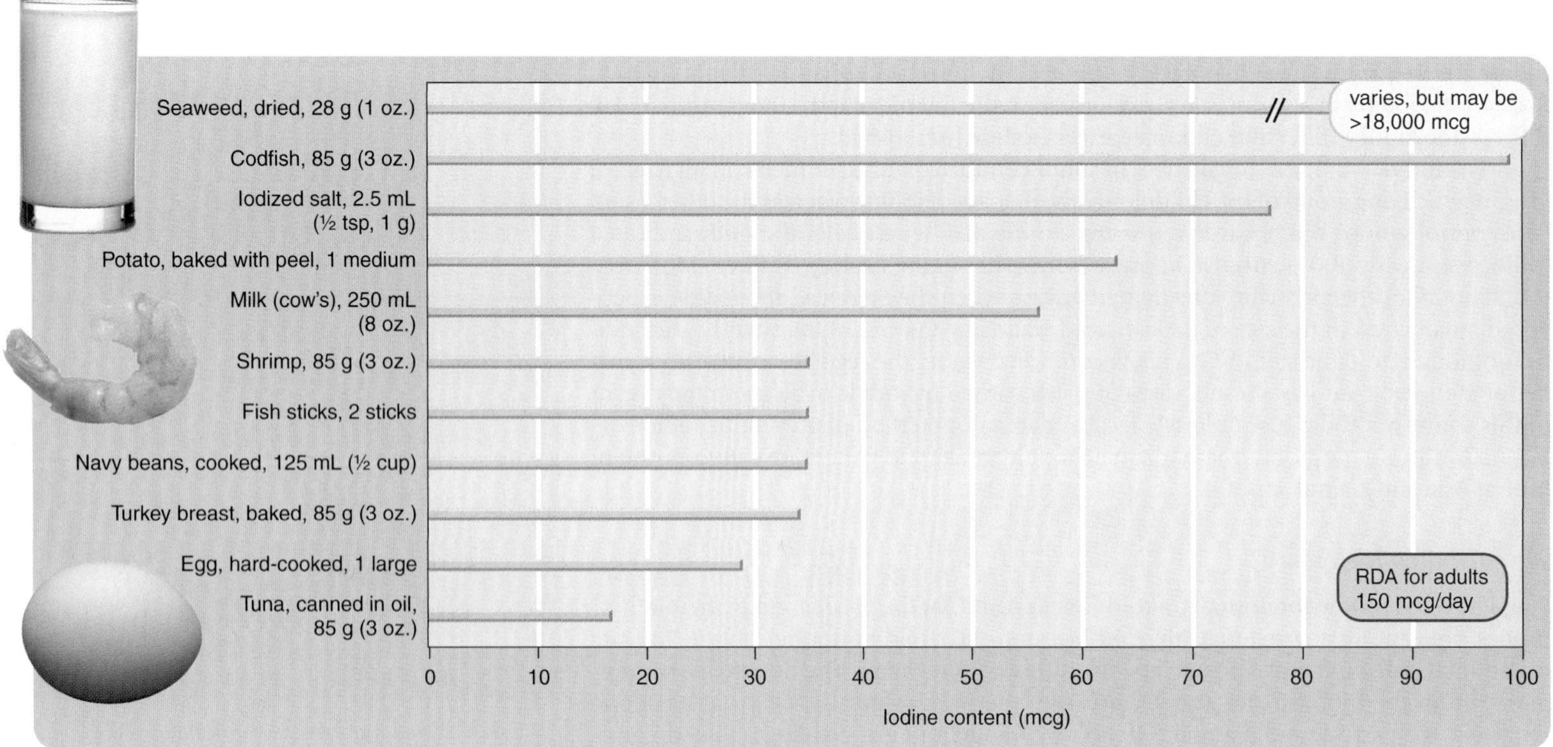

Figure 9.28 Iodide content of selected foods.

Source: Data from Higdon, J: *Iodine.* Micronutrient Information Center, Linus Pauling Institute, Oregon State University. Updated 2003. http://lpi.oregonstate.edu/infocenter/minerals/iodine/ Accessed: May 19, 2006

a condition called **cretinism** (*kre'-tin-ih-zim*). Babies with cretinism have permanent brain damage, reduced intellectual functioning, and growth retardation (see Fig. 9.27). Worldwide, iodide deficiency is the most common cause of preventable brain damage.[71] Pregnant women can reduce the risk of giving birth to infants with cretinism by consuming adequate amounts of iodide throughout pregnancy.

Iodide deficiency is a serious threat to health in places where soils are iodine deficient and commonly eaten foods are not fortified with the trace mineral, such as regions of Latin America, India, Southeast Asia, and Africa. Currently, international health organizations are engaging in efforts to eliminate iodide deficiency, primarily by promoting the use of iodized salt or iodide-fortified vegetable oils.

cretinism condition affecting infants of women who were iodide deficient during pregnancy

goitrogens compounds that inhibit iodide metabolism by the thyroid gland

Iodide Toxicity The UL for iodide is 1.1 mg per day.[47,68] Over time, consuming very high amounts of iodide can cause thyroid gland enlargement and reduced production of thyroid hormone. These side effects are the same as those that occur when diets are deficient in iodide.

Selenium (Se)

Selenium is widespread in Earth's crust, but soils can vary widely in their content of the trace mineral. Areas of western United States, including parts of Colorado and South Dakota, have unusually high concentrations of selenium in soil. Certain types of plants that grow in these places accumulate toxic levels of the mineral. Livestock that graze on the selenium-rich plants often ingest poisonous amounts of the trace mineral. In horses and cattle, selenium toxicity can cause hair and weight loss, malformed hooves that can separate from the animals' feet, muscle weakness and loss of muscular function (paralysis), and death. The majority of Canadian soil contains safe levels of selenium.

Why Is Selenium Necessary?

In the body, selenium functions as a component of several proteins referred to as selenoproteins (*sell'-in-oh-pro'-teens*). Many selenoproteins are antioxidants. Other selenoproteins are necessary for the normal functioning of the immune system and thyroid gland. The results of a few human studies indicate a relationship between selenium intake and risk of cancer.[72,73,74] Populations that consumed selenium-rich diets or took selenium supplements tended to have lower risk of prostate, colon, and other cancers than groups of people whose diets lacked the mineral.[74,75] However, more research is needed to determine whether selenium supplementation is useful for cancer prevention.

Sources of Selenium

Although the selenium content of foods varies, nuts, fish, whole-grain products, and meats are generally rich sources of the trace mineral (Fig. 9.29). Because Brazil nuts have very high selenium contents, people should not eat these nuts regularly.[76] Selenium is used to fortify a few types of foods, such as yeast and garlic.[73]

Did You Know?

Raw vegetables, particularly turnips, cabbage, brussels sprouts, cauliflower, and broccoli, contain **goitrogens**. These compounds inhibit iodide metabolism by the thyroid gland, and as a result, reduce thyroid hormone production. Unless people eat large amounts of raw vegetables that contain goitrogens, or they are iodide deficient, they do not need to be concerned about eating these foods.[71] Furthermore, cooking vegetables destroys goitrogens.

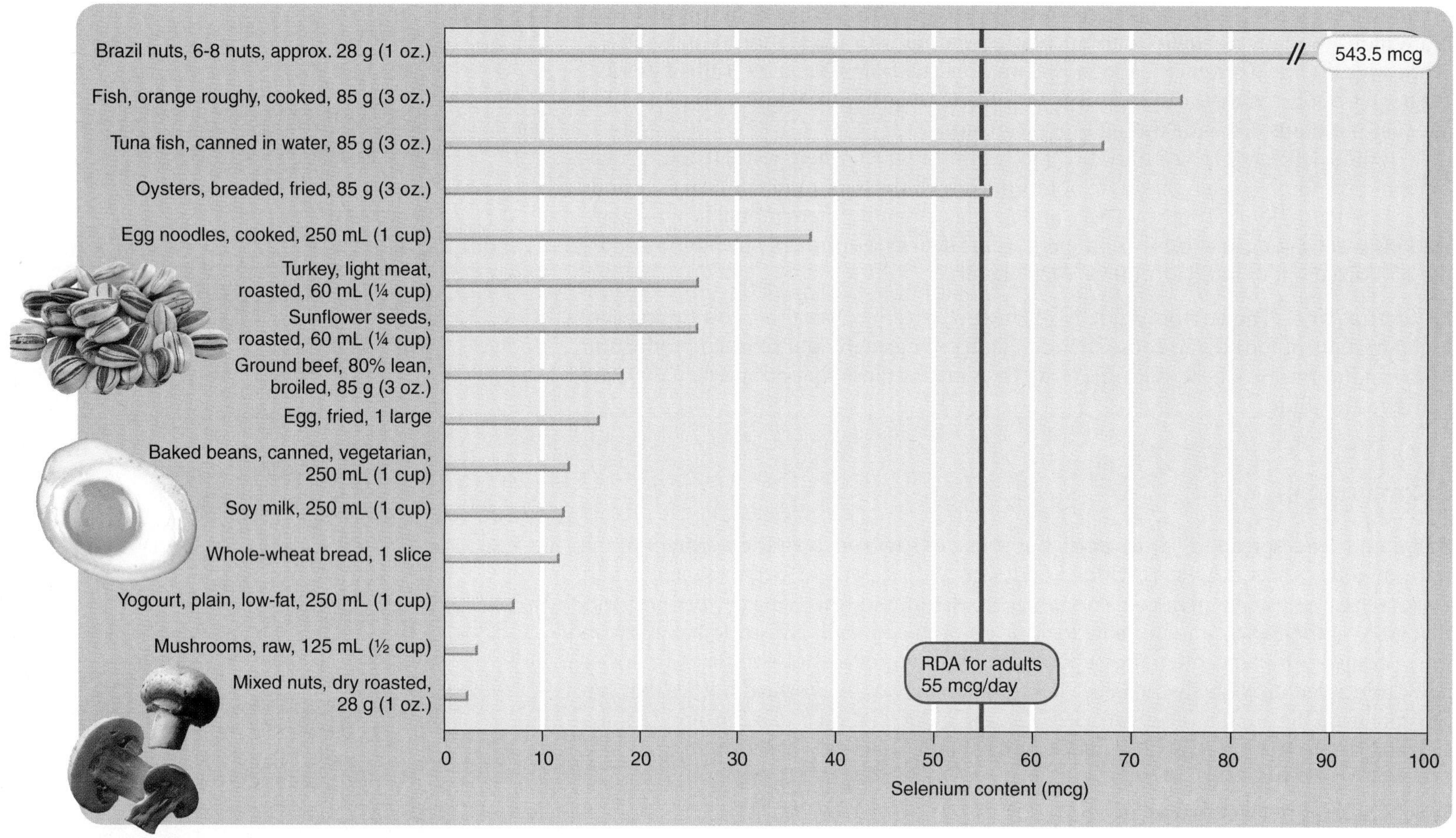

Brazil nuts, 6-8 nuts, approx. 28 g (1 oz.) — 543.5 mcg
Fish, orange roughy, cooked, 85 g (3 oz.)
Tuna fish, canned in water, 85 g (3 oz.)
Oysters, breaded, fried, 85 g (3 oz.)
Egg noodles, cooked, 250 mL (1 cup)
Turkey, light meat, roasted, 60 mL (¼ cup)
Sunflower seeds, roasted, 60 mL (¼ cup)
Ground beef, 80% lean, broiled, 85 g (3 oz.)
Egg, fried, 1 large
Baked beans, canned, vegetarian, 250 mL (1 cup)
Soy milk, 250 mL (1 cup)
Whole-wheat bread, 1 slice
Yogourt, plain, low-fat, 250 mL (1 cup)
Mushrooms, raw, 125 mL (½ cup)
Mixed nuts, dry roasted, 28 g (1 oz.)
RDA for adults 55 mcg/day
0 10 20 30 40 50 60 70 80 90 100
Selenium content (mcg)

Figure 9.29 Selenium content of selected foods.

Source: Data from U.S. Department of Agriculture, Agricultural Research Service, USDA Nutrient Data Laboratory: Selenium, Se (mcg) content of selected foods per common measure, sorted by nutrient content. *USDA national nutrient database for standard reference, release 19.* 2006.

Dietary Adequacy

According to recent survey data, the average Canadian's diet meets the RDA for selenium.[77] Some medical researchers, however, think people should consume amounts of selenium that are higher than the RDA (200 mcg/day), because the trace mineral may protect against certain chronic diseases, particularly prostate and colorectal cancer.[72,73]

Selenium Deficiency In Canada, selenium deficiency is uncommon, but the condition may occur in people who have serious digestive tract conditions that interfere with the mineral's absorption. Selenium deficiency reduces thyroid gland activity and can lead to goiter. The deficiency also depresses immune system function and may contribute to the development of heart disease and cancer. In parts of China where the soil lacks selenium and the population consumes locally produced foods, diets typically contain inadequate amounts of selenium. Certain types of cancer and a form of heart disease are common in these areas of China. At this time, two major studies are underway to investigate whether there is an association between selenium intake and cancer. Scientific evidence, however, does not support the use of selenium supplements to prevent or treat CVD.[76,78,79]

Selenium Toxicity The UL for selenium is 400 mcg per day.[75] In Canada, selenium toxicity (selenosis) (*sell'-in-o-sis*) is rare.[74] Chronic selenosis, however, can occur from drinking well water that naturally contains too much selenium. Additionally, selenium toxicity can develop by taking megadoses of dietary supplements, particularly those containing inorganic selenium, over several weeks or years.[80] In humans, signs and symptoms of chronic selenosis include brittle fingernails, loss of hair and nails, garlic-like body odour, nausea, vomiting, and fatigue.

Chromium (Cr)

The importance of chromium as an essential trace mineral in human diets has been recognized only for about the past 40 years. The results of scientific studies suggest that chromium plays an important role in maintaining proper carbohydrate and lipid metabolism. The human digestive tract absorbs only about 0.4 to 2.5% of the chromium in foods; the remainder is excreted in the feces.[81,82] Thus, the concentration of chromium in human tissues is generally low.

Why Is Chromium Necessary?

Most cells require the hormone insulin to obtain glucose from the bloodstream. Chromium may enhance insulin's action on cell membranes, and in a way, help to "hold the door open" for glucose's entry into the cells. Although cells need chromium to enable glucose to enter them, scientists do not know how the mineral accomplishes this task.

Sources of Chromium

Although chromium is widely distributed in foods, most foods contain less than 2 mcg of the mineral per serving.[81,82] Information regarding the chromium content of various foods is difficult to find, because most reliable food composition tables do not include this trace mineral. In general, meat and whole-grain products, yeast, and some fruits and vegetables are good sources of chromium. Like selenium, the amount of chromium in plant foods reflects the chromium content of soils where crops are grown.

Dietary Adequacy

The adult AIs for chromium are 25 mcg per day for young women and 35 mcg per day for young men.[21] Well-balanced diets typically contain these amounts of chromium. On average, Canadian adults consume diets that meet or exceed their AIs for chromium.[82]

Chromium Deficiency Signs of chromium deficiency are impaired glucose tolerance and elevated blood cholesterol and triglyceride levels. The mechanism by which chromium influences cholesterol metabolism is not known but may involve enzymes that control the body's cholesterol production. Cases of chromium deficiency have been reported in people maintained on special formula diets that did not contain chromium as well as in severely malnourished children.

Can people who have diabetes experience better blood glucose regulation by taking chromium supplements? A recent review of scientific research indicated mixed results when people took chromium supplements to improve their blood glucose levels. In some of the studies, chromium supplements were helpful for people with diabetes, but the results of other studies indicated no such benefits.[83] Furthermore, most people who have diabetes are not chromium deficient.[83]

Chromium Toxicity The form of chromium that is naturally in foods has not shown to produce toxicity, so no UL has been set for the trace mineral. The long-term safety of taking various chromium supplements is unknown. Data from a study using cells of mice indicated chromium picolinate may damage human DNA.[84] This finding raises concern, because damaged DNA can result in cancer. Therefore, taking supplemental chromium may be risky (see Table 11.7 on p. 401).

Concept Checkpoint

20. What is the difference between iron deficiency and iron deficiency anemia? What are the signs and symptoms of iron deficiency anemia? Which members of the population are most at risk of iron deficiency?
21. What is hemochromatosis? Identify at least three signs or symptoms of hemochromatosis. How is the condition treated?
22. Describe signs and symptoms of zinc deficiency in humans.
23. What is a goiter? What is cretinism? How can cretinism be prevented?
24. Which foods are rich sources of selenium?
25. What is the major role of chromium in the body?
26. Prepare a table for trace minerals that includes information about each trace mineral's major role or roles in the body, food sources, and signs and symptoms of the mineral's deficiency as well as toxicity disorders. Check your table against the information provided in Table 9.9.

Ultratrace Minerals

A few minerals, including nickel, arsenic, and silicon, are found in very small amounts in the body, but their roles in the body are unclear. At present, this group of minerals, referred to as ultratrace minerals, are not classified as essential nutrients. Table 9.11 summarizes the possible functions, suggested human intakes, and food sources of six ultratrace minerals. Although there are reports of severe illness and deaths resulting from environmental exposure to high amounts of ultratrace minerals, foods generally do not contain toxic amounts of these minerals.

TABLE 9.11 *Summary of Six Ultratrace Minerals*

Mineral	Possible Functions	Suggested Daily Human Intakes	Dietary Sources
Arsenic (As)	• Amino acid metabolism • DNA synthesis	12–25 mcg (insufficient data to determine UL)	Fish, grains, cereals
Boron (B)	• Regulation of ion transport across cell membranes • Steroid hormone metabolism	1–13 mg (UL: 20 mg/day)	Fruit, leafy vegetables, peanuts, beans, wine
Lithium (Li)	• Reproduction • Maintenance of appropriate mood	1000 mcg (no UL has been established)	Water supply, grains, vegetables
Nickel (Ni)	• Amino acid and fatty acid metabolism	25–35 mcg (UL: 1 mg/day)	Chocolate, nuts, beans, whole grains
Silicon (Si)	• Connective tissue, including bone formation	25–30 mg (insufficient data to determine UL)	Root vegetables, whole grains
Vanadium (V)	• Glucose metabolism • Tooth and bone mineralization	10 mcg (UL: 1.8 mg/day)	Shellfish, mushrooms, black pepper, parsley, dill

Sources: Data from Food and Nutrition Board, Institute of Medicine: *Dietary Reference Intakes for vitamin A, vitamin K, arsenic, boron, chromium, copper, iodine, iron, manganese, molybdenum, nickel, silicon, vanadium, and zinc.* Washington, DC: Standing Committee on the Scientific Evaluation of Dietary Reference Intakes. National Academy Press, 2006. Schrauzer, GN: Lithium: Occurrence, dietary intakes, nutritional essentiality. *Journal of the American College of Nutrition*, 21(1):14, 2002.

Concept Checkpoint

27. What is the key difference between an ultratrace mineral and a major or a trace mineral?
28. Identify at least four minerals that are classified as ultratrace minerals.
29. Prepare a table for arsenic, boron, lithium, nickel, silicon, and vanadium that includes information about each ultratrace mineral's possible function and major food sources. Check your table against the information provided in Table 9.11.

Chapter 9 Highlight
Bottled Water versus Tap Water

Today, preparing for a class often involves bringing a laptop computer, a notebook, something to write with, and a bottle of cold water into the classroom. Even many university professors keep a bottle of water nearby as they lecture. Not long ago, most Canadians got their water from a tap. Now, many Canadians are turning away from the tap and choosing to drink bottled water instead. If you prefer drinking bottled water over tap water, you are part of a growing trend. According to data provided by the Beverage Market Corporation, each Canadian consumed 60 litres of bottled water in 2005.[1A] That amount of bottled water is more than twice the amount consumed in 1999. The Canadian population drinks more water than milk, juice, or any other beverage.[2A]

You may have also heard the terms "soft water" and "hard water." Hard water is any water containing an appreciable quantity of dissolved minerals. Soft water is treated water in which the only positively charged ion is sodium. The minerals in water give it a characteristic taste. Some natural mineral waters are highly sought for their flavour and the health benefits they may confer. Soft water, on the other hand, may taste salty and may not be suitable for drinking. In addition, hard water may cause mineral deposits which may harm household plumbing.

Why do so many Canadians drink bottled water when tap water is much less costly? Results of a North American survey of adults found that taste and convenience were the major reasons they chose bottled water over other beverages. Other factors that influenced people's decision to drink bottled water included "trust in its treatment," source of the water, and health concerns.[3A]

For most Canadians, bottled water is usually unnecessary and expensive, as it is often very similar to tap water. Consumers need to be aware that the water in some bottled water products actually came from a municipal water supply. However, when public water supplies are disrupted by hurricanes, tornadoes, or earthquakes, drinking bottled water may be a consumer's only option. If testing indicates the water supply may pose a threat to public health, consumers are warned through media, and a "boil order"—boiling water for ten minutes to kill harmful microorganisms—may be issued.

Health Canada and the Canadian Food Inspection Agency share responsibility for the regulation of bottled water in Canada.[4A] In Canada, bottled water is regulated as a food and therefore it must comply with the *Food and Drugs Act.* Health Canada defines bottled water as "water which has been packaged in sealed containers for human consumption. The water can

come from a variety of sources including springs, aquifers, or municipal supplies and may be treated to make it fit for human consumption."[5A] While bottled water is regulated federally as a food, the tap water distributed by municipalities is regulated by the appropriate province or territory.[6A] However, Health Canada is involved in the development of the *Guidelines for Canadian Drinking Water Quality*.[7A] These guidelines are developed through the Federal-Provincial-Territorial Committee on Drinking Water, which includes members from the provinces, territories, and Health Canada's Healthy Environment and Consumer Safety Branch. They contain guidelines for microbiological, chemical, physical, and radiological contaminants. For each contaminant, the guidelines establish the maximum acceptable concentration of the substance that can be permitted in water used for drinking. They are used by the provinces and territories as the basis for their own drinking water standards. Table 9.A defines common types of water used for bottling.

Ozone may be added to spring or mineral water during the bottling process as a disinfectant to inhibit the growth of harmful microorganisms. Ozone is also effective in removing objectionable odours and flavours because it breaks down into oxygen which improves taste and other qualities.

TABLE 9.A

Definitions for Classifying Some Types of Water

Water	Definition
Artesian water	Water from a well that taps a confined aquifer.
Mineral water	Water containing not less than 250 ppm (parts per million) total dissolved solids and originating from a geologically and physically protected underground water source. No minerals may be added to mineral water.
Purified water	Water produced by distillation, deionization, reverse osmosis, or other suitable processes.
Sparkling bottled water	Treated water that contains the same amount of carbon dioxide it had when it emerged from its source.
Spring water	Water from an underground formation from which the water flows naturally to the surface of the earth at an identified location.

*For more information on Canadian drinking water quality, visit http://www.hc-sc.gc.ca/ewh-semt/water-eau/drink-potab/index-eng.php.

References for Chapter 9 Highlight

1A. International Bottled Water Association: *Bottled water: More than just a story about sales growth*. 2006. www.bottledwater.org/public/2006_Releases/2006–04–13_bevmkt.htm.

2A. Garriguet D: Beverage consumption on Canadian adults. *Health Reports*, 19(4):23–9, 2008.

3A. International Bottled Water Association: *Survey: American's poor drinking habits contradict knowledge of health risks*. 2000. www.bottledwater.org/public/whatis_main.htm. Accessed: June 3, 2006.

4A. Canadian Food Inspection Agency: *Bottled water*. http://www.inspection.gc.ca/english/fssa/labeti/inform/wateaue.shtml. Accessed: June 23, 2010.

5A. Health Canada: *Food and nutrition: Frequently asked questions about bottled water*. http://hc-sc.gc.ca/fn-an/securit/facts-faits/faqs_bottle_water-eau_embouteillee-eng.php#a1. Accessed: June 23, 2010.

6A. Health Canada: *Environmental and workplace health: Drinking water*. http://www.hc-sc.gc.ca/ewh-semt/water-eau/drink-potab/index-eng.php. Accessed: June 23, 2010.

7A. Health Canada: *Environmental and workplace health: Canadian drinking water guidelines*. http://www.hc-sc.gc.ca/ewh-semt/water-eau/drink-potab/guide/index-eng.php. Accessed: June 23, 2010.

SUMMARY

Water is a simple compound that does not undergo digestion. In the body, water is a major solvent that often participates directly in chemical reactions. Water's other physiological roles include transporting substances, removing waste products, lubricating tissues, and regulating body temperature and acid-base balance. Water does not provide energy for the body. Depending on a person's age, sex, and body composition, about 45 to 75% of his or her body is water.

The body maintains a balance between intracellular and extracellular fluids primarily by controlling concentrations of ions in each fluid compartment. Maintenance of intracellular water volume depends largely on the intracellular concentration of potassium and phosphate ions. Maintenance of extracellular water volume depends primarily on the extracellular concentration of sodium and chloride ions. If the normal concentrations of these ions change too much, water shifts out of a compartment, and cells shrink or swell as a result.

Total water intake includes water from beverages and foods. About 80% of a person's total water intake is from beverages. Most of the water that enters the digestive tract is absorbed. Metabolic water is another source of water for the body.

The body loses water in urine, perspiration, exhaled air, feces, and insensible perspiration. A healthy person's average daily total water input equals his or her average output. Environmental factors, physiological conditions, and lifestyle practices can alter the body's fluid balance.

The kidneys are the major regulator of the body's water content and ion concentrations. In a healthy person, the kidneys maintain proper hydration by filtering excess ions from blood. When the kidneys remove ions such as sodium, water follows and becomes the main component of urine. Kidneys also remove drugs and metabolic waste products from the bloodstream.

To avoid overheating, the body must dissipate the excess heat into the environment, primarily by perspiration. When water evaporates from skin, it takes some heat along with it, cooling the body.

The AI for total water intake is 2.7 L for young women and 3.7 L for young men. These amounts do not need to be consumed in the form of fluids, because most solid foods and metabolic water contribute some water to the body.

Thirst is the primary regulator of fluid intake. The majority of healthy people meet their AI for water by letting thirst be their guide. Under certain conditions, however, elderly individuals, sick persons, and people who work or exercise outdoors, especially in hot conditions, are at risk of dehydration.

Minerals are a group of elements in Earth's rocks, soils, and natural water sources. About 15 mineral elements have known functions in the body and are necessary for human health. The three groups of dietary minerals are major minerals, trace minerals, and ultratrace minerals. The essential nature of ultratrace minerals has not been fully determined.

Some minerals function as inorganic ions or structural components of tissues; other minerals are components of various enzymes, hormones, or other organic molecules. Cells cannot metabolize minerals for energy. The body, however, needs certain minerals to catalyze specific chemical reactions that release energy from macronutrients. "Lack of energy" is often a symptom of these particular mineral deficiency disorders. Excessive amounts of minerals in the body can disrupt normal cell functioning, causing toxicity. Most foods contain small amounts of minerals. When the body's needs for minerals increase, the bioavailability of minerals generally increases to meet the demand.

Calcium is a major structural component of bones and teeth, and the mineral is necessary for blood clotting, muscle contraction, nerve transmission, and cell metabolism. Calcium absorption depends on vitamin D. Milk and milk products are rich calcium sources. Although women are at risk of developing osteoporosis as they age, various lifestyle modifications help reduce this risk.

Sodium, the major positively charged ion found outside cells, is vital for maintaining fluid balance and transmitting nerve impulses. The typical Canadian diet provides high amounts of sodium, primarily from processed foods and table salt. Diets high in sodium are associated with increased risk of hypertension.

Hypertensive individuals have greater risk of CVD, kidney failure, and damage to other organs than people with normal blood pressures. Advanced age, African ancestry, obesity, physical inactivity, cigarette smoking, and excess alcohol and sodium intakes are major risk factors for hypertension. Treatment for hypertension usually includes following dietary modifications and making some other lifestyle changes.

Potassium, the major positively charged ion found inside cells, has functions that are similar to those of sodium. Potassium-rich diets may lower blood pressure, reduce the risk of developing kidney stones, and possibly decrease bone loss. Plant foods, meat, and milk are good sources of potassium.

Magnesium is a cofactor for numerous chemical reactions and is needed for nerve and heart function.

Although many Canadians do not consume recommended amounts of magnesium, cases of magnesium deficiency rarely occur among healthy members of the population. Plant foods are good sources of magnesium.

Iron is a critical component of hemoglobin, myoglobin, and cytochromes. Hemoglobin in red blood cells transports oxygen from the lungs to the tissues. Iron deficiency can result in iron deficiency anemia, a condition characterized by decreased production of red blood cells. People suffering from anemia fatigue easily and lack interest in activities. In children, anemia interferes with growth and development.

Iron absorption depends on the body's need for the mineral and form of iron in food. Heme iron is better absorbed than nonheme iron. Meat and liver are among the best sources of dietary iron. Women of child-bearing age have higher needs for iron than men because of menstrual blood loss. Throughout the world, iron deficiency–related disorders are common. People who have hereditary hemochromatosis develop iron toxicity, because they absorb too much iron.

Zinc functions as a cofactor that activates many enzymes. Zinc is involved in growth and development, antioxidant activity, immune function, and taste. Zinc deficiency can result in growth failure, loss of appetite, as well as reduced intellectual and decreased immune function. Animal foods are the best dietary sources of zinc, but whole grains, peanuts, and legumes are also good sources of the trace mineral.

Iodide is needed to make thyroid hormone. When the diet lacks iodide, the thyroid gland enlarges, forming a goiter. The iodine content of the soil in which a plant is grown affects the iodide content of the plant food. Cretinism can occur in infants born to women who were iodide deficient during pregnancy. Iodide deficiency is rare in Canada because table salt is fortified with iodide. However, the deficiency is a major health problem in parts of the world where people consume diets that lack iodide.

Selenium functions as a component of selenoproteins, many of which are antioxidants. Other selenoproteins are involved in the normal functioning of the immune system and thyroid gland. The selenium content of the soil in which a plant is grown affects the selenium content of the plant food. Meat, fish, nuts, whole grains, and seeds are good sources of selenium.

Chromium enhances the action of insulin. Chromium is found in meats and whole grains. More research is needed to determine the effects of taking chromium supplements.

A few minerals, including nickel, arsenic, and silicon, are found in very small amounts in the body, but their roles in the body are unclear. At present, these minerals, referred to as ultratrace minerals, are not classified as essential nutrients.

Recipe for Healthy Living

Easy Orange-Strawberry Smoothie

When made with skim milk or low-fat yogourt, smoothies are a tasty, low-fat, calcium- and potassium-rich snack. They are also easy to prepare—this recipe takes less than ten minutes to make. For variety, substitute a banana, mango, or raspberries for the strawberries, or use lime sherbet instead of orange sherbet. Experimenting with different fruits and flavoured sherbets makes it easy to individualize smoothies, depending on your preferences and the fruit that's available. You'll need a sturdy blender to combine the ingredients.

The following recipe makes about three, 250 mL (8-oz.) servings. Each serving supplies approximately 200 kcal, 7 g protein, 3 g fat, 343 mg calcium, 564 mg potassium, 103 mg sodium, 1 mg zinc, 5 mcg selenium, and 70 mg of vitamin C.

INGREDIENTS:

60 mL (¼ cup) frozen orange juice concentrate, calcium-fortified
250 mL (1 cup) orange sherbet
375 mL (1½ cups) low-fat, plain yogourt
250 mL (1 cup) fresh strawberries, washed with leafy "caps" removed
2 ice cubes

14%
14%
72%
Fat
Protein
Carbohydrate

PREPARATION STEPS:

1. Place all ingredients, except ice cubes, in blender.
2. Blend until smooth. Add ice cubes and blend again, until ice is crushed.
3. Serve.
4. Refrigerate or freeze unused portion in a covered container. Partially thaw frozen smoothie before blending again.

Personal Dietary Analysis

Using the DRIs

1. Refer to your three-day food log from the Personal Dietary Analysis feature in Chapter 3.

   a. Find the RDA/AI values for minerals under your life stage/gender group category in the DRI tables (see the inside front cover of this book). Write those values under the "My RDA/AI" column in the table below.

   b. Review your personal dietary assessment. Find your three-day average intakes of iron, calcium, zinc, sodium, potassium, and magnesium. Write those values under the "My Average Intake" column of the table.

   c. Calculate the percentage of the RDA/AI you consumed for each mineral by dividing your intake by the RDA/AI amount and multiplying the figure you obtain by 100. For example, if your average intake of iron was 9 mg per day, and your RDA for the mineral is 18 mg per day, you would divide 18 mg by 9 mg to obtain .50. To multiply this figure by 100, simply move the decimal point two places to the right, and replace the decimal point with a percentage sign (50%). Thus, your average daily intake of iron was 50% of the RDA. Place the percentages for each mineral under the "% of My RDA/AI" column.

   d. Under the ">, <, =" column, indicate whether your average daily intake was greater than (>), less than (<), or equal to (=) the RDA/AI.

2. Use the information you calculated in the first part of this activity to answer the following questions:

   a. Which of your average mineral intakes equalled or exceeded the RDA/AI?

   b. Which of your average mineral intakes was below the RDA/AI?

   c. What foods would you eat to increase your intake of the minerals that were less than the RDA/AI levels? (Review sources of the minerals in Chapter 9.)

   d. Turn in your completed table and answers to your instructor.

Personal Dietary Analysis: Minerals

Mineral	My RDA/AI	My Average Intake	% of My RDA/AI	>, <, or =
Iron				
Calcium				
Zinc				
Sodium				
Potassium				
Magnesium				

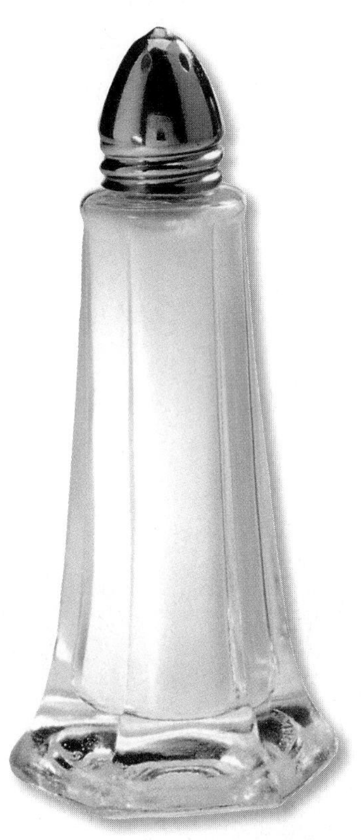

CRITICAL THINKING

1. Before the advent of refrigeration, salting meat was a common way of preventing microbes from spoiling the food. Explain why salting was effective as a means of food preservation.
2. A friend of yours refuses to drink tap water because she thinks it's contaminated. She drinks only bottled water or well water. If she asks you to explain why you drink tap water, what would you tell her?
3. A group of food manufacturers is considering fortifying some of their products with iron, chromium, boron, and iodide. Explain why you think they should or should not fortify the foods with each of these minerals.
4. What advice would you give a total vegetarian (vegan) concerning his need for calcium, iron, potassium, magnesium, and zinc?
5. Consider your family history and lifestyle to determine whether you are at risk of osteoporosis. If you are at risk, what steps can you take at this point in your life to reduce your chances of developing this disease?
6. Consider your family history and lifestyle to determine whether you are at risk of hypertension. If you are at risk, what steps can you take at this point in your life to reduce your chances of developing this disease?
7. In a televised interview, a person claiming to be a doctor recommends taking zinc, iron, and selenium supplements to enhance muscular strength and endurance. Discuss why you would or would not follow this person's advice.

PRACTICE TEST

Select the best answer.

1. Which of the following statements is false?
   a. Lean tissue contains more water than fat tissue.
   b. Water is a major solvent.
   c. Generally, young women have more body water than young men.
   d. Water does not provide energy.
2. If the extracellular fluid has an excess of sodium ions,
   a. sodium ions move into cells.
   b. the fluid moves to the outside of cells.
   c. phosphate and calcium ions are eliminated in feces.
   d. all of the above
3. Which of the following foods has the lowest percentage of water?
   a. tomato
   b. orange
   c. whole-grain bread
   d. vegetable oil

4. In Canada, table salt is fortified with
   a. iron.
   b. selenium.
   c. potassium.
   d. iodide.
5. Which of the following foods is not a good source of calcium?
   a. butter
   b. American cheese
   c. canned sardines
   d. kale
6. Henry is concerned about his risk of osteoporosis. Which of the following characteristics is a modifiable risk factor for this chronic condition?
   a. family history
   b. racial/ethnic background
   c. physical activity level
   d. age
7. The primary source of sodium in the typical Canadian's diet is
   a. mineral water.
   b. unprocessed foods.
   c. fresh fruit.
   d. table salt.
8. Which of the following populations has the highest risk of hypertension?
   a. people with African ancestry
   b. young, physically active Asian men
   c. Hispanic women who do not drink alcohol
   d. young adults who consume high amounts of fruit
9. Sources of heme iron include
   a. fortified grain products.
   b. beef.
   c. spinach.
   d. cast-iron cookware.
10. Worldwide, the most common nutrient deficiency disorder is ______ deficiency.
    a. iodide
    b. cobalt
    c. iron
    d. calcium
11. Which of the following statements is false?
    a. Iodide is necessary for normal thyroid function.
    b. In Canada, milk is usually fortified with iodide.
    c. Having too much or too little iodide in the diet can cause the thyroid gland to enlarge.
    d. Saltwater fish and other seafood are sources of iodide.

Answers to Chapter 9 Quiz Yourself

1. Your body constantly loses water through insensible perspiration, a form of water loss that is not the same as sweat. **True.** (p. 280)
2. Gram for gram, cottage cheese contains more calcium than plain yogourt. **False.** (p. 290)
3. Potassium, sodium, and chloride ions are involved in fluid balance. **True.** (p. 278)
4. Arsenic is an ultratrace mineral. **True.** (p. 320)
5. In general, plants are good dietary sources of iron because the plant pigment chlorophyll contains iron. **False.** (pp. 304, 308)

Please visit Connect at

www.mcgrawhillconnect.ca

Chapter **10**

Energy Balance and Weight Control

Chapter Learning Outcomes

After reading Chapter 10, you should be able to:

1. Describe the uses of energy by the body and explain the concept of energy balance.
2. Identify factors that influence body weight.
3. Discuss how BMI is used to determine whether a person's weight is healthy.
4. Describe ways to measure body composition.
5. List major health risks associated with excess body fat.
6. Plan a long-term weight-loss regimen that is safe and effective.
7. Evaluate popular weight-reduction diets for safety and long-term effectiveness.
8. Identify surgical procedures for severe obesity.
9. Describe treatments for underweight.
10. Identify major eating disorders, and discuss risk factors and treatments for these conditions.

Have you noticed the array of magazines available to readers today? The headline on one of the popular women's magazine covers announces in large, bright pink letters: "LOSE BIG—diet tricks that really work." A photo of chocolate brownies, cookies, and fudge nearly fills the magazine's cover. The magazine next to it contains recipes for rich desserts.

Another magazine cover displays a decorated cake and the statement: "Drop 3 inches of belly fat—every week." The magazine next to it suggests a way you can "Double your weight-loss success!" To ensure that the cover grabs your attention, an appealing-looking pie appears in the lower left-hand corner. Month after month, the magazines' covers and tables of contents seem to remain the same. When it comes to attracting readers, magazine covers that hype "new" weight-loss diets and recipes for rich desserts are a winning combination. The demand for weight-loss diets that promise success and recipes for high-calorie desserts indicates what is happening in our society today—many Canadians are too fat, preoccupied with losing weight, and yet they want to eat whatever they want and still lose weight.

An overweight or obese (overfat) person generally weighs more than what is considered healthy for his or her height.[1] At one time, people referred to height/weight tables to determine whether their body weights were "ideal" or "desirable." Today, medical experts use body composition (percentage of body fat) and the **body mass index (BMI)** to judge whether an adult's weight is *healthy*. BMI is a numerical value based on the relationship between body weight and risk of chronic health problems associated with excess body fat.[2] Healthy BMIs range from 18.5 to 24.9. The risk of developing serious chronic disorders such as type 2 diabetes, cardiovascular disease (CVD), and hypertension increases as the BMI approaches or exceeds 30.0, the minimum value for the obese range.[3,4,5]

Overweight and **obesity**, conditions characterized by too much body fat, are the most common nutritional disorders in Canada. According to data collected from the Canadian Community Health Survey (CCHS), about half of Canadian adults were either overweight or obese in 2004; approximately 23% of the adults were obese.[6] What's more startling, the percentage of overweight and obese children more than doubled between 1981 and 1997, and more recent reports suggest the problem of youth overweight and obesity is worsening.[7]

The prevalence of overweight among Canadian and American children and adolescents has risen sharply since the mid-1970s. Results of a national survey conducted from 1981 to 1996 indicated that the number of overweight Canadian youth doubled.[8] Over this same period, the BMI of Canadian children rose nearly 0.1 kg/m^2 per year for both sexes at most ages.[9] Public health experts are very concerned about the increase because overweight children have higher risk of maturing into obese adults than children who are not overweight.

In Canada, some reports have indicated that more than 19% of boys and girls in Grade 3 are overweight, or have a body mass index (BMI) above the 95th percentile for their age and gender.[9]

Although some provincial targets have been formally or informally set for population-level achievement of a *healthy body weight*, there has been no recent federal goal for reducing overweight and obesity to specified levels in Canada, though acceptable targets for BMI have been well established. It is likely that as overweight and obesity rates continue to climb in Canada, Health Canada will soon set future targets for the Canadian public with regard to increasing the percentage of Canadians with a healthy body weight (BMI between 18.5 and 24.9). Currently, nearly 60% of Canadians 20 years of age or older are either overweight or obese—a number that must be addressed in Canada.[10]

Although the prevalence of obesity among Canadians has reached epidemic proportions,[11] obesity rates ("globesity") are rising rapidly

Quiz YOURSELF

What is the difference between overweight and obesity? Why do most people gain body fat as they age? How can you tell whether a person is following a "fad" diet or a diet that is likely to be safe and effective? Are there any medications or dietary supplements that help people lose weight? Test your knowledge of energy balance and weight management concepts by taking the following quiz. The answers are on page 377.

1. You can determine whether you have an unhealthy amount of body fat simply by measuring your waistline. ______ T ______ F
2. The best way to lose weight and keep it off is to follow a low-carbohydrate, high-fat diet, such as the Atkins diet. ______ T ______ F
3. As people age, their muscle cells turn into fat cells. ______ T ______ F
4. When a person consumes more carbohydrate than needed, the excess is converted to fat and stored in fat cells. ______ T ______ F
5. Cellulite is a unique type of fat that can be eliminated by taking certain dietary supplements. ______ T ______ F

body mass index (BMI) numerical value of relationship between body weight and risk of certain chronic health problems

overweight and **obesity** condition characterized by excessive body fat

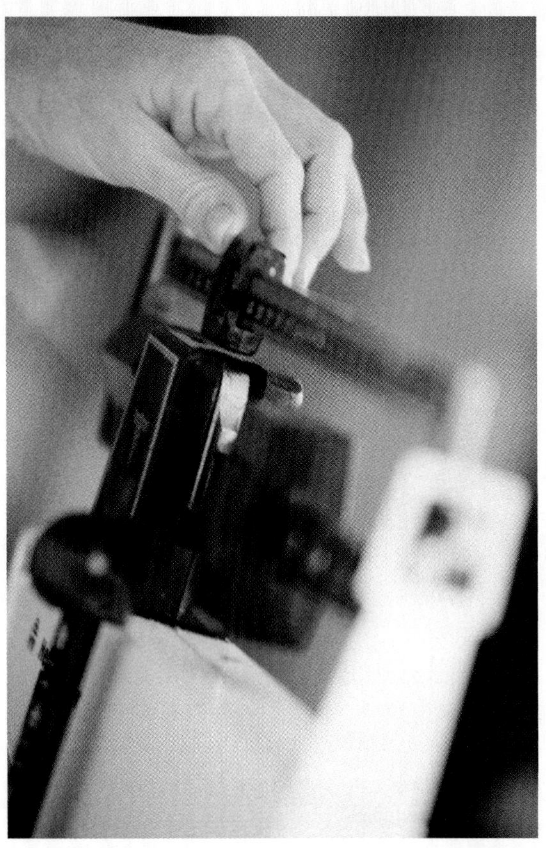

throughout the world. According to the World Health Organization (WHO), the majority of overweight and obese people live in developing countries.[12] By 2010, more obese people will reside in developing countries than in the developed world.

The Dietitians of Canada and the Canadian Paediatric Society have adopted the WHO growth charts as a means of assessing nutritional status (Table 10.1), such as normal weight, overweight, and obesity in children. The WHO considers children above the 97th percentile to be overweight, with those above the 99.9th percentile to be obese.

Losing even a small amount of excess body fat (10% of body weight) and maintaining the weight loss is often challenging for overweight or obese people. According to the limited data that is available, very few North Americans who intentionally lose weight, avoid regaining the weight for at least a year.[13,14] Because obesity is a chronic disease that is very difficult to treat effectively, preventing the condition is crucial.

Regardless of whether a person wants to maintain, lose, or gain weight, the basic principles of *energy balance* apply. By reading Chapter 10, you will learn about energy balance, health consequences linked to having too much or too little body fat, and factors that contribute to unwanted weight gain. This chapter also provides practical tips for helping you achieve or maintain a healthy body weight through sensible eating and physical activity practices.

TABLE 10.1 *Recommended Cutoffs by the WHO for Screening for Undernutrition and Overnutrition*

Age	Birth to 5 Years	5–19 Years
Underweight weight-for-age	<3rd percentile	3rd percentile
Stunted length-for-age/height-for-age	<3rd percentile	3rd percentile
Wasted weight-for-length/BMI-for-age*	<3rd percentile	3rd percentile
Risk of overweight weight-for-length/BMI-for-age	>85th percentile	not applicable
Overweight weight-for-length/BMI-for-age*	>97th percentile	>85th percentile
Obese weight-for-length/BMI-for-age*	>99.9th percentile	>97th percentile
Severe obesity BMI-for-age	not applicable	>99.9th percentile

*Weight-for-length from birth–2 years; BMI-for-age > 2 years

Source: Dietitians of Canada. *Promoting optimal monitoring of child growth in Canada: Using the new WHO growth charts.* http://www.dietitians.ca/pdf/Growth_Charts_DC_full_report_Mar12.pdf. Accessed: August 30, 2010.

Did You Know?

Cellulite, lumpy-appearing skin on thighs and buttocks of many women, is not a unique type of fat. Scientists have no clear understanding of why cellulite occurs, but it may simply be subcutaneous fat held in place by irregular bands of connective tissue. Despite claims by cosmetic manufacturers that their products eliminate cellulite, there are no effective ways to smooth the skin's dimpled appearance.[19]

Body Composition

The body is composed of two major compartments: **fat-free mass** (lean tissues) and **total body fat**. Fat-free mass is comprised of body water; mineral-rich tissues, such as bones and teeth; and protein-rich tissues, including muscles and organs.[15] Total body fat includes adipose tissue and "essential fat." Essential fat is in cell membranes, certain bones, and nervous tissue. Essential fat is vital for survival. Adipose tissue contains adipose cells that are specialized for storing triglycerides (fat). Overweight and obese people have excessive amounts of adipose tissue.

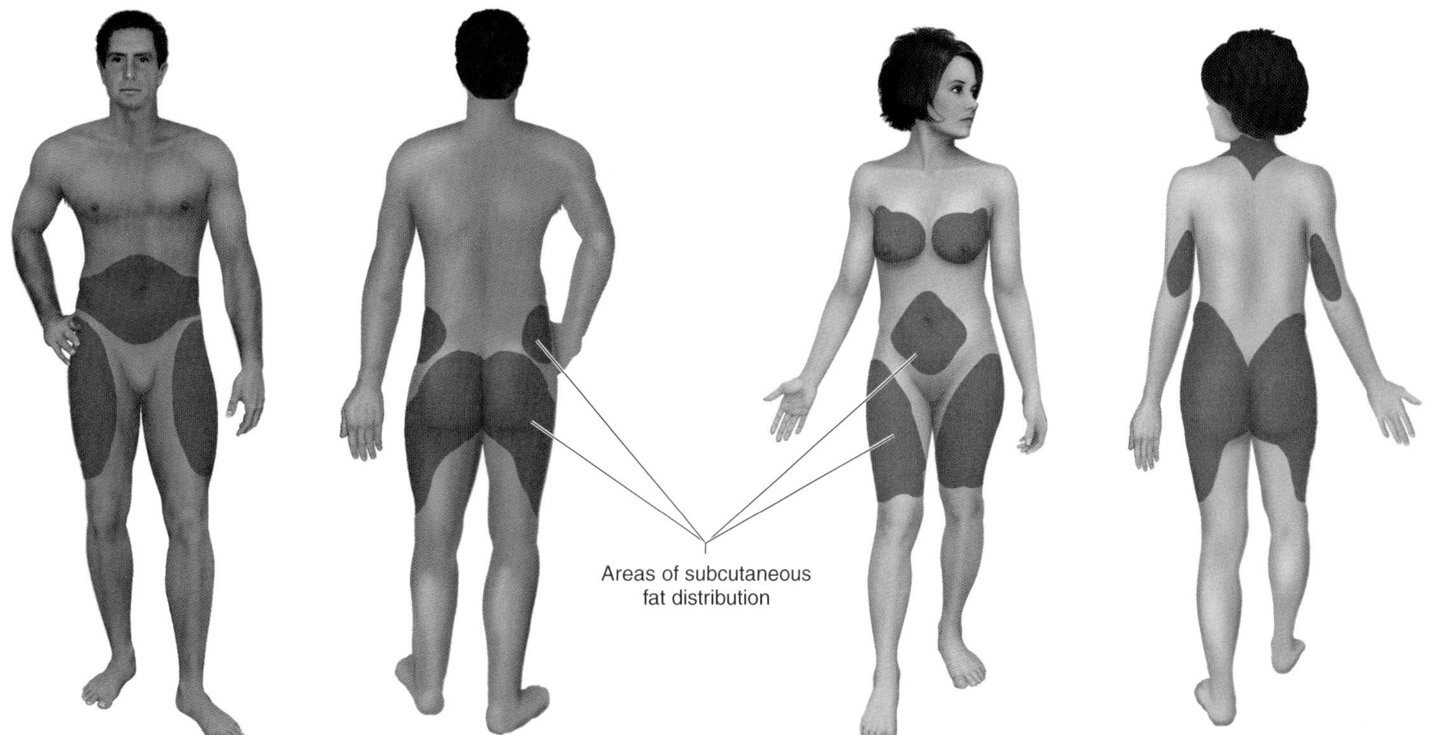

Figure 10.1 Subcutaneous fat distribution. Distinct patterns of subcutaneous fat occur in various regions of men's and women's bodies, especially in the breasts, thighs, abdominal area, and buttocks.

Adipose Tissue

Every cell contains some lipid, but the major function of an adult **adipose** ("fat") **cell** is to store a droplet of fat (see Fig. 6.13 on p. 158). When food is plentiful, adipose cells remove excess fat from the bloodstream for storage. As the amount of fat stored in adipose cells increases, the size of each cell expands, and the body gains weight. At one time, scientists thought the body could only produce fat cells during periods of rapid growth, such as childhood. However, the body can also develop more fat cells when overeating occurs in adulthood, especially in cases of extreme obesity.[16] Once fat cells form, scientists think the cells remain, unless they die or are surgically removed. Adipose tissue is not inert tissue but actually functions as an endocrine organ.

When the body needs energy, adipose cells release fat for other cells to use as fuel. As each adipose cell loses some fat, it becomes smaller, and the body loses weight as a result. In addition to storing and releasing fat, adipose cells secrete numerous proteins, some of which have roles in regulating food intake, glucose metabolism, and immune responses.[17]

Subcutaneous (*sub* = under; *cutaneous* [*qu-tay'-nee-us*] = skin) tissue holds skin in place over deeper tissues such as muscles. Subcutaneous tissue also contains adipose cells. When subcutaneous tissue has more adipose cells than other kinds of cells, it is referred to as subcutaneous fat.[18] Subcutaneous fat helps insulate the body against cold temperatures and protects muscles and bones from bumps and bruises. Distinct patterns of subcutaneous fat occur in various regions of men's and women's bodies, especially in the breasts, thighs, abdominal area, and buttocks (Fig. 10.1). In addition to subcutaneous fat, the body has *visceral* fat, deposits of fat located deep within the abdomen.

fat-free mass lean tissues

total body fat essential and storage fat

adipose cell specialized cell that stores fat

What Is Brown Fat?

Adult adipose tissue is creamy white in appearance and may be referred to as "white fat." Brown fat cells (brown adipose tissue, or BAT) are specialized adipose cells that are more richly supplied with blood and contain more mitochondria, the energy-generating organelles, than white fat tissue (Fig. 10.2). BAT uses fat for generating heat, whereas white fat tissue stores fat.

Figure 10.2 Brown fat. Brown fat tissue has more mitochondria and is more richly supplied with blood than white fat tissue.

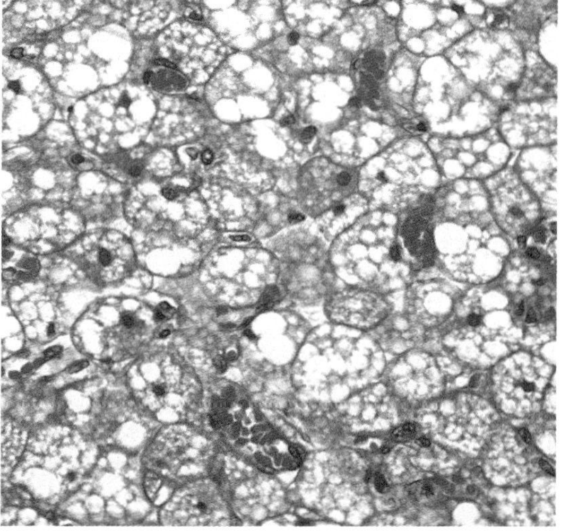

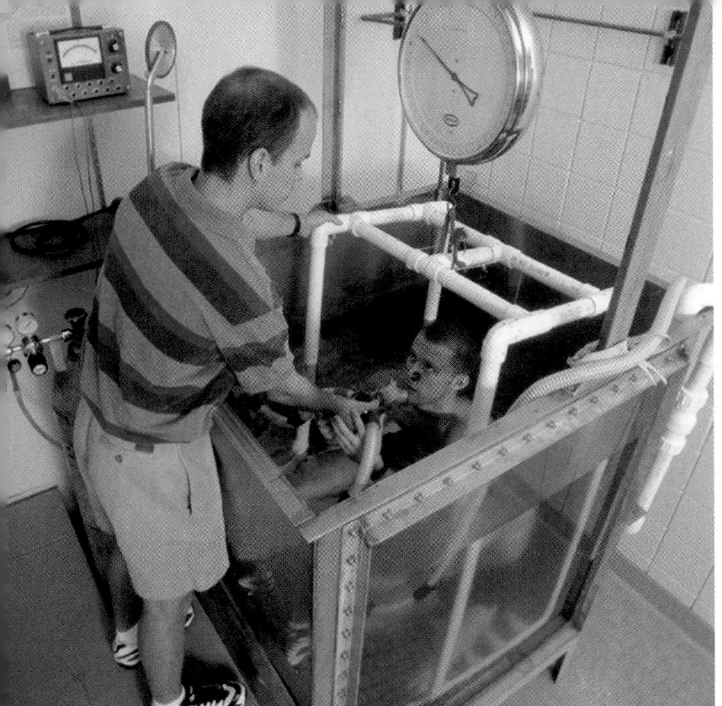

Figure 10.3 Underwater weighing. Underwater weighing involves comparing a person's weight on land to his or her weight when completely submerged in a tank of water.

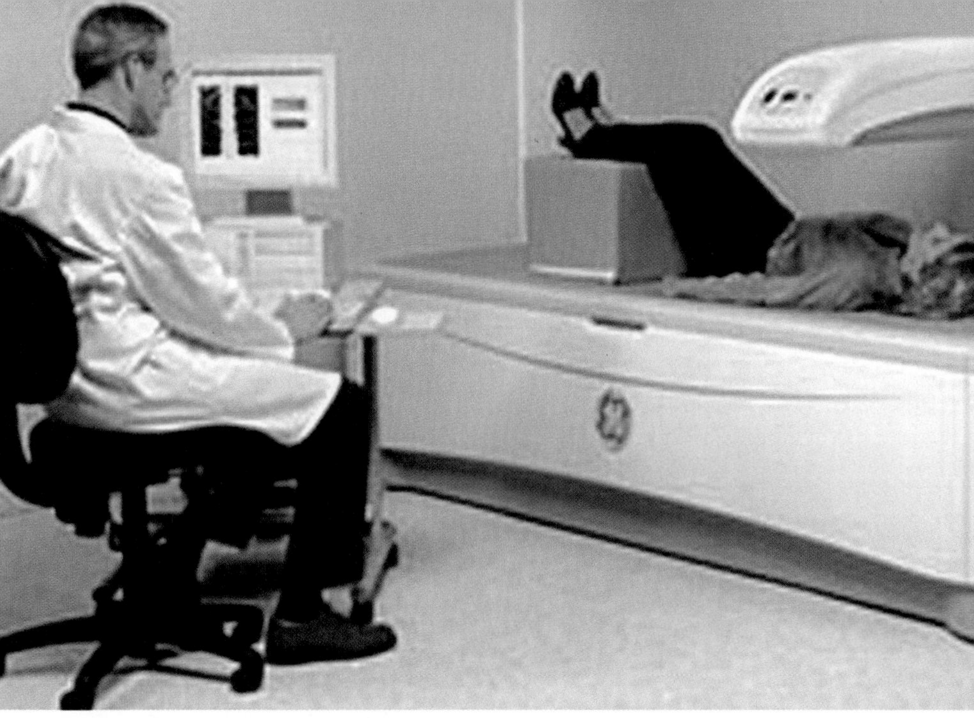

Figure 10.4 Dual-energy X-ray absorptiometry (DXA). Although DXA is a highly accurate way to estimate body fat content, the equipment is very expensive and not widely available outside of clinical settings.

Human infants have deposits of BAT in their upper backs and abdomens. In infants, BAT may be important for maintaining normal body temperature, because the cells generate body heat without the need to shiver. Although adult humans have no BAT, their white fat cells may have the potential to acquire brown fat cells' fat-burning ability.[20] Thus, some medical researchers think finding ways to "switch on" the development of BAT in adults may help people lose or control their weight, because brown fat cells "waste" energy as heat.

Promoters of certain dietary supplements claim their products contain ingredients that eliminate "hard to burn" brown fat in the thighs and abdominal area. These claims are untrue. The fat in those regions is primarily white fat. Furthermore, why would overweight or obese people want to eliminate BAT—if they had it?

Measuring Body Composition

When you weigh yourself on a scale, you cannot determine whether your weight is healthy. Why? It is healthier to have more fat-free tissue than fat tissue, but the scale does not distinguish between these two major components of your body. Information concerning your body's composition, especially its *percentage* of fat, can help you predict your risk of obesity-related diseases.

There is no direct way to measure a living person's percentage of body fat. Nevertheless, scientists can use indirect methods of measuring body fat, such as "underwater weighing," dual-energy X-ray absorptiometry, bioelectrical impedance, and skinfold thicknesses. The following sections describe these methods of assessing body composition, including their advantages and disadvantages.

underwater weighing technique of estimating body composition that involves comparing weight on land to weight when completely submerged in a tank of water

dual-energy X-ray absorptiometry (DXA) technique of estimating body composition that involves scanning the body with multiple low-energy X-rays

bioelectrical impedance technique of estimating body composition in which a device measures the conduction of a weak electrical current through the body

skinfold thickness measurements technique of estimating body composition in which calipers are used to measure the width of skinfolds at multiple body sites

Underwater Weighing

Underwater weighing involves comparing a person's weight "on land" to his or her weight when completely submerged in a tank of water (Fig. 10.3). Lean tissue is denser than water; fat tissue is not as dense as water. Thus, a person who has more body fat will weigh less when under water than a person who has more lean tissue. Underwater weighing method can be an accurate way of assessing body composition. However, the method is not a convenient, easy, inexpensive, or practical way to estimate body fat, because it requires special testing facilities.

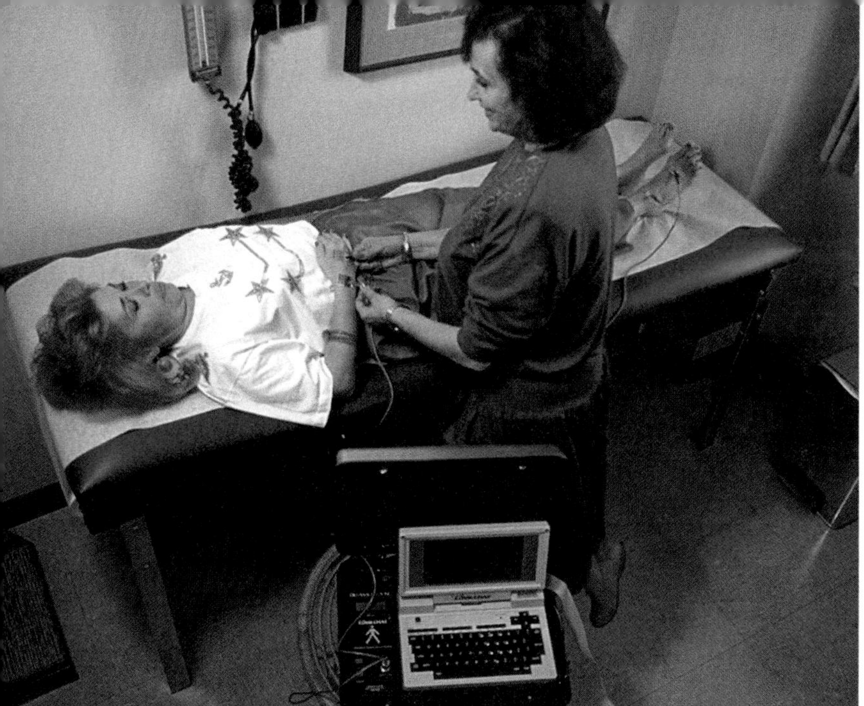

Figure 10.5 Bioelectrical impedance. The use of a device that measures bioelectrical impedance is a quick and painless way to estimate body fat content.

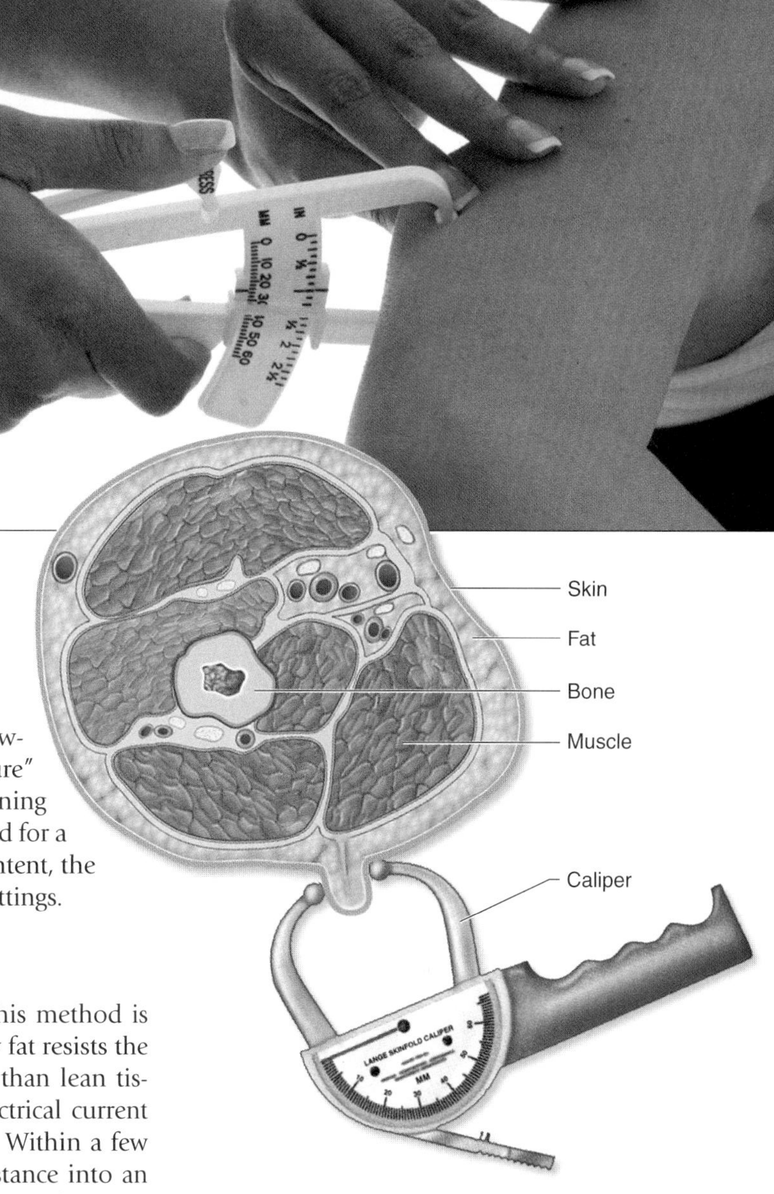

Figure 10.6 Measuring skinfold thickness. Body fat content can be estimated by measuring skinfold thicknesses using a special device (skinfold caliper) at multiple body sites, such as the triceps muscle of the arm.

Dual-Energy X-Ray Absorptiometry (DXA)

Dual-energy X-ray absorptiometry (DXA) involves the use of multiple low-energy X-rays to scan the entire body. The method provides a detailed "picture" of internal structures, including fat deposits (Fig. 10.4). During the scanning process, the equipment emits a dose of radiation that is lower than that used for a chest X-ray. Although DXA is a highly accurate way to estimate body fat content, the equipment is very expensive and not widely available outside of clinical settings.

Bioelectrical Impedance

Bioelectrical impedance is a quick way to estimate body fat content. This method is based on the principle that water and electrolytes conduct electricity. Body fat resists the flow of electricity, because fat tissue contains less water and electrolytes than lean tissue. The bioelectrical impedance device sends a painless, low-voltage electrical current via wires connected to electrodes placed on the subject's skin (Fig. 10.5). Within a few seconds, the device converts information about the body's electrical resistance into an estimate of total body fat. The method is fairly accurate, as long as the subject's hydration status is normal. Consumers can purchase a bioelectrical impedance device that resembles a bathroom scale, but scientific data about the machine's accuracy is lacking, and many of these devices pass the electrical current through only half the body.

Skinfold Thickness

A common technique for estimating total body fat involves taking **skinfold thickness measurements** at multiple body sites, such as over the triceps muscle of the arm (Fig. 10.6). The width of a skinfold indicates the depth of the subcutaneous fat at that site. To perform the measurements, a trained person pinches a section of the subject's skin, gently pulls it away from underlying muscle tissue, and uses special calipers to measure the thickness of the fat. After taking the measurements, the values are incorporated into a mathematical formula that provides a fairly accurate estimate of the subject's amount of body fat.

Skinfold thickness measurements are relatively easy and inexpensive to perform, but the technique may underestimate total body fat when used on overfat subjects. However, by combining data collected from skinfold, waist and hip circumference, and body frame (skeletal joint) measurements, researchers can obtain more reliable estimates of an individual's total body fat.[21]

Extremely obese people are far more likely to develop the serious chronic diseases associated with excess body fat and die prematurely than people who have BMIs between 18.5 and 30.0.

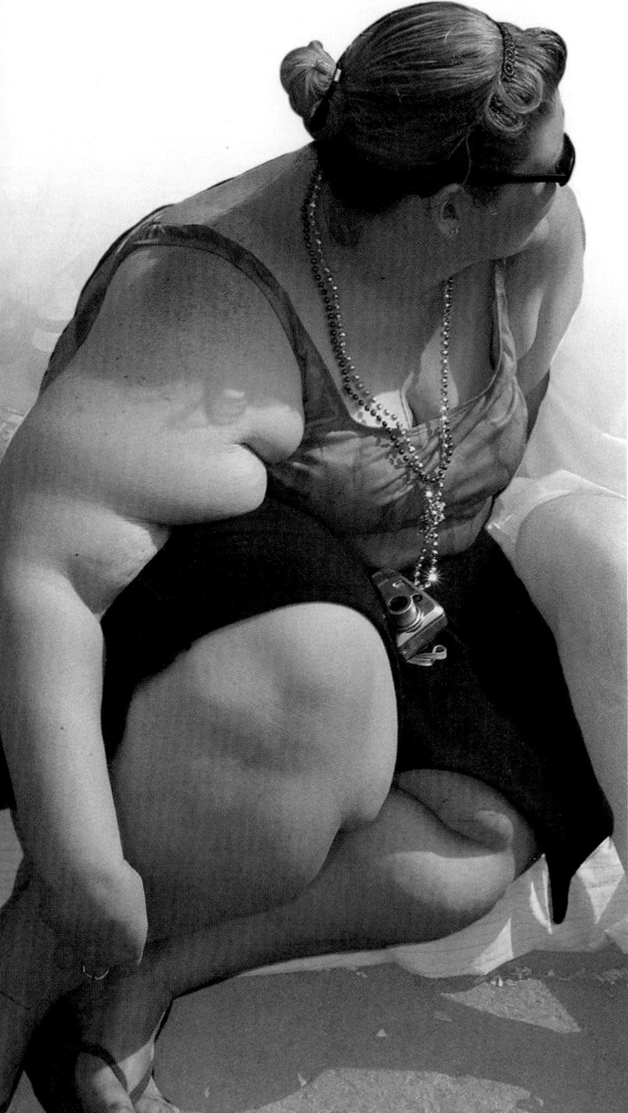

TABLE 10.3 *Adult Weight Status Categories (BMI)*

BMI	Weight Status
Below 18.5	Underweight
18.5 to 24.9	Healthy
25.0 to 29.9	Overweight
30.0 to 39.9	Obese
40 and above	Extremely obese

Source: National Heart, Lung, and Blood Institute: *The practical guide: Identification, evaluation, and treatment of overweight and obesity in adults.* NIH Publication 00-4084, 2000. www.nhlbi.nih.gov/guidelines/obesity/prctgd_b.pdf. Accessed: July 8, 2006.

TABLE 10.2 *Adult Body Weight Classification by Percentage of Body Fat*

	Body Fat (%)	
Classification	Men	Women
Healthy	13 to 21%	23 to 31%
Overweight	22 to 25%	32 to 37%
Obese	26 to 31%	38 to 42%
Extremely obese	32% or more	43% or more

Source: Adapted from Food and Nutrition Board: Dietary Reference Intakes for energy, carbohydrate, fiber, fat, fatty acids, cholesterol, protein, and amino acids (macronutrients). Table 5.5, page 126, 2005. www.nap.edu/openbook/0309085373/html/126.html. Accessed: March 20, 2007.

How Much Body Fat Is Too Much?

Some body fat is essential for good health, but too much adipose tissue, especially visceral fat, can interfere with the body's ability to function normally. Percentages of body fat can be used to develop weight classifications for adults. According to one such classification system, a man is overweight when his body is 22 to 25% fat; a woman is overweight when her body is 32 to 37% fat (Table 10.2).[2] A man is obese when fat comprises 26% or more of his body; a woman is obese when fat makes up 38% or more of her body. It is important to note that the average healthy young woman has more body fat than the average healthy young man, because she needs the extra fat for hormonal and reproductive purposes.

Adults tend to gain adipose tissue as they age, but for elderly persons, some additional fat does not necessarily contribute to serious health problems. The extra fat may actually provide some health benefits, such as providing an energy reserve for a very ill person who cannot eat. Furthermore, the extra padding of fat may protect a person from being injured by falling.

Using BMI to Classify Body Weight

Table 10.3 presents adult weight classifications based on BMI ranges. *Overweight* adults have BMIs that range from 25.0 to 29.9; *obese* adults have BMIs that range from 30.0 to 39.9. People whose BMIs are 40 or higher are classified as *extremely obese*. Extremely obese people are far more likely to develop the serious chronic diseases associated with excess body fat and die prematurely than people who have BMIs that range from 18.5 to 30.0.

Muscle is denser than fat, therefore, many muscular people may have BMIs in the overweight range, yet they have healthy percentages of body fat. For example, a muscular athlete with a BMI of 25.0 is more likely to be healthy than a sedentary person who also has a BMI of 25.0. Therefore, BMIs should not be applied to highly muscular individuals. However, most people with BMIs of 30 or higher are too fat, even if they are athletic.

How Can I Calculate My BMI?

To calculate your BMI, you can use the following formula:

$$\text{Weight (kg)/ht (m)}^2$$

For example, a person who weighs 64 kg (141 lbs.) and is 160 cm or 1.60 m (5′3″ or 63″) has a BMI of approximately 25.0. This person's BMI is just above the upper limit of the healthy range.

$$\text{Calculation: } 64 / 1.60^2 = 64 / 2.56 = 25.0$$

Concept **Checkpoint**

1. Which tissues comprise total body fat and which comprise fat-free mass?
2. Discuss conditions in which fat cells can increase in size and number.
3. Why is it necessary to have some body fat?
4. List three roles for subcutaneous fat.
5. What is cellulite?
6. Describe differences between brown fat tissue and white fat tissue.
7. Describe three different methods of measuring body fat, including drawbacks of each method.
8. Explain why a healthy woman has more body fat than a healthy man.
9. A young man's body is 13% fat. According to this information, is he overweight or obese?
10. A young woman's BMI is 26.2. According to this information, is this woman likely to be healthy, overweight, obese, or extremely obese?

Overweight and Obesity: Effects on Health

People with BMIs greater than 25 have increased risks of CVD, hypertension, and type 2 diabetes. Cancers of the gallbladder, pancreas, cervix, uterus, breast, colon, rectum, and kidney are more common in overweight and obese people. Furthermore, obese patients have high risk of experiencing serious complications during and after surgery. Such patients often require more anesthesia and their incisions are more likely to become infected than surgical patients whose weights are within the healthy range. Compared to people with healthy BMIs, obese people are more likely to die prematurely from all causes. Based on the data collected from the National Population Health Survey, it is estimated that being obese at 40 years of age is associated with a loss of over 7 years of life for Canadian women and nearly 6 years of life for men.[22]

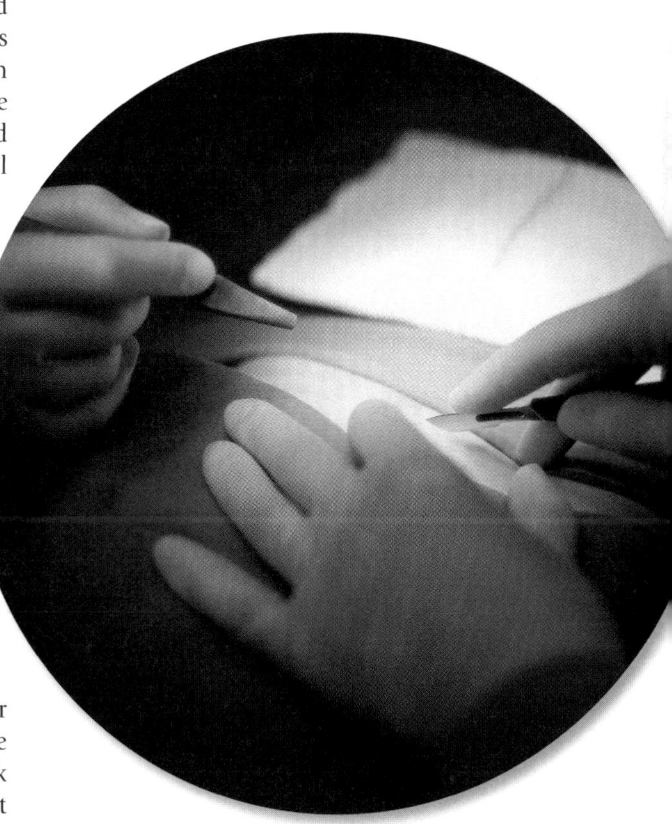

Overfat people are more likely to develop osteoarthritis, a painful chronic condition that affects joints and interferes with the person's ability to move.[23,24,25] Obese people typically have difficulty carrying out routine daily activities, especially those that require walking, carrying, kneeling, and stooping. Additionally, obese people are more likely to suffer from chronic heartburn as well as *sleep apnea*, a condition that causes breathing to stop periodically during sleep. As a result, people suffering from sleep apnea are often very tired and sleepy when awake.

Obese men and women are more likely to have fertility problems than people with healthy BMIs. *Polycystic ovary disease* often affects obese women and can reduce the women's chances of becoming pregnant. During pregnancy, obese women have high risk of *gestational diabetes* and a form of hypertension that can be deadly.[26] Additionally, obese pregnant women are at greater risk for stillbirths or giving birth to babies with birth defects than are pregnant women who have lower BMIs.

A person's mental health and self-esteem can be negatively affected by his or her "weight problem." Many Canadians admire slim and muscular body builds over obese body shapes. Thus, overfat people often suffer from poor self-images because they think their bodies are unattractive. The general public often views obesity as a condition that results from lack of willpower and the inability to "push oneself away from the table." Thus, many overfat people also deal with the negative attitude (stigma) that many people have toward them.[3] People who are not overfat often characterize obese persons as lazy, stupid, and sloppy.[27] The stigma of obesity can result in discriminatory practices that limit an obese person's chances for career opportunities. It is not surprising that depres-

gynoid obesity condition characterized by excessive subcutaneous fat

android obesity condition characterized by excessive abdominal fat

TABLE 10.4 *Health Problems Associated with Excess Body Fat*

Overweight and obesity increase the risk of:	
Cardiovascular disease (CVD)	Chronic low back pain
Hypertension	Loss of mobility
Type 2 diabetes	Fatty liver disease (not alcohol related)
Metabolic syndrome	Erectile dysfunction in men (impotence)
Polycystic ovary syndrome	Low-grade inflammation
Infertility	Gastroesophageal reflux disorder (GERD)
Elevated blood lipid levels	Psychological depression
Gallstones	Certain cancers
Sleep apnea	Skin ulcers
Osteoarthritis	Premature death

Sources: Jackson Y and others: Summary of the 2000 Surgeon General's listening session: Toward a national action plan on overweight and obesity. *Obesity Research* 10(12):1299, 2002; Virji A, Murr MM: Caring for patients after bariatric surgery. *American Family Physician*, 73(8):1403, 2006.

sion tends to accompany obesity. Table 10.4 lists these and other major health problems associated with excessive body fat.

Figure 10.7 Body fat distribution: Typical sex differences. Some people, especially women, tend to store extra fat below the waist, primarily in the buttocks and thighs (*a*). Men tend to store extra fat deep in the upper or central region of their bodies (*b*).

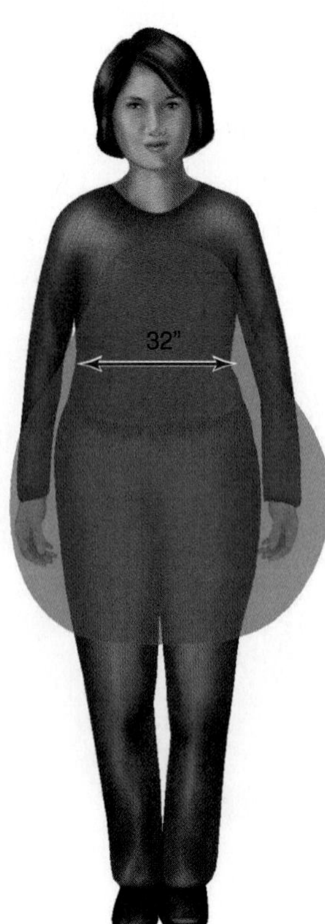

a. Lower-body fat distribution (gynoid: pear shape)

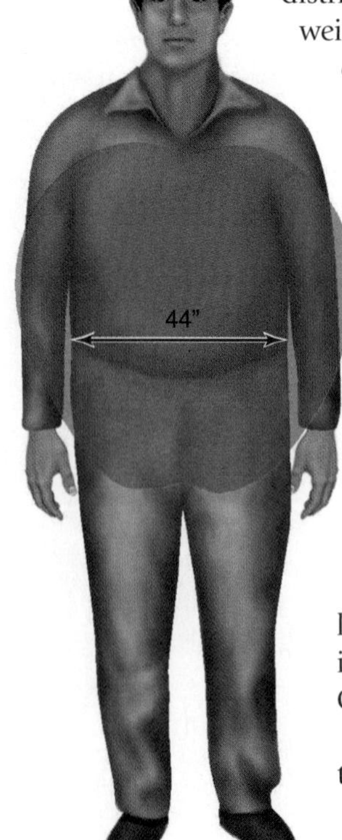

b. Upper-body fat distribution (android: apple shape)

Body Fat Distribution and Its Effects on Health

The results of medical research suggest that the distribution of excess body fat is more closely associated with obesity-related diseases than the percentage of total body fat. Some people, especially women, tend to store extra fat below the waist, primarily subcutaneously in the buttocks and thighs (Fig. 10.7a). Having this particular pattern of fat distribution (a "pear shape") adds stress to hip and knee joints that must carry the extra weight, but the pattern is not associated with increased risk of more serious chronic diseases such as type 2 diabetes. This pattern of fat distribution is often referred to as ***gynoid adiposity***.

Men tend to store extra fat deep in the upper or central region of their bodies. This visceral body fat distribution is often called ***android adiposity***. **Android obesity** is characterized by a large "pot belly" that spreads beyond buttocks and thighs. A person with upper-body obesity is sometimes described as having an "apple" body shape (see Fig. 10.7b). Regardless of their sex, people with upper-body obesity have higher risks of the serious health-related problems associated with excess body fat than people who have lower-body obesity.

Some medical researchers think upper-body obesity contributes to certain chronic diseases because the surplus of abdominal fat cells releases too many fatty acids into the *portal vein* that leads directly to the liver.[28] When flooded with fatty acids, the liver has difficulty using the lipids to make lipoproteins. When this occurs, the fatty acids circulate in blood, possibly disrupting muscle and liver glucose metabolism.[28] Furthermore, adipose cells, particularly those located deep in the abdominal region, make substances that produce inflammation in the body.[29] These inflammatory factors may also increase risks of type 2 diabetes, CVD, and hypertension.

A quick and easy method to determine your risk of obesity-related disorders is to measure your *waist circumference*. Figure 10.8 shows the recommended placement of the tape measure. Note the positioning of the tape at the top of the hip bones and not necessarily at the narrowest point.[30,31] It is also important to use a measuring tape that does not stretch. Android obesity is defined by a waist circumference of greater than 40 inches in men and greater than 35 inches in women.[30]

Concept Checkpoint

11. List at least six different serious health problems that are associated with having too much body fat, and being obese in particular.

12. What is the "stigma" of obesity?

13. Which of the two major types of body fat distribution is more likely to pose serious health risks? Which chronic diseases are more likely to develop in people who have this pattern of excess fat deposition?

14. What is a quick and easy way to determine whether a person's body fat distribution is likely to result in serious health problems, such as type 2 diabetes?

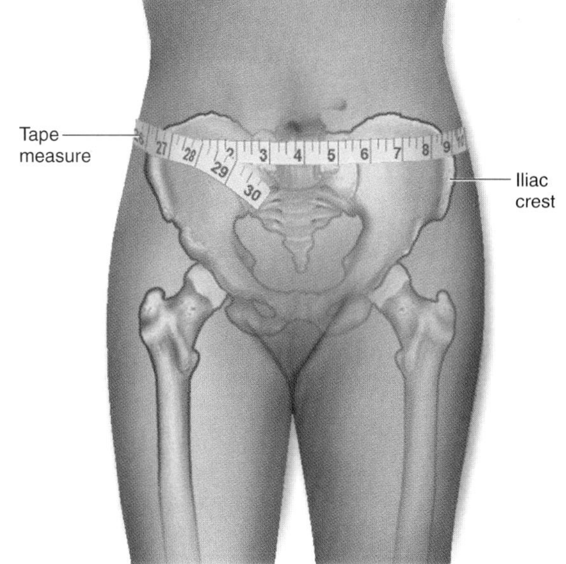

Figure 10.8 Measuring waist circumference. A quick and easy method to determine a person's risk of obesity-related disorders is to measure the individual's waist circumference. Note the positioning of the tape at the top of the hip bones and not necessarily at the narrowest point. Additionally, the tape should be held around the waist, parallel to the floor.

Energy for Living

Regardless of what you are doing—eating, watching television, studying, exercising, even sleeping—your body needs a constant supply of energy to function. **Energy** is defined as the capacity to perform work. There are several forms of energy, but heat, mechanical, chemical, and even electrical energy occur in living things. The total amount of energy is *constant*, that is, the amount remains the same, because energy cannot be created or destroyed. Nevertheless, the various forms of energy can be stored, released, moved, or transformed from one kind to another. The following section discusses how human cells obtain energy.

Energy Intake

Just as a car engine uses a mixture of gasoline, ethanol, and oxygen to run properly, your body uses a mixture of *biological fuels* and oxygen to do its work. For humans, biological fuels are foods and beverages that contain macronutrients (**energy intake**). For some individuals, nonnutrient alcohol (ethanol) also provides energy. Under normal conditions, our cells metabolize primarily glucose and fatty acids, but small amounts of amino acids are also used for energy.

Cells release the energy stored in biological fuels by breaking bonds within the compounds' molecules. The energy that is released can be captured and stored in special compounds, such as **adenosine triphosphate (ATP)**, until it is needed. Cells obtain only about 40% of the energy that was in macronutrients by forming ATP. Cells release the remaining energy as heat. Figure 10.9 summarizes events that result in macronutrient storage or breakdown for energy. The diagram in Appendix D shows the complex chemical pathways that most cells use to generate ATP from the metabolism of glucose, fat, and amino acids.

energy capacity to perform work

energy intake calories from foods and beverages that contain macronutrients and ethanol

adenosine triphosphate (ATP) biological compound that stores energy

Did You Know?

Advertisements for vitamin or mineral supplements often claim that the supplements can "boost" energy levels. Certain vitamins and minerals are needed to regulate energy metabolism, and deficiencies of these nutrients can reduce the body's ability to obtain energy from macronutrients. However, the body does not obtain energy from vitamins or minerals. Therefore, taking vitamin/mineral supplements will not increase the energy level of a person who is adequately nourished.

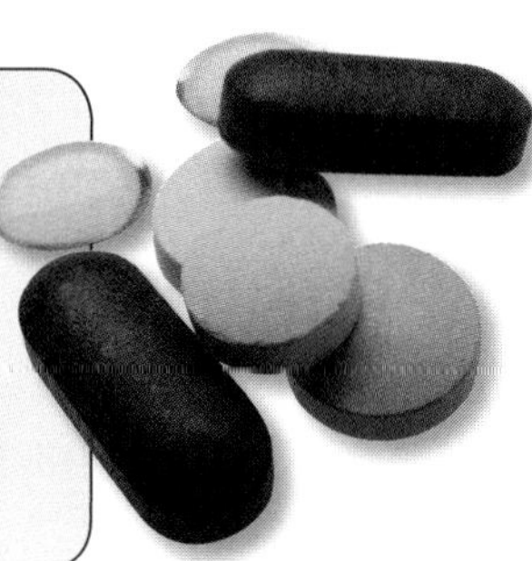

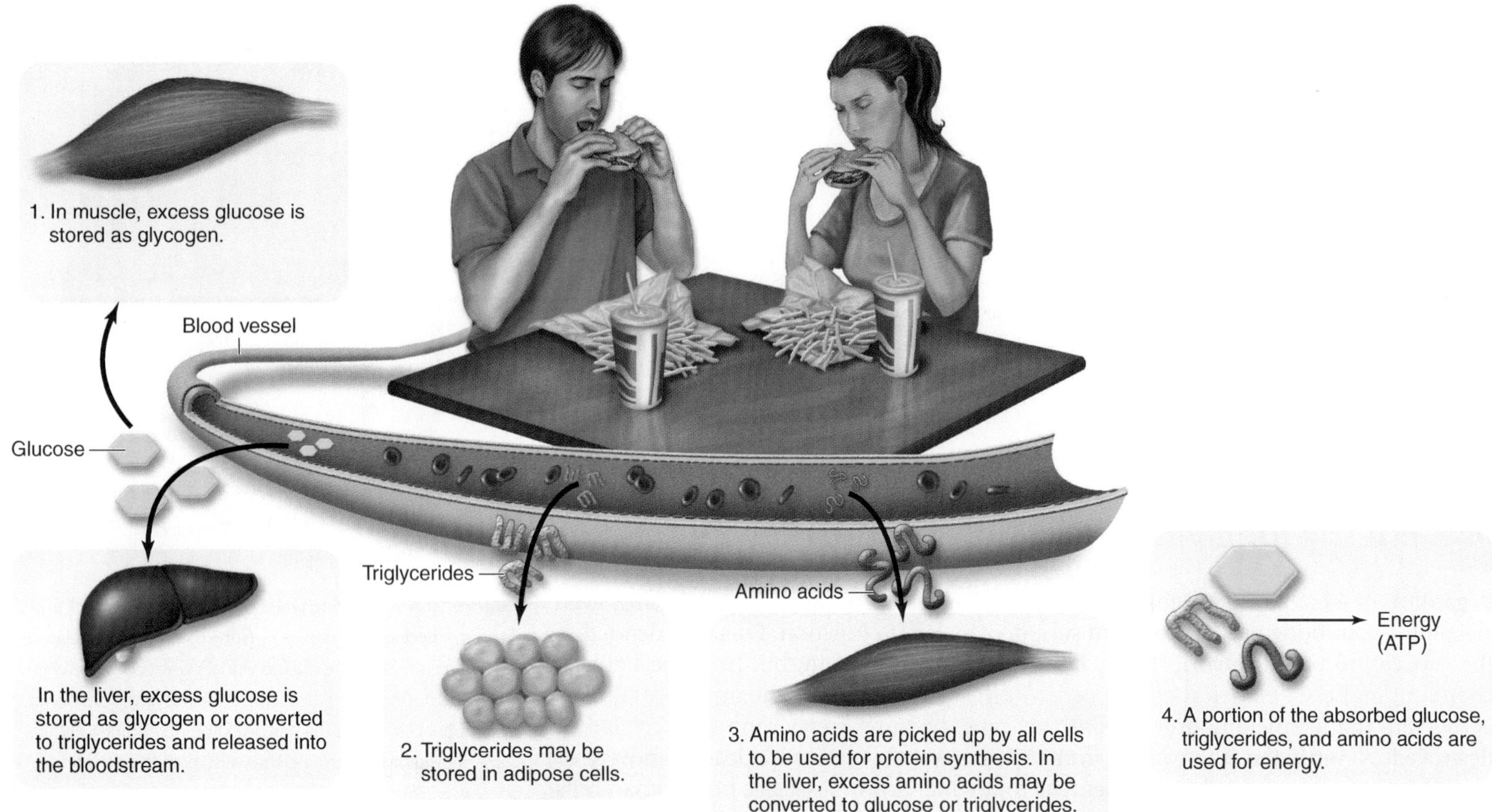

Figure 10.9 What happens to macronutrients? (*a*) After being absorbed, macronutrients are used for energy or stored as glycogen or fat. (*b*) When energy is needed to fuel cells, macronutrients are released from storage and metabolized to synthesize ATP.

Energy Output

Energy output (energy *expenditure*) refers to the energy (calories) cells use to carry out their activities. For example, muscle cells need energy to contract, liver cells use energy to convert toxic compounds to safer substances, and intestinal cells need energy to absorb certain nutrients. The following sections discuss the major ways the body uses food energy.

Basal and Resting Metabolism

Metabolism refers to all chemical changes, or reactions, that constantly occur in living cells. Anabolic reactions require energy to occur; catabolic reactions release energy. **Basal metabolism** is the minimal number of calories the body uses for vital physiological activities after fasting and resting for 12 hours. Basal metabolic processes include breathing, circulating blood, and maintaining constant liver, brain, and kidney functions. Basal metabolism does not encompass energy needed for skeletal muscle movements (physical activity), digestion of food, and absorption and processing of nutrients. For most adults, basal metabolism accounts for about 50 to 70% of the body's total energy use.[32]

The **resting metabolic rate (RMR)** refers to the body's rate of energy use a few hours after resting and eating. A person's RMR is slightly higher than his or her BMR (basal metabolism rate). Although there is a difference between the BMR and RMR, researchers often use the terms interchangeably in their publications.[33]

Thyroid hormone, secreted by the thyroid gland, regulates metabolism (see Fig. 9.11 on p. 289). A person who has an overactive thyroid gland produces too much thyroid hormone. As a result, this person has a higher than normal metabolic rate. Signs and symptoms of excess thyroid hormone production (hyperthyroidism) include feeling warm, sweaty, nervous, and restless; having rapid heart rate and chronic diarrhea; and losing weight despite eating considerable amounts of food.[34] You might think that

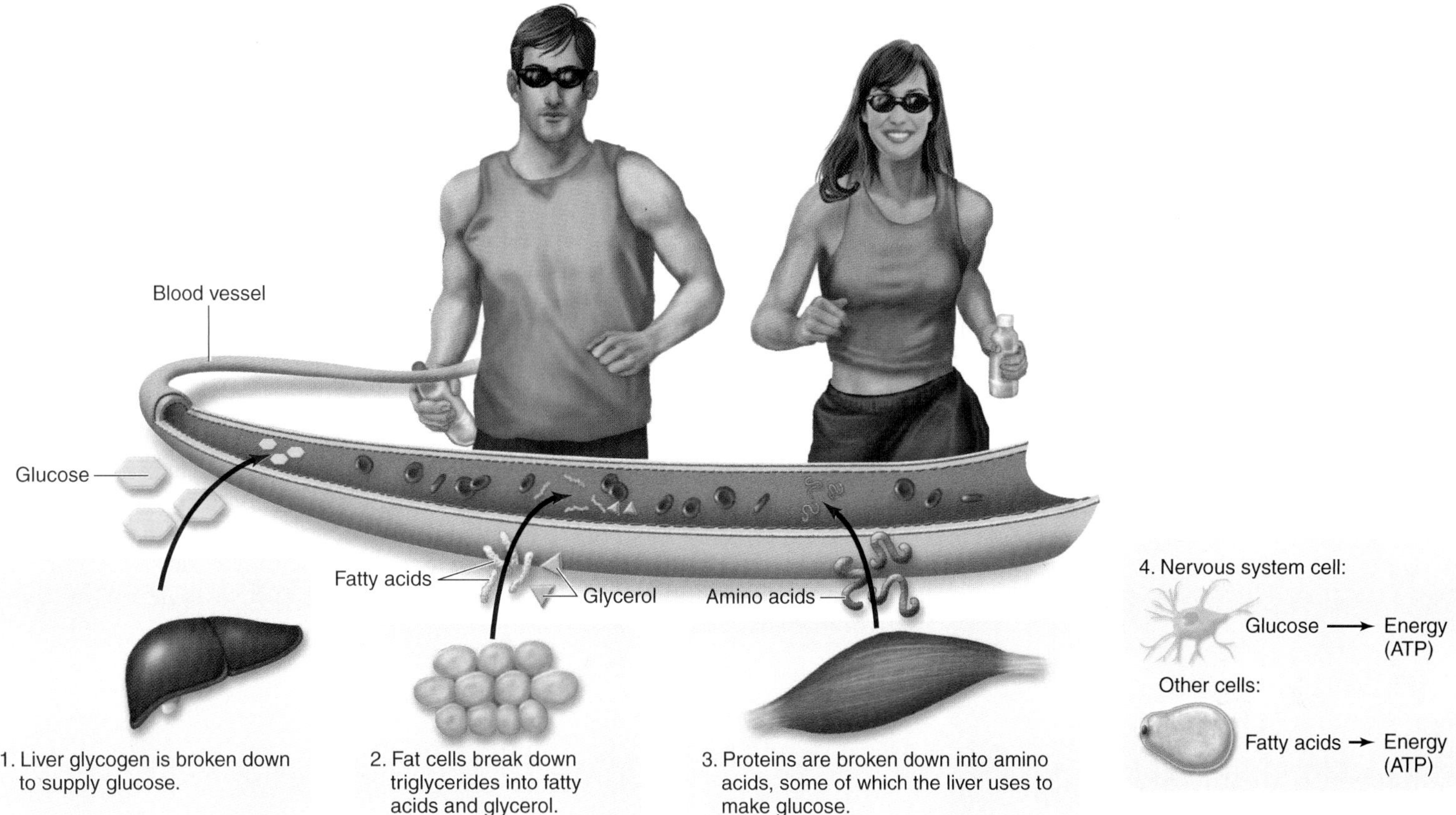

b.

hyperthyroidism is the key to treating unwanted weight gain, but the condition can have serious side effects, such as elevated blood pressure and heart failure. A person who suffers from *hypothyroidism* does not produce enough thyroid hormone, and as a result, he or she has a lower than normal metabolic rate. This individual typically complains of feeling cold, lacking energy and interest in usual activities, being constipated, and gaining weight easily. Treatment for a hypoactive thyroid gland generally includes medication that contains a form of thyroid hormone.

Although a decline in normal thyroid hormone levels results in lower than normal metabolic rates, many overweight or obese people have thyroid hormone levels that are within the normal range. However, an individual who secretes slightly less thyroid hormone than other persons may be more likely to become obese.[35]

energy output calories cells use to carry out their activities

basal metabolism minimal number of kilocalories the body uses to support vital activities after fasting and resting for 12 hours.

resting metabolic rate (RMR) body's rate of energy use a few hours after resting and eating

thyroid hormone secretion of the thyroid gland that regulates metabolism

Factors that Influence the Metabolic Rate In addition to thyroid hormone, numerous factors can increase or decrease basal metabolic rates. Thus, metabolic rates vary among individuals. Factors that influence basal metabolism include the following:

- *Body composition.* Lean body mass is the major factor that influences the metabolic rate.[2] Muscle tissue, a component of lean body mass, is more metabolically active than fat tissue. In general, a person who has more muscle mass will have a higher metabolic rate than someone with less muscle tissue.
- *Gender.* Males generally have higher metabolic rates than women because they tend to have more lean body mass.
- *Body surface area.* A tall slender person who weighs 68 kg (150 lbs.) has a higher metabolic rate than a shorter person who also weighs 68 kg (150 lbs.). Why? The body constantly loses energy in the form of heat that moves to the skin's surface and then into the environment. Because the taller person's body has more surface area than the shorter person's body, the taller individual has to generate more heat energy to replace that which is lost.

- *Age.* Basal metabolism declines as one grows older, primarily due to the loss of fat-free tissues such as muscle.[32] After 20 years of age, a woman's BMR declines about 2% and a man's BMR about 3% per decade.[32] Therefore, the average adult needs about 150 fewer kilocalories daily per decade as he or she ages.[32] As many adults grow older, they think their muscles have "turned into" fat. A muscle cell, however, cannot transform itself into a fat cell. During the aging process, lean tissue mass shrinks, as cells from muscle, bone, and organs die and are not replaced. Fat cells, however, can continue to develop throughout life, especially when a person overeats consistently. When adipose tissue expands in size, it can fill in spaces formerly occupied by muscle and organ tissues. Regular exercise helps build and preserve lean body mass, and to some extent, people can maintain a higher metabolic rate by being physically active as they grow older.
- *Calorie intake.* Calorie intake also affects the metabolic rate. The body conserves energy use when calorie intakes are very low or lacking altogether. In one study, subjects who consumed 800 kcal per day for 10 days experienced about a 6% decline in their resting metabolic rates.[36] To enhance the rate of weight loss, an overfat person should reduce caloric intake while maintaining a normal metabolic rate. Because very-low-calorie diets reduce the metabolic rate, such diets are not generally recommended for weight loss.

The following factors increase the metabolic rate:

- Fever
- Stimulant drugs (caffeine, for example)
- Pregnancy
- Milk production in a female who has given birth
- Recovery after exercise[33]

Calculating Metabolic Energy Needs Your basal metabolic rate is fairly constant from day to day.[37] Thus, you can estimate your daily metabolic rate by following a "rule of thumb" formula:

Formula for men = 1.0 kcal/kg/hr

Formula for women = 0.9 kcal/kg/hr

To estimate the number of calories you need for your basal metabolism, first convert your weight in pounds to kilograms by dividing your weight by 2.2. (A kilogram is approximately 2.2 pounds.)

______ lb. ÷ 2.2 lb. = ______ kg

Then, depending on your sex, use one of the following formulas:

______ kg × 0.9 (women) = ______ kcal/hr

______ kg × 1.0 (men) = ______ kcal/hr

Finally, use this hourly basal metabolic rate to estimate your basal metabolic rate for an entire day by multiplying the hourly value by 24.

______ kcal/hr × 24 hr = ______ kcal/day

These calculations only provide an estimate of your daily metabolic rate. To estimate your Estimated Energy Requirement (EER) for a 24-hour period, you need to add kilocalories used for physical and other activities to your BMR figure.

Energy for Physical Activity

Physical activity, voluntary skeletal muscle movement, increases energy expenditure above basal energy needs. The number of kilocalories expended for a particular physical activity depends largely on the type of activity, how long it is performed (duration), the degree of effort (intensity) used while performing the activity, and the weight of the person. A heavy person expends more kilocalories when performing the same activity, for the same duration, and at the same intensity than a lighter person. Why? The muscles of the heavier person must work harder to move the larger body. Generally, activities that use the largest muscles of the body (quadriceps, gluteal muscles, and hamstrings) expend the greatest level of energy.

To estimate your energy needs for physical activity, you need to keep a detailed diary that lists every physical activity you performed each day and the number of minutes that you spent engaging in each activity. Adults should accumulate 60 minutes of activity on most days. Table 10.5 lists various physical activities and the approximate number of kilocalories an individual expends per pound of body weight while performing each activity for a minute. For example, a 68-kg (150-lb.) person who walks for 30 minutes (5.6 km/hr, or 3.5 mph) burns approximately 149 kcal during the walk ($150 \times 30 \times 0.033$). Cells still need to carry out vital metabolic activities while one is engaging in physical activities, therefore the figures in Table 10.5 also take into account the energy needed for resting metabolism.

The number of calories you need for physical activity can vary widely, depending on how active you are each day. Because you can control the type, intensity, and duration of your physical activities, you can manipulate your energy output to increase, decrease, or maintain your weight.

TABLE 10.5 *Approximate Energy Expenditures of Selected Physical Activities*

Physical Activity	Approximate kcal/kg/min
Lying quietly	0.022
Sitting and writing	0.026
Stretching	0.019
Standing while doing light work, cleaning, etc.	0.059
Bowling	0.027
Swimming (front crawl, 18 m [20 yds.]/min)	0.068
Walking (5.6 km/hr [3.5 mph])	0.033
Light gardening/yard work	0.073
Dancing	0.073
Golf (walking and carrying clubs)	0.073
Bicycling (< 16 km/hr [10 mph])	0.042
Hiking (5 km/hr [3 mph])	0.092
Basketball (recreational)	0.108
Weightlifting	0.052
Walking (8 km/hr [5 mph])	0.054
Swimming (front crawl, 41 m [45 yds.]/min)	0.119
Soccer	0.130
Running/jogging, steady pace (8 km/hr [5 mph])	0.132
Aerobic dance	0.132
Basketball (competitive)	0.143
Bicycling (24 km/hr [15 mph])	0.160
Wrestling	0.196

Sources: U.S. Department of Health and Human Services: *Dietary Guidelines for Americans 2005*; Williams M: *Nutrition for health, fitness, and sport*. 8th edition. New York: McGraw-Hill, 2007.

thermic effect of food (TEF) energy used to digest foods and beverages as well as absorb and further metabolize the macronutrients

nonexercise activity thermogenesis (NEAT) involuntary skeletal muscular activities such as fidgeting

Thermic Effect of Food (TEF)

The body needs a relatively small amount of energy to digest foods and beverages as well as absorb and further process the macronutrients. The energy used for these tasks, generally 5 to 10% of total caloric intake, is referred to as the **thermic effect of food (TEF)**. For example, if your energy intake was 3000 kcal per day, TEF would account for 150 to 300 kcal.

Nonexercise Activity Thermogenesis (NEAT)

Nonexercise activity thermogenesis (*thermo* = heat; *genesis* = production) or **NEAT** refers to *involuntary* skeletal muscle activity, that is, physical activity that a person does not consciously control. NEAT activities include shivering, fidgeting, maintaining muscle tone, and maintaining body posture when not lying down. Studies have shown that people typically expend 100 to 800 kcal daily as NEAT.[32] It is possible that some individuals resist weight gain from overeating because they have higher than average energy expenditures for NEAT. Nevertheless, the contribution of NEAT to overall calorie needs is fairly small for most people.

Putting It All Together

To estimate your daily energy expenditure, you could add the kilocalories you burned for basal metabolism, physical activity, TEF, and NEAT in a day. However, an easier method is to use one of the formulas published by the Food and Nutrition Board of the Institute of Medicine (FNB).[2] The following formulas are for men and women who are 19 years of age or older.

Men

$$\textbf{Estimated Energy Requirement (EER)} = 662 - (9.53 \times \text{AGE}) + \text{PA} \times (15.91 + \text{WT } 539.6 \times \text{HT})$$

Women

$$\textbf{Estimated Energy Requirement (EER)} = 354 - (6.91 \times \text{AGE}) + \text{PA} \times (9.36 \times \text{WT } 726 \times \text{HT})$$

The variables in the formulas are:

AGE = age in years

PA = physical activity estimate (Table 10.6)

WT = weight in kg (lb. ÷ 2.2)

HT = height in metres (in. ÷ 39.4)

TABLE 10.6 *Physical Activity Level Estimates*

Activity Level	PA (Men)	PA (Women)
Sedentary (no exercise)	1.00	1.00
Low activity (for example, walking the equivalent of 2 miles/day at 3 to 4 mph)	1.11	1.12
Active (for example, walking the equivalent of 7 miles/day at 3 to 4 mph)	1.25	1.27
Very active (for example, walking the equivalent of 17 miles/day at 3 to 4 mph)	1.48	1.45

Source of data: Food and Nutrition Board, National Institute of Medicine: *Dietary Reference Intakes for energy, carbohydrate, fiber, fat, fatty acids, cholesterol, protein, and amino acids (macronutrients)*. Washington, DC: National Academies Press, 2005.

To try using the formula, consider a 22-year-old woman who is 165 cm or 1.65 m (5′5″ or 65″) in height, weighs about 66 kg (145 lbs.), and has a low level of physical activity. With this information, you can determine the missing values for the formula.

This young woman's age is **22** and her value for physical activity level (PA) is **1.12**. To convert her weight in pounds to kilograms, divide her weight by 2.2.

$$\mathbf{145 \div 2.2 = 65.9\ kg}$$

To convert her height to metres, divide her height (in.) by 39.4.

$$\mathbf{65.0 \div 39.4 = 1.65\ metres\ (rounded\ value)}$$

Now we can "plug" these values into the formula for a woman.

Estimated Energy Requirement (EER) $= 354 - (6.91 \times 22) + 1.12 \times (9.36 \times 65.9 + 726 \times 1.65)$

To solve the equation, move from left to right, but do the math in the parentheses first.

$$EER = 354 - (6.91 \times 22)$$

$$EER = 354 - 152.02$$

$$354 - 152.02 = 201.98$$

$$EER = 201.98 + 1.12 \times (9.36 \times 65.9 + 726 \times 1.65)$$

Now, do the math in the remaining parentheses on the right. Multiply the first two numbers in the parentheses together:

$$9.36 \times 65.9 = 616.82$$

Multiply the next two numbers together:

$$726 \times 1.65 = 1197.9$$

Add the two products together:

$$616.82 + 1197.9 = 1814.72$$

Plug this value into the formula and multiply $1.12 \times 1814.72 = 2032.49$, and then add the left and right sides of the formula together:

$$EER = 201.98 + 2032.49 = 2234.47$$

$$\mathbf{EER = approx.\ 2234\ kcal/day}$$

To estimate your EER, complete the Personal Dietary Analysis activity near the end of this chapter.

Concept **Checkpoint**

15. Using the "rule of thumb" formula, estimate the daily basal metabolic energy needs of a woman who weighs 84 kg (185 lbs.).
16. List the four major ways the body uses energy (energy output).
17. For most people, which form of energy expenditure uses the most energy on a daily basis?
18. Discuss at least five factors that influence basal metabolic rate.
19. Of the four major ways the body uses energy, which one is most easily altered?
20. Explain the differences between TEF and energy needs for physical activity.
21. What is NEAT? List at least three ways the body expends energy by NEAT.

energy equilibrium calorie intake equals calorie output

negative energy balance calorie intake is less than calorie output

positive energy balance calorie intake is greater than calorie output

Energy Balance

Understanding the concept of energy balance is critical to understanding why most people gain, lose, or maintain weight. Your body is in a state of **energy equilibrium** and "balanced" when your calorie intake from food and beverages equals your calorie output for basal metabolism, physical activity, TEF, and NEAT (Fig. 10.10). By maintaining a balanced energy state, your weight will remain relatively stable over time.

If your calorie intake is lower than your calorie output, you are in **negative energy balance**. In this state, your body needs more calories to carry out its activities than your diet is supplying. Therefore, your body metabolizes stored fat for energy. Weight loss results from being in a negative energy state. Over time, you will notice your clothes have become baggy as your adipose tissue shrinks.

If your calorie intake from macronutrients (and alcohol) is greater than your calorie output, you are in a state of **positive energy balance**. In this state, your body stores excess dietary fat in adipose cells. Additionally, the body converts surplus dietary carbohydrate, protein, and alcohol to fat and stores that fat in adipose cells. Weight gain results from being in a positive energy state, and eventually, you will notice that your clothes seem to have shrunk.

Positive energy balance is necessary for pregnant women, because extra calories are needed to add new tissues that support the pregnancy. Positive energy balance also occurs during periods of growth, such as during fetal development, infancy, childhood,

Did You Know?

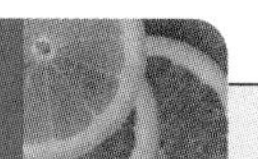

Have you heard of the "Freshman 15," the popular belief that college and university students gain 15 pounds (7 kg) during their first year? Results of scientific studies confirm that first-year students are likely to gain weight, but the increase is much less than 15 pounds—only 3 pounds (1–2 kg) on average.[38] In one study, 290 college and university students were weighed at the beginning of their first year and again at the completion of their second year. During their first two years, 70% of the students participating in the study gained weight, on average, about 9 pounds (4 kg).[39]

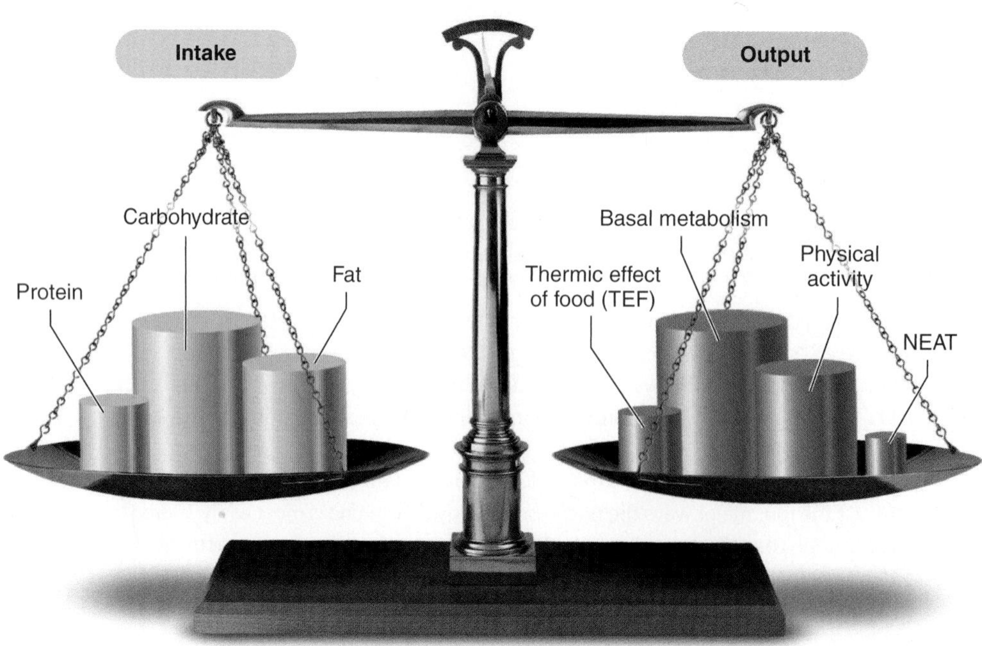

Figure 10.10 Energy balance. Your energy state is in equilibrium and "balanced" when your calorie intake from food and beverages equals your calorie output for basal metabolism, physical activity, TEF, and NEAT.

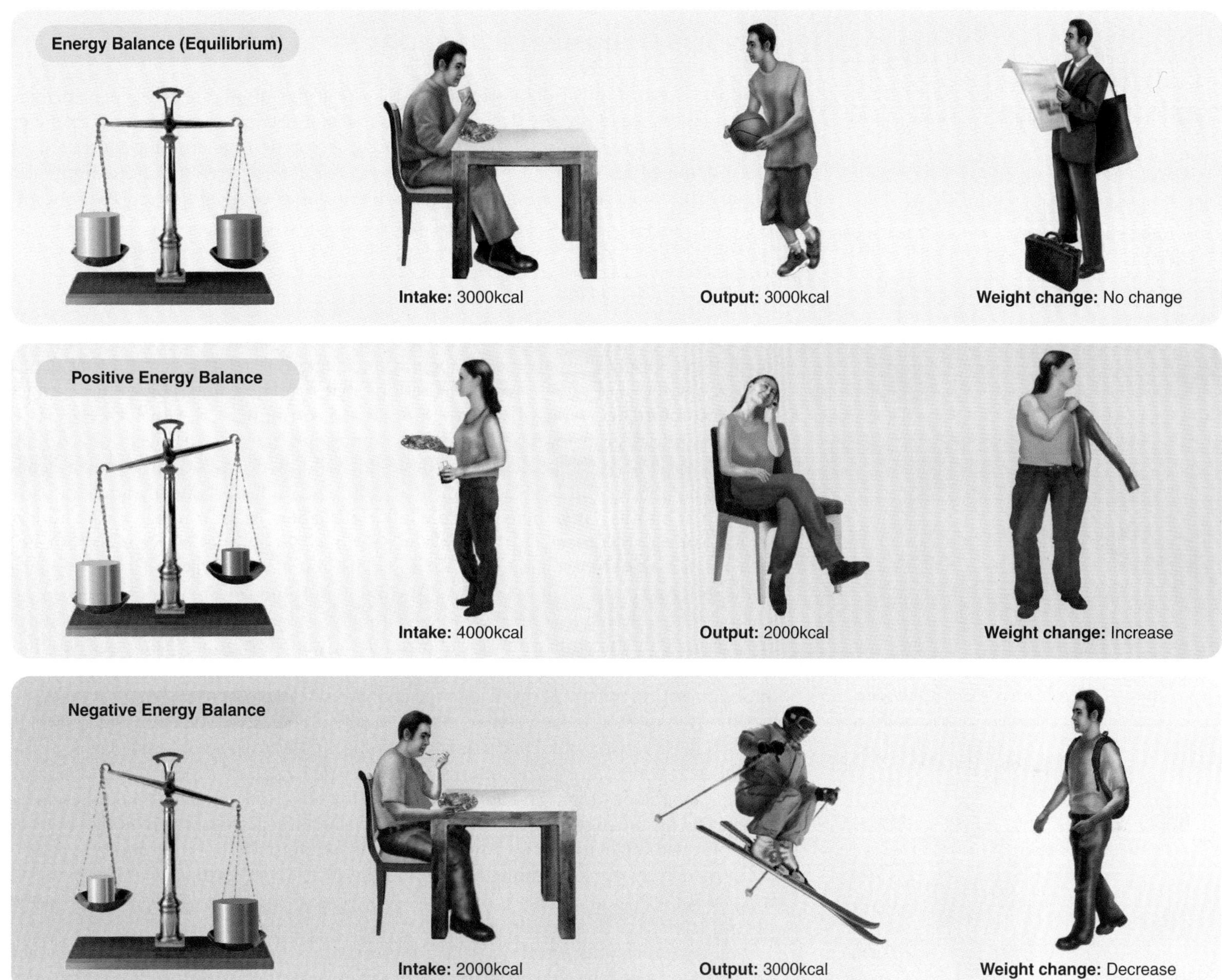

Figure 10.11 The body's possible energy states. This figure presents three possible energy states. In energy equilibrium, individuals consume the same amount of energy as they expend, and as a result, they experience no weight change. In a positive energy state, individuals consume more energy than they expend, and as a result, they gain weight. In a negative energy state, individuals consume less energy than they expend, and as a result, they lose weight. Maintenance of energy balance—matching calorie intake to calorie output over the long term—is critical for controlling body weight.

and adolescence. Over time, however, even a small positive energy balance can cause anyone's weight to increase, regardless of his or her age. Maintenance of energy balance—matching calorie intake to calorie output over the long term—is critical for controlling body weight (Fig. 10.11).

Concept Checkpoint

22. What happens to a person's body weight when he or she is in a state of positive energy balance?
23. When is it desirable for a person to be in a positive energy balance state?
24. When is a person in a negative energy balance state?

hunger uncomfortable feeling that drives a person to consume food based on a physiological need for nourishment

appetite a psychological desire for food, which can exist in the absence of hunger

satiety sense that enough food or beverages have been consumed to satisfy hunger

orexins peptides that may contribute to hunger in humans

ghrelin hormone that stimulates eating behaviour

leptin hormone that reduces hunger and inhibits fat storage in the body

What Causes Overweight and Obesity?

Although an excess intake of calories in relation to calorie output causes weight gain, there is no simple *cause* of obesity. To lose weight, a person needs to create a negative energy state by eating fewer calories, expending more calories than the amount consumed, or taking both actions. For many people, however, it is not easy to alter calorie input and output. Physiological, environmental, behavioural, psychological, and socio-economic forces influence a person's calorie intake and expenditure.

Physiological Factors

From a physiological standpoint, eating behaviour is complex and largely involves interactions among the nervous, endocrine, and digestive systems as well as fat tissue. *Hunger*, *appetite*, and *satiety* are key sensations that regulate eating behaviour. **Hunger** is an uncomfortable feeling that drives a person to consume food, which can be based on falling blood sugar levels, an empty gastrointestinal tract, or the need for a certain nutrient. **Appetite** is the psychological desire for food, which can occur in the absence of hunger. Suppose you have had a meal at 6:00 p.m. and subsequently attend a party at 7:30 p.m. At this party, there is a table full of delicious foods. You aren't truly hungry because you are still processing the meal you consumed 90 minutes earlier; your desire for these foods represents your appetite. Our appetite for food when it is available is a genetic predisposition almost all humans have. The notion of taking advantage of food resources when they were available (even if we weren't hungry) was a trait that allowed us to survive as a species. Our ancestors who were able to take advantage of food resources when they were plentiful and store the excess energy as fat, and were able to make these fat stores last through a period of famine, were able to survive and pass along their genetic material to us. However, most of us now live in a dramatically different set of circumstances, where food energy is very plentiful and our requirement for physical activity each day is greatly diminished, which has led to dramatically increased rates of overweight and obesity among Canadian children and adults. **Satiety** is the sense that enough food or beverages have been consumed to satisfy hunger. Although certain regions of the hypothalamus in the brain are thought to control hunger and satiety, scientists do not fully understand how the human body regulates eating behaviour (Fig. 10.12).[18] According to one hypothesis, an area of the hypothalamus monitors the blood and suppresses hunger when blood glucose levels rise to a certain point after eating. Scientists think another area of the hypothalamus functions as a "hunger centre." Recently, researchers discovered that certain cells in the hypothalamus secrete **orexins**, peptides that may contribute to hunger in humans. These findings provide support for the hypothesis that the hypothalamus plays a major role in regulating eating behaviour.

Figure 10.12 The hypothalamus. Within the brain, a structure called the hypothalamus is involved in hunger regulation.

Other signals to seek food or stop eating originate from the digestive tract. As time between eating increases, **ghrelin** (*greh'-lin*), a hormone secreted mainly by the stomach, stimulates eating behaviour. Some scientists think that reducing ghrelin production or activity is the key to helping people lose or maintain their weight. In addition to releasing ghrelin, the stomach signals "it's time to eat" by contracting, causing hunger pangs. As the contractions become stronger, the person usually eats or drinks something to relieve the discomfort. The stomach also influences satiety. During meals, the stomach stretches as it fills. The sensation that the stomach has reached its capacity can make a person stop eating. Nevertheless, many overfat persons do not recognize the sensation of stomach fullness, and as a result, they may eat even when they should not be hungry. It is important to recognize that ghrelin is one of more than 100 hormones involved in satiety, and the combination of many chemical and physiological influences control hunger and satiety.

Adipose tissue also plays a role in regulating food intake and body weight. Adipose cells secrete **leptin**, a hormone that reduces hunger and inhibits fat storage in the body. When researchers administer leptin to genetically engineered mice that cannot synthesize the hormone, the rodents lose weight, because the hormone reduces the animals' interest in eating and increases their rate of fat metabolism.[40] Studies involving humans, however, generally find that obese people produce high amounts of leptin, but their bodies resist the hormone's hunger-suppressing action.[41] Scientists are conducting research to determine why leptin loses its effectiveness in obese individuals, or whether "*leptin-resistance*" is what leads these many overweight and obese individuals to their current level of body composition.

Food Composition Factors

Dietary factors, particularly amounts of fat and certain carbohydrates in diets, can influence body fat production and appetite. Fatty foods are more energy dense than foods that contain more carbohydrate, protein, and water than fat.[42] Thus, high-fat diets are associated with excess calorie intakes and rising obesity rates.[11,43] However, some medical researchers think the consumption of the simple carbohydrate fructose is associated with the current obesity epidemic. High fructose intakes may result in weight gain because the sugar decreases satiety and stimulates fat synthesis in the body.[44] For a more extensive review of the role that carbohydrates may play in weight gain, see the "Are Carbohydrates Fattening?" section of Chapter 5.

Genetic Factors

Genetics play a major role in the development of obesity. Most physical characteristics are inherited, including metabolic rate, hormone production, body frame size, and pattern of fat distribution. All of these characteristics affect body weight.

Some rats and mice are genetically predisposed to become obese because they have inherited genes for "thrifty metabolisms." Rodents with thrifty metabolisms have bodies that are more efficient at storing excess energy as fat than rodents that do not have such metabolisms. It is possible that humans who gain weight easily have genes that code for thrifty metabolisms as well. In ancient times, food was often scarce, and people had to eat as much as they could when food was available. During times when food was plentiful, individuals who had thrifty metabolisms stored more of the excess energy from food as body fat than persons who did not have such efficient metabolisms. The people who lacked thrifty metabolisms wasted the excess food energy as body heat. As a result, the energy "thrifty" people were more likely to survive periods of starvation than the other persons. In many modern societies, however, high-calorie food is available 24 hours a day and starvation is unlikely. As a result, having thrifty metabolisms is no longer beneficial because depositing excess body fat often results in serious health problems.

If you gain weight easily, you may have inherited a thrifty metabolism. To prevent becoming overfat, you need to be physically active and make careful food choices. On the other hand, you probably do not have a thrifty metabolism if you can eat a lot of food and have difficulty gaining weight.

Medical researchers have identified several genes that contribute to human fatness. For example, genes control leptin production by adipose cells. Certain mice become obese because they lack genes for synthesizing leptin (Fig. 10.13). Researchers are interested in developing medications that regulate the influence of certain genes over metabolism and hormone production. If research indicates that such medications are safe and effective, they could help people manage their weight over the long term.

Figure 10.13 Genetic obesity in mice. Certain genetically engineered mice (the mouse on the left) become obese because they lack genes for synthesizing leptin.

defended body weight scientific notion that body fat content is genetically predetermined

What's the Set-Point Theory? The majority of people who intentionally lose weight regain the weight over time. According to the **defended body weight** theory (also often called the set-point theory), the body's fat content (and therefore, body weight) is, in general, genetically predetermined. The set point acts like a home thermostat, except that it regulates body weight instead of temperature. For example, a person infected with an intestinal virus tends to lose weight because he or she has no interest in eating for a few days. During and after recovery, the person generally regains the lost weight. This observation provides support for the set-point theory.

Biochemical and metabolic studies also support the set-point theory. When calorie intakes are reduced, blood thyroid hormone levels decline, depressing the normal basal metabolic rate. Additionally, the caloric cost of performing weight-bearing activities decreases when a person loses weight. As a result, an activity that required 100 kcal before weight loss may only burn 80 kcal after weight loss. Furthermore, weight loss appears to make the body become more efficient at storing calories from macronutrients as fat. When a person gains weight and stays at that weight for a while, his or her body tends to establish a new and higher set point. According to the theory, all these changes protect the body from losing weight and explain why weight loss is so difficult to achieve and maintain.

Opponents of the set-point theory argue that weight does not remain constant throughout adulthood—the average person gains weight slowly, at least until old age. Thus, body weight may result more from lifestyle practices and environmental influences than predetermined biological controls such as a set point.

Environmental Influences

How does the presence of such appealing food affect your appetite?

Consider your eating behaviour during a typical holiday meal that includes a variety of attractive tasty foods. After eating the meal, your hunger should be satisfied, but as soon as pie or cake is placed on the table, do you "find some room" in your stomach for some dessert? If you often eat when you are not hungry, then you are probably aware of the effect your environment can have on your appetite. **Appetite** is the psychological desire to eat appealing food.

Food advertising is an aspect of the environment that has a powerful influence on your food choices. To entice you to buy their products, food manufacturers usually appeal to your senses, emphasizing the appearance and taste of food, in particular. Recently, a television ad for a fast food chain promoted a hamburger that has three beef patties, three slices of cheese, and six bacon slices topped with mayonnaise. According to information at the fast food company's Web site, this burger provides 800 kcal. The site, however, does not tell you that 800 kcal is more than one-third of a day's calorie needs for an average person! How do you respond when you see food advertisements on television? Do the ads make you hungry or eager to try a new food product?

Over the past 30 years, portion sizes of many popular foods, especially restaurant items, have become larger.[42] People may choose to purchase "supersized" portions of foods because they like the idea of getting more for their money. In many instances, however, "more" means *more* fat and calories per serving. According to some nutrition experts, the increased consumption of oversized portions of restaurant foods contributes to the obesity epidemic in North America.[11,45]

Even consuming a small amount of extra energy can result in weight gain. One pound of body fat represents about 3500 kcal. Therefore, you will gain a pound of fat if you accumulate 3500 more calories than your body needs. Consider this: If you consume only 100 extra calories and maintain the same level of physical activity each day, you will consume an extra 36 500 kcal in a year. By the end of that year, you will gain about 4 to 5 kg (10 lbs.; 36 500 kcal ÷ 3500 kcal)!

Our environment also affects whether we choose to be sedentary or physically active. In our homes, we rely on a variety of "energy-saving" devices such as dishwashing machines, TV remote controls, and garage door openers to work for us. Outside our homes, we use cars, elevators, escalators, and other motorized devices, instead of our feet,

TABLE 10.7 *Average Daily Energy Intake for Canadians, 19 to 30 Years Old, 1972; 2004*

Sex/Age (years)	Food Consumption Patterns Report – Average Daily Energy Intake (kcal)	Canadian Community Health Survey 2.2 Average Daily Energy Intake (kcal)	Percentage Change
Males 19 to 30	3374	2660	–21%
Females 19 to 30	2001	1899	–5%

Source: Health Canada: *Food consumption patterns report* (1977); Canadian Community Health Survey, Cycle 2.2, Nutrition (2004).

to move us from place to place. With the help of machines, our lives are considerably easier, but we are consuming more calories than in the past. Table 10.7 presents average daily energy intake of Canadian males and females who were 19 to 30 years of age during national surveys conducted in 1972 and 2004.

Note in Table 10.7 that average daily energy intake of Canadian males who were 19 to 30 years of age decreased by approximately 21% in approximately 30 years. However, the average daily energy intake of females in that age group decreased by only 5% from 1972 to 2004. According to the principles of energy balance, excess energy intake in relation to energy output results in weight gain.

Many Canadians have "desk jobs" that require little muscular movement. When we have some leisure time, we often spend it performing tasks that involve sitting—watching television, playing computer games, or chatting with people on the Internet. This increased level of physical inactivity has significant costs to the Canadian health care system.[46] Results from the 2004 Canadian Community Health Survey showed that 48% of Canadians 12 or older (12.7 million people) were inactive in their leisure time.[47]

According to experts with the Public Health Agency of Canada, Canadian adults should perform 60 minutes of daily activity at a moderate or greater intensity on most days, and children and youth should perform 90 minutes of moderate or greater physical activity.[48] Healthy Canadian adults over 65 years of age should also perform at least 30 to 60 minutes of moderate-intensity physical activity (brisk walking, for example) most days of the week, and slowly work up to this level 10 minutes at a time until the goal is reached.[48] Adults who include exercise in their weight-loss plan may need to engage in at least 60 minutes of moderate-intensity activity each day to achieve long-term maintenance of lower body weight. Table 3.1 (p. 63) lists examples of moderate-intensity physical activities.

If you live on or near a university or college campus, your environment probably provides ample opportunities for engaging in exercise and sports, such as tennis courts, swimming pools, and weight-training rooms. It is relatively easy to be physically active while you are in university, *if you choose to be*. After you graduate, consider what you will do to maintain a healthy level of physical activity each day, especially if you have a sedentary job. How likely are you to use the staircase in a building when you see the elevator? Will you keep a pair of comfortable shoes at work so that you can walk for at least 20 minutes during lunch?

Did You Know?

Regular exercise, such as walking, can shrink abdominal fat,[49,50] but it is not possible to "spot-reduce" by exercising a fatty body part intensely. The energy needed to fuel muscle activity comes from fatty deposits within muscle tissue and the rest of the body. Exercise, however, can improve muscle tone so that fat tissue appears less flabby.

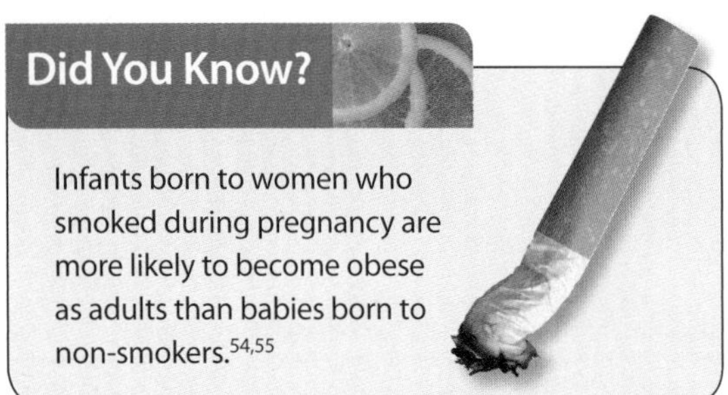

Did You Know?

Infants born to women who smoked during pregnancy are more likely to become obese as adults than babies born to non-smokers.[54,55]

Genes and Environment: Interactions

It is difficult to determine the extent to which an obese person's genetic makeup or environment contributes to his or her excess body weight. Children are more likely to develop obesity if one or both of their parents are obese. In one study, children of obese parents had more than twice the risk of becoming obese adults than children of parents who were not obese.[51,52] In another study, infants of obese women had double the risk of being obese at 2 years of age than infants of non-obese mothers.[53] These and other findings support the hypothesis that obesity is an inherited trait. Nevertheless, genes do not control everything about our health, including our weight. Environmental and other factors can modify the expression of genes. For example, a child whose parents are obese because they eat a lot of energy-dense foods and avoid physical activity may have inherited genes that increase risk for obesity. However, children of obese parents may avoid becoming obese if they adopt a physically active lifestyle and do not overeat. On the other hand, these children may become obese if they follow their parents' poor eating habits and sedentary lifestyle. So, overweight and obesity is likely a combination of inherited genes and inherited lifestyle.

Other Factors that Influence Weight

Socio-economic factors such as low income and education levels are associated with increased likelihood of overweight and obesity among Canadians. Level of education appears to be a stronger influence over BMI than income. In a survey of over 29 000 adults, 27.5% of the subjects who had less than a high school education were obese, whereas 17.4% of the subjects who earned bachelor degrees were obese.[56] However, the prevalence of overweight and obesity is increasing among *all* members of the Canadian and U.S. population, including people who have high incomes and are well educated, though those with the lowest socio-economic indices have the highest likelihood of being obese.[11,22,57]

Psychological factors such as mood and self-esteem influence eating behaviours and body weight. Many people eat not because they are hungry, but because they are bored, anxious, angry, or depressed. Results of a study involving nearly 2300 people 50 years of age or older suggest that an obese person who is not depressed is twice as likely to become depressed within a year as a person whose weight is healthy.[58] Researchers, however, cannot easily determine whether being obese causes depression or being depressed causes obesity.

Among some segments of Canadian society, the ideal female figure is slim but curvy and the ideal male physique is trim and muscular. As a result, societal pressures inspire many young women to idealize underweight. Consider the body shapes of many fashion models, professional ballerinas, and successful young actresses. These young women have so little subcutaneous fat, some of their bones protrude from under their skin. In their relentless efforts to pursue such unrealistic body shapes, many young women adopt unhealthy and potentially life-threatening eating practices. The Chapter 10 Highlight focuses on eating disorders, including *anorexia nervosa*.

Societal pressures inspire many young women to idealize underweight people, especially thin female celebrities.

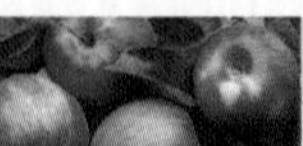

Concept Checkpoint

25. What is hunger? What is appetite? What is satiety?
26. Describe the roles that leptin, the hypothalamus, and the stomach play in regulating hunger.
27. Under what conditions would having "thrifty genes" benefit a person?
28. What is the set-point theory?
29. What is the difference between hunger and appetite?
30. Describe how the environment influences a person's food intake and physical activity level.
31. Provide at least three examples of ways that socio-economic, psychological, and societal factors can influence eating behaviour.

Weight Loss and Its Maintenance

Before you embark on an effort to lose (or gain) weight, an important first step is determining whether it is even necessary to change your weight. The need for changing your weight should be based on your overall health and family history of weight-related diseases. If you are dissatisfied with your body weight and shape, consider the following questions. Are you physically healthy at your present weight? If your BMI is within the healthy range, why do you think you need to lose or gain weight?

Consulting a BMI table such as the one in Figure 10.14 that indicates the range of healthy weights for a particular height (BMIs of 18.5 up to 24.9) can be helpful. According to this chart, an adult whose height is 165 cm (5′5″) has a healthy weight range of about 50 to 68 kg (111 to 149 lbs.).

To determine your BMI range using the table in Figure 10.14, locate your height in the left-most column with your left index finger, then locate your weight along the bottom line of the graph with your right index finger. Read across the row with your left finger and up from the bottom with your right finger, until your fingers meet. Note the BMI range where the two fingers meet. According to this graph, is your BMI in the healthy range?

The next step, if necessary, is setting a reasonable and realistic goal weight. It is important to note that an overweight or obese person does not have to shed a lot of weight to reduce risk factors associated with CVD, stroke, and type 2 diabetes. Just losing 5 to 10% of excess body fat can increase beneficial high-density lipoprotein levels (HDL cholesterol), reduce elevated blood pressure and triglyceride levels, and improve glucose tolerance.[3]

Figure 10.14 Adult BMI chart. Are you at a healthy weight?

Source of data: www.nhlbi.nih.gov/guidelines/obesity/bmi_tbl.pdf

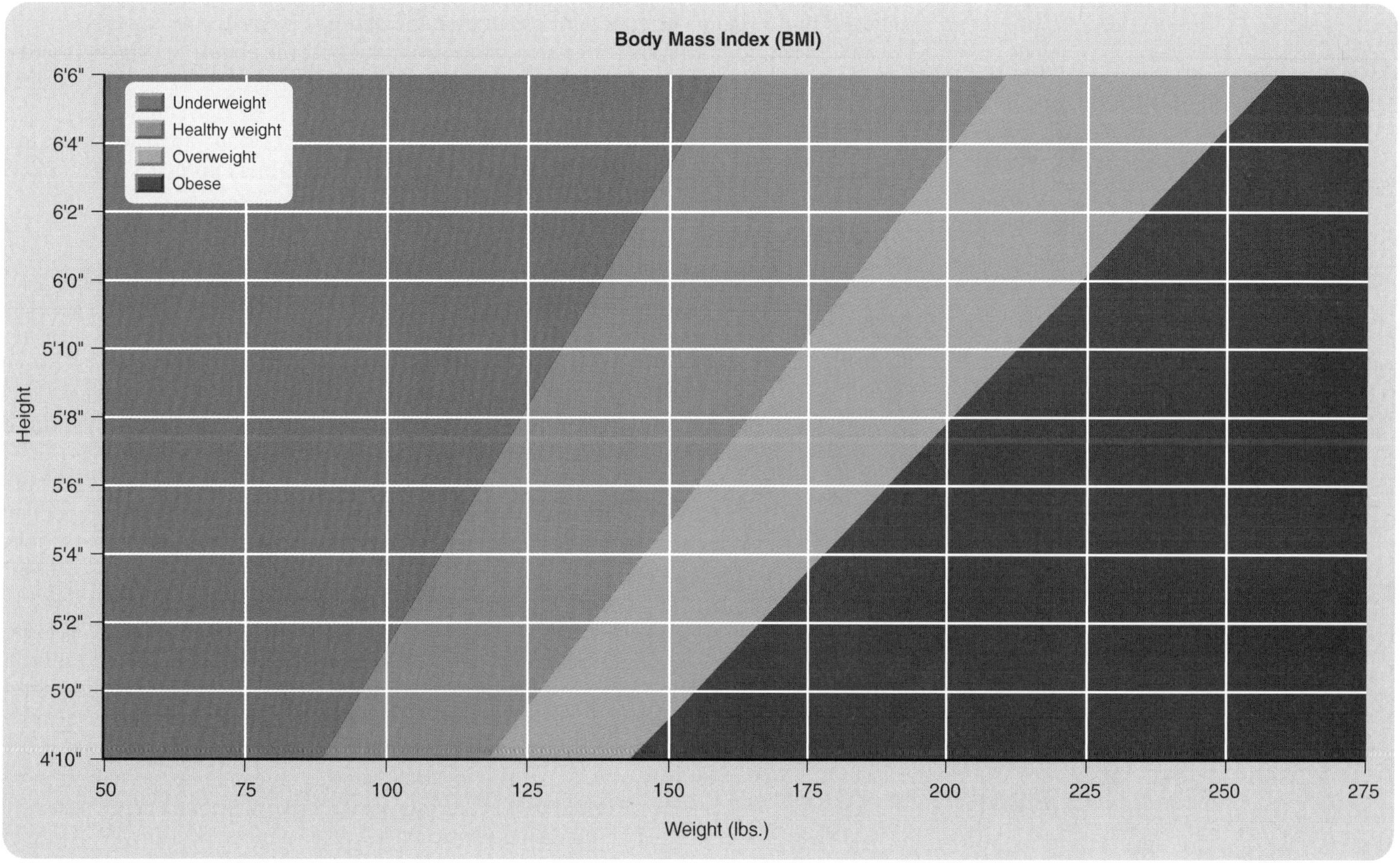

TABLE 10.8 *Key Features of Reliable Weight-Loss Plans*

A sound weight-loss plan:
• Is safe and effective.
• Meets nutritional, psychological, and social needs.
• Incorporates a variety of common foods from all food groups.
• Fosters slow but steady weight loss (1–3 kg per month).
• Does not require costly devices or diet books.
• Accommodates family and restaurant meals, parties and special occasions, ethnic foods, and food likes.
• Does not make the dieter feel deprived.
• Emphasizes readily available nutritious foods.
• Promotes changing habits that discourage overeating.
• Encourages regular physical activity.
• Provides suggestions for obtaining social support.
• Can be followed for a lifetime.

Features of Medically Sound Weight-Loss Plans

Table 10.8 presents key features of reliable weight-loss plans. Such plans should be safe and effective, as well as flexible enough to meet the dieter's nutritional, psychological, and social needs. A medically sound weight-loss diet should emphasize a wide variety of low-calorie, readily available nutritious foods and be adaptable to the dieter's food likes and dislikes. Furthermore, reliable weight-loss plans should provide suggestions for altering environments that foster overeating and sedentary behaviours. Before beginning any weight-loss diet, overfat people need to obtain their physician's approval, especially if they have serious health conditions, such as type 2 diabetes, or they are over the age of 40 (men) or 50 (women).

Key Factors

Despite claims made in advertisements and infomercials, there are no quick cures for overweight and obesity. Successful weight loss and long-term weight maintenance involve four key elements: motivation, calorie reduction, regular physical activity, and behaviour modification.

Motivation

The motivation to lose weight and keep it off requires an overfat person to recognize that there is a need to change his or her behaviour and become committed to making those changes permanent. For some people, this recognition occurs when they are diagnosed with a health disorder that is associated with excess body fat. Nevertheless, many overfat people choose not to lose weight. The commitment to lose weight and enjoy better health must become far more important than the desire to overeat.

Weight-loss "triggers" often serve as motivators. For some people, seeing themselves in an unflattering photograph, being advised by their physicians to lose weight, or being unable to enjoy activities because being obese restricts their movement triggers the decision to lose weight. According to results of a large survey, adult Americans most frequently cited "medical advice" as the reason for their weight-loss efforts.[59]

Calorie Reduction

To lose a pound of weight, a person needs to create a negative energy state of 3500 kcal. A reasonable rate of weight loss is one-half to 1 pound of fat per week.[30] Overfat persons can usually accomplish this rate of loss by reducing their calorie intake or increasing their physical activity (energy output) by 300 to 500 kcal per day.[30] Overweight or obese people can lose about 1 to 2 pounds per week by cutting their calorie intakes even further—by 500 to 1000 kcal per day.[60] Although many dieters would like to shed more than 1 kg (2 lbs.) per week, health experts recommend a slow and steady rate.

According to guidelines issued by the U.S. National Institutes of Health, reasonable calorie intakes for adults who want to lose weight range from 1000 to 1200 kcal per day for women and 1200 to 1600 kcal per day for men; however, similar specific calories targets have not been established for Canadians.[30] At these calorie intake levels, careful food choices are necessary to obtain nutritionally adequate diets. Certain diets severely limit food intake and provide fewer than 800 kcal per day. Such *very-low-calorie diets* are not recommended for most overfat persons as they are overly restrictive, and it is unlikely that individuals will be able to sustain this type of intake pattern. People who follow very-low-calorie diets may lose a lot of weight rapidly, but they regain the weight quickly after they "go off" the diet and return to their former eating habits.

The healthiest way to lower intake of total calories is to reduce consumption of added sugars, fats, and alcohol.[61,62] People can also achieve negative energy states by reducing calorie intake *and* increasing physical activity. Nevertheless, a survey of adults

who were trying to lose weight indicated that only one-third reported combining the two weight-loss strategies.[63]

One problem with the notion of "*a diet*" is that this term suggests a beginning and an end. Healthy eating isn't what we do for a few weeks or months. Healthy eating is a pattern of making the healthiest dietary intake decisions the majority of the time, throughout our lives. Increasing consumption of watery, high-fibre foods that are not energy dense, such as fruits and vegetables, may be helpful for individuals attempting weight loss. Such foods are more likely to provide satiety sooner than energy-dense foods, and as a result, reduce the person's calorie intake.[64] No particular diet or food has a "metabolic advantage" by promoting greater calorie burning by the body. A dieter's goal should be reducing total calorie intake while obtaining all essential nutrients.

Eventually, a person who intentionally loses weight by reducing calorie intake and increasing physical activity reaches a weight *plateau*. When this occurs, the dieter is in energy balance. To continue losing weight, the person must reduce his or her calorie intake or increase physical activity beyond the present levels. For someone who is consuming only 1000 to 1200 kcal per day, cutting calories even further can lower the metabolic rate, hindering continued weight loss and making maintenance of lost weight more difficult.

Regular Physical Activity

It is difficult to burn much energy without being physically active. By increasing their physically active level and burning more calories, dieters do not need to limit their food intake as excessively as they would by relying on calorie reduction alone to lose weight. You do not need to jog for 10 km to reap the benefits of engaging in regular physical activity. Moderate-intensity activities, such as those listed in Table 3.1 (p. 63), are recommended for people who want to lose or manage their weight.

Did You Know?

A *pedometer* is a small device that records the number of steps a person takes while engaging in physical activities. If you would like to monitor your steps, you can purchase an inexpensive pedometer in sporting goods stores. The one shown in the photo clips onto socks or belts.

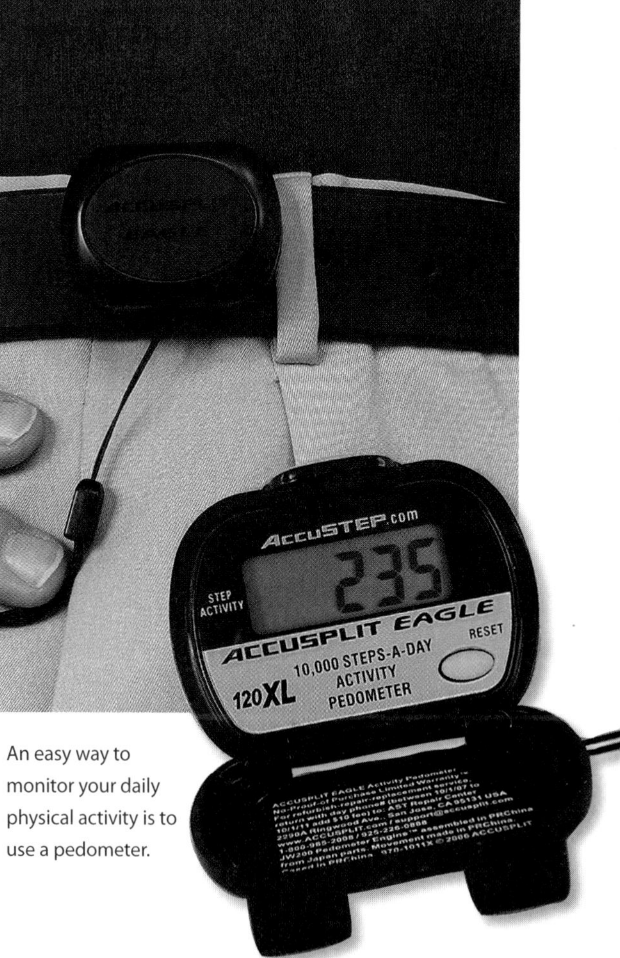

An easy way to monitor your daily physical activity is to use a pedometer.

Behaviour Modification

Controlling calorie intake and increasing physical activity are easier to accomplish if overfat persons analyze their faulty behaviours, identify eating *cues* and "problem" behaviours, and develop ways to change the behaviours. Eating cues are usually environmental factors that stimulate eating behaviour, such as seeing an ad for a fast food restaurant or smelling freshly baked brownies when walking past a bakery. Identifying such cues can enable people to recognize effects of the signals and avoid inappropriate ones, whenever possible. By analyzing their food-related behaviours, overfat individuals can often determine the circumstances in which they tend to overeat.

Did You Know?

Results of scientific studies suggest that watching television is associated with obesity among children and adults.[5,65,66] In addition to being a sedentary activity, television viewing is often combined with eating high-fat foods.

Cues can also help overfat people lose weight. If, for example, you are trying to lose weight, posting an unflattering photograph of yourself on the refrigerator or pantry door can serve as a reminder to stay on course with your behaviour modification plan.

Although the process may seem slow, people are more likely to change ingrained habits by focusing on changing one behaviour at a time. For example, many people snack on energy-dense foods and drinks while watching television. To change this habit, a person could decide to eat only at the kitchen table and avoid all food and beverage consumption while sitting in front of a TV.

For individuals who want to lose (or gain) weight, keeping records of food intake and physical activities can be helpful for estimating daily calorie input and output. However, overfat persons often underestimate their calorie intake and overestimate their energy output.[67,68] Therefore, people need to record information about food choices and physical activity habits accurately.

Read Nutrition Facts tables to compare calorie and fat contents of packaged foods.

Tips for Modifying Food- and Exercise-Related Behaviours The following suggestions may help a person lose excess weight as well as maintain a lower, healthier body weight.

- **Planning Menus**
  1. Plan meals and snacks to cover three or more days and use the plan to prepare grocery lists.
  2. When menu planning, include sources of protein, unsaturated fat, and complex carbohydrates in meals and snacks.
  3. Avoid labelling certain foods as "off limits." Depriving yourself of such items can result in bingeing on the "forbidden" food. Learning to analyze why you have difficulty controlling your intake of these foods and developing strategies to learn how to reduce your intake of them can be very helpful.

- **Grocery Shopping**
  1. To reduce the likelihood of making impulsive food choices, shop for food *after* eating.
  2. Shop from a grocery list. If a food isn't on your list, ask yourself if you really need to buy it, and if it will hinder or help your weight-loss efforts.
  3. Read food labels to compare calorie and fat contents per serving.

- **Food Preparation**
  1. Reduce the use of fat in cooking; bake, broil, or roast meats instead of frying them.
  2. Add less fat to foods such as cooked vegetables before serving or eating them.
  3. If you sample foods while preparing them, consider the amounts you ate and reduce your portion sizes at mealtimes accordingly.
  4. Prepare only enough food to provide one limited-size portion for yourself. Using measuring cups and a small scale for weighing food can be helpful.
  5. Serve food on smaller plates and eat with smaller spoons.
  6. Take your usual-size portion and return one-third to one-half of it to the serving dish or container.
  7. Remove serving dishes from the table. Keeping foods or their containers in sight can encourage overeating.

Using a small scale for weighing food can be helpful for limiting portion sizes.

- **Eating Behaviour**
  1. Keep nutrient-dense low-calorie snack foods, such as fresh fruits and vegetables, on hand.
  2. Eat meals and snacks at scheduled times; don't skip meals, especially breakfast.
  3. Eat all food in a "dining" area; avoid eating while engaged in other activities, such as reading a book or watching television.

4. Slow down the pace of meals by putting eating utensils down between mouthfuls and eating more slowly.
5. Leave some food on your plate.
6. Become a "defensive eater." Practise ways to refuse food graciously or request smaller portions. Be aware of people, especially relatives and friends, who *sabotage* your weight-loss efforts. Examples of such sabotage include a person who repeatedly offers calorie-dense foods to you, even though you have turned down the food and this person knows you are trying to lose weight.

- **Holidays and Parties**

1. Beforehand, think about what you will eat and drink while attending the event. Practise polite ways to decline food.
2. Consider limiting your food intake before the special occasion to avoid consuming too many calories for the day.
3. Eat a low-calorie snack about an hour before the occasion.
4. Drink fewer alcoholic beverages. Replace alcoholic beverages with ice water or diet soft drinks.

- **Restaurants**

1. Avoid fried menu items or those made with butter, gravy, or cream sauce.
2. Choose pasta with red sauce instead of white sauce.
3. Request salad dressing "on the side" so that you can control the amount.
4. Think "small." Order an entree and share it with another person.
5. Don't be a member of the "clean plate club." Ask your server for a carryout container when he or she brings your order to the table. Then divide the food in half and place one half in the container. Be sure to refrigerate the leftovers within two hours after the meal, and then eat them for a meal the following day.
6. If you choose a dessert item, share it with others.
7. Avoid eating regularly at fast food outlets.
8. When at fast food outlets, make substitutions, such as a salad instead of a fried fish sandwich, a regular hamburger instead of a specialty burger, or a roasted chicken sandwich instead of a breaded and fried chicken sandwich. Order a diet soft drink or water instead of a regular soft drink. If possible, order a baked potato instead of fries.

- **Physical Activity**

1. Choose physical activities that you enjoy and can do without the need for expensive equipment.
2. Increase the time you spend walking each day. Keep walking shoes where you can see them.
3. Reduce the amount of time you spend sitting. For example, do more household chores yourself.
4. Take stairs instead of elevators or escalators whenever possible.
5. Park your car farther from your destination and walk, if you feel it is safe to do so
6. Perform calisthenics or lift handheld weights while watching television.
7. Adopt moderate-intensity activities for your leisure time. For example, join a coed volleyball club or take a ballroom dancing class.

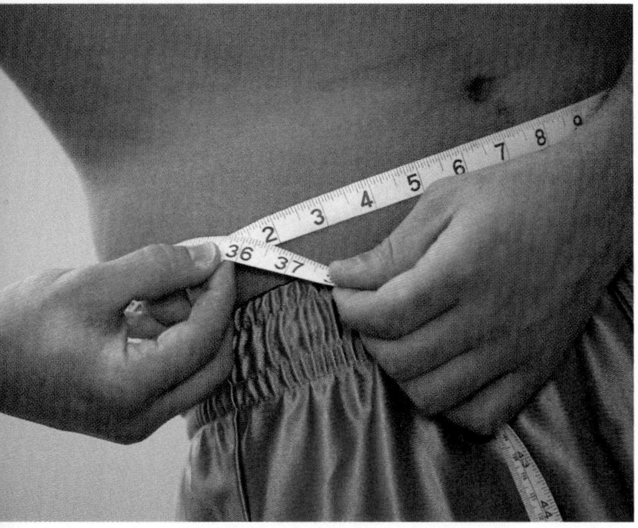

- **Self-Monitoring**

  1. Set reasonable weight-loss goals, for example, losing 2 kg (about 4 lbs.) in one month. When you achieve that goal, then set another reasonable goal, and continue with this process until the goal weight is achieved.
  2. Use a special notebook to use as a food and exercise diary and keep it you can see it—near the kitchen table, refrigerator, or pantry, for example.
  3. In the diary, note the time and place of eating as well as the type and amount of food eaten. Also record who was present and your mood when you ate meals and snacks.
  4. Use the diary to identify your food-related problem areas, such as eating when bored or depressed.
  5. In the exercise section of the diary, record the form of moderate-intensity exercise you performed and the number of minutes you spent engaging in that activity each day. Try to achieve at least 150 minutes of moderate-intensity activities each week.
  6. Measure your waistline weekly and keep a record of the measurements.
  7. Weigh yourself at least once a week, preferably at the same time and without clothing. However, don't rely only on your weight as an indication of your progress. Regular exercise often increases muscle mass that can result in weight gain or failure to lose weight. However, adding muscle mass is healthier than maintaining too much body fat.

- **Rewards for New Behaviours**

  1. Plan non-food motivators or rewards for specific behaviours. For example, "I'll buy a pair of slacks that are one size smaller than what I currently wear and hang them where I can see them…" or "I'll buy that DVD I've wanted when I lose 2 kg (4 lbs.)."
  2. Encourage family and friends to provide praise and encouragement for your efforts to manage your weight. Let family, friends, and associates know that you are trying to lose weight and you'd appreciate their help and support. Thank them when you receive their praise and support.

- **Changing Negative Thought Patterns**

  1. Don't get discouraged by occasional setbacks—relapses can be expected when changing behaviours. For example, "OK, so I lost control and had too much to eat at the wedding. That's to be expected. I just need to get back on track. I'll pull in the reins on my eating for the next day and exercise more."
  2. Think positively about progress. "I didn't lose any weight this week, but I didn't gain any either. I must be losing fat and getting trimmer—those slacks fit better than they did two months ago."
  3. Counter negative thoughts with positive statements. "Next time, I'll eat two cookies instead of four. This afternoon, I'll just have to walk a little longer and harder to burn off those extra calories."

Food & Nutrition *tips*

- When you are hungry, drink some skim milk or eat a banana, an apple, a few whole dates, or a handful of raisins.
- Skipping meals can contribute to fatigue. Eating breakfast and small in-between-meal snacks can provide the carbohydrates needed to maintain blood glucose levels.
- Include foods that supply complex carbohydrate, including fibre, in each meal to provide a sense of fullness and satiety.

Community-Based Weight-Loss Programs

Many communities offer a variety of weight-loss programs. Registered dietitians often conduct weight-loss classes at hospitals or universities. Dietitians have extensive training in foods, metabolism, nutrition, dietetics, and counselling methods to help people design safe and effective weight-loss plans. If a physician prescribes dietary counselling by a registered dietitian, Canada's publicly funded health care system will cover the cost of such treatment.

Commercial programs such as Weight Watchers have diet plans that have been developed by dietitians, but members who have lost weight while following the plan usually conduct local meetings. Before joining any weight-loss program, consumers should obtain answers to the following questions:

- How much does the program cost? Do I pay when I attend meetings? Do I need to sign a contract? If so, for what length of time?
- Do I have to buy special foods or dietary supplements?
- Is nutrition counselling provided? Do the persons providing nutrition counselling and information have degrees in nutrition and dietetics from accredited colleges or universities? How much contact will I have with a counsellor?
- Does the plan emphasize the importance of making lifestyle changes, including ways to increase physical activity?
- Does the program's advertising include questionable weight-loss claims and deceptive testimonials?

Individuals who lose excess weight and maintain the weight loss tend to eat regular meals, including breakfast.

Successful Dieters—How Do They Manage Their Weight?

The U.S. National Weight Control Registry tracks a group of over 4000 adult Americans, mostly women, who have lost at least 30 pounds (13 to 14 kg) and maintained the weight loss for at least one year.[13] Information about members' nutrition- and exercise-related practices provides some insights into lifestyle practices that foster losing excess weight and maintaining the lower weight. Registry members tend to:

- Eat low-calorie, low-fat, high-carbohydrate diets;[69] on average, a member's estimated calorie intake is 1800 kcal per day, with fat comprising about 25% of total calories.
- Maintain the same diet regimen every day of the week.
- Eat regular meals, including breakfast almost every day.
- Weigh themselves at least once a week; many members weigh themselves daily.
- Burn about 400 kcal by exercising at least 60 minutes daily.[70]
- Eat a limited variety of nutritious foods.[69]

Concept Checkpoint

32. What are the four key elements that are necessary for weight loss and maintenance?
33. List at least six features of reliable weight-loss plans or programs.
34. What questions would it be wise for consumers to have answered before they join a weight-loss group or plan?
35. List at least three steps that members of the U.S. National Weight Control Registry often take to maintain their reduced body weights.

Medical Treatments for Obesity

Obese patients are often unsatisfied with the amount of weight they lose while following fad as well as conventional diets. The frustration of repeated dieting leads some obese persons to turn to physicians for prescription medications and surgical procedures for managing their weight.

Weight-Loss Medications

Some obese people are candidates for taking prescribed medications to aid their weight-loss efforts. Such candidates generally have BMIs of 30 or more, or they have waist circumferences that exceed 40 inches (men) or 35 inches (women). Presently, no weight loss medications or agents are available for sale in Canada as they have not been approved for use by Health Canada. In the United States, the only weight-loss medication approved by the U.S. Food and Drug Administration (FDA) for long-term use is orlistat (Xenical). When orlistat is taken along with a meal, the medication reduces fat digestion by about 30%. The undigested fat is eliminated in the feces and can cause an oily, unpleasant discharge. The fat carries fat-soluble vitamins along with it, and these micronutrients are eliminated in feces as well. Therefore, patients using orlistat often need to take a multiple vitamin supplement. In 2007, the FDA approved sales of the non-prescription form of orlistat ("Alli") as a weight-loss aid for adults.

The typical patient who takes one of the approved medications for a year can expect to lose less than 5 kg (11 lbs.).[71] Overfat people need to recognize that in some instances, prescription medications can aid their weight-loss efforts, but these drugs do not replace the need to reduce calorie intake and increase physical activity.

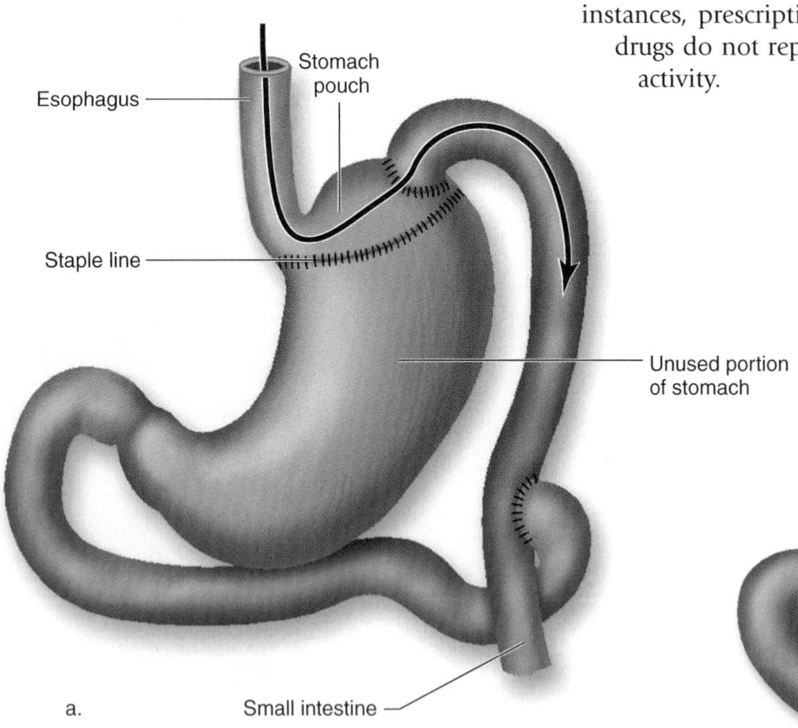

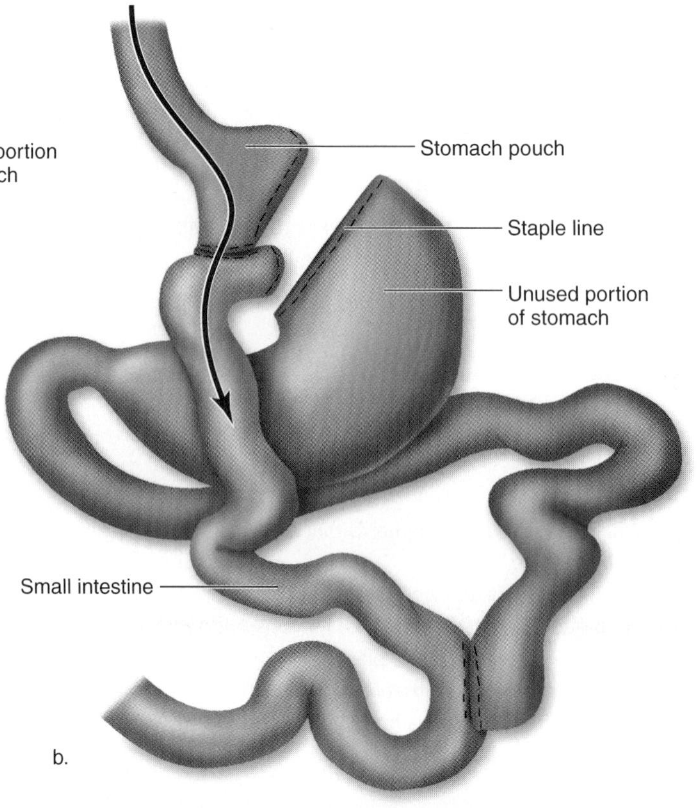

Figure 10.15 Gastric bypass surgeries. (*a*) The Roux-en-Y gastric bypass procedure reduces the obese patient's stomach capacity to about 45 mL (1.5 oz.). Additionally, the surgeon cuts the small intestine and attaches the lower end of it to the newly formed stomach pouch. (*b*) A more drastic form of gastric bypass surgery involves completely separating the newly formed small stomach pouch from the lower part of the stomach.

Bariatric Surgical Procedures

Bariatric (*bar-ee-a'-tric*) **medicine** is the medical specialty that focuses on the treatment of obesity. Currently, bariatric surgery is the only effective method of treating extreme obesity.[24,72] Such surgical procedures drastically reduce the size of an obese person's stomach, markedly limiting his or her food intake. As a result, obese patients are able to lose more than 50% of their excess weight.[72] Aside from helping obese people lose considerable amounts of weight and maintain the loss, bariatric surgery often produces dramatic health benefits. Patients often achieve normal blood pressure, glucose, and triglyceride levels after surgery.

bariatric medicine medical specialty that focuses on the treatment of obesity

In Canada and the United States, the most common surgical approach to treating obesity is the *Roux-en-Y* (*ru-en-wi'*) *gastric bypass*.[73] During this operation, the surgeon staples across the upper part of the stomach to create a small pouch. This procedure reduces the obese patient's stomach capacity to about 45 mL (1.5 oz.), which is approximately the volume of one egg. (Normally, the stomach's capacity is about 946 mL (32 oz.) Additionally, the surgeon cuts the small intestine and attaches the lower end of it to the newly formed stomach pouch (see Fig. 10.15a). The "bypassed" section of the intestine does not receive food, so digestion and absorption are reduced as a result of the surgery. Another, more drastic form of gastric bypass surgery involves stapling, and then completely separating the newly formed small stomach pouch from the lower part of the stomach (see Fig. 10.15b).

By performing the *adjustable gastric banding* procedure, the bariatric surgeon creates the small stomach pouch with an adjustable band instead of fixed surgical staples (Fig. 10.16). By adjusting the tightness of the band, the surgeon determines the size of the stomach. The gastric banding procedure is easier to perform and safer than the other types of bariatric surgery.[72,73]

Bariatric surgery results in weight loss partly because the stomach pouch fills quickly with food, and patients experience satiety sooner than prior to surgery. Moreover, overeating causes discomfort or vomiting. Thus, people who undergo such surgical procedures must make major lifestyle changes, such as the need to plan and consume frequent, small meals. If nutrition education does not accompany bariatric surgery, frequently patients slowly return to their previous eating patterns and stretch the stomach pouch. The stretching of

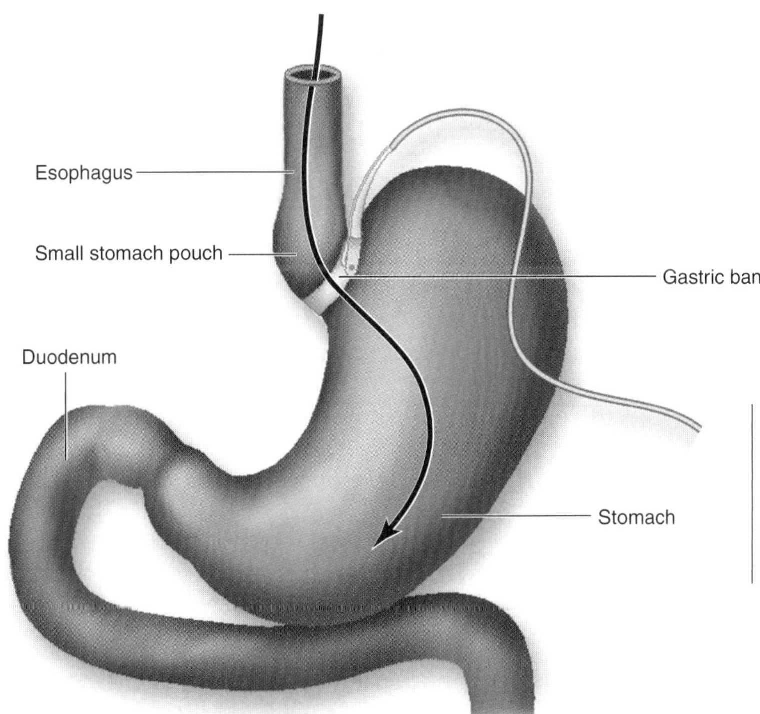

Figure 10.16 Adjustable gastric banding. When performing the adjustable gastric banding procedure, the surgeon creates the small stomach pouch with an adjustable band instead of fixed surgical staples. By adjusting the tightness of the band, the surgeon determines the size of the stomach.

the stomach pouch usually results in eventual regain of the weight loss associated with this form of bariatric surgery.

Complications often associated with bariatric surgery include intestinal blockage and bleeding, ulcer or blood clot formation, and wound infections. About 1% of patients who undergo bariatric surgical procedures die as a result.[24] After surgery, patients can develop iron deficiency and some bone loss. However, patients can reduce their risk of nutrient deficiencies by taking vitamin and mineral supplements.

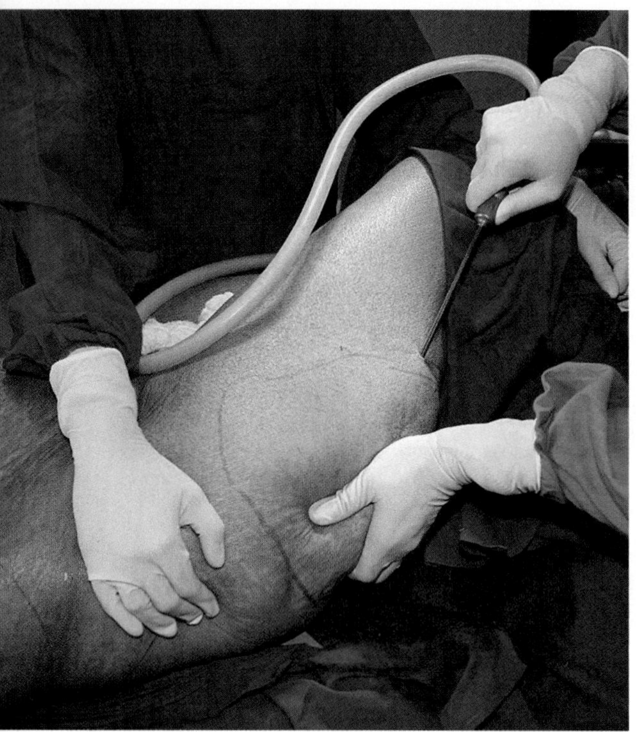

Figure 10.17 Liposuction. Liposuction is a surgical procedure that involves inserting a pencil-thin tube into an incision in the skin and suctioning the excess fat out of the body.

What Is Liposuction?

Liposuction is a surgical method of reducing the size of local fat deposits. Liposuction is not intended to treat obesity, but it can help a person improve the contours of his or her body. This procedure involves inserting a pencil-thin tube into an incision in the skin and suctioning the excess fat out of the body (Fig. 10.17). This procedure has risks, such as infection, permanent dimpling of the skin at the suctioning site, and blood clots that can be deadly. Liposuction is usually considered cosmetic rather than necessary surgery; therefore, public and private health insurance plans are not likely to cover its costs. Despite the expense and risks, liposuction is the most common type of cosmetic surgery in Canada and the United States.[74]

A highly promoted treatment involves injecting chemicals into subcutaneous fat tissue that supposedly "dissolves" the fat without the need for surgical suctioning. (The procedure may make you wonder what happens to the fat after it "dissolves.") At this point, there is no reliable scientific evidence to support the safety and effectiveness of this method.[75]

Concept **Checkpoint**

36. Explain how sibutramine (Meridia) and orlistat (Xenical) can aid weight-loss efforts.

37. Describe two different bariatric surgeries. Why is bariatric surgery effective? Compared to gastric stapling procedures, what is a major advantage of gastric banding?

38. What is liposuction? List three risks associated with this procedure.

liposuction surgical method of reducing the size of local fat deposits

fad trendy practice that has widespread appeal for a period of time, but then becomes no longer fashionable

Unreliable Weight-Loss Methods

Each year, North Americans spend well over $50 billion on products and services promoted to help them lose weight.[76] Some overweight or obese people join commercial weight-loss programs that have "good track records" for encouraging successful weight loss and maintenance. Other overfat persons obtain individual dietary counselling from a registered dietitian to help them lose weight. By recognizing that it took months and probably years to gain the excess fat, individuals may be more likely to accept advice and diets that result in slow but steady weight loss. However, many overweight and obese people seek "quick fixes" to lose weight, such as *fad* diets and dietary supplements promoted to "burn" or "melt" fat fast.

Fad Diets

A **fad** is a trendy practice that has widespread appeal among a population, but after a period of time, people lose interest in the practice and it becomes no longer fashionable. Table 10.9 presents some popular fad weight-loss diets and their features. People often

TABLE 10.9 *Examples of Popular Fad Weight-Loss Diets*

Approach	Examples	Features	Outcomes
Restricted carbohydrates	Dr. Atkins New Diet Revolution; Calories Don't Count; The Complete Scarsdale Medical Diet; Enter the Zone; Sugar Busters; South Beach Diet (especially initial phase); Protein Power	Generally less than 100 g of carbohydrate daily	Ketosis due to excess burning of fat; may cause fatigue; high saturated fat intake may increase blood cholesterol levels; constipation, headaches, and bad breath
Low fat	The Rice Diet; The Macrobiotic Diet (some versions); Pritikin Diet; T-Factor Diet; Fit or Fat; The McDougall Plan; Lean Bodies; Turn Off the Fat Genes; The Pasta Diet; Eat More, Weigh Less; G-Index Diet	Generally less than 20% of calories from fat Limited or no sources of animal protein Limited nuts and seeds	Excess fibre may result in increased intestinal gas Difficult to follow for long periods because food choices are so limited Limited food choices may lead to feelings of food deprivation
Diets with gimmicks	Dr. Berger's Immune Power Diet; Fit for Life; The Beverly Hills Diet; F-Plan Diet; The Princeton Diet; Eat to Win; Cabbage Soup Diet; Grapefruit Diet; Eat Right for Your Type	Promotes certain nutrients, foods, or combinations of foods as having unique, magical, or previously unreported weight-loss-promoting properties	Malnutrition if followed for a long period Such diets generally do not encourage changing exercise and food-related habits

lose weight while following fad diets; however, they usually regain much of the weight that was lost while "on the diet" when they resume their prior eating and other lifestyle habits. Too often, people think of a weight-loss diet as a temporary change in their eating habits. Achieving a healthy body weight and maintaining that weight requires making lifestyle changes that a person adopts for the rest of his or her life.

Fad diets often rely on *gimmicks*. A gimmick is a novel feature that makes the diet seem to be unique and more likely to work than other diets. Some fad diets use the gimmick of emphasizing one food or food group while excluding almost all others. The cabbage soup and grapefruit diets are examples of fad diets that promote eating single foods. Dieters may lose some weight while following eating plans that restrict food variety, but the weight loss occurs because the diet is low in calories, not because cabbage, grapefruit, or other "special food" contains compounds that cause rapid weight loss. Following such diets for a few days often results in boredom and monotony. Eventually, dieters abandon such restrictive menu plans because they just cannot face another cup of cabbage soup or bowl of grapefruit. Weight regain occurs when dieters return to their former eating habits—the habits that contributed to their original overweight or obese conditions.

Fad diets will come and go. However, if you examine any diet plan carefully, you can determine whether it is probably a fad. A typical fad diet:

- Offers a "quick fix," that is, the diet promotes rapid weight loss without calorie restriction and increased physical activity.
- Limits food selections from a few food groups and dictates specific rituals, such as eating only fruit for breakfast or eating only certain food combinations.
- Requires buying a book or various gimmicks, such as expensive dietary supplements, weight-loss patches, or cellulite-reducing creams.
- Uses outlandish and unscientific claims to support its usefulness. For example, the "Beverly Hills Diet" book promoted the notion that people become fat because food "gets stuck" in their bodies, rots, and produces toxins. Another author of a fad diet book claimed people can lose weight by following diet plans based on their blood types. These notions and recommendations are not supported by scientific evidence.
- Relies on testimonials from famous people or connects the diet to trendy places such as Beverly Hills, California, and South Beach, Florida.
- Does not emphasize the need to change eating habits and physical activity patterns.

Advertising campaigns use celebrities to promote weight-loss supplements. Here, the late model Anna Nicole Smith appears in an advertisement for TrimSpa.

Low-Carbohydrate Approaches

Fad weight-loss diets that severely limit carbohydrate intakes and are high in protein and saturated fat include the Dr. Atkins' New Diet Revolution, Scarsdale Diet, and Four-Day Wonder Diet. A weight-reduction diet is low carbohydrate if it eliminates or severely restricts the intake of carbohydrate-rich foods such as breads, cereals, fruits, vegetables, and sweets. The lack of variety often leads to boredom with the selection of foods, and as a result, people lose weight because they tend to eat less.

Low-carbohydrate diets usually produce rapid weight loss initially, primarily because the body loses water. Why? The body produces less glycogen when carbohydrate intake is low and uses much of its stored glycogen to supply glucose for energy. Tissues maintain about three grams of water with each gram of glycogen, so a reduction in body glycogen content results in the need for less water to store with it. The kidneys eliminate the excess water in urine. Furthermore, a very-low-carbohydrate intake causes the liver to produce glucose, mostly from certain amino acids supplied by the body's tissue proteins. Protein tissue also contains a lot of water. When protein-rich tissues are dismantled and their amino acids used for energy, the water that was stored with the proteins also ends up in urine.

An analysis of five studies indicated that after six months, people on low-carbohydrate diet plans lost an average of about 3 kg (7 lbs.) more than people on low-fat diets.[77] After a year, however, there was no difference in weight loss between the two groups of dieters. Furthermore, subjects who followed low-carbohydrate diets had higher total cholesterol and LDL cholesterol ("bad" cholesterol) levels. Long-term studies are needed to determine whether low-carbohydrate diets increase the risk of CVD.

Figure 10.18 Toxic herbal supplement. In 2003, Baltimore Orioles pitcher Steve Bechler's death was linked to ephedra. Bechler had taken a large dose of an ephedra-containing supplement a few hours before he died.

Very-Low-Fat Approaches

Very-low-fat diets are actually very-high-carbohydrate diets. These diets supply approximately 5 to 10% of calories from fat and generally result in rapid weight loss when followed consistently. The most notable are the Pritikin Diet and Dr. Dean Ornish's "Eat More, Weigh Less" diet plans. Very-low-fat diets are not harmful for healthy adults, but they are difficult to follow for the long term. Fat contributes to the flavour and texture of foods. Extremely low-fat diets are not tasty, and they eliminate many foods that are usually high on peoples' favourite foods' lists, such as ice cream and meat. Although grains, fruits, and vegetables are nutrient-dense foods, eating them repeatedly and without fat can cause "diet boredom."

Dietary Supplements for Weight Loss

Many overweight and obese people are attracted to dietary supplements for weight loss because they believe promoters' claims that their products are "magic bullets" for shedding unwanted weight quickly and effortlessly.[78] Although over 50 individual types of weight-loss supplements are available, many of these products have not been scientifically tested in humans for safety and effectiveness.

The FDA (Food and Drug Administration) and the FTC (Federal Trade Commission) are the regulatory bodies in the United States that protect public health by assuring the safety and security of the food supply and prevent food manufacturers from making frivolous statements. In Canada, Health Canada establishes policies, regulations, and standards related to the safety and nutritional quality of all food and drugs. The Canadian Food Inspection Agency is responsible for enforcing the food safety policies and standards set by Health Canada.[79]

In 2004, the FDA banned the sale of most dietary supplements that contained the natural stimulant ephedra (*eh-feh'-dra*) or ephredra-related compounds, after the agency received reports of serious side effects and even deaths resulting from use of these products. These types of products have never been approved for use in Canada.

TABLE 10.10 *Summary of Selected Weight-Loss Supplements*
Science-Based Findings

Supplement	Usefulness	Side Effects/Safety Concerns (Usual Doses)
Beta-hydroxy-betamethylbutyrate	May decrease adipose tissue and increase lean body mass, but more research is needed	None reported
Chinese diet pills, Chaso Diet Capsules, Chaso Genpi	Not determined	Linked to illness and deaths in Japan; may contain the active drug fenfluramine
Chitosan	Doubtful	May cause gastrointestinal discomfort including nausea, constipation, and intestinal gas
Chromium picolinate	May enhance weight loss to a small extent	None reported, but may damage DNA
*Dieter's Teas*ᵻ	Not effective	May cause intestinal discomfort and have laxative effects; may cause irregular heart rate; linked to deaths
Ephedrine (ma huang, ephedra, ephedra sinica, sida cordifolia, pinellia, and ephedrine with caffeine)	Ephedrine-containing products promote shortterm weight loss but also increase risk of serious side effects. Ephedra-containing dietary supplements are banned in Canada and the United States.	May cause rapid heart rate, elevated blood pressure, dizziness, sweating, headache, and sleep disturbances; Linked to heart attacks, strokes, and deaths
GHB (gamma hydroxybutyrate, liquid ecstasy, GBL)¶	GHB is illegal in Canada and the United States, except for FDA-approved studies.	May cause nausea, vomiting, delusions, seizures, breathing difficulties, and coma; linked to more than 45 deaths in the United States
Garcinia cambogia (hydroxycitric acid, HCA)	Conflicting results, but overall evidence does not suggest usefulness	May cause headache and gastrointestinal discomfort
Glucomannan	May be effective, but more research is needed	None reported
Guar gum	Not effective	May cause diarrhea and intestinal gas
Hoodia (P57)‡	May suppress appetite	None reported from consuming the stem of hoodia, a type of cactus that is used as a food and appetite suppressant by San bushmen of South Africa. Hoodia is not recommended for children or pregnant females. Currently scientists are investigating the physiological effects of P57, the active chemical in hoodia.
Plantago psyllium	Not effective	None reported
Pyruvate	Not effective	None reported
Spirulina (blue-green algae)	Not effective	Unknown

Sources: Pittler MH, Ernst E: Dietary supplements for body-weight reduction: A systematic review. *American Journal of Clinical Nutrition* 79:529, 2004 Saper RB and others: Common dietary supplements for weight loss. *American Family Physician* 70:1731, 2004.

ᵻ Kurtzweil P: Dieter's brews make tea time a dangerous affair. *FDA Consumer* 31 (no pages cited), 1997. www.fda.gov/fdac/features/1997/597_tea.html

¶ Nordenberg T: The death of the party: All the rave, GHB's hazards go unheeded. *FDA Consumer* 34:14, 2000.

‡ Tahiliani M: *New dietary ingredient notification for Hoodia Gordonii.* 2004. www.fda.gov/ohrms/dockets/dockets/95s0316/95s-0316-rpt0238-04-Hoodia-Gordonii-Tahiliani-vol173.pdf.

The death in 2003 of Steve Bechler, Baltimore Orioles baseball player, was linked to ephedra (Fig. 10.18).[80] Table 10.10 presents science-based findings about some popular weight-loss supplements, including their potential usefulness and safety concerns. At this point, medical experts do not recommend any weight-loss supplement.[78]

Analyzing Advertising Hype for Weight-Loss Supplements

Maybe you've heard or read remarkable claims for weight-loss products such as "Lose weight while you sleep," "Lose 30 pounds in just 30 days," and "Eat anything you want and still lose weight." In general, advertising claims that a product promises quick and easy weight loss are too good to be true. According to an investigation conducted in the United States by the Federal Trade Commission (FTC) in 2001, 55% of the 300 advertisements for weight-loss products included false or misleading claims.[81] It is not uncommon for Canadian consumers to fall victim to this form of nutrition misinformation.

The FTC study identified several features, including typical claims, for popular weight-loss products and services. The agency's report also provided reasons why you should be skeptical of such features when they are used in magazine ads, television infomercials, or Web sites. According to FTC, you should be wary of claims that the product or service:

- *Causes rapid and extreme weight loss.* Ads commonly use outrageous claims such as "Lose up to 18 pounds in one week!" to attract consumers. The use of the modifier up to means that the person using the product could lose considerably less than 18 pounds a week.

- *Requires no need to change dietary patterns or physical activity.* Principles of energy balance do not support claims such as "Lose weight without dieting or strenuous exercise" and "Eat as much as you want—the more you eat, the more you'll lose." Regular exercise and moderate energy intake are necessary for weight loss and long-term maintenance.
- *Results in permanent weight loss.* Claims such as "Discover the secret to permanent weight loss" and "Lose weight and keep it off" often appear in ads. These claims target consumers who have lost weight but gained it back and are wary of weight-loss products. Long-term weight loss is difficult to achieve without calorie reduction and regular exercise, and claims that permanent weight loss can result simply from using a product are questionable.[81]
- *Is scientifically proven or doctor endorsed.* Some ads claim their product or service has been "clinically tested," "scientifically proven," or "physician recommended." Scientific testing of the product or service supposedly occurred at "respected" or "leading" medical centres or universities. However, most ads do not provide information about testing sites or journals where the results were published. Such information is critical for assessing the reliability of claims. Endorsements by "doctors" or medical professionals can be misleading. A doctor could be someone with a bogus doctorate degree (PhD) or a PhD in a non-scientific field. Moreover, consumers need to be aware that the "professionals" pictured or featured in the ads may be models or fictional characters.
- *Includes a money-back guarantee.* Consumers should recognize that a product does not necessarily work just because it is guaranteed. The FTC frequently sues companies that fail to return money to dissatisfied consumers as their ads guaranteed.
- *Is safe.* Ads may include safety-related claims, such as "proven 100% safe" or "safe, immediate weight loss." Additionally, the term "natural" often accompanies safety claims, implying that "natural" weight-loss products are safer than prescribed weight-loss treatments. Despite such assurances, weight-loss supplement manufacturers usually have little scientific evidence to support safety claims, particularly concerning long-term use of their products.
- *Is supported by satisfied customers.* Ads for weight-loss products or services typically feature testimonials from satisfied users. The assumption is that if the product worked for the person providing the testimonial, it should work for anyone. According to the FTC, testimonials generally provide little reliable information about what consumers can expect from using the product.
- *Displays before-and-after photos.* Many ads use photos of "satisfied" customers to support claims that their weight-loss products are effective. In the typical "before" photo, the subject has poor posture, no smile, unkempt hair, and unfashionable, unflattering clothing. In the "after" photo, the person stands with his or her shoulders held back and abdomen tucked in. Additionally, the subject is usually smiling and appears more attractive than in the "before" photo. If you read carefully, you may find disclaimers in small print, such as "results not typical" at the bottom of the "after" photo.

Concept **Checkpoint**

39. What is a "fad" diet? List at least four typical features of fad diets.
40. Why do fad diets and dietary supplements promoted for weight loss appeal to overfat people?
41. Identify at least four popular weight-loss supplements and indicate whether each supplement is safe and effective.
42. Discuss at least three features or claims that are commonly used in ads for weight-loss products or services.

underweight describes person with a BMI of less than 18.5

Gaining Weight

In some societies, being underweight is more socially acceptable than being overweight or obese. Nevertheless, many underweight individuals are just as interested in gaining weight, especially muscle mass, as many overfat persons are interested in losing weight. An **underweight** individual has a BMI that is less than 18.5. Factors that contribute to underweight include genetics, lifestyle practices, chronic diseases, and psychological disturbances.

It is often difficult to pinpoint a cause of underweight; multiple factors contribute to having a lower than average body weight. Individuals who inherit higher resting metabolic rates, tall body frames, or both may find it difficult to gain weight. Excessive physical activity can result in low body weight. Compared to sedentary adults, the bodies of rapidly growing, physically active children and adolescents have higher energy needs. If these children do not consume enough energy, they can lose weight. Chronic diseases such as cancer, tuberculosis, AIDS, and inflammatory bowel disease, often result in severe weight loss that is difficult to treat. Some people who suffer from depression fail to eat enough food to support their energy needs, and they lose weight as a result.

If a person's BMI was within the healthy range before excessive weight loss occurred, an evaluation by a physician may be necessary to determine the cause or causes of the loss, especially when the underweight person has not tried to lose weight. A thorough medical examination can rule out possible reasons for unintentional weight loss, such as hormonal imbalances, depression, cancer, and infectious or digestive tract diseases.

For an underweight person, gaining weight can be just as challenging as losing weight is for an overfat person. To gain weight, underweight adults can gradually increase their consumption of calorie-dense foods, especially those high in healthy fats. Fatty fish, such as salmon; olives; avocados; seeds; low-fat cheeses; nuts and nut butters; bananas, and granola made with dried fruit, seeds, and nuts are high-calorie nutritious food choices with low saturated-fat content. Additionally, underweight people can replace beverages such as soft drinks with more nutritious calorie sources, such as 100% fruit juices, smoothies, and milkshakes made with peanut butter and reduced-fat ice cream. Encouraging a regular meal and snack schedule also aids in weight gain and maintenance.

Sometimes people who are underweight are too busy to eat, and as a result, their caloric intakes are too low to support weight gain. If physical activity habits contribute to their inability to increase their weight, underweight people can find ways to be less active. If their weight remains low, underweight persons can add muscle mass through a

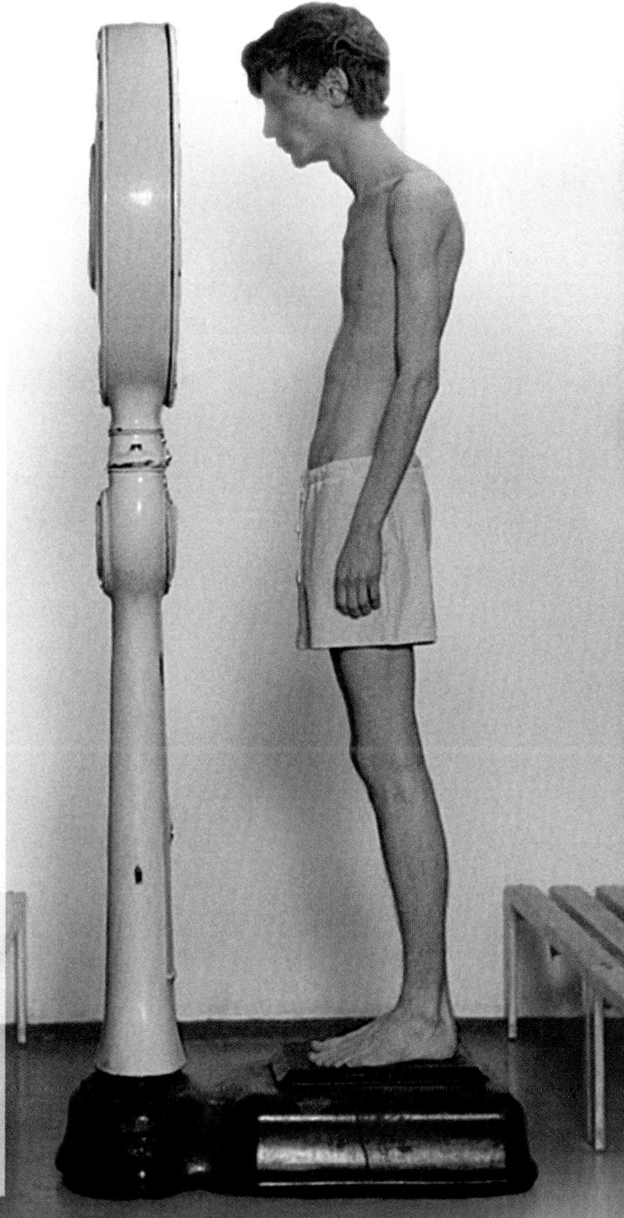

Many underweight individuals are interested in gaining weight, especially muscle mass.

resistance-training (weight-lifting) program, but they must increase their calorie intake to support the additional exercise. Otherwise, gaining muscle tissue is not likely to occur.

In many instances, healthy underweight people may have to accept their body builds. Furthermore, they can realize the health benefits of being lean and the sheer enjoyment of being able to eat a variety of foods without gaining weight. For the typical slim person, the passage of time is usually all that is necessary for weight gain to occur, as the aging process is often accompanied with increasing body fat.

Concept **Checkpoint**

43. List at least three health conditions that are often associated with underweight.

44. Discuss at least three measures an underweight person can take to gain lean mass safely.

Chapter 10 Highlight

Over the Deep Edge

By the time she was in Grade 11, Emily M. was on top of her world. She had been president of her Grade 9 class and captain of the cheerleading squad. Although she was academically and socially successful, Emily sensed that her peers were jealous of her. Also, she was concerned about her weight—59 kg (130 lbs.). At 157 cm (5′2″), her BMI (23.8) was within the healthy range. Nevertheless, Emily began an effort to lose some weight after she overheard a teacher commenting that her cheerleading uniform was too tight.

At first, Emily's food choices were healthy, but soon she began skipping breakfast. Eventually, she stopped eating on alternative days, and when she did eat, she ate mostly fruit, vegetables, and some bagels with cream cheese. She avoided milk but drank lots of diet soft drinks. Occasionally, she would *binge eat,* that is, lose control over her restrictive eating practices. During such food binges, Emily consumed large amounts of fat-free ice cream and sugar-coated cereal. However, she did not practise *purging,* self-induced vomiting and other techniques intended to prevent macronutrients from being absorbed by the digestive tract.

While limiting her food intake, Emily increased her calorie output. She burned calories during intense cheerleading workouts that lasted 90 minutes every day after school. Following the exhaustive workouts, she would run around the school's track, thinking to herself, "I may pass out any second…" yet she continued to run.

As Emily lost weight, people began to take notice of her appearance and she received compliments. According to Emily, "The positive attention fuelled continued dieting…it [dieting] took me over." Although she was hungry all the time, she suppressed the urge to eat. When her weight loss became excessive, her parents were very concerned about her health. Although Emily agreed to see therapists to obtain counselling, at that point, she was not ready to be helped.

After graduating from high school, Emily moved to Nova Scotia, a considerable distance from her family, so she could attend university. A few months after making the move, she woke up in the middle of the night—her heart was racing, and she thought she was having a heart attack. She called her mother and cried, "I can't live like this anymore." Fearing her daughter was going to die, Emily's mother flew to Nova Scotia. At this point, Emily weighed about 41 kg (90 lbs.). She finally realized she wanted to live, and to live, she had to eat.

When Emily returned home, she threw out the bathroom scale. She promised herself not to skip meals, and she limited her exercise regimen to an hour a day. Within a few months, her weight climbed to 55 kg (120 lbs.). Although she felt her body was getting back to normal, she decided to obtain counselling to help deal with the emotional and physical changes she was experiencing.

Today, Emily is healthy, employed as a nanny for three children, married, and is again attending university, part-time. Emily loves being around children. Her motivation to maintain a healthy weight for her height is fuelled by her realization that she must have some body fat to become pregnant someday. Her advice, "The decisions you're making now affect you forever. Take care of your body; nurture it, and remember—not everyone is meant to be a supermodel!"

Emily suffered from *anorexia nervosa*, a serious eating disorder that is more common among young women than young men. Fortunately, she was able to recover completely from this disorder. Many people who suffer from anorexia nervosa do not regain healthy body weights—some even die as a result of starvation.

What is an eating disorder? How can you distinguish quirky eating behaviours from harmful eating disorders? What are the typical signs of eating disorders? How are eating disorders treated? After reading the Chapter 10 Highlight, you will find the answers to these questions.

Disordered Eating or Eating Disorder?

With the prevalence of obesity rising rapidly in the Canada, it is not surprising that many Canadian adolescents and young adults are concerned about their body shapes and weights. Furthermore, the media constantly bombards us with images of the "ideal" body. Television shows and movies often portray thin women or muscular men as happy and successful. Excessive concern about body size and social pressure to avoid weight gain can lead to *disordered eating*, chaotic and abnormal food-related practices such as skipping meals, limiting food choices, following fad diets, and bingeing on food. Disordered eating behaviours are temporary and often occur when a person is under a lot of stress or wants to lose weight to improve his or her appearance. When a person adopts disordered eating behaviours as a lifestyle, practices can become harmful and difficult-to-treat *eating disorders*.

Eating disorders are psychological disturbances that lead to certain physiological changes and serious health complications.[1A] According to the Canada-based National Eating Disorders Information Centre, as many as 10% of Canadian females and 1% of Canadian males suffer from anorexia nervosa, bulimia nervosa, or "eating disorders not otherwise specified," such as binge-eating disorder.[1A] In most cases, eating disorders develop during adolescence or early adulthood, but these conditions may begin at any age. A recent Canadian study suggests as many as 27% of Ontario girls between 12 and 18 years of age may be engaged in problematic eating or weight-loss patterns.[1A] A person who has an eating disorder typically experiences problems adjusting to the demands of work and school as well as relationships.

eating disorders psychological disturbances that lead to certain physiological changes and serious health complications

anorexia nervosa (AN) severe psychological disturbance characterized by self-imposed starvation

The causes of eating disorders are unknown, but genetic, social, and psychological factors contribute to their development. Risk factors for eating disorders include being a female, having low self-esteem, experiencing sexual abuse as a child, being teased about weight, dieting repeatedly to lose weight, having a perfectionist personality, and being in a dysfunctional family.[2A] Mood and anxiety disorders as well as substance abuse often accompany these conditions, but it is not clear whether eating disorders cause psychological problems or are the result of mental disturbances. Thus, treatment of eating disorders is complex, involving more than just dietary counselling.

If you or someone you know has an eating disorder, it is important to seek help for the condition as early as possible—before the behaviour becomes highly ingrained or the affected person's life is at risk. In academic environments, professional help is commonly available at student health centres and student guidance/counselling facilities on university campuses.

Anorexia Nervosa

Anorexia nervosa (AN) is a severe psychological disturbance characterized by self-imposed starvation that results in malnutrition and low body weight. In developed countries, AN affects about 1 in 200 women.[3A] Although men also develop AN, women comprise 90% of cases. People suffering from AN:

- Maintain BMIs of 17.5 or less.
- Have distorted body images. Patients deny they are too thin and they are overly concerned about becoming fat.
- Are obsessed with losing weight.
- Avoid "fattening foods."
- Engage in one or more of the following practices:
  - self-induced vomiting
  - abuse of laxatives or diuretics
  - excessive exercise regimens
  - use of appetite suppressants

- Display signs of hormonal imbalances such as delayed puberty, loss of menstrual periods in females, and loss of sexual interest and functioning in males.
- Are depressed and anxious.[2A]

Young women suffering from AN have lower than normal estrogen levels that not only result in failure to menstruate but also can accelerate bone loss and cause premature osteoporosis. Other physical signs of the condition include severe constipation; widespread delicate, dense, white hairs on the skin (lanugo hair); and shrunken breasts and buttocks. People with AN often wear layers of clothing to keep warm, because they lack adequate subcutaneous fat and they want to hide their extremely thin appearances.

Effective treatment for AN usually involves a team of health professionals, including registered dietitians, physicians, nurses, and mental health counsellors, who are specially trained to treat the condition.[1A] Dietitians work with patients to restore healthy weight and promote healthy attitudes toward food and gaining weight. Additionally, dietitians are sources of accurate food and nutrition information for patients with AN and other eating disorders. A key goal of treatment is for patients to achieve and maintain healthy BMIs.

People suffering from AN have a high risk of dying from starvation, electrolyte imbalances, or suicide.[4A] Five percent of people with AN eventually die as a result of the disorder.[5A] Although nearly 50% of patients fully recover from AN, the illness becomes chronic in about 20% of cases. AN patients who binge eat and then follow up binges with *purging* activities, such as self-induced vomiting or laxative abuse, are more likely to have poor long-term outcomes.[5A] On the other hand, patients who do not binge eat or purge and have good relationships with their parents are more likely to recover.

Bulimia Nervosa

An estimated 1.5% of women and 0.5% of men in the Canadian population have **bulimia nervosa**, a condition characterized by cyclic episodes of overeating (bingeing) and calorie-restrictive dieting.[1A] As in cases of anorexia nervosa, females are more likely to have bulimia nervosa than males. People with "bulimia" often consume cakes, cookies, ice cream, and other high-fat high-carbohydrate foods during binges. After a binge, the person attempts to *purge* the calories consumed during binges by vomiting and abusing laxatives, diuretics, or enemas. Another way a bulimic person attempts to avoid gaining weight after a binge is by exercising excessively.

People with bulimia frequently induce vomiting by thrusting fingers deep into their mouths, and as a result, scrape their knuckles. Thus, characteristic signs of bulimia nervosa are bite marks and scars on the knuckles. Dentists often identify people who practise bulimia because the acid in vomit erodes the enamel on the surface of teeth, especially the backs of teeth.

The practice of inducing vomiting leads to many of the health problems associated with bulimia nervosa. Repeated vomiting can cause:

- Blood chemistry abnormalities; blood potassium can drop dramatically, altering heartbeat and increasing risk of sudden death.
- Swelling of the salivary glands in the mouth as a result of infection or irritation.
- Tears and bleeding of the esophagus.

Unlike people suffering from anorexia nervosa, people with bulimia are often difficult to identify by their appearances, because they tend to have BMIs in the normal or overweight

bulimia nervosa eating disorder characterized by cyclic episodes of bingeing and calorie-restrictive dieting

range. Furthermore, they usually hide their binge-purge behaviours from others. Many people with the condition lie about their food-related behaviours to family and friends, and they resort to shoplifting groceries because they cannot afford to buy such large amounts of food. Persons with bulimia nervosa often have low self-esteem, and they feel guilty and depressed after a binge. The compelling need to binge and purge eventually becomes a preoccupation for people with bulimia, and as a result, they become less involved in social activities and more isolated. Some people show behavioural characteristics of both anorexia nervosa and bulimia nervosa, because the illnesses can overlap. About half of the women diagnosed as having anorexia nervosa eventually develop signs of bulimia.

Effective treatment for bulimia nervosa, as for anorexia nervosa, requires a team of medical professionals who have experience treating eating disorders. A key goal of treatment is having patients with bulimia develop a plan to eat normally.[1A] Dietitians can help people with the disorder by providing reliable nutrition information and suggestions for developing healthy eating patterns. For example, patients may be encouraged to keep a food diary to monitor their food intake and help identify situations that trigger binge episodes. Psychotherapy can also help patients learn to change unhealthy beliefs about themselves, accept themselves, and use alternative methods—other than bingeing—to cope with stressful situations. Additionally, patients may need to take certain prescribed medications, particularly antidepressants. Up to 60% of people with bulimia nervosa improve with treatment.[2A]

Binge-Eating Disorder and Night Eating Syndrome

People with *binge-eating disorder (BED)* or *night eating syndrome (NES)* do not display all the signs of people suffering from anorexia nervosa or bulimia nervosa. BED and NES are characterized by episodic food binges that are not followed by purging. During binges, a person with BED typically isolates him- or herself and consumes large quantities of calorie-dense foods, such as ice cream, cookies, sweets, and potato chips. According to estimates, 1 to 2% of North Americans suffer from binge-eating disorder.[1A] A person with NES is not hungry in the morning but wakes up during the night to binge eat. Although obesity does not always accompany BED and NES, these abnormal eating patterns are more common among overfat persons.[6A]

Stressful events and feelings of loneliness, anxiety, depression, anger, isolation, and frustration can trigger a food binge. People who experienced sexual and physical abuse as children are at risk of BED.[7A] The condition may develop in people who never learned to express and deal appropriately with their negative feelings. While bingeing, the person may feel better, but after the episode of overeating, this individual usually feels depressed, ashamed, guilty, and disgusted with him- or herself. In some cases, a person with BED eventually develops anorexia nervosa or bulimia nervosa.[1A]

Treatment for BED usually includes individual and group therapy. A major goal of treatment is to reduce the patient's frequency of binges. In therapy, the BED patient learns how to eat in response to hunger rather than emotional needs or external factors, such as the presence of food. Some experts feel that learning to eat all foods—but in moderation—is an effective behavioural goal for binge eaters. This practice may prevent people with BED from feeling deprived and frustrated. Antidepressants may also be helpful because such medications can improve the patient's negative moods that often trigger food binges.

Female Athlete Triad

Women participating in appearance-based competitive sports that require low body mass, such as gymnastics, swimming, and distance running, are at risk of disordered eating practices and eating disorders. The **female athlete triad** is a condition characterized by disordered eating, lack of menstrual periods (amenorrhea [*a-men-ohree'-a*]), and osteoporosis.[8A] According to clinical reports, 15 to 60% of female athletes display disordered eating practices, such as frequent fasting.[8A] Severe food restriction and chronic emotional stress can result in lower blood estrogen levels that, in turn, cause amenorrhea. Furthermore, estrogen is needed to maintain bone mineral mass. Thus, young women with low estrogen levels have less dense and weaker bones than normal, increasing their risk of bone and stress fractures.

Patients with symptoms of the female athlete triad should seek treatment from a multidisciplinary team of health professionals. The goal of treatment is improving the nutritional state of the patient to reverse the signs and symptoms of her disordered eating practices. However, highly competitive athletes may not be willing to accept necessary treatment plans. Until she recovers, the female athlete may need to decrease the time she spends in training or the intensity of her workouts by 10 percent.[8A]

female athlete triad condition characterized by disordered eating, lack of menstrual periods, and osteoporosis

References for Chapter 10 Highlight

1A. National Eating Disorder Information Centre: *Understanding statistics on eating disorders.* www.nedic.ca/knowthefacts/statistics.shtml. Accessed: December 2009.

2A. Nicholls D, Viner R: Eating disorders and weight problems. *British Medical Journal* 330:950, 2005.

3A. Torpy JM and others: Anorexia nervosa. *The Journal of the American Medical Association* 295:2684, 2006.

4A. Gucciardi E and others: Eating disorders. *BMC Women's Health* 4:S21, 2004.

5A. Steinhausen H-C: The outcome of anorexia nervosa in the 20th century. *American Journal of Psychiatry* 159:1284, 2002.
6A. Tanofsky-Kraft M, Yanovski SZ: Eating disorder or disordered eating? Non-normative eating patterns in obese individuals. *Obesity Research* 12:1361, 2004.
7A. Striegel-Moore RH and others: Abuse, bullying, and discrimination as risk factors for binge eating disorder. *American Journal of Psychiatry* 159:1902, 2002.
8A. Birch K: Female athlete triad. *British Medical Journal* 330:244, 2006.

SUMMARY

The prevalence of overweight and obesity has reached epidemic proportions in Canada and the United States and throughout the world. Nearly two-thirds of Canadian adults are now overweight or obese; approximately one-quarter of the adults are obese. The prevalence of obese Canadian and American infants, children, and adolescents has risen sharply over the past 25 years.

The body is composed of two major compartments: total body fat and fat-free mass. Overweight and obese people have excessive adipose tissue. Percentage of body fat is associated with risks of obesity-related diseases. According to certain standards, a man is overweight when his body is 22 to 25% fat; a woman is overweight when her body is 32 to 37% fat. A man is obese when fat comprises 26% or more of his body; a woman is obese when fat makes up 38% or more of her body.

In addition to percentage of body fat, medical experts use BMI to determine whether one's weight is healthy. BMIs of 18.5 to 24.9 are healthy; BMIs of 25.0 to 29.9 are in the overweight range. Persons with BMIs of 30.0 or more are obese. People with BMIs greater than 25 have increased risks of CVD, hypertension, type 2 diabetes, and certain cancers. Compared to people with healthy BMIs, obese people are more likely to die prematurely from all causes.

Body fat distribution is associated with obesity-related diseases. Excessive upper-body fat (apple shape) is associated with increased risks of CVD, type 2 diabetes, and hypertension. Waist circumferences that exceed 40 inches (men) or 35 inches (women) are linked to obesity-related diseases.

Biological fuels are foods and beverages that contain macronutrients and the nonnutrient alcohol. Under normal conditions, human cells metabolize primarily glucose and fatty acids, but small amounts of amino acids are also used for energy. Cells release the energy stored in biological fuels by breaking bonds within the molecules. Cells obtain only about 40% of the energy that was in macronutrients by forming ATP. Cells release the remaining energy as heat.

Basal or resting metabolism, physical activity, TEF, and NEAT account for total energy use by the body. Metabolism requires the largest share of an average person's daily energy needs. Various factors including thyroid hormone, body composition, gender, and age influence the metabolic rate. Physical activity is energy use by skeletal muscle movement. TEF is the increase in energy needs that occurs during digestion, absorption, and processing of nutrients in food. NEAT is energy use for involuntary skeletal muscle activities, such as shivering.

Energy balance is a state in which a person's calorie intake from food and beverages equals his or her calorie output for metabolism, physical activity, TEF, and NEAT. Negative energy balance occurs when calorie output is greater than calorie intake, resulting in weight loss. Positive energy balance occurs when calorie intake is greater than calorie output, resulting in weight gain.

There is no simple cause for obesity. From a physiological standpoint, eating behaviour is complex and largely involves interactions among the nervous, endocrine, and digestive systems as well as fat tissue. Dietary and inherited factors also influence body weight. Additionally, overfat people may have inherited genes for "thrifty metabolisms." According to the set-point theory, the body's fat content is genetically predetermined. The set point may protect the body from losing weight and explain why weight loss is so difficult to achieve and maintain.

Environmental factors, such as food advertising, can have a powerful influence on food choices and appetite. The increased consumption of oversized portions of restaurant foods may be partly responsible for the obesity epidemic. The environment also influences people's patterns of physical activity. According to the Public Health Agency of Canada, healthy adults under 65 years of age should perform 60 minutes of moderate-intensity physical activity five days of the week.

A reliable weight-loss plan is safe and effective, and the plan should meet the dieter's nutritional, psychological, and social needs. Successful weight loss and long-term weight maintenance involve four key elements: motivation, calorie reduction, regular physical activity, and behaviour modification.

A pound of adipose tissue supplies about 3500 kcal. If energy output exceeds calorie intake by about 500 kcal per day, a person can expect to lose a pound of fat per week. The healthiest way to lower total calorie intake is to reduce consumption of added sugars, fats, and alcohol. A dieter's goal should be reducing total calorie intake while obtaining all essential nutrients.

Members of the National Weight Control Registry have lost weight and maintained their lower weights by eating a low-calorie, low-fat, high-carbohydrate diet; maintaining the same diet regimen every day; eating regular meals, including breakfast; weighing themselves frequently; exercising at least 60 minutes daily; and eating a limited variety of nutritious foods.

Certain medications can enhance weight loss when combined with a plan that includes calorie restriction and regular exercise. Bariatric surgeries reduce the stomach volume of people with extreme obesity.

People can lose weight while following fad diets, but they usually regain much of the weight that was lost when they resume their prior eating and other lifestyle habits. Achieving a healthy body weight and maintaining that weight requires making lifestyle changes that a person adopts for the rest of his or her life. No dietary supplement is recommended for weight loss.

Underweight can be caused by various factors, such as genetics, excessive physical activity, and certain diseases. To gain weight, an underweight person generally needs to increase portion sizes, eat more calorie-dense foods, and reduce physical activity, if excessive.

Personal Dietary Analysis

1. Consider your eating behaviours.
   a. Does your emotional state influence your eating behaviour? For example, do you eat certain foods when you feel "stressed-out" or depressed? Which foods do you eat under these circumstances? Describe a situation in which you ate in response to an emotional state instead of being hungry.
   b. Discuss the influence that food advertising has over your eating practices.
   c. Besides emotional state and food advertising, what other factors influence your eating habits?
2. Estimate your energy requirement by using one of the following formulas—choose the appropriate formula for your gender group.

Men 19 Years and Older:

Estimated Energy Requirement (EER) = 662 – (9.53 × AGE) PA × (15.91 × WT + 539.6 × HT)

Women 19 Years and Older:

Estimated Energy Requirement (EER) = 354 – (6.91 × AGE) + PA × (9.36 × WT + 726 × HT)

The variables in the formulas are:

AGE = age in years

PA = physical activity estimate (see Table 10.6)

WT = weight in kg (lb. ÷ 2.2)

HT = height in metres (in. ÷ 39.4)

Recipe for Healthy Living

Did You Make that Dip?!

When it's time to entertain your friends, you can make a fiesta dip that will disappear quickly and provide plenty of compliments too. Fresh cilantro and dried cumin give recipes a distinctive "Mexican" flavour. Bean dip recipes often include canned refried beans and cheeses that are high in fat. This lower-fat version uses canned red beans and reduced-fat cheese. You can save time by using canned fat-free refried beans (yes, there is such a product). You can also substitute commercially prepared salsa for the homemade version, but you may find that making salsa with fresh ingredients is worth the extra effort. If you like a "hotter" salsa, use jalapeño peppers instead of mild green chili peppers. When preparing hot peppers, be careful to avoid touching your eyes or inside of your nose until after you have thoroughly washed your hands with soap and water. The peppers contain *capsaicin*, the highly irritating chemical used in pepper spray, which causes intense burning when in contact with mucous membranes.

This recipe makes approximately eight 60-mL (¼-cup) servings. Each serving (without tortilla) supplies approximately 115 kcal, 6.5 g protein, 4.8 g fat, 19.0 mg vitamin C, 65 mcg folate, 360 mg potassium, 274 mg sodium, 1.4 mg iron, and 4.0 g fibre.

SALSA LAYER INGREDIENTS:

1 large, fresh ripe tomato
¼ medium onion, finely chopped
1 clove garlic, finely minced
1 118 mL (4-oz.) can of mild green chilies (peeled and diced)
45 mL (3 Tbsp) chopped fresh cilantro leaves

GUACAMOLE LAYER INGREDIENTS:

1 ripe, black-skinned avocado (slightly soft)
juice of ½ lime
⅛ tsp dried cumin (a spice)
⅛ tsp ground black pepper

OTHER LAYERS:

1 414- to 473-mL (14- to 16-oz.) can red beans
250 mL (1 cup) shredded fat-reduced cheddar cheese

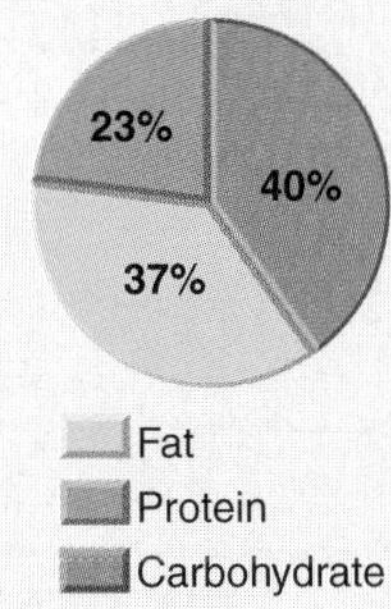

PREPARATION STEPS:

1. Cover an 8" dinner plate with a sheet of heavy-duty aluminum foil.
2. Wash cilantro in cool water and shake off excess water. Wash tomato, avocado, and lime in cool water. Set cilantro and fruits aside on paper towels.
3. Use a sharp knife to *mince* (finely chop) onion, garlic, and cilantro on a cutting board. Place in small bowl.
4. Add chilies to the onion, garlic, and cilantro mixture. Stir gently until well mixed.
5. *Dice* (cut into small pieces) tomato and add to minced ingredients. You've made *salsa*.
6. To make guacamole, remove skin and seed from avocado. In a small bowl, dice avocado into small pieces and sprinkle with lime juice. Add cumin and black pepper to avocado mixture and set aside.
7. Drain juice from beans and rinse them with cool water. Mash beans with the back of a large spoon; bean mixture will be lumpy.
8. Spread mashed beans evenly on the plate, leaving about 2 cm from the edge of the plate free of beans.
9. Cover beans with individual layers of salsa and guacamole, and top with shredded cheese.
10. Loosely cover layered dip with clear plastic wrap and refrigerate.
11. To serve, spoon dip on pieces of soft tortillas.

CRITICAL THINKING

1. Kim and Kevin weigh the same and have similar swimming skills. While in a swimming pool, Kim floats easily when she extends her arms and legs in the water. When Kevin extends his arms and legs and tries to float in the pool, he sinks. Why is Kim able to float more easily than Kevin?
2. Why does your body "warm up" when you exercise?
3. An advertisement for a weight-loss supplement claims that the mixture of herbs in the product increases the metabolic rate by 150%. Explain why you would or would not recommend this product to someone who wants to lose weight.
4. Explain why it is usually difficult to pinpoint a *cause* of obesity.
5. Why are most people who lose weight unable to maintain the lower body weight over time?
6. If your BMI is within the overweight or obese range, discuss your reasons for being interested or not interested in losing weight. If you want to lose weight, what lifestyle changes will you make?
7. If your BMI is within the underweight range, discuss your reasons for being interested or not interested in gaining weight. If you want to gain weight, what lifestyle changes will you make?
8. If your BMI is in the healthy range, discuss steps you can take to maintain a healthy body weight as you grow older.

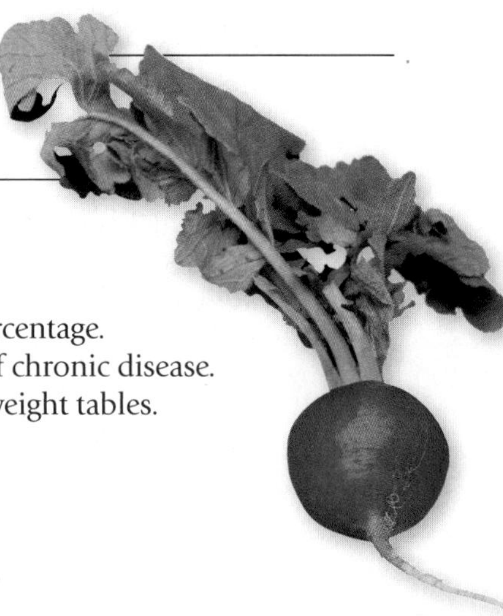

PRACTICE TEST

Select the best answer.

1. Body mass index (BMI) is
   a. a standard used to calculate a person's body fat percentage.
   b. based on a relationship between weight and risk of chronic disease.
   c. gradually being replaced by more reliable height/weight tables.
   d. none of the above
2. ______ cells are specialized to store fat.
   a. Carcinoma
   b. Megaloblastic
   c. Neural
   d. Adipose
3. ______ fat deposits are located deep within the abdomen.
   a. Subcutaneous
   b. Visceral
   c. Cellulite
   d. Brown

4. ______ relies on the principle that lean tissue is denser than water.
   a. Bioelectrical impedance
   b. Underwater weighing
   c. Dual-energy X-ray absorptiometry
   d. none of the above
5. A healthy body fat percentage for women is
   a. 3–10%.
   b. 23–31%.
   c. 32–37%.
   d. 40–50%.
6. For most adults, basal metabolism accounts for ______ of the body's total energy use.
   a. 10–20%
   b. 21–49%
   c. 50–70%
   d. over 70%
7. Basal metabolism includes energy needs for
   a. breathing and circulating blood.
   b. performing physical activity.
   c. digesting food.
   d. absorbing nutrients.
8. Which of the following statements is true?
   a. Women generally have higher metabolic rates than men.
   b. Thyroid hormone levels influence BMR.
   c. A person who has more muscle mass will have a lower BMR than someone with less muscle tissue.
   d. When a person has a fever, his or her BMR drops below normal.
9. Negative energy balance occurs when
   a. the body needs more calories than the diet supplies.
   b. fat storage in the body increases.
   c. energy intake is higher than energy output.
   d. the thermic effect of food equals NEAT.
10. ______ is a hormone that reduces hunger and inhibits fat storage in the body.
   a. Coumadin
   b. Leptin
   c. Ghrelin
   d. Orexin
11. Members of the National Weight Control Registry tend to
   a. skip breakfast regularly.
   b. follow low-carbohydrate/high-protein diets.
   c. exercise two to three times per week.
   d. eat meals regularly, including breakfast.

Answers to Chapter 10 Quiz Yourself

1. You can determine whether you have an unhealthy amount of body fat simply by measuring your waistline. **True.** (p. 338)
2. The best way to lose weight and keep it off is to follow a low-carbohydrate, high-fat diet, such as the Atkins diet. **False.** (p. 364)
3. As people age, their muscle cells turn into fat cells. **False.** (p. 342)
4. When a person consumes more carbohydrate than needed, the excess is converted to fat and stored in fat cells. **True.** (p. 346)
5. Cellulite is a unique type of fat that can be eliminated by taking certain dietary supplements. **False.** (p. 332)

Please visit Connect at

Chapter **11**

Nutrition for Physically Active Lifestyles

Chapter Learning Outcomes

After reading Chapter 11, you should be able to:

1. List five health benefits of a physically active lifestyle.
2. Differentiate between anaerobic and aerobic use of energy, and identify advantages and disadvantages of each.
3. Plan nutritionally adequate, high-carbohydrate menus.
4. Estimate an athlete's energy and protein needs.
5. List at least five ergogenic aids that athletes often use, and describe their effects on health and physical performance.
6. Design a personal fitness regimen that suits your interests and lifestyle.

Bicycling for weeks through quaint villages and over steep mountains in France; swimming for miles in the chilly English Channel while being buffeted by waves; lifting metal disks that weigh more than the weightlifter—the extent to which some people push their bodies is truly amazing. Superior athletes seem to thrive on performing gruelling physical feats that require extraordinary stamina, strength, and energy.

Millions of Canadians admire competitive athletes for their physical accomplishments and enjoy watching them perform. However, approximately two-thirds of adults in Canada do not obtain the recommended levels of physical activity to promote health benefits.[1] Even when Canadians have the time, many choose not to be physically active.

The human body is designed for **physical activity**, movement that results from skeletal muscle contraction. Most of the physical activities you perform each day are *unstructured*, for example, shopping for groceries or doing household tasks. **Exercise** refers to physical activities that are usually planned and structured for a particular purpose, such as having fun or increasing muscle mass. Both forms of physical activity can benefit your health.

Physical fitness is the ability to perform moderate- to vigorous-intensity activities without becoming excessively fatigued. A *physically fit* person has the strength, endurance, flexibility, and balance to meet the physical demands of daily living, exercise, and sports. Proper nutrition is essential for optimal physical fitness and sports performance.

Regardless of whether you aspire to be a world-class athlete or simply want to be healthier, regular exercise should be a part of your daily routine. Physically inactive people do not have to perform high-intensity structured workouts daily to improve their health.[2] According to the recommendations of Canadian health experts, healthy adults under 65 years of age should perform moderate-intensity physical activity for 60 minutes daily, five days a week.[3,4]

After reading Chapter 11, you will learn about the benefits of a physically active lifestyle, different cellular energy systems, and dietary practices that are appropriate for athletes and other physically active people. This chapter also provides practical tips for planning an exercise routine that you can follow for a lifetime.

Quiz YOURSELF

What is ATP? How much protein is needed for optimal muscular development? Are there any dietary supplements that can improve muscle strength and endurance safely? To test your nutrition and fitness knowledge, take the following quiz. The answers are on page 409.

1. People who exercise regularly can reduce their risk of type 2 diabetes. ______T ______F
2. Sports drinks are not useful for fluid replacement. ______T ______F
3. Protein is the body's preferred fuel for muscular activity. ______T ______F
4. Heatstroke is a serious illness that requires immediate professional medical treatment. ______T ______F
5. While at rest, skeletal muscles metabolize more glucose than fat for energy. ______T ______F

physical activity movement resulting from contraction of skeletal muscles

exercise physical activities that are usually planned and structured for a purpose

physical fitness ability to perform moderate- to vigorous-intensity activities without becoming excessively fatigued

Benefits of Regular Exercise

Millions of North Americans suffer from chronic illnesses that can be prevented or improved by exercising more often.[2] People who exercise regularly can substantially reduce their risks of serious chronic conditions, including cardiovascular disease (CVD), type 2 diabetes, hypertension, obesity, osteoporosis, and certain cancers.[2] As Figure 11.1 illustrates, you can gain physical as well as psychological benefits by performing moderate-intensity physical activity regularly. Furthermore, you may achieve even greater health benefits by increasing the duration, frequency, and intensity (physical effort) of your exercise routine.

Determining the Intensity of Physical Activity

Intensity refers to the level of exertion used to perform an activity. Duration and type of physical activity, as well as body weight, influence the intensity of skeletal muscle movement. Thus, activities such as walking and bicycling can be classified as either moderate- or vigorous-intensity physical activity depending on the rate at which the activities are performed as well as the weight of the person performing them. See Table 3.1 (p. 63) for examples of physical activities that are generally classified as moderate or vigorous intensity.

Figure 11.1 Benefits of being physically active. Regular physical activity improves health in several ways.

target heart rate zone heart rate range that reflects intensity of physical exertion

There are a few ways to determine the intensity of exercise. One way is to judge your level of exertion based on physical signs, such as breathing rate and sweat production. While exercising at the moderate-intensity level, you should be aware of your muscular effort, but you should also be able to chat with an exercise partner comfortably.

A popular method of estimating the intensity of exercise is to use a percentage of your *age-related maximum heart rate*. To calculate your age-related maximum heart rate, subtract your age from 226 (men) or 220 (women). Your **target heart rate zone** is the range of heart rate that reflects the intensity of your exertion during physical activity. For moderate-intensity physical activity, your target heart rate zone should be 50 to 70% of your age-related maximum heart rate.[5,6] To determine your moderate-intensity "zone," take your age-related maximum heart rate and multiply this figure by 0.50 and 0.70. For example, the age-related maximum heart rate of a 20-year-old woman is 200 beats per minute (220 minus 20). Multiply 200 beats per minute (bpm) by 0.50 to calculate the 50% value and multiply 200 bpm by 0.70 to obtain the 70% level. This woman's target heart rate zone for moderate-intensity activities is 100 to 140 bpm.

Moderate-intensity physical activities expend 3.5 to 7.0 kcal per minute.[7] To "burn" (*oxidize* or *metabolize*) more energy and give your heart a more vigorous workout, you can engage in physical activities that expend more than 7 kcal per minute.[7] Such physical activities usually require considerable muscular effort and result in significant increases in breathing rate and perspiration. Examples of vigorous physical activities include jogging, running, aerobic dancing, swimming laps, or bicycling uphill.

To exercise vigorously, your target heart rate should be 70 to 85% of your age-related maximum heart rate.[5,6] To calculate this range, follow the same formula that you used to determine the range for moderate-intensity activity, except you need to change "0.50 and 0.70" to "0.70 and 0.85." A 20-year-old woman, for example, would have an estimated maximum age-related heart rate of 200 bpm, and the 70 to 85% levels would range from 140 to 170 bpm. If you have any serious health problems, ask your physician to help you determine your target zone.

You can measure your heart rate (pulse) easily by finding the *radial artery* in your wrist. Locate the radial artery by gently placing your index and middle fingers on the underside of your wrist by the thumb as shown in Figure 11.2. Count your pulse for ten seconds, and then multiply that number by six to determine your heart rate for one minute. Your heart rate begins to decline as soon as you stop exercising, so you need to practise taking your pulse while still working out.

Figure 11.2 Finding the radial artery. To locate the radial artery, gently place your index and middle fingers on the underside of your wrist, by the thumb, as shown.

Physical Activity Guide

The Public Health Agency of Canada developed a physical activity guide to help people add more physical activity into their daily routines (Fig. 11.3).[2] This guide presents various activities that need to be performed regularly and provides practical suggestions for increasing the intensity of various routine activities. For example, you'll exert more physical effort and expend more energy if you use stairs instead of elevators or "jog" instead of "walk" the dog.

Low-intensity, unstructured and structured physical activities form the foundation of the physical activity guide. The physical activity guide stresses that the recommended physical activity does not have to be completed all at once. To begin, many Canadians choose to perform light physical activity for short periods of time, such as 10 to 15 minutes of walking or biking. As the level of physical fitness improves, Canadians may perform more strenuous activities or perform physical activity for a longer duration. **Aerobic exercise** involves sustained, rhythmic contractions of large muscle groups in the legs and arms. Such activities raise your heart rate, giving your heart a more effective workout. Running, jogging, rapid walking, and swimming are aerobic activities. Additionally, the physical activity guide recommends performing resistance and stretching exercises at least two times a week to increase muscle mass, strength, and flexibility. Resistance exercises, such as weightlifting, can also increase bone mass. The Chapter 11 Highlight provides information concerning how to design a more formal physical fitness plan.

aerobic exercise physical activities that involve sustained, rhythmic contractions of large muscle groups

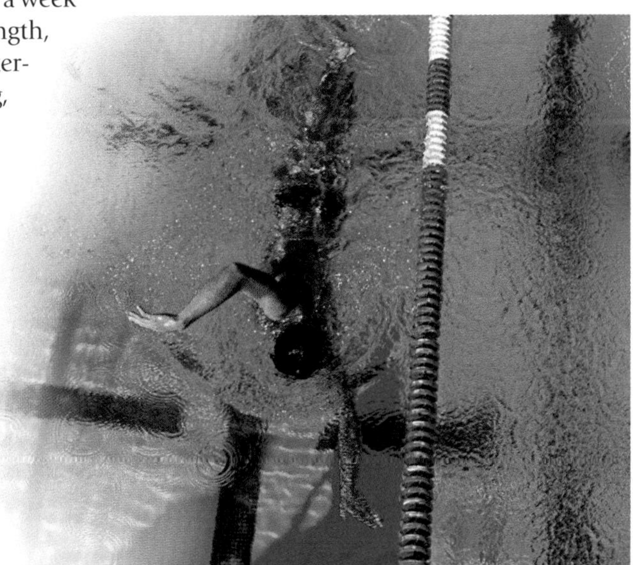

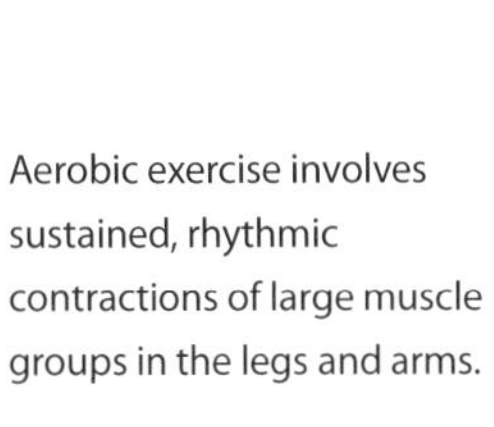

Aerobic exercise involves sustained, rhythmic contractions of large muscle groups in the legs and arms.

Figure 11.3 Physical activity guide. The Public Health Agency of Canada developed this guide to help Canadians include more physical activity into their daily routines.

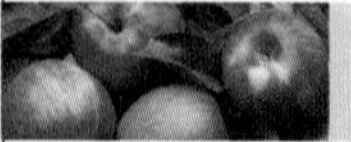

Concept Checkpoint

1. What is the difference between physical activity and exercise?
2. Define physical fitness.
3. List at least five health benefits of performing moderate-intensity exercise regularly.
4. To obtain some health benefits, what is the minimum amount of time an adult should spend engaging in exercise each day?
5. What are at least two benefits of performing resistance exercise regularly?
6. Calculate the target heart rate range for a 24-year-old person performing moderate-intensity physical activity.

Energy for Muscular Work

To move, muscles must contract, and to contract, muscles must have a source of energy. Under normal conditions, most cells, including muscle cells, metabolize a mixture of biological fuels, especially glucose and fatty acids. Muscle cells also metabolize a small amount of amino acids from proteins to obtain energy.[8]

Energy Metabolism

Cells obtain energy by means of a complex series of chemical reactions that progressively break down (*catabolize*) macronutrients and alcohol to release the energy stored within these compounds' chemical bonds. Cells lose much of this energy as heat, but they capture some of the energy in *high-energy compounds* such as **adenosine triphosphate (ATP)**. ATP forms when an *inorganic phosphate* group (P_i) bonds with **adenosine diphosphate (ADP)**; the chemical bond traps the energy (Fig. 11.4). Note in Figure 11.4 that ADP has two inorganic phosphate groups and ATP has three inorganic phosphate groups.

Glucose is the most useful biological fuel, because the simple sugar can be catabolized when free oxygen (O_2) is unavailable (**anaerobic**) or available (**aerobic**). Catabolic processes involve *oxidation*, the removal of electrons from compounds to create new compounds. During **glycolysis** (*glyco* = carbohydrate [particularly sugar]; *lysis* = breakdown), the first stage of glucose oxidation, glucose (a six-carbon molecule) is degraded to form two **pyruvate** molecules (three-carbon molecules) under anaerobic conditions (Fig. 11.5a). Glycolysis produces a small amount of ATP.

If oxygen is available, pyruvate undergoes further oxidation in a stepwise series of chemical pathways called *aerobic respiration*. Pyruvate moves from the fluid within cells (cytoplasm) into **mitochondria** (Fig. 11.5b). Mitochondria are often referred to as "powerhouses," because much of the energy stored in glucose or other biological fuels is released within these organelles. In mitochondria, pyruvate undergoes complete degradation, and as a result, cells generate more additional ATP than just that produced during glycolysis. Furthermore, carbon dioxide (CO_2) and ATP are produced. Oxygen is a key player in this phase of the process, because the element bonds to hydrogen atoms that were released from pyruvate, forming water (H_2O) (see Fig. 11.5b). When cells completely oxidize glucose to release the energy stored in its carbon-hydrogen bonds, the end products are simply CO_2 and H_2O. Most of the CO_2 is exhaled, and the H_2O produced metabolically can help maintain proper body water volume. Besides glucose, triglycerides (fat), amino acids, and alcohol are also sources energy for production of ATP. Figure 11.6 summarizes the pathways that dietary protein, carbohydrate, and fat follow during energy metabolism. For more detailed illustrations of the metabolic pathways that biological fuels undergo, see Appendix D.

adenosine triphosphate (ATP) high-energy compound, major direct energy source for cells

adenosine diphosphate (ADP) high-energy compound, by-product of ATP use

anaerobic conditions that lack free oxygen

aerobic conditions that require free oxygen

glycolysis first stage of glucose oxidation

pyruvate compound that results from anaerobic breakdown of glucose

mitochondria organelles that generate ATP from macronutrients

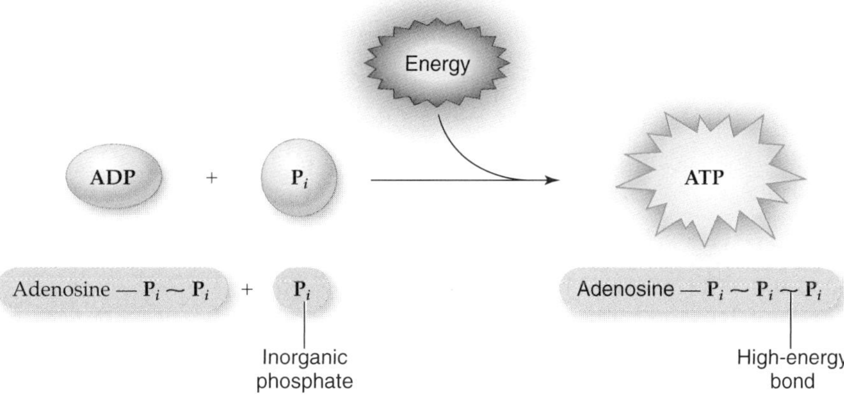

Figure 11.4 **ATP.** Cells capture and store energy by forming ATP from ADP and inorganic phosphate (P_i).

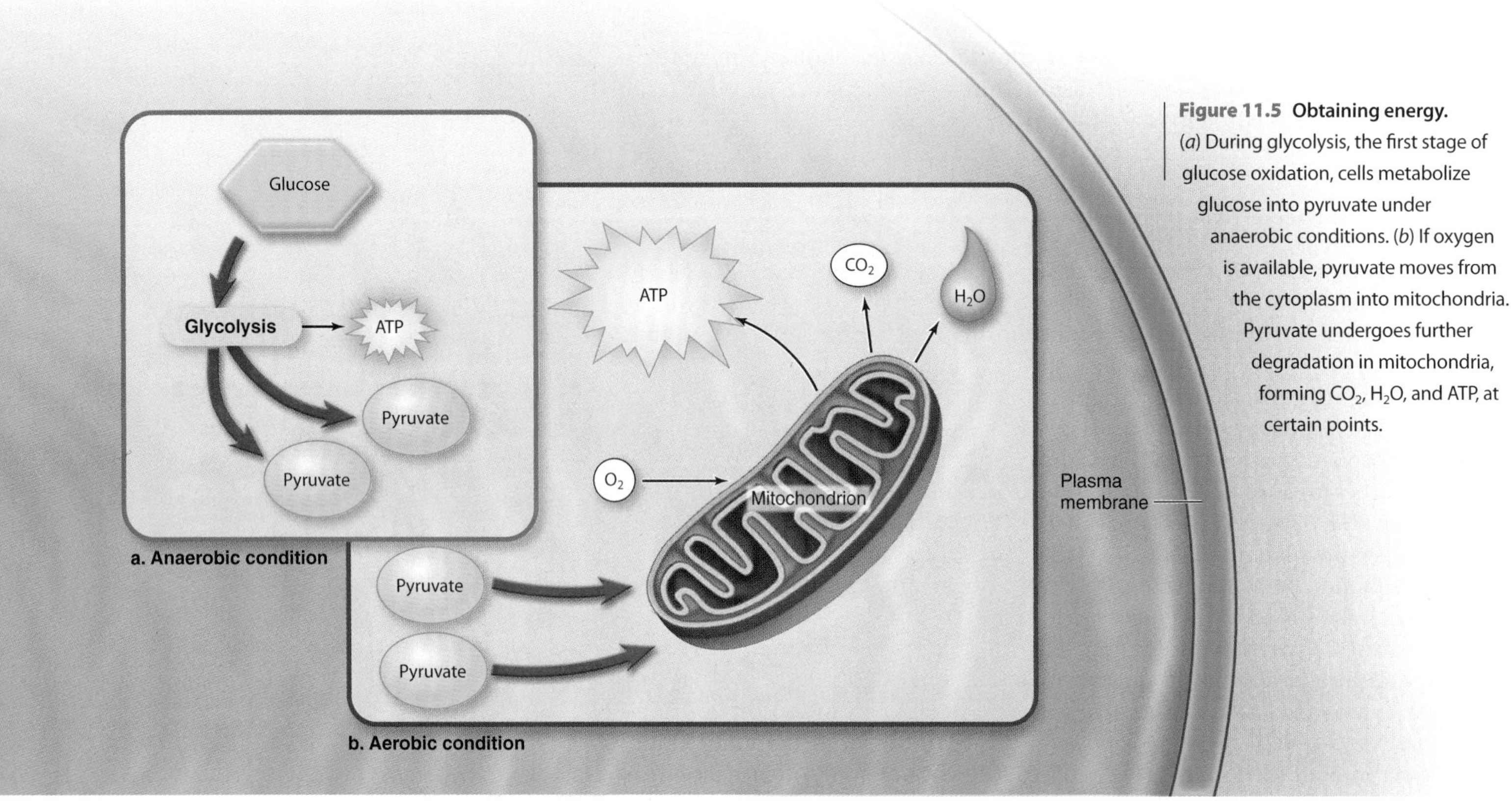

Figure 11.5 Obtaining energy. (*a*) During glycolysis, the first stage of glucose oxidation, cells metabolize glucose into pyruvate under anaerobic conditions. (*b*) If oxygen is available, pyruvate moves from the cytoplasm into mitochondria. Pyruvate undergoes further degradation in mitochondria, forming CO_2, H_2O, and ATP, at certain points.

Did You Know?

Human cells can convert certain amino acids into glucose, but the cells are unable to make glucose from fatty acids.

How Do Cells Use ATP?

ATP is the primary source of direct energy for all cells. ATP is often referred to as "energy currency," because it functions like money. Just as you save money until it is needed to make a purchase, your cells save energy in ATP until it is needed to power cellular work.

When a cell needs some energy to drive a chemical reaction, it uses an enzyme to break the bond between the last two phosphate groups of ATP (Fig. 11.7). This process releases the energy stored in the bond (*ATP-energy*) and reforms ADP and P_i. Thus, cells can recycle their supplies of ADP and P_i. Cells do not store much ATP, so they must constantly replace their supply of the high-energy compound by recycling ADP and P_i.

Energy Systems for Exercising Muscles

Gram for gram, fat supplies more energy than carbohydrate. Fatty acids, however, are not a very useful fuel for intense, brief exercise, such as a 100-metre sprint. Why? A fatty acid molecule is metabolized aerobically, while brief intense activity such as sprinting is an

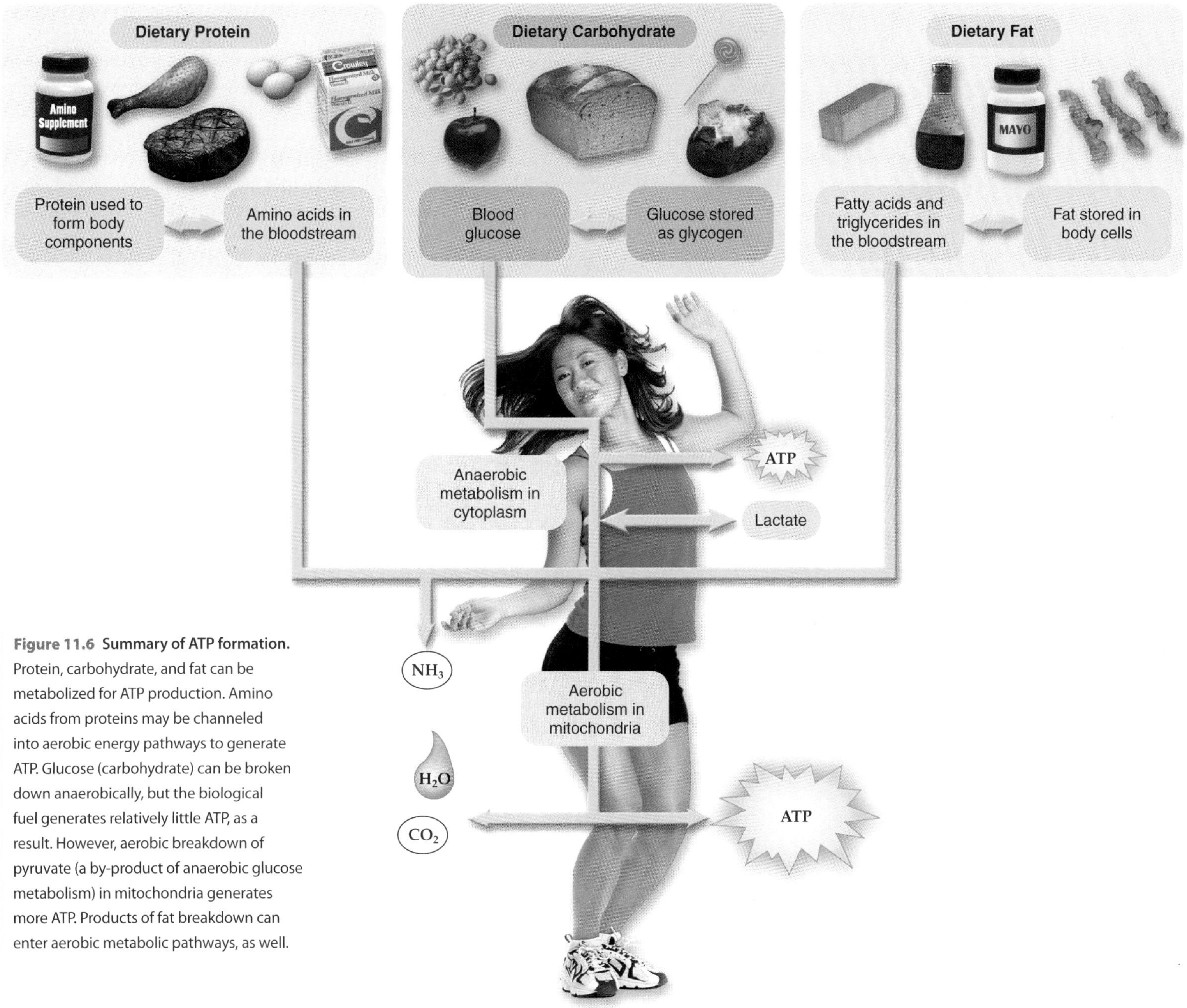

Dietary Protein
Amino Supplement
Protein used to form body components
Amino acids in the bloodstream
Dietary Carbohydrate
Blood glucose
Glucose stored as glycogen
Dietary Fat
MAYO
Fatty acids and triglycerides in the bloodstream
Fat stored in body cells
ATP
Anaerobic metabolism in cytoplasm
Lactate
NH3
Aerobic metabolism in mitochondria
H2O
CO2
ATP

Figure 11.6 Summary of ATP formation. Protein, carbohydrate, and fat can be metabolized for ATP production. Amino acids from proteins may be channeled into aerobic energy pathways to generate ATP. Glucose (carbohydrate) can be broken down anaerobically, but the biological fuel generates relatively little ATP, as a result. However, aerobic breakdown of pyruvate (a by-product of anaerobic glucose metabolism) in mitochondria generates more ATP. Products of fat breakdown can enter aerobic metabolic pathways, as well.

Energy to perform cellular functions
ATP
ADP + Pi
Adenosine — Pi ~ Pi ~ Pi
Adenosine — Pi ~ Pi + Pi

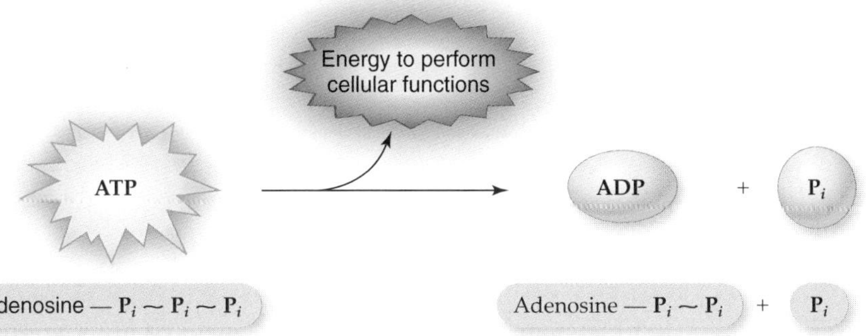

Figure 11.7 Energy from ATP. When a cell needs energy to drive a chemical reaction, it uses an enzyme to break the bond between the last two phosphate groups of ATP, releasing the energy stored in the bond and reforming ADP and Pi.

During a brief bout of intense anaerobic exercise, glucose is a major source of energy for working muscles.

anaerobic activity. Thus, cells need more oxygen to metabolize a fatty acid molecule than to burn a glucose molecule. During a brief bout of intense exercise, the heart and lungs do not have enough time to deliver much oxygen to muscles. Under these conditions, glucose is a major source of energy. For physical activities that last longer and are less intense, muscles can use more fat for energy, because the lungs are able to supply them with enough oxygen.

Muscle cells rely on three major systems to obtain energy—the *PCr-ATP, lactic acid,* and *oxygen systems.* The PCr-ATP and lactic acid systems do not need oxygen to produce ATP. Thus, these systems metabolize glucose under anaerobic conditions, such as when a person holds his or her breath while sprinting or lifting a heavy load. As the duration of the activity increases, muscle cells need to form considerably more ATP. To meet this demand, muscle cells depend heavily on the oxygen system to metabolize glucose and fat.

The three energy-releasing systems do not function independently of each other during intense physical exertion—each contributes ATP-energy to power intense muscular activity.[9] The following sections provide more information about these major energy systems.

PCr-ATP Energy System

A resting muscle cell contains only a small amount of ATP that can be used immediately. This amount of ATP is enough to contract a muscle maximally for only about one second.[10] Muscle cells have another type of high-energy compound—**phosphocreatine (PCr)**—that enables the cells to produce more ATP quickly under anaerobic conditions. To make the ATP, cells break down PCr into *creatine* and P_i, releasing energy to form ATP from ADP and P_i (Fig. 11.8a). Cells do not use PCr directly to power their activities; the compound provides the energy to resupply ATP.

By breaking down PCr to form ATP, muscle cells can obtain enough energy to function during intense events lasting about six seconds.[11] However, the PCr-ATP system can be activated instantly, replenishing ATP fast enough to meet the energy demands of the swiftest and most powerful muscle movements, such as jumping, lifting, throwing, and sprinting. When the intense activity stops and there is no need to maintain high levels of ATP, an inorganic phosphate group bonds with creatine to recycle PCr (see Fig. 11.8b). Muscle cells, however, do not make or store much PCr.

phosphocreatine (PCr) high-energy compound used to reform ATP under anaerobic conditions

lactic acid compound formed from pyruvate during anaerobic metabolism

Lactic Acid Energy System

When physical activity lasts longer than a few seconds, the PCr-ATP energy system cannot keep up with the demand for energy, and muscle cells must metabolize glucose to generate more ATP. The immediate source of glucose for working muscles is glycogen that is stored within the muscles.[12] The liver also helps supply glucose for muscles by degrading glycogen and releasing glucose molecules into the bloodstream.

In anaerobic conditions, muscle cells metabolize glucose to pyruvate and then convert pyruvate to **lactic acid** (Fig. 11.9a). The degradation of glucose to lactic acid produces a small amount of ATP—only enough to sustain vigorous physical exertion for 30 to 40 seconds.[11] Lactic acid accumulates in muscles and converts to a related substance, *lactate*. Although certain muscle cells can use lactate as a fuel, some of the compound enters the bloodstream (Fig. 11.9b). The liver removes lactate from blood and can convert the compound into glucose (Fig. 11.9c). The liver may then release the glucose into the bloodstream to help meet muscles' demand for fuel, or use the simple sugar to make glycogen (Fig. 11.9d).

Hydrogen ions (H^+) form as a result of the conversion of lactic acid to lactate. The accumulation of H^+ in muscle tissue contributes to muscle acidity, a condition that can lead to muscle fatigue and declining physical performance.

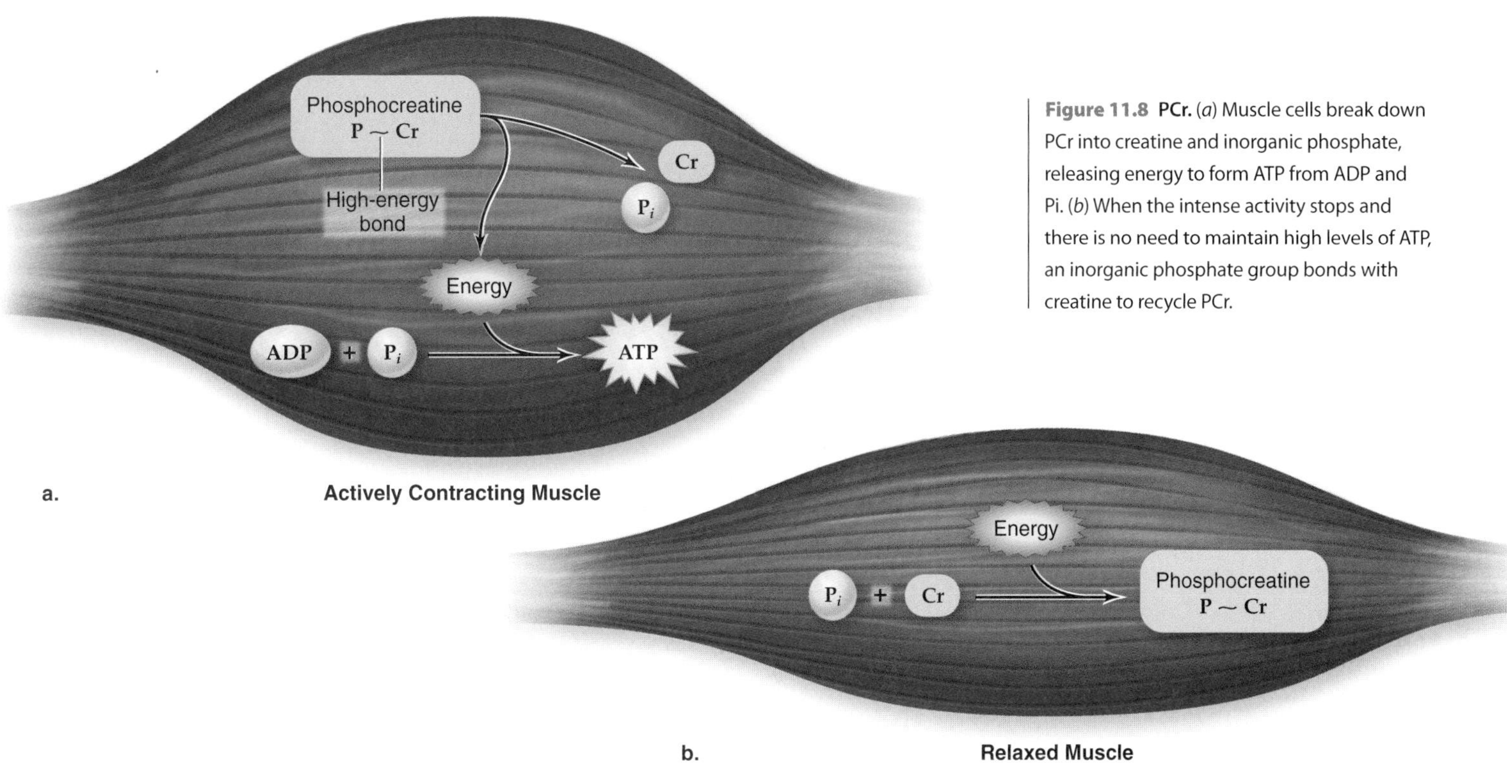

Figure 11.8 PCr. (*a*) Muscle cells break down PCr into creatine and inorganic phosphate, releasing energy to form ATP from ADP and Pi. (*b*) When the intense activity stops and there is no need to maintain high levels of ATP, an inorganic phosphate group bonds with creatine to recycle PCr.

Figure 11.9 Lactic acid. (*a*) In anaerobic conditions, muscle cells rapidly metabolize glucose to pyruvate and then to lactate. (*b*) Lactate enters the bloodstream. (*c*) The liver can remove lactate from blood, convert it into glucose, and release the simple sugar into the bloodstream, if the fuel is needed. (*d*) If the body does not need the energy, the liver converts glucose to glycogen.

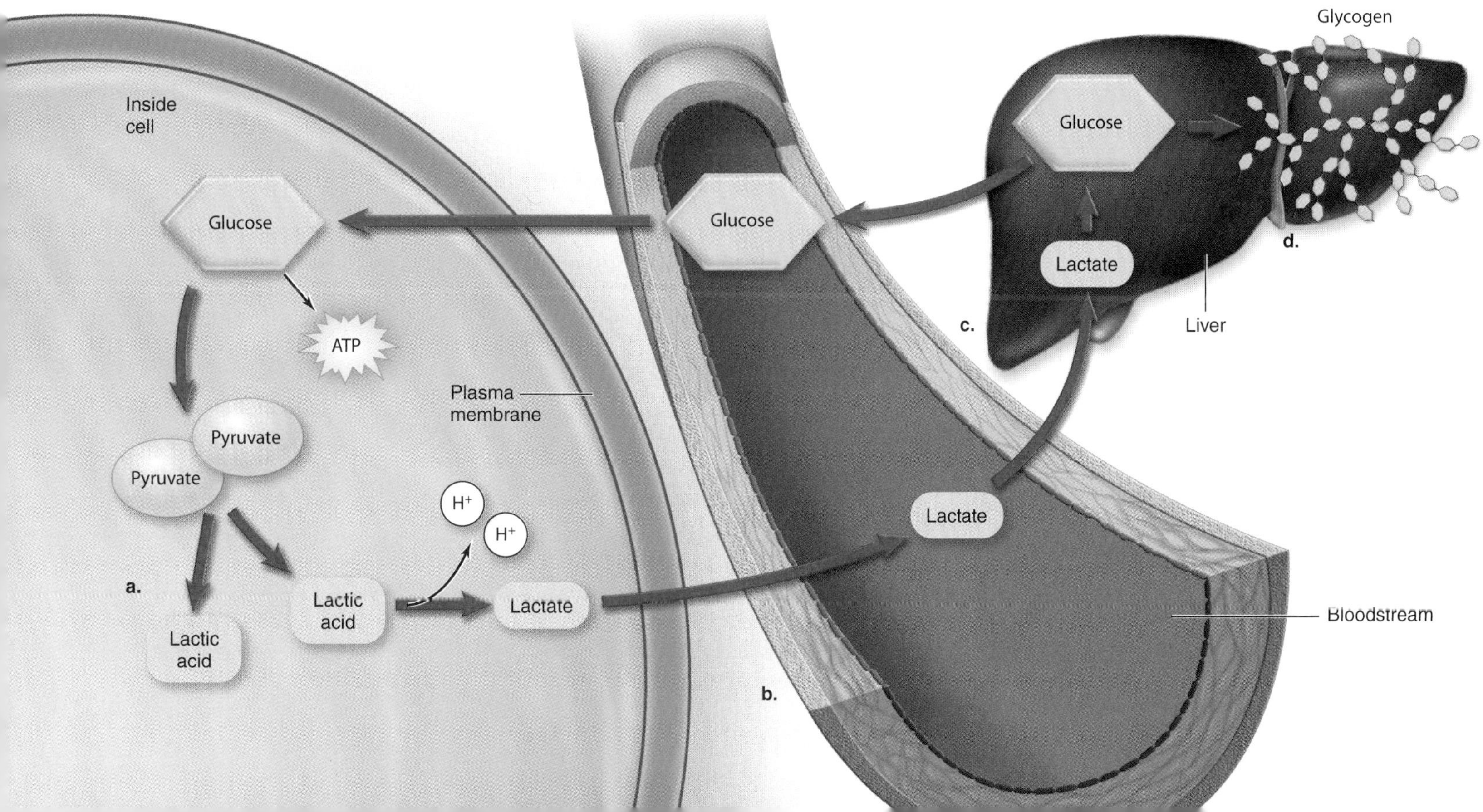

Even well-trained athletes experience muscle fatigue as the time they spend performing intense muscular exertion increases. This marathon runner collapsed as she crossed the finish line of the 28th Annual U.S. Marine Corps Marathon. Photo: LCPL Richard A. Burkdall, USMC.

Oxygen Energy System

You would not be able to enjoy activities such as walking at a fast pace, swimming laps, playing a game of soccer or basketball, as well as other continuous types of physical activity, if your muscles depended only on the anaerobic energy systems. When muscle cells have plenty of oxygen, such as during low- to moderate-intensity exercise, they can metabolize glucose completely to CO_2 and H_2O. In fact, the availability of oxygen enables cells to produce about 18 times more ATP-energy than the amount produced by anaerobic systems. The ability to obtain this amount of energy is useful for endurance athletes, because it allows their muscle cells to contract repeatedly for hours.

Aerobic Capacity The ability of your heart and lungs (sometimes referred to as the *cardiorespiratory system*) to deliver oxygen to muscles determines your capacity for intense aerobic physical activity. Scientists can use special equipment to estimate maximal oxygen intake (*aerobic capacity* or *VO_2max*) during vigorous physical exertion. A simple way to determine if you are nearing your aerobic capacity is to engage in vigorous exercise and note when your breathing rate increases to the point that you cannot carry on a conversation.

You can increase your aerobic exercise capacity by engaging in an endurance training program that gradually increases the intensity level of activities. Such training improves your muscle cells' ability to generate ATP rapidly.[13] However, even highly trained athletes experience muscle fatigue after increasing the time they usually spend performing intense muscular exertion.

Did You Know?

As people grow older, their aerobic capacities decline with each passing decade. By being physically active, however, even elderly persons can maintain a higher degree of aerobic capacity than their sedentary counterparts. It's never too late to begin a training program to improve physical fitness. If you have existing health problems, you should have a complete medical checkup and obtain your physician's "OK" before beginning a moderate-intensity fitness program.

TABLE 11.1 *Energy Sources for Muscles**

Source/System	When in Use	Examples of Activities
ATP	At all times	All types
Phosphocreatine (PCr)	All exercise initially; short bursts of exercise thereafter	Shot put, high jump
Carbohydrate		
Anaerobic	High-intensity exercise, especially lasting 30 seconds to 2 minutes	200-metre sprint
Aerobic	Exercise lasting 2 minutes to 3 hours or more; the higher the intensity of exercise, the greater the use	Basketball, swimming, jogging
Fat	At rest	Sitting
	Exercise lasting more than a few minutes; low- to moderate-intensity physical activities	30-minute brisk walk
Protein	Low amounts during all exercise, slightly more during endurance exercise, especially when carbohydrate fuel is lacking	Long-distance running

* Note that at any given time, more than one energy system is operating.

Source: Adapted from Wardlaw GM, Smith AM: *Contemporary nutrition*. 6th ed. New York: McGraw-Hill, 2006.

Fat or Carbohydrate for Fuelling Exercise?

The intensity of a physical activity largely influences the relative amounts of fatty acids and glucose that muscles metabolize for energy.[14,15] Glucose supplies only about 40% of the energy needed to sustain a person who is resting or engaged in very light to light activities, such as watching TV, typing, and walking. Fat is the primary fuel muscles use while resting or engaged in low- to moderate-intensity physical activities.[14] During high-intensity exercise, the rate of fat oxidation decreases while glucose oxidation increases.[16] Table 11.1 presents various energy sources for resting and contracting muscles.

An individual's level of training influences the ratio of glucose to fatty acids that his or her muscles use during exercise. Trained endurance athletes tend to oxidize more fat when exercising at the same intensity than untrained persons.[17,18] As a result, muscle cells of trained athletes "spare" glycogen, that is, they conserve their supply of glucose.[15] By sparing their glycogen supplies, athletes can enhance their capacity to exercise longer.

Concept Checkpoint

7. How is glycogen used during exercise?
8. How is ATP formed? How do cells use ATP?
9. Explain how each energy system supplies ATP for muscles. Which energy systems operate under anaerobic conditions?
10. How can you improve your aerobic capacity?
11. When is fat a major source of energy for muscles?

General Dietary Advice for Athletes

Athletes often manipulate their diets to lose or gain weight, increase their muscular strength, and prevent or delay fatigue during exercise. Although an athlete's diet plays a major role in determining if he or she finishes first or last in a competitive event, *genetic*

genetic endowment inherited physical characteristics that can affect physical performance

endowment and *physical training* are the most crucial factors that influence athletic performance.[10] **Genetic endowment** refers to inherited physical characteristics that can affect an athlete's physical performance, such as body size, shape, and composition. Regardless of how well an athlete eats, if this person lacks the physical traits that are necessary for success in his or her chosen sport, the athlete will find it difficult to compete effectively. Athletes must also be highly motivated to compete and engage in a well-designed intensive training program to maximize their physical capabilities. Nevertheless, optimizing an athlete's diet may provide a competitive advantage, especially for sporting events in which hundredths of a second can mean the difference between finishing in first or second place.

Athletes and coaches often believe misinformation concerning the value of dietary supplements, certain foods, and fad diets for optimizing physical health and performance. Such beliefs can lead to diet-related practices that are useless and a waste of money. In some cases, however, these practices are harmful, or even deadly.

Sports nutrition focuses on applying nutrition principles and research findings to improving athletic performance. This section of Chapter 11 provides specific dietary recommendations that are appropriate for athletes and other physically active people. If you would like additional information on sports nutrition, contact a registered dietitian. Other reliable sources of sports nutrition include the Web sites of the Coaching Association of Canada (www.coach.ca), the American College of Sports Medicine (www.acsm.org), and the Centers for Disease Control and Prevention (www.cdc.gov/nccdphp/dnpa). If you are interested in studying sports nutrition, check with your academic advisor to determine whether your college or university offers sports nutrition courses.

Optimizing an athlete's diet may provide a competitive advantage.

Energy for Athletic Performance

Compared to non-athletes, athletes generally need more energy to support their physically active lifestyles.[19] Male athletes who train or compete aerobically for more than 90 minutes daily need at least 50 kcal per kilogram of body weight per day (kcal/kg/day); their female counterparts need 45 to 50 kcal/kg/day.[20] Thus, athletes may require 3000 kcal per day or more to support their energy needs and maintain their weight. Table 11.2 presents three sample daily menus that are nutritionally adequate; supply approximately 3000, 4000, and 5000 kcal per day; and provide ample amounts of carbohydrate. Chapter 3 provides general information to help you plan nutritious menus.

How can athletes tell if they are consuming enough energy? One way is to have them keep accurate food records and use the information to estimate their daily calorie intakes. Athletes can also monitor their body weights and have their skinfold thicknesses measured regularly. If their weights were within the healthy BMI range before training and they start to lose weight during training, the individuals should consume more food until they regain their pre-training weights. Consuming an additional 500 to 700 kcal per day, especially by eating calorie- and nutrient-dense foods such as nuts and dried fruit, is a healthy way for anyone to boost his or her calorie intake. Athletes who gain too much body fat can increase their energy output by spending more time in training. Overfat athletes can also reduce their food intake by about 200 to 500 kcal per day, until they are in the healthy body mass index (BMI) range. In general, a good way to reduce energy intake is to limit portions of fatty foods.

For most physically active people, fat should supply 20 to 35% of energy, which is within the range recommended for the general population.[21,22] Trained endurance athletes may adapt to long-term, very-high-fat diets (65% or more of total energy) without harming their performance.[22,23] Nevertheless, the bulk of scientific evidence does not support the use of high-fat diets for athletes.[19] Furthermore, very-low-fat diets (< 15% of total energy from fat) are not recommended for healthy, physically active people. Not only are very low-fat diets difficult to follow for the long term, such diets may also be harmful.[19,24]

TABLE 11.2 *Sample Daily 3000, 4000, and 5000 kcal Menus*

3000 kcal	4000 kcal	5000 kcal
65% carbohydrate	66% carbohydrate	66% carbohydrate
21% fat	23% fat	22% fat
17% protein	14% protein	15% protein
Breakfast	**Breakfast**	**Breakfast**
Skim milk, 250 mL (1 cup)	Skim milk, 250 mL (1 cup)	Skim milk, 250 mL (1 cup)
Cheerios, 500 mL (2 cups)	Cheerios, 500 mL (2 cups)	Cheerios, 500 mL (2 cups)
Bagel, 1	Bran muffins, 2	Bran muffins, 2
Cherry preserves, 5 mL (1 tsp)	Orange, 1	Orange, 1
Oat bran muffin, 1		
Low-fat cream cheese, 15 mL (1 Tbsp)		
Snack	**Snack**	**Snack**
Oatmeal-raisin cookies, 2	Chopped dates, 187 mL (¾ cup)	Low-fat plain yogourt, 250 mL (1 cup)
		Chopped dates, 250 mL (1 cup)
Lunch	**Lunch**	**Lunch**
Chicken breast, skinless roasted, 55 g (2 oz.)	Macaroni & cheese, 625 mL (2½ cups)	Chicken enchilada, 1
Whole-wheat bread, 2 slices	Romaine lettuce, 250 mL (1 cup)	Romaine lettuce, 250 mL (1 cup)
Provolone cheese, 28 g (1 oz.)	Garbanzo beans, 250 mL (1 cup)	Garbanzo beans, 250 mL (1 cup)
Mayonnaise, 5 mL (1 tsp)	Grated carrots, 125 mL (½ cup)	Shredded carrots, 187 mL (¾ cup)
Raisins, 325 mL (1⅓ cup)	French dressing, 30 mL (2 Tbsp)	Chopped celery, 125 mL (½ cup)
Cranberry juice, 375 mL (1½ cups)	Apple juice, 250 mL (1 cup)	Seasoned croutons, 28 g (1 oz.)
Low-fat vanilla yogourt, 250 mL (1 cup)		French dressing, 30 mL (2 Tbsp)
		Whole-wheat bread, 2 slices
		Soft margarine, 15 mL (1 Tbsp)
Snack	**Snack**	**Snack**
Banana, 1	Whole-wheat bread, 2 slices	Banana, 1
Oatmeal-raisin cookie, 1	Margarine, 5 mL (1 tsp)	Bagel, 1
	Grape jelly, 30 mL (2 Tbsp)	Cream cheese, 15 mL (1 Tbsp)
Dinner	**Dinner**	**Dinner**
Lean broiled beef, sirloin, 75 g (3 oz.)	Skinless, roasted turkey breast, 50 g (2 oz.)	Lean broiled beef, sirloin, 125 g (5 oz.)
Romaine lettuce, 250 mL (1 cup)	Mashed potatoes, 500 mL (2 cups)	Mashed potatoes, 500 mL (2 cups)
Garbanzo beans, 250 mL (1 cup)	Peas and onions, 250 mL (1 cup)	Soft margarine, 10 mL (2 tsp)
Italian dressing, 30 mL (2 Tbsp)	Soft margarine, 10 mL (2 tsp)	Spinach egg noodles, 375 mL (1½ cups) cooked
Spinach egg noodles, 375 mL (1½ cups) cooked	Mango, 1	Grated parmesan cheese, 30 mL (2 Tbsp)
Soft margarine, 5 mL (1 tsp)	Skim milk, 250 (1 cup)	Green beans, 250 mL (1 cup)
Green beans, 250 mL (1 cup)		Oatmeal-raisin cookies, 3
Skim milk, 125 mL (½ cup)		
	Snack	**Snack**
	Pasta, 250 mL (1 cup) cooked	Air-popped popcorn, 500 mL (2 cups)
	Parmesan cheese, 50 g (2 oz.)	Raisins, 83 mL (⅓ cup)
	Cranberry juice, 250 mL (1 cup)	Cranberry juice, 500 mL (2 cups)

Source: Adapted from Wardlaw GM, Hampl JS: *Perspectives in nutrition*. New York: McGraw-Hill, 2007.

Focusing on Carbohydrate Intake

Recommended diets for athletes supply 60% or more of energy from carbohydrates. To maintain adequate muscle glycogen, athletes should consume 6 to 10 grams of carbohydrate per kilogram of body weight daily.[19] Glycogen depletion is a major cause of fatigue during endurance exercise. By consuming several servings of grains, starchy vegetables, and fruits daily, an athlete can obtain enough carbohydrate to maintain adequate liver and muscle glycogen stores.

To calculate your recommended range of carbohydrate intake, multiply your weight in kilograms by 6 and then by 10. For example, a 66-kg (145-lb.) female athlete should consume between 396 and 660 g of carbohydrate each day. If she requires 3000 kcal per day to maintain her weight and physical activity level, and she consumes 60% of her energy from carbohydrates, she will obtain about 450 g of carbohydrate, which is within the recommended range.

It is important to keep in mind that there is no "one size fits all" diet plan that specifies amounts of carbohydrate-rich foods for pre-event, event, or post-event meals and snacks. Diets for athletes should be individualized and based on factors such as the athlete's sex, body size and weight, sport and training level, and exposure to environmental conditions, as well as personal experiences and food preferences. Furthermore, athletes should test any dietary strategies during practices or trials—several days or weeks before a competitive event.

Pre-Event Meals and Snacks

About two to four hours before an endurance activity, athletes can eat a low-fat meal that supplies at least 100 g of carbohydrate, because such meals may increase the athletes' exercise capacity.[25] Eating fatty foods such as sausage, bacon, sauces, and gravies is not recommended because they take longer to digest than low-fat foods.[10] Although some nutritionists advise athletes to exclude high-fibre foods from pre-event meals, there is a lack of scientific evidence to support this recommendation. Nevertheless, athletes can have different responses to eating high-fibre diets prior to events; individuals who react negatively may find it necessary to avoid eating high-fibre foods until after competing. Table 11.3 provides some menu ideas for high-carbohydrate, low-fat pre-event meals that supply 500 to 600 kcal and approximately 100 g of carbohydrate.

The longer the period before the start of an event, the larger the meal can be, because there will be more time for the stomach to empty and some digestion to occur prior to the activity. Many athletes, however, are anxious before competing and may experience nausea and vomiting if they eat at this time. Other athletes feel comfortable consuming a high-carbohydrate, low-fat meal or snack prior to an event.

TABLE 11.3 *High-Carbohydrate, Low-Fat Pre-Event Meals*

Meal A	Meal B	Meal C
Instant oatmeal, cooked, 1 packet	Yogourt, strawberry, low-fat, 250 mL (1 cup)	Cornflakes, ready-to-eat cereal, 187 mL (¾ cup)
Fresh peaches, sliced, 125 mL (½ cup)	Bagel, whole, 4" diam.	Skim milk, 250 mL (1 cup)
Orange juice, 250 mL (1 cup)	Mayonnaise-type salad dressing, skim, 10 mL (2 tsp)	Orange juice, 125 mL (½ cup)
Toast, 1 slice	Roasted turkey breast, 28 g (1 oz.)	Toast, 2 slices
Jelly, 5 mL (1 tsp)		Soft margarine, 5 mL (1 tsp)
Skim milk, 250 mL (1 cup)		Jelly, 10 mL (2 tsp)

TABLE 11.4 *Energy and Macronutrient Contents of Selected Foods*

Food and Amount	kcal	Carbohydrate (g)	Protein (g)	Fat (g)
Macaroni, plain, cooked, 250 mL (1 cup)	221	43.20	8.12	1.30
Spaghetti, cooked, 250 mL (1 cup)	220	42.83	8.12	1.30
Rice, instant, white, cooked, 250 mL (1 cup)	194	41.16	4.60	0.58
Egg noodles, cooked, 250 mL (1 cup)	221	40.26	7.26	3.31
Baked potato, ½ large	139	31.62	3.74	0.19
Corn, canned, drained, 250 mL (1 cup)	133	30.49	4.30	1.64
Bagel, ½, 4" diam.	144	28.04	5.51	0.84
Grapes, 250 mL (1 cup)	104	27.33	1.09	0.24
Banana, 1 med. (approx. 7" long)	105	26.95	1.29	0.39
Baked beans, 125 mL (½ cup)	119	26.85	6.03	0.47
Crackers, 6 rectangular saltines	154	25.53	3.32	4.09
Orange juice, unsweetened, 250 mL (1 cup)	110	25.05	1.99	0.69
Cornflakes, 250 mL (1 cup)	101	24.28	1.88	0.03
Pretzels, 28 grams (1 oz.)	108	22.61	2.93	0.75
Cooked oatmeal, plain, 250 mL (1 cup)	129	22.44	5.43	2.13
Apple, 1 med. (approx. 3" diam.)	72	19.06	0.36	0.23
Yogourt, low-fat, plain, 250 mL (1 cup)	154	17.25	17.86	3.80
English muffin, ½	67	13.11	2.53	0.51
Bread, white, 1 slice	66	12.65	2.19	0.82
Skim milk, 250 mL (1 cup)	83	12.15	8.26	0.20
Tortilla, corn, ready-to-cook, 6" diam. (1)	58	12.12	1.48	0.65
Soy milk, 250 mL (1 cup)	127	12.08	10.98	4.70

Source: USDA: *USDA national nutrient database for standard reference*, release 19, 2006. www.nal.usda.gov/fnic/foodcomp/search/.

carbohydrate loading practice of manipulating physical activity and dietary patterns to increase muscle glycogen stores

High-carbohydrate, low-fat food choices for pre-event meals or snacks include cereal with skim milk, bagels, dried fruit, pretzels and a sports drink, cooked oatmeal with fruit, baked potato topped with yogourt, and toasted bread with jam. Table 11.4 presents commonly eaten foods that are high in carbohydrate and relatively low in fat. Food eaten about an hour before competing should be blended or liquid to promote rapid stomach emptying. Examples of such foods are low-fat smoothies or liquid meal-replacement formulas, such as "instant breakfast" products.

What Is Carbohydrate Loading? A healthy person stores about 6 g of glycogen per kilogram of body weight. Therefore, an individual who weighs 75 kg (165 lbs.) stores about 450 g of glycogen. This amount of glycogen supplies 1800 kcal, which is enough energy to enable the person to bicycle at 21 km/hr (13 mph) for about 4 hours and 15 minutes. Endurance athletes who have more muscle glycogen at the start of an event may be able to exercise longer than those who do not have as much muscle glycogen. **Carbohydrate loading** involves manipulating dietary and physical activity patterns, a few days before an event, to increase muscle glycogen stores well above the normal range.[26,27,28]

According to one type of carbohydrate loading technique, an athlete trains intensely seven days before competing. Over the next three days, the person gradually reduces the duration of his or her daily aerobic workouts (tapering) and during this period, the athlete eats a mixed diet that contains moderate amounts of carbohydrate (about 300 g/day). During the next three days, the athlete can exercise lightly or rest.

About two to four hours before an endurance event, athletes can eat a low-fat meal that supplies at least 100 g of carbohydrate, such as a bowl of cornflakes, fruit, milk, toast, and juice.

The athlete also switches from a moderate-carbohydrate to a high-carbohydrate diet—one that supplies 400 to 700 g of carbohydrate per day.[10]

About 3 g of water are incorporated into muscle tissue along with each gram of glycogen. Thus, carbohydrate loading adds water to muscles. Although this fluid aids in maintaining proper hydration status, some individuals experience muscle stiffness and unwanted weight gain as a result of carbohydrate loading. Athletes who would like to determine whether a carbohydrate-loading regimen helps their performance should try the regimen during training to experience its effects. Rather than promote carbohydrate loading, many nutrition and human performance experts simply recommend that athletes routinely follow a high-carbohydrate diet and consume certain forms of carbohydrate during prolonged exercise.

Consuming Carbohydrate during Events

When athletes exercise vigorously for longer than 60 minutes, their glycogen supplies become depleted. At this point, athletes report they have "hit the wall," that is, they feel unable to maintain a competitive pace. While performing prolonged physical activity, athletes can delay reaching "the wall" by consuming 30 to 60 g of carbohydrate per hour of activity.[19]

Sports drinks are a convenient way to obtain a source of glucose during lengthy and vigorous physical activities. Commercially available sports drinks are usually sweetened with nutritive sweeteners such as sucrose, glucose, fructose, or maltodextrin. Such beverages typically provide 15 to 27 g of carbohydrate per 355-mL (12-oz.) serving. Foods or drinks that are concentrated sources of fructose are not recommended, because large amounts of this particular simple sugar may cause gastrointestinal upset. In addition to supplying carbohydrate, sports drinks contain water and electrolytes, such as sodium, that can benefit athletes during prolonged physical effort. Sports gels are also good sources of simple carbohydrate, but they generally supply very little fluid. Therefore, it is important for athletes who consume these products to drink enough water to maintain proper hydration during endurance events.

Consuming Carbohydrates during Exercise Recovery

During a post-event meal, starchy foods, such as pasta, can be served to boost an athlete's carbohydrate consumption.

After completing exhaustive physical activity, trained athletes can replenish nearly all of their glycogen stores within a few days, provided they rest and eat a high-carbohydrate diet. During a post-event meal, starchy foods such as whole-grain bread, mashed potatoes, pasta, and rice can be served to boost athletes' carbohydrate consumption. Athletes who train intensely each day need to consume 8 to 10 g of carbohydrate per kilogram of body weight to replenish their muscle glycogen stores.[10] To restore their supply of muscle glycogen quickly after an event, athletes can consume sports drinks, candy, sugar-sweetened soft drinks, and fruit or fruit juices.

What about Protein?

One of the most controversial topics in nutrition is the amount of protein needed to support athletic performance. Many athletes are convinced that consuming ample amounts of protein from animal foods and taking protein or amino acid supplements is necessary to improve their physical performance and body build. The adult RDA for protein is 0.8 g per kilogram of body weight.[29,30] A review of the nutritional practices of elite athletes indicated that individuals training for aerobic sports consumed 1.1 to 3.0 g of protein per kilogram of body weight per day, whereas those training for anaerobic sports, such as weightlifting, consumed 1.1 to 3.2 protein per kilogram of body weight per day.[20] Are such high protein intakes recommended or even necessary?

Under normal conditions, carbohydrate and fat are the primary fuels for cellular activity, and protein provides no more than 15% of the body's energy needs. Thus, protein is not a major biological fuel. During prolonged physical activity, muscles lose some protein because they metabolize certain amino acids for energy.[31] To spare protein so that the nutrient can be used for muscle tissue growth and repair instead of for energy, it is very important for physically active people to consume adequate amounts of carbohydrate and fat.

After strenuous exercise, muscle cells repair damaged muscle tissue by using available amino acids to synthesize new proteins. Thus, having adequate amounts of amino acids in muscle tissue promotes positive nitrogen balance after exercise.[32,33] After engaging in intense physical activity, athletes may be able to enhance protein synthesis in their muscles by eating protein-rich foods.[31,34,35] Compared to non-athletes, however, the typical athlete consumes more food to meet his or her increased energy needs, and as a result, obtains plenty of dietary protein.[35] Therefore, healthy active Canadians who eat varied diets that supply adequate energy do not need to take protein or amino acid supplements.[22] If people consume excess protein from foods or supplements and they do not need the energy, the amino acids in these proteins will not be used for building or repairing muscles. Instead, the body converts the extra amino acids into fat for storage in adipose tissue.

Protein: Recommendations for Athletes

Despite conventional wisdom that athletes have higher protein requirements than non-athletes, there are no specific protein RDAs for endurance or resistance athletes. Members of the National Academy of Sciences review scientific research and establish RDAs. A recent report published by the Academy states that "...no additional dietary protein is suggested for healthy adults undertaking resistance or endurance exercise."[29] Nevertheless, the RDA for protein may not apply to athletes involved in training or competition. According to joint recommendations issued by the American Dietetic Association, Dietitians of Canada, and the American College of Sports Medicine, endurance and resistance athletes should consume 1.2 to 1.4 g of protein per kilogram of body weight per day and 1.6 to 1.7 g of protein per kilogram of body weight per day, respectively.[19] Although these amounts of protein are considerably higher than the RDAs for non-athletes, they do not appear to be harmful for *healthy* physically active people.

Raising the Bar?

"Lasting energy," "fast fuel," "optimal energy"—such claims are used to promote so-called "energy" bars, gels, and drinks. Energy or sports bars are essentially cookies made from soy and milk proteins that are fortified with vitamins, minerals, and fibre. Sugary syrups hold these ingredients together. *High-protein* energy bars may appeal to athletes who think proteins are a source of energy and enhance muscular development. However, proteins are not a major biological fuel, and they are not "quick energy" sources, because the liver must process amino acids before they can be used for energy. Moreover, eating more protein than the body needs does not build muscle tissue. People need to follow a resistance training program to enlarge their skeletal muscles safely.

Granola bars, fruit-filled cookies, and fresh or dried fruits are less expensive and more natural sources of energy and nutrients than energy or sports bars. You can make your own "energy" bars by following the recipe in the Recipes for Healthy Living feature later in this chapter. If you prefer to eat commercial energy bars, check the products' Nutrition Facts table to determine amounts of carbohydrates and other nutrients that are in a serving. By eating several energy bars daily, you may ingest high amounts of iron, vitamin A, and other micronutrients. Therefore, consider energy bars as occasional snacks and not as meal replacements. Table 11.5 presents approximate energy and macronutrient contents per 100 g of various popular energy bars and gels.

High-protein energy bars may appeal to athletes who think proteins are a source of energy and enhance muscular development.

TABLE 11.5 *Popular Energy Bars and Gels: Energy and Macronutrient Contents/100 g*

Product	Energy kcal/100 g	Carbohydrates g/100 g	Protein g/100 g	Fat g/100 g
PowerBar Performance (cookies & cream)	370	66.2	12.3	4.6
PowerBar ProteinPlus (cookies & cream)	385	48.7	29.5	7.7
PowerBar PowerGel (vanilla)	268	65.9	0	0
Luna Bar (peanut butter cookies)	375	47.9	28.8	12.5
Clif Bar (chocolate chip)	368	66.2	28.8	7.4
Clif Shot (vanilla gel)	312	78.1	0	0
Balance Bar (chocolate)	400	44.0	28.0	12.0
Balance CarbWell (chocolate peanut butter)	400	44.0	28.0	16.0

Sources: Clif Bar & Company, www.clifbar.com; Luna Bar, www.lunabar.com; Balance Bar Food Company, www.balance.com; Power Bar, www.powerbar.com.

caffeine naturally occurring stimulant drug

heat cramps heat-related illness characterized by painful muscle contractions

Energy drinks usually contain sugars and a lot of **caffeine**, a stimulant drug that is naturally in coffee and tea. When consumed in moderate amounts, caffeine can increase alertness and decrease fatigue.[36,37] Some energy drinks also contain the amino acid *taurine* and herbal substances such as ginseng. Although the body uses taurine, the compound is not required by humans. Ginseng may enhance the stimulating effects of caffeine.[38] The "Ergogenic Aids: Separating Fact from Fiction" section, later in this chapter, provides more information about caffeine, ginseng, and some other substances that are promoted for enhancing physical performance.

TABLE 11.6 *Heat-Related Illnesses: Signs and Symptoms*

Heat cramps
• Painful muscle spasms
Heat exhaustion
• Muscle cramps
• Weakness
• Light-headedness
• Lack of interest in doing things
• Headache
• Nausea
Heatstroke
• Severe weakness
• High fever (over 40°C/104°F)
• Lack of sweating
• Rapid, shallow breathing
• Irritability and confusion
• Coma

Focusing on Fluids

The Adequate Intake (AI) for total water intake is approximately 2.7 L (11 cups) and 3.7 L (15 cups), for young women and men, respectively.[39,40] Athletes generally require more water than non-athletes to keep their bodies cool during muscular activity. Many factors, however, influence a person's hydration status. Among athletes in particular, differences in sports, fitness levels, and environmental conditions affect fluid needs. For example, sweating can cause runners to lose 750 to 2000 mL (3 to 8 cups) of water per hour.[35] Even a small degree of dehydration can lead to declines in an athlete's endurance, strength, and overall performance. Moreover, body temperature rises when dehydration occurs, increasing the risk of heat-related illness.

Heat-Related Illness

As the environmental temperature and humidity increase, the evaporation of sweat from skin slows, and the body has difficulty cooling itself by perspiring. Ineffective sweating contributes to fatigue, makes the heart work harder, and raises the risk of *heat-related illness*. Table 11.6 presents three major types of heat-related illnesses and their common signs and symptoms.

Many athletes are familiar with **heat cramps**. These painful muscle *spasms* (involuntary contractions) can affect any muscle, but they usually occur in the back, abdominal, or calf muscles. The cause of heat cramps is unclear, but the spasms may result from the loss of electrolytes in sweat.[10] Treatment of heat cramps includes resting, drinking juice or a sports drink, and gently stretching and massaging the affected muscles.[42]

Heat exhaustion can occur after heavy exercise in warm conditions, especially when fluid intake has been inadequate. A person suffering from heat exhaustion sweats excessively and has a body temperature of around 39 °C (102 °F).[42] Other signs of the illness include cool, moist, grey-coloured skin and rapid, weak pulse. To treat heat exhaustion, move the victim to a cool or shady place and have the person lie on his or her back, with legs slightly elevated above chest level. Furthermore, cool the person by fanning, spraying with cool water, or giving a cool sponge bath. It is also very important to have the victim drink cool water or a sports drink. People with heat exhaustion should be monitored closely, because the condition can rapidly develop into *heatstroke*.

Heatstroke is the most dangerous form of heat-related illness. Signs of heatstroke include elevated body temperature (more than 40 °C/104 °F); lack of sweating; rapid, shallow breathing; irritable and confused behaviour; and loss of consciousness (coma).[42] Heatstroke is a medical emergency that needs to be treated by trained medical staff. If you suspect that a person has heatstroke, summon emergency medical assistance immediately (dial "911") and move the victim to a cool environment. While waiting for professional medical care to arrive, you can spray or sponge the patient with cool water.

heat exhaustion heat-related illness that can occur after intense exercise

heatstroke most dangerous form of heat-related illness

To reduce the risk of heat illnesses, athletes and other physically active people should replace fluid losses that occur during prolonged exertion.

Replenishing Fluids

To reduce the risk of heat illnesses, athletes and other physically active people should avoid exercising under extremely hot, humid conditions and replace fluid losses that occur during prolonged exertion. According to recommendations recently established by the International Marathon Medical Directors Association (IMMDA), thirst protects athletes from consuming too little or too much fluid.[43] Experts with this organization no longer recommend drinking fluids even if you are not thirsty, because this practice can lead to water intoxication (*hyponatremia*). However, athletes should avoid losing more than 2% of their body weight during exercise.[41]

To estimate the amount of fluids needed to replace water loss during exercise (*rehydration*), athletes can weigh themselves prior to exercising and then calculate 2% of their body weight (0.02 × weight). After working out, athletes should weigh themselves again. If the difference between pre-exercise and post-exercise body weights is more than 2%, fluid replacement is necessary during such activities. For example, if you weigh 68 kg (150 lbs.), 2% of that weight is 1.36 kg (3 lbs.) (0.02 × 68). Therefore, you should drink enough fluids to avoid losing 3 or more pounds when you train or compete. In general, you can replace each pound that you lose during exercise by drinking 625 to 750 mL (2½ to 3 cups) of fluid.[10] For example, if your usual weight is 150 pounds and you weigh 149 pounds immediately after exercising, you lost 1 pound of body fluids during the activity. The next time you exercise under similar conditions, you can consume 625 to 750 mL (2½ to 3 cups) of water during the activity to maintain your body's water balance. Why do you need to drink 50% more fluids than you lost in sweat? After exercise, rehydration may stimulate the kidneys to produce more urine than normal, thus you need to drink the extra fluids to achieve proper hydration.[10] As noted in Chapter 9, alcoholic beverages have a diuretic effect on the body and are not recommended for rehydration.

Do I Need a Sports Drink? Sports drinks provide some nutritional benefits beyond those of plain water. These beverages usually contain simple carbohydrates, a source of energy that can enhance performance during endurance activities. Recommended products contain about 21 g of carbohydrate per 355-mL (12-oz.) serving, or about 6% carbohydrate by weight. Drinks with sugar contents above 10%, such as soft drinks or fruit juices, are not recommended because they may cause intestinal discomfort. Sodium and other electrolytes in sports beverages help maintain blood volume, enhance the absorption of water and carbohydrate from the intestinal tract, and stimulate thirst.

Sports drinks provide some nutritional benefits beyond those of plain water.

Food & Nutrition *tip*

Compared to commercially available sports drinks, diluted fruit juices with added sugar and salt are less expensive sources of water, sodium, and simple sugars. You can prepare your own "sports" drink by adding 60 mL (¼ cup) of orange juice, 60 mL (¼ cup) of sugar, and 9 mL (⅛ tsp) of table salt to 887 mL (30 oz.) of water or club soda. Pour the beverage into a quart pitcher, cover, and refrigerate until needed.

Should you drink water or a sports drink during competition? According to the IMMDA, fluids beyond water are necessary when workouts or events last longer than 30 minutes.[43] Although electrolytes are lost in sweat, the quantities lost in shorter periods can be easily replaced by consuming foods and beverages, such as water or fruit juice, after the event.

It is possible to drink too much water and develop water intoxication (see Chapter 9). Endurance athletes, especially poorly trained individuals, may compete at relatively low exercise intensities for prolonged periods. Under these conditions, the athletes do not sweat as much, therefore they do not need to replace as much water as better-trained athletes who exercise at higher intensities. Regardless of training level, athletes who drink too much water can dilute the level of sodium in their blood and develop serious and even deadly side effects. Although sports drinks generally contain sodium, these beverages are mostly water, therefore consuming excessive amounts of sports drinks can contribute to fluid overload.[44] To avoid water intoxication, athletes should drink water according to their thirst. If an athlete gains weight while exercising, he or she may be retaining too much fluid.

Intense exercise may stimulate the body's natural antioxidant defence system.

Antioxidant Vitamins

During aerobic physical activities, skeletal muscles use more oxygen and generate more free radicals than resting muscle tissue.[45] Exercise can produce a temporary imbalance between free radical generation and the ability of antioxidants to counteract them. Scientific evidence suggests that such *oxidative stress* may contribute to muscle fatigue and damage. Nevertheless, results of studies that examined whether antioxidant vitamin supplements enhanced athletic performance generally concluded that performance was not improved, unless there was a pre-existing deficiency of those particular vitamins.

Findings of some scientific studies indicate that free radicals generated during intense exercise may stimulate the body's natural antioxidant defence system. Thus, the oxidative stress produced during exercise might have benefits, and blocking this process by taking antioxidant vitamin supplements may not be desirable.[45,46]

Currently, antioxidant vitamin supplements are not recommended for athletes.[45] Athletes should be cautious about taking such supplements based on anecdotes or advertising claims, because there is not enough scientific evidence concerning the long-term effects of using these products. Rather than experiment on themselves with antioxidant supplements, athletes should follow diets that contain foods naturally rich in antioxidants, such as fruits, vegetables, whole-grain breads and cereals, and vegetable oils.

Iron

The body needs iron to produce red blood cells, transport oxygen, and obtain energy. Thus, iron deficiency can negatively affect athletic performance. Young female athletes are likely to develop iron deficiency because of their menstrual blood losses—bleeding is a cause of iron deficiency. Athletes who follow low-calorie or vegetarian (especially vegan) diets are also at risk of iron deficiency, because their food choices may be low in iron. Additionally, distance runners may develop low iron status, because intense prolonged workouts can lead to gastrointestinal bleeding.

In the early phase of their training, endurance athletes often develop *sports anemia*, a temporary condition that results from an increase in the liquid portion of blood (*plasma*), rather than iron deficiency.[10] The effects of sports anemia on physical performance are unknown. Nevertheless, it can be difficult to differentiate between sports anemia and true iron deficiency anemia. It is a good idea for athletes, especially females, to have their iron status checked at the beginning of a training season and at least once during midseason. If an athlete is iron deficient, a physician needs to determine the cause and prescribe treatment.

Calcium

Athletes, especially those who are total vegetarians or who restrict their consumption of dairy products to lose weight, can have marginal or low calcium intakes. This practice may result in weak bones that fracture easily, as well as osteoporosis later in life. Additionally, female athletes who have irregular or no menstrual cycles may be deficient in the hormone estrogen. Although weight-bearing exercise, such as jogging, improves bone density, estrogen is necessary for maintaining healthy bones. Female athletes who develop menstrual cycle abnormalities should consult a physician to determine the cause. Decreasing the amount of training or gaining weight may restore a regular menstrual pattern. For information about the *female athlete triad*, see the Chapter 10 Highlight; Chapter 9 provided information about osteoporosis.

Concept Checkpoint

12. What are some practical ways to assess whether an athlete's energy intake is adequate?
13. Why should athletes be concerned about their carbohydrate intakes before, during, and after prolonged intense physical activity?
14. Identify at least five high-carbohydrate, low-fat foods.
15. Explain why athletes do not need to take protein or amino acid supplements.
16. Why should athletes be concerned about their bodies' fluid status?
17. What are major signs and symptoms of heat cramps, heat exhaustion, and heatstroke?
18. When is consuming a sports drink a better choice than plain water for rehydration?
19. Explain why you would or would not recommend that an athlete take antioxidant supplements.
20. Explain why iron deficiency can impair an athlete's physical performance.
21. For young female athletes, what is the significance of having irregular or no menstrual cycles on bone health?

Ergogenic Aids: Separating Fact from Fiction

ergogenic aids foods, devices, dietary supplements, or drugs used to improve physical performance

Athletes often use **ergogenic aids**—foods, devices, dietary supplements, and even drugs ("doping")—to improve their physical performance. Bee pollen, dried adrenal glands from cattle, seaweed, freeze-dried liver flakes, and ginseng are among the dietary supplements that athletes consume as they hope to gain the competitive edge over their sports' rivals. However, no reliable scientific evidence supports the effectiveness of most dietary supplements purported to have ergogenic effects. Nevertheless, many athletes firmly believe in the value of the performance-enhancing aids that they use. In many instances, the perceived benefits are more likely to result from the placebo effect than actual physiological changes (see Chapter 2).

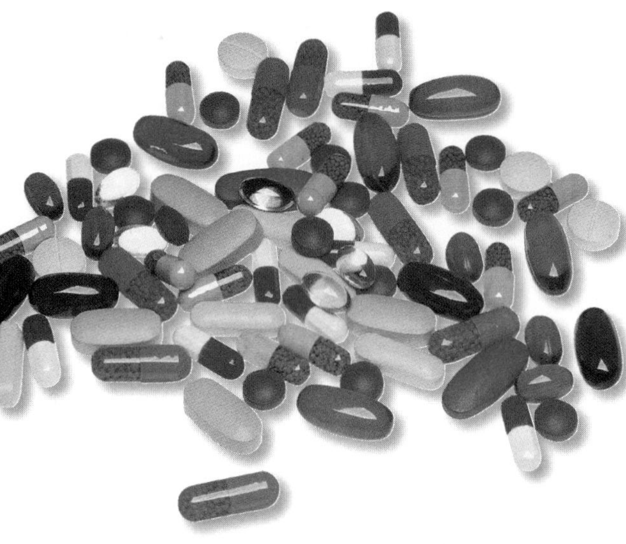

A few dietary substances and practices can enhance physical performance. These ergogenic aids include sufficient water and electrolytes, carbohydrates, and a balanced and varied diet consistent with the *Eating Well with Canada's Food Guide* recommendations. For athletes, meeting carbohydrate and fluid needs—along with overall nutrient needs—is the most important ergogenic aid.

Athletes should be skeptical of claims made for any substance until its ergogenic effects and long-term safety have been determined by researchers who are not associated with the supplement industry. Rather than searching for a "magic bullet" to enhance their performance, athletes should concentrate their efforts on improving their dietary habits, training routines, and sports techniques. Nutrient supplements should be used for specific dietary deficiencies, such as preventing iron deficiency or boosting calcium intakes.

Table 11.7 summarizes science-based findings regarding caffeine, carnitine, creatine, and some other dietary supplements and ergogenic aids that are popular among athletes. It is important to note that certain dietary supplements are known to be unsafe, and the use of others are restricted or banned by major athletic organizations or are not approved for use in Canada. For example, in 2004 FDA banned the use of ephedrine-containing supplements. Ephedrine (ephedra, ma huang) increases central nervous system activity but the drug can cause serious, even deadly side effects. The following section discusses the ergogenic properties of caffeine.

Caffeine raises the level of fatty acids in blood, and as a result, exercising muscles can use more fat for energy.

Caffeine

Worldwide, caffeine is the most widely used ergogenic aid.[47,48] Caffeine raises the level of fatty acids in blood, and as a result, exercising muscles can use more fat for energy. Caffeine also enhances the ability of skeletal and heart muscles to contract and increases mental alertness. Although consuming even small amounts of caffeine may help endurance athletes, the National Collegiate Athletic Association (NCAA) limits the amount of caffeine that athletes can have in their bodies during competition. Athletes who have more than 15 micrograms of caffeine per millilitre (mcg/mL) of their urine can be banned.[49] Nevertheless, the World Anti-Doping Agency (WADA) does not prohibit the use of caffeine and these guidelines govern the use of performance enhancing substances in the Canadian Interuniversity Sport (CIS) competitions.[50,51]

People who are not regular caffeine consumers may experience shakiness, rapid heart rate, sleep disturbances, diarrhea, and frequent urination after ingesting relatively high amounts of the stimulant drug. Caffeine is addictive; discontinuing its use results in *withdrawal*, temporary unpleasant side effects, especially headache.

It is important to understand that the quick "energy" boost provided by "energy drinks" is a result of caffeine or other stimulants contained in the products.[52,53] Nevertheless, energy drinks also provide calories if they are sweetened with added sugars. Table 11.8 compares the caffeine and calorie contents of popular beverages including an energy drink ("Red Bull"). Note that a 250-mL (8.5-oz.) serving

TABLE 11.7 *Evaluation of Some Popular Ergogenic Supplements/Aids*

Substance	Claim	Current Science-Based Findings Concerning Claims	Side Effects
Caffeine	Enhances fat metabolism Increases alertness	Consuming 3 to 9 mg of caffeine per kg of body weight about one hour before events may benefit certain athletes.	High doses can cause nervousness, shakiness, and sleep disturbances. Intakes of more than 600 mg (1500 to 2000 mL of coffee) can produce levels of caffeine in urine that are banned by the National Collegiate Athletic Association (NCAA).
Creatine	Enhances muscular endurance and strength Increases lean muscle mass	May enhance performance of sprinters and weightlifters	High doses may cause kidney damage, especially in persons with kidney disease.
Carnitine	Boosts fat metabolism during exercise	No significant effect on performance	None reported
Beta-hydroxy-beta-methylbutyrate (HMB)	Decreases protein metabolism, increasing muscle mass	May increase muscle mass, but evidence is weak	None reported, but results of long-term use are unknown.
Branched chain amino acids	Provides energy for muscles	Mixed or no beneficial results	Mild at high doses
Glucosamine	Aids in repairing damaged joints	Generally no beneficial results	None reported
Chromium	Increases lean mass	No benefit	Toxic level: intakes above 400 mcg daily
Coenzyme Q10	Enhances cardiac function, delays fatigue	No benefit	Long-term safety is unknown.
Bee pollen	Shortens muscle recovery time Increases muscular strength and endurance	No benefit	May cause allergic reactions in sensitive persons
Ginseng	Combats fatigue and improves stamina	May have mild stimulant effects	Results of most clinical studies (200 to 1600 mg/day) indicate that ginseng does not improve physical performance, but more research is needed.
Anabolic steroids	Increases muscle mass and strength	Increases protein synthesis In Canada and the United States, legal use requires physician's prescription.	Side effects include: bloody liver cysts; increased risk of cardiovascular disease, hypertension, and reproductive problems; mood swings and aggressive behaviour ("roid rage"); sleep disturbances Banned by many sports organizations
Gamma hydroxybutyric acid (GHB)	Increases muscle mass by acting like an anabolic steroid	Illegal—Health Canada and the FDA have not approved GHB for production or sale in Canada or the United States.	Vomiting, dizziness, shakiness, and seizures May cause death
Human growth hormone	Increases muscle mass and fat metabolism	Most studies indicate no benefit.	May increase height as well as size of the heart and other internal organs Very dangerous, can be deadly International Olympic Committee bans the use of growth hormone.
DHEA and androstenedione ("andro")	Increases the body's steroid production	No benefit	May be dangerous Banned by International Olympic Committee In 2004, the FDA warned companies to stop manufacturing products that contain "andro." Not approved for use in Canada.

Sources: Wardlaw GM, Hampl JS: *Perspectives in nutrition*. New York: McGraw-Hill, 2007; Ahrendt DM: Ergogenic aids: Counseling the athlete. *American Family Physician* 63:913, 2001; Kiwdwe D, Pantuso T: Panax ginseng. *American Family Physician* 68:1539, 2003; Hsu C-C and others: American ginseng supplementation attenuates creatine kinase level induced by submaximal exercise in human beings. *World Journal of Gastroenterology* 11:5327, 2005; Liang MT and others: Panax notoginseng supplementation enhances physical performance during endurance exercise. *Journal of Strength and Conditioning Research* 19:108, 2005; U.S. Department of Health and Human Services: *HS launches crackdown on products containing andro*. 2004. www.fda.gov/bbs/topics/news/2004/hhs_031104.html.

TABLE 11.8 *Caffeine Content of Selected Beverages*

Beverage and Amount	kcal	Caffeine (mg)
Coffee, Tim Hortons, large, 1 milk, 1 sugar	55*	140*
Coffee, Starbucks, grande, 473 mL (16 oz.)	140**	259 ***
Coffee, brewed from grounds, unsweetened, 250 mL (8.5 oz.)	2	104
Red Bull, 250 mL (8.5 oz.)	118	80
Coffee, instant plain, prepared, 250 mL (8 oz.)	5	62
Cola with caffeine	136–151	29–99
Tea, brewed, unsweetened	2	47
Tea, ready-to-drink, 355-mL (12-oz.) can	133	17
Chocolate drink	109	2

* TDL Group Corp.: Nutrition Information. http://www.timhortons.com/ca/en/menu/nutrition-calculator.html

**Starbucks beverages: Nutrition information. www.starbucks.com/retail/nutrition_beverages.asp

****Caffeine content of common beverages*. Updated 2006. MayoClinic.com: Tools for healthier lives. www.mayoclinic.com/health/caffeine/AN01211/

Source: USDA: *USDA national nutrient database for standard reference, release 19.* 2006. www.nal.usda.gov/fnic/foodcomp/search/

of brewed coffee supplies more caffeine but fewer kilocalories than the same amount of the energy drink. However, amounts of caffeine in brewed coffee can vary widely, depending on preparation methods. "Stay awake" pills and chewing gums are concentrated sources of caffeine that can be purchased without a prescription.

Concept **Checkpoint**

22. Why do many athletes use ergogenic aids?
23. Identify three ergogenic aids that have been banned by at least one athletic association.
24. Identify at least three foods or beverages that are rich sources of caffeine.
25. Discuss the ergogenic effects that caffeine can have on the body.

Chapter 11 Highlight
Developing a Personal Physical Fitness Plan

Healthy adults under 65 years of age should perform moderate-intensity physical activity for 60 minutes daily, while children should achieve a minimum of 90 minutes each day and older adults over the age of 65, should aim for 30 to 60 minutes of activity daily.[1A]

Most healthy people can gradually increase their level of physical activity. Health problems that require a preliminary medical evaluation are obesity, cardiovascular disease (or family history of CVD), hypertension, type 2 diabetes (or family history), shortness of breath after mild exertion, and arthritis. Additionally, pregnant women should check with their physicians before starting an exercise regimen.

When developing your personal physical fitness plan, first consider your fitness goals. For example, if you want to lose weight, how much do you want to lose and how many weeks will it take to lose that amount? Do you want to focus more on strengthening your muscles or improving your aerobic capacity? Then determine when you can work out and whether you'll need to join a fitness facility such as a gym or purchase special equipment such as handheld weights. For a comprehensive fitness program, make sure to include aerobic, resistance, and stretching activities into your weekly exercise regimen. The following fitness plan has three stages: initiation, improvement, and maintenance phases.

Initiation

The first three to six weeks of your new exercise program is the *initiation* stage. Start by incorporating short periods of physical activity into your daily routine. For example, you can walk more often, take the stairs instead of the elevator, and do more housework, gardening, or other activities that cause you to "huff and puff" a bit. Furthermore, you can strive to reduce the time that you spend in sedentary activities.

The goal is to accumulate a total of 60 minutes of moderate-intensity types of activities most days of the week. If necessary, the time that you spend engaging in the activity each day can occur in three or more short intervals lasting 10 to 20 minutes. If you do not have 60 minutes to spend on exercising, try increasing the intensity of the activities during shorter bouts of exercise to obtain some health benefits.

Improvement and Maintenance

The next five or six months of the program is the *improvement* stage, in which you increase the intensity and duration of exercises. When you begin the improvement phase, exercise at an intensity that's near the lower end of your target heart rate zone. As you progress and become more physically fit, you can increase the intensity by exercising at a higher heart rate.

By the end of the improvement stage, you may notice that you have reached your goals, and you don't seem to be making further gains in your fitness. This plateau marks the beginning of your *maintenance* stage. At this point, you can evaluate your personal fitness plan, and if you would like to make new goals, this is the time to develop them. If you are satisfied with your fitness level, continue with your present program. Discontinuing exercise gradually results in *detraining*, declining physical fitness.

Components of a Workout Regimen

Ideally, you should establish a regular time for exercising that fits into your daily routine. To be effective, your aerobic workout program needs to include the following components:

1. *Warm-up.* Warming up muscles can increase your joints' range of motion (flexibility) and may decrease your risk of injury. Stretching for five to ten minutes is a good way to warm up. Start with smaller muscle groups such as the arms and progressively work toward stretching larger muscle groups in the legs and abdomen. Hold your position in the stretch for 15 seconds and do not bounce. If stretching causes pain, stop immediately. "No pain, no gain" is not true—pain is an indication of injury. Another way to warm up is to perform five to ten minutes. To obtain substantial health benefits, people should engage in some form of aerobic activity regularly of the anticipated activity but at a low intensity. For example, if you walk for fitness, warm up by walking at a slower pace.
2. *Aerobic workout.* To obtain substantial health benefits, you should engage in some form of aerobic activity regularly. A comprehensive aerobic workout emphasizes the *type*, *duration*, *frequency*, *intensity*, and *progression* of exercise.
   - **Type:** The kinds of exercise you choose should increase your heart and breathing rates and involve rhythmic movements of large muscle groups in the legs. Examples include brisk walking, running, swimming, and cycling. If you swim, add

| To obtain substantial health benefits, people should engage in some form of aerobic activity regularly.

some *weight-bearing activities*, such as walking, to your fitness plan. Weight-bearing exercises place stress on your bones, improving their strength.

- **Duration:** Duration is the amount of time spent in an exercise session. A session should generally last at least 20 to 30 minutes, depending on intensity, not including time spent warming up and cooling down. Ideally, the exercise session should be continuous (without stopping), but multiple ten-minute bouts of moderate to intense activity with rest periods in between are also acceptable.
- **Frequency:** The frequency of exercise describes the number of times that the activity is performed, generally on a weekly basis. To derive significant health benefits, the frequency of aerobic exercise should be at least five times per week. By exercising daily, you can enjoy even greater benefits.
- **Intensity:** Health benefits can occur when you achieve at least a moderate level of intensity during exercise (see Table 3.1 on p. 63).
- **Progression:** Progression, the final component of a comprehensive fitness plan, refers to the gradual increase in the frequency, intensity, and duration of exercise that occurs over a period.

3. *Cool down.* To cool down, you can repeat the same stretches you performed during warming up. Stretch for five to ten minutes. Cooling down may prevent injury and reduce muscle soreness.

What about Strength (Resistance) Training?

Strength training, such as weightlifting, is an important part of a comprehensive physical fitness plan. Strength training should be done two to four days per week. To start, warm up by stretching for five to ten minutes. Then perform a group of eight to ten exercises that strengthen major muscle groups of the upper body and lower body. Cool down for five to ten minutes at the end of each session.

Fitness centres have machines that provide resistance for various muscle groups. For resistance training outside of gymnasiums or fitness clubs, you can purchase simple elastic exercise cords designed to increase muscular strength (Fig. 11.A). For increasing upper arm strength, a set of inexpensive handheld weights can be kept in a convenient location for performing resistance exercise regularly, such as near the TV. The weights should allow you to perform at least one set of 8 to 15 repetitions.[2A] When you can do more than 15 repetitions with relative ease, consider increasing the weight slightly.

Mixing It Up

To make your exercise routine more enjoyable, include several types of physical activities in your weekly regimen. For example, jogging one day might be followed by swimming the next day. Adding variety to a program not only keeps you from becoming bored with your workouts but also strengthens different muscle groups in your body and reduces your risk of injury. Additionally, invite a friend or relative to be your exercise partner. Having an exercise partner may provide additional motivation and encouragement to exercise regularly.

Figure 11.A Increasing muscle strength. This individual is using a simple rubber exercise cord to increase muscular strength.

Some overfat people do not experience significant weight loss while following an exercise regimen. However, they still benefit from regular physical activity. Initially, exercise programs for obese people should emphasize non-weight-bearing activities, such as swimming, water aerobics, and bicycling. As obese people lose weight and become more fit, they can add weight-bearing activities to their plans.

Whatever physical activities you choose to include in your fitness program, they should be enjoyable and easy to become routine. You can apply the dietary principles of variety, balance, and moderation to your exercise routine:

- **Variety:** Perform several different activities to exercise different muscle groups.
- **Balance:** For overall fitness, balance your exercise regimen by including activities that build cardiovascular endurance, muscular strength, and flexibility.
- **Moderation:** Focus on exercising to keep fit, without overdoing it and injuring yourself. You don't need to work out vigorously every day to become healthier.

To learn more about the health benefits of physical fitness, determine your level of fitness, or develop a personal fitness program, access the following Web sites:

www.shapeup.org
www.fitness.gov
www.presidentschallenge.org
www.acefitness.org/default.aspx

References for Chapter 11 Highlight

1A. Public Health Agency of Canada: Healthy Living Unit: *Canada's physical activity guide to healthy active living*. www.phac-aspc.gc.ca/hp-ps/hl-mvs/pag-gap/index-home-accueil-eng.php. Accessed: September 9, 2010.

2A. Why everyone needs strength training. *University of California–Berkeley Wellness Letter*, p. 4, May 2004.

SUMMARY

Many North Americans lead sedentary lives. Canadians can manage their weight more effectively and reduce their risk of developing the major causes of death and disability by engaging in at least 30 minutes of moderate-intensity physical activity on most days of the week. Furthermore, most people can achieve even greater health benefits by increasing the duration, frequency, and intensity of their physical activities.

Regular physical activity reduces the risk of dying prematurely and developing heart disease, diabetes, and high blood pressure. Additionally, regular exercise builds and maintains healthy bones, muscles, and joints; helps reduce blood pressure in people who have high blood pressure; reduces the risk of developing certain cancers; aids weight-control efforts; helps older adults become stronger and reduces their risk of falls; reduces risk of sleep disorders, depression, and anxiety; and promotes psychological well-being. Millions of Canadians suffer from chronic illnesses that can be prevented or improved by exercising more often.

ATP is the major form of energy used by cells. Phosphocreatine (PCr) can rapidly reform ATP from its breakdown product ADP, but PCr supplies are limited. To generate ATP, muscle cells can metabolize carbohydrate, fat, and protein. In muscle cells, glucose molecules are broken down through a series of steps to yield lactic acid (in anaerobic conditions) or CO_2 plus H_2O (in aerobic conditions).

The proportions of macronutrients used for energy largely depend on the intensity of the physical activity. Fat is a key aerobic fuel for muscle cells, especially at low-intensity exercise. At rest and during light activity, muscles burn primarily fat for energy needs. In comparison, little protein generally is used to fuel muscles. During brief bouts of intense physical effort, the cardiorespiratory system is unable to deliver adequate oxygen to muscles. Under such anaerobic conditions, muscle cells metabolize glucose rather than fat for energy, but their ability to sustain the release of energy for intense activity is limited. Muscle cells can obtain far more energy when in aerobic conditions.

Sports nutrition focuses on applying nutrition principles and research findings to improving athletic performance. Athletes often manipulate their diets to enhance their body contours, increase their muscular strength, and prevent or delay fatigue during exercise. Although diet is important, genetic endowment and physical training are the most crucial factors that influence athletic performance.

A high-carbohydrate diet can be beneficial for athletes, and carbohydrate-rich foods should form the foundation of pre-event meals. Many athletes consume more protein than they require. Despite marketing claims, protein supplements are unnecessary. By eating their usual food choices, most athletes can meet their protein needs.

Physically active people need to be concerned about their fluid intakes. Fluid replacement should be based on thirst and loss of body weight while exercising. Consuming a source of electrolytes, such as a sports drink, can be helpful, especially when the duration of intense exercise exceeds 30 minutes. It is important to avoid over-consumption of water because of the risk of water intoxication.

Athletes often ingest certain substances, including herbal products, because they believe these substances have ergogenic effects. Scientific evidence, however, does not suggest that most of these substances are effective. Furthermore, long-term safety of many ergogenic aids has not been determined and use of some substances is restricted or banned by various athletic organizations.

Recipes for Healthy Living

Nutty Energy Bars

You can use the following recipe to make your own "energy bars." This recipe makes eight 4″ × 2″ bars. Each bar supplies approximately 253 kcal, 8 g protein, 13 g fat, 26 g carbohydrate, 3 g fibre, and 4.9 mg iron.

INGREDIENTS:

Oil cooking spray
1 egg, large
375 mL (1½ cups) instant oats, dry
60 mL (¼ cup) almonds, slivered
60 mL (¼ cup) enriched wheat flour
125 mL (½ cup) smooth peanut butter
15 mL (1 Tbsp) vegetable oil
125 mL (½ cup) honey
2–3 mL (½ tsp) ground cinnamon
5 mL (1 tsp) vanilla

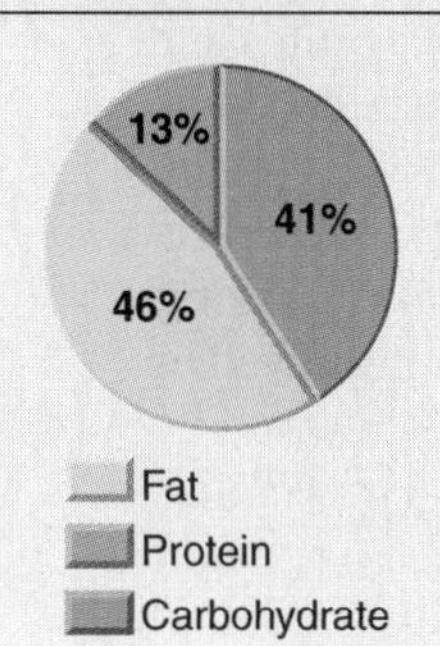

PREPARATION STEPS:

1. Preheat oven to 350°F.
2. Spray "nonstick" oil on the inside bottom and sides of an 8″ × 8″ pan.
3. Crack open the egg, drop the egg's contents into a medium-size bowl, and discard the shell. Using a fork, beat the egg until its yolk is completely mixed with the egg white.
4. Add remaining ingredients to the egg and stir until well-blended. Mixture will be thick, like cookie dough.
5. Using a large spoon, press dough into the bottom of pan, covering the inside of the pan evenly.
6. Bake for 12 to 14 minutes.
7. Cool completely before cutting into eight 2″ × 4″ bars.

Spiral Pasta Salad

Athletes often rely on pasta dishes to help maintain or replenish their glycogen supplies. There are many different forms of pasta, including shells, tubes, and twisted pieces called rotini. This quick and easy pasta salad recipe uses rotini mixed with fresh green pepper, tomato, onion, and garlic. The recipe makes two 250-mL (1-cup) servings. Each serving supplies approximately 260 kcal, 52 g carbohydrate, 4 g protein, 2.5 g fibre, 4 g fat, 2 mg iron, 250 mg potassium, and 144 mcg folate.

INGREDIENTS:

2800 mL (1⅓ cups uncooked) rotini pasta
1 small garlic clove, minced
15 mL (1 Tbsp) finely chopped onion
325 mL (1⅓ cups) chopped green pepper
325 mL (1⅓ cups) chopped tomato
30 mL (2 Tbsp) lite mayonnaise-type salad dressing
pinch of black pepper

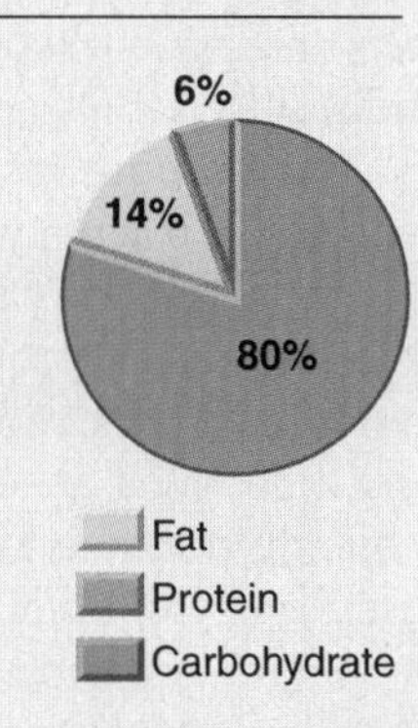

PREPARATION STEPS:

1. Prepare rotini according to package directions but do not add salt to boiling water.
2. Drain cooked rotini.
3. Gently mix rotini with other ingredients.
4. Serve hot or cold.

CRITICAL THINKING

1. Using the recommendation to achieve 60 minutes of moderate or greater intensity physical activity at least five days of the week (see Chapter 3), analyze your weekly physical activity habits. Does your participation in various physical activities meet the minimum recommendations? If not, which physical activities are you willing to include in your weekly routine to improve your fitness level?
2. Calculate your target heart rate zone for moderate-intensity as well as vigorous-intensity activities.
3. Why do human cells rely far more on glucose and fat for energy than protein?
4. Your neighbour is planning to run in a marathon. What advice would you give him concerning fluid intake before and during the event?
5. One of your friends is a competitive athlete. She tells you that she ordered an amino acid supplement from the manufacturer's Web site. According to testimonials posted at the site, the supplement improves athletic performance. What would you tell her about the general effectiveness of such products?

PRACTICE TEST

Select the best answer.

1. Miranda is physically fit. She has
   a. an increased risk of osteoporosis.
   b. the strength, endurance, and flexibility to meet the demands of daily living.
   c. a greater need for vitamins and minerals than other women.
   d. none of the above
2. During glycolysis, the body
   a. converts two fatty acid molecules into one glucose molecule.
   b. synthesizes one amino acid molecule from one carbon dioxide molecule and two oxygen molecules.
   c. breaks down one glucose molecule to form two pyruvate molecules.
   d. none of the above
3. A ______ physical activity generally requires a high degree of exertion.
   a. vigorous
   b. basic
   c. moderate
   d. precise
4. Aerobic activities
   a. enable muscles to use less oxygen than normal.
   b. do not require voluntary muscular contractions.
   c. force muscle cells to use more vitamins and minerals for energy.
   d. involve sustained, rhythmic contractions of certain large skeletal muscles.

5. Which of the following statements is true?
   a. Resistance exercises do not help build bone mass.
   b. Sedentary activities do not require much energy to perform.
   c. Anaerobic energy systems need large quantities of oxygen to produce ATP.
   d. all of the above
6. Amy is studying quietly. Under these conditions, her muscles are using primarily ______ for energy.
   a. fat
   b. glucose
   c. amino acids
   d. ketones
7. Carbohydrate loading
   a. provides a competitive edge for award-winning sprinters, bodybuilders, and weightlifters.
   b. involves manipulating dietary patterns and physical activities prior to an endurance event.
   c. often results in short-term weight loss and positive energy balance.
   d. is generally recommended for long-term weight control for athletes.
8. Which of the following foods is high carbohydrate and low fat?
   a. dried fruit
   b. pretzels
   c. toast spread with strawberry jam
   d. all of the above
9. Caffeine
   a. is the most widely used ergogenic aid in the world.
   b. reduces the level of fatty acids in blood.
   c. is nonaddictive.
   d. decreases mental alertness.
10. Drinking large amounts of water
    a. is generally safe.
    b. is necessary for physically active persons even if they are not thirsty.
    c. can result in water intoxication.
    d. improves athletic performance.
11. Which of the following beverages contains caffeine?
    a. Red Bull
    b. tea
    c. chocolate milk
    d. all of the above
12. Under aerobic conditions, cells breakdown glucose to form
    a. carbon dioxide and water.
    b. acetyl Co-A and sorbitol.
    c. beta-carotene and glutamine.
    d. phosphocreatine and ADP.

13. Human cells release most of the energy stored in carbohydrates, fats, and amino acids as
    a. electricity.
    b. phosphocreatine.
    c. ATP.
    d. heat.
14. To obtain energy under aerobic conditions, cells need
    a. ribose.
    b. oxygen.
    c. methionine.
    d. alanine.
15. _____ is an immediate and direct source of energy for cells.
    a. LDP
    b. Glycogen
    c. ATP
    d. Phospholipid

Answers to Chapter 11 Quiz Yourself

1. People who exercise regularly can reduce their risk of type 2 diabetes. **True.** (p. 379)
2. Sports drinks are not useful for fluid replacement. **False.** (p. 397)
3. Protein is the body's preferred fuel for muscular activity. **False.** (p. 394)
4. Heatstroke is a serious illness that requires immediate professional medical treatment. **True.** (p. 397)
5. While at rest, skeletal muscles metabolize more glucose than fat for energy. **False.** (p. 389)

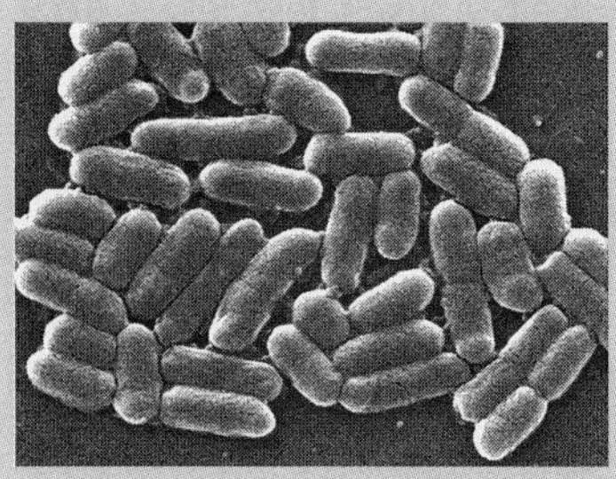

Chapter **12**

Food Safety Concerns

Chapter Learning Outcomes

After reading Chapter 12, you should be able to:

1. List some common types and sources of microbes that can cause food-borne illness.
2. Identify the government's role in protecting the food supply.
3. Describe procedures that can reduce the risk of food-borne illness.
4. Identify various food preservation methods.
5. List at least three functions of food additives.
6. Identify sources of contaminants in food.
7. Discuss the pros and cons of pesticide use.

In August 2006, Jill K. was adjusting to her first semester in graduate school and training for her third marathon race. About three days a week, Jill would run 5 to 13 km (3 to 8 miles) a day. On weekends, she would jog longer distances, up to 30 km (about 18 miles) at a time. While in training, Jill ate a high-carbohydrate diet that emphasized nutrient-dense foods such as whole grains, fruits, and vegetables.

A few days before Labour Day, Jill bought a package of raw baby spinach and used about half of the bag to prepare a large spinach salad. About three or four days after eating the salad, she developed a fever, body aches, and severe intestinal cramps. When the young woman discovered a lot of blood in her bowel movements, she went to a hospital emergency room. Jill told emergency room staff about her bloody diarrhea, but they dismissed her illness as "just food poisoning" and prescribed an antibiotic for her to take. After being discharged from the emergency room, she went to a nearby pharmacy to have the prescription filled. Jill was so weak, she passed out as she left the pharmacy. Some people found her and took her back to the emergency room, where she was admitted into the hospital. Jill was hospitalized for two and a half weeks, spending much of that time in the intensive care unit. At one point, her kidneys stopped functioning properly and her physicians feared she would die. She survived the terrible ordeal.

Within a few weeks, public health investigators determined that Jill and similar victims had something in common—they had eaten raw baby spinach. The culprit lurking in the spinach was a type of bacteria called *E. coli* O157:H7. **Bacteria** are simple, single-cell microorganisms. Some bacteria, such as *E. coli* O157:H7, cause infectious diseases in humans.

By the end of October, food safety experts identified cattle manure from nearby ranches as a possible source of the bacteria that tainted the baby spinach leaves. The manure might have been in water used to irrigate the spinach fields or spread on the spinach fields. Public health experts, however, were unable to determine the origin of the bacterial contamination.[1]

Today, Jill feels "back to normal." She has returned to graduate school and is running again. In June 2007, she completed a marathon, running the 42.2 km (26.2-mile) race in 4 hours and 37 minutes. She washes her hands a lot, cooks meat thoroughly, and washes ready-to-eat vegetables even though they are pre-washed. Not surprisingly, she avoids eating spinach. According to Jill, "If you ever have bloody diarrhea, go to the hospital and insist the ER staff find out why you are bleeding."

Each year, an estimated 13 million Canadians become ill from various **food-borne illnesses**.[2] Of those persons who contract such ailments, approximately 2 to 3% develop chronic health problems. There are more than 250 food-borne illnesses;[3,4] preventing these diseases is a major public health objective.

In 2008, a listeriosis outbreak linked to Maple Leaf Foods in Ontario killed 22 people; there were a total of 41 confirmed cases linked to the Maple Leaf plant.[5] In response, Maple Leaf Foods voluntarily recalled many of their products and has since implemented improved cleaning and sanitation practices in their plants.

In 2000, *E. Coli* infection linked to the water supply in Walkerton, Ontario, cost seven residents their lives and made ill an estimated 2500 others.[6] The catastrophe cost taxpayers an estimated $64.5 million and impacted the lives of hundreds.[7]

Food-borne as well as water-borne illnesses can occur when microscopic agents (*microbes*) or their toxic by-products enter food or water, and then they are consumed. Disease-causing microbes are referred to as **pathogens**. Many kinds of food-borne pathogens infect the digestive tract, inflaming the tissues and causing an "upset stomach" within a few hours after being ingested. A few types of food-borne pathogens multiply in the human intestinal tract, enter the bloodstream, and cause general illness when they invade other tissues. Other pathogens do not sicken humans directly, but these microbes secrete poisons (*toxins*) into food. When the food is eaten, the toxins can irritate the intestinal tract and cause a type of food-borne illness called **food intoxication** (or food poisoning).

In Canada, water-borne pathogens are not major health threats. Therefore, Chapter 12 focuses primarily on food-borne illness, including common sources of these infections in Canada and the United States. Additionally, this chapter presents safe food-handling practices and examines the safety of our food supply.

Quiz YOURSELF

Which foods are most likely to be responsible for food-borne illness? How can you reduce the risk of contracting one of these illnesses? Which government agencies monitor the safety of the Canadian and U.S. food supply? After reading Chapter 12, you will learn answers to these questions. Test your knowledge of food safety by taking the following quiz. The answers are found on page 443.

1. Aflatoxins are the most common sources of food-borne illness in Canada and the United States. _____ T _____ F
2. In Canada, foods such as ready-to-eat cereals, commercially canned vegetables, and orange juice are common sources of food-borne illness. _____ T _____ F
3. Certain fungi, such as button mushrooms, are safe to eat. _____ T _____ F
4. The Canadian Food Inspection Agency (CFIA) regulates the proper use of pesticides in Canada. _____ T _____ F
5. The best way to tell if a food is safe to eat is to smell it. _____ T _____ F

bacteria simple single-celled microorganisms

food-borne illness infection caused by microscopic disease-causing agents in food

pathogens disease-causing microbes

food intoxication illness that results when poisons produced by certain microbes contaminate food and irritate the intestinal tract

Jill K.

Protecting Our Food

Canada has one of the safest food supplies in the world, primarily the result of a team effort conducted by cooperating federal, provincial, and municipal agencies that regulate and monitor the production and distribution of food. The Canadian Food Inspection Agency (CFIA)[8] and Agriculture and Agri-Food Canada[9] under the mandate of Health Canada protect consumers by regulating the country's food industry. Provincial departments of agriculture and public health agencies also play an invaluable role in protecting Canadians from food-borne illness.

To help protect our food supply, CFIA performs many important tasks, such as regulating nearly all domestic and imported food sold in Canada and enforcing the food safety policies and standards set forth by Health Canada.[10] Additionally, CFIA and Health Canada establish standards for safe food manufacturing practices, such as Hazard Analysis and Critical Control Point (HACCP) programs.[11] HACCP is a science-based, systematic approach to preventing food-borne illness by predicting which hazards are most likely to occur in a food production facility.[12] When a hazard is identified, food manufacturers can then take appropriate measures to prevent the illness. If necessary, CFIA or provincial public health officials can take certain enforcement actions, such as requesting that a food manufacturer recall an unsafe item so that it is removed from store shelves.[12] Another important function of provincial public health agencies is educating the general public about safe food-handling practices.

Although Health Canada oversees the safety of most foods, Health Canada, CFIA, and provincial public health inspectors enforce food safety laws for domestic and imported meat and poultry products. CFIA staff inspect beef, poultry, and other food animals for diseases before and after slaughter, and the agency also ensures that meat and poultry processing plants meet federal standards.[13] Additionally, CFIA staff collect and analyze food samples to check for the presence of microbial and other unwanted and potentially harmful material in foods.[13] If a food hazard is identified, CFIA officials can ask meat and poultry processors to recall their unsafe products. Additionally, food safety experts with CFIA and provincial public health agencies conduct programs to educate people about proper food-handling practices. For more information, visit CFIA's Web site at www.inspection.gc.ca.

The responsibility for making sure Canadian drinking water supplies are safe is shared between the federal, provincial, territorial, and municipal governments.[14] The day-to-day responsibility of providing safe drinking water to the public rests with the individual provinces and territories, while local municipalities usually oversee the day-to-day operations of the water treatment facilities.[14] Health Canada's Water Quality and Health Bureau takes the leadership role in water science and research. Health Canada's Water Quality and Health Bureau protects the health of all Canadians by developing the *Guidelines for Canadian Drinking Water Quality* in partnership with the provinces and territories. These guidelines are used by every municipality and jurisdiction in Canada and are the basis for the drinking water quality requirements for all Canadians.[14]

Provincial and municipal officials work with CFIA and other federal agency staff to implement national food safety standards for foods produced and sold within each province.[8] Local public health departments, for example, are responsible for inspecting restaurants, grocery stores, dairy farms, and local food-processing companies. In many communities, restaurants are required to post their sanitation rating where customers can easily see it. Local health departments can close restaurants that do not receive high enough ratings and prevent them from reopening until food safety hazards have been corrected.

After you obtain foods and bring them into your home, it becomes your responsibility to reduce the risk of food-borne illness by handling the items properly. However, if you suspect that something you consumed made you or a family member very sick, you should contact your physician for treatment. The physician may decide to report the case of food-borne illness to local public health officials so that they can investigate and determine the source of your infection.

In many communities, restaurants must display their rating for sanitation where customers can easily see it. Local health departments can close restaurants that do not receive high enough ratings and not allow them to reopen until food safety hazards have been corrected.

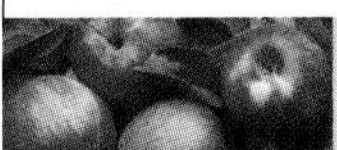

Concept **Checkpoint**

1. Discuss the roles of Health Canada, CFIA, and Agriculture and Agri-Food Canada in protecting the Canadian food supply.
2. How do local health departments protect consumers from food-borne illness?

Microbes in Food

For thousands of years, people have used certain microbes to produce a variety of foods, including hard cheeses, raised breads, pickled foods, and alcoholic beverages. When microorganisms metabolize nutrients in food, they often secrete substances that alter the colour, texture, taste, and other characteristics of the food in beneficial and desirable ways. Other kinds of microbes grow and multiply in food, but their metabolic by-products spoil the food, making it unfit for human consumption. When pathogens are in food, they can make the item unsafe to eat.

A **contaminated food** (or beverage) is no longer wholesome—pure or safe for human consumption. Contamination generally occurs when something that may or may not be harmful enters food or beverages unintentionally. Such contaminants include pathogens, insect parts, residues of compounds used to kill insects that destroy food crops, and metal fragments from food processing equipment. The following section discusses how pathogens can contaminate our food.

Did You Know?

You can't always rely on your senses to judge the wholesomeness of a food. A food can taste, smell, and appear safe to eat, but it may contain pathogens and/or their toxic by-products.

How Pathogens Enter Food

The microbes that cause food-borne illness can live practically anywhere—in air, water, soil, and sewage, as well as on various surfaces. Our skin, nasal passages, and large intestines have vast colonies of various kinds of microbes, some of which can be pathogenic. Animals, including cats, dogs, reptiles, cattle, and poultry, can also harbour harmful microbes on and in their bodies, especially in their intestinal tracts. Because pathogens are found throughout your environment, there are numerous ways that the microbes can contaminate your food. To reduce your risk of food-borne illness, you need to be aware of how pathogens can enter foods. The section, "Preventing Food-Borne Illness," later in this chapter discusses specific steps you can take to reduce the chances of contracting or spreading food-borne illness.

contaminated food item that is impure or unsafe for human consumption

Common Routes for Transmitting Pathogens

One common route for transmitting harmful microbes involves *vermin*, animals that often live around sewage or garbage, such as flies, cockroaches, mice, and rats. When vermin land on or crawl across filth, they pick up pathogens on their feet and can transfer them to humans, if they come in contact with food. To reduce your risk of food-borne illness, keep flies, cockroaches, and other vermin away from your food.

Poor personal hygiene practices frequently transfer microbes to food. People can contaminate their hands with pathogens when they come in contact with feces, such as while using the toilet or changing a baby's soiled diaper. Furthermore, animals harbour pathogens in their feces as well as on their skin and fur. If children prepare or eat foods after stroking animals at "petting" zoos or playing with pets, they can transmit these microbes to themselves or others. Thus, it is important for people to wash their hands before preparing foods. Children (and many adults) often need to be reminded to wash their hands.

To reduce your risk of food-borne illness, keep flies, cockroaches, and other vermin away from your food.

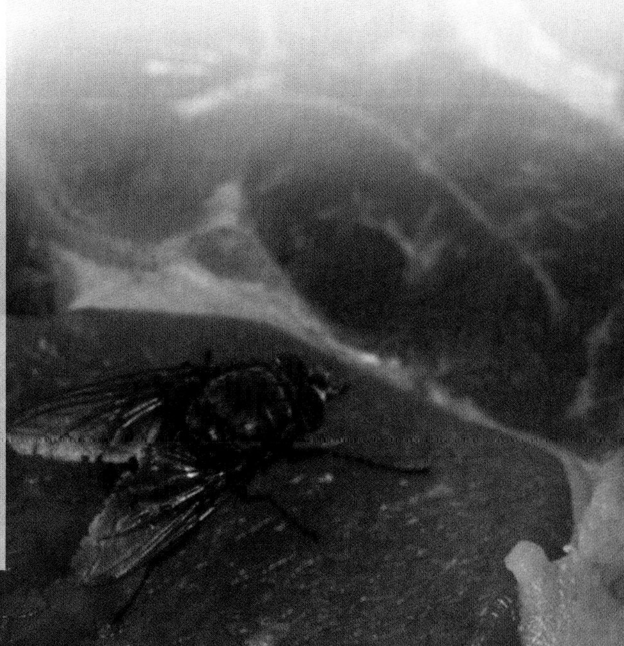

cross-contamination unintentional transfer of pathogenic microbes from one food to another

pasteurization process that kills the pathogens in foods and beverages as well as many microbes responsible for spoilage

Improper food handling frequently results in food-borne illness. A common practice is failing to wash cutting boards and food preparation utensils after they come in contact with raw meat or poultry. The contaminated boards and utensils are then used to prepare other foods. As a result of this practice, **cross-contamination** is likely to occur, because the pathogens in one food are transferred to another food, contaminating it. If that food is eaten raw, such as carrots in a salad, it carries a high risk of food-borne illness. Failing to cook foods properly can also increase the likelihood of food-borne illness. **Pasteurization** is a special heating process used by many commercial food producers to kill pathogens. In Canada, for example, most juices[15] and milk[16] have been pasteurized before they are marketed. A later section of this chapter, "Food Preservation," discusses other ways of preserving foods.

High-Risk Foods

Not all foods are likely to harbour pathogens. To survive and multiply, most microbes need warmth, moisture, and a source of nutrients, and some also require oxygen. In general, high-risk foods are warm, moist, and protein-rich, and they have a neutral or slightly acidic pH. Many of the foods we eat every day, such as meats, eggs, and milk, and products made from milk, fit this description. Table 12.1 presents some high-risk foods and the primary food-borne pathogens they may contain. The acronym FATTOM (food, acidity, time, temperature, oxygen, and moisture) can be used as an aid to remember the six favourable conditions required for the growth of food-borne pathogens.

Concept Checkpoint

3. Discuss at least three ways pathogens can contaminate human foods.
4. With regard to food preparation, what is cross-contamination?
5. What is pasteurization?
6. Discuss conditions that favour the survival and multiplication of food-borne pathogens.
7. Identify at least four foods that are high risk for supporting pathogens.

Certain pets, particularly reptiles such as this box turtle, are sources of *Salmonella*. Anyone who touches turtles or other potential *Salmonella* carriers should wash their hands thoroughly after handling the animals.

TABLE 12.1 *Summary of Some High-Risk Foods and Their Primary Pathogens*

Raw or Undercooked Animal Food	Typical Menu Item	Common Pathogens
Beef	Rare hamburger Steak tartare Carpaccio	*Salmonella* species *E. coli* O157:H7
Pork	Sausage Pork roast	*Trichinella*
Poultry	Chicken, turkey, duck	*Salmonella* species *Campylobacter jejuni*
Eggs	Quiche, hollandaise sauce, eggs Benedict, homemade mayonnaise, meringue pies, mousse, tiramisu, chicken croquettes, rice balls, stuffing, French toast, crab cakes, eggnog, Caesar salad, homemade ice creams and frozen custards	*Salmonella enteritidis*
Raw fish/finfish	Sushi; lightly cooked fish; raw-marinated, cold-smoked fish; ceviche, tuna carpaccio	*Anisakis* *Vibrio parahaemolyticus*
Shellfish	Oysters Clams	*Vibrio vulnificus and other Vibrio species* Hepatitis A *Norovirus*
Milk and milk products	Raw or unpasteurized milk, some soft cheeses such as Camembert and Brie	*Listeria monocytogenes* *Salmonella species* *Campylobacter jejuni* *E. coli* O157:H7

Source: FDA Center for Food Safety and Applied Nutrition: *Managing food safety: A manual for the voluntary use of HACCP principles for operators of food service and retail establishments*. 2006. www.cfsan. fda.gov/~dms/hret2-a3.html.

Food-Borne Illness

Signs and symptoms of food-borne (and water-borne) illnesses generally involve the digestive tract and include nausea, vomiting, diarrhea, and intestinal cramps. However, most pathogens have an *incubation period*, a length of time in which they grow and multiply in the digestive tract before they cause illness. Thus, if you develop signs and symptoms of a food-borne illness, you might have difficulty identifying the source of the infection. Was the vomiting and diarrhea that you experienced at 3 a.m. the result of eating soft-cooked eggs for breakfast 18 hours earlier or the sliced deli chicken you ate for lunch two days ago?

Various factors influence whether an individual becomes ill after consuming a food or beverage that has been contaminated with a pathogen. The number of pathogenic microbes in a food or the amount of toxin it contains can contribute to the risk and severity of a food-borne illness. Furthermore, individuals vary in their vulnerability to many food-borne pathogens. In general, high-risk groups are pregnant women, very young children, the elderly, and persons who suffer from serious chronic illnesses or weakened immune systems.

In most cases, otherwise healthy individuals who suffer from common types of food-borne illness recover completely and without professional medical care within a few days. However, vomiting, diarrhea, and other signs of illness can be so severe, the patient requires hospitalization. You should consult a physician when an intestinal disorder is accompanied by one or more of the following signs: fever (oral temperature above 38.6°C/101.5°F), bloody bowel movements, prolonged vomiting that reduces fluid intake, diarrhea that lasts more than three days, or dehydration.[3] Many people mistakenly report that they have the "stomach *flu*," when they actually are suffering from a food- or water-borne illness. "Flu" or *influenza* is an infectious disease caused by specific viruses that invade the respiratory tract. Influenza is characterized by coughing, fever, weakness, and body aches. On the other hand, food-borne illness primarily affects the digestive system and not the respiratory system. Intestinal cramps, diarrhea, and vomiting are *not* typical signs and symptoms of influenza, and coughing is not a usual sign of a food-borne illness. Thus, it is inaccurate to call a bout of diarrhea and intestinal cramps the "stomach flu."

Did You Know?

Honey, even commercially processed brands of the sweetener, should not be fed to infants because they may contain *Clostridium botulinum* spores. The spores can grow in an infant's intestinal tract, produce toxin, and cause botulism (see Chapter 5). Older children and adults can consume honey safely, because their immune systems prevent the spores from growing.

Concept **Checkpoint**

8. Identify at least three typical signs and symptoms of food-borne illness.
9. When should a person suffering from a food-borne illness seek professional medical help?
10. Discuss the differences between a food-borne illness and "the flu."

Improperly cooked or handled meat, poultry, eggs, and foods made with eggs are common sources of *Staphylococcus aureus*. The bacteria produce a toxin that results in food-borne illness.

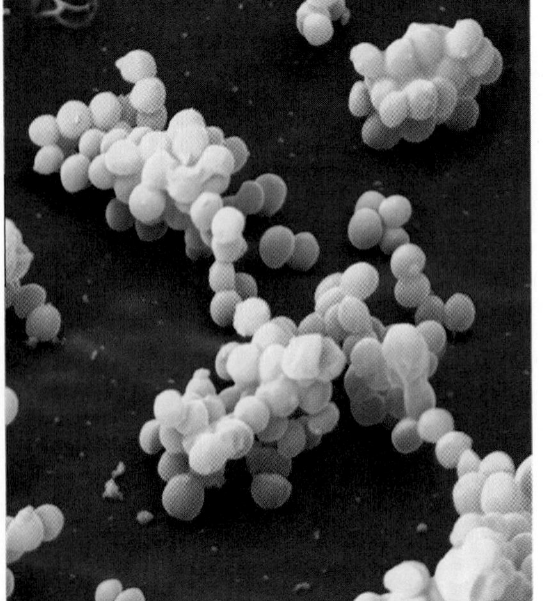

Sources of Food-Borne Pathogens

The major kinds of pathogens are bacteria, viruses, protozoans, and fungi. In Canada, *bacteria* and *viruses* are responsible for most cases of food-borne illness.[17] The following sections take a closer look at some of the major pathogens that can cause food-borne illness.

Bacteria

Bacteria are single-cell microorganisms that do not have the complex array of organelles that plant and animal cells contain. Some bacteria can live without oxygen, such as in canned or vacuum-packed foods. Other types of bacteria transform into inactive resistant forms called *spores* when living conditions are less than ideal. If the environment becomes more hospitable, the spores revert to the active bacterial state.

Many kinds of bacteria are pathogens that cause food-borne illness, including forms of *Campylobacter*, *Clostridium*, *Escherichia*, *Listeria*, *Salmonella*, and *Staphylococcus* (*kam'-pih-low-bak'-ter, klo-strid'-e-um, esh'-ear-i'-ke-ah, lis-te'-re-ah, sal'-mo-nell-ah, staff'-il-lo-cawk'-kiss*). Table 12.2 summarizes some general information about common bacterial sources of food-borne illness in Canada.

TABLE 12.2 *Common Sources of Food-Borne Illness: Bacteria*

Bacterium	High-Risk Foods	Approx. Time of Onset	Typical Signs and Symptoms
Bacillus cereus (toxin)	Meat, poultry, and starchy foods (rice, potatoes, puddings, some soups)	10–16 hours	Abdominal cramps, watery diarrhea, nausea
Campylobacter jejuni	Raw, undercooked poultry; raw milk; contaminated water	2–5 days	Diarrhea, abdominal cramping, vomiting, fever, bloody diarrhea (sometimes)
Clostridium botulinum (toxin)	Vacuum-packed foods, improperly canned foods, garlic-in-oil mixtures Honey may contain spores.	12–72 hours	Vomiting, diarrhea, blurry or double vision, difficulty swallowing, muscular weakness Can be fatal
Clostridium perfringens (toxin)	Cooked meat, poultry, casseroles, gravies	8–16 hours	Watery diarrhea, abdominal cramps, fever (rarely)
Escherichia coli O157:H7 (toxin)	Raw ground beef, raw seed sprouts, raw leafy greens, fresh fruit, raw milk, unpasteurized juices, foods contaminated with feces	1–8 days	Intestinal cramps, diarrhea, bloody diarrhea, kidney failure Can be fatal
Listeria monocytogenes	Raw meat and poultry, raw milk, fresh soft cheese made from raw milk, liver pâté, smoked seafood, deli meats and salads, hot dogs	9–48 hours for GI tract signs and symptoms, 2–6 weeks for invasive disease	Fever, muscular aches, vomiting, diarrhea In pregnant women, the infection can lead to stillbirth (birth of a dead fetus) or premature birth.
Salmonella species	Raw or undercooked meat, poultry, seafood, and eggs; raw seed sprouts; raw vegetables; unpasteurized juice	1–3 days	Nausea, vomiting, fever, chills, headache, abdominal cramps, diarrhea Infection can be fatal in infants, the elderly, and people suffering from chronic illness.
Shigella species	Raw vegetables, herbs, and other foods that were contaminated as a result of poor food-handling practices	24–48 hours	Abdominal cramps, fever, diarrhea that may contain blood and mucus
Staphylococcus aureus (toxin)	Meats, poultry, and eggs; foods made with eggs, such as potato, egg, macaroni, and egg salads; certain homemade ice creams, custards, and cream-filled pastries Cooked foods are often contaminated as a result of improper food handling practices.	30 minutes to 8 hours	Diarrhea, nausea, vomiting, abdominal cramps, weakness, fever (occasionally)
Vibrio vulnificus	Raw oysters and other raw or undercooked seafood	1–7 days	Vomiting, diarrhea, abdominal cramps
Yersinia enterocolitica	Raw vegetables, undercooked pork, contaminated water, unpasteurized milk	2–3 days	Diarrhea, fever, vomiting, abdominal pain

Sources: National Institute of Allergy and Infectious Diseases: *Foodborne diseases*. Updated 2006. www.niaid.nih.gov/factsheets/foodbornedis.htm; U.S. Food and Drug Administration, Center for Food Safety and Applied Nutrition: *Bad bug book: Foodborne pathogenic microorganisms and natural toxins handbook*. Updated 2006. www.cfsan.fda.gov/~mow/app2.html.

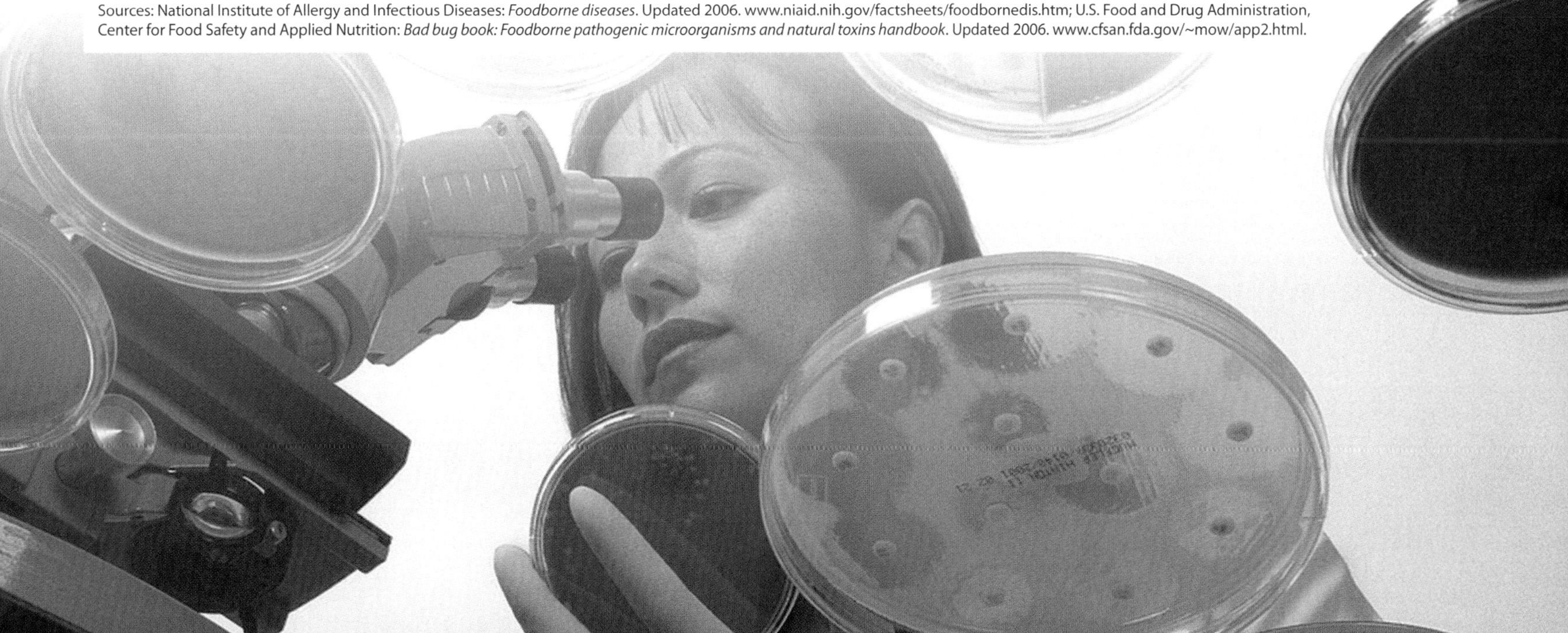

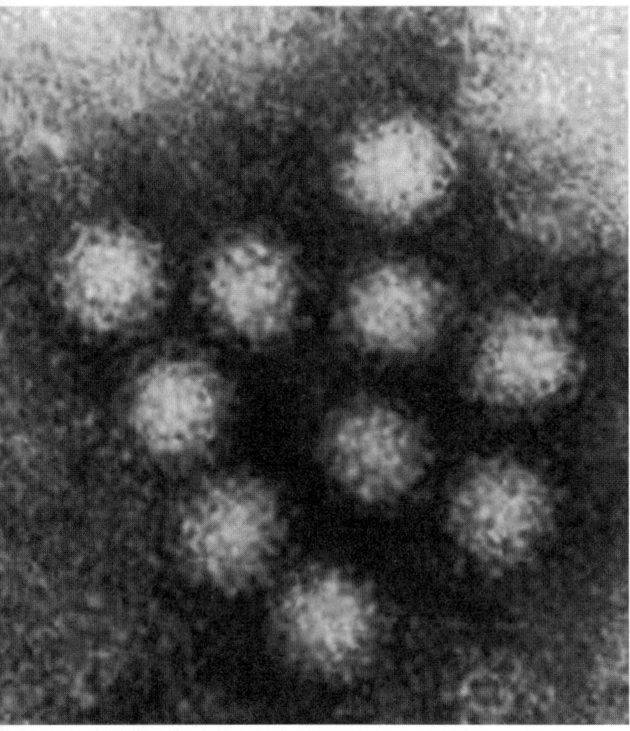

Figure 12.1 Norovirus. A virus, such as this Norovirus, is simply a piece of genetic material coated with protein.

TABLE 12.3 *Common Sources of Food-Borne Illness: Viral*

Virus	High-Risk Foods	Approx. Time of Onset	Typical Signs and Symptoms
Norovirus	Food or water that has been contaminated with infected feces, enabling the virus to be spread person-to-person	1–2 days	Vomiting; watery, non-bloody diarrhea; abdominal cramps; nausea; low-grade fever (occasionally)
Rotavirus	Food or water that has been contaminated with infected feces Most children have been infected by 2 years of age.	2 days	Fever, abdominal pain, vomiting, watery diarrhea Worldwide, thousands of children die each year as a result of *rotavirus* infection. In 2006, Health Canada approved a vaccine to prevent rotaviral infections in children.
Hepatitis A (HAV)	Food or water that has been contaminated with HAV from feces	15–50 days	Fever, loss of appetite, nausea, vomiting, diarrhea, muscle aches, general weakness May have signs of liver inflammation, such as jaundice (indicated by yellow discoloration of skin and whites of eyes), liver enlargement, and dark-coloured urine Most people recover after a few weeks, but in rare cases, the illness is deadly.

Sources: Centers for Disease Control and Prevention: *CDC technical fact sheet about noroviruses*. www.cdc.gov/ncidod/dvrd/revb/gastro/ noro-factsheet.pdf. Accessed: September 25, 2006; Centers for Disease Control and Prevention: Rotavirus. Reviewed June 2006. www.cdc.gov/ncidod/drvd/revb/gastro/rotavirus.htm. Accessed: September 25, 2006; Fiore AE: Hepatitis A transmitted by food. *Clinical Infectious Disease* 38:705, 2004.

virus microbe consisting of a piece of genetic material coated with protein

parasite organism that lives in or on another organism, often deriving nourishment from its host

protozoans single-celled microorganisms that have complex cell structures

fungi simple organisms that live on dead or decaying organic matter

Viruses

Viruses are another common source of food-borne infection (Table 12.3). A **virus** is simply a piece of genetic material coated with protein (Fig. 12.1). Viruses must invade a living cell to produce more viruses. Unlike certain bacteria, viruses do not secrete toxins, and therefore, they do not cause food intoxication. Contaminated food or water, however, can transmit viruses to humans and cause food infection.

Parasites

A **parasite** is an organism that lives in or on another living thing, often deriving nourishment from its host. Some parasites, such as *Giardia* (*jee-ar'-de-ah*) and *Cryptosporidium* (*krip'-toe-spo-rid'-ee-um*), are **protozoans** (*pro-toe-zoe'-ans*), single-celled microorganisms that have a more complex cell structure than bacteria. Protozoans are often responsible for causing travellers' diarrhea; the Chapter 12 Highlight discusses this condition. In addition to protozoans, food-borne parasites include types of worms such as *Trichinella* (*trick'-ah-nell'-ah*) and *Anisiakis* (*ah'ni-sa'-kis*) (Fig. 12.2).[18] Table 12.4 provides information about parasites that can cause food-borne infections. Most Canadians who become infected with parasites that are common in Canada recover when they receive proper treatment. Nevertheless, some infected persons suffer long-term health problems, and even die, as a result of the illnesses.

Giardia is a parasitic protozoan, a single-celled microorganism that has a more complex cell structure than bacteria.

TABLE 12.4 *Common Sources of Food-Borne Illness: Parasites*

Parasite	High-Risk Foods	Approx. Time of Onset	Typical Signs and Symptoms
Cryptosporidium	Foods prepared with contaminated water or by people whose hands were contaminated with infected feces	1–12 days	Profuse, watery diarrhea; abdominal pain; fever; nausea; vomiting; weight loss
Giardia	Consumption of contaminated water, including water from lakes, streams, swimming pools High-risk groups include travellers to certain countries, hikers, and people who swim in or camp by lakes and streams.	1–3 days	Sudden onset of explosive watery diarrhea, abdominal pain, loss of appetite
Toxoplasma	Raw or partially cooked infected meat, especially pork, lamb, or deer meat Accidentally ingesting infected cat feces	10–13 days	Fever, headache, muscle aches, rash Pregnant women should avoid contact with cat feces, because the parasite can infect their unborn offspring, causing eye or brain damage.
Trichinella	Raw or undercooked infected meat, especially pork, bear, seal, and walrus meat	4–28 days	Initially: nausea, vomiting, diarrhea, fatigue, fever, abdominal discomfort Later: headaches, chills, cough, eye swelling, muscle and joint pain In severe cases, death can occur.
Anisakis	Raw or undercooked infected seafood	1 hour to 2 weeks	Tickling sensation in throat and vomiting or coughing up a worm In severe cases, severe abdominal pain that may be mistaken for appendicitis.

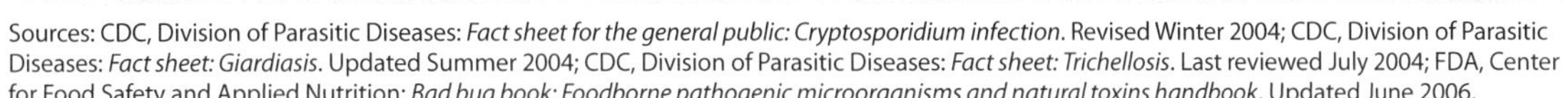

Sources: CDC, Division of Parasitic Diseases: *Fact sheet for the general public: Cryptosporidium infection*. Revised Winter 2004; CDC, Division of Parasitic Diseases: *Fact sheet: Giardiasis*. Updated Summer 2004; CDC, Division of Parasitic Diseases: *Fact sheet: Trichellosis*. Last reviewed July 2004; FDA, Center for Food Safety and Applied Nutrition: *Bad bug book: Foodborne pathogenic microorganisms and natural toxins handbook*. Updated June 2006.

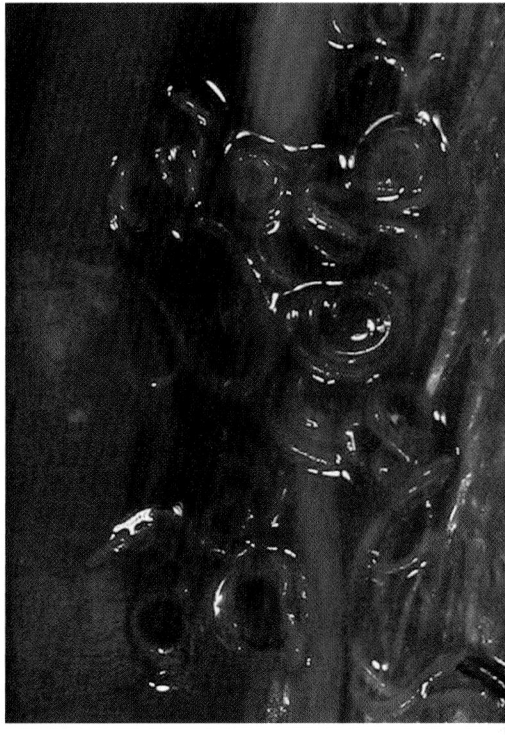

Figure 12.2 ***Anisakis.*** *Anisakis* is a type of worm that can be transferred to humans who eat raw fish.

Fungi

Fungi such as moulds, yeast, and mushrooms are simple life forms that live on dead or decaying organic matter. Certain fungi, such as button mushrooms and the mould in blue cheese, are beneficial and edible. Other fungi are responsible for spoiling foods, such as bread moulds, or causing allergic reactions in sensitive people. A serious concern is the toxicity of several varieties of wild mushrooms. Cases of severe illness and death have been reported as a result of people picking and eating toxic wild mushrooms after mistaking them for edible varieties (Fig. 12.3). Nevertheless, fungi are not a major source of food-borne illness in Canada or the United States.

Certain fungi, such as button mushrooms and the mould in blue cheese, are beneficial and edible.

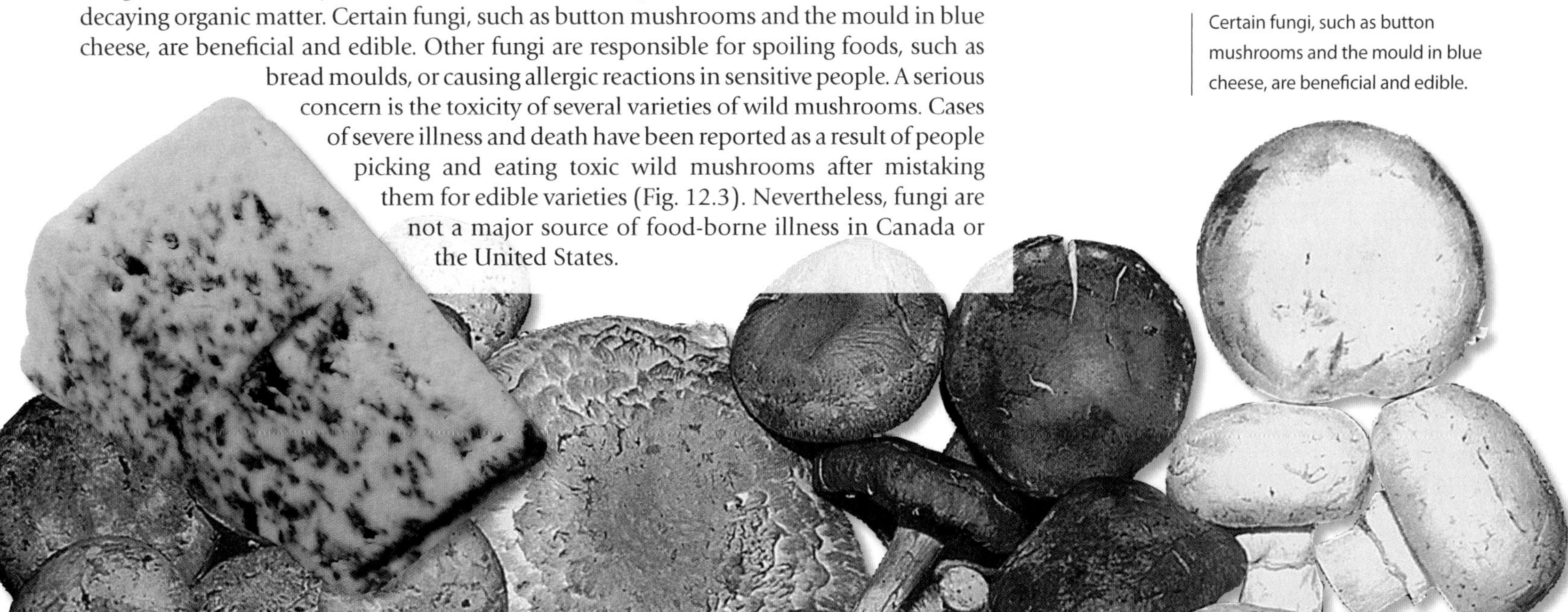

Figure 12.3 Deadly mushrooms. Severe illness and even death can occur if people pick and eat toxic mushrooms, such as this Amanita mushroom, after mistaking them for edible varieties.

Certain moulds produce *aflatoxins*, substances that can cause severe illness, particularly liver damage, and even death when consumed. Improperly stored tree nuts, peanuts, and corn can be sources of aflatoxins. In some regions of the world, especially Africa and Southeast Asia, people often eat foods that are contaminated with aflatoxin-producing moulds. Rates of liver cancer are high in these places. Thus, medical researchers think there is an association between exposure to aflatoxins and development of liver cancer. At present, the aflatoxins of most concern for Canadians would come through foods grown in the tropics and imported in Canada, as the aflatoxins associated with any Canadian products are typically associated with animal feeds.[19]

Concept **Checkpoint**

11. Identify at least three bacterial sources of food-borne illness in Canada.
12. Identify three viruses that are sources of food-borne illness in Canada.
13. Identify three parasites that can cause food- or water-borne illness in Canada.
14. What are aflatoxins?

Preventing Food-Borne Illness

In many instances, you cannot control the safety of foods that are prepared in restaurants or other places outside your home. However, you can greatly reduce your risk of food-borne illness by following some important rules, most of which require changing risky food selection, preparation, and storage practices.

In addition, the Canadian Partnership for Consumer Food Safety Education provides information to assist Canadians to practise safe food-handling and preparation methods to reduce the risk of microbial food-borne illness.[2] The Canadian Partnership for Consumer Food Safety Education Web site (www.canfightbac.org) provides useful food safety tips and promotes a Fight BAC! campaign (Fig. 12.4) that highlights four simple steps Canadians can take to help prevent food-borne illness.[2] It is also important to note that many local health units in Canada offer certification in food safety training, and many employers in the food industry require this certification.

Figure 12.4 Fight BAC! The Canadian Partnership for Consumer Food Safety Education promotes food safety through this four-step campaign to prevent food-borne illness.

Purchasing Food

To reduce your risk of food-borne illness:

- When shopping in a supermarket, select frozen foods and highly perishable foods, such as meat, poultry, or fish, last.
- Avoid precut bagged produce or salads.
- Check "best by" dates on packaged perishable foods. Choose meats and other animal products with the latest dates.
- Don't buy food in damaged containers; for example, avoid containers that leak, bulge, or are severely dented, or jars that are cracked or have loose or bulging lids.
- Open egg cartons and examine eggs—don't buy cartons that have cracked eggs.
- Purchase only pasteurized milk, cheese, and fruit and vegetable juices (check the label).
- Purchase only the amount of produce needed for a week's menus. The longer you keep fresh fruits and vegetables, the more likely they will spoil.

Before purchasing eggs, open the carton and check the eggs—don't buy cartons that have any cracked eggs.

- Pack meat, fish, and poultry in separate plastic bags, so their drippings don't contaminate each other and your other groceries.
- After shopping for food, take groceries home immediately. Refrigerate or freeze meat, fish, egg, and dairy products promptly.
- Store whole eggs in their carton, even if your refrigerator has a place for storing eggs. Egg cartons are designed to keep eggs fresh longer than a refrigerator's egg compartment.

Setting the Stage for Food Preparation

Contaminated hands and food preparation surfaces spread pathogens. To reduce the risk of food-borne illness:

- Wash hands thoroughly with hot, soapy water for at least 20 seconds before and after touching food (Fig. 12.5).
- Use a fresh paper towel or clean hand towel to dry hands. Reserve dish towels for drying pots, pans, and cooking utensils that are not washed and dried in a dishwasher.
- Before preparing food, clean food preparation surfaces, including kitchen counters, cutting boards, dishes, knives, and other food preparation equipment with hot, soapy water. You can kill most pathogens when you clean and *sanitize* food preparation surfaces with a solution made by adding a tablespoon of bleach to 3.75 L (1 gal.) of water. However, avoid getting the bleach solution on coloured fabrics or surfaces that can be damaged by bleach (granite, for example).
- CFIA recommends cutting boards with unmarred surfaces made of easy-to-clean, nonporous materials, such as plastic, marble, or glass. If you prefer to use wooden cutting boards, make sure they are made of a non-absorbent hardwood, such as oak or maple, and have no obvious seams or cracks.
- Replace cutting boards when they become streaked with cuts, because these grooves can be difficult to clean thoroughly and may harbour bacteria.
- If possible, have one cutting board reserved for meats, fish, and poultry; another cutting board for fruits and vegetables; and a third board for breads. Clean all cutting boards in the dishwasher or with hot, soapy water. You can also sanitize cutting boards with a diluted bleach solution.
- Sanitize food preparation surfaces and equipment that have come in contact with raw meat, fish, poultry, and eggs as soon as possible to destroy pathogens that may be present. In addition, sanitize kitchen sponges and wash kitchen towels frequently.

Figure 12.5 Proper handwashing. Remember these six steps to ensure proper handwashing.

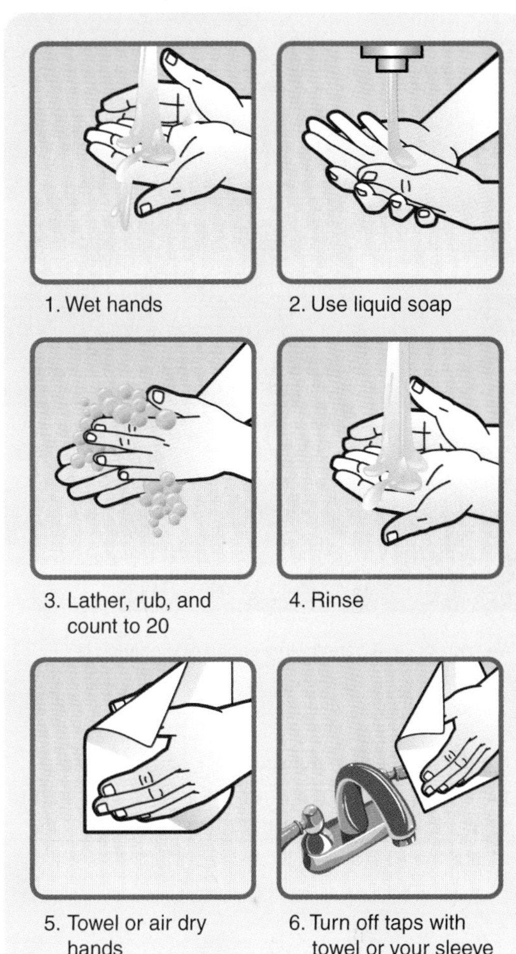

Wash hands thoroughly with hot, soapy water for at least 20 seconds before and after touching food.

| Wash produce in water before eating or preparing it.

Preparing Food

To reduce your risk of food-borne illness:

- Don't use foods from containers that leak, bulge, or are severely dented or from jars that are cracked or have loose or bulging lids.
- Don't use foods from containers that have damaged safety seals, because the food they contain may have been contaminated.
- Don't taste or use food that spurts liquid or has a bad odour when the can is opened.
- Read product labels to determine whether foods need to be refrigerated after their packages are opened.
- Before preparing fresh produce, carefully wash the foods under running water to remove dirt and bacteria clinging to the surface. Bacteria can be sticky, so scrub the peel with a vegetable brush if it is to be eaten. Even if you plan to remove the skin or peel, wash the produce before you cut it.
- If a food has a *small* amount of mould, you can cut out the mouldy portions, and also remove some of the unaffected portions around it. If the mouldy area is large, don't eat the food. **When in doubt, throw the food out.**

Maintaining the Proper Temperature of Foods

Most microbes grow well when the temperature of a high-risk food is between 4°C and 60°C (40°F and 140°F)—the "danger zone" (Fig. 12.6).[20] Cooking foods to the proper temperature destroys food-borne viruses and bacteria, such as *Norovirus* and *E. coli* O157:H7. To be safe, a product must be cooked to an internal temperature that is high enough to destroy harmful pathogens and certain bacterial toxins. Using a meat thermometer is a reliable way to ensure that meat, poultry, thick pieces of fish, and egg-containing dishes have reached the proper internal temperature, without over-cooking. Table 12.5 indicates recommended minimum internal temperatures for cooking these foods.

Meat thermometers must be used properly. In general, the thermometer should be placed in the thickest part of the muscle tissue, away from bone, fat, or gristle (Fig. 12.7). If the thermometer is inserted incorrectly, or placed in the wrong area, the reading may not accurately reflect the internal temperature of the product.

Microwave cooking can result in uneven heating that does not destroy microbes in the cool spots. While cooking a food in a microwave oven, keep the dish covered, and stop the oven occasionally to stir the food. Stirring the food reduces uneven heating. Microwave cooking is not recommended for stuffed foods; during cooking, the temperature of the stuffing may not be high enough to kill pathogens.[21]

Chilling food slows the growth of microbes in the items, but some bacteria can grow even at proper refrigeration temperatures. Freezing does not kill bacteria or inactive viruses in food; the process just halts the microbes' ability to multiply. As frozen food thaws, the bacteria and viruses resume their activities and can cause illness.

A major challenge for food handlers involves keeping large amounts of high-risk foods at safe temperatures when they are served from a single container. Food that is near the sides of the container may stay hotter or colder than food that is near or in the centre of the container. As shown in Figure 12.8, chilled foods should be kept covered and served from a shallow container filled with ice. Hot foods should be kept covered and be served from shallow, heated pans. The best simple advice to follow: "Keep hot foods hot and cold foods cold."

Figure 12.6 Temperature guide for food safety. Most pathogenic microbes grow well when the temperature of risky food is between 4°C and 60°C (40°F and 140°F)—the "danger zone."

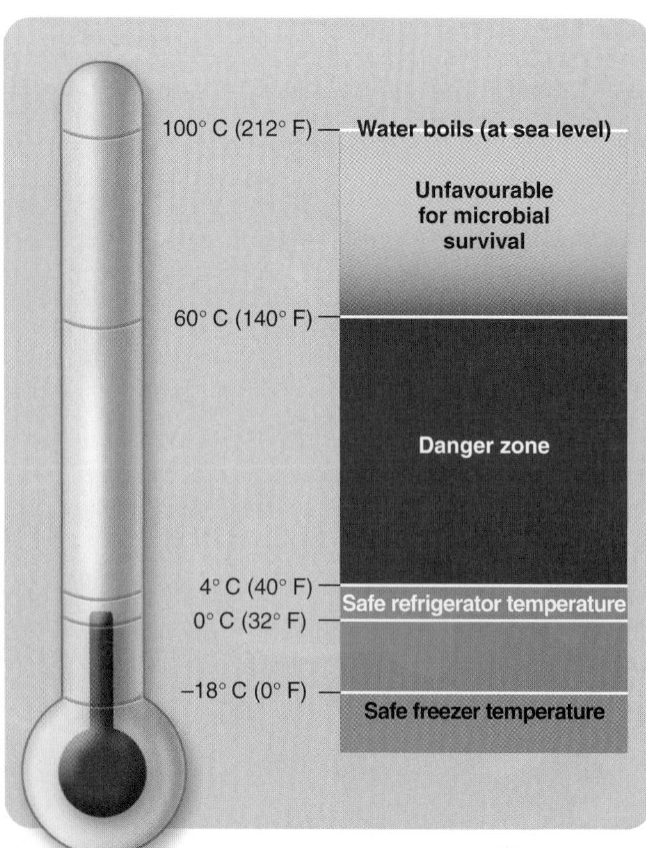

TABLE 12.5 *Recommended Safe Minimum Internal Temperatures*

Food	Safe Minimum Internal Temperature (°C/°F)
Beef steaks and roasts	63/145
Fish	63/145
Pork	71/160
Ground beef	71/160
Egg dishes	71/160
Chicken breasts	74/165
Whole poultry	74/165

Source: U.S. Department of Agriculture, Food Safety and Inspection Service: *"Is it done yet?"* Revised April 2006. www.fsis.usda.gov/PDF/IsItDoneYet_ Magnet.pdf.

To reduce your risk of food-borne illness:

- Always thaw high-risk foods in the refrigerator, or under cold running water, or in a microwave oven.
- Cook foods immediately after thawing. Do not refreeze.
- Marinate food in the refrigerator, and if marinating meat, fish, or poultry, discard the marinade.
- Don't remove cold foods from the refrigerator or hot foods from the stove until it is time to serve them.

Figure 12.7 Meat thermometer. Using a meat (food) thermometer is a reliable way to ensure that the cooked item has reached the proper internal temperature.

Figure 12.8 Keep cold foods cold. Chilled foods, especially picnic items, should be kept covered, in a shallow container, and placed in another container that is filled with ice.

Did You Know?

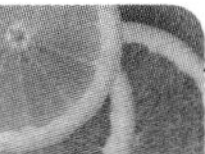

Have you heard about the "five-second rule"? Supposedly, food that drops on the floor will not pick up microbes if it is picked up within five seconds. A study determined that this is a food-related myth. As soon as food touches a contaminated surface such as a floor, microbes adhere to it.[22]

Eating raw fish, such as some forms of sushi, can be safe for most healthy people if the fish is very fresh before being commercially frozen and then thawed.

Raw Fish

Eating raw fish, such as sushi, can be safe for most healthy people if the fish is very fresh before being commercially frozen and then thawed. While frozen, the fish must maintain an internal temperature of −12°C (10°F) for seven days. The freezing step is important because very cold temperatures can kill parasites that are often in fish tissues. If you choose to eat uncooked fish, purchase it from reputable establishments that have high standards for quality and sanitation. Nevertheless, it is prudent to not eat any raw animal products, including fish.

Ground Meats, Poultry, and Fish

Ground meats, poultry, and fish are highly perishable and must be thoroughly cooked to avoid being a source of food-borne illness. The interior portion of an intact piece of raw animal flesh is free of bacteria, because the tissues are not exposed to air. However, ground meats, fish, and poultry products are often contaminated with microbes. Prior to being ground up, the surface of a chunk of meat, fish, or poultry may contain relatively harmless concentrations of pathogens. The grinding process, however, mixes the pathogens throughout the meat. At the same time, grinding the meat greatly increases its surface area, exposing more of the protein-rich tissues to microbes in air. Furthermore, the meat grinder can be a source of pathogens and can spread them to the food product, especially if the machine was not properly cleaned after its last use. The particles of food that remained in the grinder can provide food for pathogenic microorganisms. Therefore, surfaces that touch ground meats should be cleaned carefully.

To reduce your risk of food-borne illness:

- Cook beef, poultry, pork, thick pieces of fish, and egg-containing dishes thoroughly, using a meat thermometer to check for doneness.
- Cook eggs until the yolk and white have solidified and no "runniness" remains.
- Heat alfalfa and other types of sprouts until they are steaming, because fresh sprouts may be contaminated with pathogenic bacteria.
- Properly cooked seafood should not be shiny, and it should be firm but flake easily when touched with a fork.
- Bake stuffing separately from poultry or wash the poultry cavity thoroughly and stuff the bird immediately before cooking. Make sure the temperature of the stuffing reaches 74°C (165°F). After cooking, transfer the stuffing to a clean bowl for serving or storage.
- Serve meat, poultry, and fish on a clean plate—never use the same plate that held the raw product. For example, when grilling hamburgers, don't put cooked items on the plate that was used to carry the raw meat to the grill.
- Picnic foods require special attention because outdoor temperatures may favour rapid bacterial growth. Keep cold salads and desserts on ice. Meats should be cooked completely at a picnic site. Do not partially cook foods in advance and plan to finish cooking them at the picnic.

Prior to being ground up, the surface of a chunk of meat, fish, or poultry may contain relatively harmless concentrations of pathogens. The grinding process mixes the pathogens throughout the meat.

Storing and Reheating Food

After food is cooked, careless food handling continues to set the stage for the growth of pathogens. Food-borne pathogens thrive at *room temperature*, temperatures that are between 16°C and 43°C (60°F and 110°F). A common practice is to let hot or cold foods remain on the table at room temperature for a few hours. Although you may not feel like clearing the table after eating, it is a good idea to cover leftovers and refrigerate or freeze them as soon as you are done eating, or within two hours. Do this by separating the food into as many shallow pans as needed to provide a large surface area for faster cooling. There is no need to let hot foods cool before chilling or freezing them.

To reduce your risk of food-borne illness, follow these food storage tips:

- Check your refrigerator's temperature regularly to make sure it stays below 4°C (40°F). Keep the refrigerator as cold as possible without freezing milk and lettuce.
- Cook ground meats and poultry soon after purchasing. If this is not possible, freeze the ground items.
- Raw fish, shellfish, and poultry are highly perishable. It is best to cook these foods or freeze them the day they are purchased.
- Use refrigerated ground meat and patties within one to two days and use frozen meat and patties within three to four months after purchasing them. Table 12.6 presents recommended time limits for refrigeration and freezer storage of foods. Foods that are stored in the freezer for longer than recommended periods often develop unappealing flavours. Note that ground meats are more perishable than intact cuts of meat.
- Use refrigerated leftovers within four days. The Recipes for Healthy Living feature near the end of this chapter has a chilled chicken salad recipe that uses leftover chicken.
- Reheat leftovers to 74°C (165°F); reheat gravy to a rolling boil to kill pathogenic bacteria that may be present.

TABLE 12.6 *Cold Storage Time Limits for Perishable Foods*

Product	Storage Period in Refrigerator (4°C/40°F)	Storage Period in Freezer (−18°C/0°F)
Fresh meat		
Ground meat	1–2 days	3–4 months
Steaks and roasts	3–5 days	6–12 months
Fresh pork		
Chops	3–5 days	4–6 months
Ground	1–2 days	3–4 months
Roasts	3–5 days	4–6 months
Cured meats		
Luncheon meat	3–5 days	1–2 months
Sausage	1–2 days	1–2 months
Gravy	1–2 days	2–3 months
Fresh fish		
Lean (such as cod, flounder, haddock)	1–2 days	Up to 6 months
Fatty (such as perch, salmon)	1–2 days	2–3 months
Fresh chicken (whole)	1–2 days	12 months
Parts	1–2 days	9 months
Giblets	1–2 days	3–4 months
Dairy products		
Cheese (swiss, brick, processed cheese)	3–4 weeks	Not recommended
Milk	5 days	1 month
Ice cream, ice milk	—	2–4 months
Eggs		
Fresh, in shell	3 weeks	—
Hard-cooked	1 week	—

Source: FDA: The unwelcome dinner guest: Preventing food-borne illness. *FDA Consumer Magazine* 25, 2003. www.fda.gov/fdac/reprtints/dinguest.html.

Figure 12.9 Storing risky foods in the refrigerator. To avoid cross-contamination, store raw meats, poultry, fish, and shellfish on lower shelves of the refrigerator so that they are separated from foods that are to be eaten raw.

Did You Know?

During an electrical power outage, you can keep refrigerated food safely for only about four hours—if you don't open the refrigerator door. A full freezer can maintain its cold temperature for about 48 hours (24 hours if the freezer is half full), if the freezer door remains closed.[24,25] For more information about handling perishable foods during an emergency, visit the following CFIA Web site at www.inspection.gc.ca/english/fssa/concen/tipcon/emurge.shtml.

Cross-contamination is not only a threat during food preparation; it can also become a problem during food storage. Therefore, keep all foods, including leftovers, covered while they are in the refrigerator. This practice can prevent drippings from foods that are often contaminated, such as raw chicken, from tainting other foods. Furthermore, store raw meats, fish, poultry, and shellfish on lower shelves of the refrigerator so that they are separated from foods that are to be eaten raw (Fig. 12.9).

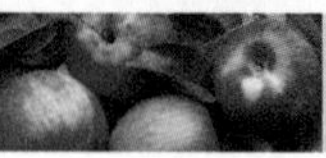

Concept Checkpoint

15. List at least four rules for reducing the risk of food-borne illness when you purchase foods and beverages.
16. List at least five rules for reducing the risk of food-borne illness when you prepare and cook foods.
17. List at least three rules for reducing the risk of food-borne illness when you store cooked foods.
18. Explain why ground meat and poultry often are sources of food-borne illness.
19. What preparation steps can be taken to make fish safer to eat raw?
20. What temperature range encourages rapid multiplication of pathogens?
21. Explain how to best orient foods in your refrigerator to avoid cross-contamination.

Be alert for signs of unsafe food-handling practices when you eat out. Make sure tabletops, dishes, and eating utensils are clean; custard, pudding, pies, and salad bar foods are chilled and kept on ice; and hot foods are hot and served from a heated food bar. Also be wary of perishable foods in vending machines, especially those selling sandwiches. If your serving of meat, poultry, or fish does not appear to be thoroughly cooked, ask the waiter to return the item to the kitchen to be heated again. These tips also apply to foods prepared for dormitory residents.

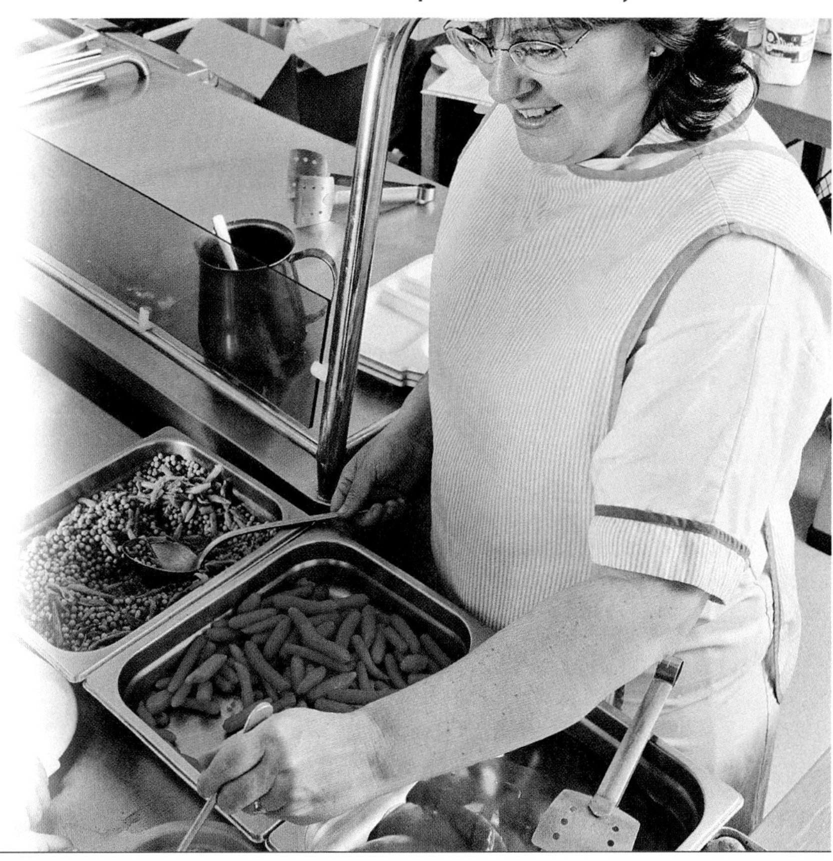

When eating out, make sure tabletops, dishes, and eating utensils are clean; custard, pudding pies, and salad bar foods are chilled and kept on ice; and hot foods are hot and served from a heated food bar.

Food Preservation

If nothing is done to preserve a fresh food, the item soon undergoes various chemical changes that eventually result in spoilage. Preserving food extends its shelf life. **Shelf life** refers to the period of time that a food can be stored before it spoils. Heating is one of the oldest ways to preserve foods. Heat can kill or deactivate pathogens, and the process also destroys naturally occurring enzymes in foods that can contribute to food spoilage.

Fermentation is an ancient method of food preservation that is still used to produce a variety of foods, including yogourt, wine, pickles, and sauerkraut. The fermentation process involves adding certain bacteria or yeast to food. These microbes use sugars in the food to make acids and alcohol, chemicals that hinder the growth of other types of bacteria and yeast that can spoil food.

For centuries, people preserved meats, fruits, and other foods that had high water contents by adding salt or sugar to them. To grow, bacteria need plenty of water; yeasts and moulds can grow when less water is available. Adding sugar or salt to foods draws water out of cells, including bacteria, fungi, protozoans, and worms.

shelf life period of time that a food can be stored before it spoils

fermentation process used to preserve or produce a variety of foods, including pickles and wine

Dried fruits such as raisins have a longer shelf life than grapes, their natural counterparts.

As a result, these pathogens are less likely to survive in sugary or salty foods. Drying reduces a food's water content. Dried fruits such as raisins, for example, have a longer shelf life than grapes, their natural counterparts.

Today we can add pasteurization, refrigeration, freezing, canning, irradiation, additives, and *aseptic* processing to the list of food preservation techniques (Table 12.7). Aseptic processing involves sterilizing a food and its package separately, before the food enters the package. The **sterilization** process destroys all microorganisms and viruses. After undergoing aseptic packaging, boxes of sterile foods and beverages, such as milk or juices, can remain free of microbial growth for several years, while sitting on supermarket or pantry shelves. However, once the containers of these products are opened, the foods or beverages have the same shelf life as their counterparts that have not undergone aseptic processing.

Home-Canned Foods

When food is canned, commercial food production methods require heating the food to certain temperatures for specified times. Thus, unless the can or jar has been damaged,

TABLE 12.7 *Summary of Food Preservation Methods*

Method	Means of Effectiveness	Examples of Foods
Heating (cooking, pasteurization, aseptic processing)	Kills or deactivates spoilage and pathogenic microbes, destroys enzymes that result in food spoilage	Most foods
Adding salt/sugar	Binds water, decreasing the amount available for microbes	Ham, bacon, fish, pickled foods
Smoking	Kills spoilage microbes, destroys enzymes that result in food spoilage Smoking is a method of heating. The process involves salting food before smoking and refrigerating or freezing the food after smoking.	Meats, fish
Curing	Retards the growth of *C. botulinum* and stabilizes the flavour of the food Additives such as sodium nitrate and nitrite are used to cure meat, fish, or poultry.	Luncheon meats, smoked fish
Chilling/freezing	Slows molecular movement, retarding microbial and enzymatic activity	Most foods
Drying (dehydration)	Removes much of the moisture in food that microbes need to survive	Fruit, herbs, meat jerkies, seeds
Fermenting	Produces acids and alcohol that interfere with the survival of unwanted microbes	Alcoholic beverages, yogourt, cheeses, soy sauce
Canning	Kills spoilage microbes, destroys enzymes in food that result in spoilage, removes oxygen that certain microbes need to survive	Meat, fish, poultry, fruits, vegetables, milk
Irradiating	Destroys most pathogens, delays sprouting (potatoes)	Spices, potatoes, raw meats, fresh fruits

Sources: Hilderbrand KS: *Smoking fish at home—safely*. PNW 238, 2003. extension.oregonstate.edu/catalog/pdf/pnw/pnw238.pdf;
National Center for Home Food Preservation: *How do I?* 2003. www.uga.edu/nchfp/search.html.

properly processed canned foods should be free of pathogens. Certain home-canned foods, however, may contain the microorganism *Clostridium botulinum* (*C. botulinum*) that causes *botulism* or its toxin. The home-canning process may kill *C. botulinum* bacteria in the food, but their spores or toxin may remain. That is why home-canned, *low-acid* foods such as beans and corn should be boiled for ten minutes before eating. Foods made with vinegar, tomatoes, or citrus juices are usually high-acid foods, and as a result, such items are not likely to be sources of *C. botulinum*. The *botulinum* toxin is highly poisonous; never taste a home-canned low-acid food before boiling it.

Figure 12.10 Irradiating food. A food microbiologist places a batch of hot dogs into the gamma radiation source to rid them of food-borne pathogens.

Irradiation

The process of food irradiation preserves food by using a high amount of energy to kill pathogens such as *Salmonella* and *E. coli* O157:H7 (Fig. 12.10). The processes used to irradiate foods do not make the items radioactive. The energy passes through the food, as in microwave cooking, and no radioactive material is left behind. The energy is strong enough to destroy the genetic material as well as cell membranes or cell walls of insects and microbes. As a result, irradiation is a highly effective way of killing insects and microorganisms that may be in foods. However, radiation is not always an effective way to destroy viruses.[26] It is important to recognize that even when foods, especially meats, have been irradiated, once their packaging has been opened, the foods can still become contaminated.

Irradiation extends the shelf life of spices, dry vegetable seasonings, meats, seeds, shell eggs, and fresh fruits and vegetables. Except for dried seasonings, packages that contain irradiated foods must be labelled with the international food irradiation symbol, the Radura, and include a statement indicating the product has been treated by irradiation (Fig. 12.11).

Irradiation of food is not a new technology; in 1963, U.S. food manufacturers were given approval to irradiate wheat flour. Today, France, Israel, Russia, and China are among the countries that use irradiation to preserve various foods. In Canada, only a handful of foods, including potatoes, onions, wheat, and flour, are approved for irradiation.[27] Currently, irradiation is not used widely on food commodities in Canada. The main use of irradiation in Canada has been on spices. Nevertheless, some consumer groups claim that irradiation diminishes the nutritional value of food and leads to the formation of harmful compounds, such as **carcinogens**, cancer-causing substances. According to medical experts with Health Canada, the World Health Organization (WHO), the U.S. Food and Drug Administration (FDA), and the Centers for Disease Control and Prevention (CDC), irradiated foods are safe to eat.[27,28] Furthermore, irradiation causes little or no nutritive losses. Despite such assurances, many Canadians are skeptical about the safety of irradiated foods, and they avoid purchasing such products.

Figure 12.11 Radura symbol. The Radura symbol indicates the food in this package has been irradiated.

Concept Checkpoint

22. Define shelf life.

23. Identify four methods of food preservation and explain how each method extends the shelf life of foods.

24. What preparation step can be taken to make home-canned, low-acid foods safe to eat?

25. What is a carcinogen?

sterilization process that kills or destroys all microorganisms and viruses

carcinogens cancer-causing substances

Preparing for Disasters

This aerial photo shows people waiting to be rescued from the roof of a house that was surrounded by floodwater in New Orleans, Louisiana, on August 30, 2005. After Hurricane Katrina struck New Orleans, thousands of people were saved after they moved to their roofs or attics.

In late August 2005, Hurricane Katrina devastated the central Gulf Coast region of the United States. At least 1800 individuals lost their lives and more than 250 000 people were displaced from their homes as a result of the hurricane. Media coverage of the storm's aftermath showed desperate conditions as people lived in their attics or on their roofs, waiting to be rescued. What steps can you take to have enough water and food available to survive hurricanes, earthquakes, or other serious emergency situations?

A supply of clean water and wholesome food is necessary for surviving disasters such as hurricanes and earthquakes. The Chapter 12 Highlight provides instructions for sanitizing water. The following recommendations may help sustain you and your loved ones for several days:

- Store at least 2 L (½ gal.) of water per person per day. Ideally, you should have at least a 3- to 5-day supply of drinking water, or at least 10 L (2.5 gal.) of water for each person in a household. Children and breast-feeding women may need more than 2 L (½ gal.) of water per day. Also, more water may be necessary for people living in warm climates. Furthermore, store extra water for food preparation, personal hygiene, dishwashing, and pets.
- Water should be maintained in a cool place and in sturdy plastic bottles with tight-fitting lids.
- Avoid storing water in areas where toxic substances, such as gasoline and pesticides, are stored. Over time, toxic vapours from these products may penetrate the plastic and contaminate the water.
- Change stored water every six months.
- Drink only bottled, boiled, or treated water until you are certain the public water supply is safe.
- If you have time to prepare, fill a bathtub with water to use if it becomes necessary. The water, however, will need to be sanitized before consuming.
- If you drink bottled water, make sure the seal has not been broken.

If your emergency water supply is inadequate, you can consume melted ice cubes from the freezer, canned fruit juices, and water drained from an undamaged water heater. Water stored in the tank of the toilet (not the bowl) is also fit to drink. Pets can drink toilet bowl water that has not been treated with a toilet bowl sanitizer. Water in swimming pools and spas can be used for personal hygiene needs but not for drinking. Never drink water from car radiators, home heating systems, and water beds. Alcohol and caffeinated beverages contribute to dehydration and, therefore, should be avoided.

Emergency Food Supply

A disaster can easily disrupt your access to safe food, therefore, you should store at least a three-day supply of food for emergency use. Choose foods that have a long storage life, require no refrigeration, and can be eaten without cooking, such as canned meats, fruits, and vegetables. If you have pets, you should also keep a supply of pet foods. Table 12.8 lists foods that can be included in your emergency food supply. Also store a manual can opener, paper plates, and eating utensils.

If stored under proper conditions, unopened canned or boxed foods will remain fresh for about two years. Before storing food, use a permanent marking pen to write the date on the package. You should use and replace foods before they lose their freshness or reach their expiration date. An ideal food-storage location is a cool, dry, dark place. Do not store foods near gasoline, oil, paints, and petroleum-based solvents, because some food products absorb their odours. You can protect food from rodents and insects by storing them in airtight containers or plastic storage bins.

If you have no electricity, consume perishable food in your refrigerator or freezer before using your emergency food supply. However, discard cooked foods after they have been at room temperature for two hours. Do not eat food that appears or smells spoiled or is from cans that are leaking or bulging.

To prepare meals safely after a disaster, you will need to store:

- A camp stove or charcoal grill.
- Fuel for cooking, such as charcoal. **Never** cook food on a camp stove or charcoal grill indoors. The fumes contain *carbon monoxide,* an odourless deadly gas.
- Matches.
- Cooking and eating utensils.
- Paper plates, cups, and towels.
- Heavy-duty aluminum foil.

For more information about emergency preparedness, visit the following Web site provided by Public Safety Canada: www.getprepared.gc.ca.

TABLE 12.8 *Foods to Store for Emergency Situations*

• Canned meats, fish, fruits, and vegetables
• Canned fruit juices
• Unopened boxes of cereal, low-salt crackers, and trail mix
• Prewrapped fruit-filled granola bars
• Peanut or other nut butters
• Raisins and other dried fruit
• Dry milk powder
• Baby foods

Concept **Checkpoint**

26. Develop an emergency food- and water-supply plan for your home. Identify at least five foods that are appropriate for an emergency food supply.

27. In case public water supplies are disrupted, identify at least three sources of drinking water in homes that are safe for humans. Identify at least two sources of water that are unsafe to drink.

food additive any substance that becomes incorporated into food during production, packaging, transport, or storage

colour additives dyes, pigments, or other substances that provide colour to food

Food Additives

Technically, a **food additive** is a substance added to food that influences the product's characteristics, including taste or colour. Food manufacturers incorporate *direct* or *intentional additives* into their products for various reasons. Such additives may make food easier to process, more nutritious, stay fresh longer, or taste better.

Many direct food additives help maintain the safety of foods by limiting the growth of bacteria that cause food-borne illness. Other additives protect against the action of enzymes that can lead to undesirable changes in the food's colour and taste. Such unwanted chemical changes occur when enzymes that are naturally in certain foods are exposed to the oxygen in air. *Antioxidant additives,* including vitamins E and C and a variety of *sulphites,* can prevent oxygen from reacting with these enzymes. **Colour additives** are dyes, pigments, or other substances that provide colour to foods, drugs, or cosmetics, such as beta-carotene in margarine and FD&C (Food, Drug, & Cosmetic) Red No. 40 in cherry-flavoured cough syrup. Table 12.9 lists common types of direct food additives (including colour additives), their uses, examples of products that contain the additives, and names of specific additives.

Colour additives are dyes, pigments, or other substances that provide colour to foods, drugs, or cosmetics.

Sulphites are sulphur-containing food additives that limit the growth of food spoilage microbes and prevent enzymatic browning of certain foods, such as pieces of fruit and vegetables. Some people, however, are sensitive or allergic to sulphites, and they can have severe reactions when they ingest the compounds. CFIA and Health Canada require manufacturers who add sulphites to foods and beverages to indicate on their products' package labels that these chemicals are among the ingredients.[30] For more information about sulphites, visit Health Canada's Web site about the additive at www.hc-sc.gc.ca/fn-an/securit/allerg/fa-aa/allergen_sulphites-sulfites-eng.php.

Indirect additives, such as compounds from a food's wrapper or container, can enter food as it is packaged, transported, or stored. Indirect additives, however, have no purpose. Certain international organizations regulate *all* food additives to ensure processed foods and their packaging are safe.[29]

Food Safety Legislation: Food Additives

According to Health Canada, "A food additive is any chemical substance that is added to food during preparation or storage and either becomes a part of the food or affects its characteristics for the purpose of achieving a particular technical effect. Substances that are used in food to maintain its nutritive quality, enhance its keeping quality, make it attractive or to aid in its processing, packaging or storage are all considered to be food additives. However, some substances that aid in the processing of food, under certain conditions, are considered to be food processing aids, not food additives."[31]

Many of these food additives have long histories of being safe, and were deemed safe after undergoing scientific testing. Food additives are regulated in Canada according to the *Food and Drug Regulations*.[31]

Examples of food additives include colouring agents to give foods an appetizing appearance, anti-caking agents to keep powders such as salt free-running, preservatives to prevent or retard spoilage in food, and certain sweeteners used to sweeten foods without adding to the caloric value of these foods.

Under the *Food and Drug Regulations*, food additives do not include the following:

- Food ingredients such as salt, sugar, starch
- Vitamins, minerals, amino acids
- Spices, seasonings, flavouring preparations

TABLE 12.9 *Common Types of Direct Food Additives*

Type of Additive	Functions	Typical Products	Examples of Specific Ingredients
Preservatives	Prevent food spoilage	Jellies, beverages, baked goods, cured meats, cereals, snack foods	Ascorbic acid, citric acid, sodium benzoate, calcium propionate, sodium erythorbate, BHA, BHT, EDTA, sulphites
Sweeteners	Add sweetness	Processed foods, beverages, baked goods, sugar substitutes	Sucrose, glucose, mannitol, corn syrup, aspartame, sucralose
Flavours and spices	Add specific flavours	Puddings, pie fillings, gelatins, cake mixes, candies, soft drinks	Natural flavourings, artificial flavourings, spices
Flavour enhancers	Enhance flavours already present	Snack foods	Monosodium glutamate (MSG), hydrolyzed soy protein
Nutrients	Replace nutrients lost during processing, boost levels of nutrients naturally in food	Flour, grains, cereals, margarine, juice, energy bars	Thiamin hydrochloride, riboflavin, niacin, niacinamide, folic acid, beta-carotene, ascorbic acid
Emulsifiers	Keep oily and watery ingredients from separating	Salad dressings, peanut butter, chocolate, frozen desserts	Soy lecithin, mono- and diglycerides, polysorbates
Leavening agents	Promote rising of certain baked goods	Baked goods	Baking soda, monocalcium phosphate, calcium carbonate
Stabilizers, thickeners, binders	Provide uniform texture and improve "mouth feel"	Frozen desserts, puddings, sauces	Gelatin, pectin, guar gum, carregeenan
Colour additives	Enhance natural colours, provide colour to colourless and "fun" foods as well as medications and cosmetics	Processed foods, including candies, snack foods, margarine, cheese, soft drinks, gelatin, drug capsules, cough syrup, lipstick	FD&C Blue No. 1, FD&C Red No. 40, beta-carotene, caramel colour

Source: Modified from International Food Information Council and U.S. Food and Drug Administration: *Food ingredients and colors*. 2004. www.cfsan.fda.gov/~dms/foodic.html.

- Agricultural chemicals
- Veterinary drugs
- Food packaging materials

Health Canada publishes a food additives dictionary for additives used in Canada; visit www.hc-sc.gc.ca/fn-an/securit/addit/diction/index-eng.php.

Did You Know?

According to the results of numerous scientific studies, food additives do not cause hyperactivity or learning disabilities in children.

Other Substances in Foods

Various substances can accidentally enter food during processing. Although such contaminants can blend into a food, they are not food additives. Common biological and physical food contaminants are insect parts, rodent feces or urine, dust and dirt, and bits of metal or glass from machinery used to process food. Although some of these substances may not be harmful to health, most people find it unappealing to have filth and other unintentional ingredients in their foods.

Very small amounts of unavoidable, naturally occurring substances such as dirt and insect parts are in foods, because they are not harmful when consumed in minute amounts. Health Canada and CFIA established guidelines concerning amounts of certain materials that are permitted in specific foods, such as mould and rodent hairs in paprika or insect eggs in canned orange juice. Products harmful to consumers are subject to regulatory action whether or not they exceed the action levels.

Chemical contaminants also enter foods unintentionally. Toxic metals, such as lead, cadmium, and mercury, are naturally in our environment, and these elements may also be in our food. Poisonous human-made compounds such as *benzene* and *polychlorinated biphenols (PCBs)* are in the environment as well. Toxic metals or poisonous compounds resulting from human manufacturing practices can pollute sources of water used by consumers (well water, for example). Canadians who drink water from municipal supplies can be assured that the water is analyzed regularly to determine its concentrations of toxic substances.[14] However, people who rely on privately owned wells should have the water tested routinely.

What Is Benzene?

Health Canada has investigated soft drinks and other beverages for the presence of benzene, following U.S. reports that trace levels of benzene had been found in some soft drinks. Secondary to its investigation, Health Canada has concluded that soft drinks and other beverages available for sale in Canada are safe.[32] This conclusion is based both on these findings and on the cooperative actions taken by the soft drink industry to reformulate products where necessary.

Late in 2005, FDA received reports that low levels of benzene had been detected in some soft drinks that contained ascorbic acid (vitamin C) and a group of food additives called benzoate (*ben'-zo-ate*) salts. Benzene is a cancer-causing agent present in the environment from natural and manufactured sources. After receiving the reports, the FDA's Center for Food Safety and Applied Nutrition (CFSAN) surveyed benzene levels in soft drinks. The survey's findings indicated that the vast majority of beverages sampled, including those containing both benzoate salts and ascorbic acid, contained either no detectable amounts of benzene or amounts that were very low and within the range allowed by the U.S. water standard.[33]

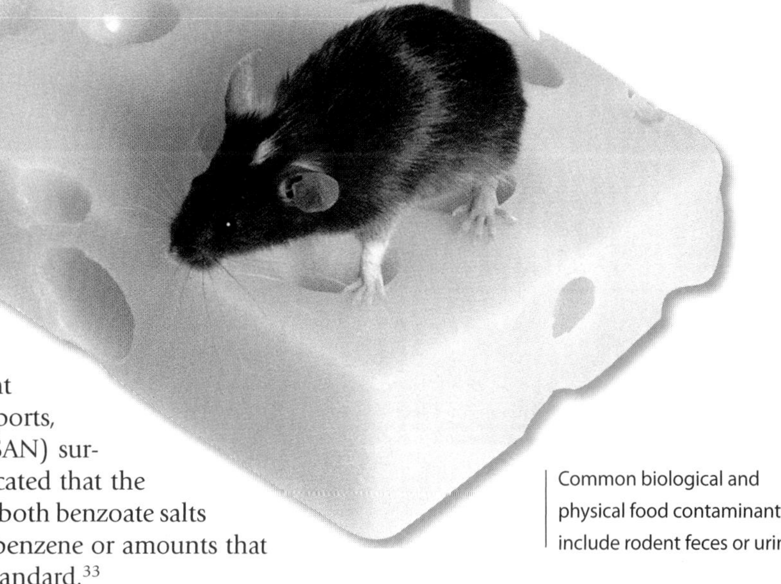

Common biological and physical food contaminants include rodent feces or urine.

Did You Know?

Lead is a highly toxic mineral that may be in candies imported from Mexico and in traditional ethnic folk remedies, especially *greta, azarcon, ghasard*, and *ba-baw-san*. Therefore, it is prudent to avoid ingesting these candies or folk remedies.

Herbicides are the most widely used type of pesticide in agriculture. Note the protective gear worn by this farmworker as he handles a herbicide.

pesticide substance that people use to kill or control unwanted insects, weeds, or other organisms

insecticides substances used to control or kill insects

rodenticides substances used to kill mice and rats

herbicides substances used to destroy weeds

fungicides substances used to limit the spread of fungi

tolerances maximum amounts of pesticide residues that can be in or on each treated food crop

What Are Pesticides?

A **pesticide** is any substance that people use to control or kill unwanted insects, weeds, rodents, fungi, or other organisms. There are several different kinds of pesticides. **Insecticides** control or kill insects; **rodenticides** kill mice and rats; **herbicides** destroy weeds; and **fungicides** limit the spread of fungi, such as mould and mildew. Over one *billion* tons of pesticides are used in Canada and the United States annually.[34] Herbicides are the most widely used type of pesticide in agriculture.[34]

Pesticide Residue Tolerances The use of pesticides in modern farming practices has helped increase crop yields, reduce food costs, and protect the quality of many agricultural products. However, many pesticides leave small amounts (*pesticide residues*) in or on treated crops, including fruits, vegetables, and grains, even when they are applied correctly. Concentrations of pesticide residues often decrease as food crops are washed, stored, processed, and prepared. Nevertheless, some of these substances may remain in fresh produce, such as apples or peaches, as well as in processed foods, such as canned applesauce or peaches.

Health Canada regulates the proper use of pesticides in Canada under the Pest Management Regulatory Agency (PMRA),[35] though municipalities and provinces have the authority to set further conditions on the use of pest control substances. The agency can limit the amount of a pesticide that is applied on crops, restrict the frequency or location of the pesticide's application, or require the substance be used only by specially trained, certified persons. PMRA also sets pesticide **tolerances**, maximum amounts of pesticide residues that can be in or on each treated food crop under the *Pest Control Products Act* (PCPA).[35] A pesticide tolerance includes a margin of safety, so the maximum pesticide residue that is allowed to be in or on a food is much lower than amounts that can cause negative health effects.[34]

Non-chemical Methods of Pest Management Although PMRA focuses on chemical methods of managing pests, the agency also promotes non-chemical pest management techniques that may be safer for humans and the environment. Integrated pest management (IPM) involves using a variety of methods for controlling pests while limiting damage to the environment. IPM methods include growing pest-resistant crops, using predatory wasps to control crop-destroying insects, and trapping adult insect pests before they can reproduce. Biologically based pesticides, such as sex hormones (pheromones) that attract pesky insects to predators or traps and viruses that infect insects and weeds, are becoming increasingly popular among farmers (Fig. 12.12). Such methods are often safer for humans than traditional chemical pesticides.

Figure 12.12 Helpful insect. A predatory insect, the spined soldier bug (left), makes a meal of a Mexican bean beetle larva. Bean beetle larvae are devastating pests of snap and soybeans. The spined soldier bug's pheromone may help farmers control many insects that eat crops.

It is important to note that IPM permits the use of chemical pesticides, but only as needed to enhance the effects of non-chemical methods. Studies suggest that IPM techniques generally increase crop yields and economic profits, while reducing the use of chemical pesticides.[34] As IPM programs become more widely adopted, conventional farmers will depend less on the use of chemical pesticides.

Fruits and vegetables grown without use of pesticides are available and may bear an "organic" label (see Chapter 3 for information about organic foods). These products generally are more expensive than those grown using pesticides, and they are not necessarily safer or more nutritious than conventionally produced foods.

How Safe Are Pesticides? Pesticides used in agriculture have both beneficial and unwanted effects. Pesticides help protect the food supply and make food crops available at reasonable cost. Nevertheless, pesticides have the potential to harm humans, animals, or the environment because they are designed to kill or otherwise negatively affect organisms. If a pesticide is applied improperly to cropland, it may remain in the soil, be taken up by plant roots, decompose to other compounds, or enter groundwater and waterways. Winds may carry pesticides in air and dust to distant locations. Each path can be a route to the human food chain (Fig. 12.13).

Figure 12.13 Pesticide pathways. If a pesticide is applied improperly to cropland, it may remain in the soil, be taken up by plant roots, decompose to other compounds, or enter groundwater and waterways. Winds may carry pesticides in air and dust to distant locations. Each path can be a route to the human food chain.

The potential harmful effects of a pesticide in food depends on the particular chemical and how effectively the body can eliminate it, its concentration in the food, how much and often it is eaten, and the consumer's vulnerability to the substance. Tolerable amounts of pesticide residues on or in foods are extremely small. However, it is possible that exposure to small amounts of these chemicals regularly may enable the substances to accumulate in the body and produce toxicity or initiate cancer.[36,37] Health experts have studied rates of cancers among people who have close contact with pesticides, such as farmers and pesticide applicators. Among the people who applied pesticides, the likelihood of developing lip cancer was elevated. The risk of prostate cancer was also elevated, but primarily among applicators with a family history of this type of cancer.[38] Environmental health experts will continue to monitor the effects of pesticides on humans.

Concept Checkpoint

28. What is a food additive? What is the difference between direct and indirect food additives?
29. What is a colour additive?
30. List two substances added to foods that are not considered food additives in Canada.
31. Are the benzene levels in Canadian soft drinks a concern?
32. What is an unintentional food additive? Provide at least three examples of such additives.
33. What is a pesticide? Provide at least three examples of types of pesticides.
34. Define integrated pest management and provide an example of this method.
35. Which Canadian agency regulates the use of pesticides?
36. What is a pesticide tolerance?
37. Explain how pesticides can enter the human food chain.

Chapter 12 Highlight
Avoiding "The Revenge"

If you like travelling to foreign countries and enjoy sampling exotic cuisines in these places, one thing you don't need to encounter is *travellers' diarrhea (TD)*. Also referred to as "Montezuma's Revenge" and "Tut's Tummy," TD can ruin your vacation. By taking some precautions, however, your digestive system can stay healthy while travelling abroad.

TD results from consuming food or water contaminated with pathogens. The illness is characterized by the abrupt onset of abdominal cramps and loose or watery bowel movements. Additional symptoms may include nausea, vomiting, intestinal bloating, and fever. TD generally lasts three to four days without treatment, but signs and symptoms may persist in a small percentage of infected travellers.

Unless precautions are taken, TD is likely to occur during or shortly after travelling in regions where sanitary water supplies are not always available, people have less than ideal personal hygiene practices, and untreated human feces are used for fertilizer. In about 85% of cases, pathogenic bacteria, particularly a form

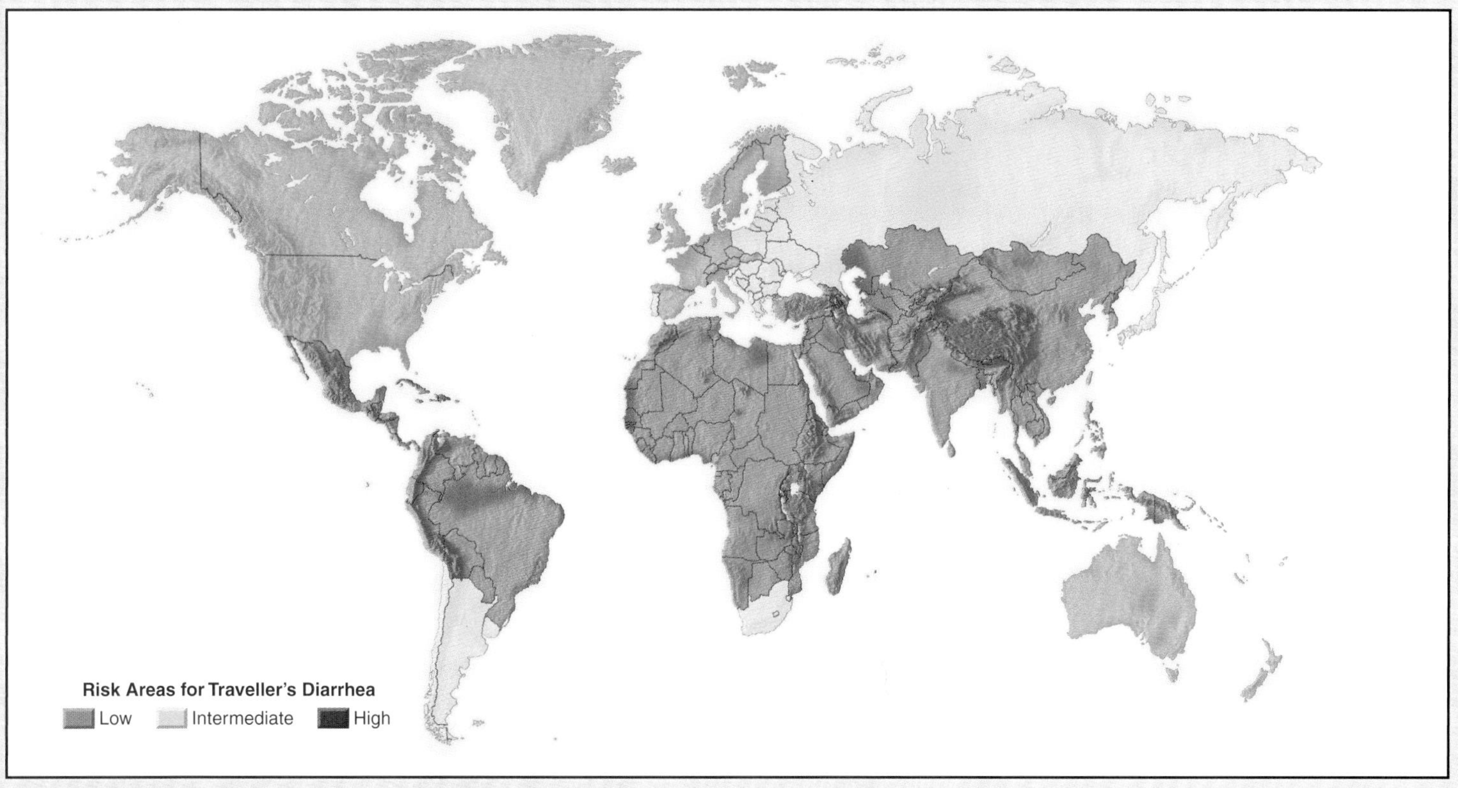

Figure 12.A Areas of risk for travellers' diarrhea. This map presents regions of the world where the risks are low, intermediate, and high.

of *E. coli*, cause TD.[1A] Parasitic protozoans such as *Giardia* and *Cryptosporidium* ("Crypto") account for about 10% of TD cases. When travellers suffer from persistent symptoms, the illness is likely to be the result of a parasitic rather than a bacterial infection.

It is important to note that a trip to every foreign destination is likely to include the risk of TD. Figure 12.A presents regions of the world where the risks are low, intermediate, and high. Low-risk countries include Canada, the United States, Australia, New Zealand, Japan, and countries in northern and western Europe. Intermediate-risk countries include those in eastern Europe, South Africa, and some of the Caribbean islands. High-risk areas include most of Asia, the Middle East, Africa, and Central and South America. On average, 30 to 50% of travellers will develop TD during a one- to two-week stay in a high-risk area.[1A]

Reducing Your Risk of TD

Experts at the CDC recommend several approaches for reducing your risk of TD. These include following instructions regarding food and beverage selection, avoiding contact with contaminated waterways, sanitizing drinking water, and using medications that may prevent TD.

When you visit places where risk of contracting TD is moderate to high, avoid consuming food or beverages purchased from street vendors. Before you eat meat or other high-risk foods, make sure they are fully cooked and served hot. Avoid raw foods that have been washed in water, such as fresh fruits, raw vegetables, and salads. Don't eat fresh fruit without peeling it first. Avoid water, ice, and beverages diluted with water or ice, such as reconstituted fruit juices and iced drinks. Don't drink fresh fluid milk or milk products that have not been pasteurized. Safe beverages include those that are bottled and sealed; bottled beer and wine may also be safe to drink. If boiled water is used to make tea and coffee, these beverages may be safe to consume. Use bottled water to wash hands, brush teeth, and take medication.

TD can be spread when pathogens from human or animal feces are in sources of water, including swimming pools, lakes, rivers, and other bodies of water. Accidentally swallowing even small amounts of contaminated water can cause illness. Swimming pools that contain chlorinated water may be safe places to swim, if the disinfectant and pH levels are properly maintained. However, some pathogens are resistant to levels of chlorine commonly used to disinfect swimming pools. Thus, you should also avoid swallowing chlorinated swimming pool water.

How Can I Sanitize Drinking Water?

Boiling is the most reliable method to make impure water safe to drink.[1A] Water should be brought to a vigorous rolling boil for one minute and allowed to cool to room temperature without adding ice. This procedure will kill bacterial and parasitic causes of TD at all altitudes and viruses at low altitudes. To inactivate viruses at altitudes greater than 2000 m (6562 ft.), water should be boiled three 3 minutes or *chemical disinfection* should be used after the water has boiled for one minute.

Chemical Disinfection

Disinfection methods kill large numbers of microorganisms, reducing the likelihood of infection. Chemical disinfection with iodine or chlorine is an alternative method of sanitizing water when boiling water is not practical. Two reliable methods for disinfecting water with iodine are the use of tincture of iodine and tetraglycine hydroperiodide tablets. To reduce the risk of TD, follow the manufacturer's instructions for sanitizing water with these chemicals. Keep in mind, however, that chemical disinfection is not a reliable method of killing Crypto.

Filtering Water

Microstrainer filters can remove bacteria and protozoans from drinking water, but most of these filters do not remove viruses (Fig. 12.B). To destroy viruses, you should disinfect the water with iodine or chlorine after using microstrainer filters. Filters collect organisms from water, so wash your hands with sanitized water after handling used filters. A travellers' guide to buying water filters for removing Crypto and *Giardia* can be found at the following Web site: www.cdc.gov/ncidod/dpd/parasites/cryptosporidiosis/factsht_crypto_prevent_water.htm.

Preventive Medications

Before you leave Canada to enter a high-risk region, see your physician for his or her recommendations for preventing TD. You can also take medications that contain bismuth subsalicylate (BSS), the active ingredient in Pepto-Bismol, to reduce the risk of TD. Side effects of BSS commonly include nausea, constipation, and blackening of the tongue and bowel movements. BSS is not recommended for children under 3 years of age, and the medication should be avoided by people who are allergic to aspirin or have certain chronic conditions. Therefore, check with your physician before taking BSS along when you travel to other countries.

Treating TD

Because pathogenic bacteria are often the cause of TD, antibiotics are the primary method of treating the condition.[1A] In Canada, physicians often prescribe antibiotics for their patients to bring with them when they travel out of the country. When used in combination with antibiotics, antimotility agents can be helpful. These medications, such as loperamide, the active ingredient in Imodium, slow the muscular activity of the digestive tract and can provide relief from the diarrhea associated with TD. Loperamide, however, is not recommended for children who are less than 2 years of age.

BSS taken as 30 mL (1 oz.) of liquid or two chewable tablets every 30 minutes for eight doses may shorten the severity of symptoms and duration of the illness. As mentioned earlier, however, people suffering with TD should check with a physician before using BSS as a treatment.

Dehydration can be a serious complication of TD. To prevent dehydration, it is important for people suffering from TD to replace fluids and electrolytes lost by vomiting and diarrhea. However, travellers should remember to use only beverages that are sealed or carbonated. If fluid loss is severe, it's best to obtain professional medical treatment.

Reference for Chapter 12 Highlight

1A. Health Canada: *Canada communicable disease report*, 15 March 2001. Vol. 27 (ACS-3)/(DCC-3) Statement on Travellers' Diarrhea. www.phac-aspc.gc.ca/publicat/ccdr-rmtc/01pdf/acs27-3.pdf. Accessed: June 30, 2010.

Figure 12.B Microstrainer filter. Microstrainer filters can remove bacteria and protozoans from drinking water, but most of these filters do not remove viruses.

SUMMARY

In Canada, an estimated 13 million people become ill from various food-borne illnesses each year. Food-borne illness occurs when microscopic pathogens or their toxic by-products enter food (or beverages) and are consumed. Many kinds of pathogens infect the digestive tract; other types of food-borne pathogens do not sicken humans directly, but these microbes secrete toxins into food. When the food is eaten, the toxins irritate the intestinal tract and cause food intoxication.

Canada has one of the safest food supplies in the world, primarily the result of a team effort conducted by cooperating federal, provincial, and local agencies that regulate and monitor the production and distribution of food. Health Canada and CFIA are the key federal agencies that protect consumers by regulating the country's food industry. Other team members include public health agencies as well as provincial and local governments.

People use certain microbes to produce a variety of foods, including hard cheeses, raised breads, pickled foods, and alcoholic beverages. When microorganisms metabolize nutrients in food, they often secrete substances that alter the colour, texture, taste, and other characteristics of the food in beneficial and desirable ways. Other kinds of microbes grow and multiply in food, but their metabolic by-products spoil the food, making it unfit for human consumption. When pathogens are in food, they can make the item unsafe to eat. Food contaminants include pathogens, insect parts, residues of compounds used to kill insects that destroy food crops, and metal fragments from food processing equipment.

The microbes that cause food-borne illness can live practically anywhere. Common routes for transmitting harmful microbes to food involve vermin, poor personal hygiene practices, and improper food preparation and storage practices.

To grow, most microbes need warmth, moisture, and a source of nutrients, and some microorganisms also need oxygen. In general, high-risk foods are warm, moist, and protein-rich, and they have a neutral or slightly acidic pH. Such foods include meat, poultry, milk and milk products, and eggs.

Many factors influence whether an individual becomes ill after eating food or drinking a beverage that has been contaminated with a pathogen. The number of pathogens in a food or the amount of toxin it contains can contribute to the risk and severity of a food-borne illness. Furthermore, people vary in their vulnerability to many food-borne pathogens. In general, high-risk groups are pregnant women, very young children, the elderly, and persons who suffer from serious chronic illnesses or weakened immune systems.

Signs and symptoms of food- or water-borne illnesses primarily involve the digestive tract and include nausea, vomiting, diarrhea, and intestinal cramps. In most cases, otherwise healthy persons who suffer from common types of food-borne illness recover completely within a few days. Medical treatment should be obtained when an intestinal disorder is accompanied by fever, bloody bowel movements, prolonged vomiting and diarrhea, and/or dehydration.

The major kinds of pathogens are bacteria, viruses, protozoans, and fungi. In Canada, bacteria and viruses are responsible for most cases of food-borne illness. Bacteria are single-cell microorganisms. Some bacteria can live without oxygen; other types of bacteria transform into spores when living conditions are less than ideal. A virus is simply a piece of genetic material coated with protein. Viruses must invade a living cell to produce more viruses. A parasite is an organism that lives in or on another organism, often deriving nourishment from its host. Fungi such as moulds, yeast, and mushrooms are simple life forms that live on dead or decaying organic matter.

People can reduce their risk of food-borne illness by following some important rules, most of which require changing risky food selection, preparation, and storage practices. Cooking foods is an effective way to destroy pathogens. After food is cooked, however, careless food handling sets the stage for the growth of pathogens. A simple rule to follow is: "Keep hot foods hot and cold foods cold." Other simple rules include wash hands and surfaces often, don't cross-contaminate, heat foods to proper temperatures, and chill foods promptly.

For centuries, people preserved foods by heating, adding salt or sugar, fermenting, and drying. More modern methods of food preservation include pasteurization, refrigeration, freezing, canning, aseptic processing, preservative additives, and irradiation. According to medical experts, irradiated foods are safe to eat, but many Canadians avoid purchasing such products.

Direct food additives can make food easier to process, more nutritious, stay fresh longer, taste better or appear more attractive. An indirect food additive is a substance that becomes incorporated into food during production, packaging, transport, or storage. Unintentional food additives are substances that accidentally are in foods, such as dirt, rodent hairs, pesticide residues, and metals that enter the food and water from the environment. A pesticide is any substance that people use to kill or control unwanted insects, weeds, rodents, or other organisms. The use of pesticides in modern agricultural practices has helped increase crop yields, reduce food costs, and protect the quality of many agricultural products. PMRA regulates the proper use of pesticides and sets pesticide tolerances. IPM methods control agricultural pests while limiting damage to the environment.

Agricultural pesticides have both beneficial and unwanted effects. Pesticides help protect the food supply and make food crops available at reasonable cost. Nevertheless, these substances may harm humans, animals, or the environment. The potentially harmful effects of pesticide residues in food depends on the particular chemical, its concentration in the food, how much and often it is eaten, and the consumer's vulnerability to the substance. Environmental health experts continually monitor the effects of pesticides on humans.

Recipe for Healthy Living

Very Easy Chicken Salad

Chicken that's properly prepared, cooked, and stored is a safe, nutritious, economical food. A good way to use up day-old cooked chicken is to make chicken salad. If you don't have leftover chicken, you can use rotisserie chicken that many supermarkets offer in their deli sections. This recipe is unusual, because it includes seedless grapes and sunflower seeds. (You can substitute day-old cooked turkey for chicken and chopped apple or dried apricots for the grapes.)

The chicken salad recipe makes approximately three 1-cup servings. A serving of this salad supplies approximately 300 kcal, 23 g protein, 16 g fat, 3.5 g fibre, and 190 mg sodium.

INGREDIENTS:

- 312 mL (1¼ cup) cooked and chilled, skinless, boneless chicken meat (approximately 1 whole chicken breast)
- 1 medium stalk celery, washed and chopped
- 125 mL (½ cup) sweet red onion, skinned and finely chopped
- 125 mL (½ cup) washed seedless red or green grapes, halved
- 125 mL (½ cup) unsalted roasted sunflower seeds
- ⅛ tsp curry powder
- ⅛ tsp ground black pepper
- 60 mL (¼ cup) low-fat mayonnaise-type salad dressing

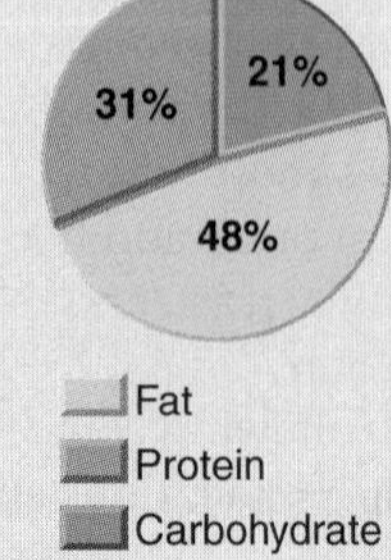

PREPARATION STEPS:

1. Cut chicken into small pieces and place in a large bowl.
2. Add the rest of the ingredients to the chicken and gently mix until well blended.
3. Serve on a bed of washed romaine lettuce leaves or as a sandwich filling.

CRITICAL THINKING

1. Prepare a food safety checklist that can be used in your household.
2. Consider your usual food preparation practices. After having read Chapter 12, which of your food preparation practices are unsafe?
3. Consider your usual food storage practices. After having read Chapter 12, which of your food storage practices are unsafe?
4. For lunch on Monday, you visited a restaurant and ordered a hamburger, French fries, baked beans, and a container of orange juice. Two days later, you developed nausea, vomiting, fever, chills, headache, abdominal cramps, and diarrhea. You suspect Monday's lunch made you sick. Was the hamburger, fries, beans, or juice the most likely source of your infection? Why? Which food-borne pathogen was the most likely suspect for causing the intestinal disorder? In the future, what steps can you take to reduce the likelihood that the food makes you sick again?
5. Develop a pamphlet to educate consumers about food-borne illness.

PRACTICE TEST

Select the best answer.

1. ______ are disease-causing microbes.
   a. Pathogens
   b. Toxins
   c. Teratogens
   d. Oxidants
2. The ______ is the primary government agency that oversees the safety of most foods in Canada.
   a. Canadian Food Inspection Agency (CFIA)
   b. Agricultural Research Service (ARS)
   c. Centers for Disease Control and Prevention (CDC)
   d. Environmental Protection Agency (EPA)
3. Which of the following foods is most likely to support the growth of pathogens?
   a. overripe bananas
   b. pasteurized milk
   c. raw ground meat
   d. commercially canned tomato soup
4. Food-borne illnesses are usually characterized by
   a. flu-like signs and symptoms.
   b. coughing, sneezing, and respiratory inflammation.
   c. megaloblastic anemia and nervous system defects.
   d. abdominal cramps, diarrhea, and vomiting.

5. In Canada, common sources of food-borne illness include all of the following, except
   a. *Norovirus*.
   b. *Staphylococcus aureus*.
   c. *fungi*.
   d. *Salmonella*.
6. Aflatoxins are
   a. responsible for 30% of food-borne illnesses in Canada.
   b. poisonous compounds produced by certain bacteria.
   c. a type of parasitic worm.
   d. none of the above
7. Which of the following practices can help reduce the growth of food-borne pathogens?
   a. washing hands before preparing food
   b. keeping cold foods cold and hot foods hot
   c. cooking foods to proper internal temperatures
   d. all of the above
8. Which of the following substances are not direct food additives?
   a. sulphites
   b. enrichment nutrients
   c. pesticide residues
   d. all of the above
9. Irradiation of food is
   a. an untested technology.
   b. not recommended, because the process increases nutrient losses.
   c. currently mainly used on spices in Canada.
   d. a common method of food preservation in the United States.
10. Which of the following food preservation processes effectively destroys microbes?
    a. freezing
    b. sterilization
    c. smoking
    d. all of the above

11. _____ is the commercial heating process that destroys harmful bacteria in milk and fruit juices.
    a. Sporulation
    b. Sedimentation
    c. Detoxification
    d. Pasteurization
12. When you visit countries that are less developed than Canada, you can reduce your risk of travellers' diarrhea by
    a. eating whole fresh fruits and vegetables.
    b. avoiding water that has not been bottled and sealed.
    c. purchasing foods from street vendors.
    d. all of the above
13. A _____ is a substance that kills weeds.
    a. rodenticide
    b. herbicide
    c. fungicide
    d. none of the above
14. Which of the following temperatures is recommended for storing chilled foods in a refrigerator?
    a. 4°C (40°F)
    b. 18°C (65°F)
    c. 25°C (77°F)
    d. 100°C (212°F)
15. To reduce the risk of food-borne illness, raw poultry should be cooked to an internal temperature of at least
    a. 4°C (40°F).
    b. 60°C (140°F).
    c. 74°C (165°F).
    d. 100°C (212°F).

Answers to Chapter 12 Quiz Yourself

1. Aflatoxins are the most common sources of food-borne illness in Canada and the United States. **False.** (p. 420)
2. In Canada, foods such as ready-to eat cereals, commercially canned vegetables, and orange juice are common sources of food-borne illness. **False.** (p. 414)
3. Certain fungi, such as button mushrooms, are safe to eat. **True.** (p. 419)
4. The Canadian Food Inspection Agency (CFIA) regulates the proper use of pesticides in Canada. **False.** (p. 434)
5. The best way to tell if a food is safe to eat is to smell it. **False.** (p. 413)

Please visit Connect at
www.mcgrawhillconnect.ca

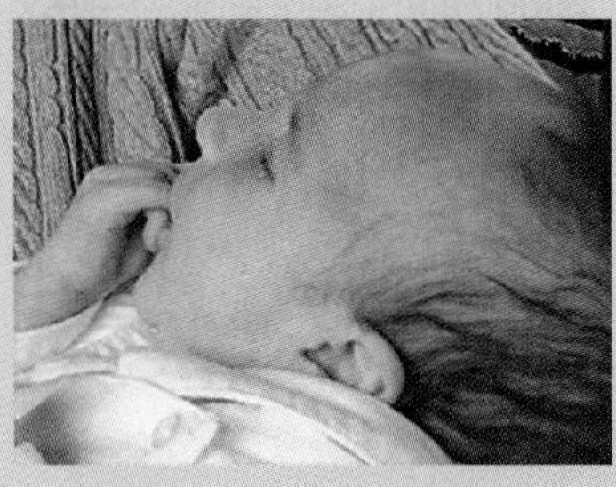

Chapter **13**

Nutrition for a Lifetime

This portrait features four generations of a Canadian family—newborn Mitchell is held by his grandmother; her daughter, the infant's mother, is on the left; and the baby's great-grandmother proudly stands behind them. Thanks to technological and medical advances that occurred during the twentieth century, Mitchell has an excellent chance of enjoying a healthy, long life.

Chapter Learning Outcomes

After reading Chapter 13, you should be able to:

1. List major physiological changes that occur during pregnancy and identify typical nutrition-related discomforts of pregnancy.
2. Identify the range of weight that healthy adult women should gain during pregnancy.
3. Discuss the effects that pregnancy-induced hypertension and gestational diabetes can have on pregnancy.
4. Identify nutrients that may need to be supplemented during pregnancy.
5. Describe the physiological processes involved in lactation and breast-feeding.
6. Compare the nutritional composition of infant formula with breast milk and identify at least three advantages of breast-feeding.
7. Explain the rationale for delaying the introduction of solid foods to infants until they are 4 to 6 months of age.
8. Summarize practical suggestions for encouraging healthy eating habits among children.
9. Identify some major nutrition-related health concerns facing Canadian children and teenagers.
10. Identify at least three physiological changes that occur during the normal aging process.
11. Discuss how the aging process can affect an individual's nutrient needs.

If you are a woman, are you pregnant? Do you already have children? If you have children, were they breast-fed or formula-fed? Do you live with and help care for an elderly parent or grandparent? These may seem to be personal questions, but many undergraduate university students do not fit the stereotype of being 18 to 22 years of age, having no children, and residing away from home.

Most of the nutrition recommendations presented in this textbook apply to people who are "adults"—loosely defined as the period when a person is 19 to 70 years of age.[1] Chapter 13 focuses on the differing nutrition needs and health concerns of people who are in specific *life stages*. These particular life stages are the **prenatal period**, or pregnancy, the time between conception and birth; **lactation**, milk production for breast-feeding; infancy; childhood; adolescence; and the older adult period that generally spans from 70 years of age until death.

Why is it necessary to learn some basic information about nutrition-related concerns during various life stages? If you do not have children, you may become a parent in the future. If your parents and grandparents are relatively young and vigorous now, you can expect them to experience declining physical functioning as they grow older. Finally, you need to recognize that most of these changes are normal and will affect you as well.

Today in Canada, many of the leading causes of death are chronic diseases, such as heart disease and cancer.[2] Long-term health-related practices, including dietary and physical activity habits, often contribute to the development of these diseases. Whether you enjoy overall good health or suffer from one or more disabling physical ailments as you grow older depends not only on your lifestyle choices but also on several other factors, including your heredity, relationships, environment, income, education level, and access to health care.

Quiz YOURSELF

What steps can young women take to prepare for pregnancy? Compared to breast milk, do infant formulas provide the same health benefits for infants? When is the best time to begin feeding solid foods to infants? Which nutrients are most likely to be deficient in diets of older adults? After reading Chapter 13, you will learn answers to these questions. Test your knowledge of nutrition during the certain life stages by taking the following quiz. The answers are found on page 487.

1. During pregnancy, a mother-to-be should double her food intake because she's "eating for two." ______ T ______ F
2. The natural size of a woman's breasts is not a factor in determining her ability to breast-feed her baby. ______ T ______ F
3. Within the first month after a baby is born, Canadian dietitians recommend adding solid foods to the infant's diet. ______ T ______ F
4. Over the past 30 years, the prevalence of overweight has increased among Canadian school-age children. ______ T ______ F
5. Compared to younger persons, older adults have lower risks of nutritional deficiencies. ______ T ______ F

From Fertilized Egg to Newborn

"It's positive!" Each day, the results of pregnancy testing are a source of excitement, relief, or concern for thousands of women. Many pregnancies in Canada are unplanned. Therefore, all sexually active women of child-bearing age should be aware of their likelihood of becoming pregnant. Whether a pregnancy is planned or not, dietary practices, before and during pregnancy, play a major role in the course of the pregnancy and the primary outcome—a healthy infant.

prenatal period time between conception and birth; pregnancy

lactation milk production

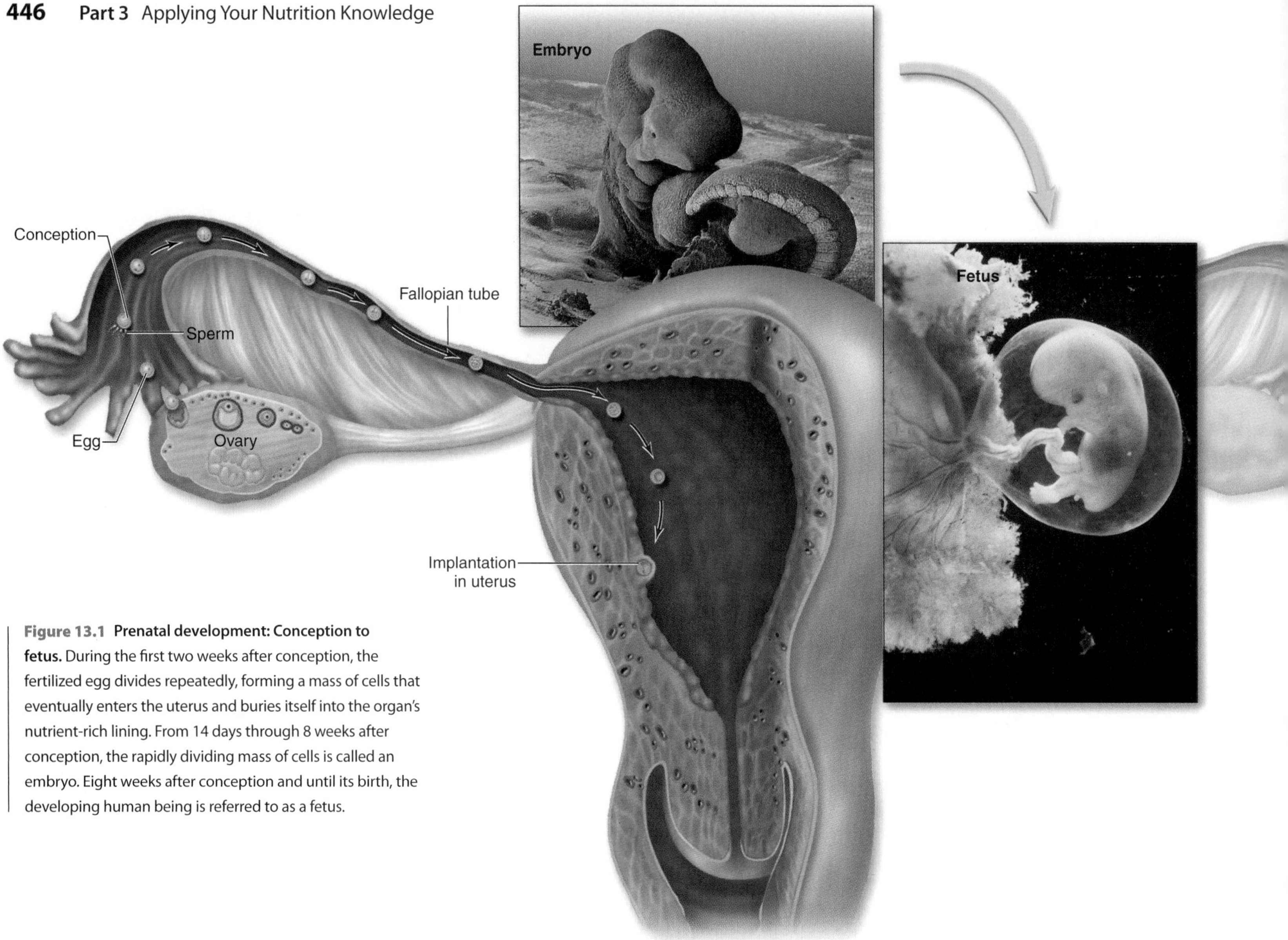

Figure 13.1 Prenatal development: Conception to fetus. During the first two weeks after conception, the fertilized egg divides repeatedly, forming a mass of cells that eventually enters the uterus and buries itself into the organ's nutrient-rich lining. From 14 days through 8 weeks after conception, the rapidly dividing mass of cells is called an embryo. Eight weeks after conception and until its birth, the developing human being is referred to as a fetus.

conception moment when a sperm enters an egg (fertilization)

uterus female reproductive organ that protects the developing organism during pregnancy

embryo human organism from 14 days to 8 weeks after conception

fetus human organism from 8 weeks after conception until birth

The prenatal period (*gestation*) encompasses the time from **conception**, the moment a male sperm cell enters a female egg cell, until the birth of a *full-term* infant, about 38 to 42 weeks later. During the first two weeks after conception, the fertilized egg (*ovum*) divides repeatedly, forming a mass of cells that enters the woman's **uterus**, the female reproductive organ that protects the developing organism. The mass of cells buries itself into the nutrient-rich lining of the uterus and continues to develop. For the next six weeks, the rapidly dividing mass of cells, called an **embryo**, increases in size and forms organs. Eight weeks after conception, the developing human being is referred to as a **fetus** (Fig. 13.1).

The prenatal period is often divided into three stages, or *trimesters*. During the first trimester, the embryo/fetus develops most of its organs, and by the end of this period, the fetus can move. The first trimester is a critical stage in human development because nutrient deficiencies or excesses and exposure to toxic compounds, such as alcohol, are most likely to have devastating effects on the embryo/fetus. However, many women who are in their first trimester do not realize they are pregnant.

As the second trimester begins, the fetus is still very tiny, about 6.5 to 7.5 cm (2½ to 3 in.) in length, and weighs only about 25 to 30 g (1 oz.). However, the fetus is beginning to look more like a human infant—it has fully formed arms, hands, fingers, legs, feet, and toes. The fetus's organs continue to grow and mature in their ability to function. As the fetus moves around, its mother becomes increasingly aware of its presence within her body.

placenta organ of pregnancy that connects the uterus to the embryo/fetus via the umbilical cord

low-birth-weight (LBW) infant infant generally weighing less than 2.5 kg (5½ lbs.) at birth

preterm infant born before 37 weeks of pregnancy

By the beginning of the third trimester, the fetus is approximately 30 cm (12 in.) long and weighs about 675 to 900 g (1½ to 2 lbs.). During this trimester, the fetus will nearly double in length and multiply its weight by three to four times. Thus, the fetus usually weighs about 2700 to 3600 g (6 to 8 lbs.) and is 48 to 53 cm (19 to 21 in.) long by the time it is full-term and ready to be born.

Throughout the prenatal period, the embryo/fetus depends entirely on its mother for survival. During most of the pregnancy, the expectant mother nourishes her embryo/fetus through the **placenta**, the organ of pregnancy that connects the uterus to the embryo/fetus via the *umbilical cord* (see Fig. 13.1). The role of the placenta is to transfer nutrients and oxygen from the mother's bloodstream to the embryo/fetus. Additionally, the placenta transfers wastes from the embryo/fetus to the mother's bloodstream so that her body can eliminate them. Unfortunately, the placenta does not filter many microbes and toxic substances, such as alcohol and nicotine, from the mother's blood. Thus, agents of infection and harmful chemicals can pass through the placenta, enter the embryo/fetus, and cause disease, birth defects, or embryonic/fetal death.

A full-term baby is defined as having spent at least 37 weeks developing within the uterus. Thus, 37 weeks gestation is considered the time required for a baby to be physiologically mature enough to thrive after birth. A fetus's weight depends on the supply of nutrients that it receives through the placenta.[3] If the placenta fails to grow properly, the developing fetus is likely to be born too soon and be lighter than average at birth.

Low-Birth-Weight and Preterm Newborns

Birth weight is a major factor that determines whether a baby is healthy and survives his or her first year of life.[4] *High-birth-weight* newborns generally weigh more than 4 kg (8.8 lbs.). When compared to newborns with healthy weights, high-birth-weight infants may experience injuries during birth.[5] **Low-birth-weight (LBW) infants** generally weigh less than 2.5 kg (5½ lbs.) at birth. Pregnant females who are 45 to 54 years of age or under 15 years of age are more likely to give birth to low-birth-weight infants than women in other age groups.[4] Additionally, women who smoke during pregnancy are at risk to have LBW babies.[6]

LBW is often associated with premature or *preterm births*. It is estimated that 13 million babies are born prematurely each year around the world.[7] Canada ranks a close second to Japan with regard to the decrease in infant mortality in the past 35 years, and in the proportion of babies who are **preterm**, that is, they occurred before the 37th week of pregnancy.[4,8] Preterm birth and LBW are leading causes of death among Canadian infants who are less than 28 days of age.[8] About 2% of births are *very preterm*, that is, the infants are born before 32 weeks of gestation. Very preterm infants are more likely to have serious health problems and die soon after birth than babies delivered after 32 weeks of pregnancy.[9]

A very preterm infant who is born after about 26 weeks of pregnancy may survive if cared for in a hospital nursery for high-risk newborns (Fig. 13.2). However, the tiny infant's body will not have stores of fat and certain minerals that normally accumulate during the last month of pregnancy. Additionally, very preterm babies are likely to have conditions that complicate their medical care and food intake, such as breathing difficulties and weak sucking and swallowing abilities.

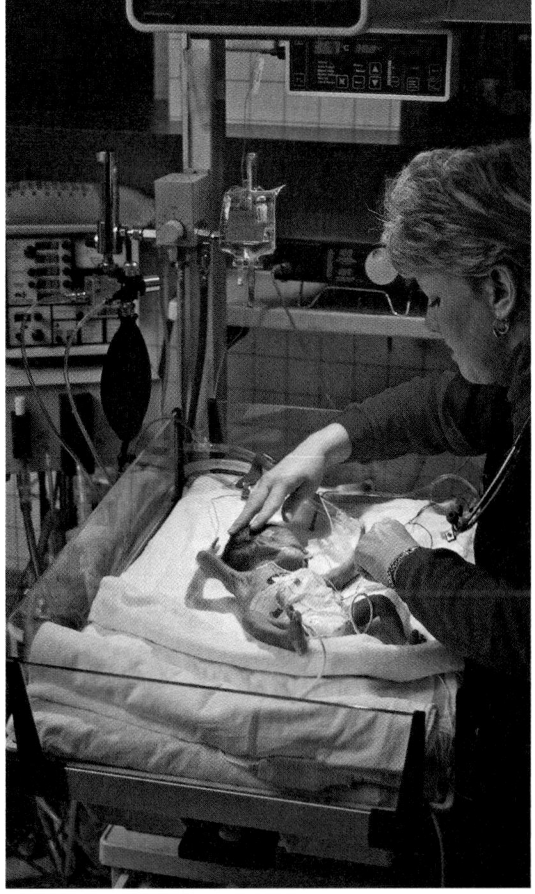

Figure 13.2 Very preterm infant. A very preterm infant may survive if cared for in a hospital nursery for such high-risk newborns.

Concept Checkpoint

1. When is an embryo referred to as the fetus?
2. What is the role of the placenta?
3. What is a major factor that determines whether a newborn baby is healthy and survives its first year of life?
4. What is a preterm birth?

prolactin hormone that stimulates milk production after delivery

morning sickness nausea and vomiting associated with pregnancy

Pregnancy

During pregnancy, a woman's body undergoes major physiological changes, such as increased blood volume, breast size, and levels of several hormones. These adaptations enable her body to nourish and maintain the developing embryo/fetus, as well as produce milk for her infant after its birth. However, some of the physical changes cause discomfort for the pregnant woman.

Common Nutrition-Related Signs of Pregnancy

In the first trimester, most women experience physical signs that they are pregnant, such as enlarged breasts and morning sickness. Other common nutrition-related signs as well as complaints of pregnancy include extreme tiredness, swollen feet, constipation, and heartburn. In most cases, such discomforts do not create serious complications and they resolve within a few months.

Breast Changes

During pregnancy, hormones signal the breasts to increase in size in preparation for lactation. The mother's pituitary gland in the brain produces **prolactin**, a hormone that stimulates the development of milk-producing tissue in the breasts. However, a pregnant woman's breasts do not form milk, because high levels of progesterone, a hormone that helps maintain pregnancy, inhibit milk production.[10] After birth, the level of progesterone drops rapidly, essentially removing the "brakes" from the breasts' ability to produce milk.

Morning Sickness

A common sign of pregnancy is **morning sickness**, nausea that is sometimes accompanied with vomiting. The term *morning sickness* is misleading because the queasy feeling can occur at any time of the day. The cause of this unpleasant condition is unclear but may be the result of the pregnant woman's body adapting to higher levels of female hormones. Additionally, emotional stress and certain foods can contribute to nausea. The condition generally begins early in the first trimester, and most women are no longer affected by the 16th week of pregnancy.[11] However, some women experience nausea and vomiting occasionally throughout their pregnancies.

To help control mild morning sickness, pregnant women can avoid odours and foods, such as fried or greasy foods, that trigger nausea. Some women find that eating crackers and drinking some water helps reduce the likelihood of feeling nauseated, especially before they get out of bed in the morning. Furthermore, eating smaller but more frequent meals and nutritious snacks can be helpful. If the nausea and vomiting are severe or the sickness persists beyond the fourth month of pregnancy, the pregnant woman should contact her physician for treatment. During pregnancy, excessive vomiting is harmful because it can lead to dehydration and weight loss.

Fatigue in Pregnancy

Early in pregnancy, the mother's blood volume expands to approximately 150% of normal. The number of red blood cells, however, increases by only 20 to 30%, and this change occurs more gradually. As a result, the pregnant woman develops *physiological anemia*, a condition characterized by a lower concentration of red blood cells in the bloodstream.

This form of anemia is a normal response to pregnancy, rather than the result of inadequate nutrient intake. Nevertheless, physiological anemia may be responsible for the extreme tiredness experienced by pregnant women during their first trimester. As their red blood cell numbers increase, expectant mothers report having more energy, especially during the second trimester. By the third trimester, however, most pregnant women are easily fatigued again, possibly because carrying a rapidly growing fetus is physically demanding.

What Is Edema?

High levels of certain hormones can cause various tissues to retain fluid during pregnancy. Although the extra fluid causes some minor swelling (edema), especially in the hands and feet, the condition is normal. In most cases, mild edema does not require treatment such as restricting salt intake or taking diuretics. Edema, however, can be a sign of trouble if hypertension and the appearance of extra protein in the urine accompany the swelling. A later section of this chapter discusses hypertension during pregnancy.

Digestive Tract Discomforts

During pregnancy, certain hormones produced by the placenta relax muscles of the digestive tract. As a result, intestinal movements slow down and digested material takes longer to pass through the tract, increasing the likelihood of constipation (see the "Fibre and the Digestive Tract" section of Chapter 5). To help prevent constipation, pregnant women should consume adequate amounts of fibre and fluids. During pregnancy, the Adequate Intake (AI) for fibre is 28 g per day, and the AI for total water is 3 L per day;[1] for women who are not pregnant, the current recommendation from Health Canada for fibre intake is 14 g per 1000 kcal consumed each day. If constipation persists after making these dietary changes, the pregnant woman should discuss this concern with her physician.

Heartburn is another common complaint of pregnant women. As the fetus grows, the uterus pushes upward in the mother's abdominal cavity and applies pressure on her stomach (Fig. 13.3).[12] When this occurs, stomach acid can enter the esophagus, causing

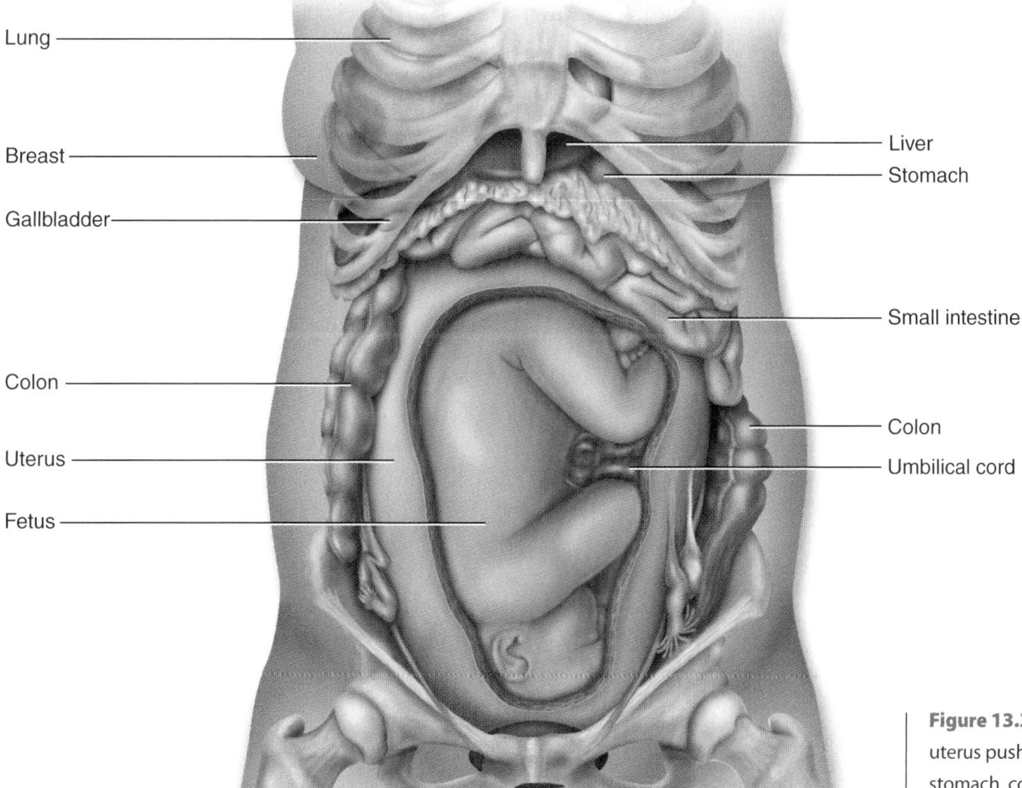

Figure 13.3 Heartburn during pregnancy. As the fetus grows, the uterus pushes upward and applies pressure to the pregnant woman's stomach, contributing to heartburn.

TABLE 13.1 *Comparing Selected DRIs: 25-Year-Old Non-pregnant and Pregnant Women*

Energy/ Nutrient	Non-pregnant	Pregnant
Kilocalories	Estimated Energy Requirement (EER)	First trimester = EER + 0
		Second trimester = EER + 340
		Third trimester = EER + 452
Protein¶	46 g/day	71 g/day
Vitamin C¶	75 mg/day	85 mg/day
Thiamin¶	1.1 mg/day	1.4 mg/day
Niacin¶	14 mg/day	18 mg/day
Folate¶	400 mcg/day	600 mcg/day
Vitamin D*	5 mcg/day	5 mcg/day
Calcium*	1000 mg/day	1000 mg/day
Iron¶	18 mg/day	27 mg/day
Iodine¶	150 mcg/day	220 mcg/day

¶ RDA

* AI

Source of data: Institute of Medicine: *Dietary Reference Intakes: The essential guide to nutrient requirements*. Otten JJ and others, eds. Washington, D.C.: National Academies Press, 2006.

heartburn (see the Chapter 4 Highlight). To help avoid heartburn, the pregnant woman can consume smaller meals, avoid lying down after eating, eat less fatty foods, and learn to identify and avoid foods that seem to contribute to heartburn. If heartburn continues to be bothersome, the woman should consult her physician and discuss other ways to treat the condition.

Pregnancy: General Dietary Recommendations

Ideally, women of child-bearing age should take steps to ensure good health before becoming pregnant. For example, women can analyze the nutritional adequacy of their diets and choose to eat foods that correct any marginal or deficient intakes. Prior to pregnancy, sedentary women can begin an exercise regimen; overweight or obese women can lose some excess weight; and women who smoke can join smoking cessation programs. The time to remedy faulty lifestyle practices and increase the chance of having a healthy pregnancy and baby is long before pregnancy occurs. Due to the increased requirement for folate during the first trimester of pregnancy, it is recommended that any women of child-bearing age consume 400 mcg per day of folate. Since the first trimester is when women may not yet realize they are pregnant, it is recommended that women of child-bearing age consume a daily multivitamin and mineral supplement containing folic acid, preferably containing 400 mcg of folic acid. Pregnant woman are advised to take 600 mcg per day of folate.

During pregnancy, the mother-to-be should follow a diet that meets her own nutritional needs as well as those of her developing offspring. Depending on the trimester, an expectant woman's requirements for energy (calories), protein, and many other nutrients are greater than her needs prior to pregnancy. Nevertheless, a pregnant woman does not need to double her usual food intake just because she is "eating for two." Table 13.1 compares Recommended Dietary Allowances (RDA) and Adequate Intakes (AI) for energy and selected nutrients that apply to healthy 25-year-old non-pregnant and pregnant women.

Energy Needs

In the first trimester, a pregnant woman's daily energy requirement (*Estimated Energy Requirement*, or *EER*) is essentially the same as a non-pregnant woman's, because the embryo/fetus is quite small (see Table 13.1). However, the fetus grows rapidly during the second and third trimesters, and the pregnant woman requires more energy and nutrients to support its growth as well as her own body's needs. During the second trimester, the expectant mother should consume approximately 340 more kilocalories per day than her pre-pregnancy EER. Throughout the third trimester, she should add about 450 kcal per day to her pre-pregnancy EER (see Table 13.1). If a woman is physically active during her pregnancy, she may need to increase her kilocalorie intake by even more than these levels. Why? As the pregnant woman gains weight, her muscles require more energy to move her body. The average expectant mother, however, reduces her physical activity level during the third trimester, conserving energy.

Folate and Iron Needs

A pregnant woman's requirements for folate and iron are 50% higher than those of a non-pregnant woman. It is important for women to enter pregnancy with adequate folate status, because embryos need the vitamin to support rapid cell division. As discussed in Chapter 8, pregnant women who are folate deficient are at high risk of giving birth to infants with neural tube defects, such as spina bifida (see Fig. 8.30 on p. 255). To obtain adequate folate, women of child-bearing age as well as pregnant women should include rich food sources of folate in their diets, such as green leafy vegetables, and take a vitamin/mineral supplement that supplies at least 400 mcg of *folic acid*, a form of folate.

As the pregnant woman's blood volume expands, her need for iron increases because her body must make more hemoglobin for the extra red blood cells. Additionally, the woman's body transfers iron to the fetus to build its stores of the mineral. If women fail to meet their iron needs during pregnancy, their iron stores can be severely depleted, and they can develop iron deficiency anemia. Pregnant women who are iron deficient are at high risk of giving birth prematurely and having low-birth-weight infants.[13]

Even when their diets include good sources of iron such as red meats and enriched cereals, pregnant women often need a supplemental source of iron. Thus, most physicians recommend special prenatal multiple vitamin/mineral supplements that contain iron for their pregnant patients.

Menu Planning for Pregnant Women

Rather than view pregnancy as a time to splurge by eating energy-dense empty-calorie foods, the mother-to-be should obtain the extra calories from nutrient-dense foods. For example, drinking an additional 250 mL (1 cup) of skim milk, eating a bowl of an enriched whole-grain cereal, and taking a prenatal supplement each day can supply extra kilocalories as well as protein, fibre, and micronutrients. Table 13.2 presents a day's meals and snacks for a 25-year-old woman who is in her second trimester of pregnancy. Her pre-pregnancy EER was 2060 kcal, so her sample menu is based on the *Eating Well with Canada's Food Guide* recommendations for 2400 kcal, enough to cover her increased EER during this trimester.

TABLE 13.2 *Sample Menu for a 25-Year-Old Pregnant Woman (Second Trimester)*

Breakfast
187 mL (¾ cup) cooked oatmeal, made with 125 mL (½ cup) skim milk and sprinkled with 60 mL (¼ cup) raisins
125 mL (½ cup) calcium-fortified orange juice
Mid-morning snack
125 mL (½ cup) calcium-fortified orange juice
1 rectangular graham cracker
30 mL (2 Tbsp) peanut butter
Lunch
Cheese sandwich
2 slices whole-grain bread
1 slice cheddar cheese
2 slices tomato
60 mL (¼ cup) leaf lettuce
10 mL (2 tsp) mayonnaise-type low-calorie salad dressing
250 mL (1 cup) apple slices
250 mL (1 cup) skim milk
125 mL (½ cup) orange sherbet
Mid-afternoon snack
1 whole-grain English muffin, toasted
15 mL (1 Tbsp) soft margarine
10 mL (2 tsp) jelly
125 mL (½ cup) skim milk
Dinner
Broiled salmon filet, 140 g (5 oz.)
313 mL (1¼) cups mixed salad greens
15 mL (1 Tbsp) low-calorie Italian dressing
125 mL (½ cup) enriched white rice
250 mL (1 cup) steamed broccoli
2 small dinner rolls
15 mL (1 Tbsp) soft margarine
Evening snack
250 mL (1 cup) frozen yogourt

Is Fish Safe to Eat during Pregnancy?

Fish and shellfish (e.g., clams, shrimp, and crabs) are excellent sources of many minerals, omega-3 fatty acids, and high-quality protein. However, most fish and shellfish contain very small amounts of mercury, a toxic mineral.[14] For most healthy adults, ingesting amounts of mercury that are generally in fish and shellfish is not thought to be harmful. Certain kinds of fish and shellfish, however, contain higher levels of mercury than others. When a pregnant woman eats these foods, the mercury in them can eventually reach the developing fetus and damage its nervous system. According to recommendations issued by Health Canada, women who may become pregnant, are pregnant, or are breast-feeding their babies should:

- Eat at least two servings (75 g/2.5 oz. each) of fish per week that are generally known to contain no or minute amounts of mercury, such as shrimp, canned light tuna, salmon, pollock, and salmon. (Albacore tuna contains more mercury than canned light tuna, but eating up to four servings of albacore tuna per week is allowed.)
- Avoid eating types of fish that often contain high amounts of mercury, particularly shark, swordfish, king mackerel, and tilefish.

Health Canada also recommends that caregivers should only feed smaller quantities (one to two servings per week) of fish that contain higher amounts of mercury (such as albacore tuna) to young children because their nervous systems are still developing.[14]

What about Cravings?

The stereotype of a pregnant woman who craves pickles and ice cream is not simply a myth—cravings are common during this stage of life. However, ask pregnant women to identify the foods they crave, and you are likely to get a variety of responses. The causes of cravings are unknown but may be responses to the hormonal changes associated with pregnancy, or to the emotional state of the mother-to-be. In other instances, specific food cravings may simply reflect the pregnant woman's family traditions. Unless food cravings contribute to excess weight gain, they are generally harmless.

According to Health Canada recommendations, women who may become pregnant, are pregnant, or are breast-feeding their babies should eat at least two servings of fish per week that generally contain small amounts of mercury.

pica craving non-food items

Some women develop **pica**, the craving of non-food items such as laundry starch, chalk, cigarette ashes, and soil. Some studies have linked pica with iron and zinc deficiency, but it is not clear if pica is the result or cause of such deficiencies. Pregnant women should refrain from practising pica, especially eating clay or soil. Soil may contain substances that interfere with the absorption of minerals in the intestinal tract. Furthermore, eating soil can be harmful because the dirt may be contaminated with toxic substances, such as lead and pesticides, and pathogenic microbes.

TABLE 13.3 *Distribution of Weight Gain during Pregnancy*

Tissue	Approximate Grams (Pounds)
Maternal	
Blood	1400 (3.0)
Breasts	900 (2.0)
Uterus	900 (2.0)
Fat, protein, and retained fluid	5000 (11.0)
Fetus	3400 (7.5)
Placenta	675 (1.5)
*Amniotic fluid**	900 (2.0)

* Protective fluid that surrounds fetus.

Source: March of Dimes: Weight gain during pregnancy. www.marchofdimes.com/pnhec/159_153.asp.

Weight Gain during Pregnancy

Nearly all pregnant women experience weight gain. In fact, gaining an appropriate amount of weight is crucial during pregnancy. How much weight a woman should gain depends on her pre-pregnancy body mass index (BMI). According to experts with the Society of Obstetricians and Gynaecologists of Canada (SOGC), women who were underweight prior to pregnancy should gain 12.7 to 18.2 kg (28 to 40 lbs.); women whose pre-pregnancy weights were within the healthy range can expect to gain 11.4 to 15.9 kg (25 to 35 lbs.). Women who were overweight before they became pregnant should gain 6.8 to 11.4 kg (15 to 25 lbs.), and obese women should gain at least 6.8 kg (15 lbs.) during pregnancy.[15] The recommendations are higher for women who are pregnant with more than one fetus. For example, a healthy woman who is carrying twins may gain as much as 20 kg (45 lbs.) during pregnancy.[16]

Underweight women who do not gain enough weight during pregnancy are at risk of having preterm or LBW infants. Underweight pregnant women should try to reach healthy weights by the end of the first trimester and then meet the recommended weight gain goals. Obese women have a greater risk of developing hypertension as well as type 2 diabetes during pregnancy. However, overfat women should not try to lose weight during pregnancy because calorie restriction may harm the fetus.

In Canada, pregnant women often gain more weight than recommended amounts.[17] Expectant mothers who gain about 18.2 kg (40 pounds) or more during their pregnancies are more likely to give birth to high-birth-weight babies.[18] Such large babies tend to have more health problems than babies whose birth weights are within the healthy range. Furthermore, women who gain excess weight during pregnancy are at risk of retaining the extra weight long after their babies are born.

Accounting for the Weight Gain

It is important to understand that much of the weight a woman gains during a healthy pregnancy is not body fat. By the end of a full-term pregnancy, the average fetus weighs about 3.4 kg (7½ lbs.), and the placenta and amniotic fluid that surround the fetus account for about 1.6 kg (3½ lbs.). The remaining weight is comprised of tissues and fluids the mother's body gains during pregnancy (*maternal weight gain*). Table 13.3 indicates the typical distribution of weight that is gained during this life stage.

Figure 13.4 Rate of weight gain: Healthy pregnancy. This chart illustrates the rate of maternal weight gain that typically occurs during a healthy pregnancy.

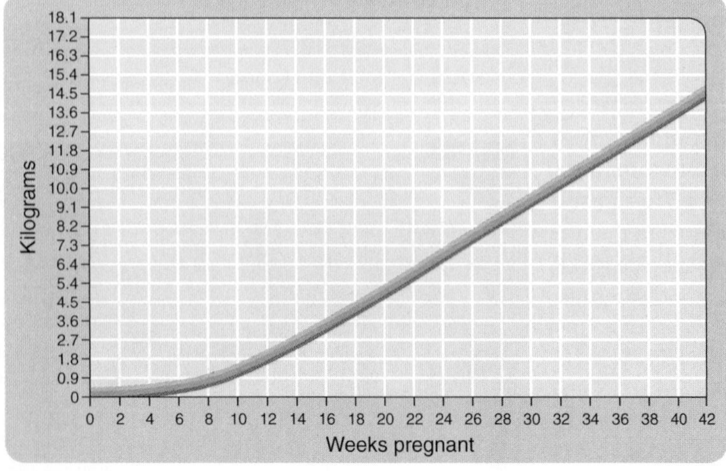

Rate of Weight Gain

Not only is the amount of weight that an expectant mother gains important, but also the rate of the gain. Most pregnant women add up to 1.8 kg (4 lbs.) of weight during the first trimester. Throughout the rest of their pregnancies, women typically gain at a faster rate, 1.4 to 1.8 kg (3 to 4 lbs.) *each* month.[16] Figure 13.4 charts the course of weight gain in a healthy pregnancy. Note how the rate reaches a steady pace of about 0.45 kg (1 lb.) per week during the second and third trimesters.

The Importance of Prenatal Care

Ideally, women of child-bearing age should plan for pregnancy and receive dietary advice before becoming pregnant. If this is not possible, *prenatal care* should begin early in pregnancy, because many medical problems that may occur during this life stage can be diagnosed and treated before the health of the mother or her fetus are threatened. **Prenatal care** is specialized to meet the health care needs of pregnant women. Routine prenatal health care includes measuring and monitoring the pregnant woman's weight, blood pressure, blood glucose level, and uterine growth. The prenatal health care provider may also discuss various concerns with the expectant mother such as morning sickness, safe types of physical activity, what to expect during the birth process, and basic infant care skills. Additionally, the health care provider can advise the pregnant woman to make appropriate lifestyle choices, such as avoiding the use of tobacco, alcohol, and illegal substances.

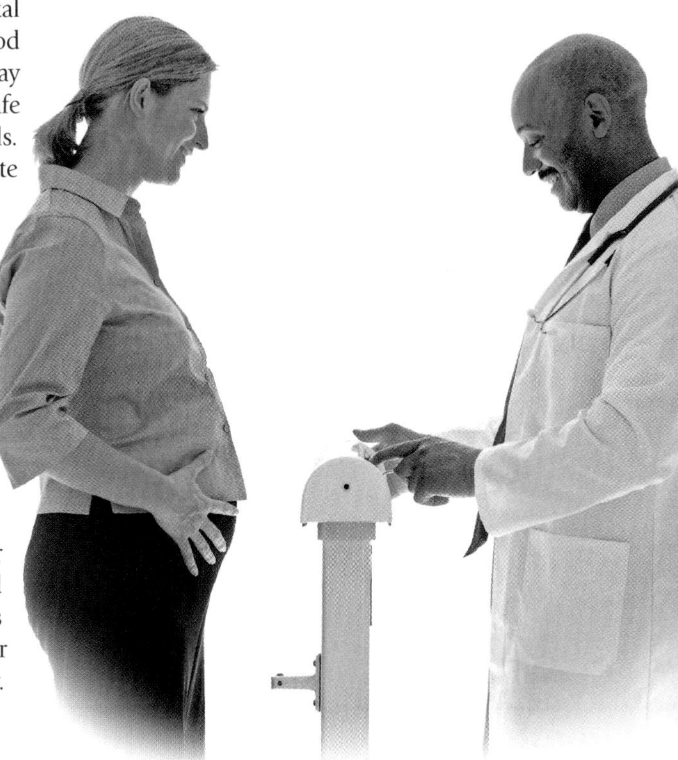

Proper nutrient intake during pregnancy is also vital to ensure long-term health as the baby grows into adolescence and adulthood. The **Barker hypothesis** (www.thebarkertheory.org) suggests that a fetus deprived of nutrients in utero subsequently has a reduced level of fetal growth, which is strongly associated with chronic conditions later in life. The increased susceptibility occurs secondary to adaptations made by the fetus in an environment limited in its supply of nutrients. These conditions include obesity, diabetes, coronary heart disease, and hypertension.

According to a report from the Centers for Disease Control and Prevention, women who receive no prenatal care have increased risk for pregnancy-related death.[19]

During pregnancy, it is important for a woman to decide whether she will breast-feed her baby. According to results of one survey, women chose breast-feeding over bottle-feeding because the practice was better for their babies' health, more natural, and more likely to encourage bonding with their infants.[20] The best food for a new baby is breast milk; pregnant women who decide to breast-feed their babies should inform their physicians and learn as much as they can about breast-feeding early in their pregnancy.

Gestational Diabetes

About 4% of pregnant women develop type 2 diabetes during pregnancy (*gestational diabetes*). When a woman has gestational diabetes, her fetus receives too much glucose and converts the excess into fat. Thus, women with this form of diabetes often give birth to high-birth-weight babies. After birth, these infants often have difficulty controlling their own blood glucose levels and are at risk of becoming overweight as children.

Gestational diabetes can be detected during routine prenatal care. Diet and exercise are usually necessary to treat the condition, but in some cases, insulin injections are required. After giving birth, the blood glucose values of women who developed diabetes during pregnancy generally return to normal. However, women who experienced gestational diabetes are at higher risk of developing type 2 diabetes later in life. For more information about diabetes, see Chapter 5.

Pregnancy-Induced Hypertension (PIH)

Rapid weight gain, especially after the fifth month of pregnancy, could be a sign of a serious type of hypertension called **pregnancy-induced hypertension (PIH)**. PIH is commonly referred to as preeclampsia (*pre-e-klamp'-see-a*). Preeclampsia is characterized by sudden, dramatic increase in weight that is due to edema, particularly of the hands and face; hypertension; protein in urine; and abnormal liver function.[21] If a woman suffering from preeclampsia develops convulsions, her condition is called eclampsia (*e-klamp'-see-a*).

Hypertension is a common complication of pregnancy. According to an Australian study involving over 250 000 women, hypertension was present in almost 10% of pregnancies; about 4% of pregnant women developed PIH.[22] Pregnant women who have high risk of PIH are those who are under 17 or over 35 years of age, have a history of diabetes or hypertension, and are carrying more than one fetus.

prenatal care specialized health care for pregnant women

pregnancy-induced hypertension (PIH) type of hypertension that can develop during pregnancy

Most pregnant women can continue their pre-pregnancy exercise regimens, especially those that include low- or moderate-intensity activities.

In Canada, approximately 400 000 women become pregnant each year.[23] Most Canadian women have normal pregnancies and deliver healthy infants, but some women do not experience normal pregnancies or have healthy infants. PIH is a leading cause of pregnancy-related death.[19] At present, the only effective treatment for PIH is delivering the fetus. Unfortunately, infants born before the 24th week of pregnancy are unlikely to survive. However, if the fetus is more mature, its mother may be hospitalized for treatment until the fetus has a better chance of surviving after the birth. Nevertheless, babies born to hypertensive mothers are more likely to be LBW.

Drug Use

Exposure to alcohol and tobacco is harmful to the embryo/fetus. Women who drink alcohol during pregnancy are at risk of having a child with fetal alcohol syndrome (FAS) (see Fig. 6.G on p. 179). Scientists do not know if there is a "safe" amount of alcohol that pregnant women can consume, therefore, women of child-bearing age who are sexually active or pregnant should avoid alcoholic beverages. The Chapter 6 Highlight provides more information about FAS.

Compared to pregnant women who do not smoke cigarettes, expectant mothers who smoke are at higher risk of giving birth too early and having LBW babies. Furthermore, expectant mothers who smoke cigarettes may increase the risk of having babies with birth defects or that die of *sudden infant death syndrome (SIDS)*. SIDS is the sudden, unexplained death of an infant younger than 1 year old and the leading cause of death for babies between 1 month and 1 year of age.[24]

The use of illegal drugs, herbal supplements, and medications during pregnancy can also harm the embryo/fetus. Ideally, the time to quit abusing illegal drugs is before pregnancy. Pregnant women should consult their physicians before using herbal supplements or taking any drugs, even over-the-counter medications.

What about Physical Activity?

Women can derive many benefits from being physically active during pregnancy, including enhanced muscle tone and strength, reduced edema, and improved mood and sleep. Most pregnant women can continue their pre-pregnancy exercise regimens, especially those that include low- or moderate-intensity activities. However, the exercise routine should not result in weight loss. Recommended activities generally include walking, cycling, swimming, or light aerobics. Pregnancy is not the time to begin an intense fitness regimen or perform high-risk physical activities. Activities that are risky and should be avoided include downhill skiing; contact sports such as judo, soccer, and basketball; and scuba diving.[25] Pregnant women should discuss their physical activity practices and needs with their physicians. Some expectant women, such as those experiencing PIH or premature labour contractions, may need to restrict their physical activity.

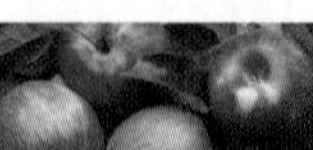

Concept Checkpoint

5. Identify at least three different nutrition-related signs of pregnancy.
6. According to recommendations of the Society of Obstetricians and Gynaecologists of Canada, how much weight should a healthy woman gain during pregnancy? How much weight if she was underweight before becoming pregnant? How much weight should a woman gain if she was overweight before pregnancy?
7. Why is having adequate folate and iron status important for pregnant women?
8. Discuss the harmful effects that a pregnant woman's alcohol consumption and cigarette smoking can have on her embryo/fetus.

Infant Nutrition

Rapid physical growth characterizes infancy, the life stage that extends from birth to about 2 years of age. During the first four to six months of life, a healthy baby doubles its birth weight, and by 1 year of age, an infant's birth weight has tripled. Additionally, an infant's length increases by 50% during its first year of life. Thus, if a baby girl weighs 3.2 kg (7 lbs.) and is 51 cm (20 in.) long at birth, you would expect her to weigh 9.5 kg (21 lbs.) and be 76 cm (30 in.) long by her first birthday (Fig. 13.5).

Compared to older children, an infant needs more energy and nutrients, per gram of body weight, to support its rapid growth.[1] If an infant's diet lacks adequate energy and nutrients, the baby's growth may slow or even stop. The following sections take a closer look at infant nutrition, including breast-feeding and other infant-feeding practices.

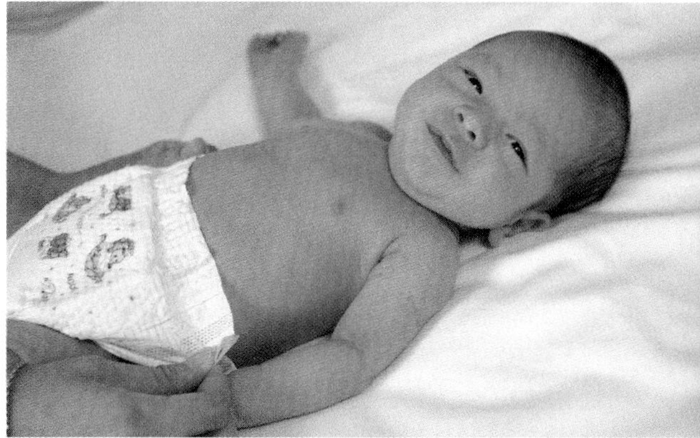

a.

b.

Figure 13.5 Growth rates during infancy. A healthy newborn baby (*a*) grows rapidly during its first year. During the first four to six months of life, a baby doubles its birth weight, and by 1 year of age, an infant's birth weight has tripled (*b*). Additionally, an infant's length increases by 50% during its first year of life.

infant formula synthetic food that simulates human milk

colostrum initial form of breast milk that contains anti-infective properties

Breast Milk Is Best

Two hundred years ago, if a new mother was unable to breast-feed her baby, the child faced certain death—unless a woman who was producing breast milk could be located to suckle (*nurse*) the infant. Today, a new mother can choose to nurse her baby or feed the child an **infant formula**, a synthetic food that simulates human milk. Although both foods provide adequate nutrition for infants, Canadian and American infants who are not breast-fed have a higher infant mortality rate than babies who receive breast milk.[26,27]

Human milk is uniquely formulated to meet the nutrient needs of a newborn baby. During the first couple of days after giving birth, the new mother's breasts produce **colostrum** (*co-loss'-trum*), a yellowish fluid that does not look like milk. (Some women report colostrum leaked from their breasts late in the pregnancy.)[27] By the end of the first week of lactation, colostrum has undergone a transition to *mature milk*. If you compare the appearance of mature human milk to cow's milk, you will notice that breast milk is more watery than cow's milk and may have a slightly bluish colour.

If they are unaware that colostrum is secreted by breasts soon after birth, women may think something is wrong with their ability to produce milk. However, colostrum is a very important first food for babies, because the fluid contains antibodies and immune system cells that can be absorbed by the infant's immature digestive tract. Colostrum also contains a substance that encourages the growth of a type of bacteria, *Lactobacillus bifidus* (*L. bifidus*), in the infant's GI tract. Such biologically active substances help an infant's body fight infections and hasten the maturation of the baby's immune system. Thus, breast-fed infants have lower risks of diarrhea, allergies, and gastrointestinal, respiratory, and ear infections than formula-fed infants.[28] Furthermore, breast-fed babies may be less likely to develop childhood asthma, leukemia, obesity, and type 1 diabetes than infants who are not breast-fed.[28,29]

Human milk is a rich source of lipids, including cholesterol, and fatty acids such as linoleic acid, *arachidonic acid* (*ARA*), and *docosahexaenoic acid* (*DHA*). An infant's nervous system, especially the brain and eyes, depends on ARA and DHA for proper development. Furthermore, the fat in breast milk helps supply the energy needed to maintain the infant's overall growth.

The practice of breast-feeding also provides some important advantages for parents, particularly the new mother. Breast-feeding is more convenient and economical than using infant formula. Human milk is readily available—there is no need to purchase cans of infant formula and have them on hand. As milk leaves the breast, it is always fresh, free of bacteria, and ready-to-feed without mixing, bottling, or warming. Because human milk production requires a considerable amount of energy, lactating women can lose the extra body fat gained during pregnancy faster than mothers who use infant formula. Additionally, women who breast-feed their babies have lower risks of breast cancer (before menopause) and ovarian cancer than women who do not breast-feed. Some of these benefits depend on whether women breast-feed exclusively, that is, provide no other foods, and

Canadian infants who are breast-fed have a lower infant mortality rate than babies who are not.

oxytocin hormone that elicits the let-down response and causes the uterus to contract

the number of months the mother nurses her infant. Table 13.4 lists these and several other advantages of breast-feeding.[26,28]

The Milk Production Process—Lactation

When an infant suckles, nerves in the mother's nipple signal her brain to release prolactin and **oxytocin** (*ox-e-tose'-in*) into her bloodstream. Prolactin stimulates specialized cells in breasts to form milk. These cells carry out the lactation process by synthesizing some nutrients and removing others from the mother's bloodstream and adding them to her milk. Oxytocin plays a different role in establishing successful lactation. This hormone signals breast tissue to "let down" milk. The *let-down reflex* enables milk to travel in several tubes (ducts) to the nipple area. A reflex is a physical response that is automatic and not under conscious control. When let-down occurs, the infant removes the milk by continued sucking (Fig. 13.6). Shortly before the flow of milk begins, the lactating woman often feels a tingling sensation in her nipples, a signal that let-down is occurring.

Embarrassment, emotional stress and tension, pain, and fatigue can easily block the let-down reflex. For example, if a lactating mother is tense or upset, let-down does not occur, and her infant will not be able to obtain milk when it suckles. When this happens, the hungry infant becomes frustrated and angry, and the mother may respond by becoming even more tense and upset, setting up a vicious cycle. At this point, new mothers often give up breast-feeding, reporting that they tried to suckle their babies, but they were unable to "produce" milk.

Lactating women need to be aware of the connection between their emotional state and failure to let-down. To smooth the path to successful lactation, it helps if new mothers are in a comfortable, relaxed environment when they breast-feed their babies. When lactation and breast-feeding are well established, the let-down response often occurs without the need for suckling. For example, the mother's let-down reflex may be triggered just by thinking about nursing her infant or hearing it cry.

Did You Know?

The size of a woman's breasts does not influence her ability to breast-feed her infant. However, certain surgical procedures used to enlarge or decrease breast size can disrupt the nerves and milk-producing tissue in the breasts. Women who had surgery to alter their breasts may be able to produce milk after giving birth, but their infants' growth rates should be monitored to make sure the babies are obtaining enough milk.[30]

TABLE 13.4 *Advantages of Breast-feeding*

Advantages for Infants
Human milk:
• Is free of bacteria as it leaves the breast.
• Supplies antibodies and immune cells.
• Is easily digested.
• Reduces risk of food allergies, especially to proteins in infant formulas and cow's milk.
• Changes in composition over time to meet the changing needs of a growing infant.
• Contains zinc, iron, and other minerals in highly absorbable forms.
• Decreases risks of ear, intestinal, and respiratory infections.
• May reduce the risk of asthma, obesity, and type 1 diabetes in childhood.
Advantages for New Mothers
Breast-feeding:
• Reduces uterine bleeding after delivery.
• Promotes shrinkage of the uterus to its pre-pregnancy size.
• Decreases the risk of breast cancer (before menopause) and ovarian cancer.
• May promote maternal weight loss.
• May enhance bonding with the infant.
• Is less expensive and more convenient than feeding infant formula.

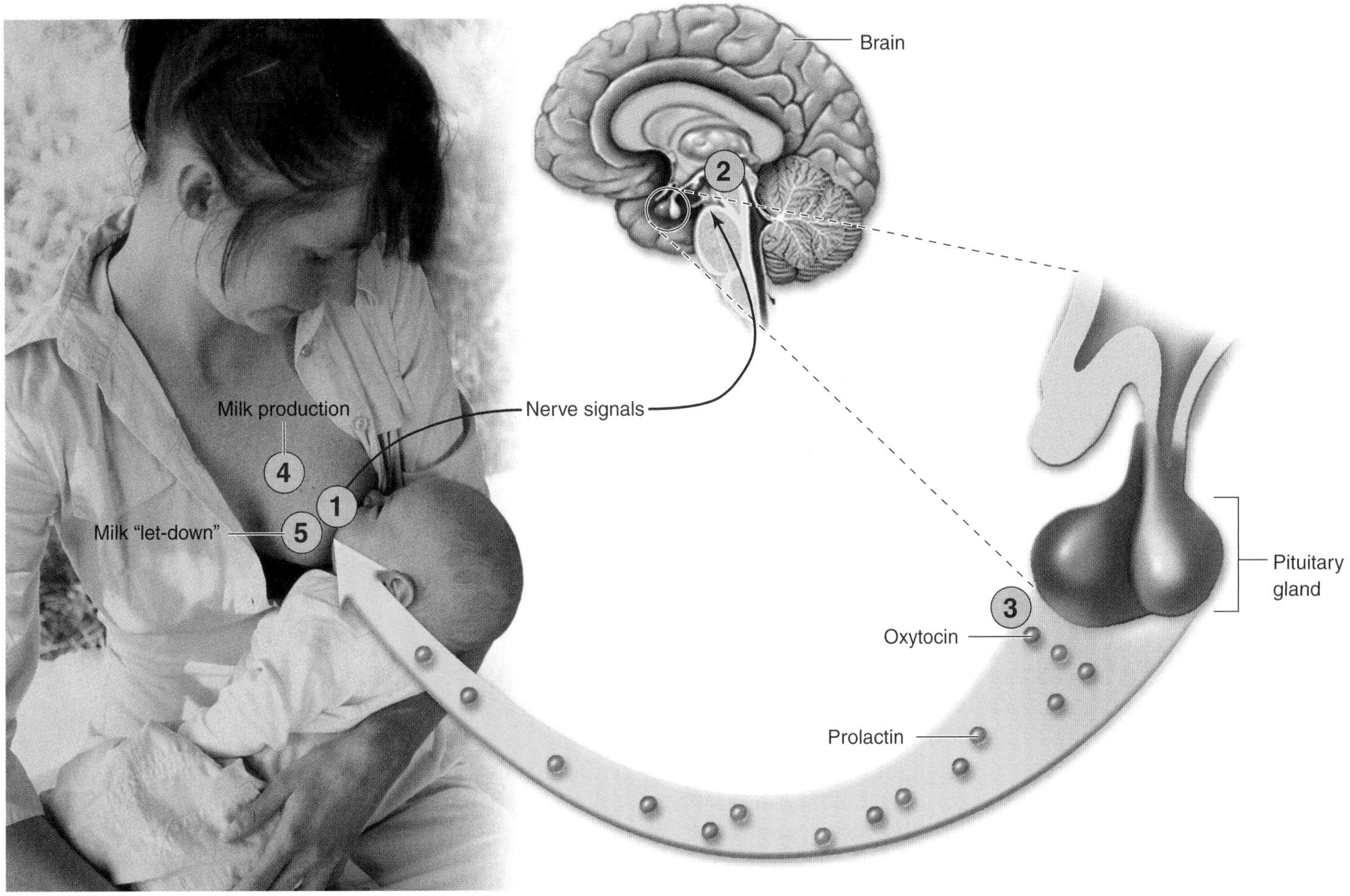

Figure 13.6 Prolactin and oxytocin. (1) A baby's sucking stimulates nerves in the nipple that signal the pituitary gland in the mother's brain (2) to release prolactin and oxytocin into her bloodstream (3). Prolactin stimulates milk-producing cells in breasts to form milk (4). Oxytocin triggers breast tissue to "let down" milk, a process that enables milk to travel via ducts to the nipple area (5).

Breast-feeding is a skill, and like other skills, it takes some practice to fully master. Thus, it may take a few weeks for the new mother to feel comfortable with the process. By persevering, she and her baby are likely to become a successful breast-feeding team.

Typically, a lactating woman produces over 750 mL (3 cups) of milk per day.[10] It is important to recognize that milk production relies on "supply and demand." The more the infant suckles (demand), the more milk its mother's breasts produce (supply). However, if milk is not fully removed from the breasts, milk production soon ceases. This is likely to occur when infants are not hungry, because they have been given baby food and formula to supplement breast-milk feedings.

Did You Know?

When a new mother breast-feeds her newborn immediately after delivery, oxytocin signals her uterus to contract, reducing the risk of excessive uterine bleeding.

Dietary Planning for Lactating Women

Milk production requires approximately 800 kcal every day. However, the lactating woman's daily energy needs can be met by adding only about 300 to 400 kcal to her pre-pregnancy EER. The difference between the energy needed for milk production and the recommended energy intake can enable the new mother to lose the extra body fat she accumulated during pregnancy. This loss is more likely to occur if she continues breast-feeding her baby for six months or more and increases her physical activity level. A woman, for example, who needed 2000 kcal before becoming pregnant would require about 2400 to 2600 kcal daily during lactation. To help plan meals and snacks that are

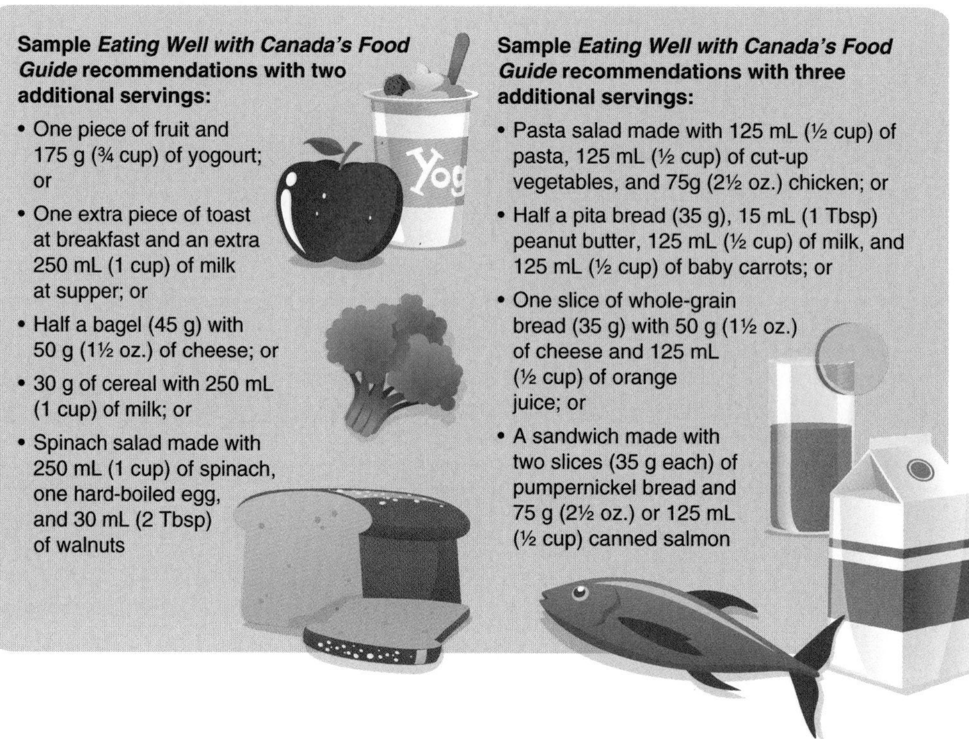

Figure 13.7 ***Eating Well with Canada's Food Guide* recommendations for breast-feeding women.** Breast-feeding women typically require a few more calories. For most women, this means an extra two or three food guide servings each day in addition to their recommended number of food guide servings.

nutritionally adequate, she can follow the *Eating Well with Canada's Food Guide* recommendations (Fig. 13.7).

No special foods are necessary to sustain milk production. However, a lactating woman should drink fluids every time her infant suckles to help her maintain adequate milk volume and keep her body properly hydrated. For as long as she breast-feeds her baby, the lactating mother should limit her intake of alcohol- and caffeine-containing beverages because her body secretes these drugs into her milk. A woman who breast-feeds her baby should also check with her physician before using any medications, even over-the-counter and herbal products, because such substances may also end up in her breast milk.

Did You Know?

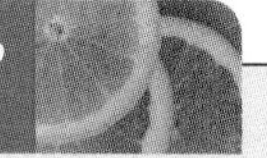

In Canada, newborns are given vitamin K with the parents' permission to protect them against excessive bleeding.

Is Breast Milk a Complete Food?

Health Canada and Dietitians of Canada recommend that new mothers breast-feed their infants exclusively during their babies' first six months of life.[28] According to experts with Health Canada, it is not necessary to supplement young infants' diets with other fluids, such as water, infant formula, and juices, or solid foods such as baby food.[28] After an infant reaches 6 months of age, breast-feeding should continue, but the infant can also be offered some appropriate solid foods. Dietitians of Canada promotes breast-feeding combined with infant foods until the child's first birthday. However, there is no reason why children cannot be breast-fed for longer periods. Throughout the world, many mothers continue to nurse their babies well past the babies' first birthdays, but in Canada, this practice is less common.

Although breast milk is highly nutritious, it is not a complete food for all infants. Human milk may contain inadequate amounts of vitamins D and B-12, and the minerals iron and fluoride. Health Canada recommends all breast-fed infants be given a supplement that supplies 400 IU of vitamin D per day (although the DRI is 200 IU), until they are consuming that amount of the vitamin from food or infant formula.[28] Exposing the infant to some sun can also help meet part of the child's vitamin D needs. If a lactating woman is a total vegetarian and she does not consume a source of vitamin B-12, she should consult her physician concerning the need for vitamin B-12 supplementation. When breast-fed infants are about 6 months old, they should also be consuming some iron-containing solid foods, because the amount of iron in their mother's milk may no longer meet their needs. Before giving any dietary supplements to the babies, parents or caregivers should discuss their infant's nutritional needs with the child's physician.

A question commonly asked is whether the breast-fed infant needs additional water, particularly in hot weather or if the child is suffering from diarrhea, vomiting, or fever. Human milk provides adequate water intake for healthy infants who are exclusively breast-fed.[31] However, it is important to obtain prompt professional medical care to prevent an ill baby from becoming dehydrated.

Quitting Too Soon

Nearly all healthy women are physically capable of breast-feeding their infants, but the Canadian Breastfeeding Foundation (www.canadianbreastfeedingfoundation.org) estimates while nearly 85% of Canadian mothers attempt breast-feeding, only 15% are able to meet the recommendation to exclusively breast-feed for the first six months.[31] The World Health Organization (WHO) estimates that 1.5 million infants die each year around the world because they are not breast-fed.[32]

Women who breast-feed their newborns may stop the practice prior to the Health Canada recommendation to exclusively breast-feed until 6 months of age.[28] There are many reasons why women discontinue nursing their infants too soon. New mothers often quit because they lack information about and support for breast-feeding their babies. Some women discontinue breast-feeding because of uncertainty over how much milk their babies are consuming. Baby bottles are marked to indicate millilitres, so a mother who bottle-feeds her infant can easily measure the amount of formula consumed. A lactating mother, however, has to observe her baby for cues indicating the child is full. When a breast-feeding baby is no longer interested in nursing and stops, its mother has to assume the infant is satisfied with the feeding. A well-nourished breast-fed infant will gain weight normally and generally have six or more wet diapers as well as one or two soft bowel movements per day. Parents or caregivers who are concerned about their infants' food intake or nutritional status should consult their physician immediately.

Many new mothers discontinue breast-feeding before their babies are 6 months old, because they need to return to work and have caregivers feed their babies. Although lactating women can learn to express milk from their breasts and preserve it for later feedings, many workplaces do not have comfortable, private facilities for women to express milk and then store it safely.

To enhance the likelihood that a nursing mother continues to breast-feed, it is helpful to enlist the support of a female relative or friend who has successfully breast-fed their children. Furthermore, the woman's partner needs to understand and appreciate the function of the human breast as a source of nearly perfect nourishment for infants. New mothers are unlikely to begin and continue nursing their babies without their partners' support. La Leche League is an international organization dedicated to providing education and support for breast-feeding women (1-800-LALECHE or www.lalecheleague.org). Also, hospitals may employ lactation consultants or specialists. Lactation consultants are often nurses who are trained to provide information and advice about breast-feeding. For more information about breast-feeding visit the Canadian Breastfeeding Foundation Web site (above) or www.cdc.gov/breastfeeding.

This mother is using an electric device to express milk in a private room at her workplace. She will chill the milk and give it to her baby's caregiver for bottle feeding.

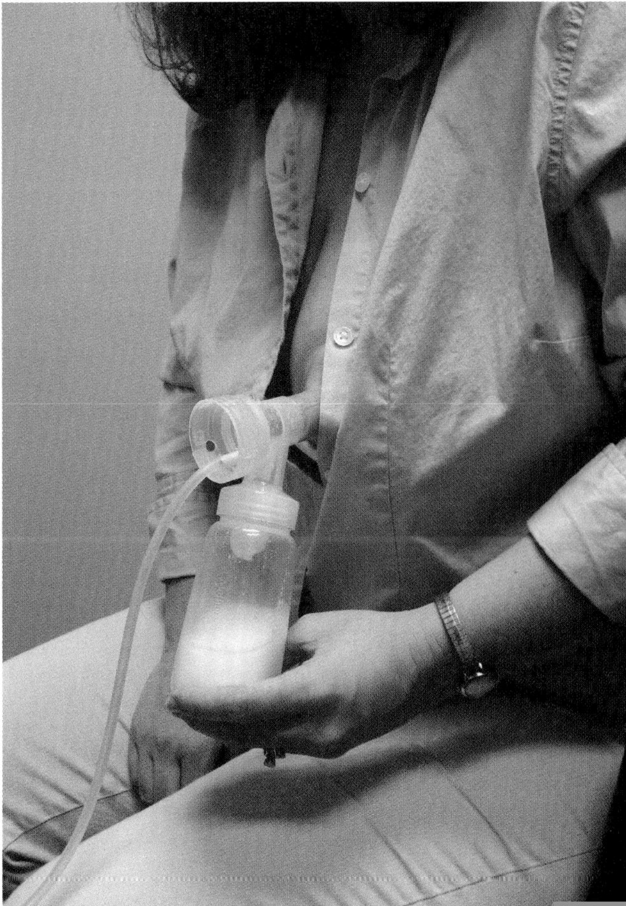

Figure 13.8 Infant formulas. Infant formulas provide a safe and nutritionally adequate source of nutrients for babies who are not breast-fed.

Infant Formula-Feeding

Not every woman wants or is able to breast-feed her baby. Infant formulas are a safe and nutritionally adequate source of nutrients for babies who are not breast-fed (Fig. 13.8). To produce artificial milk for babies, infant formula manufacturers alter cow's milk to improve its digestibility and nutrient content. Infant formulas generally contain heat-treated proteins from cow's milk, lactose and/or sucrose, and vegetable oil. Infant formulas generally lack cholesterol, but some of these products have the fatty acids DHA and ARA added to them. Vitamins and minerals are added to the product, and in some instances, infant formula contains higher levels of micronutrients than human milk. Although infant formulas mimic the water, macronutrient, and micronutrient content of human milk, their compositions are not identical to human milk (Table 13.5). Formula manufacturers have been unable to duplicate human antibodies and other unique immune system factors that are in breast milk. Thus, the "breast is best!"

An interesting feature of human milk is that its fat content changes during each feeding, which usually lasts about 20 minutes. In the beginning of the session, the mother's milk is low in fat, but as her infant continues to suckle, the fat content of her milk gradually increases.[33] The higher fat content of the "hind milk" may make the baby feel satisfied and, as a result, discontinue feeding. Infant formulas, however, have uniform composition, that is, they do not change their fat contents during a feeding session. Thus, the mother or infant caregiver is more likely to control the amount of formula the baby consumes, possibly leading to overfeeding. Nevertheless, the overall energy content of human milk is about the same as that of infant formulas.

Experts with Health Canada recommend that caregivers provide an iron-fortified infant formula for babies who are not breast-fed.[28] Not all infant formulas contain iron, so it is important to read the product's label before purchasing it. Formula-fed babies may also need a source of fluoride, but caregivers should check with their infants' physicians before providing a supplement containing the mineral. For babies who are allergic to infant formulas made from cow's milk proteins, similar products made with soy or other proteins are available.

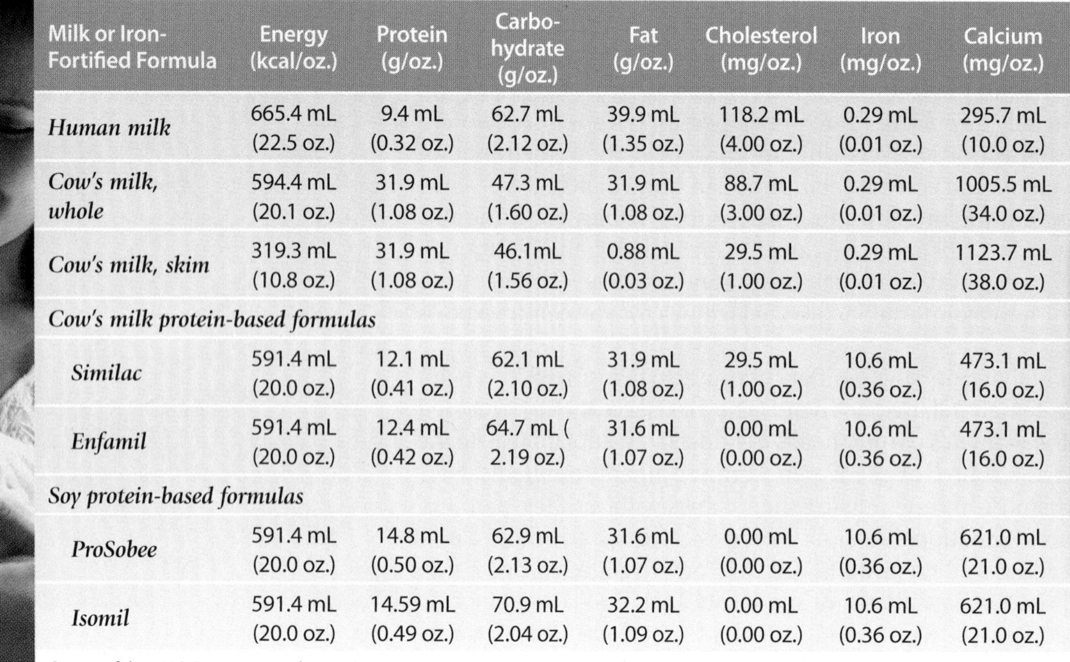
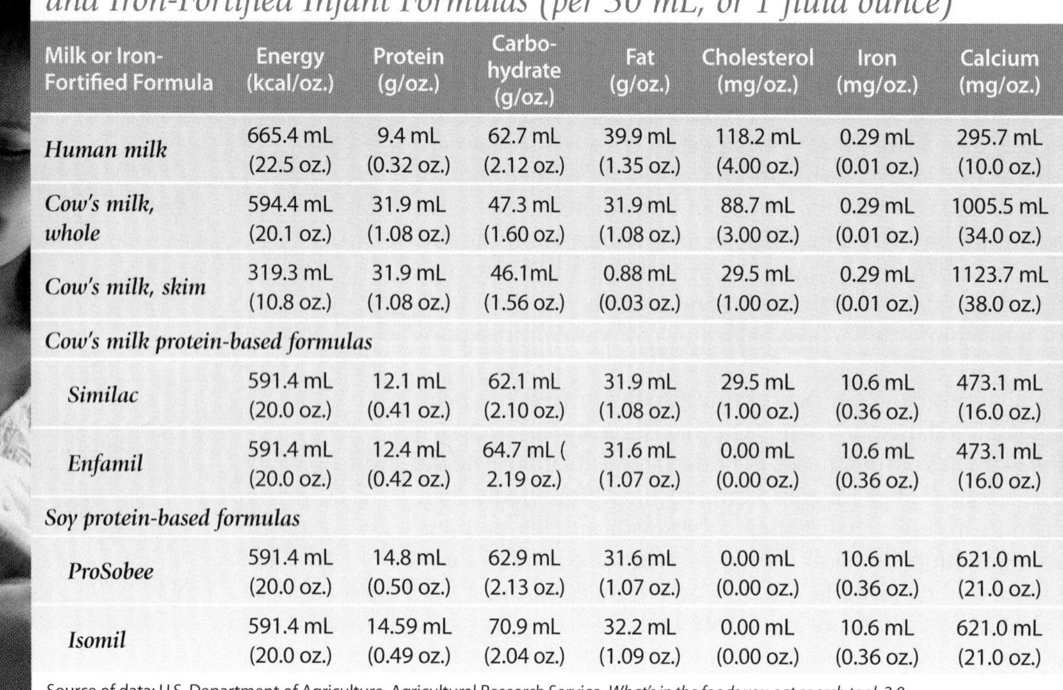

TABLE 13.5 *Comparing Approximate Compositions of Human Milk, Cow's Milk, and Iron-Fortified Infant Formulas (per 30 mL, or 1 fluid ounce)*

Milk or Iron-Fortified Formula	Energy (kcal/oz.)	Protein (g/oz.)	Carbohydrate (g/oz.)	Fat (g/oz.)	Cholesterol (mg/oz.)	Iron (mg/oz.)	Calcium (mg/oz.)
Human milk	665.4 mL (22.5 oz.)	9.4 mL (0.32 oz.)	62.7 mL (2.12 oz.)	39.9 mL (1.35 oz.)	118.2 mL (4.00 oz.)	0.29 mL (0.01 oz.)	295.7 mL (10.0 oz.)
Cow's milk, whole	594.4 mL (20.1 oz.)	31.9 mL (1.08 oz.)	47.3 mL (1.60 oz.)	31.9 mL (1.08 oz.)	88.7 mL (3.00 oz.)	0.29 mL (0.01 oz.)	1005.5 mL (34.0 oz.)
Cow's milk, skim	319.3 mL (10.8 oz.)	31.9 mL (1.08 oz.)	46.1mL (1.56 oz.)	0.88 mL (0.03 oz.)	29.5 mL (1.00 oz.)	0.29 mL (0.01 oz.)	1123.7 mL (38.0 oz.)
Cow's milk protein-based formulas							
Similac	591.4 mL (20.0 oz.)	12.1 mL (0.41 oz.)	62.1 mL (2.10 oz.)	31.9 mL (1.08 oz.)	29.5 mL (1.00 oz.)	10.6 mL (0.36 oz.)	473.1 mL (16.0 oz.)
Enfamil	591.4 mL (20.0 oz.)	12.4 mL (0.42 oz.)	64.7 mL (2.19 oz.)	31.6 mL (1.07 oz.)	0.00 mL (0.00 oz.)	10.6 mL (0.36 oz.)	473.1 mL (16.0 oz.)
Soy protein-based formulas							
ProSobee	591.4 mL (20.0 oz.)	14.8 mL (0.50 oz.)	62.9 mL (2.13 oz.)	31.6 mL (1.07 oz.)	0.00 mL (0.00 oz.)	10.6 mL (0.36 oz.)	621.0 mL (21.0 oz.)
Isomil	591.4 mL (20.0 oz.)	14.59 mL (0.49 oz.)	70.9 mL (2.04 oz.)	32.2 mL (1.09 oz.)	0.00 mL (0.00 oz.)	10.6 mL (0.36 oz.)	621.0 mL (21.0 oz.)

Source of data: U.S. Department of Agriculture, Agricultural Research Service. *What's in the foods you eat search tool, 2.0.* www.ars.usda.gov/Services/docs.htm?docid=7783.

What about Cow's Milk?

Why not feed fresh fluid cow's milk to an infant? Cow's milk is too high in minerals and protein and does not contain enough carbohydrate to meet an infant's nutrient needs (see Table 13.5). In addition, infants have more difficulty digesting **casein** (*kay'-seen*), the major protein in cow's milk, than the major proteins in human milk. Cow's milk can also contribute to intestinal bleeding and iron deficiency.[28,34] Thus, whole cow's milk should not be fed to infants until they are 1 year of age.[28] Furthermore, fat-reduced and skim cow's milk are too low in energy to be given to most children until they are 2 years of age.

Allergies Allergies are immune-system responses to the presence of foreign proteins in the body. Allergies to proteins in foods, especially cow's milk proteins, often begin in infancy and may persist through childhood. Signs and symptoms of food allergies typically include the following:

- Vomiting, diarrhea, intestinal gas and pain, bloating, or constipation
- Itchy, swollen, or reddened skin
- Runny nose and breathing difficulties, such as asthma

Compared to breast-fed infants, formula-fed babies have a greater risk of food allergies. When a woman has a personal or family history of food allergies, she may be able to prevent her children from developing such allergies, if she breast-feeds her babies exclusively for six months. Infants rarely develop allergic reactions to food proteins that enter breast milk from the mother's bloodstream.

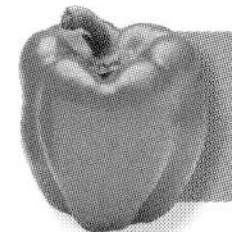

Food & Nutrition *Tips*

Do not heat infant formula or human milk in a microwave oven. The heat can destroy immune factors in human milk and create hot spots that can scald an infant's tongue.

Did You Know?

Concentrated or ready-to-use infant formulas are highly perishable. Once a container of liquid infant formula has been opened, the product can remain in the refrigerator for only one day. Any formula that remains in the bottle after a feeding should be discarded, because it will be contaminated by enzymes in the infant's saliva and bacteria.

Introducing Solid Foods

Before 6 months of age, babies' nutritional needs can generally be met with human milk and/or infant formula. According to Health Canada experts, solid foods should not be introduced to infants until they are about 6 months of age.[28] At this age, many infants need the additional calories supplied by solid foods. Breast-fed babies may also need a dietary source of iron, because their stores of the mineral are usually exhausted about six months after birth. Nevertheless, caregivers should continue to provide human milk or iron-fortified infant formula as the foundation of the baby's diet for the first year.

Many new parents are anxious to start feeding their young infants solid food. However, babies are not physically mature enough to consume solids before they are 4 to 6 months of age. For example, a baby's kidney functions are quite limited until the child is about 4 to 6 weeks of age. Additionally, an infant's digestive tract cannot readily digest starch before the child is about 3 months old.

Infants are born with the **extrusion reflex**, an involuntary response that occurs when a solid or semisolid object is placed in an infant's mouth. As a result of this reflex, a young baby thrusts its tongue forward, pushing the object out of its mouth. Thus, trying to feed the infant solid foods is a messy, frustrating process, as the child automatically pushes the food out of its mouth. Liquid foods, such as breast milk or infant formula, do not elicit the extrusion reflex, so the baby swallows fluids.

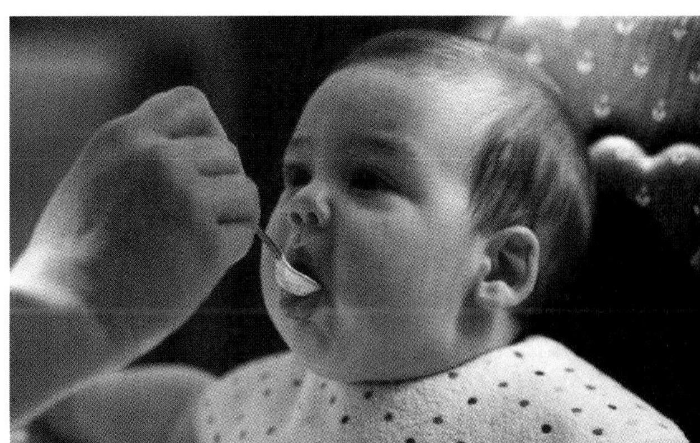

casein major protein in cow's milk

extrusion reflex involuntary response in which a young infant thrusts its tongue forward when a solid or semisolid object is placed in its mouth

weaning gradual process of shifting from breast-feeding or bottle-feeding to drinking from a cup and eating solid foods

Did You Know?

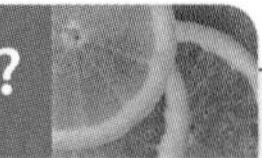

Many parents think adding solid foods to infants' diets helps babies sleep through the night. Actually, this developmental milestone generally occurs around 3 to 4 months of age, regardless of what infants are eating.

As the infant reaches 4 to 6 months of age, the extrusion reflex disappears, and the child has developed the physiological abilities to digest, metabolize, and excrete a wider range of foods. Moreover, a 6-month-old infant can usually sit up with back support and coordinate muscular control over his or her mouth and neck movements. These signs indicate the baby is ready physically to eat solid foods, is less likely to choke on such foods, and can turn his or her head away from food when full.

Weaning is the gradual process of shifting an infant from breast-feeding or bottle-feeding to drinking from a cup and eating solid foods. Most pediatricians recommend introducing an iron-fortified infant cereal as the first solid food. A commercial brand of infant rice cereal is the best to offer, because it is least likely to cause allergies. After feeding the infant cereal for the first time, caregivers should offer the food to the baby for at least four days and observe the infant for signs and symptoms of food allergy. If the infant appears to tolerate rice cereal, caregivers can add a new food to the baby's diet, such as another type of baby cereal or a cooked strained vegetable. As each new food is introduced, caregivers should wait two to four days before adding a different food to the child's diet.[28]

A commercial brand of infant rice cereal is best to introduce first, because it is least likely to cause allergies.

Foods that frequently cause allergic responses in infants include egg whites, chocolate, nuts, and cow's milk. Therefore, caregivers should not offer these foods to babies. Also, it is important to avoid giving mixed foods such as casseroles or commercially prepared baby food "dinners" to infants. If the baby has an allergic response after eating a food mixture, it will be difficult to determine which ingredient was responsible. Serving mixed foods is acceptable when the child has eaten each ingredient individually without having an allergic response. Many babies outgrow food allergies during childhood, but some children remain allergic to the foods through adulthood.

Many varieties of strained baby food are available at the supermarket. Single food items, such as carrots or peas, are more nutrient-dense choices for feeding infants than mixed dinners and desserts. Most brands have no added salt, but some fruit desserts contain a lot of added sugar. As an alternative, caregivers can prepare their own baby food by taking plain, unseasoned cooked foods and pureeing them in a blender. If a large amount of the item is blended, the pureed food can be poured into an ice cube tray, covered with a plastic bag, and frozen. When it is feeding time, an ice cube portion of the baby food can be popped out of the tray and warmed. The Recipes for Healthy Living feature later in this chapter includes an applesauce recipe that both children and adults will enjoy.

At about 6 to 8 months of age, the baby's first set of teeth, the "primary teeth" begin to appear. These teeth are important for proper nutrition because they help the child bite and chew food.

Single food items, such as carrots or peas, are more nutrient-dense choices for feeding infants than mixed dinners and desserts.

By 8 to 12 months of age, most infants can use their fingers to pick up and chew "finger foods" such as crackers, toast, and cooked string beans. Babies can also hold a bottle and practise drinking from a special cup ("sippy cup") that has a lid with a spout (Fig. 13.9). Babies need to practise self-feeding skills, even if it means playing with food and creating messes. By about 10 months of age, many infants are mastering self-feeding and making the transition from baby foods to menu items the rest of the family enjoys.

Figure 13.9 Learning to drink from a cup. After a baby learns to hold a bottle, the child can practise holding a "sippy cup" and learn how to drink from it.

When feeding solid foods to an infant:

- Use a baby-sized spoon—a small spoon with a broad handle.
- Hold the infant comfortably on your lap, as for breast-feeding or bottle-feeding, but in a more upright position to ease swallowing.
- Add some breast milk or infant formula to the cereal, and place a small dab of the semisolid food on the spoon's tip. Gently place the spoon on the infant's tongue and tilt it so that the food slides onto the tongue. If the infant spits it out, don't continue with the feeding.
- Expect the infant to take only two or three bites during these early feeding sessions.

What Not to Feed an Infant

By the end of the first year, an infant should be consuming many different foods—grain products, meats, fruits, and vegetables—along with breast milk or infant formula. Introducing a baby to various foods helps the child learn about different tastes, odours, and textures. However, certain foods and beverages are not appropriate for infants. Avoid feeding an infant the following:

- **Honey.** This product may contain spores of *Clostridium botulinum* that can produce a potentially fatal toxin in children who are under 1 year old (see Chapter 12).
- **Excessive infant formula or human milk.** An infant may require about 750 mL (25 oz.) of human milk or infant formula daily.[35] A child who drinks too much milk may not eat enough solid foods that contain nutrients lacking in milk.
- **Semisolid baby cereal in a baby bottle that has the nipple opening enlarged.** This practice contributes to overfeeding and does not help the child learn self-feeding skills.
- **Candy, flavoured gelatin water, or soft drinks.** These items provide few micronutrients.
- **Small pieces of hard or coarse foods.** Foods such as hot dogs (unless finely cut into sticks, not coin shapes), whole nuts, grapes, chunks of cooked meat, raw carrots, popcorn, and peanut butter can cause choking. Caregivers should supervise meals to keep young children from stuffing too much food in their mouths.
- **Excessive amounts of apple or pear juice.** The fructose and *sorbitol*, a sugar alcohol, contained in these juices can lead to diarrhea. Also, if the infant drinks fruit juice or fruit drinks rather than breast milk or infant formula, the child may not be receiving adequate amounts of calcium and other essential minerals.
- **Unpasteurized (raw) milk.** Raw milk may be contaminated with bacteria or viruses.
- **Goat's milk.** Goat's milk is low in iron, folate, and vitamins C and D.

Babies need to practise self-feeding skills, even if it means playing with food and creating messes.

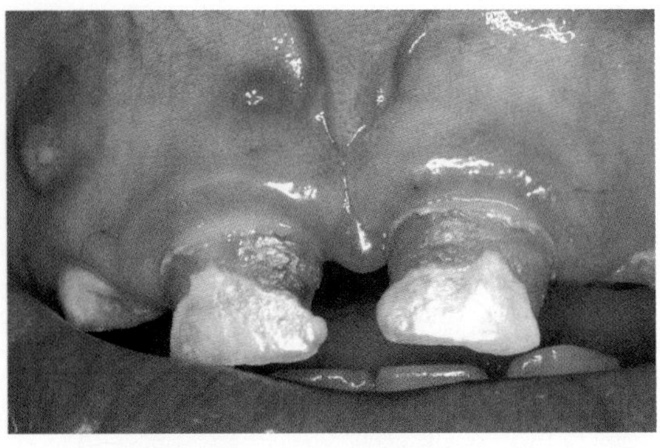

Figure 13.10 Baby bottle caries. This infant has baby bottle caries. To reduce the risk of baby bottle caries, infants should be given only water in a baby bottle at bedtime.

Baby Bottle Caries

At bedtime, many caregivers place infants in their cribs with a baby bottle containing formula, juice, or a sugar-sweetened drink. This practice is not recommended, because the sleepy infant sucks slowly, allowing the carbohydrate-containing fluid to bathe the child's teeth and provide a source of nutrients for bacteria that stick to teeth. These bacteria produce acids that dissolve tooth enamel, causing cavities to form in the teeth (*dental caries*). Dentists often refer to this condition as "baby bottle caries" (Fig. 13.10). To reduce the risk of baby bottle caries, infants should be given only water in their bedtime bottle.

Monitoring an Infant's Growth

During routine "well baby" checkups, a health professional usually measures the infant's length, weight, and head *circumference* (see Fig. 13.11). Head circumference measurements assess brain growth, which occurs at a rapid rate during the first 18 months of life. The three values are then compared to those indicating typical growth patterns displayed on growth charts available at the Centers for Disease Control and Prevention Web site (www.cdc.gov/growthcharts/cdc_charts.htm). The charts display percentile divisions; a percentile ranks the child's size among other children who are the same age and gender. If an infant boy's length, for example, is at the 90th percentile according to the length-for-age chart, he is the same length or taller than 90% of the other boys his age. Furthermore, this child is the same length or shorter than 10% of boys his age. If the infant's rate of growth slows down too much or is higher than normal, the child's physician should investigate whether a medical or nutritional problem is responsible for the unusual measurements.

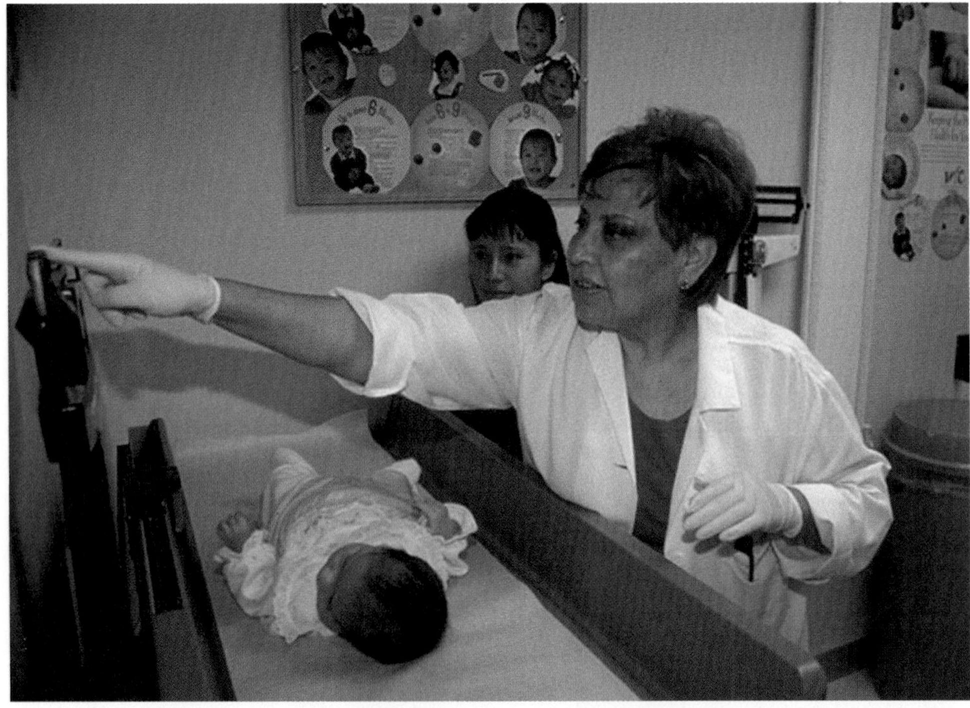

Figure 13.11 Measuring growth rates during infancy. During routine checkups, a health professional usually measures the infant's recumbent length, weight, and head circumference.
USDA Photo by: Ken Hammond

Concept **Checkpoint**

9. What is the let-down reflex?
10. How does lactation affect a new mother's energy needs?
11. What is colostrum, and why is it a valuable first food for breast-fed babies?
12. According to the recommendations of Health Canada, how many months should infants be breast-fed exclusively?
13. List at least five benefits that infants derive from breast-feeding.
14. Identify at least three benefits that women derive from breast-feeding their babies.
15. Compare the energy, macronutrient, and calcium contents of 30 mL (1 oz.) of human milk with 30 mL (1 oz.) of cow's milk.
16. Identify at least three physiological indications that an infant is ready to eat solid foods.
17. Describe three ways that a health care practitioner can monitor an infant's growth.

Childhood

Childhood can be divided into the preschool period (2 to 5 years of age) and the school-age period (6 to 11 years of age). The rapid growth rate that characterizes the first 12 months of life tapers off quickly during the preschool years and proceeds at a slow but steady rate until the end of childhood. If an average infant's growth rate did not slow down, he or she might weigh about 86 kg (190 lbs.) and be about 1.7 m (5′7″) tall by 3 years of age! However, the average 3-year-old weighs about 14.5 kg (32 lbs.) and is about 91 cm (3′) in height.

The preferred growth standard for children who are 2 to 20 years of age is the *body mass index for age (BMI-for-age)*. The BMI-for-age is a number calculated from the child's height and weight. BMI charts for children are both gender- and age-specific (see Appendix H, available on *Connect* at www.mcgrawhillconnect.ca). A child whose BMI is between the 85th and 95th percentile is "at risk of overweight" and a child whose BMI is at or above the 95th percentile is "overweight," which corresponds to overweight and obesity respectively in adults.

As the growth rate slows after infancy, preschoolers' appetites decrease because they do not need as much food. Parents and other caregivers must recognize that a 3-year-old child should not be expected to eat as eagerly as he or she did as an infant. Furthermore, children do not have the stomach capacity to eat adult-size portions of foods (Fig. 13.12). When planning meals and snacks for children who eat relatively little food, caregivers should emphasize nutrient-dense foods, such as lean meats, low-fat milk products, whole-grain cereals, fruits, nuts, and vegetables. Although many ready-to-eat cereals are sweetened with sugar, it is not necessary to eliminate such foods. Caregivers, however, should read product labels and choose varieties with less added sugar. Additionally, it is important to monitor children's intake of sweets, because sugary items can crowd out more nutritious foods from their diets.

Table 13.6 presents a day's food selections, based on *Eating Well with Canada's Food Guide* recommendations, that are appropriate for children who are 2 to 8 years of age. Recall that fish and seafood are in the Meat and Alternatives food group. Caregivers should include fish in children's meals regularly, especially fish that are rich sources of omega-3 fatty acids, such as salmon. However, commercially fried fish, including fish sticks, should be avoided, because of their high fat content.[36]

Snacks

Snacking is not necessarily a bad habit, especially if snacks are nutrient dense and fit into the child's overall diet. Preschool children have relatively small stomachs, so nutritious

Figure 13.12 **Age-appropriate portion sizes.** Healthy young children should not be expected to eat adult-size portions of food. Each of these children is eating half a sandwich, a reasonable amount for their age.

TABLE 13.6 *Preschool and Young Children: Daily Food Plan Based on* Eating Well with Canada's Food Guide *Recommendations*

Energy/Food Group	2 to 3 Years	4 to 8 Years
Kilocalories*	1150	1400
Grain Products	3 servings	4 servings
Vegetables and Fruit	4 servings	5 servings
Milk and Alternatives	2 servings	2 servings
Meat and Alternatives	1 serving	1 serving
Oils	30–45 mL	30–45 mL

* Kilocalorie estimates are based on age and active levels of physical activity.

Source: Health Canada: *Eating Well with Canada's Food Guide*. www.hc-sc.gc.ca/fn-an/food-guide-aliment/index-eng.php.

TABLE 13.7 *Nutritious Snacks*

Nutritious Snacks
• Peanut butter spread on graham crackers
• Fruit smoothies (see Chapter 9 Recipes for Healthy Living)
• Fruit salad (or cut-up fruit)
• Mini-pizzas (half an English muffin, topped with tomato sauce and Mozzarella cheese, and heated in toaster oven or microwave oven)
• Plain, low-fat yogourt topped with granola or fresh fruit
• Pasta salad
• Peanuts, cashews, or sunflower seeds
• Fruitpops
• Leftovers (pizzas, macaroni and cheese, lasagna)
• Quick breads, such as banana bread
• Cheese melted on whole-grain crackers
• Dried fruit
• Trail mix
• Ready-to-eat cereal
• Vegetable sticks dipped in hummus

snacks can be offered at mid-morning or mid-afternoon, when the child is likely to become hungry between meals. A 4- or 5-year-old child can safely eat raw vegetables without fear of choking. Thus, a platter of raw or lightly cooked carrots; broccoli flowerets; slices of green, yellow, and red peppers; and mushrooms served as a snack may be accepted. Nutritious dips, such as the yogourt dip in the Recipes for Healthy Living feature later in this chapter, may make raw vegetables more appealing to children. Table 13.7 lists some nutritious snacks that children tend to like.

Fostering Positive Eating Behaviours

Parents often refer to their preschool children as "picky eaters," because the youngsters do not eat everything offered to them. Furthermore, it is not unusual for children to have "food jags," periods in which they refuse to eat a food that they liked in the past, or only want to eat a particular food such as peanut butter and jelly sandwiches or cereal and milk. Picky eating and food jags may be expressions of a child's growing need for independence. Caregivers should avoid nagging, forcing, and bribing children to eat. Instead, caregivers can offer the child a variety of healthy foods each day and allow the youngster to choose which items and how much to eat.

It is not unusual for children to have "food jags," periods in which they insist on eating a particular food such as cereal and milk.

Many children, especially preschool children, resist eating new foods. The temperature, appearance, texture, and taste of a food influence whether children will sample it. For example, young children often reject lumpy or hot-temperature foods. Sometimes children object to having foods mixed together such as in stews and casseroles, even though they like the ingredients when served separately. It is not unusual for young children to dislike vegetables that have strong flavours or odours such as broccoli, onions, and asparagus. The idea of eating vegetables may become more appealing when children help grow, select, or prepare fresh produce. Nevertheless, it is important to recognize that everyone, including children, is entitled to dislike certain foods.

Eating vegetables may become more appealing when children help grow, select, or prepare fresh produce.

The social atmosphere can make mealtimes enjoyable or unbearable, which in turn, influences a child's desire to eat. Mealtimes should be happy, social occasions to enjoy healthful foods with parents or other caregivers. The kitchen table should not become a battleground in which adults use threats or bribes to force children to eat unfamiliar foods. For example, avoid telling a child, "You'll just sit there until you clean your plate" or "You can have a cupcake, if you eat your peas." When a child refuses to eat, have the youngster remain at the table for a while. If the child continues to be disinterested in eating, remove the food and wait until the next scheduled meal or snack.

Healthy children are not in danger of starving if they skip a meal. A child who is not hungry at mealtimes may have eaten a snack before the meal at a friend's home. If a child's lack of appetite persists, caretakers should consult the child's physician to rule out illness.

Common Food-Related Concerns

Nutrition-related problems that often affect preschool children are iron deficiency, dental caries, food allergies, and overweight. Additionally, vegetarian diets can also pose problems if they are not planned to meet children's nutrient needs.

Iron Deficiency

Iron deficiency can lead to decreased physical stamina, learning ability, and resistance to infection. The best way to prevent iron deficiency in children is to provide foods that are good sources of iron, such as lean meat and enriched breads and cereals. Milk and other milk products are poor sources of iron, so caregivers may need to limit daily servings of foods from this food group. Preschool children should consume 500 mL (2 cups) per day of skim or low-fat milk or equivalent milk products.[37] Chapter 9 provides more information about iron deficiency.

Dental Caries

Many preschool children have had one or more dental caries by the time they enter school. If dental caries are not treated, jaw pain, gum infection, and tooth loss can occur. The following tips can help reduce the risk of dental caries in children:

- Brush teeth with a pea-sized amount of fluoride-containing toothpaste twice daily.
- Provide routine pediatric dental care.
- Provide fluoridated drinking water.
- Avoid eating retentive (sticky), sugary snacks, especially between meals.
- If preschoolers want to chew gum, chewing sugarless gum can reduce the risk of dental caries.[38]

Allergies

Although any food can trigger allergic reactions among preschool children, the most common food *allergens* are peanuts, tree nuts (e.g., walnuts and pecans), fish, shellfish, milk, eggs, soybeans, and wheat. A child who is extremely allergic to a food may have an adverse reaction just by being in the room where that food is being cooked or eaten. For a small number of children, avoiding foods that produce allergic responses is a matter of life and death.

The best treatment for a food allergy is avoiding exposure to the problem food. Parents and other caregivers must learn to read the list of ingredients on labels to determine whether products contain foods an allergic child should avoid. Furthermore, caregivers should inform adults who have contact with the child about the youngster's need to avoid the offending food. A registered dietitian can assist caregivers in planning menus that meet the allergic child's nutrient needs. It is also common for children to outgrow food allergies and intolerances, so parents can attempt to carefully reintroduce foods as children grow older.

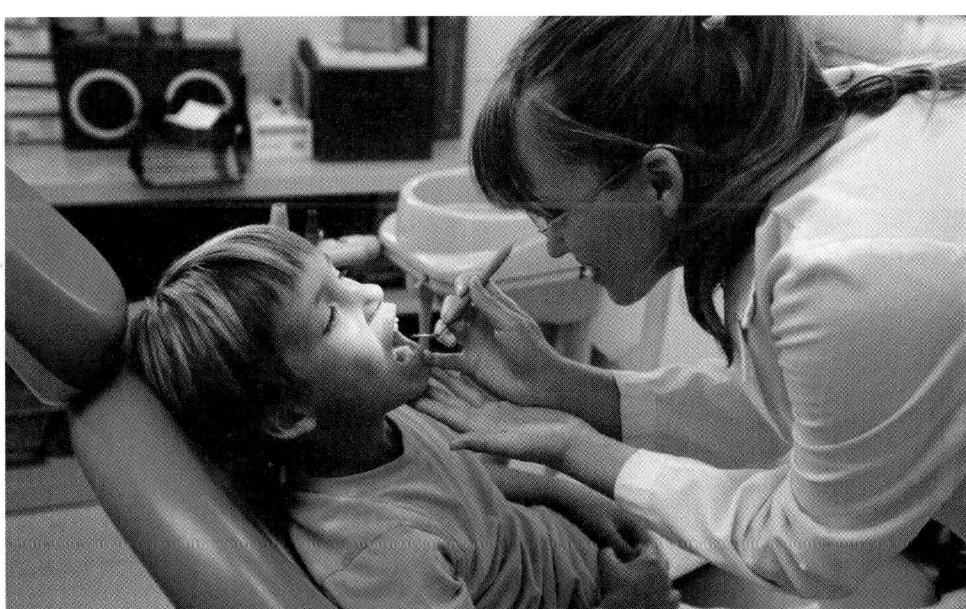

To reduce the risk of dental caries, children should receive regular dental checkups.

- Foods with bright colours, crisp textures, and sweet or mild flavours usually appeal to children. When planning meals, consider including foods with these attractive characteristics.
- As a parent, you may want to consider having the "one bite policy." According to this policy, your child should try at least one bite of each new food provided at mealtimes. If you don't like a particular food that is offered, you should follow the "one bite policy" as well. Taste the item—you may discover that you like it.
- To stimulate your child's appetite, try serving food on a small colourful plate that is designed to appeal to young children.
- Keep in mind that you are your children's role model for food choices and physical activity habits. If you eat a variety of nutrient-dense foods and are physically active, your children are likely to eat such foods and be active as well.

To help reduce the likelihood that young children become overweight, caregivers need to provide opportunities for youngsters to be physically active.

Overweight

An overweight preschooler's BMI is greater than or equal to the 95th percentile for his or her sex and age (see Appendix H, available on *Connect* at www.mcgrawhillconnect.ca). Since the 1970s, the prevalence of overweight among Canadian preschool children has increased dramatically and in the U.S. has tripled.[39,40] The increase in the prevalence of overweight among Canadian preschoolers is concerning because being overweight as a child is highly correlated with being overweight as an adult, and being an overweight adult increases all-cause mortality among Canadians.[41]

There is no single cause of overweight in children, but researchers have identified factors that are associated with the development of the condition. These factors include having a family history of obesity, high birth weight, and obese family members. Furthermore, youngsters who spend a lot of time at sedentary activities, such as watching television or playing computer games, and consume too much fried foods and sugar-sweetened carbonated beverages are also at risk of overweight in childhood.[42]

Medical experts have not determined the best long-term treatment program for overweight children.[43] Furthermore, because of the lack of long-term success with programs designed to treat adult overweight and obesity, *preventing* overweight in childhood may be the best course of action. To help reduce the likelihood that young children become overweight, caregivers need to promote healthy eating practices and physically active lifestyles for all family members by setting a healthy living example: eating healthy, being physically active, and providing opportunities for youngsters to be physically active.

Concept **Checkpoint**

18. What is a "food jag"?
19. Discuss effects that iron deficiency can have on children.
20. List at least three steps caregivers can take to reduce the risk of dental caries in children.
21. List at least four foods that commonly trigger allergic responses in children.
22. Identify at least four factors that contribute to overweight among children.

School-Age Children

By the time children are 6 years of age, many have adopted diets that are not nutritionally adequate.[42] Compared to preschoolers, older children often skip breakfast, and they typically consume more foods away from home, larger portions of food, and more fried foods and sweetened beverages. School-age children also tend to reduce their intakes of milk products as well as fruits and vegetables, except fried potatoes. As a result, diets of many school-age children provide too much sodium while supplying inadequate amounts of other minerals, particularly calcium and potassium.[44]

Table 13.8 presents a day's food recommendations for healthy children 9 to 13 years of age, based on the *Eating Well with Canada's Food Guide* recommendations.

Caregivers can help improve children's diets by encouraging youngsters to eat breakfast regularly. Children who routinely eat breakfast are more likely to have better diets and healthier body weights than children who skip this meal.[45] Breakfast menus do not need to feature traditional fare such as bacon, eggs, waffles, or pancakes. For example, leftovers from the previous night's dinner can be eaten for breakfast. Convenient "fast breakfasts" that school-age children can prepare quickly include ready-to-eat cereal with

TABLE 13.8 *School-Age Children: Daily Food Plan Based on* Eating Well with Canada's Food Guide *Recommendations*

Energy/Food Group	Boys and Girls 9–13 Years
Kilocalories*	1600
Grains	6 servings
Vegetables and Fruit	6 servings
Milk and Alternatives	3–4 servings
Meat and Alternatives	1–2 servings
Oils	30–45 mL

* Kilocalorie estimates are based on age and active levels of physical activity.

Source: Health Canada: *Eating Well with Canada's Food Guide*. www.hc-sc.gc.ca/fn-an/food-guide-aliment/index-eng.php.

milk and fruit, cottage cheese and fruit, a peanut butter and jelly sandwich, or yogourt topped with trail mix or pieces of fresh fruit.

Parents and other caregivers need to be concerned about foods that are available at school and obtain answers to the following questions. What kinds of foods are offered for school breakfasts and lunches? Does the school have vending machines accessible to youngsters? If so, what kinds of foods and beverages are sold from these machines? Do vending machines offer competitively priced nutrient-dense foods? What can be done to ensure that the machines and the school's cafeteria provide nutritious foods that children will eat? Furthermore, what efforts are being made to teach children about proper nutrition while they are in school?

Parents and other caregivers need to be concerned about their children's food choices.

Common Nutrition-Related Concerns

Public health experts are alarmed about the increasing prevalence of overweight among school-age children in Canada and the United States.[39] The following sections take a closer look at the problems associated with excess body fat during childhood and other nutrition-related concerns such as multiple vitamin/mineral supplements and vegetarianism.

Overweight

An overweight school-age child's BMI is greater than or equal to the 95th percentile for his or her sex and age (see Appendix H, available on *Connect* at www.mcgrawhillconnect.ca). In Canada, the prevalence of overweight among school-age children (aged 7 to 13 years) more than tripled from 5% in 1981 to approximately 16% in 1997, and it continues to increase.[46] According to findings of the National Health and Nutrition Examination Survey (NHANES) in the U.S., about 19% of 6- to 11-year-old children were overweight in 2003–2004.[40] And the 2004 Canadian Community Health Survey concluded that 18% of 6- to 11-year-old children and 20% of 12- to 17-year-olds were overweight. This percentage is much higher than those obtained in similar national surveys conducted about 30 years earlier (Fig. 13.13).

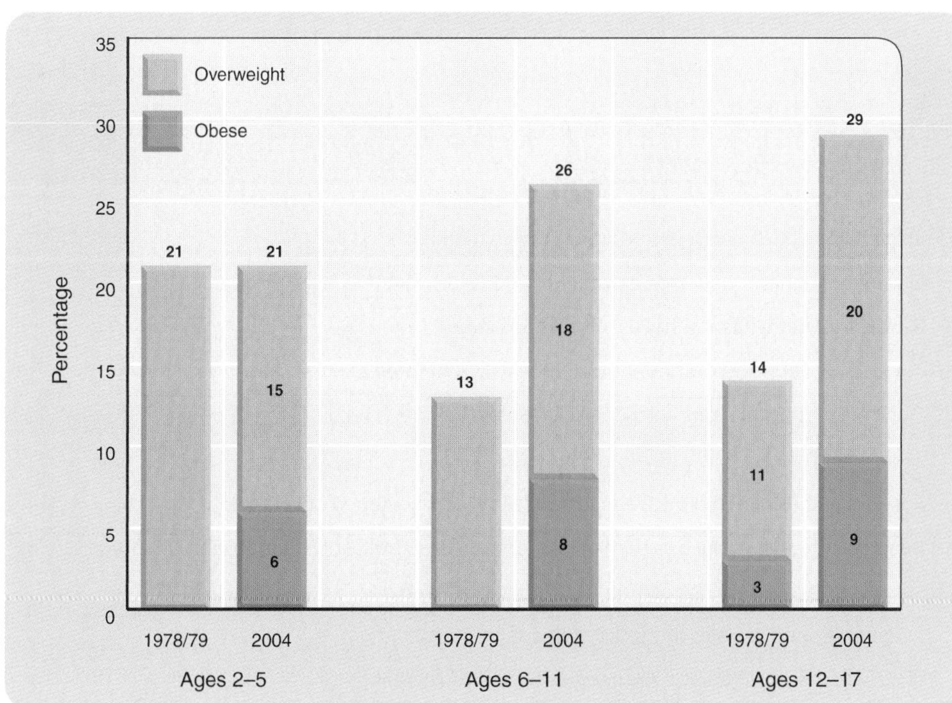

Figure 13.13 Overweight among Canadian children. Prevalence of overweight and obesity by age group among Canadian children age 2 to 17 years, 1978/9 and 2004.*

* For the purposes of this study, Health Canada defined overweight as a child having a BMI between the 85th and 95th percentile and obese as a BMI above the 95th percentile for age- and sex-matched criteria. Today in Canada, at "risk of overweight" and "overweight" are generally used in place of "overweight" and "obese" to reflect these criteria respectively.

Data sources: 2004 Canadian Community Health Survey: Nutrition; Canada Health Survey 1978/79.

Note: The obesity rates for the 2–5 and 6–11 age groups from the 1978/79 Canada Health Survey are not available.

Overfat children often have higher than normal blood pressure, cholesterol, and glucose levels.[46,47] Children who have elevated blood pressure, cholesterol, and glucose levels are at risk to develop hypertension, heart disease, and type 2 diabetes later in life. Overfat children are also more likely to experience depression, have low self-esteem, and become obese as adults.[46,48]

In most cases, no single factor is responsible for causing overweight in childhood. Overweight and obesity tend to "run in families," but genetics does not account for all individual differences in body weight. Environmental factors—such as frequent consumption of fast foods, easy access to energy-dense foods, and lack of safe areas for playing outdoors—also contribute to overweight in childhood. Caregivers may need to limit the overweight child's intakes of sugared soft drinks, fried chicken, french fries, whole milk, and other empty-calorie or fatty foods. These items often replace more nutrient-dense or lower-calorie foods in children's diets.

When helping a child lose weight, caregivers should avoid scolding or nagging the youngster, because doing so can make the child rebel against adults, feel unloved and depressed, and dislike his or her body shape. As a result of harbouring such negative feelings, an overweight child may become vulnerable to developing disordered eating practices or eating disorders.

Aside from making poor dietary choices, physical inactivity also contributes to excessive weight gain in childhood. The average Canadian child spends more than two hours a day watching television, and many children spend even more of their leisure time each day playing computer and video games. A recent study found that more than 80% of Canadian youth in grades 6 to 10 exceeded two hours per day of total screen time.[42] Child health experts recommend caregivers limit children's TV viewing and video-game playing to less than two hours per day.[49] Children need at least 60 to 90 minutes of moderate- or greater-intensity physical activity, most days of the week. Thus, it is important to assess an overweight youngster's daily physical activity level and encourage the child to be more physically active. Table 13.9 presents common physical activities that children usually enjoy.

Caregivers can ask their children's teachers about opportunities for youngsters to be physically active while they are in school. For example, how often do children participate in the school's physical education classes? Are boys and girls active during recess? If

TABLE 13.9 *Popular Physical Activities for Children*

• Dancing
• Playing tag
• Jumping rope
• Biking
• Shooting hoops with a basketball
• Swimming
• Rollerblading
• Playing soccer or "kickball"
• Skateboarding

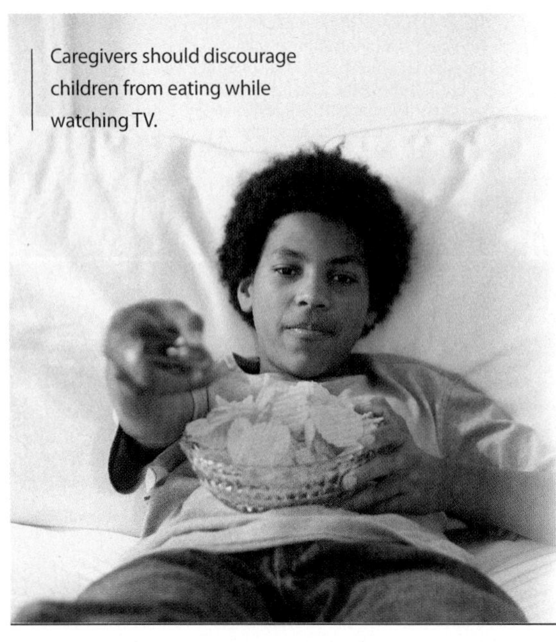

Caregivers should discourage children from eating while watching TV.

The following tips can help you improve your child's diet:

- Guide your family's food choices rather than dictate what they eat.
- Eat meals together as a family as often as possible.
- If necessary, reduce the amount of fat, especially saturated and trans fat, in your family's diet.
- Don't place your child on a restrictive diet, unless the diet is recommended by the child's physician.
- Avoid using food as a reward or punishment.
- Encourage the child to drink water instead of sugar-sweetened beverages.
- Keep healthy snacks (such as skim or low-fat milk, fresh fruit, and vegetables) on hand.
- Serve at least five servings of fruits and vegetables each day.
- Discourage eating meals or snacks while watching TV.
- Encourage the child to eat a nutrient-dense breakfast daily.

children are not obtaining enough physical activity during the day, their caregivers can enroll them in afterschool sports or community-based exercise programs. Being physically active will help children not only to attain healthy body weights but also *maintain* healthy body weights later in life.

Parents and other caregivers are primary role models for children. Before trying to alter their children's weight, caregivers should evaluate their own weights, as well as eating and physical activity practices. Often, everyone in a family reaps healthful benefits from eating more meals prepared and eaten at home and becoming more physically active.

Vegetarianism

Vegetarian diets can be nutritionally adequate for children, but careful planning is necessary to make sure youngsters obtain enough energy, high-quality protein, vitamin B-12, iron, calcium, and zinc. Nuts, seeds, ready-to-eat cereals, and fortified soy milk can supply some of the nutrients that tend to be low in vegan diets. Additionally, vegan children will need a source of vitamin D, such as regular sun exposure. For more information about vegetarianism, see Chapter 7.

Do Children Need Multiple Vitamin/ Mineral Supplements?

In general, multiple vitamin/mineral supplements are not necessary for healthy children who eat a variety of foods from all food groups, including ready-to-eat cereals that are fortified with micronutrients. However, children's diets may supply inadequate amounts of iron and zinc, especially if youngsters eat little or no meats or other rich food sources of these minerals. Children who refuse to eat meat or follow vegan diets may benefit from taking a children's multiple vitamin/mineral supplement. Regardless of one's age, taking nutrient supplements is no substitute for eating a varied and nutritious diet.

Concept **Checkpoint**

23. Discuss how young children's eating patterns often change when they enter school.
24. Identify at least three health consequences of overweight during childhood.
25. How much physical activity is recommended for school-age children?
26. List at least three tips for improving diets of school-age children.

If children are not obtaining enough physical activity during the day, their caregivers can enroll them in afterschool sports or community-based exercise programs.

Adolescence

Adolescence is the life stage in which a child matures physically into an adult. During adolescence, the reproductive organs increase in size and begin functioning properly. Furthermore, individuals attain their full height by the end of adolescence.[50] During this life stage, youth also develop emotionally, intellectually, and socially as they prepare for their adult roles.

Healthy adolescents learn to function independently of their adult caregivers. Thus, youths face a variety of lifestyle choices, including decisions regarding eating and physical activity habits. Such decisions often set the stage for the quality of their health in adulthood. For many teens, however, pressure to conform to fads and be influenced by other adolescents ("peer pressure") negatively affects their diets and overall health.

Puberty signals the end of childhood. Most boys experience puberty when they are between 12 and 16 years of age; most girls begin puberty between 10 and 12 years of age.[12] Puberty is a period characterized by dramatic physical changes, including increases in height and weight, known as the *growth spurt*. During growth spurts, adolescent girls tend to accumulate both lean and fat tissue, whereas adolescent boys tend to gain mostly lean tissue. Most girls begin their growth spurt between 10 and 13 years of age. Boys begin their growth spurt later than girls—generally when they are between 12 and 15 years of age. Girls usually begin menstruating during their growth spurt. A girl's skeletal growth is almost complete about two years after her first menstrual period, whereas boys typically continue to gain stature until they are in their early 20s. Figure 13.14 shows a group of adolescents who are about the same age but are at different stages of physical maturity.

adolescence life stage in which a child matures physically into an adult

When their growth spurts begin, adolescents eat more to support their higher energy needs. If maturing boys and girls choose to eat nutritious foods and maintain a high level of physical activity, they can take advantage of their increased hunger without gaining excess body fat. The *Eating Well with Canada's Food Guide* can provide the basis for healthy adolescents to plan nutritionally adequate meals and snacks (Table 13.10).

Figure 13.14 Different rates of physical maturity. Although these adolescents are about the same age, they are in different stages of physical maturity.

Nutrition-Related Concerns of Adolescents

Many people establish their future eating habits and physical activity practices when they are teenagers. According to results of some provincial surveys, the majority of youth in Canada are not getting sufficient servings from the *Eating Well with Canada's Food Guide* food groups, though it appears as much as 25% of their energy intake is coming from the *other foods* group.[49]

Adolescents whose diets rely heavily on fatty foods purchased at fast food restaurants or vending machines may be setting the stage for the development of obesity, type 2 diabetes, heart disease, and other serious chronic diseases. Overweight, eating disorders, and low iron and calcium intakes are major nutrition-related concerns of adolescents. Youth, especially teenage girls, are at risk of developing disordered eating practices and eating disorders. You can learn more about eating disorders by reading the Chapter 10 Highlight.

TABLE 13.10 *Teens: Daily Food Plan Based on* Eating Well with Canada's Food Guide *Recommendations*

Energy/Food Group	14- to 18-Year-Old Girls	14- to 18-Year-Old Boys
Kilocalories*	1900	2800
Grain Products	6 servings	7 servings
Vegetables and Fruit	7 servings	8 servings
Milk and Alternatives	3–4 servings	3–4 servings
Meat and Alternatives	2 servings	3 servings
Oils	30–45 mL	30–45 mL

* Kilocalorie estimates are based on age and active levels of physical activity.

Source: Health Canada: *Eating Well with Canada's Food Guide*. www.hc-sc.gc.ca/fn-an/food-guide-aliment/index-eng.php.

Did You Know? 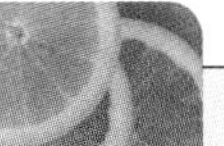

Many teenagers are plagued by *acne*—pimples, blackheads, and reddening of the skin—that often occurs on the face, upper back, and chest. Many people think acne is caused by eating certain foods, especially greasy foods and chocolate. However, no scientific evidence links specific foods with acne. According to physicians who treat skin disorders (*dermatologists*), hormonal changes normally associated with puberty cause acne.[51]

Overweight

In Canada, the prevalence of overweight is rising rapidly among adolescents. Overweight adolescents have a 70% chance of maturing into overweight or obese adults.[46]

Although the prevalence of overweight has increased for all North American children over the past few decades, rates vary among youngsters of different ethnic/racial groups. The most striking difference is the prevalence of overweight among non-Hispanic white and non-Hispanic black, female teenagers. In 2003–2004, about 15% of white girls between 12 and 19 years of age were overweight compared to about 25% of the black girls in this age group.[40] Reasons for this disparity are unclear.

Physical inactivity contributes to overweight among adolescents. Teenagers need to perform at least 60 minutes of moderate-intensity physical activity every day, or at least five or more days of the week.[52] Many teens spend much of their leisure time using a computer, playing video games, or watching television.

Overweight and Atherosclerosis Although it is unusual for young adults to have heart attacks or strokes, the process of atherosclerosis begins in childhood and continues during adolescence.[53] High blood glucose, cholesterol, and blood pressure levels are major risk factors for atherosclerosis. The prevalence of type 2 diabetes and hypertension is increasing among overweight Canadian adolescents.[41,46] Thus, medical experts are concerned that many overfat teenagers with type 2 diabetes, elevated blood cholesterol, or hypertension will develop atherosclerosis prematurely.

Weight Loss for Adolescents In many cases, overweight teenagers who are experiencing their growth spurt do not need to lose weight, because their lengthening skeletons eventually add inches to their height. However, these youth may need to slow their rate of weight gain so that they are less likely to be overfat when their skeletal growth stops. Before embarking on a weight-loss program, overfat teens should be evaluated by a physician to determine how much weight they should lose. After the assessment, the physician can refer the overweight adolescent to a registered dietitian for specific help in planning a calorie-reduced diet.

Appropriate weight-loss diets for overfat teenagers should provide adequate amounts of essential nutrients while providing just enough energy to support normal growth. Caregivers and health professionals should encourage heavy teenagers to achieve gradual weight loss without relying on fad diets, disordered eating behaviours, or diet pills. To avoid regaining lost weight, formerly overfat teens must be motivated to continue practising healthy eating habits and increased physical activity levels for the rest of their lives.

Iron and Calcium Intakes

Adolescent boys may become iron deficient during their growth spurt, because their iron intakes do not keep up with their bodies' needs for the mineral. Adolescent girls are also at risk of iron deficiency, especially if their diets lack iron-rich foods and they have heavy menstrual blood losses. Iron deficiency leads to increased fatigue and decreased ability to concentrate and learn. Teenagers need to understand why iron is important for good health and incorporate reliable food sources of the mineral in their diets (see Chapter 9). Over the last 20 years, many adolescents have switched from drinking milk to soft drinks. Dietitians and other nutrition experts are concerned that many adolescents have inadequate calcium intakes because of this practice. Inadequate calcium intake during adolescence is associated with decreased bone mass and increased likelihood of bone fractures later in life. To encourage youth to consume adequate amounts of calcium, parents or other caregivers should explain the importance of the mineral to bone health and provide calcium-rich foods and beverages during meals and snacks. Adolescents should consume 750 mL (3 cups) per day of skim or low-fat milk or equivalent milk products daily.[37] Furthermore, teenagers need to be aware that physical activity can strengthen bones whereas smoking cigarettes is a risk factor for *osteoporosis*, a condition characterized by loss of bone density. To learn more about this condition, see the "What Is Osteoporosis?" section of Chapter 9.

Adolescents should consume 750 mL (3 cups) per day of skim or low-fat milk or equivalent milk products daily.

Vegetarianism

Some teenagers adopt vegetarian diets as a way of defining their identity and asserting independence from their caregivers. Although vegetarian diets can be healthy alternatives to the typical Canadian diet, some youth use vegetarianism to mask disordered eating behaviours (see the Chapter 10 Highlight).[54] When planning their diets, teenage vegans need to include foods that supply adequate amounts of calcium, iron, and zinc, as well as vitamins D and B-12. For information to help plan well-balanced, nutritionally adequate diets, teens can use the recommendations of the *Eating Well with Canada's Food Guide* that are appropriate for their age, sex, and physical activity level.[37] Chapter 7 discusses vegetarianism in more detail.

Concept **Checkpoint**

27. At what age does the adolescent growth spurt usually occur in boys? At what age does the growth spurt generally occur in girls?
28. Identify at least three health consequences that overweight adolescents are likely to experience.
29. Why are intakes of iron and calcium important during adolescence?

Nutrition for Older Adults

life expectancy length of time an average person born in a specific year can expect to live

Life expectancy is the length of time a person born in a specific year, such as 1900, can expect to live.[55] One hundred years ago, the top three leading causes of death for North Americans were pneumonia, influenza, and other infectious diseases. By 2008, life expectancy in Canada rose to a record high—78 years for men and 83 years for women.[55] Major factors that contributed to increased life expectancy during the past century include improved diets, housing conditions, and public sanitation, as well as advances in medicine.

According to Canadian statistics, less than 12% of the Canadian population were 65 years of age or older in 1991.[56] By 2011, government experts estimate that about 14% of Canadians will be in this age group. Canadians who are the "oldest old"—85 years of age or older—comprise one of the fastest-growing segments of the Canadian population (Fig. 13.15). It is estimated that in 2031, 9 million Canadians will be elderly. This is expected to represent 22% of the Canadian population.[56]

Although more Canadians are living longer than their ancestors, they are not necessarily living well. For the first time in recorded Canadian history, the House of Commons Standing Committee on Health has predicted Canadian life expectancy will begin to decline.[57] Chronic diseases top the list of leading causes of death in Canada (Table 13.11). These diseases are associated with lifestyles that include smoking, eating a poor diet, and being physically inactive.[57]

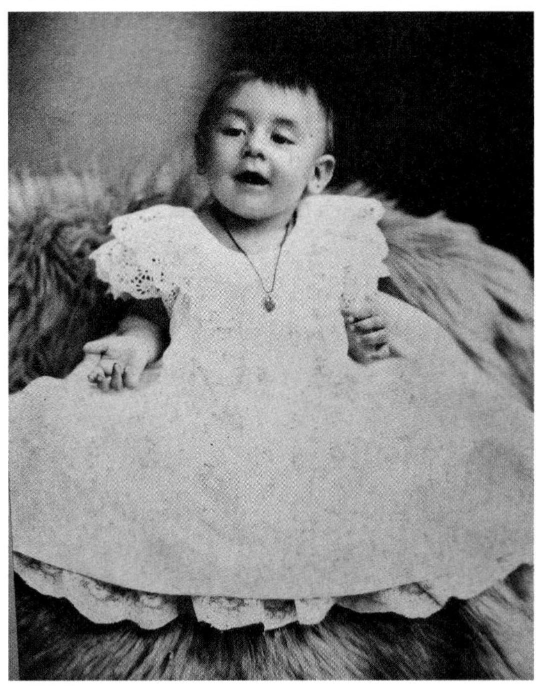

George John Blum of St. Louis, Missouri, circa 1900. In 1900, the life expectancy of a baby born in the United States was only 47 years.

The Aging Process

The aging process begins at conception and is characterized by numerous predictable physical changes. By the time you are 65 years of age, you will have reached the final

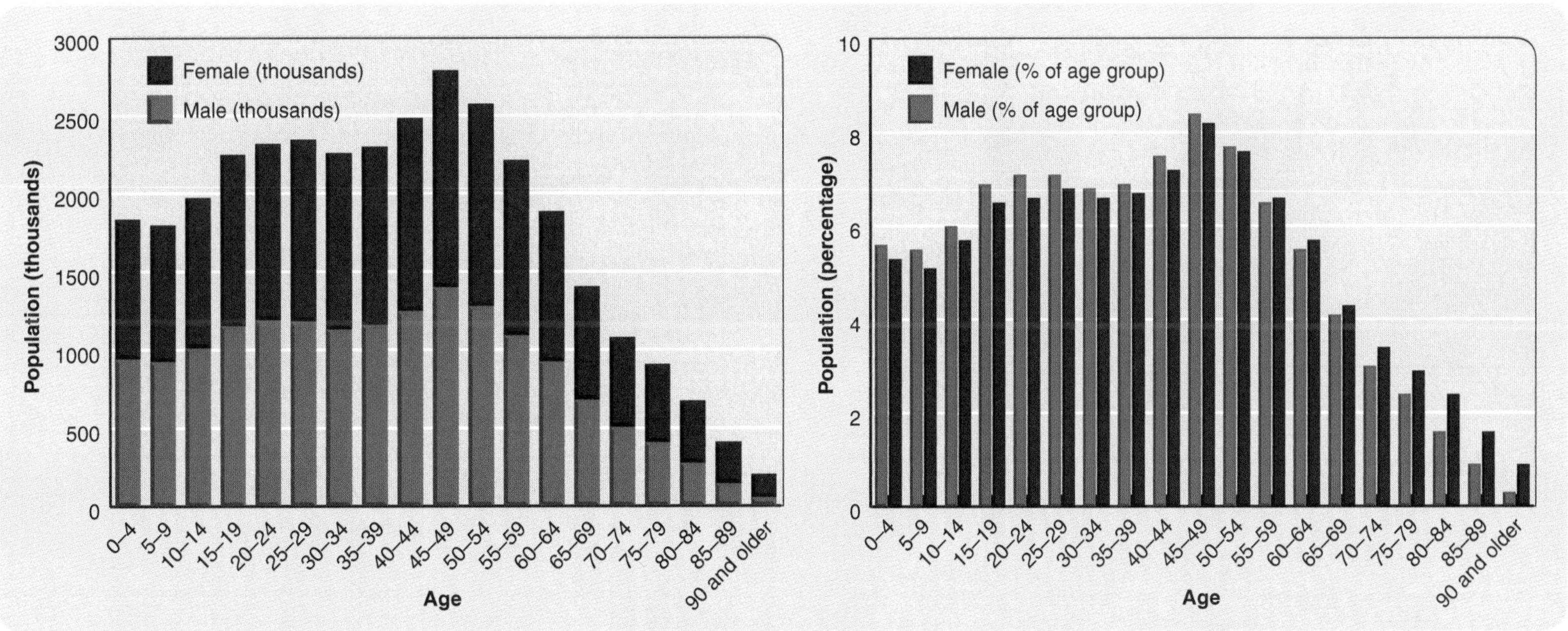

Figure 13.15 Canadian population by sex and age. Currently, nearly 14% of the Canadian population is over the age of 65 years, and 1.8% are over the age of 85 years.

Source: Statistics Canada, CANSIM, table (for fee) 051-0001.

TABLE 13.11 *Ten Leading Causes of Death for Canadians, Both Sexes, All Ages*

1. Heart disease
2. Cancer
3. Stroke
4. Chronic, lower respiratory disease
5. Unintentional injuries (accidents)
6. Diabetes mellitus
7. Alzheimer's disease
8. Influenza and pneumonia
9. Kidney disease
10. Septicemia

Source: Public Health Agency of Canada: Leading causes of death, Canada, 2005, males and females combined. 2004. www.phac-aspc.gc.ca/publicat/lcd-pcd97/table1-eng.php.

senescence declining organ functioning and increased vulnerability

lifespan maximum number of years an organism can live

life stage, *older adulthood*. What causes people to age is unclear. Scientists who study the aging process have learned that cell structure and function inevitably decline with time, leading to many of the physiological changes shown in Table 13.12.[50] Eventually, most cells lose the ability to regenerate their internal parts, and they die. As more and more cells in an organ die, the organ loses its functional capacity, and as a result, other organs fail and body systems are adversely affected. When this happens, the person soon dies. **Senescence** (*seness'-enz*) refers to declining organ functioning and increased vulnerability to disease that occurs after a person reaches physical maturity.[50]

Extending the Human Lifespan

Lifespan refers to the maximum number of years an organism such as a human can live. To date, the longest documented human lifespan is 122 years (Fig. 13.16). Some scientists think the human lifespan can be lengthened considerably just by making certain dietary changes. The Chapter 13 Highlight takes a closer look at the role of diet and longevity.

Growing old is a normal and natural process. Your body ages, regardless of dietary and other health-related practices you follow. Nevertheless, scientists have found a strong genetic component to human longevity. If you have ancestors who are very old or lived to be 90 years of age or more, you may have inherited "longevity genes." If your ancestors were not so fortunate, to some extent, you can control the rate at which you age. How? By

TABLE 13.12 *Aging: Normal Physiological Changes*

Body System	Changes
Digestive	Reduced saliva, gastric acid, and intrinsic factor secretion; increased heartburn and constipation
Skin, hair, and nails (integument)	Greying hair; drier skin and hair; skin loses elasticity and forms wrinkles; skin bruises easily
Musculoskeletal	Bone-forming cells become less active, resulting in bone loss that can lead to tooth loss and bones that fracture easily; fractures heal more slowly; joints become stiff and painful; muscle mass declines, resulting in loss of strength and stamina.
Nervous	Decreased brain weight, reduced production of neurotransmitters, delayed transmission of nervous impulses, loss of short-term memory, and reduced sensory abilities (e.g., vision, hearing, smell, and taste)
Lymphatic (immune)	Reduced functioning resulting in increased vulnerability to cancer and infections
Circulatory	Hardening of the arteries, reduced cardiac output, increased risk of blood clots
Endocrine	Decreased production of reproductive, growth, and thyroid hormones
Respiratory	Reduced lung capacity, increased vulnerability to respiratory infections
Urinary	Increased loss of functional kidney cells, resulting in decreased blood filtration rate; loss of bladder control
Reproductive	Men: Decreased male hormone production and sperm count Women: Declining female hormone production, cessation of menstrual cycles, and loss of fertility

Figure 13.16 Oldest human being. When the French woman Jeanne Calment died in 1997 at 122 years of age, she was documented as the world's longest living human being.

making responsible healthy lifestyle decisions while you are still young, such as selecting a nutritious diet, exercising regularly, and avoiding tobacco. Your focus should not be simply on living longer but on living longer *and* healthier.

Older Adults: Common Nutrition-Related Concerns

Compared to younger persons, older adults have greater risk of nutritional deficiencies because of physiological changes associated with the normal aging process. Other factors that can influence an older person's nutritional status include illnesses, medications, low income, and lack of social support. Diets of older adults, particularly older women, often provide inadequate amounts of vitamins D, A, C, and B-12 and minerals such as calcium, iron, and zinc.[58] Results of a survey of more than 1700 older adults indicated that subjects often failed to consume recommended amounts of grain and milk products, vegetables, and fruits.[59] Furthermore, most subjects were overfat with BMIs equal to or greater than 25. The following sections discuss some of the major health concerns that often affect the nutritional status of older adults. Some of these conditions have been discussed in previous chapters.

Changes in Body Weight

As the human body ages, its need for energy decreases.[1] In senescence, muscle mass declines as some muscle cells shrink or die. The loss of muscle mass leads to a decrease in muscular strength and basal metabolism. Additionally, the aging body loses lean tissue and gains fat tissue. Increased body fat results from overeating and lack of physical activity, but even athletic men and lean women typically gain some central body fat after they are 50 years of age. Being overfat may increase the bone density of older adults and result in stronger bones,[60] but having too much body fat increases the risk of type 2 diabetes, hypertension, cardiovascular disease, and osteoarthritis. For more information about overweight and obesity, see Chapter 10.

People who are over 70 years of age often lose weight. Several factors contribute to weight loss among older adults. Elderly persons may eat less because they have lost the ability to taste and smell food. Loss of teeth and difficulty swallowing can also result in decreased food consumption. Additionally, social and economic factors often play a role in reduced food intake. Many older people live alone and on fixed incomes, circumstances that are associated with depression and inability to afford adequate amounts of nutritious food. In many instances, very old people refuse to eat, and as a result, lose considerable amounts of weight, a situation that hastens their death.

For older adults who find that food no longer tastes "good," adding more spices may improve the taste of food, and as a result, stimulate weak appetites. Efforts to make mealtimes social events, such as inviting friends to share potluck meals together, can enhance older adults' mental outlooks and spark their interest in eating. Older adults can increase or maintain their weight by consuming energy-dense snacks between meals, such as cheese, milkshakes, nuts, or oatmeal cookies. If weight loss becomes significant, a physician should be consulted to determine the cause.

Physical Inactivity

Many of the undesirable physical changes we associate with growing old are the result of a lifetime of physical inactivity. Regardless of a person's age, a physically active lifestyle increases muscle strength and mobility, improves balance, slows bone loss, and boosts emotional well-being. Most older adults can benefit from performing aerobic and strength training activities regularly (Fig. 13.17). Before embarking on a program to increase physical fitness, however, sedentary older adults should consult their physicians concerning appropriate activities.

Figure 13.17 It's never too late. Most older adults can benefit from performing aerobic and strength-training activities regularly.

Did You Know?

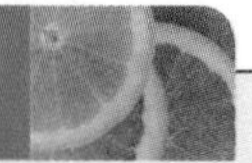

You're never too old to gain some benefits from exercise. Even very old people can increase their muscular strength significantly by exercising for only 40 minutes per week.[50]

Tooth Loss

In the 1950s, the majority of older Canadian adults had lost all their natural teeth.[61] Since then, the percentage of older adults who retain all or most of their teeth has increased in Canada. Tooth loss is related to long-term poor dental hygiene, cigarette smoking, and dietary practices. By following recommended dental hygiene practices, obtaining regular dental care, and avoiding tobacco use, you can greatly increase your chances of keeping most of your teeth as you age.

Excessive tooth loss can lead to faulty eating habits. People who lack teeth often avoid crisp or chewy foods, such as fresh fruits, vegetables, whole-grain cereals, and meat. According to results of an eight-year study involving nearly 32 000 men, subjects who had lost all or several teeth consumed less dietary fibre, vitamin E, and polyunsaturated fat than those who had maintained most of their teeth.[62] Although dentures that replace natural teeth can enable some people to chew normally, many older adults do not like to wear them because they can be uncomfortable. When a person has difficulty chewing food, serving soft foods such as ground meats, cooked vegetables, pureed fruits, and puddings can stimulate the individual's appetite.

Intestinal Tract Problems

Constipation is a major complaint of older adults. By increasing their intakes of fibre-rich foods, such as whole-grain products and vegetables, older adults may be able to have more regular bowel movements (see the "Fibre" section of Chapter 5). Dehydration contributes to constipation, so older persons should make sure their fluid intake is adequate.

As a person ages, his or her stomach secretes less hydrochloric acid (HCl) and intrinsic factor. These changes can contribute to poor absorption of vitamin B-12 and the development of pernicious anemia. Older adults may be able to meet their vitamin B-12 needs by eating foods fortified with the micronutrient or taking vitamin B-12 supplements. Some older adults, however, must take injections of the B vitamin to prevent pernicious anemia (see Chapter 8). Older persons are also at risk of iron deficiency, because reduced stomach acid production may hinder iron absorption. Furthermore, many older adults take aspirin regularly, and this practice can cause intestinal bleeding that can lead to iron deficiency anemia. Intestinal ulcers and cancer can also cause blood loss from the digestive tract. The discovery of blood in bowel movements needs to be reported to a physician—regardless of one's age.

Many older adults take one or more prescription drugs daily. Although such medications can improve health and quality of life of elderly persons, some drugs interfere with the body's absorption and/or use of certain nutrients. Additionally, older adults often take one or more dietary supplements regularly. According to a survey conducted in 2001, about 70% of persons over 65 years of age reported that they currently used at least one vitamin or other dietary supplement.[63] Certain dietary supplements, including herbal products, can reduce or amplify the effects of prescribed medications. Therefore, older adults should notify their physicians about their use of all dietary supplements. A few foods also interfere with prescribed drugs. Grapefruit juice, for example, can alter the potency of certain medications that are used to lower blood pressure or cholesterol.

Although dentures that replace natural teeth can enable some people to chew normally, many older adults do not like to wear them because they can be uncomfortable.

Depression in Older Adults

About 15% of community-dwelling older persons and as many as 25% of elderly people living in nursing homes suffer depression.[64] Situations that contribute to depression among the elderly population include coping with chronic illness or loss of mobility, and isolation and loneliness as family members and friends die or move away. If the depressed person loses interest in cooking and eating, weight loss and nutrient deficiencies are likely to occur. In many instances, depression can be managed with medication, but social support and psychological counselling may be necessary as well. Without proper treatment, depressed persons are at risk of alcoholism and suicide. In fact, you may be surprised to learn that suicide rates of older adult Canadians are higher than rates for members of other age groups.[65]

Older adults dining together at senior apartments.

Dietary Planning in Older Adulthood

The *Eating Well with Canada's Food Guide* recommendations can provide the basis for planning nutritionally adequate meals and snacks for healthy older adults (see Table 13.13).[37] However, amounts of foods recommended in these diet plans may not provide enough vitamin D and vitamin B-12 for elderly persons. By regularly consuming fortified and/or enriched foods, older adults can increase their intakes of these micronutrients. In many instances, older adults can also benefit from taking a daily multiple vitamin/mineral supplement.

Friends, relatives, and health care personnel should be alert for indications of poor nutrient intakes among older people, especially those who are at risk and live in nursing homes or other long-term-care facilities. For example, family members can make sure the older adult's nutrient needs are met by visiting the person's residence during mealtimes, observing the foods that are offered, and if necessary, helping the older adult eat. Additionally, monitoring the elderly individual's weight can indicate whether long-term food intake has been adequate. Older adults who live at home may need help planning nutritionally adequate diets. In these instances, registered dietitians can be consulted to provide personalized dietary advice.

Community Nutrition Services for Older Adults

In Canada, most large communities offer special nutrition programs for independent-living older adults, such as congregate meals and home-delivered meals. The

TABLE 13.13 *Daily Food Plan Based on* Eating Well with Canada's Food Guide *Recommendations for Healthy Persons Aged 51+ Years*

Energy/Food Group	Females	Males
Kilocalories*	1800	2200
Grain Products	6 servings	7 servings
Vegetables and Fruit	7 servings	7 servings
Milk and Alternatives	3 servings	3 servings
Meat and Alternatives	2 servings	3 servings
Oils	30–45 mL	30–45 mL

* Sedentary level of physical activity. This values decrease with age.

Source: Health Canada: *Eating Well with Canada's Food Guide*. www.hc-sc.gc.ca/fn-an/food-guide-aliment/index-eng.php

Food & Nutrition Tips

The following suggestions can help caregivers improve nutrient intakes of elderly persons:

- Emphasize nutrient-dense foods when planning daily menus.
- Try new foods, seasonings, and ways of preparing foods.
- Have easy-to-prepare nutrient-dense foods on hand for times when the older person is too tired to cook large meals.
- Serve meals in well-lit or sunny areas, and plan appealing meals by using foods with different flavours, colours, shapes, textures, and smells.
- Plan occasions for the older adult to share cooking responsibilities and eat meals with friends or relatives.
- Encourage the older person to eat at a senior centre whenever possible. Investigate community resources for helping the older adult obtain groceries, cook, or manage other daily care needs.
- Encourage the older adult to be physically active.
- If biting and chewing are difficult for an elderly person, chop, grind, or blend tough or crisp foods.
- Prepare extra amounts of soup, stew, or casserole so that leftovers can be frozen for future meals.

home-delivered meal program may be called Meals on Wheels, if it is sponsored by the local private or public agencies (Fig. 13.18). The Chapter 1 Highlight provides more information about these popular community-based nutrition services for older adults.

You can obtain information regarding locally available nutrition services for older people from medical clinics, private practitioners, hospitals, and other provincial and local health organizations in your area. To learn more about nutrition-related programs for older adults, visit the following Web sites:

Canadian Centre for Activity and Aging:
www.uwo.ca/actage/research/applied_research.html
Meal Call (links to Meals on Wheels for Canada):
www.mealcall.org/canada/index.htm
Dietitians of Canada: www.dietitians.ca/seniors

Figure 13.18 Meals on Wheels. Many communities in Canada offer the Meals on Wheels program in which volunteers deliver nutritious meals prepared at a senior centre to qualified, homebound older adults.

Concept Checkpoint

30. What is the difference between life expectancy and lifespan?
31. Identify at least five physiological changes that are associated with the normal aging process.
32. Explain why nutrient needs for older adults are often higher than those for younger persons.
33. List at least four nutrients that are often lacking in diets of older adults.
34. Suggest at least three ways caregivers can improve nutrient intakes of older persons.
35. What is Meals on Wheels?

Chapter 13 Highlight

In Search of the Fountain

In 1513, Spanish explorer Juan Ponce de León (Fig. 13.A) sailed to the southeastern coastal region of North America and discovered an area he named "Land of Flowers" (Florida). Ponce de León was on a mission to find gold, but he was also eager to locate a natural spring that supposedly had magical powers. According to Native Americans in the area, elderly people who drank the spring's water regained their youthful looks and vigour. Unfortunately, Ponce de León never found gold or the mythical "fountain of youth" in Florida. Nevertheless, many older adults still seek ways to combat aging, especially by taking certain hormones and dietary supplements promoted for their age-defying properties. Older North Americans spend considerable amounts of money on such products, some of which may be harmful in the long run.[1A] Promoters of anti-aging formulas or therapies claim their treatments can stop, and even reverse, the process of aging. Is there any reliable scientific evidence to support claims that you can take something to stay young longer?

Figure 13.A Ponce de León.

Claims that a nutritional fountain of youth exists are simply not true. There is little credible scientific evidence to support the use of anti-aging therapies that include taking hormones such as *dehydroepiandrosterone (DHEA)*[2A] or megadoses of vitamins and antioxidants. At this point, there is no way to prevent aging from following its natural course in humans.[3A] Nevertheless, researchers are conducting experiments to better understand the process of aging and the keys to longevity.

According to *biogerontologists*, scientists who study the biology of aging, longevity results from the body's ability to maintain and repair the damage done by a lifetime of exposure to the environment and the effects of everyday "wear and tear."[4A] Some multicellular organisms are able to live longer, when they can improve their abilities to repair damage to their DNA, reduce the toxicity of free radicals, and replace non-functioning cells. Antioxidants reduce the toxic effects of free radicals (see Chapter 8), and organisms produce a variety of antioxidants to control free radical production. In scientific laboratories, a species of tiny flies commonly called "fruit flies" had their genes for antioxidant synthesis modified by genetic engineering. As a result, these fruit flies lived longer than non-genetically modified fruit flies.[5A] Although the genetically engineered flies provide intriguing evidence that it is possible to extend the normal life expectancy of an organism by modifying its DNA, the production of a genetically engineered human being raises numerous ethical concerns.

One area of biogerontological research that shows some promise is the use of *calorie restriction (CR)* to extend longevity. Since the 1930s, scientists have studied the effects of CR on the health and lifespans of various species of multicellular organisms. According to the research findings, CR can increase lifespans of various organisms, including rodents, fish, flies, and worms.[6A]

Despite the growing body of scientific evidence, researchers do not fully understand how CR enhances longevity. Moreover, there are no long-term studies that examine the effects of consuming a high-quality, but calorie-restricted diet in humans. In a 6-month study involving 48 healthy men, subjects who followed a nutritious but very-low-calorie diet (about 900 kcal/day) experienced reductions in body temperature, fasting insulin levels, and signs of reduced DNA damage.[7A] These physiological adaptations to such calorie-restricted diets may be biological indicators of a lengthening human lifespan, but at present, no one is certain of their significance.

Some scientists hypothesize that prolonged CR is not necessary for achieving life-extending benefits. In a small study of 16 non-obese adults, participants fasted every other day for 3 weeks.[8A] Results of this study indicated that the subjects lost weight and total body fat, but they did not develop most of the physiological changes associated with lengthening the lifespan. Furthermore, the subjects reported being hungry on fasting days, indicating people may be unlikely to follow the diet for the long run. Even if scientists provide evidence that any form of CR adds some years to the human lifespan, would you be interested in reducing your food intake to such a drastic extent? How enjoyable would your life be if you ate only 900 kcal daily? What is important to you: How long you can live, or how *well* you live?

The science of biogerontology is still in its beginning stages; researchers have much to learn about the aging process before they can develop safe ways to enhance longevity. We already know that you can reduce your risk of dying prematurely from chronic diseases such as heart disease, hypertension, type 2 diabetes, and many forms of cancer by adopting healthy lifestyles. Rather than wait until the fountain of youth becomes a reality, you can take charge of your health now by consuming a nutritionally adequate diet, obtaining regular moderate- to vigorous-intensity physical activity, maintaining a healthy weight, avoiding tobacco products, limiting your alcohol consumption, and having regular physical checkups.

References for Chapter 13 Highlight

1A. U.S. General Accounting Office: *Antiaging products pose potential for physical and economic harm*. Special Committee on Aging, GAO-01-1129, 2001.

2A. Celec P, Stárka L: Dehydroepiandrosterone—Is the fountain of youth drying out? *Physiological Research* 52:397, 2003.

3A. Olshansky SJ and others: Position statement on human aging. *Journals of Gerontology, Series A, Biological Sciences and Medical Sciences* 57:B292, 2002.

4A. Rattan SIS: Anti-ageing strategies: Prevention or therapy? *EMBO Reports* 6:S25, 2005.

5A. Johnson FB and others: Molecular biology of aging. *Cell* 96:291, 1999.

6A. Heilbronn LK, Ravussin E: Calorie restriction and aging: A review of the literature and implications for studies in humans. *American Journal of Clinical Nutrition* 78:361, 2003.

7A. Heilbronn LK and others: Effect of 6-month calorie restriction on biomarkers of longevity, metabolic adaptation, and oxidative stress in overweight individuals: A randomized controlled trial. *Journal of the American Medical Association* 295:1539, 2006.

8A. Heilbronn LK and others: Alternate-day fasting in nonobese subjects: Effects on body weight, body composition, and energy metabolism. *American Journal of Clinical Nutrition* 81:69, 2005.

SUMMARY

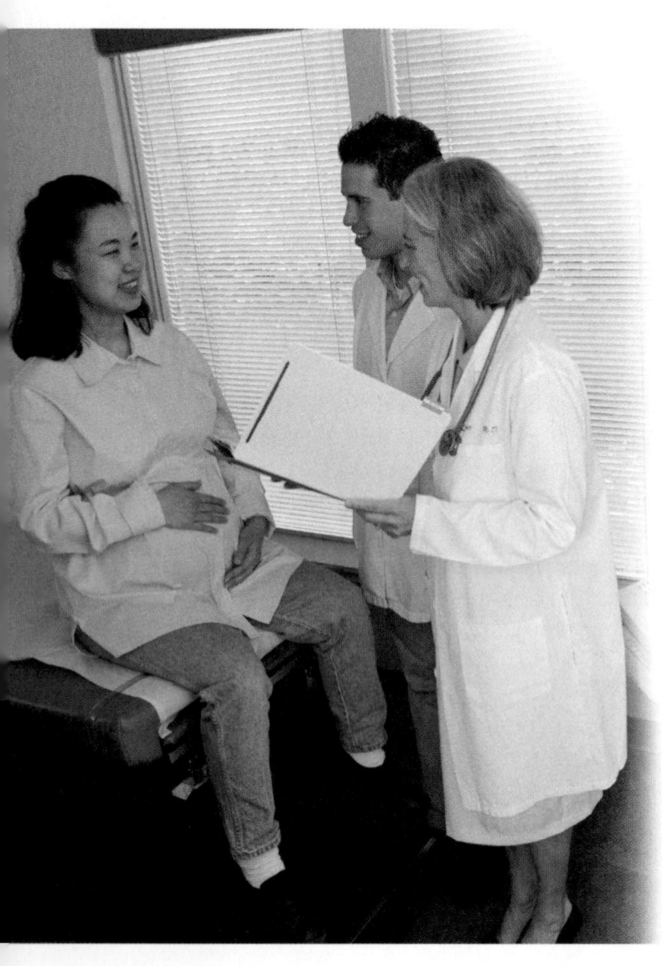

The leading causes of death for Canadians are chronic diseases—heart disease, cancer, and stroke. Lifestyles, especially dietary practices and physical activity patterns, contribute to the development of these chronic conditions. Other factors that influence a person's overall health include heredity, relationships, environment, income, education level, and access to health care.

Embryonic/fetal life is characterized by rapid rates of cell division, resulting in a dramatic increase in cell numbers. The first trimester of pregnancy is a critical stage in human development, because inadequate or excessive nutrient intakes as well as exposure to toxic compounds can have devastating effects on the embryo/fetus during this period. The placenta is the organ of pregnancy that transfers nutrients and oxygen from the mother's bloodstream to her embryo/fetus. The placenta also transfers wastes from the embryo/fetus to the mother's bloodstream so that her body can eliminate them. Infectious agents and harmful chemicals can pass through the placenta, enter the embryo/fetus, and cause disease, birth defects, or embryonic/fetal death.

Women of child-bearing age should take steps to ensure they are in good health prior to becoming pregnant. During pregnancy, the woman's body undergoes various physiological changes. These changes enable her body to nourish and maintain the developing fetus, as well as produce milk for her infant after its birth. A pregnant woman should follow a diet that meets her own nutritional needs as well as those of her developing offspring. During the second and third trimester, the pregnant woman's energy needs increase beyond her pre-pregnancy energy requirement. Additionally, needs for certain vitamins and minerals increase during pregnancy. The mother-to-be can use the *Eating Well with Canada's Food Guide* recommendations to develop nutritionally adequate daily menus, but she may also need to take a prenatal vitamin/mineral supplement.

Women whose pre-pregnancy weights were within the healthy range can expect to gain 11.4 to 15.9 kg (25 to 35 lbs.) during pregnancy. Women who gain excess weight during pregnancy may retain the extra weight long after delivery. Most women gain up to 1.8 kg (4 lbs.) during the first trimester; they gain 1.3 to 1.8 kg (3 to 4 lbs.) each month during the second and third trimesters.

Monitoring weight gain is an important aspect of prenatal care. Rapid weight gain, especially after the fifth month of pregnancy, could be a sign of pregnancy-induced hypertension (PIH). Underweight women who do not gain enough weight during pregnancy are at risk of having preterm or low-birth-weight infants. Obese women have greater risk of developing hypertension and type 2 diabetes during pregnancy. However, women should not try to lose weight while they are pregnant.

Breast milk is the best first food for infants, because it is uniquely formulated to meet the nutrient needs of a newborn human being. Furthermore, human milk contains biologically active substances that help an infant's immune system. Compared to babies who are not breast-fed, breast-fed infants have lower risks of allergies, as well as gastrointestinal, respiratory tract, and ear infections. Women who breast-feed their babies can also derive some important benefits from the practice, such as losing extra fat gained during pregnancy.

Prolactin stimulates the development of milk-producing tissue in the breasts of a pregnant woman. After delivery, this hormone stimulates milk production. When an infant suckles, nerves in the nipple signal the mother's brain to release prolactin and oxytocin into her bloodstream. Oxytocin is necessary for the let-down reflex and also causes the uterus to contract. Milk production relies on "supply and demand." If the breasts are not emptied fully, milk production soon ceases. To support milk production, the lactating mother needs about 400 to 500 extra kilocalories daily.

Growth is very rapid during infancy; birth weight doubles in four to six months, and length increases by 50% in the first year. Health care practitioners can assess growth in infants and children by measuring body weight, height (or length), and head circumference over time. For the first six months, the infant's nutrient needs can be met by human milk or iron-fortified infant formula. Breast-fed babies need vitamin D, and possibly iron and fluoride supplements.

Most infants do not need solid foods before 6 months of age. At this age, the child's GI tract can digest complex foods, the baby can sit up with support, he or she no longer has the extrusion reflex, and the risk of developing food allergies has decreased. The first solid food offered to babies should be an iron-fortified infant cereal. Other foods should be added one at a time, and the child should be observed for allergy signs and symptoms. Whole cow's milk should not be fed to babies until they are 1 year of age.

It is normal for a preschooler's appetite to decline as the child's growth rate tapers off. Additionally, it is not unusual for preschool children to be "picky eaters" or embark on "food jags." Caregivers should avoid nagging, forcing, and bribing children to eat, but instead offer a variety of healthy food choices and allow the child to choose what and how much to eat. Nutrition-related problems that often affect preschool children are iron deficiency, dental caries, overweight, and food allergies.

School-age children often skip breakfast, and they tend to consume more foods away from home, larger portions of food, and more fried foods and sweetened beverages. Children who eat breakfast are more likely to have better diets and healthier body weights than children who skip this meal. Diets of many school-age children do not supply recommended amounts of calcium and potassium while providing too much sodium.

Public health experts are very concerned about the increasing prevalence of overweight among children in Canada and the United States. Overfat children have higher risks of elevated blood pressure, cholesterol, and glucose levels than children whose weights are within the healthy range. Overfat children may also have higher risk of hypertension, heart disease, and type 2 diabetes later in life. Such children are also more likely to experience depression, have low self-esteem, and become obese as adults.

A young child matures physically into an adult during adolescence. Adolescents face a variety of lifestyle choices, including decisions regarding eating and physical activity habits. For many teens, pressure to conform to fads and be influenced by other adolescents negatively affects their diets and overall health. Overweight, eating disorders, and low iron and calcium intakes are major nutrition-related concerns of adolescents.

The aging process is characterized by numerous predictable physical changes. Senescence refers to declining organ functioning and increased vulnerability to disease that occurs after a person reaches physical maturity. Aging is not a disease, and diseases that often accompany old age are not an inevitable aspect of aging. Many of the chronic ailments that are associated with senescence can be managed, delayed, and even prevented. Although genetics play a role in determining longevity, lifestyle practices and environmental conditions influence a person's rate of aging. People may be able to live longer and healthier by making responsible healthy lifestyle decisions while they are still young.

Compared to younger persons, older adults have greater risk of nutritional deficiencies because of physiological changes associated with the normal aging process. Other factors that can influence an older person's nutritional status include illnesses, tooth loss, medications, low income, depression, and lack of social support. Diets of older adults, particularly older women, often provide inadequate amounts of vitamins D, A, C, and B-12 and minerals such as calcium, iron, and zinc. Friends, relatives, and health care personnel should be alert for indications of poor nutrient intakes among older people, especially those who live in nursing homes or other long-term-care facilities.

Recipes for Healthy Living

Homemade Applesauce

It takes a little bit of work, but once you've eaten homemade applesauce, you're unlikely to eat commercially prepared applesauce again. This version has no added sugar, salt, or spices and is suitable for infants to eat. If you're not making the sauce for a baby, you may want to add a dash of cinnamon to it. You'll need a two-quart saucepan with a lid, and a strainer.

To make applesauce for a baby, cook the apples and strain the sauce. Spoon it into a clean ice cube tray, tightly cover the tray with a freezer plastic bag, and place in freezer. Whenever you want to feed your baby some applesauce, just pop one of the cubes out of the tray and heat it gently in a small saucepan. Apricots, pears, and peaches can be substituted for apples. This recipe makes approximately eight ice cube–sized servings. Each serving supplies approximately 36 kcal, 3.2 mg vitamin C, 74 mg potassium, and 1.6 g fibre.

INGREDIENTS:

4 medium apples (7 cm/2¾" diam.), preferably Jonathan apples
2 Tbsp water

PREPARATION STEPS:

1. Wash apples in warm water.
2. Peel skin from apples.
3. Cut small pieces of apple away from the core, avoiding any seeds, and place the fruit in a saucepan.
4. Add water to saucepan. Cover the saucepan with its lid and cook on high heat for about two minutes.
5. Reduce heat to simmer, and cook fruit for about 10 minutes. Stir occasionally with a large spoon, mashing the fruit.
6. Place strainer over a small bowl. Spoon cooked fruit into the strainer and mash it through the strainer. If sauce is lumpy, return it to the strainer and repeat the straining process.
7. Serve the applesauce while warm, or cover and refrigerate it. You can also freeze the sauce in an ice cube tray as described previously.

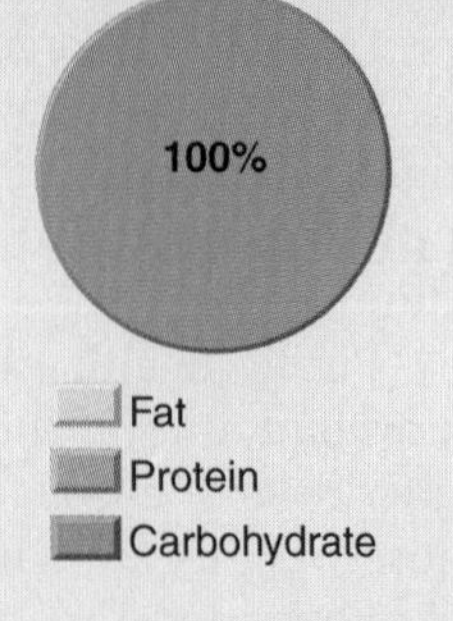

Recipes for Healthy Living

Vegetable Dip

You can make low-fat versions of fruit or vegetable dips by replacing sour cream or mayonnaise in recipes with plain, low-fat yogourt. This vegetable dip recipe makes approximately five 60-mL (¼-cup) servings of dip. Each serving provides approximately 46 kcal, 3 g protein, 2 g fat, 90 mg calcium, 160 mg sodium, and 120 mg potassium.

INGREDIENTS:

250 mL (1 cup) plain, low-fat yogourt
45 mL (3 Tbsp) calorie-reduced ranch dressing
1 mL (¼ tsp) curry powder (optional)

PREPARATION STEPS:

1. In a small bowl, combine yogourt with the dressing and stir until well blended.
2. Refrigerate until served.
3. Serve chilled in a bowl that is surrounded with fresh pieces of raw vegetables.
4. Discard any remaining dip.

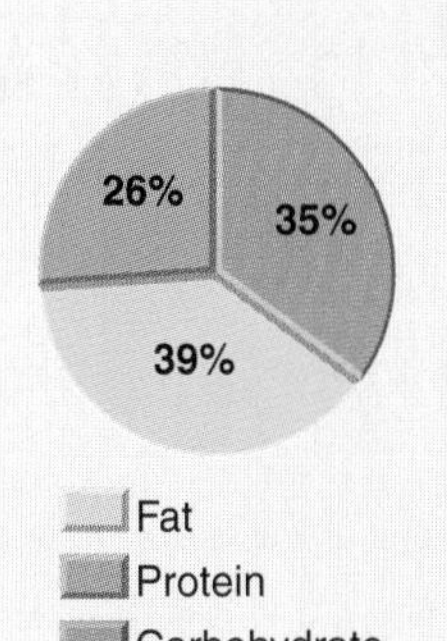

CRITICAL THINKING

1. One of your friends just found out that she's pregnant. Although her BMI is within the healthy range, she is concerned about gaining too much weight during pregnancy. What advice would you provide concerning the need to gain some weight during this life stage? If your friend's pre-pregnancy weight was 57 kg (125 lbs.), how much weight would be appropriate for her to gain during pregnancy?

2. Your pregnant friend wants your advice concerning whether she should breast-feed or formula-feed her baby. After reading Chapter 13, what information would you provide to help your friend decide to breast-feed?

3. Olivia is a healthy 2-month-old baby. Olivia's mother Kara wants to replace Olivia's iron-fortified infant formula with the same fresh fluid 2% milk that she drinks. What advice would you give to Kara concerning the appropriateness of making such a decision?

4. Marcus is 3 years old and his BMI is in the overweight range. His caregivers are also overweight, but they seem to be concerned about Marcus's excess body weight. What advice would you provide his caregivers to help Marcus achieve a healthy BMI?

5. Are your parents, grandparents, and great-grandparents still alive? If any of your ancestors died before they were 60 years of age, can you identify their causes of death and factors that contributed to their deaths? What lifestyle changes can you make now that can help you achieve a longer, healthier lifetime?

6. Use the *Eating Well with Canada's Food Guide* recommendations to design a day's menu for a 70-year-old woman who obtains 30 to 60 minutes of physical activity daily.

PRACTICE TEST

Select the best answer.

1. The embryo/fetus develops most of its organs during the
   a. preconception period.
   b. first trimester.
   c. second trimester.
   d. third trimester.
2. The placenta cannot
   a. transfer nutrients from the mother's bloodstream to the embryo/fetus.
   b. eliminate waste products from the embryo/fetus.
   c. prevent all toxic substances from reaching the embryo/fetus.
   d. all of the above
3. During the first trimester, a pregnant woman's daily energy requirement is ______ her daily energy needs before she became pregnant.
   a. 300 kcal lower than
   b. about the same as
   c. 300 kcal higher than
   d. 500 kcal higher than
4. Women with pre-pregnancy weights within the healthy range should gain ______ during pregnancy.
   a. 4.5 to 9.1 kg (10 to 20 lbs.)
   b. 9.1 to 11.4 kg (20 to 25 lbs.)
   c. 11.4 to 15.9 kg (25 to 35 lbs.)
   d. 15.9 to 22.7 kg (35 to 50 lbs.)
5. Preeclampsia is a form of ______ that can develop during pregnancy.
   a. hypertension
   b. diabetes
   c. hypertriglyceridemia
   d. anemia
6. Which of the following statements is true?
   a. A woman's energy needs are higher during the first trimester than at any other time in pregnancy.
   b. Using infant formula to bottle-feed a baby is more convenient and less expensive than breast-feeding a baby.
   c. Oxytocin is necessary for the let-down reflex to occur.
   d. Health Canada recommends feeding fresh whole milk to infants when they are 6 months of age.

7. A healthy infant who weighs about 3000 grams (6.5 lbs.) at birth can be expected to weigh ______ by her first birthday.
   a. 5.9 kg (13.0 lbs.)
   b. 7.5 kg (16.5 lbs.)
   c. 8.8 kg (19.5 lbs.)
   d. 10.7 kg (23.5 lbs.)
8. Breast-fed infants are ______ than babies who are fed infant formula.
   a. more likely to have diarrhea
   b. less likely to have cystic fibrosis
   c. more likely to have respiratory infections
   d. less likely to have ear infections
9. Infants are physically ready to start eating solid foods when they are ______ of age.
   a. 4 to 6 weeks
   b. 4 to 6 months
   c. 6 to 12 months
   d. 12 to 14 months
10. The first solid food offered to an infant should be
   a. iron-fortified infant rice cereal.
   b. mixed baby-food dinners.
   c. french fries.
   d. cooked egg whites.
11. Which of the following foods is not a common source of food allergens?
   a. peanuts
   b. eggs
   c. milk
   d. applesauce
12. Which of the following factors is associated with increased risk of overweight during childhood?
   a. having a family history of obesity
   b. eating three to five servings of fresh fruit daily
   c. being a low-birth-weight infant
   d. all of the above
13. Which of the following factors can influence an older person's nutritional status?
   a. illnesses
   b. medications
   c. income level
   d. all of the above

Answers to Chapter 13 Quiz Yourself

1. During pregnancy, a mother-to-be should double her food intake because she's "eating for two." **False.** (p. 450)
2. The natural size of a woman's breasts is not a factor in determining her ability to breast-feed her baby. **True.** (p. 456)
3. Within the first month after a baby is born, Canadian dietitians recommend adding solid foods to the infant's diet. **False.** (p. 461)
4. Over the past 30 years, the prevalence of overweight has increased among Canadian school-age children. **True.** (p. 468)
5. Compared to younger persons, older adults have lower risk of nutritional deficiencies. **False.** (p. 477)

Please visit Connect at

www.mcgrawhillconnect.ca

Appendices

Appendix A

English–Metric Conversions and Metric-to-Household Units

Metric-English Conversions

Length

English (USA)	Metric
inch (in.)	= 2.54 cm, 25.4 mm
foot (ft.)	= 0.30 m, 30.48 cm
yard (yd.)	= 0.91 m, 91.4 cm
mile (statute) (5280 ft.)	= 1.61 km, 1609 m
mile (nautical) (6077 ft, 1.15 statute mi.)	= 1.85 km, 1850 m

Metric	English (USA)
millimetre (mm)	= 0.039 in. (thickness of a dime)
centimetre (cm)	= 0.39 in.
metre (m)	= 3.28 ft., 39.4 in.
kilometre (km)	= 0.62 mi., 1091 yd., 3273 ft.

Weight

English (USA)	Metric
grain	= 64.80 mg
ounce (oz.)	= 28.35 g
pound (lb.)	= 453.60 g, 0.45 kg
ton (short—2000 lb.)	= 0.91 metric tonne (907 kg)

Metric	English (USA)
milligram (mg)	= 0.002 grain (0.000035 oz.)
gram (g)	= 0.04 oz. (1/28 of an oz.)
kilogram (kg)	= 35.27 oz., 2.20 lb.
metric tonne (1000 kg)	= 1.10 tons

Volume

English (USA)	Metric
cubic inch	= 16.39 cc
cubic foot	= 0.03 m^3
cubic yard	= 0.765 m^3
teaspoon (tsp)	= 5 mL
tablespoon (tbsp)	= 15 mL
fluid ounce	= 0.03 litre (30 mL)*
cup (c)	= 237 mL
pint (pt.)	= 0.47 litre
quart (qt.)	= 0.95 litre
gallon (gal.)	= 3.79 litres

Metric	English (USA)
millilitre (mL)	= 0.03 oz.
litre (L)	= 2.12 pt.
litre	= 1.06 qt
litre	= 0.27 gal.

1 litre ÷ 1000 = 1 millilitre or 1 cubic centimetre (10^{-3} litre)
1 litre ÷ 1,000,000 = 1 microlitre (10^{-6} litre)

*Note: 1 mL = 1 cc

Metric and Other Common Units

Unit/Abbreviation	Other Equivalent Measure
milligram/mg	1/1000 of a gram
microgram/μg	1/1,000,000 of a gram
decilitre/dl	1/10 of a litre (about ½ cup)
millilitre/ml	1/1000 of a litre (5 mL is about 1 tsp)
International Unit/IU	Crude measure of vitamin activity generally based on growth rate seen in animals

Fahrenheit–Celsius Conversion Scale

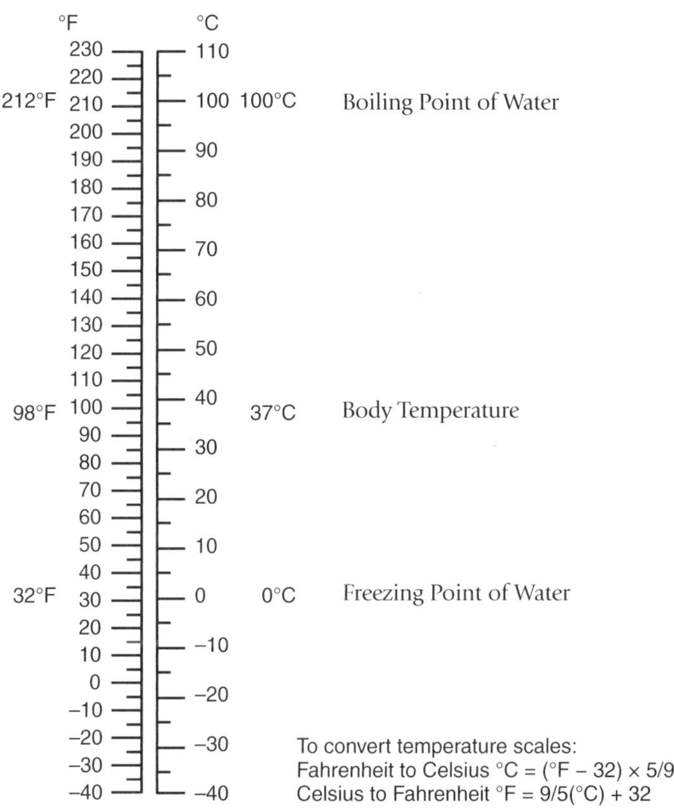

Household Units

3 teaspoons	= 1 tablespoon	1 cup	= 8 fluid ounces
4 tablespoons	= ¼ cup	1 cup	= ½ pint
5⅓ tablespoons	= ⅓ cup	2 cups	= 1 pint
8 tablespoons	= ½ cup	4 cups	= 1 quart
10⅔ tablespoons	= ⅔ cup	2 pints	= 1 quart
16 tablespoons	= 1 cup	4 quarts	= 1 gallon
1 tablespoon	= ½ fluid ounce		

Appendix B
Canadian Food Guide

The information in this appendix includes advice on dietary patterns, as well as regulations that apply to food labelling. Previous **Recommended Nutrient Intakes (RNIs)** for nutrients have been replaced by the Dietary Reference Intakes (DRIs) that apply to Canadian and U.S. residents. These are listed on the inside cover. Both Canadian and American scientists worked on the various DRI committees, coming up with a set of harmonized Dietary Reference Intakes for both countries.

Summary of the Nutrition Recommendations for Canadians

The Canadian federal department responsible for helping Canadians maintain and improve their health is Health Canada. The Office of Nutrition Policy and Promotion is within the Health Products and Food Branch of Health Canada and focuses on nutrition. Health Canada's National Dietary Guidance programs have been in existence since the 1930s and have always relied on scientific and other related evidence. Since 1977, a pattern of eating that meets nutrient needs and reduces the risk of chronic diseases has been promoted. In the 1990s, dietary guidance included *Canada's Guidelines for Healthy Eating* and *Food Guide to Healthy Eating* as well as *Nutrition for a Healthy Pregnancy* and *Nutrition for Healthy Term Infants*. The *Recommended Nutrient Intakes (RNI)*, a Canadian version of the RDA, was published in 1990.

In 1995, the U.S. Institutes of Medicine (IOM) brought together Canadian and American scientists to work on various committees, which came up with a set of harmonized Dietary Reference Intakes for both countries. The DRIs replaced the previous RNIs and a new set of recommendations (EAR, AI, RDA, UL) similar to those in the United States were adopted in Canada. Adoption of the DRIs in Canada led to a review and subsequent revision of *Canada's Food Guide to Healthy Eating* and *Guidelines for Healthy Eating*.

The revised *Canada's Food Guide* (Fig. B.1) was released in early 2007. The basic message to Canadians is to "Eat Well" with *Canada's Food Guide*. Learning more about *Canada's Food Guide* will help Canadians know how much food they need, what types of foods are better for them, and the importance of physical activity in their day.

In addition, if Canadians have the amount and type of food recommended and follow the tips included in *Eating Well with Canada's Food Guide*, this will help them:

- Meet their needs for vitamins, minerals, and other nutrients.
- Reduce their risk of obesity, type 2 diabetes, heart disease, certain types of cancer and osteoporosis.
- Contribute to their overall health and vitality.

Eating Well with Canada's Food Guide (Fig. B.1) places foods into four groups: Vegetables and Fruit; Grain Products; Milk and Alternatives; and Meat and Alternatives. *Eating Well with Canada's Food Guide* also includes information on the recommended number of food guide servings per day, examples of what one food guide serving is, and how to make each food guide serving count within each food group (Fig. B.2) and at each meal (Fig. B.3). Recommendations

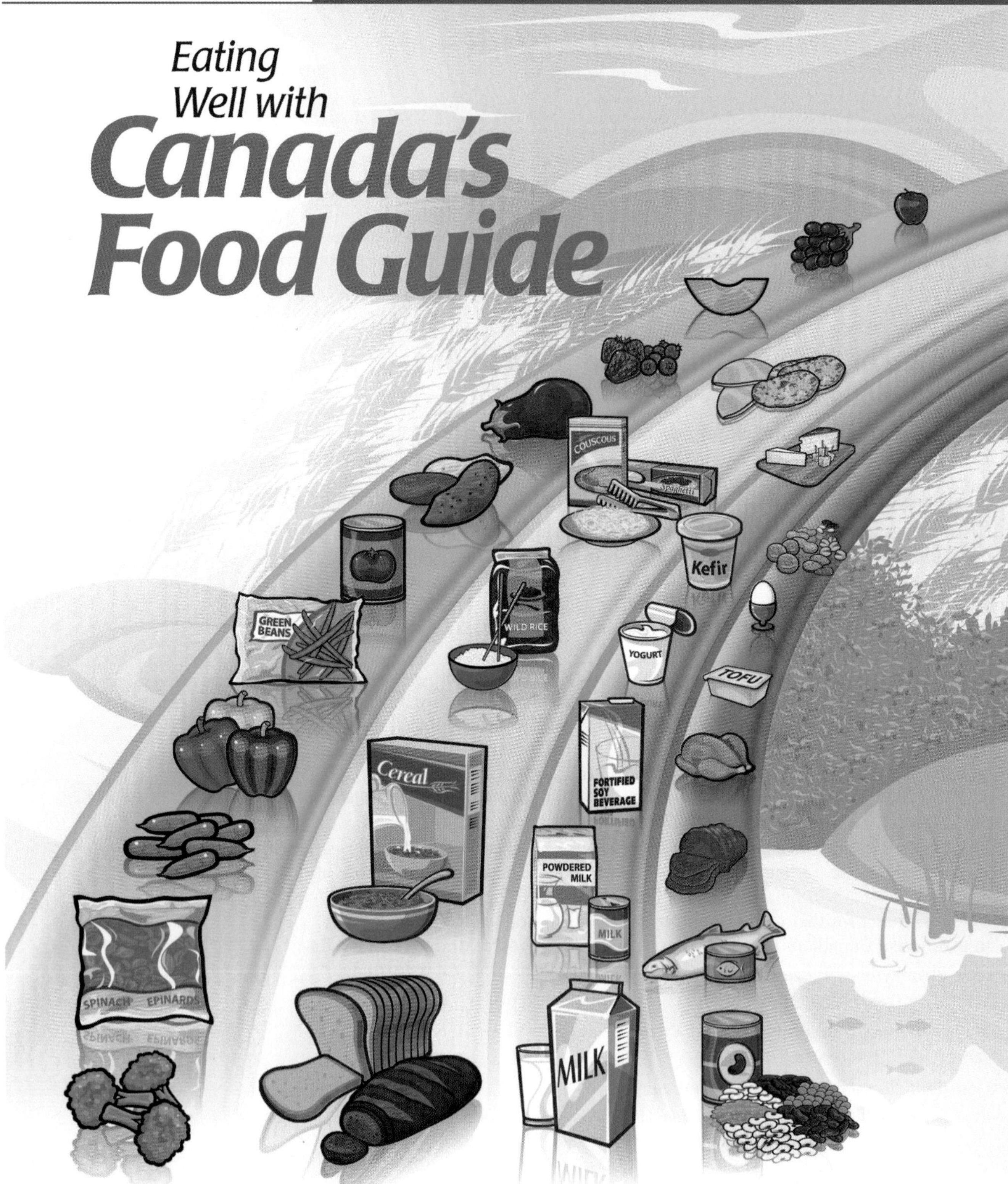

Figure B.1
Eating Well with Canada's Food Guide.

Recommended Number of Food Guide Servings per Day

	Children			Teens		Adults			
Age in Years	2-3	4-8	9-13	14-18		19-50		51+	
Sex	Girls and Boys			Females	Males	Females	Males	Females	Males
Vegetables and Fruit	4	5	6	7	8	7-8	8-10	7	7
Grain Products	3	4	6	6	7	6-7	8	6	7
Milk and Alternatives	2	2	3-4	3-4	3-4	2	2	3	3
Meat and Alternatives	1	1	1-2	2	3	2	3	2	3

The chart above shows how many Food Guide Servings you need from each of the four food groups every day.

Having the amount and type of food recommended and following the tips in *Canada's Food Guide* will help:

- Meet your needs for vitamins, minerals and other nutrients.
- Reduce your risk of obesity, type 2 diabetes, heart disease, certain types of cancer and osteoporosis.
- Contribute to your overall health and vitality.

Figure B.2 Information about food guide servings from *Eating Well with Canada's Food Guide*.

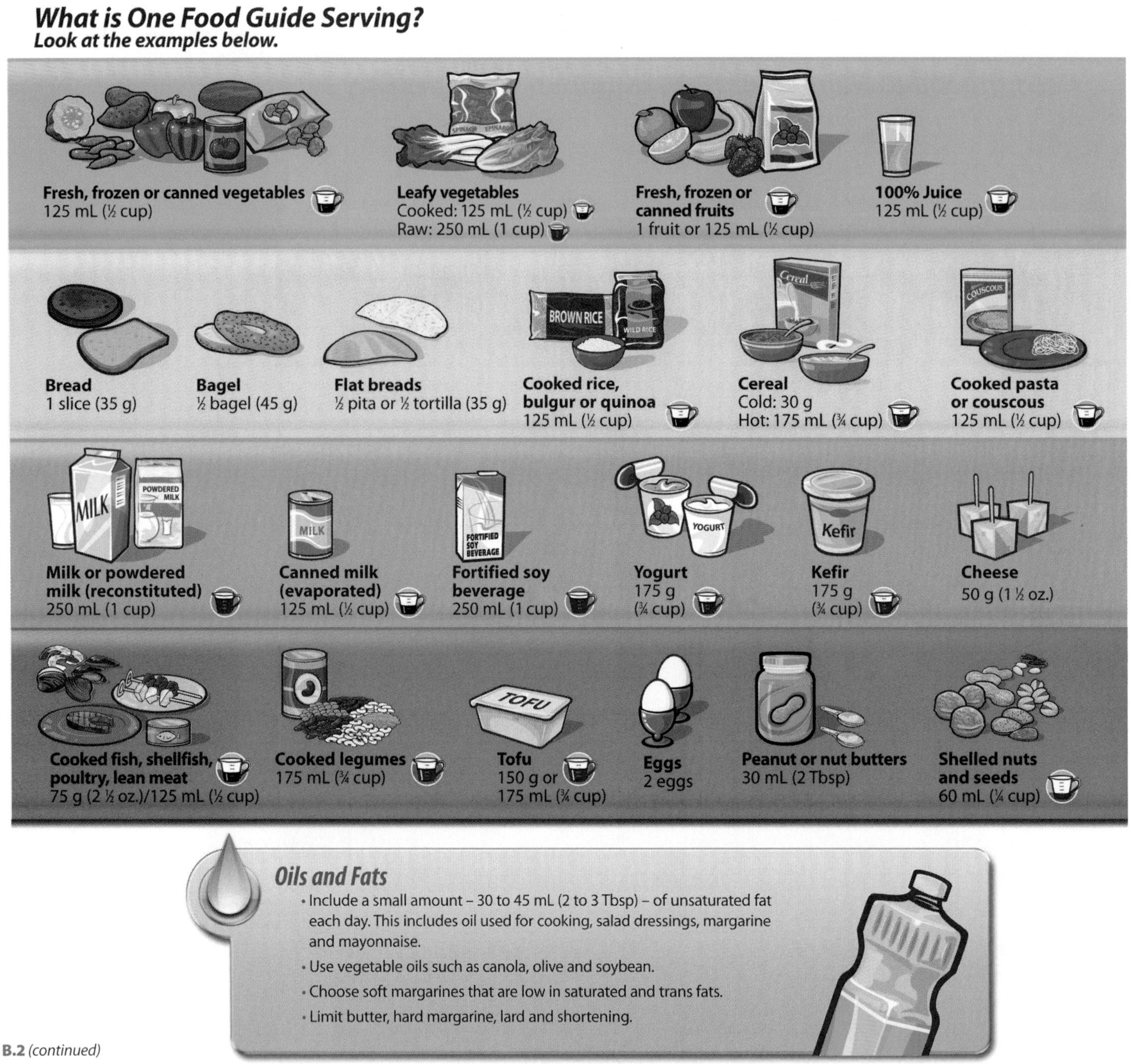

What is One Food Guide Serving?
Look at the examples below.

Fresh, frozen or canned vegetables
125 mL (½ cup)

Leafy vegetables
Cooked: 125 mL (½ cup)
Raw: 250 mL (1 cup)

Fresh, frozen or canned fruits
1 fruit or 125 mL (½ cup)

100% Juice
125 mL (½ cup)

Bread
1 slice (35 g)

Bagel
½ bagel (45 g)

Flat breads
½ pita or ½ tortilla (35 g)

Cooked rice, bulgur or quinoa
125 mL (½ cup)

Cereal
Cold: 30 g
Hot: 175 mL (¾ cup)

Cooked pasta or couscous
125 mL (½ cup)

Milk or powdered milk (reconstituted)
250 mL (1 cup)

Canned milk (evaporated)
125 mL (½ cup)

Fortified soy beverage
250 mL (1 cup)

Yogurt
175 g
(¾ cup)

Kefir
175 g
(¾ cup)

Cheese
50 g (1 ½ oz.)

Cooked fish, shellfish, poultry, lean meat
75 g (2 ½ oz.)/125 mL (½ cup)

Cooked legumes
175 mL (¾ cup)

Tofu
150 g or
175 mL (¾ cup)

Eggs
2 eggs

Peanut or nut butters
30 mL (2 Tbsp)

Shelled nuts and seeds
60 mL (¼ cup)

Oils and Fats

- Include a small amount – 30 to 45 mL (2 to 3 Tbsp) – of unsaturated fat each day. This includes oil used for cooking, salad dressings, margarine and mayonnaise.
- Use vegetable oils such as canola, olive and soybean.
- Choose soft margarines that are low in saturated and trans fats.
- Limit butter, hard margarine, lard and shortening.

Figure B.2 *(continued)*

are also included about the types and amounts of oils and fats to consume, along with guidance to enjoy a variety of foods and to satisfy your thirst with water (Fig. B.2). *Eating Well with Canada's Food Guide* emphasizes the combination of eating well and being active every day (Fig. B.4). The new Canadian Nutrition Facts table is also highlighted in the *Eating Well with Canada's Food Guide* with the message to "Read the label" (Fig. B.4). Finally, specific nutrition advice for different ages and stages is included (Fig. B.5). "My Food Guide," a Web-based interactive tool that will help you personalize the information found in the *Eating Well with Canada's Food Guide,* is available at www.hc-sc.gc.ca/fn-an/food-guide-aliment/myguide-monguide/index_e.html.

Make each Food Guide Serving count...
wherever you are – at home, at school, at work or when eating out!

- **Eat at least one dark green and one orange vegetable each day.**
  - Go for dark green vegetables such as broccoli, romaine lettuce and spinach.
  - Go for orange vegetables such as carrots, sweet potatoes and winter squash.
- **Choose vegetables and fruit prepared with little or no added fat, sugar or salt.**
  - Enjoy vegetables steamed, baked or stir-fried instead of deep-fried.
- **Have vegetables and fruit more often than juice.**

- **Make at least half of your grain products whole grain each day.**
  - Eat a variety of whole grains such as barley, brown rice, oats, quinoa and wild rice.
  - Enjoy whole grain breads, oatmeal or whole wheat pasta.
- **Choose grain products that are lower in fat, sugar or salt.**
  - Compare the Nutrition Facts table on labels to make wise choices.
  - Enjoy the true taste of grain products. When adding sauces or spreads, use small amounts.

- **Drink skim, 1%, or 2% milk each day.**
  - Have 500 mL (2 cups) of milk every day for adequate vitamin D.
  - Drink fortified soy beverages if you do not drink milk.
- **Select lower fat milk alternatives.**
  - Compare the Nutrition Facts table on yogurts or cheeses to make wise choices.

- **Have meat alternatives such as beans, lentils and tofu often.**
- **Eat at least two Food Guide Servings of fish each week.***
  - Choose fish such as char, herring, mackerel, salmon, sardines and trout.
- **Select lean meat and alternatives prepared with little or no added fat or salt.**
  - Trim the visible fat from meats. Remove the skin on poultry.
  - Use cooking methods such as roasting, baking or poaching that require little or no added fat.
  - If you eat luncheon meats, sausages or prepackaged meats, choose those lower in salt (sodium) and fat.

Enjoy a variety of foods from the four food groups.

Satisfy your thirst with water!

Drink water regularly. It's a calorie-free way to quench your thirst. Drink more water in hot weather or when you are very active.

* Health Canada provides advice for limiting exposure to mercury from certain types of fish. Refer to www.healthcanada.gc.ca for the latest information.

Figure B.2 *(continued)*

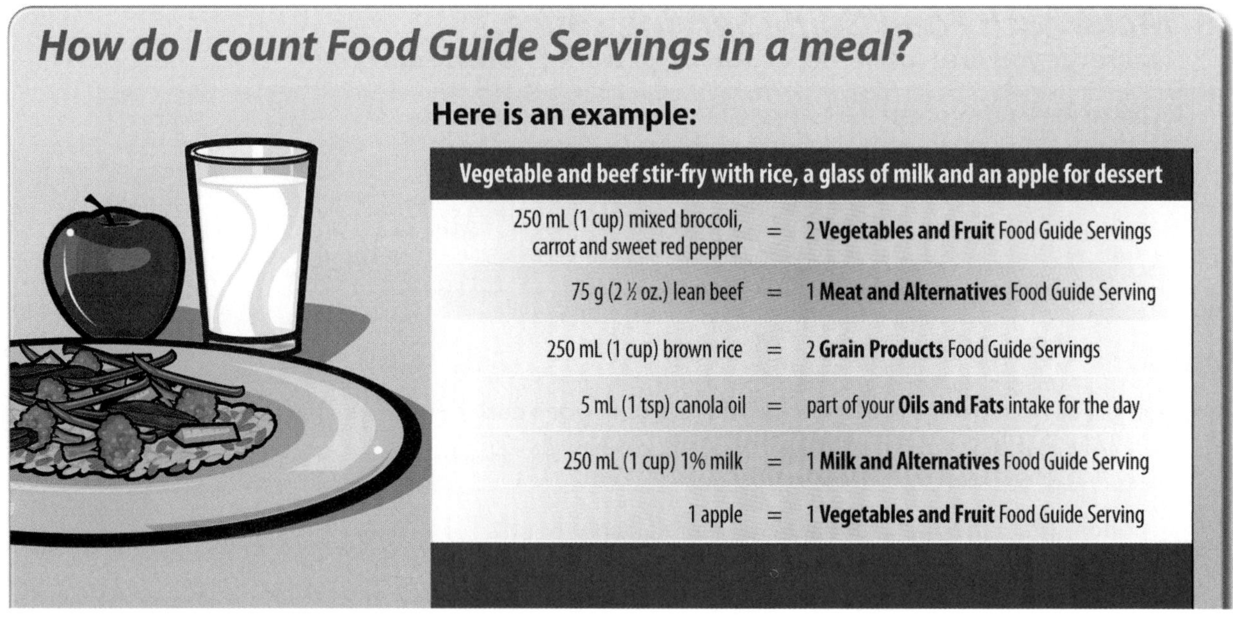

How do I count Food Guide Servings in a meal?

Here is an example:

Vegetable and beef stir-fry with rice, a glass of milk and an apple for dessert		
250 mL (1 cup) mixed broccoli, carrot and sweet red pepper	=	2 **Vegetables and Fruit** Food Guide Servings
75 g (2 ½ oz.) lean beef	=	1 **Meat and Alternatives** Food Guide Serving
250 mL (1 cup) brown rice	=	2 **Grain Products** Food Guide Servings
5 mL (1 tsp) canola oil	=	part of your **Oils and Fats** intake for the day
250 mL (1 cup) 1% milk	=	1 **Milk and Alternatives** Food Guide Serving
1 apple	=	1 **Vegetables and Fruit** Food Guide Serving

Figure B.3 How to count food guide servings in a meal.

Nutrition Labels

New labelling requirements were published on January 1, 2003. The new regulations require most food labels to carry a mandatory Nutrition Facts table listing Calories and 13 key nutrients.

How to Read the Canadian Nutrition Label

The Regulations provide for the optional declaration of the number of Calories both from fat and from saturates plus *trans*. Recommendations on the % of Calories from fat apply to the total diet rather than to an individual food. Therefore, inclusion of the % of Calories from fat in the Nutrition Facts table may be confusing and is not permitted.

The Nutrition Facts table provides information on saturated and *trans* fatty acids, shown to raise serum cholesterol levels. The declaration of the other groups of fatty acids, monounsaturates, omega-3, and omega-6 polyunsaturates, is optional unless claims are made, in which case all three must be declared.

Potassium is not included as a mandatory nutrient of the Nutrition Facts table because it is not considered to be a nutrient of general public health importance. The declaration of potassium, however, is mandatory when a claim is made for the sodium or salt content of a food that contains an added potassium salt.

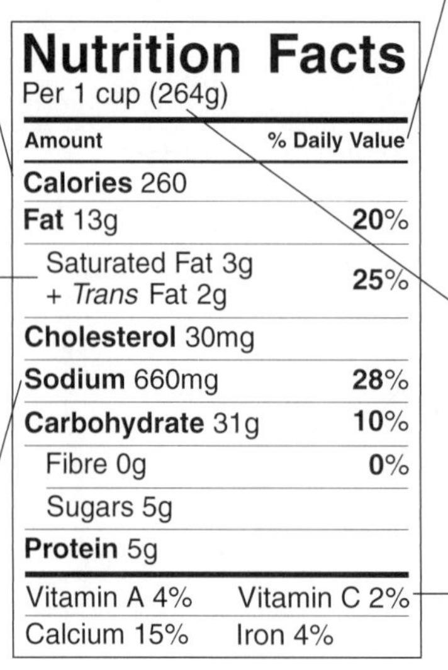

Nutrition Facts
Per 1 cup (264g)

Amount	% Daily Value
Calories 260	
Fat 13g	20%
Saturated Fat 3g + *Trans* Fat 2g	25%
Cholesterol 30mg	
Sodium 660mg	28%
Carbohydrate 31g	10%
Fibre 0g	0%
Sugars 5g	
Protein 5g	
Vitamin A 4%	Vitamin C 2%
Calcium 15%	Iron 4%

g = gram
mg = milligram

Daily Value is a comparison standard comprised of
(*a*) vitamin or mineral amounts referred to in the definition of a recommended daily intake for that vitamin or mineral
(*b*) nutrient amounts referred to in the definition of reference standard for that nutrient

Serving size is stipulated for various foods.

The amount of vitamins and minerals is expressed as a percentage of the Daily Value per serving of stated size.

Eat well and be active today and every day!

The benefits of eating well and being active include:

- Better overall health.
- Lower risk of disease.
- A healthy body weight.
- Feeling and looking better.
- More energy.
- Stronger muscles and bones.

Be active

To be active every day is a step towards better health and a healthy body weight.

Canada's Physical Activity Guide recommends building 30 to 60 minutes of moderate physical activity into daily life for adults and at least 90 minutes a day for children and youth. You don't have to do it all at once. Add it up in periods of at least 10 minutes at a time for adults and five minutes at a time for children and youth.

Start slowly and build up.

Eat well

Another important step towards better health and a healthy body weight is to follow *Canada's Food Guide* by:

- Eating the recommended amount and type of food each day.
- Limiting foods and beverages high in calories, fat, sugar or salt (sodium) such as cakes and pastries, chocolate and candies, cookies and granola bars, doughnuts and muffins, ice cream and frozen desserts, french fries, potato chips, nachos and other salty snacks, alcohol, fruit flavoured drinks, soft drinks, sports and energy drinks, and sweetened hot or cold drinks.

Read the label

- Compare the Nutrition Facts table on food labels to choose products that contain less fat, saturated fat, trans fat, sugar and sodium.
- Keep in mind that the calories and nutrients listed are for the amount of food found at the top of the Nutrition Facts table.

Nutrition Facts
Per 0 mL (0 g)

Amount	% Daily Value
Calories 0	
Fat 0 g	**0** %
Saturates 0 g	**0** %
+ Trans 0 g	
Cholesterol 0 mg	
Sodium 0 mg	**0** %
Carbohydrate 0 g	**0** %
Fibre 0 g	**0** %
Sugars 0 g	
Protein 0 g	

Vitamin A	0 %	Vitamin C	0 %
Calcium	0 %	Iron	0 %

Limit trans fat

When a Nutrition Facts table is not available, ask for nutrition information to choose foods lower in trans and saturated fats.

Take a step today...

✓ Have breakfast every day. It may help control your hunger later in the day.

✓ Walk wherever you can – get off the bus early, use the stairs.

✓ Benefit from eating vegetables and fruit at all meals and as snacks.

✓ Spend less time being inactive such as watching TV or playing computer games.

✓ Request nutrition information about menu items when eating out to help you make healthier choices.

✓ Enjoy eating with family and friends!

✓ Take time to eat and savour every bite!

For more information, interactive tools, or additional copies visit Canada's Food Guide on-line at: www.healthcanada.gc.ca/foodguide

or contact:

Publications
Health Canada
Ottawa, Ontario K1A 0K9
E-Mail: publications@hc-sc.gc.ca
Tel.: 1-866-225-0709
Fax: (613) 941-5366
TTY: 1-800-267-1245

Également disponible en français sous le titre : Bien manger avec le Guide alimentaire canadien

This publication can be made available on request on diskette, large print, audio-cassette and braille.

 HC Pub.: 4651 Cat.: H164-38/1-2007E ISBN: 0-662-44467-1

Figure B.4 Recommendations to eat well and be active from *Eating Well with Canada's Food Guide.*

Advice for different ages and stages...

Children

Following *Canada's Food Guide* helps children grow and thrive.

Young children have small appetites and need calories for growth and development.

- Serve small nutritious meals and snacks each day.
- Do not restrict nutritious foods because of their fat content. Offer a variety of foods from the four food groups.
- Most of all... be a good role model.

Women of childbearing age

All women who could become pregnant and those who are pregnant or breastfeeding need a multivitamin containing **folic acid** every day. Pregnant women need to ensure that their multivitamin also contains **iron**. A health care professional can help you find the multivitamin that's right for you.

Pregnant and breastfeeding women need more calories. Include an extra 2 to 3 Food Guide Servings each day.

Here are two examples:

- Have fruit and yogurt for a snack, or
- Have an extra slice of toast at breakfast and an extra glass of milk at supper.

Men and women over 50

The need for **vitamin D** increases after the age of 50.

In addition to following *Canada's Food Guide*, everyone over the age of 50 should take a daily vitamin D supplement of 10 μg (400 IU).

Figure B.5 Advice for different ages and stages from *Eating Well with Canada's Food Guide*.

The new regulations make nutrition labelling mandatory on most food labels using a new format. The regulations also update requirements for nutrient content claims and permit, for the first time in Canada, diet-related health claims for foods.

Templates for Canadian "Nutrition Facts" Tables

Bilingual Label

Nutrition Facts Valeur nutritive Per 125 mL (87 g) / 0par 125 mL (87 g)	
Amount / **Teneur**	**% Daily Value** / **% valeur quotidienne**
Calories / Calories 80	
Fat / Lipids 0.5 g	**1** %
Saturated / saturés 0 g + *Trans* / trans 0 g	**0** %
Cholesterol / Cholestérol 0 mg	
Sodium / Sodium 0 mg	**0** %
Carbohydrate / Glucides 18 g	**6** %
Fibre / Fibres 2 g	**8** %
Sugars / Sucres 2 g	
Protein / Protéines 3 g	
Vitamin A / Vitamine A	2 %
Vitamin C / Vitamine C	10 %
Calcium / Calcium	0 %
Iron / Fer	2 %

English Label

Nutrition Facts Per 125 mL (87 g)			
Amount			**% Daily Value**
Calories 80			
Fat 0.5 g			**1** %
Saturated 0 g + *Trans* 0 g			**0** %
Cholesterol 0 mg			
Sodium 0 mg			**0** %
Carbohydrate 18 g			**6** %
Fibre 2 g			**8** %
Sugars 2 g			
Protein 3 g			
Vitamin A	2 %	Vitamin C	10 %
Calcium	0 %	Iron	2 %

French Label

Valeur nutritive par 125 mL (87 g)			
Teneur			**% valeur quotidienne**
Calories 80			
Lipids 0,5 g			**1** %
saturés 0 g + trans 0 g			**0** %
Cholestérol 0 mg			
Sodium 0 mg			**0** %
Glucides 18 g			**6** %
Fibres 2 g			**8** %
Sucres 2 g			
Protéines 3 g			
Vitamine A	2 %	Vitamine C	10 %
Calcium	0 %	Fer	2 %

g = gram
mg = milligram

New Canadian Nutrition Facts Label for Children Under Two Years of Age

Nutrition Facts Per 1 jar (126 mL)			
			Amount
Calories			110
Fat			0g
Sodium			10 mg
Carbohydrate			27g
Fibre			4g
Sugars			18g
Protein			0g
% Daily Value			
Vitamin A	6%	Vitamin C	45%
Calcium	2%	Iron	2%

g = gram
mg = milligram

Recommended Daily Intakes and Reference Standards

The following are the Recommended Daily Intakes and Reference Standards used on Nutrition Facts tables for persons 2 years of age and older.*†‡

Dietary Constituent	Amount	Dietary Constituent	Amount
Fat	**65 g**	*Folacin*	220µg
The sum of saturated fatty acids and trans fatty acids	**20 g**	*Vitamin B12*	2µg
Cholesterol	**300 mg**	*Pantothenic acid or pantothenate*	7mg
Carbohydrate	**300 g**	*Vitamin K*	**80 mg**
Fibre	**25 g**	*Biotin*	**30 µg**
Sodium	**2400 mg**	*Calcium*	1100 mg
Chloride	**3400 µg**	*Phosphorus*	1100 mg
Potassium	**3500 mg**	*Magnesium*	250 mg
Vitamin A	1000 RE	*Iron*	14 mg
Vitamin D	5 µg	*Zinc*	9 mg
Vitamin E	10 mg	*Iodide*	160 µg
Vitamin C	60 mg	*Selenium*	**50 µg**
Thiamin, thiamine or vitamin B1	1.3 mg	*Copper*	**2 mg**
Riboflavin or vitamin B2	1.6 mg	*Manganese*	**2 mg**
Niacin	23 NE	*Chromium*	**120 µg**
Vitamin B6	1.8 mg	*Molybdenum*	**75 µg**

*RE = retinol equivalents

†NE = niacin equivalents

‡Together these constitute the Daily Values used on the Canadian Nutrition Facts table. Note that Reference Standards are bolded.

Approved Nutrient Content Claims for Canada

The following is a sample of approved nutrient content claims for food labels (for the complete list of regulations see www.inspection.gc.ca/english/fssa/labeti/guide/ch7be.shtml#a7_25).

Energy

- *Free of energy:* The food provides less than 5 Calories or 21 kilojoules per reference amount and serving of stated size.
- *Low in energy:* The food provides 40 Calories or 167 kilojoules or less per reference amount and serving of stated size.
- *Reduced in energy:* The food is processed, formulated, reformulated, or otherwise modified so that it provides at least 25% less energy per reference amount of a similar food.
- *Lower in energy:* The food provides at least 25% less energy per reference amount of a similar food.
- *Source of energy:* The food provides at least 100 Calories or 420 kilojoules per reference amount and serving of stated size.
- *More energy:* The food provides at least 25% more energy, totalling at least 100 more Calories or 420 more kilojoules per reference amount of a similar food.

Protein

- *Low in protein:* The food contains no more than 1 g of protein per 100 g of the food.
- *Source of protein:* The food has a protein rating of 20 or more, as determined by official method FO-1, *Determination of Protein Rating*, October 15, 1981, (*a*) per reasonable daily intake; or (*b*) per 30 g combined with 125 mL of milk, if the food is a breakfast cereal.

- *Excellent source of protein:* The food has a protein rating of 40 or more, as determined by official method FO-1, *Determination of Protein Rating,* October 15, 1981, (*a*) per reasonable daily intake; or (*b*) per 30 g combined with 125 mL of milk, if the food is a breakfast cereal.
- *More protein:* The food (*a*) has a protein rating of 20 or more, as determined by official method FO-1, *Determination of Protein Rating,* October 15, 1981, (*i*) per reasonable daily intake, or (*ii*) per 30 g combined with 125 mL of milk, if the food is a breakfast cereal; and (*b*) contains at least 25% more protein, totalling at least 7 g more, per reasonable daily intake compared to the reference food of the same food group or the similar reference food.

Fat

- *Free of fat:* The food contains less than 0.5 g of fat per reference amount and serving of stated size.
- *Low in fat:* The food contains 3 g or less of fat per reference amount and serving of stated size and, if the reference amount is 30 g or 30 mL or less, per 50 g.
- *Reduced in fat:* The food is processed, formulated, reformulated, or otherwise modified so that it contains at least 25% less fat than the reference amount of a similar food.
- *Lower in fat:* The food contains at least 25% less fat per reference amount of the food, than the reference amount of the reference food of the same food group.
- *100% fat-free:* The food (*a*) contains less than 0.5 g of fat per 100 g; (*b*) contains no added fat.
- *No added fat:* The food contains no added fats or oils set out in Division 9, or added butter or ghee, or ingredients that contain added fats or oils, or butter or ghee.
- *Free of saturated fatty acids:* The food contains less than 0.2 g saturated fatty acids and less than 0.2 g *trans* fatty acids per reference amount and serving of stated size.
- *Low in saturated fatty acids:* (1) The food contains 2 g or less of saturated fatty acids and *trans* fatty acids combined per reference amount and serving of stated size. (2) The food provides 15% or less energy from the sum of saturated fatty acids and *trans* fatty acids.
- *Reduced in saturated fatty acids:* The food is processed, formulated, reformulated, or otherwise modified without increasing the content of *trans* fatty acids, so that it contains at least 25% less saturated fatty acids per reference amount of the food than the reference amount of the similar reference food.
- *Lower in saturated fatty acids:* The food contains at least 25% less saturated fatty acids and the content of *trans* fatty acids is not higher per reference amount of the food, than the reference amount of the reference food of the same food group.
- *Free of* trans *fatty acids:* The food contains less than 0.2 g of *trans* fatty acids per reference amount and serving of stated size.
- *Reduced in* trans *fatty acids:* The food is processed, formulated, reformulated, or otherwise modified without increasing the content of saturated fatty acids, so that it contains at least 25% less *trans* fatty acids per reference amount of the food than the reference amount of the similar reference food.
- *Lower in* trans *fatty acids:* The food contains at least 25% less *trans* fatty acids and the content of saturated fatty acids is not higher per reference amount of the food compared to the reference amount of a similar food.
- *Source of omega-3 polyunsaturated fatty acids:* The food contains 0.3 g or more of omega-3 polyunsaturated fatty acids per reference amount and serving of stated size.
- *Source of omega-6 polyunsaturated fatty acids:* The food contains 2 g or more of omega-6 polyunsaturated fatty acids per reference amount and serving of stated size.

Cholesterol

- *Free of cholesterol:* The food contains less than 2 mg of cholesterol per reference amount and serving of stated size.
- *Low in cholesterol:* The food contains 20 mg or less of cholesterol per reference amount and serving of stated size (if the reference amount is 30 g or 30 mL or less, per 50 g).
- *Reduced in cholesterol:* The food is processed, formulated, reformulated, or otherwise modified so that it contains at least 25% less cholesterol per reference amount of a similar food.
- *Lower in cholesterol:* The food contains at least 25% less cholesterol per reference amount of a similar food.

Sodium or Salt

- *Free of sodium or salt:* The food contains less than 5 mg of sodium per reference amount and serving of stated size.
- *Low in sodium or salt:* The food contains 140 mg or less of sodium per reference amount and serving of stated size.
- *Reduced in sodium or salt:* The food is processed, formulated, reformulated, or otherwise modified so that it contains at least 25% less sodium per reference amount of a similar food.
- *Lower in sodium or salt:* The food contains at least 25% less sodium per reference amount of the food.
- *No added sodium or salt:* The food contains no added salt, other sodium salts, or ingredients that contain sodium that functionally substitute for added salt.
- *Lightly salted:* The food contains at least 50% less added sodium than the sodium added to a similar reference food.

Sugars

- *Free of sugars:* The food contains less than 0.5 mg of sugars per reference amount and serving of stated size.
- *Reduced in sugars:* The food is processed, formulated, reformulated, or otherwise modified so that it contains at least 25% less sugars, totalling at least 5 g less, per reference amount of the food.
- *Lower in sugars:* The food contains at least 25% less sugars, totalling at least 5 g less, per reference amount of the food.
- *No added sugars:* The food contains no added sugars, no ingredients containing added sugars or ingredients that contain

sugars that functionally substitute for added sugars.

Fibre

- *Source of fibre:* The food contains 2 g or more (*a*) of fibre per reference amount and serving of stated size, if no fibre or fibre source is identified in the statement or claim; or (*b*) of each identified fibre or fibre from an identified fibre source per reference amount and serving of stated size, if a fibre or fibre source is identified in the statement or claim.
- *High source of fibre:* The food contains 4 g or more (*a*) of fibre per reference amount and serving of stated size, if no fibre or fibre source is identified in the statement or claim; or (*b*) of each identified fibre or fibre from an identified fibre source per reference amount and serving of stated size, if a fibre or fibre source is identified in the statement or claim.
- *Very high source of fibre:* The food contains 6 g or more (*a*) of fibre per reference amount and serving of stated size, if no fibre or fibre source is identified in the statement or claim; or (*b*) of each identified fibre or fibre from an identified fibre source per reference amount and serving of stated size, if a fibre or fibre source is identified in the statement or claim.
- *More fibre:* The food contains at least 25% more fibre, totalling at least 1 g more, if no fibre or fibre source is identified in the statement or claim, or at least 25% more of an identified fibre or fibre from an identified fibre source, totalling at least 1 g more, if a fibre or fibre source is identified in the statement or claim compared to reference amount of a similar food.

Light and Lean

- *Light in energy or fat:* The food meets the conditions set out for the subject "reduced in energy" or "reduced in fat."
- *Lean:* The food (*a*) is meat or poultry that has not been ground, a marine or fresh water animal or a product of any of these; and (*b*) contains 10% or less fat.
- *Extra lean:* The food (*a*) is meat or poultry that has not been ground, a marine or fresh water animal or a product of any of these; and (*b*) contains 7.5% or less fat.

Approved Health Claims for Nutrition Labels

If a manufacturer follows specific guidelines addressing both the nutrients noted in the claim as well as guidelines pertaining to other nutrients in a food, the following health claims can be made:

- A healthy diet containing foods high in potassium and low in sodium may reduce the risk of high blood pressure, a risk factor for stroke and heart disease.
- A healthy diet with adequate calcium and vitamin D, and regular physical activity, help to achieve strong bones and may reduce the risk of osteoporosis.
- A healthy diet low in saturated and *trans* fats may reduce the risk of heart disease.
- A healthy diet rich in a variety of vegetables and fruit may help reduce the risk of some types of cancer.
- Foods very low in starch and fermentable sugars can make the following health claims:
- Won't cause cavities;
- Does not promote tooth decay;
- Does not promote dental caries; or is
- Non-cariogenic.

Appendix C
Daily Values Table

Nutrition Facts
Serving Size 1 cup (38 g)
Servings Per Container 18
Amount Per Serving
Calories 100
Calories from Fat 20
% Daily Value*
Total Fat 2g **3%**
Saturated Fat 0g 0%

The Daily Values Used on Food Labels in the United States, with a Comparison to the Latest RDAs and Other Nutrient Standards

Dietary Constituent	Unit of Measure	Current Daily Values for People over 4 Years of Age	RDA or Other Current Dietary Standard: Males, 19 Years Old	RDA or Other Current Dietary Standard: Females, 19 Years Old
Total fat†	g	<65	—	—
Saturated fatty acids†	g	<20	—	—
Protein†	g	50	56	46
Cholesterol§	mg	<300	—	—
Carbohydrate†	g	300	130	130
Fibre	g	25	38	25
Vitamin A	µg Retinol activity equivalents	1000	900	700
Vitamin D	International units	400	200	200
Vitamin E	International units	30	22–33	22–33
Vitamin K	µg	80	120	90
Vitamin C	mg	60	90	75
Folate	µg	400	400	400
Thiamin	mg	1.5	1.20	1.10
Riboflavin	mg	1.7	1.30	1.10
Niacin	mg	20	16	14
Vitamin B-6	mg	2	1.30	1.30
Vitamin B-12	µg	6	2.40	2.40
Biotin	mg	0.3	0.03	0.03
Pantothenic acid	mg	10	5	5
Calcium	mg	1000	1000	1000
Phosphorus	mg	1000	700	700
Iodide	µg	150	150	150
Iron	mg	18	8	18
Magnesium	mg	400	400	310
Copper	mg	2	0.9	0.9
Zinc	mg	15	11	8
Sodium‡	mg	<2400	1500	1500
Potassium‡	mg	3500	4700	4700
Chloride‡	mg	3400	2300	2300
Manganese	mg	2	2.3	1.8
Selenium	µg	70	55	55
Chromium	µg	120	35	25
Molybdenum	µg	75	45	45

Abbreviations: g = gram, mg = milligram, µg = microgram

*Daily Values are generally set at the highest nutrient recommendation in a specific age and gender category. Many Daily Values exceed current nutrient standards. This is in part because aspects of the Daily Values were originally developed in the early 1970s using estimates of nutrient needs published in 1968. The Daily Values have yet to be updated to reflect the current state of knowledge.

†These Daily Values are based on a 2000 kcal diet, instead of RDAs, with a caloric distribution of 30% from fat (and one-third of this total from saturated fat), 60% from carbohydrate, and 10% from protein.

‡The considerably higher Daily Values for sodium and chloride are there to allow for more diet flexibility, but the extra amounts are not needed to maintain health.

§Based on recommendations of U.S. federal agencies.

Appendix D
Energy Metabolism

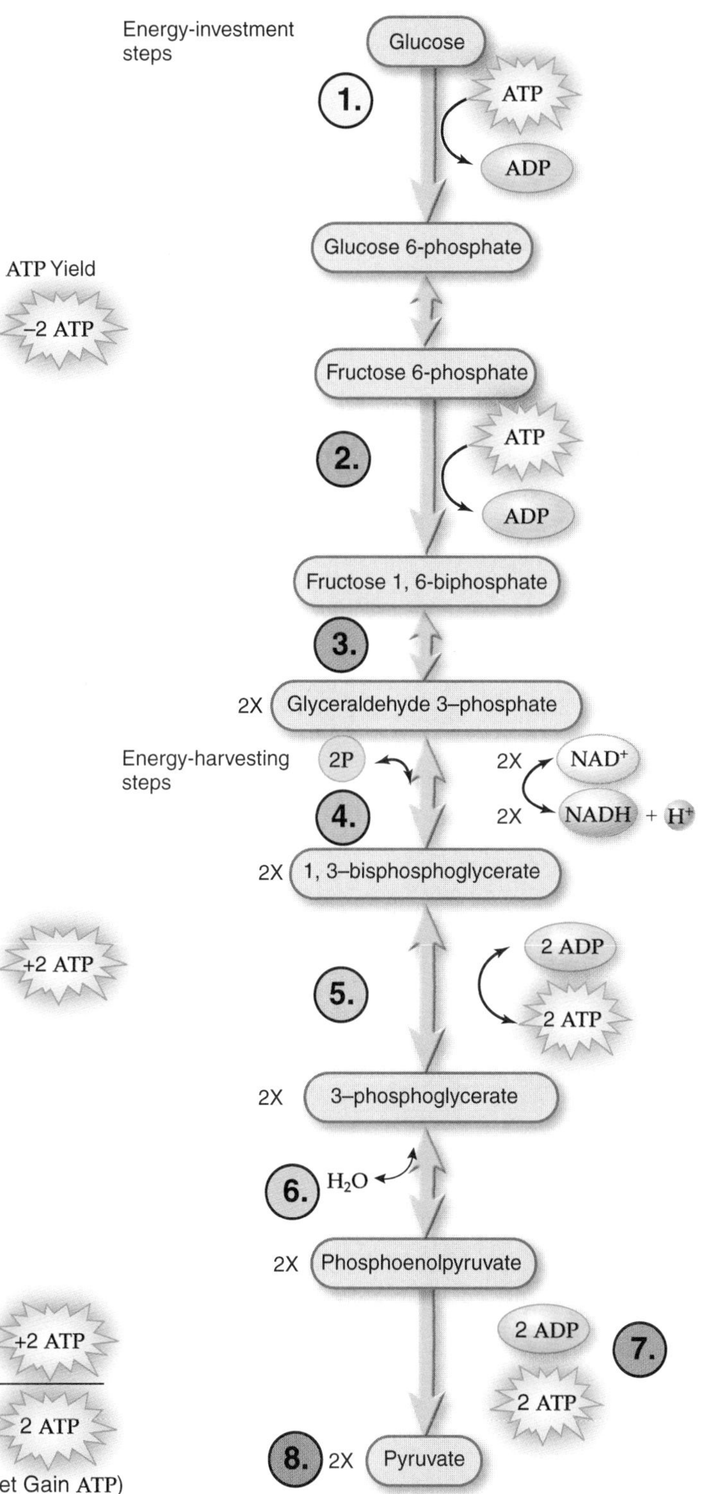

1. Adding phosphate to glucose using ATP produces an activated molecule.

2. Rearrangement, followed by a second addition of phosphate using ATP, produces fructose 1, 6-biphosphate.

3. The 6-carbon molecule is split into two 3-carbon-phosphate molecules.

4. Oxidation, followed by the addition of phosphate produces 2 NADH + $2H^+$ molecules and two 3-carbon-phosphate-phosphate molecules.

5. Removal of 2 phosphate groups by 2 ADP molecules produces 2 ATP molecules and two 3-carbon-phosphate molecules.

6. Removal of water produces two 3-carbon-phosphate molecules.

7. Removal of 2 phosphate groups by 2 ADP molecules produces 2 ATP molecules.

8. Pyruvate is the end product of the glycolysis pathway. Generally pyruvate enters mitochondria for further breakdown.

Figure D.1 Glycolysis, step by step. This metabolic pathway begins with glucose and ends with pyruvate. Net gain of two ATP molecules can be calculated by subtracting those used during the energy-investment steps from those produced during the energy-harvesting steps. Text in boxes explains the reactions.

Pyruvate
Transition Reaction
CO_2
NAD^+
CoA
NADH + H^+
Acetyl-CoA
Pyruvate is first metabolized in a transition reaction to acetyl-CoA. It is acetyl-CoA that actually enters the citric acid cycle. In the process, NADH + H^+ is produced and CO_2 is lost.

Intermediates of the citric acid cycle, such as oxaloacetate, can leave the cycle and go on to form other compounds, such as glucose. Thus, the citric acid cycle should be viewed as a traffic circle rather than as a closed circle.

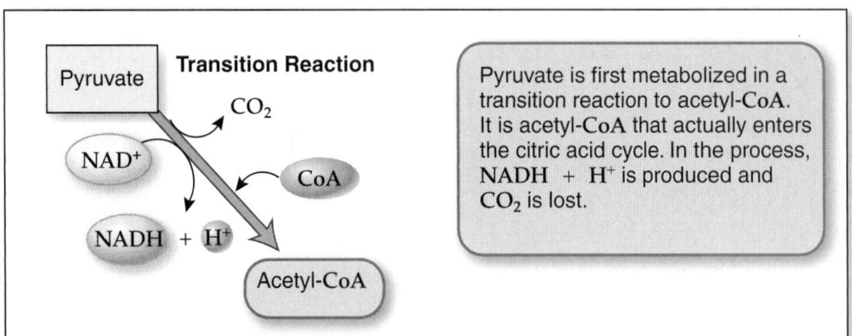

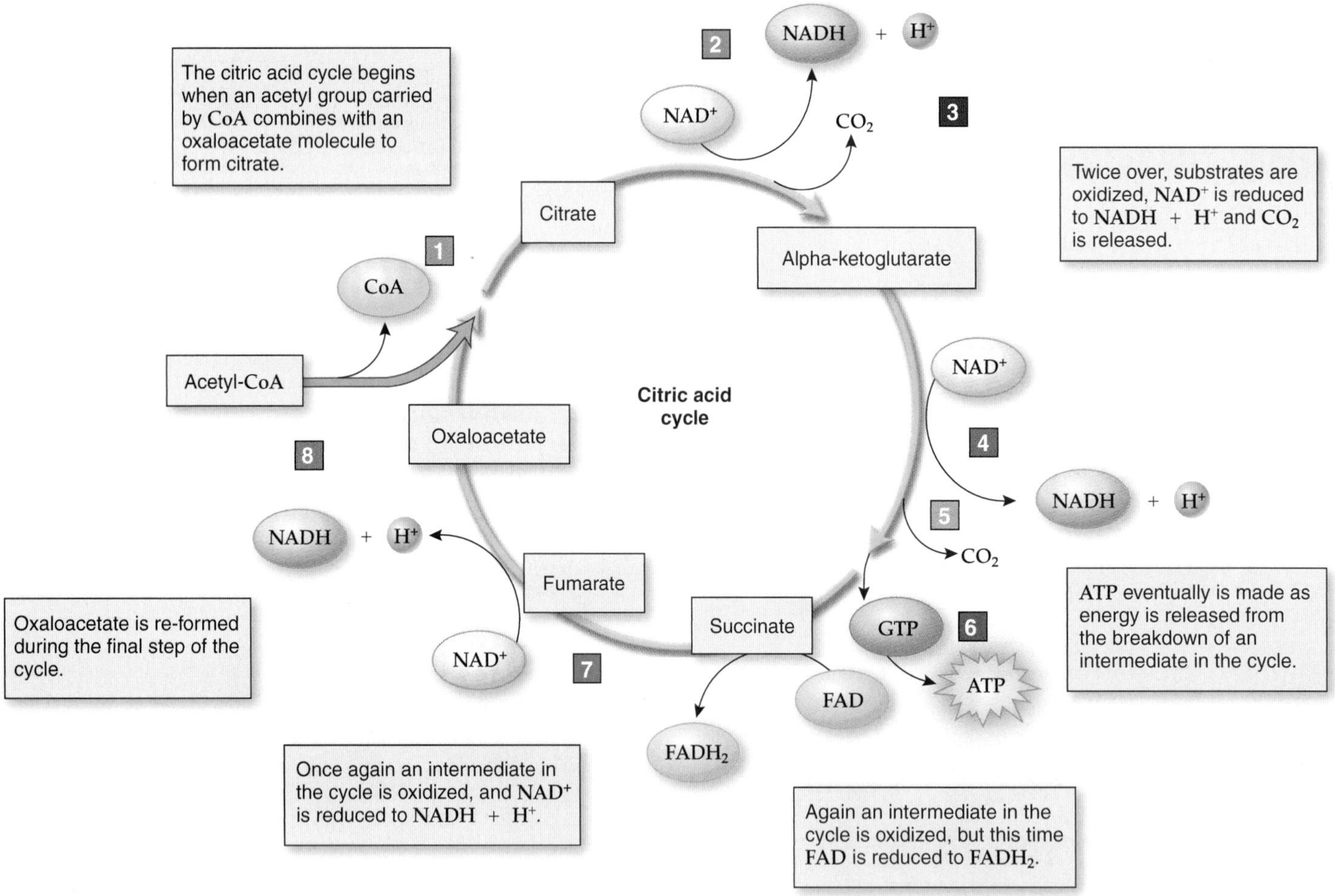

The citric acid cycle begins when an acetyl group carried by CoA combines with an oxaloacetate molecule to form citrate.
2
NADH + H^+
NAD^+
CO_2
3
Twice over, substrates are oxidized, NAD^+ is reduced to NADH + H^+ and CO_2 is released.
Citrate
1
CoA
Alpha-ketoglutarate
Acetyl-CoA
NAD^+
Citric acid cycle
Oxaloacetate
4
8
NADH + H^+
NADH + H^+
5
CO_2
Fumarate
Succinate
GTP
6
ATP
ATP eventually is made as energy is released from the breakdown of an intermediate in the cycle.
Oxaloacetate is re-formed during the final step of the cycle.
NAD^+
7
FAD
$FADH_2$
Once again an intermediate in the cycle is oxidized, and NAD^+ is reduced to NADH + H^+.
Again an intermediate in the cycle is oxidized, but this time FAD is reduced to $FADH_2$.

Figure D.2 The transition reaction and the citric acid cycle. The net result of one turn of this cycle of reactions (steps 1–8) is the oxidation of an acetyl group to two molecules of CO_2 and the formation of three molecules of NADH + H^+ and one molecule of $FADH_2$. One GTP molecule also results, which eventually forms ATP. The citric acid cycle turns twice per glucose molecule. Note that oxygen does not participate in any of the steps in the citric acid cycle. It instead participates in the electron transport chain.

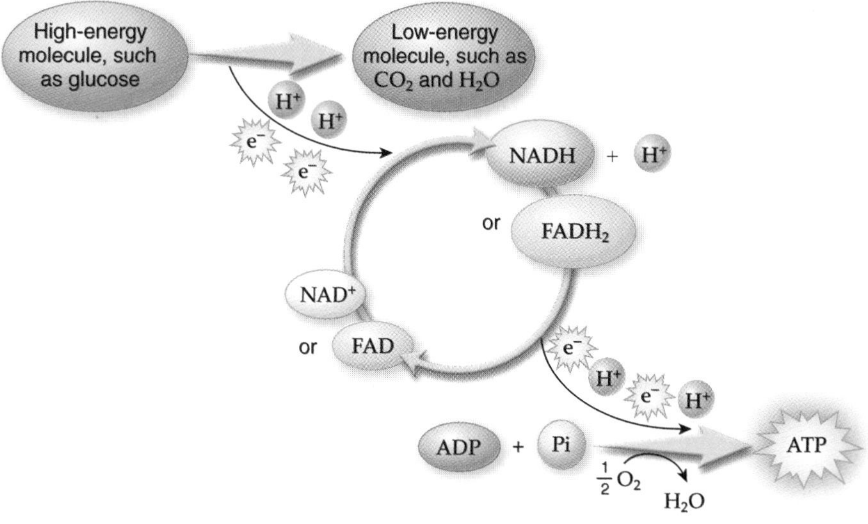

Figure D.3 Simplified depiction of electron transfer in energy metabolism. High-energy compounds, such as glucose, give up electrons and hydrogen ions to NAD^+ and FAD. The NADH + H^+ and $FADH_2$ that are formed transfer these electrons and hydrogen ions, using specialized electron carriers, to oxygen to form water (H_2O) The energy yielded by the entire process is used to generate ATP from ADP and P_i.

Appendix E
References

Chapter 1

1. Tremblay MS, Katzmarzyk PT, & Willms JD: Temporal trends in overweight and obesity in Canada, 1981–1996. *International Journal of Obesity and Related Metabolic Disorders*, 26(4):538–43, 2002.
2. Tremblay MS, & Willms JD.: Secular trends in the body mass index of Canadian children. *Canadian Medical Association Journal*, 163(11):1429–33, 2000.
3. World Health Organization Statistics 2006: Death and DALY estimates by cause, 2002. http://www.who.int/entity/healthinfo/statistics/bodgbddeathdalyestimates.xls. Accessed: February 2009.
4. Health Canada. *Maintaining healthy habits: Eat well and be active today and every day*. Updated 2007. http://www.hc-sc.gc.ca/fn-an/food-guide-aliment/maintain-adopt/index-eng.php. Accessed: February 2009.
5. Health Canada. 2003. Natural Health Products Regulations, Part II. *Canada Gazette*, 137(13).
6. National Center for Complementary and Alternative Medicine. *Herbs at a Glance: Echinacea*. July 2005. http://nccam.nih.gov/health/echinacea/. Accessed: December 16, 2006.
7. Liu RH: Potential synergy of phytochemicals in cancer prevention: Mechanism of action. *Journal of Nutrition* 134(12 Suppl):3479S, 2004.
8. Canadian Cancer Society, *Progress in cancer prevention: Modifiable risk factors* http://www.cancer.ca/canada-wide/about%20cancer/cancer%20statistics/canadian%20cancer%20statistics/special%20topics/progress%20in%20cancer%20prevention%20modifiable%20risk%20factors.aspx?sc_lang=en. Accessed: May 31, 2010.
9. Gray-Donald K and others: Food habits of Canadians: reduction in fat intake over a generation. *Canadian Journal of Public Health*, 91(5):381–5, 2000.
10. Garriguet D: *Overview of Canadian eating habits*, Statistics Canada Catalogue no. 82-620-MIE — No. 2. 2004.
11. Schulze MB and others: Sugar-sweetened beverages, weight gain, and incidence of type 2 diabetes in young and middle-aged women. *Journal of the American Medical Association* 292(8):927, 2004.
12. Garriguet D: Beverage consumption on Canadian adults. *Health Reports*, 19(4):23–9, 2008.
13. What is a megadose and why do you recommend against taking megadoses of vitamins? *Johns Hopkins Medical Letter Health After 50* 13(6):8, 2001.
14. Fletcher RH, Fairfield KM: Vitamins for chronic disease prevention in adults. *Journal of the American Medical Association* 287(23):3127, 2002.
15. Huang H-Y and others: The efficacy and safety of multivitamin and mineral supplement use to prevent cancer and chronic disease in adults: A systematic review for a National Institutes of Health State-of-the-Science Conference. *Annals of Internal Medicine* 145(5):372, 2006.

Chapter 2

1. Kraut A: *Dr. Joseph Goldberger & the war on pellagra*. Office of NIH History. http://history.nih.gov/exhibits/goldberger/docs/intro_2.htm. Accessed: February 21, 2007.
2. Simoni RD and others: Copper as an essential nutrient and nicotinic acid as the anti-black tongue (pellagra) factor: The work of Conrad Arnold Elvehjem. *Journal of Biological Chemistry* 277(34):e22, 2002.
3. Marshall BJ and others: Pyloric *Campylobacter* infection and gastrointestinal disease. *Medical Journal of Australia* 142(8):439, 1985.
4. The Canadian Diabetes Association: *Diabetes: An investment for the future health of Canadians*. 2003. www.diabetes.ca/files/Standing%20Committee%20on%20finance.doc. Accessed: May 28, 2010.
5. National Center for Health Statistics. *Health, United States, 2004*. http://www.cdc.gov/nchs/hus.htm. Accessed: October 14, 2005.
6. Yamamoto S and others: Soy, isoflavones, and breast cancer risk in Japan. *Journal of the National Cancer Institute* 95(12):906, 2003.
7. Wu AH and others: Adolescent and adult soy intake and risk of breast cancer in Asian-Americans. *Carcinogenesis* 23(9):1491, 2002.
8. Hirose H and others: Soybean products and reduction of breast cancer risk: A case-control study in Japan. *British Journal of Cancer* 93(1):15, 2005. http://www.nature.com/bjc/journal/v93/n1/full/6602659a.html. Accessed: July 21, 2010.
9. Pike CC and others: Breast cancer in a multiethnic cohort in Hawaii and Los Angeles: Risk factor-adjusted incidence in Japanese equals and in Hawaiians exceeds that in whites. *Cancer Epidemiology, biomarkers, and Prevention* 11(9):795, 2002.
10. Government of Canada. Panel on Research Ethics: *Tri-council policy statement: Ethical conduct for research involving humans (TCPS)*. www.pre.ethics.gc.ca. Accessed: June 10, 2010.
11. Fricchione G. Stefano GB: Placebo neural systems: Nitric oxide, morphine and the dopamine brain reward and motivation circuitries. *Medical Science Monitor* 11(5):M554, 2005.
12. *Vitamins and dietary supplements in Canada*. Euromonitor International. Chicago. 2009.

Chapter 3

1. Food Marketing Institute: Supermarket facts: Industry overview 2005. http://www.fmi.org/facts_figs/superfact.htm. Accessed: February 2, 2007.
2. Institute of Medicine: Dietary Reference Intakes for vitamin C, vitamin E, selenium, and carotenoids. Washington, DC: National Academies Press, 2000.
3. Dieticians of Canada: Scientific Basis of EATracker. http://www.dietitians.ca/public/content/eat_well_live_well/english/eatracker/backgrounder.asp. Accessed: July 17, 2007.

4. Otten, JJ and others (eds): *Dietary Reference Intakes: The essential guide to nutrient requirements*. Institute of Medicine of the National Academies. Washington, DC: National Academies Press, 2006.
5. Barr SI and others: Interpreting and using the Dietary Reference Intakes in dietary assessment of individuals and groups. *Journal of the American Dietetic Association* 102(6):780, 2002.
6. Health Canada: Food and nutrition: Dietary Reference Intake tables. http://www.hc-sc.gc.ca/fn-an/nutrition/reference/table/index-eng.php. Accessed: July 17, 2007.
7. Health Canada: Food and nutrition. Frequently asked questions about nutrition labelling. http://www.hc-sc.gc.ca/fn-an/label-etiquet/nutrition/educat/te_quest-eng.php#a13. Accessed: July 18, 2010.
8. Health Canada: Position paper on five US health claims considered for use in Canada. http://www.hc-sc.gc.ca/fn-an/label-etiquet/claims-reclam/position_paper-enonce_position-eng.php#a3. Accessed: March 2009.
9. Health Canada: *Eating Well with Canada's Food Guide*. http://www.hc-sc.gc.ca/fn-an/food-guide-aliment/index-eng.php. Accessed: November 2009.
10. Centers for Disease Control and Prevention: Eat a colorful variety of fruits and vegetables every day: Q&A. http://www.5aday.gov/qa/index.html. Accessed: February 2, 2007.
11. Health Canada: *Eating Well with Canada's Food Guide*. A resource for educators and communicators. http://www.hc-sc.gc.ca/fn-an/alt_formats/hpfb-dgpsa/pdf/pubs/res-educat-eng.pdf. Accessed: July 17, 2007.
12. Health Canada: Policy paper – Nutraceuticals/functional foods and health claims on foods. http://www.hc-sc.gc.ca/fn-an/label-etiquet/claims-reclam/nutra-funct_foods-nutra-fonct_aliment-eng.php. Accessed: December 2009.
13. Public Health Agency of Canada: *Canada's Physical Activity Guide for Healthy Active Living*. http://www.phac-aspc.gc.ca/hp-ps/hl-mvs/pag-gap/index-eng.php. Accessed: July 2010.
14. Kritchevsky SB: A review of scientific research and recommendations regarding eggs. *Journal of the American College of Nutrition* 23(6):596, 2004.
15. Campagna, PD and others: *Physical activity levels and dietary intake of children and youth in the province of Nova Scotia – 2005*. Report for the Nova Scotia Department of Health Promotion and Protection and the Nova Scotia Department of Education. 2006.
16. Dietitians of Canada: EATracker.ca. http://www.dietitians.ca/public/content/eat_well_live_well/english/eatracker. Accessed: January 2010.
17. Health Canada: Food and nutrition: Information Sheet of Nutrition facts. http://www.hc-sc.gc.ca/fn-an/label-etiquet/nutrition/cons/cr_tearsheet-cr_fiche-eng.php. Accessed: January 2010.
18. Canadian Food Inspection Agency: Guide to food labelling and advertising. 2010. http://www.inspection.gc.ca/english/fssa/labeti/guide/toce.shtml. Accessed: June 14, 2010.
19. U.S. Food and Drug Administration, Center for Food Safety and Applied Nutrition: How to understand and use the Nutrition Facts label. Updated November 2004. http://www.cfsan.fda.gov/~dms/foodlab.html#see6. Accessed: December 20, 2006.
20. Health Canada: Food and nutrition: Canada's Food and Drugs Act & Regulations. http://www.hc-sc.gc.ca/fn-an/legislation/acts-lois/act-loi_reg-eng.php. Accessed: January 2010.
21. Canadian Food Inspection Agency. Organic Products. http://www.inspection.gc.ca/english/fssa/orgbio/orgbioe.shtml. Accessed: January 2010.
22. Dimitri C, Greene C: *Recent growth patterns in the U.S. organic foods market*. U.S. Department of Agriculture, Economic Research Service, Market and Trade Economics Division and Resource Economics Division. Agricultural Information Bulletin, No. 777, 2002. http://www.ers.usda.gov/publications/aib777/aib777c.pdf Accessed: November 27, 2007
23. Stokstad E: Organic farms reap many benefits. *Science* 296(5573):1589, 2002.
24. Williams CM: Nutritional quality of organic food: Shades of grey or shades of green? *Proceedings of the Nutrition Society* 61(1):19, 2002.
25. U.S. Department of Agriculture. What's in the food you eat *Search Tool, 2.0*. http://www.ars.usda.gov/Services/docs.htm?docid=7783 Accessed: December 16, 2006.

Chapter 4

1. Saladin KS: *Anatomy & physiology* 4th ed. Boston: McGraw-Hill Publishing Company, 2010.
2. Seeley RR and others: *Essentials of anatomy & physiology* 7th ed. Boston: McGraw-Hill Publishing Company, 2010.
3. Widmaier E and others: *Vander's human physiology* 10th ed. Boston: McGraw-Hill Publishing Company, 2006.
4. Prescott LM and others: *Microbiology* 6th ed. Boston: McGraw-Hill Publishing Company, 2005.
5. Reid G and others: Potential uses of probiotics in clinical practice. *Clinical Microbiology Reviews* 16(4):658, 2003.
6. Adolfsson O and others: Yogurt and gut function. *American Journal of Clinical Nutrition* 80(2):245, 2004.

Chapter 5

1. Tanzi, MG, Gabay MP: Association between honey consumption and infant botulism. *Pharmacotheraphy* 22(11):1479, 2002.
2. Health Canada: Healthy living: Infant botulism. http://www.hc-sc.gc.ca/hl-vs/iyh-vsv/diseases-maladies/botu-eng.php. Accessed: February 2010.
3. Canadian Diabetes Association: Sweeteners. http://www.diabetes.ca/diabetes-and-you/nutrition/sweeteners. Accessed: July 29, 2010.
4. American Dietetic Association: Position of the American Dietetic Association: Use of nutritive and nonnutritive sweeteners. *Journal of the American Dietetic Association* 104(2):255, 2004.
5. Health Canada: Food and nutrition: Aspartame. http://www.hc-sc.gc.ca/fn-an/securit/addit/sweeten-edulcor/aspartame-eng.php. Accessed: June 4, 2010.
6. Soffritti M and others: First experimental demonstration of the multipotential carcinogenic effects of aspartame administered in the feed to Sprague-Dawley rats. *Environmental Health Perspectives* 114(3):379, 2006.
7. Health Canada: Food and nutrition: Health Canada comments on the recent study relating to the safety of aspartame. http://www.hc-sc.gc.ca/fn-an/securit/addit/sweeten-edulcor/aspartame_statement-eng.php. Accessed: June 1, 2010.
8. Health Canada: Food and nutrition: Questions and answers: Saccharin. http://www.hc-sc.gc.ca/fn-an/securit/addit/sweeten-edulcor/saccharin_qa-qr-eng.php. Accessed: June 4, 2010.
9. Health Canada: Food and nutrition: Whole grains—Get the facts. http://www.hc-sc.gc.ca/fn-an/nutrition/whole-grain-entiers-eng.php. Accessed: February 2010.

10. Widmaier E and others: *Vander's human physiology* 10th ed. Boston: McGraw-Hill Publishing Company, 2006.

11. Otten JJ and others, eds.: *Dietary Reference Intakes: The essential guide to nutrient requirements*. Washington, D.C.: National Academies Press, 2006.

12. Health Canada: Food and nutrition: Dietary Reference Intake tables. http://www.hc-sc.gc.ca/fn-an/nutrition/reference/table/index-eng.php. Accessed: June 2, 2010.

13. Howarth NC and others: Dietary fiber and weight regulation. *Nutrition Reviews* 59(5):129, 2001.

14. Seeley RR and others: *Essentials of anatomy & physiology* 7th ed. Boston: McGraw-Hill Publishing Company, 2010.

15. Saladin KS: *Anatomy & physiology 4th ed*. Boston: McGraw-Hill Publishing Company, 2010.

16. Health Canada: Food and nutrition: The Canadian nutrient file. http://www.hc-sc.gc.ca/fn-an/nutrition/fiche-nutri-data/index-eng.php. Accessed: December 2009.

17. Shintani TT and others: The Hawaii diet: Ad libitum carbohydrate, low-fat multicultural diet for the reduction of chronic disease risk factors: obesity, hypertension, hypercholesterolemia, and hyperglycemia. *Hawaiian Medical Journal* 60(3):69, 2001.

18. Rolls BJ: The role of energy density in the overconsumption of fat. *Journal of Nutrition* 130(2S Suppl): 268S, 2000.

19. Shah M, Garg A: High-fat and high-carbohydrate diets and energy balance. *Diabetes Care* 19(10):1142, 1996.

20. Stubbs RJ and others: Carbohydrates, appetite, and feeding behavior in humans. *Journal of Nutrition* 131(10):2775S, 2001.

21. Bray G and others: Consumption of high-fructose corn syrup in beverages may play a role in the epidemic of obesity. *American Journal of Clinical Nutrition* 79(4): 537, 2004.

22. Schulze MB and others: Sugar-sweetened beverages, weight gain, and incidence of type 2 diabetes in young and middle-aged women. *Journal of the American Medical Association* 292(8):927, 2004.

23. CBC News: High fructose corn syrup: just another sugar? http://www.cbc.ca/health/story/2008/11/19/f-fructosecornsyrup.html. Accessed: June 4, 2010.

24. Garriguet D. Beverage consumption of children and teens. *Health Reports*, 19(4):17–22. 2008.

25. U.S. Department of Agriculture, Agricultural Research Service. Nutrient Data Laboratory: *USDA national nutrient database for standard reference, Release 19*. 2006. http://www.nal.usda.gov/fnic/foodcomp/search. Accessed: February 19, 2006.

26. Yanovski S: Sugar and fat: Cravings and aversions. *Journal of Nutrition*, 133 (3):835S, 2003.

27. Canadian Diabetes Association. http://www.diabetes.ca. Accessed: January 2010.

28. Public Health Agency of Canada: *Diabetes policy review—Report of the expert panel*. http://www.phac-aspc.gc.ca/publicat/2009/dprrep-epdrge/cont-sit-eng.php. Accessed: July 29, 2010.

29. Harrison LC, Honeyman MC: Cow's milk and type 1 diabetes: The real debate is about mucosal function. *Diabetes* 48:1501, 1999.

30. Couper JJ: Environmental triggers of type 1 diabetes. *Journal of Pediatric and Child Health* 37(3):218, 2001.

31. Akerblom HK and others: Environmental factors in the etiology of type 1 diabetes. *American Journal of Medical Genetics* 115(1):18, 2002.

32. Wasmuth HE, Kolb H: Cow's milk and immune-mediated diabetes. *Proceedings of the Nutrition Society* 59(4):573, 2000.

33. Brand-Miller JC and others: Glycemic index and obesity. *American Journal of Clinical Nutrition* 76(1):281S, 2002.

34. Ludwig DS: The glycemic index: Physiological mechanisms relating to obesity, diabetes, and cardiovascular disease. *Journal of the American Medical Association* 287(18): 2414, 2002.

35. Mayer-Davis EJ and others: Towards understanding of glycemic index and glycemic load in habitual diet: Associations with measures of glycemia in the Insulin Resistance Atherosclerosis Study. *British Journal of Nutrition* 95(2):397, 2006.

36. American Dietetic Association: *Hot topic: glycemic index*. 2005. http://www.eatright.org/cps/rde/xchg/ada/hs.xsl/nutrition_7908_ENU_HTML.htm. Accessed: February 19, 2005.

37. Finkelstein MM: The prevalence of diabetes among overweight and obese individuals is higher in poorer than in richer neighbourhoods. *Canadian Journal of Diabetes*, 32(3):190–7. 2008. http://www.diabetes.ca/documents/for-professionals/CJD--Sept_2008--Finkelstein,_M.pdf. Accessed: June 4, 2010.

38. Walker S: Prevention of type 2 diabetes. *Canadian Diabetic Care Guide*, http://www.diabetescareguide.com/en/article_vol28.html. Accessed: June 4, 2010.

39. Schulze MB and others: Glycemic index, glycemic load, and dietary fiber intake and incidence of type 2 diabetes in younger and middle-aged women. *American Journal of Clinical Nutrition* 80(2):243, 2004.

40. Sheard NF and others: Dietary carbohydrate (amount and type) in the prevention and management of diabetes: A statement by the American Diabetes Association. *Diabetes Care* 27(9):2266, 2004.

41. EatRight Ontario: The truth about sugar – FAQs. https://www.eatright-ontario.ca/en/ViewDocument.aspx?id=201. Accessed: June 3, 2010.

42. Pipeleers D and others: A view on beta cell transplantation in diabetics. *Annals of New York Academy of Science* 958:69, 2002.

43. Brien SE and Katzmarzyk PT: Physical activity and metabolic syndrome in Canada. *Applied Physiology, Nutrition and Metabolism*, 31(1):40–7, 2006.

44. Grundy SM and others: Diagnosis and management of the metabolic syndrome: An American Heart Association/National Heart, Lung, and Blood Institute scientific statement: Executive summary. *Circulation* 112:e285, 2005.

45. Lichtenstein AH and others: Diet and lifestyle recommendations revision 2006: A scientific statement from the American Heart Association Nutrition Committee. *Circulation* 114(1):82, 2006.

46. Fried SK, Rao SP: Sugars, hypertriglyceridemia, and cardiovascular disease. *American Journal of Clinical Nutrition* 78(4):873S, 2003.

47. *Food in Canada:* Lactose-free products could be better: researchers. http://www.canadianmanufacturing.com/foodincanada/news/dairynews/article.jsp?content=20090911_154859_8956. Accessed: June 21, 2010.

48. National Institute of Diabetes and Digestive and Kidney Diseases: Lactose intolerance. NIH Publication No. 06-2751, 2006. http://digestive.niddk.nih.gov/ddiseases/pubs/lactoseintolerance/index.htm. Accessed: December 28, 2006.

49. Bahna SL: Cow's milk allergy versus cow milk intolerance. *Annals of Allergy, Asthma, and Immunology* 89(6 Suppl 1):56, 2002.

50. ADHD.ca: Recognizing the symptoms. http://www.adhd.ca/portals/adhd/eng/1215452720316.html. Accessed: June 4, 2010.

51. Wolraich ML and others: The effect of sugar on behavior or cognition in children. *Journal of the American Medical Association* 274(20):1617, 1995.

52. Krummel DA and others: Hyperactivity: Is candy causal? *Critical Review of Food Science & Nutrition* 36(1–2):31, 1996.

53. World Health Organization: *Cancer: WHO World Cancer Control Programme*. 2005. http://www.who.int/cancer/en. Accessed: February 6, 2005.

54. U.S. Cancer Statistics Working Group: *United States cancer statistics: 1999–2002, incidence and mortality Web-based report version*. Atlanta (GA): Department of Health and Human Services, Centers for Disease Control and Prevention, and National Cancer Institute, 2005. http://www.cdc.gov/colorectalcancer/statistics/index.htm. Accessed: February 19, 2006.

55. Park Y and others: Dietary fiber intake and risk of colorectal cancer: A pooled analysis of prospective cohort studies. *Journal of the American Medical Association* 294(22):2849, 2005.

56. Health Canada:. Food and nutrition: Executive summary and recommendations for action. http://www.hc-sc.gc.ca/fn-an/nutrition/pol/action_healthy_eating-action_saine_alimentation-01-eng.php. Accessed: November 2009.

57. Roberts SB and others: The influence of dietary composition on energy intake and body weight. *Journal of the American College of Nutrition* 21(2):140S, 2002.

Chapter 6

1. Gurevich-Panigrahi T and others: Obesity: pathophysiology and clinical management. *Current Medicinal Chemistry* 16(4):506–21, 2009.

2. Jequier E: Pathways to obesity. International Journal of Obesity and Related Metabolic Disorders 26(Suppl 2):S12, 2002.

3. Kris-Etherton PM and others: Position of the American Dietetic Association and Dietitians of Canada: dietary fatty acids. *Journal of the American Dietetic Association* 107(9):1599–611, 2007.

4. Lewis CJ, Yetley EA: Health claims and observational human data: Relation between dietary fat and cancer. *American Journal of Nutrition* 69(Suppl):1357S, 1999.

5. Kushi L, Giovannucci E: Dietary fat and cancer. American Journal of Medicine 113 (Suppl 9B):63S, 2002.

6. Merchant AT and others: Interrelation of saturated fat, trans fat, alcohol intake, and subclinical atherosclerosis. *American Journal of Clinical Nutrition* 87(1):168–74, 2008.

7. Otten JJ and others (eds.): *Dietary Reference Intakes: The essential guide to nutrient requirements*. Washington, D.C.: National Academies Press, 2006.

8. Health Canada: Food and nutrition: Do Canadian adults meet their nutrient requirements through food intake alone? http://www.hc-sc.gc.ca/fn-an/surveill/nutrition/commun/art-nutr-adult-eng.php. Accessed: June 4, 2010.

9. Lichtenstein AH: Dietary fat, carbohydrate, and protein: Effects on plasma lipoprotein patterns. *Journal of Lipid Research* 47(8):1661, 2006.

10. Food and Nutrition Board: *Dietary Reference Intakes for energy, carbohydrate, fiber, fat, fatty acids, cholesterol, protein, and amino acids (macronutrients)*. Institute of Medicine of the National Academies, Washington, DC: National Academies Press, 2005.

11. Forman D, Bulwer BE: Cardiovascular disease: Optimal approaches to risk factor modification of diet and lifestyle. *Current Treatment Options in Cardiovascular Medicine* 8(1):47, 2006.

12. Health Canada: Food and nutrition: Frequently asked questions about nutrition labeling. http://www.hc-sc.gc.ca/fn-an/label-etiquet/nutrition/educat/te_quest-eng.php. Accessed: June 4, 2010.

13. Nestel PJ: Adulthood-prevention: Cardiovascular disease. *Medical Journal of Australia* 176(11 Suppl): S118, 2002.

14. Health Canada: Healthy living: Trans fat: It's your health. http://www.hc-sc.gc.ca/hl-vs/iyh-vsv/food-aliment/trans-eng.php#ma. Accessed: June 4, 2010.

15. Widmaier E and others: *Vander's human physiology* 10th ed. Boston: McGraw-Hill Publishing Company, 2006.

16. Stephen AM and others: Intake of carbohydrate and its components – international comparisons, trends over time, and the effects of low-fat diets. *American Journal of Clinical Nutrition*, 62:851S–67S, 1995.

17. Gray-Donald K and others: Food habits of Canadians: reduction in fat intake over a generation. *Canadian Journal of Public Health* 91:381–5, 2000.

18. Health Canada: Healthy living: Trans fat: It's your health. http://www.hc-sc.gc.ca/hl-vs/iyh-vsv/food-aliment/trans-eng.php. Accessed: June 4, 2010.

19. Health Canada: Summary of dietary recommendations for the Canadian public. 2009. http://www.hc-sc.gc.ca/fn-an/nutrition/pol/action_healthy_eating-action_saine_alimentation-table1-eng.php. Accessed: February 2009.

20. Institute of Medicine, Food and Nutrition Board. Dietary Reference Intakes for Energy, Carbohydrate, Fibre, Fat, Fatty Acids, Cholesterol, Protein, and Amino Acids (Macronutrients). Washington, DC: National Academies Press. 2002.

21. Health Canada: Articles on Canadians' nutrient intakes from food. http://www.hc-sc.gc.ca/fn-an/surveill/nutrition/commun/art-nutr-table-eng.php. Accessed: June 4, 2010.

22. Health Canada. *Eating Well with Canada's Food Guide*. 2007b.http://www.hc-sc.gc.ca/fn-an/alt_formats/hpfb-dgpsa/pdf/food-guide-aliment/print_eatwell_bienmang-eng.pdf. Accessed: February 2009.

23. Health Canada: Healthy living: Trans fat: It's your health. http://www.hc-sc.gc.ca/hl-vs/iyh-vsv/food-aliment/trans-eng.php. Accessed: June 4, 2010.

24. Heart and Stroke Foundation of Canada: Statistics. http://www.heartandstroke.ns.ca/site/c.inKMIPNlEiG/b.3668063/k.345C/Statistics.htm. Accessed: February 2009.

25. Statistics Canada: Causes of death 2004. Released 2006.

26. Public Health Agency of Canada: Economic burden of illness in Canada, 1998. Released 2002. http://www.phac-aspc.gc.ca/publicat/ebic-femc98/index-eng.php. Accessed: June 4, 2010.

27. Heart and Stroke Foundation of Canada: Prevention of risk factors. http://www.heartandstroke.ns.ca/site/c.inKMIPNlEiG/b.3668005/k.7752/Prevention_of_Risk_Factors.htm. Accessed: February 2009.

28. Statistics Canada: Mortality, summary list of causes 2005. http://www.statcan.gc.ca/pub/84f0209x/84f0209x2005000-eng.htm. Accessed: June 4, 2010.

29. Centers for Disease Control and Prevention: *National diabetes fact sheet: General information and national estimates on diabetes in the United States, 2005*. Atlanta, GA: U.S. Department of Health and Human Services, 2005. http://www.cdc.gov/diabetes/pubs/pdf/ndfs_2005.pdf.

30. American Heart Association: *Risk factors and coronary heart disease: AHA scientific position*. 2006. http://www.americanheart.org/presenter.jhtml?identifier=4726.

31. U.S. Department of Health and Human Services, National Cancer Institute. Changes in Cigarette-Related Disease Risks and Their Implication for Prevention and Control. National Institutes of Health. N.I.H. Publication No. 97-4213. Washington, D.C. February 1997.
32. Heart and Stroke Foundation of Canada: *Heart disease and stroke in Canada*. Ottawa, 1997.
33. Heart and Stroke Foundation of Canada: Living with cholesterol: Cholesterol and healthy living. 2008.
34. Blake GJ, Ridker PM: Inflammatory bio-markers and cardiovascular risk prediction. *Journal of Internal Medicine* 252(4):283, 2002.
35. Ridker PM: High-sensitivity C-reactive protein and cardiovascular risk: Rationale for screening and primary prevention. *American Journal of Cardiology* 92(4B):17K, 2003.
36. Sesso HD and others: C-reactive protein and the risk of developing hypertension. *Journal of the American Medical Association* 290(22):2945, 2003.
37. Dietschy JM: Dietary fatty acids and the regulation of plasma low density lipoprotein cholesterol concentrations. *Journal of Nutrition* 128(2Suppl):444S, 1998.
38. Dietary fat makes a comeback. *Tufts University Health & Nutrition Letter* 19(5):4, 2001.
39. Heart and Stroke Foundation of Canada: Trans fatty acids ('trans fat') and heart disease and stroke._http://www.heartandstroke.com/site/c.ikIQLcMWJtE/b.3799313/k.C112/Position_Statements__Trans_fatty_acids_position_statement.htm. Accessed: June 4, 2010.
40. AHRQ Evidence Reports Confirm that Fish Oil Helps Fight Heart Disease. Press Release, April 22, 2004. Agency for Healthcare Research and Quality, Rockville, MD. http://www.ahrq.gov/news/press/pr2004/omega3pr.htm. Accessed: November 28, 2007.
41. U.S. Department of Health and Human Services and U.S. Environmental Protection Agency: *What you need to know about mercury in fish and shellfish*. EPA-823-R-04–005, 2004. http://www.cfsan.fda.gov/~dms/admehg3.html. Accessed: November 28, 2007.
42. Health Canada: Health Canada's revised assessment of mercury in fish enhances protection while reflecting advice in *Canada's Food Guide*. http://www.hc-sc.gc.ca/ahc-asc/media/advisories-avis/_2007/2007_31-eng.php. Accessed: June 4, 2010.
43. Lichtenstein AH and others: Diet and Lifestyle recommendations Revision 2006: A Scientific statement from the American Heart Association Nutrition Committee, Cicculation 114(1):82, 2006.
44. Ganji V, Kafai MR: Demographic, health, lifestyle, and blood vitamin determinants of serum total homocysteine concentrations in the third National Health and Nutrition Examination Survey, 1988–1994. *American Journal of Clinical Nutrition* 77(4):826, 2003.
45. Heart and Stroke Foundation of Canada: Foundation study: How do diet and genes affect each other in heart disease and stroke? http://www.heartandstroke.com/site/apps/nlnet/content2.aspx?c=ikIQLcMWJtE&b=3485821&ct=6333943. Accessed: June 4, 2010.
46. Wald DS and others: Homocysteine and cardiovascular disease: Evidence on causality from a meta-analysis. *British Medical Journal* 325(7374):1202, 2002.
47. Rimm EB and others: Folate and vitamin B6 from diet and supplements in relation to risk of coronary heart disease among women. *Journal of the American Medical Association* 279(5):359, 1998.
48 Gardner, CD and others: Effect of raw garlic vs. commercial garlic supplements of plasma lipid concentrations in adults with moderate hypercholesterolemia. Archives of Internal Medicine 167 (4):346, 2007.
49. Wang X and others: Positional identification of TNFSN4, encoding OX ligand, as a gene that influences atherosclerosis susceptibility. *Nature Genetics Advance Online Publication*. March 6, 2005.
50. Hu FB and others: A prospective study of egg consumption and risk of cardiovascular disease in men and women. *Journal of the American Medical Association* 281(15):1387, 1999.
51. Rosenbloom, C: Eggs 101. Heart and Stroke Foundation of Canada posted October 2009. http://www.heartandstroke.com/site/apps/nlnet/content2.aspx?c=ikIQLcMWJtE&b=4869055&ct=7511425. Accessed: June 4, 2010.
52. Raloff J: Cholesterol medicine for eggs? *Science News Online*, 164(2), 2003. http://www.sciencenews.org/articles/20030712/food.asp. Accessed: November 28, 2007.
53. Weeks, C: Butter v. margarine - which is better? *The Globe and Mail*, March 25, 2010. http://www.theglobeandmail.com/life/health/butter-v-margarine---which-is-better/article1511588. Accessed: June 4, 2010.
54. U.S. Food and Drug Administration (FDA) Center for Food Safety and Applied Nutrition, Office of Food Labeling: *Questions and Answers about Trans Fat Nutrition Labeling* 2006. http://www.cfsan.fda.gov/~dms/qatrans2.html. Accessed: November 28, 2007.
55. Schaefer EJ: Lipoproteins, nutrition, and heart disease. *American Journal of Clinical Nutrition* 75(2):191, 2002.
56. Denke MA and others: Individual cholesterol variation in response to a margarine- or butter-based diet: A study of families. *Journal of the American Medical Association* 284(21):2740, 2000.
57. Food Safety Network: Fat Substitutes. http://www.foodsafetynetwork.ca/aspx/public/publication_detail_global.aspx?languageid=1&contenttypeid=5&id=50. Accessed: June 4, 2010.
58. Miller DL and others: Effect of fat-free potato chips with and without nutrition labels on fat and energy intakes. *American Journal of Clinical Nutrition* 68(2):282, 1998.
59. Bray GA: A 9-month randomized clinical trial comparing fat-substituted and fat-reduced diets in healthy obese men: The Ole Study. *American Journal of Clinical Nutrition* 76(5):928, 2002.

Chapter 7

1. Saladin KS: *Anatomy & physiology 4th ed*. Boston: McGraw-Hill Publishing Company, 2010.
2. Reeds PJ: Dispensable and indispensable amino acids for humans. *Journal of Nutrition* 130:1835S, 2000.
3. Food and Nutrition Board: Dietary Reference Intakes for energy, carbohydrate, fiber, fat, fatty acids, cholesterol, protein, and amino acids (macronutrients). Institute of Medicine of the National Academies, Washington, DC: National Academies Press, 2005.
4. Young VR: Soy protein in relation to human protein and amino acids nutrition. *Journal of the American Dietetic Association* 91(7):828, 1991.
5. Harmon D: 5 things you need to know about soy protein. Food Network Canada. http://www.foodnetwork.ca/guides/silk-soy/articles/Things+Need+Know+About+Protein/2774179/story.html. Accessed: June 7, 2010.
6. Messina MJ, Loprinzi CL: Soy for breast cancer survivors: A critical review of the literature. *Journal of Nutrition* 131:2095S, 2001.
7. Canadian Cancer Society: Food issues: Soy. http://www.cancer.ca/canada-wide/prevention/eat%20well/make%20healthy%20eating%20choices/food%20issues.aspx?sc_lang=en#Soy. Accessed: June 7, 2010.

8. Tomé D, Bos C: Dietary protein and nitrogen utilization. *Journal of Nutrition* 130(7):1868S, 2000.
9. Tipton KD, Wolfe RR: Exercise, protein metabolism, and muscle growth. *International Journal of Sport Nutrition and Exercise Metabolism* 11(1):109, 2000.
10. Evans WJ: Protein nutrition and resistance exercise. *Canadian Journal of Applied Physiology* 26(Suppl):S141, 2001.
11. Health Canada: Dietary Reference Intakes: Reference values for macronutrients. http://www.hc-sc.gc.ca/fn-an/nutrition/reference/table/ref_macronutr_tbl-eng.php. Accessed: June 7, 2010.
12. Health Canada: Sulphites - One of the nine most common food products causing severe adverse reactions. http://www.hc-sc.gc.ca/fn-an/securit/allerg/fa-aa/allergen_sulphites-sulfites-eng.php. Accessed: June 4, 2010.
13. Niggemann B, Gruber C: Unproven diagnostic procedures in IgE-mediated allergic diseases. *Allergy* 59(8):806, 2004.
14. Health Canada: Canadian Community Health Survey, Cycle 2.2, Nutrition (2004): Nutrient intakes from foods. http://www.hc-sc.gc.ca/fn-an/surveill/nutrition/commun/cchs_guide_escc-eng.php. 2006. Accessed: August 10, 2010.
15. Health Canada: *Eating well with Canada's food guide*. http://www.hc-sc.gc.ca/fn-an/alt_formats/hpfb-dgpsa/pdf/food-guide-aliment/print_eatwell_bienmang-eng.pdf. 2007. Accessed: February 2009.
16. Garriguet, D: Overview of Canadian eating habits. Statistics Canada Catalogue no. 82-620-MIE — No. 2. 2004.
17. Position of the American Dietetic Association and Dietitians of Canada: Vegetarian Diets. *Canadian Journal of Dietetic Practice and Research* 64(2): Summer 2003.
18. American Dietetic Association: Position of the American Dietetic Association and Dietitians of Canada: Vegetarian diets. *Journal of the American Dietetic Association* 103(6):748, 2003.
19. Nieman DC: Physical fitness and vegetarian diets: Is there a relation? *American Journal of Clinical Nutrition* 70(Suppl):570S, 1999.
20. Key TJ and others: Health effects of vegetarian and vegan diets. *The Proceedings of the Nutrition Society* 65(1):35, 2006.
21. Haddad EH and others: Dietary intake and biochemical, hematologic, and immune status in vegans compared to nonvegetarians. *American Journal of Clinical Nutrition* 70(3 Suppl):586S, 1999.
22. Anon: Neurologic impairment in children associated with maternal dietary deficiency of cobalamin—Georgia, 2001. *Morbidity and Mortality Weekly Report* 52(4):61, 2003.
23. Schaefer EJ: Lipoproteins, nutrition, and heart disease. *American Journal of Clinical Nutrition* 75(2):191, 2002.
24. Sacks FM, Katan M: Randomized clinical trials on the effects of dietary fat and carbohydrate on plasma lipoproteins and cardiovascular disease. *American Journal of Medicine* 113(Suppl 9B):13S, 2002.
25. Kelemen LE and others: Associations of dietary protein with disease and mortality in a prospective study of postmenopausal women. *American Journal of Epidemiology* 161(3):239, 2005.
26. Norat T and others: Meat, fish, and colorectal cancer risk: The European Prospective Investigation into Cancer and Nutrition. *Journal of the National Cancer Institute* 97(12):906, 2005.
27. Gonzalez CA: Nutrition and cancer: The current epidemiological evidence. *British Journal of Nutrition* 96(Suppl 1):S42, 2006.
28. Nöthlings U and others: Meat and fat intake as risk factors for pancreatic cancer: The Multiethnic Cohort Study. *Journal of the National Cancer Institute* 97(19):1458, 2005.
29. Larsson SC and others: Processed meat consumption, dietary nitrosamines and stomach cancer risk in a cohort of Swedish women. *International Journal of Cancer* 119(4):915, 2006.
30. Cho E and others: Red meat intake and risk of breast cancer among premenopausal women. *Archives of Internal Medicine* 166(20):2253, 2006.
31. Kerstetter JE and others: Low-protein intake: The impact on calcium and bone homeostasis in humans. *Journal of Nutrition* 133(3):855S, 2003.
32. Sellmeyer DE and others: A high ratio of dietary animal to vegetable protein increases rate of bone loss and the risk of fracture in postmenopausal women. *American Journal of Clinical Nutrition* 73:118, 2001.
33. Weigle DS and others: A high-protein diet induces sustained reductions in appetite, ad libitum caloric intake, and body weight despite compensatory changes in diurnal plasma leptin and ghrelin concentrations. *American Journal of Clinical Nutrition* 82(1):41, 2005.
34. Dansinger ML and others: Comparison of the Atkins, Ornish, Weight Watchers, and Zone diets for weight loss and heart disease risk reduction. *Journal of the American Medical Association* 293(1):43, 2005.
35. Paddon-Jones D and others: Protein, weight management, and satiety. *American Journal of Clinical Nutrition* 87(5):1558S–1561S, 2008.
36. World Health Organization: *Alleviating protein-energy malnutrition*. http://www.who.int/nut/pem.htm. 2003.
37. Nutrition, Division of Health Protection and Promotion, World Health Organization—Regional Office for the Eastern Mediterranean. *Protein energy malnutrition*. http://www.emro.who.int/nutrition/PDF/Protein_Malnutrition.pdf Accessed: March 6, 2007.
38. World Health Organization: *Management of the child with a serious infection or severe malnutrition*. Department of Child and Adolescent Health and Development. Geneva, Switzerland: WHO, 2000. http://www.who.int/child-adolescent-health/publications/referral_care/chap7/chap71.htm.

Chapter 8

1. Bartholomew M: "James Lind's Treatise of the Scurvy (1753)." *Postgraduate Medicine* 78:695, 2002.
2. Health Canada: *Healthy living: It's your health. The safety of vitamin E supplements*. http://www.hc-sc.gc.ca/hl-vs/iyh-vsv/food-aliment/vitam-eng.php. Accessed: March 2010.
3. Food and Nutrition Board: Dietary Reference Intakes for vitamin C, vitamin E, selenium, and carotenoids. Washington, DC: National Academy Press, 2000.
4. Vandamme EJ: Production of vitamins, coenzymes and related biochemicals by biotechnological processes. *Journal of Chemical Technology & Biotechnology* 53(4):313, 1992.
5. Guo X and others: Use of vitamin and mineral supplements among Canadian adults. *Canadian Journal of Public Health* 100(5):357–60, 2009.
6. Hernandez A: Personal communication. Kelloggs' Consumer Affairs Department, 2007.
7. Health Canada: *Food fortification proposed policy*. http://www.hc-sc.gc.ca/fn-an/alt_formats/hpfb-dgpsa/pdf/nutrition/faqs-eng.pdf. Accessed: July 27, 2010.
8. Cahill L and others: Vitamin C deficiency in a population of young Canadian adults. *American Journal of Epidemiology* 170(4):464–71, 2009.
9. U.S. National Library of Medicine and the National Institutes of Health: Thiamin (thiamine), vitamin B1. *Medline Plus*. 2006. http://www.nlm.nih.gov/medlineplus/druginfo/natural/patient-thiamin.html.

10. Food and Drug Administration, Center for Devices and Radiological Health, CDRH Consumer Information: *Microwave oven radiation.* Updated July 2006. http://www.fda.gov/cdrh/consumer/microwave.html#5.
11. Health Canada: *Microwave ovens and food safety.*http://www.hc-sc.gc.ca/hl-vs/alt_formats/pacrb-dgapcr/pdf/iyh-vsv/prod/micro-f-a-eng.pdf. Accessed: July 26, 2010.
12. Center for Food Safety and Applied Nutrition: *How long can shelf-stable foods be safely stored on the shelf?* Updated 2001. http://www.cfsan.fda.gov/~dms/a2z-s.html#shelfstable.
13. Stephensen CB: Vitamin A, infection, and immune function. *Annual Review of Nutrition* 21:167, 2001.
14. Office of Dietary Supplements: *Dietary supplement fact sheet: Vitamin A and carotenoids.* http://ods.od.nih.gov/factsheets/vitamina.asp. Accessed: February 2, 2007.
15. Fielding JM and others: Increases in plasma lycopene concentration after consumption of tomatoes cooked with olive oil. *Asia Pacific Journal of Clinical Nutrition* 14:131, 2005.
16. Otten JJ and others (eds.): Institute of Medicine: *Dietary Reference Intakes: The essential guide to nutrient requirements.* Washington, DC: National Academies Press, 2006.
17. Health Canada: *Dietary Reference Intakes: Reference values for vitamins.* http://www.hc-sc.gc.ca/fn-an/nutrition/reference/table/ref_vitam_tbl-eng.php. Accessed: July 26, 2010.
18. Health Canada: *Canadian Community Health Survey Cycle 2.2, Nutrition Focus.* http://www.hc-sc.gc.ca/fn-an/surveill/nutrition/commun/cchs_focus-volet_escc-eng.php#p1. Accessed: July 26, 2010.
19. World Health Organization: The world health report 2002: Reducing risks, promoting healthy life, 2002. http://www.who.int/whr/2002/en/.
20. Zile MH: Function of vitamin A in vertebrate embryonic development. *Journal of Nutrition* 131:705, 2001.
21. Sale TA, Stratman E: Carotenemia associated with green bean ingestion. *Pediatric Dermatology* 21(6):657, 2004.
22. Holick MF: Sunlight and vitamin D for bone health and prevention of autoimmune diseases, cancers, and cardiovascular disease. *American Journal of Clinical Nutrition* 80(6Suppl):1678S, 2004.
23. Scanlon K (ed.): Vitamin D Expert Panel Meeting: *Final report,* 2001. http://www.cdc.gov/nccdphp/dnpa/nutrition/pdf/Vitamin_D_Expert_Panel_Meeting.pdf. Accessed: February 28, 2006.
24. Deluca HF: Overview of general physiologic features and functions of vitamin D. *American Journal of Clinical Nutrition* 80:1689S, 2004.
25. Office of Dietary Supplements, National Institutes of Health: *Dietary supplement fact sheet: vitamin D.* Updated 2005. http://ods.od.nih.gov/factsheets/vitamind.asp. Accessed: March 3, 2006.
26. Canadian Cancer Society of Canada: *Vitamin D.* http://www.cancer.ca/canada-wide/prevention/vitamin%20d.aspx?sc_lang=en. Accessed: July 26, 2010.
27. Cantorna MT and others: Vitamin D status, 1, 25-dihydroxyvitamin D_3, and the immune system. *American Journal of Clinical Nutrition* 80:1717S, 2004.
28. Dietitians of Canada: *Vitamin D—Many Canadians may not be getting enough.* http://www.dietitians.ca/news/media.asp?fn=view&id=6542&idstring=. Accessed: July 27, 2010.
29. Health Canada: *Skin cancer.* http://www.hc-sc.gc.ca/hl-vs/sun-sol/expos/skin-cancer-peau-eng.php. Accessed: July 27, 2010.
30. Canadian Cancer Society: *Causes of melanoma.* http://www.cancer.ca/canada-wide/about%20cancer/types%20of%20cancer/causes%20of%20melanoma.aspx. Accessed: July 27, 2010.
31. Pettifor JM: Nutritional rickets: Deficiency of vitamin D, calcium, or both? *American Journal of Clinical Nutrition* 80:725S, 2004.
32. Hanley DA, Davison KS: Vitamin D insufficiency in North America. *Journal of Nutrition* 135:332, 2005.
33. Canadian Paediatric Society: *Pregnancy and babies – Vitamin D.* http://www.caringforkids.cps.ca/pregnancy&babies/vitamind.htm. Accessed: February 2010.
34. Health Canada: *Vitamin D for people over 50: Background.* http://www.hc-sc.gc.ca/fn-an/food-guide-aliment/context/evid-fond/vita_d-eng.php. Accessed: July 27, 2010.
35. Ebeling PR: Megadose therapy for vitamin D deficiency. *Medical Journal of Australia* 183:4, 2005.
36. Vieth R, Fraser D: Vitamin D insufficiency: no recommended dietary allowance exists for this nutrient. *Canadian Medical Association Journal* 166(12):1517–24, 2002.
37. Nesby-O'dell S and others: Hypovitaminosis D prevalence and determinants among African-American and white women of reproductive age: Third National Health and Nutrition Examination Survey, 1988–1994. *American Journal of Clinical Nutrition* 76:187, 2002.
38. Bischoff-Ferrari HA and others: Fracture prevention with vitamin D supplementation. A meta-analysis of randomized controlled trials. *Journal of the American Medical Association* 293:2257, 2006.
39. Food and Nutrition Board: Dietary Reference Intakes for calcium, phosphorus, magnesium, vitamin D, and fluoride. Washington, DC: National Academy Press, 1997.
40. Health Canada: *The safety of vitamin E supplements.* http://www.hc-sc.gc.ca/hl-vs/alt_formats/pacrb-dgapcr/pdf/iyh-vsv/food-aliment/vitam-eng.pdf. Accessed: July 27, 2010.
41. Bruno RS and others: Faster vitamin E disappearance in smokers is normalized by vitamin C supplementation. *Free Radical and Biological Medicine* 40:689, 2006.
42. Food and Nutrition Board: *Dietary Reference Intakes for thiamin, riboflavin, niacin, vitamin B-6, folate, vitamin B-12, pantothenic acid, biotin, and choline.* Washington, DC: National Academy Press, 1998.
43. Health Canada: *Riboflavin.* http://www.hc-sc.gc.ca/dhp-mps/alt_formats/hpfb-dgpsa/pdf/prodnatur/mono_riboflavin-eng.pdf. Accessed: July 27, 2010.
44. Eat Right Ontario: *Facts about folate.* http://eatrightontario.ca/en/ViewDocument.aspx?id=109&Topic=7&Cat=372. Accessed: July 27, 2010.
45. Clarke R and others: Vitamin B-12 and folate deficiency in later life. *Age and Ageing* 33:34, 2004.
46. Health Canada: *Prenatal nutrition guidelines for health professionals: Folate.* http://www.hc-sc.gc.ca/fn-an/alt_formats/hpfb-dgpsa/pdf/pubs/folate-eng.pdf. Accessed: July 27, 2010.
47. Health Canada: *Nutrients of special concern for a healthy pregnancy.* 2008. http://www.hc-sc.gc.ca/fn-an/consultation/init/prenatal/folate-cons-eng.php. Accessed: March 2010.
48. Are you getting enough of this vitamin? *Harvard Health Letter* 30:1, 2005
49. Health Link BC: *Healthy eating and healthy aging for adults.* http://www.healthlinkbc.ca/healthfiles/hfile68j.stm. Accessed: July 27, 2010.
50. Andres E and others: Food-cobalamin malabsorption in elderly patients: Clinical manifestations and treatments. *American Journal of Medicine* 118:1154, 2005.
51. Eussen SJ and others: Oral cyanocobalamin supplementation in older people with vitamin B-12 deficiency: A dose-finding trial. *Archives of Internal Medicine* 165:1167, 2005.

52. Codazzi D and others: Coma and respiratory failure in a child with severe vitamin B(12) deficiency. *Pediatric Critical Care Medicine* 6:483, 2005.
53. Food and Nutrition Board: *Dietary Reference Intakes for vitamin A, vitamin K, arsenic, boron, chromium, copper, iodine, iron, manganese, molybdenum, nickel, silicon, vanadium, and zinc.* Washington, DC: National Academy Press, 2000.
54. Naidu KA: Vitamin C in human health and disease is still a mystery? An overview. *Nutrition Journal* 2:7, 2003.
55. Health Canada: *Eating well with Canada's food guide.* 2007b. http://www.hc-sc.gc.ca/fn-an/alt_formats/hpfb-dgpsa/pdf/food-guide-aliment/print_eatwell_bienmang-eng.pdf. Accessed: February 2009.
56. Taylor EN and others: Dietary factors and the risk of incident kidney stones in men: New insights after 14 years of follow-up. *Journal of the American Society of Nephrology* 15:3225, 2004.

Chapter 9

1. Centers for Disease Control and Prevention: Hyperthermia and dehydration-related deaths associated with intentional rapid weight loss in three collegiate wrestlers—North Carolina, Wisconsin, and Michigan, November–December 1997. *Morbidity and Mortality Weekly Report* 47:105, 1998. http://www.cdc.gov/mmwr/preview/mmwrhtml/00051388.htm.
2. National Collegiate Athletic Association: *Wrestling rules and interpretations.* 2007. http://www.ncaa.org/library/rules/2007/2007_wrestling_rules.pdf. Accessed: March 28, 2007.
3. Saladin KS: *Anatomy & physiology* 4th ed. Boston: McGraw-Hill Publishing Company, 2010.
4. Food and Nutrition Board, Institute of Medicine: *Dietary Reference Intakes for water, potassium, sodium, chloride, and sulfate.* Washington, DC: National Academy Press, 2004.
5. Seeley RR and others: *Essentials of anatomy & physiology* 7th ed. Boston: McGraw-Hill Publishing Company, 2010.
6. The Kidney Foundation of Canada: How do kidneys work? www.kidney.ca. Accessed: June 13, 2007.
7. Valtin H: "Drink at least eight glasses of water a day." Really? Is there scientific evidence for "8 × 8"? *American Journal of Physiological Regulation and Integrative Comparative Physiology* 283:R993, 2002.
8. Health Canada: Dietary reference intakes, reference values for macronutrients. http://www.hc-sc.gc.ca/fn-an/nutrition/reference/table/ref_macronutr_tbl-eng.php. Accessed: June 14, 2010.
9. Widmaier E and others: *Vander's human physiology* 10th ed. Boston: McGraw-Hill Publishing Company, 2006.
10. Wiese JG and others: The alcohol hangover. *Annals of Internal Medicine* 132:897, 2000.
11. Kenney WL, Chiu P: Influence of age on thirst and fluid intake. *Medicine and Science in Sports and Exercise* 33:1524, 2001.
12. Volkert D and others: Fluid intake of community-living, independent elderly in Germany—A nationwide, representative study. *Journal of Nutrition, Health, and Aging* 9:305, 2005.
13. Bossingham MJ and others: Water balance, hydration status, and fat-free mass hydration in younger and older adults. *American Journal of Clinical Nutrition* 81:1342, 2005.
14. Yeates KE and others: Salt and water: A simple approach to hyponatremia. *Canadian Medical Association Journal* 170:365, 2004.
15. Hartung TK: Hyponatraemic states following 3,4-methylenedioxymethamphetamine (MDMA, "ecstasy") ingestion. *Quarterly Journal of Medicine* 95:431, 2002.
16. Health Canada: Health concerns: Ecstasy. http://www.hc-sc.gc.ca/hc-ps/drugs-drogues/learn-renseigne/ecstasy-eng.php. Accessed: June 14, 2010.
17. Guéguen L, Pointillart A: The bioavailability of dietary calcium. *Journal of the American College of Nutrition* 19:119S, 2000.
18. Food and Nutrition Board, Institute of Medicine: *Dietary Reference Intakes for calcium, phosphorus, magnesium, vitamin D, and fluoride.* Washington, DC: National Academy Press, 1997.
19. U.S. Department of Health and Human Services: *Bone health and osteoporosis: A report of the Surgeon General.* Rockville, MD: U.S. Department of Health and Human Services, Office of the Surgeon General, 2004. http://www.surgeongeneral.gov/library/bonehealth/content.html.
20. Montgomery H and others: Finding whole grains and calcium rich food sources on supermarket shelves. *The Forum for Family and Consumer Issues* 9: SSN 1540 5273, 2004. http://www.ces.ncsu.edu/depts/fcs/pub/9_2/grains.html. Accessed: May 2, 2006.
21. Health Canada: Dietary reference intakes, reference values for macronutrients. http://www.hc-sc.gc.ca/fn-an/nutrition/reference/table/ref_elements_tbl-eng.php. Accessed: June 14, 2010.
22. Office of Dietary Supplements, National Institutes of Health: *Calcium*, Updated 2005. http://ods.od.nih.gov/factsheets/calcium.asp. Accessed: June 13, 2006.
23. Osteoporosis Canada: What is osteoporosis? http://www.osteoporosis.ca/index.php/ci_id/5526/la_id/1.htm. Accessed: June 14, 2010.
24. Roche JJW and others: Effects of comorbidities and postoperative complication on mortality after hip fracture in elderly people: Prospective observational cohort study. British Medical Journal 331:1374, 205, doi:10.1136/bmj.38643.663843.55.
25. Raisz LG: Pathogenesis of osteoporosis: Concepts, conflicts, and prospects. *Journal of Clinical Investigation* 115:3318, 2005.
26. Osteoporosis Canada: What is osteoporosis? http://www.osteoporosis.ca/index.php/ci_id/5526/la_id/1.htm. Accessed: June 15, 2010.
27. Canadian Fitness and Lifestyle Research Institute: Preventing osteoporosis. ISSN 1205-7029 http://www.cflri.ca/pdf/e/pip21.pdf. Accessed: June 16, 2010.
28. Dieticians of Canada: Eating guidelines for osteoporosis, http://www.onpen.ca/OPEN/ViewPDF.aspx?Portal=WqWaJw%3D%3D&id=JMbrWA0%3D. Accessed: June 16, 2010.
29. Warburton DER and others: Health benefits of physical activity: The evidence. *Canadian Medical Journal* 174:801, 2006.
30. Health Canada: Seniors and aging: Osteoporosis: It's your health. http://www.hc-sc.gc.ca/hl-vs/iyh-vsv/diseases-maladies/seniors-aines-ost-eng.php. Accessed: March, 2010.
31. Jackson RD and others: Calcium plus vitamin D supplementation and the risk of fractures. *New England Journal of Medicine* 354:669, 2006.
32. Carroll MF, Schade DS: Practical approaches to hypercalcemia. *American Family Physician* 67:1959, 2003.
33. Garriguet, D: Statistics Canada, Health Reports: Sodium consumption at all ages. http://www.statcan.gc.ca/pub/82-003-x/2006004/article/9608-eng.htm. Catalogue no. 82-003-XWE. volume 18, number 2. Accessed: June 16, 2010.
34. Health Canada: Food and nutrition, the issue of sodium. http://www.hc-sc.gc.ca/fn-an/nutrition/sodium/issue-question-sodium-eng.php. Accessed: June 18, 2010.

35. Health Canada: It's your health, sodium. http://www.hc-sc.gc.ca/hl-vs/iyh-vsv/food-aliment/sodium-eng.php. Accessed: June 18, 2010.

36. Heart and Stroke Foundation of Canada: http://www.heartandstroke.ns.ca/site/c.inKMIPNlEiG/b.3667919/k.F8ED/Heart_Disease_Stroke_and_Healthy_Living.htm. Accessed: March, 2010.

37. Heart and Stroke Foundation of Canada: Statistics. http://www.heartandstroke.ns.ca/site/c.inKMIPNlEiG/b.3668063/k.345C/Statistics.htm. Accessed: March 2010.

38. Jago R and others: Prevalence of abnormal lipid and blood pressure values among an ethnically diverse population of eighth-grade adolescents and screening implications. *Pediatrics* 117:2065, 2006.

39. Godwin, M. Prehypertension and hypertension in a primary care practice. *Canadian Family Physician* 54(10):1418-1423. 2008.

40. Appel, L.J., and others: Dietary approaches to prevent and treat hypertension: A Scientific statement from the American Heart Association. Hypertension 47:296, 2006.

41. Khaw K-T and others: Blood pressure and urinary sodium in men and women: The Norfolk Cohort of the European Prospective Investigation into Cancer (EPIC-Norfolk). *American Journal of Clinical Nutrition* 80:1397, 2004.

42. Heart and Stroke Foundation of Canada: http://www.heartandstroke.ns.ca/site/c.inKMIPNlEiG/b.3668075/k.D051/Heart_Disease__High_blood_pressure_hypertension.htm. Accessed: March 2010.

43. Doorenbos CJ, Vermeij CG: Danger of salt substitutes that contain potassium in patients with renal failure. *British Medical Journal* 325:35, 2003.

44. Statistics Canada: Canadian Community Health Survey, Cycle 2.2, Nutrition (2004). 2009.

45. Office of Dietary Supplements, National Institutes of Health: *Magnesium*. Updated 2005. http://dietary-supplements.info.nih.gov/factsheets/magnesium.asp.

46. Health Canada: Magnesium. http://www.hc-sc.gc.ca/ewh-semt/pubs/water-eau/magnesium/index-eng.php. Accessed: July 19, 2010.

47. Food and Nutrition Board: *Dietary Reference Intakes for vitamin A, vitamin K, arsenic, boron, chromium, copper, iodine, iron, manganese, molybdenum, nickel, silicon, vanadium, and zinc*. Washington, DC: National Academy Press, 2000.

48. National Institute of Nutrition: Iron for health –for all ages, NIN Review No. 31, 2002.

49. World Health Organization: *Miconutrient deficiencies: Iron deficiency anemia*. 2006. http://www.who.int/nutrition/topics/ida/en. Accessed: June 13, 2006.

50. Ghosh K: Non haematological effects of iron deficiency—A perspective. *Indian Journal of Medical Sciences* 60:30, 2006.

51. National Heart, Lung, and Blood Institute: *Iron-deficiency anemia*. 2006. http://www.nhlbi.nih.gov/health/dci/Diseases/ida/ida_whatis.html. Accessed: May 16, 2006.

52. Lozoff B and others: Long-lasting neural and behavioral effects of iron deficiency in infancy. *Nutrition Reviews* 64:S34, 2006.

53. Centers for Disease Control and Prevention: *Nutrition for everyone: Iron deficiency*. http://www.cdc.gov/nccdphp/dnpa/nutrition/nutrition_for_everyone/iron_deficiency/index.htm. Accessed: March 12, 2007.

54. Sandstead HH: Causes of iron and zinc deficiencies and their effects on brain. *Journal of Nutrition* 130:347S, 2000.

55. Kazal LA: Prevention of iron deficiency in infants and toddlers. *American Family Physician* 66:1217, 2002.

56. Office of Dietary Supplements, National Institutes of Health: *Dietary supplement fact sheet: iron*. Updated 2005. http://dietary-supplements.info.nih.gov/factsheets/iron.asp. Accessed: June 13, 2006.

57. Canadian Institutes of Health Research:L Dr. Stanley Zlotnik, CIHR National/International Knowledge Translation Award. http://www.cihr.ca/e/32709.html. Accessed: June 22, 2010.

58. Toddler deaths resulting from ingestion of iron supplements. *Morbidity and Mortality Weekly Report* 42:111, 1993.

59. Canadian Hemochromatosis Society: http://www.cdnhemochromatosis.ca. Accessed: December 2009.

60. Prasad A: Zinc deficiency. *British Medical Journal* 326:409, 2003.

61. Prasad AS and others: Zinc deficiency in sickle cell disease. *Clinical Chemistry* 21:582, 1975.

62. Office of Dietary Supplements, National Institutes of Health: Zinc. 2002. http://dietary-supplements.info.nih.gov/factsheets/cc/zinc.html. Accessed: May 17, 2006.

63. Health Canada: Zinc. http://www.hc-sc.gc.ca/ewh-semt/pubs/water-eau/zinc/index-eng.php. Accessed: June 22, 2010.

64. Position of the American Dietetic Association and Dietitians of Canada: Vegetarian Diets. Canadian Journal of Dietetic Practice and Research – Vol 64 No. 2, Summer 2003.

65. Carpenter KJ: David Marine and the problem of goiter. *Journal of Nutrition* 135:675, 2005.

66. Health Canada: Bureau of Nutritional Sciences, Food Directorate, Health Protection Branch: Addition of vitamins and minerals to foods. October, 1999. http://dsp-psd.pwgsc.gc.ca/Collection/H58-1-2-1999E.pdf. Accessed: June 22, 2010.

67. Health Canada: Salt. *Food and drug regulations. Part B, Division 17*. 1997. http://www.hc-sc.gc.ca/fn-an/salt_formats/hpfb-dgpsa/pdf/legislation/e_d-text-2.pdf. Accessed: May 19, 2006.

68. Iodine Network: Frequently asked questions. http://www.iodinenetwork.net/Learning_FAQ.htm. Accessed: June 21, 2010.

69. Margen S and others. *Wellness foods A to Z*. UC Berkeley Wellness Letter, New York: Rebus, Inc., 2002.

70. Andersson M and others: Current global iodine status and progress over the last decade towards the elimination of iodine deficiency. *Bulletin of the World Health Organization* 83:518, 2005.

71. Higdon J: *Iodine*. Micronutrient Information Center, Linus Pauling Institute, Oregon State University, updated 2003. http://lpi.oregonstate.edu/infocenter/minerals/iodine. Accessed: May 19, 2006.

72. Diwadkar-Navsariwala V, Diamond AM: The link between selenium and chemoprevention: A case for selenoproteins. *Journal of Nutrition* 134:2899, 2004.

73. Whanger, PD: Selenium and its relationship to cancer: An update. British Journal of Nutrition 91(1):11, 2004.

74. Health Canada: Selenium. http://www.hc-sc.gc.ca/ewh-semt/pubs/water_eau/selenium/index-eng.php. Accessed: June 22, 2010.

75. Food and Nutrition Board: *Dietary Reference Intakes for vitamin C, vitamin E, selenium, and carotenoids*. Washington, DC: National Academy Press, 2000.

76. Office of Dietary Supplements, National Institutes of Health: *Selenium*. 2002. http://ods.od.nih.gov/factsheets/Selenium_pf.asp. Accessed: May 21, 2006.

77. The Dieticians of Canada: Eating well boosts your immunity. http://www.dietitians.ca/resources/resourcesearch.asp?fn=view&contentid=14102&resource_resourcetype=News Release&resource_language=English. Accessed: June 17, 2010.

78. Alissa EM and others: The controversy surrounding selenium and cardiovascular disease: A review of the evidence. *Medical Science Monitor* 9: RA9, 2003.
79. Eat Right Ontario: Resources: The scoop on selenium, https://www.eatrightontario.ca/en/viewdocument.aspx?id=293. Accessed: June 22, 2010.
80. Opresko DM: *Toxicity summary for selenium*. The Risk Assessment Information System, U.S. Department of Energy (DOE), Office of Environmental Management, Oak Ridge Operations (ORO) Office. Updated 1998. http://rais.ornl.gov/tox/profi les/selenium_f_V1.shtml. Accessed: May 21, 2006.
81. Office of Dietary Supplements, National Institutes of Health: Chromium. Updated 2005. http://ods.od.nih.gov/factsheets/chromium.asp. Accessed: May 22, 2006.
82. Health Canada: Chromium. http://www.hc-sc.gc.ca/ewh-semt/pubs/water-eau/chromium-chrome/index-eng.php. Accessed: June 22, 2010.
83. Yeh GY and others: Systematic review of herbs and dietary supplements for glycemic control in diabetics. *Diabetes Care* 26(4):1277, 2003.
84. Whittaker P and others: Mutagenicity of chromium picolinate and its components in *Salmonella typhimurium* and L5178Y mouse lymphoma cells. *Food and Chemical Toxicology* 43:1619, 2005.

Chapter 10

1. HealthCanada:Canadianguidelinesforbodyweightclassificationinadults. http://www.hc-sc.gc.ca/fn-an/alt_formats/hpfb-dgpsa/pdf/nutrition/weight_book-livres_des_poids-eng.pdf. Accessed: March 2010.
2. Food and Nutrition Board, National Institute of Medicine: *Dietary Reference Intakes for energy, carbohydrate, fiber, fat, fatty acids, cholesterol, protein, and amino acids (macronutrients)*. Washington, DC: National Academies Press, 2005.
3. Bray GA: Medical consequences of obesity. *Journal of Clinical Endocrinology & Metabolism* 89:2583, 2004.
4. Stein CJ, Colditz GA: The epidemic of obesity. *The Journal of Clinical Endocrinology & Metabolism* 89:2522, 2006.
5. Gilmore J: Body mass index and health. Statistics Canada, Catalogue 82-003. Health Reports, Summer 1999, Vol. 11, No. 1. http://www.statcan.gc.ca/studies-etudes/82-003/feature-caracteristique/5018868-eng.pdf. Accessed: July 15, 2010.
6. Tjepkema, M: Canadian Community Health Survey – Adult Obesity in Canada: Measured height and weight.
7. Tremblay MS, Katzmarzyk PT, & Willms, JD: Temporal trends in overweight and obesity in Canada, 1981–1996. *International Journal of Obesity and Related Metabolic Disorders* 26(4):538–543, 2002.
8. Tremblay MS & Willms JD: Secular trends in the body mass index of Canadian children. *Canadian Medical Association Journal* 163(11):1429–1433, 2000
9. Campagna PD, Amero M, Arthur M, Durant MA, Murphy R, Porter J, Rehman L, Thompson A, Wadsworth L. Physical activity levels and dietary intake of children and youth in the province of Nova Scotia – 2005. Report for the Nova Scotia Department of Health Promotion and Protection and the Nova Scotia Department of Education; 2006.
10. Heart and Stroke Foundation: Statistics. http://www.heartandstroke.com/site/c.ikIQLcMWJtE/b.3483991/k.34A8/Statistics.htm. Accessed: July 15, 2010.
11. Starky S: The obesity epidemic in Canada. Parliamentary Information and Research Service. http://www2.parl.gc.ca/Content/LOP/ResearchPublications/prb0511. Accessed: July 15, 2010.
12. World Health Organization: *Nutrition: Challenges*, 2006. http://www.who.int/nutrition/challenges/en/index.html. Accessed: June 27, 2006.
13. Wing RR, Phelan S: Long-term weight loss maintenance. *American Journal of Clinical Nutrition* 82:222S, 2005.
14. Ross R: The challenge of obesity treatment: avoiding weight regain. *Canadian Medical Association Journal*. May 12, 2009. http://www.cmaj.ca/cgi/reprint/180/10/997. Accessed: July 15, 2010.
15. Clasey JL and others: Validity of methods of body composition assessment in young and older men and women. *Journal of Applied Physiology* 86:1728, 1999.
16. Naaz A and others: Loss of cyclin-dependent kinase inhibitors produces adipocyte hyperplasia and obesity. *The FASEB Journal* 18:1925, 2004.
17. Trayhurn P: Adipose tissue in obesity—An inflammatory issue. *Endocrinology* 146:1003, 2005.
18. Saladin KS: *Anatomy & Physiology*. 4th ed. Boston: McGraw-Hill Publishing Company, 2007.
19. Avram MM: Cellulite: A review of its physiology and treatment. *Journal of Cosmetic and Laser Therapy* 6:181, 2004.
20. Tiraby C and others: Acquirement of brown fat cell features by human white adipocytes. *Journal of Biological Chemistry* 278:33370, 2003.
21. Garcia AL and others: Improved prediction of body fat by measuring skinfold thickness, circumferences, and bone breadths. *Obesity Research* 13:626, 2005.
22. Le Petit C & Berthelot JM: Healthy today, healthy tomorrow? Findings from the National Population Health Survey: Obesity: a growing issue. Statistics Canada Catalogue no. 82-618-MWE2005003 http://www.statcan.gc.ca/pub/82-618-m/2005003/pdf/4224882-eng.pdf. Accessed: July 19, 2009.
23. Jackson Y and others: Summary of the 2000 Surgeon General's Listening Session: Toward a national action plan on overweight and obesity. *Obesity Research* 10:1299, 2002.
24. Virji A, Murr MM: Caring for patients after bariatric surgery. *American Family Physician* 73:1403, 2006.
25. The Arthritis Society: Osteoarthritis. http://www.arthritis.ca/types%20of%20arthritis/osteoarthritis/default.asp?s=1&province=ns. Accessed: July 19, 2009.
26. Cedergren MI: Maternal morbid obesity and the risk of adverse pregnancy outcome. *Obstetrics & Gynecology* 103:219, 2004.
27. Friedman KE and others: Weight stigmatization and ideological beliefs: Relation to psychological functioning in obese adults. *Obesity Research* 13:907, 2005.
28. Klein S: The case of visceral fat: Argument for the defense. *Journal of Clinical Investigation* 113:1530, 2004.
29. Monzon JR and others: Lipolysis in adipocytes isolated from deep and superficial subcutaneous adipose tissue. *Obesity Research* 10:266, 2002.
30. National Heart, Lung, and Blood Institute: *The practical guide: Identification, evaluation, and treatment of overweight and obesity in adults*. HIH Publication 00-4084, 2000. http://www.nhlbi.nih.gov/guidelines/obesity/prctgd_b.pdf.
31. Klein S and others: Waist circumference and cardiometabolic risk. *Diabetes Care* 30(6):1647, 2007.
32. Roberts SB, Dallal GE: Energy requirements and aging. *Public Health Nutrition* 8:1028, 2005.
33. Williams M: *Nutrition for health, fitness, and sport*. 8th ed. New York: McGraw-Hill, 2007.

34. Hyperthyroidism. *Medline plus, medical encyclopedia*. Updated 2006. http://www.nlm.nih.gov/medlineplus/ency/article/000356.htm. Accessed: July 4, 2006.
35. Knudsen N and others: Small differences in thyroid function may be important for body mass index and the occurrence of obesity in the population. *Journal of Clinical Endocrinology & Metabolism* 90:4019, 2006.
36. Weinsier RL and others: Do adaptive changes in metabolic rate favor weight regain in weight-reduced individuals? An examination of the set-point theory. *American Journal of Clinical Nutrition* 72:1088, 2000.
37. Haugen HA and others: Variability of measured resting metabolic rate. *American Journal of Clinical Nutrition* 78:1141, 2005.
38. Hajhosseini L and others: Changes in body weight, body composition and resting metabolic rate (RMR) in first-year university freshmen students. *Journal of the American College of Nutrition* 25:123, 2006.
39. Racette SB and others: Weight changes, exercise, and dietary patterns during freshmen and sophomore years of college. *Journal of American College Health* 53:245, 2005.
40. Wasan KM, Looije NA: Emerging pharmacological approaches to the treatment of obesity. *Journal of Pharmacy and Pharmaceutical Sciences* 8:259, 2005.
41. Jequier E: Leptin signaling, adiposity, and energy balance. *Annals of the New York Academy of Sciences* 967:379, 2002.
42. Ello-Martin JA and others: The influence of food portion size and energy density on energy intake: Implications for weight management. *American Journal of Clinical Nutrition* 82: 236S, 2005.
43. Jequier E: Pathways to obesity. International Journal of Obesity and Related Metabolic Disorders 26:S12, 2002.
44. Wylie-Rosett J and others: Carbohydrates and increases in obesity: Does the type of carbohydrate make a difference? *Obesity Research* 12:124S, 2004.
45. Ledikwe JH and others: Portion sizes and the obesity epidemic. *Journal of Nutrition* 135:905, 2005.
46. Katzmarzyk P and others: The economic burden of physical inactivity in Canada. *Canadian Medical Association Journal* 163(11):1435–1440. 2000.
47. Gilmour H: Physically active Canadians. Health Reports, Statistics Canada, Catalogue 82-003, 2007.
48. Public Health Agency of Canada: Canada's physical activity guide to active healthy living. http://www.phac-aspc.gc.ca/hp-ps/hl-mvs/pag-gap/index-eng.php. Accessed: April, 2010.
49. You T and others: Addition of aerobic exercise to dietary weight loss preferentially reduces abdominal adipocyte size. *International Journal of Obesity (London)* 30:1211, 2006.
50. Eat Right Ontario: Resources: A healthy waist is good for your health! https://eatrightontario.ca/en/viewdocument.aspx?id=84. Accessed: July 20, 2010.
51. Whitaker RC and others: Predicting obesity in young adulthood from childhood and parental obesity. *New England Journal of Medicine* 337:869, 1997.
52. Carrière G: Parent and child factors associated with youth obesity. *Health Reports*, Statistics Canada, Catalogue 82-003, 2003; 14(suppl):29–39.
53. Whitaker RC: Predicting preschooler obesity at birth: The role of maternal obesity in early pregnancy. *Pediatrics* 114:e29, 2004.
54. Toschke AM and others: Early intrauterine exposure to tobacco-inhaled products and obesity. *American Journal of Epidemiology* 158:1068, 2003.
55. Reilly JJ and others: Early life risk factors for obesity in childhood: Cohort study. *British Medical Journal* 330:1357, 2005.
56. Healton CG and others: Smoking, obesity, and their co-occurrence in the United States: Cross sectional analysis. *British Medical Journal* 333:25, 2006.
57. Zhang Q, Wang Y: Trends in the association between obesity and socioeconomic status in U.S. adults: 1971–2000. *Obesity Research* 12:1622, 2004.
58. Roberts RE and others: Are the obese at greater risk for depression? *American Journal of Epidemiology* 152(2):163, 2000.
59. Bish CL and others: Diet and physical activity behaviors among Americans trying to lose weight: 2000 Behavioral Risk Factor Surveillance System. *Obesity Research* 13:596, 2005.
60. Klein S and others: Weight management through lifestyle modification for the prevention and management of type 2 diabetes: Rationale and strategies. A statement of the American Diabetes Association, the North American Association for the Study of Obesity, and the American Society for Clinical Nutrition. *American Journal of Clinical Nutrition* 80:257, 2004.
61. U.S Department of Health and Human Services: Dietary Guidelines for Americans 2005. Http://healthierus.gov/dietaryguidelines. Accessed: July 27, 2006.
62. Canadian Institute for Health Information: Improving the health of Canadians: Canadian Population Health Initiative. http://secure.cihi.ca/cihiweb/products/IHC2004_ch5_e.pdf. Accessed: July 20, 2010.
63. Kruger J and others: Attempting to lose weight: Specific practices among U.S. adults. *American Journal of Preventive Medicine* 269:402, 2004.
64. Rolls BJ and others: What can intervention studies tell us about the relationship between fruit and vegetable consumption and weight management? *Nutrition Reviews* 62:1, 2004.
65. Hu FB and others: Television watching and other sedentary behaviors in relation to risk of obesity and type 2 diabetes mellitus in women. *Journal of the American Medical Association* 289:1785, 2003.
66. Matheson DM and others: Children's food consumption during television viewing. *American Journal of Clinical Nutrition* 79:1088, 2004.
67. Irwin ML and others: Estimation of energy expenditure from physical activity measures: Determinants of accuracy. *Obesity Research* 9:517, 2001.
68. 2004 Chief Medical Officer of Health Report: Healthy weights, healthy lives. http://www.mhp.gov.on.ca/en/heal/healthy_weights.pdf. Accessed: July 20, 2010.
69. Raynor HA and others: Amount of food group variety consumed in the diet and long-term weight loss maintenance. *Obesity Research* 13:883, 2005.
70. Phelan S and others: Are the eating and exercise habits of successful weight losers changing? *Obesity* 14:710, 2006.
71. Zhaoping L and others: Meta-analysis: Pharmacologic treatment of obesity. *Annals of Internal Medicine* 142:532, 2005.
72. O'Brien PE and others: Obesity, weight loss, and bariatric surgery. *Medical Journal of Australia* 183:310, 2005.
73. Karmali S, Shaffer E: The battle against the obesity epidemic: Is bariatric surgery the perfect weapon? *Clinical and Investigative Medicine: Official Journal of the Canadian Society for Clinical Investigation* Volume 28, no 4:6–13, August 2005.
74. CBC News: In Depth: Health cosmetic surgery: Balancing risk. Last Updated April 10, 2008. http://www.cbc.ca/news/background/health/cosmetic-surgery.html. Accessed: July 21, 2010.

75. Personal communication: Professor Dee Anna Glaser, M.D. Director of Cosmetic & Laser Surgery, Department of Dermatology, Saint Louis University, St. Louis Missouri, July 11, 2006.
76. Sharma A, Freedhoff Y: "Lose 40 pounds in 4 weeks": Regulating commercial weight-loss programs. *Canadian Medical Association Journal*, February 17, 2009.
77. Nordmann AJ and others: Effects of low-carbohydrate vs. low-fat diets on weight loss and cardiovascular risk factors; a meta-analysis of randomized controlled trials. *Annals of Internal Medicine* 166:285, 2006.
78. Saper RB and others: Common dietary supplements for weight loss. *American Family Physician* 70:1731, 2004
79. Health Canada: Food safety. http://www.hc-sc.gc.ca/fn-an/securit/index-eng.php. Accessed: July 21, 2010.
80. Food and Drug Administration: FDA issues regulation prohibiting sale of dietary supplements containing ephedrine alkaloids and reiterates its advice that consumers stop using these products. *FDA News*, Feb. 6, 2004. http://www.cfsan.fda.gov/~lrd/fpephed6.html. Accessed: August 18, 2006.
81. Federal Trade Commission, Bureau of Consumer Protection: *Weight loss advertising: An analysis of current trends*. 2002. http://www.ftc.gov/bcp/reports/weightloss.pdf.

Chapter 11

1. Canadian Fitness and Lifestyle Research Institute: http://www.cflri.ca/eng/story_details.php?id=49. Accessed: April, 2010.
2. Public Health Agency of Canada: Canada's physical activity guide to active healthy living. http://www.phac-aspc.gc.ca/hp-ps/hl-mvs/pag-gap/index-eng.php. Accessed: April, 2010.
3. Public Health Agency of Canada: Canada's physical activity guide to active healthy living for older people. http://www.phac-aspc.gc.ca/hp-ps/hl-mvs/pag-gap/pdf/guide-older-eng.pdf. Accessed April, 2010.
4. Canadian Society for Exercise Physiology (CSEP) and ParticipACTION: Fact sheet – new physical activity recommendations. http://www.csep.ca/CMFiles/PAMGpdfs/CSEP_PAC%20-%20Fact%20Sheet%20-%20EN.pdf. Accessed: June 30, 2010.
5. (CDC) Physical Activity for Everyone: Measuring Physical Activity Intensity: Target Heart Rate and Estimated Maximum Heart Rate. http://www.cdc.gov/nccdphp/dnpa/physical/measuring/target_heart_rate.htm. Accessed: August 22, 2006.
6. Healthy Canada.com: Keeping track: Heart rate. http://www.healthycanada.com/component/deeppockets/content/1696-keeping-track-heart-rate. Accessed: June 23, 2010.
7. Dieticians of Canada: Scientific basis of EATracker. http://www.dietitians.ca/public/content/eat_well_live_well/english/eatracker/backgrounder.asp. Accessed: June 23, 2010.
8. Sherman WM: Metabolism of sugars and physical performance. *American Journal of Clinical Nutrition* 62:228S, 1995.
9. Gastin PB: Energy system interaction and relative contribution during maximal exercise. *Sports Medicine* 31:725, 2001.
10. Williams MH: *Nutrition for health, fitness, and sport*. 8th ed. New York: McGraw-Hill, 2007.
11. Saladin KS: *Anatomy & physiology 4th ed.* Boston: McGraw-Hill Publishing Company, 2010.
12. Shulman RG, Rothman DL: The "glycogen shunt" in "exercising muscle," a role for glycogen in muscle energetics and fatigue. *Proceedings of the National Academy of Sciences* 98:458, 2001.
13. Casaburi R: Physiologic responses to training. *Clinical Chest Medicine* 15:215, 1994.
14. Van Loon LJC and others: The effects of increasing exercise intensity on muscle fuel utilization in humans. *Journal of Physiology* 536:295, 2001.
15. Holloszy JO and others: The regulation of carbohydrate and fat metabolism during and after exercise. *Frontiers Bioscience* 3:D1011, 1998.
16. Bergman BC, Brooks GA: Respiratory and gas-exchange ratios during graded exercise in fed and fasted trained and untrained men. *Journal of Applied Physiology* 86:479, 1999.
17. Sidossis LS and others: Regulation of plasma fatty acid oxidation during low- and high-intensity exercise. *American Journal of Physiology* 72: E1065, 1997.
18. Horowitz JF, Klein S: Lipid metabolism during endurance exercise. *American Journal of Clinical Nutrition* 72:558S, 2000.
19. American Dietetic Association: Position of the American Dietetic Association, Dietitians of Canada, and the American College of Sports Medicine—Nutrition and athletic performance. *Journal of the American Dietetic Association* 100:1543, 2000.
20. Economos CD and others: Nutritional practices of elite athletes: Practical recommendations. *Sports Medicine* 16:381, 1993.
21. Institute of Medicine of the National Academies: *Dietary Reference Intakes: The essential guide to nutrient requirements*. The National Academies Press: Washington, D.C., 2006.
22. Zello, G: Dietary Reference Intakes for the macronutrients and energy: considerations for physical activity. *Applied Physiology, Nutrition, and Metabolism* 31:74–79, 2006. http://pubs.nrc-cnrc.gc.ca/rp/rppdf/h05-022.pdf. Accessed: June 24, 2010.
23. Lambert EV and others: High-fat diet versus habitual diet prior to carbohydrate loading: Effects of exercise metabolism and cycling performance. *International Journal of Sports Nutrition and Exercise Metabolism* 11:209, 2001.
24. Dreon DM and others: A very low-fat diet is not associated with improved lipoprotein profiles in men with a predominance of large low-density lipoproteins. *American Journal of Clinical Nutrition* 69:411, 1999.
25. Schabort EJ and others: The effect of a preexercise meal on time to fatigue during prolonged cycling exercise. *Medicine & Science in Sports & Exercise* 31:464, 1999.
26. Hawley JA and others: Carbohydrate loading and exercise performance: An update. *Sports Medicine* 24:73, 1997.
27. Dennis SC and others: Nutritional strategies to minimize fatigue during prolonged exercise: Fluid, electrolyte, and energy replacement. *Journal of Sports Science* 15:305, 1997.
28. Dieticians of Canada: What should I eat and drink before, during and after an endurance exercise? http://www.dietitians.ca/resources/resourcesearch.asp?fn=view&contentid=1318&resource_resourcetype=FAQ%28Frequently%20asked%20question%29%20&resource_language=English. Accessed: June 24, 2010.
29. Food and Nutrition Board: Dietary Reference Intakes for energy, carbohydrate, fiber, fat, fatty acids, cholesterol, protein, and amino acids (macronutrients). Institute of Medicine of the National Academies, Washington, DC: National Academies Press, 2005.
30. Health Canada: Dietary Reference Intakes, reference values for macronutrients. http://www.hc-sc.gc.ca/fn-an/nutrition/reference/table/ref_macronutr_tbl-eng.php. Accessed: June 14, 2010.
31. Rennie MJ, Tipton KD: Protein and amino acid metabolism during and after exercise and the effects of nutrition. *Annual Review of Nutrition* 20:457, 2000.

32. Tipton KD, Wolfe RR: Protein and amino acids for athletes. *Journal of Sports Science* 22:65, 2004.
33. Gibala MJ: Nutritional supplementation and resistance exercise: What is the evidence for enhanced skeletal muscle hypertrophy? *Canadian Journal of Applied Physiology* 25:524, 2000.
34. Maughan R: The athlete's diet: Nutritional goals and dietary strategies. *Proceedings of the Nutrition Society* 61:87, 2002.
35. Fielding RA, Parkington J: What are the dietary protein requirements of physically active individuals? New evidence on the effects of protein utilization during post-exercise recovery. *Nutrition in Clinical Care* 5:191, 2002.
36. Smith A: Effects of caffeine on human behavior. *Food and Chemical Toxicology* 40:1243, 2002.
37. Dieticians of Canada: What is caffeine? Is it bad for my health? http://www.dietitians.ca/resources/resourcesearch.asp?fn=view&contentid=6153&resource_resourcetype=FAQ%28Frequently%20asked%20question%29%20&resource_language=English. Accessed: June 25, 2010.
38. A guide to the best and worst drinks. *Consumer Reports on Health*, p. 8, July 2006.
39. Health Canada: Dietary Reference Intakes, reference values for macronutrients. http://www.hc-sc.gc.ca/fn-an/nutrition/reference/table/ref_macronutr_tbl-eng.php. Accessed: June 14, 2010.
40. Food and Nutrition Board, Institute of Medicine: *Dietary Reference Intakes for water, potassium, sodium, chloride, and sulfate*. Washington, DC: National Academy Press, 2004.
41. Coyle EF: Fluid and fuel intake during exercise. *Journal of Sports Science* 22:39, 2004.
42. Health Canada: Healthy living – extreme heat events. http://www.hc-sc.gc.ca/hl-vs/iyh-vsv/environ/heat-chaleur-eng.php. Accessed: April 2010.
43. Association of International Marathons and Road Races: *IMMDA's revised fluid recommendations for runners & walkers*. 2006. http://www.aims-association.org/guidelines_fluid_replacement.htm Accessed: August 26, 2006
44. Clark N: Salt and athletes: Shake it or leave it? *ACSM Fit Society Page*. Summer 2006. http://www.acsm.org/AM/Template.cfm?Section=Home_Page&CONTENTID=5275&TEMPLATE=/CM/ContentDisplay.cfm
45. Powers SK and others: Dietary antioxidants and exercise. *Journal of Sports Sciences* 22:81, 2004.
46. Nieman DC and others: Vitamin E and immunity after the Kona Triathlon World Championship. *Medicine and Science in Sports and Exercise* 36:1328, 2004
47. University Extension, Iowa State University: Caffeine for athletes. *Food and nutrition: Choices for health*. Updated 2006. http://www.extension.iastate.edu/nutrition/supplements/caffeine.php
48. Graham TE and others: Does caffeine alter muscle carbohydrate and fat metabolism during exercise? *Applied Physiology, Nutrition, and Metabolism* 33:1311–1318, 2008. http://article.pubs.nrc-cnrc.gc.ca/RPAS/rpv?hm=HInit&journal=apnm&volume=33&calyLang=eng&afpf=h08-129.pdf. Accessed: June 25, 2010.
49. National Collegiate Athletic Association: NCAA banned-drug classes. NCAA drug-testing programs, 2001–02. Updated 2001. http://www1.ncaa.org/membership/ed_outreach/health-safety/drug_testing/banned_drug_classes.pdf Accessed: October 4, 2006
50. World Anti-Doping Agency: *The World Anti-Doping Code. The 2007 prohibited list, international standard*. 2007. http://www.wada-ama.org/rtecontent/document/2007_List_En.pdf
51. Canadian Interuniversity Sport: Athletes guide. http://english.cis-sic.ca/information/student-athlete_info/athletes_guide. Accessed: June 25, 2010.
52. Centers for Disease Control and Prevention, National Center for Chronic Disease Prevention and Health Promotion, Division of Nutrition and Physical Activity: Does drinking beverages with added sugars increase the risk of overweight? *Research to practice series*. No. 3, September 2006. http://www.cdc.gov/nccdphp/dnpa/nutrition/pdf/r2p_sweetend_beverages.pdf
53. Health Canada: Safe use of energy drinks. http://www.hc-sc.gc.ca/hl-vs/iyh-vsv/prod/energy-energie-eng.php. Accessed: June 25, 2010.

Chapter 12

1. U.S. Food and Drug Administration: Investigation of 2006 spinach outbreak yields important information. *FDA News Digest*, March 26, 2007.
2. Canadian Partnership for Consumer Food Safety Education: http://www.canfightbac.org/en. Accessed: January, 2010.
3. National Institute of Allergy and Infectious Diseases: *Foodborne diseases*. 2006. http:www.niaid.nih.gov/factsheets/foodbornedis.htm. Accessed: September 18, 2006.
4. Ontario Ministry of Health and Long-term Care: Hazard identification and risk assessment 2007. http://www.health.gov.on.ca/english/providers/program/pubhealth/oph_standards/ophs/progstds/phep/req1/req14.pdf. Accessed: June 28, 2010.
5. Ontario Ministry of Health and Long-term Care: http://www.health.gov.on.ca/en/news/release/2008/dec/nr_20081208.aspx. Accessed: December, 2009.
6. Health Canada: Health policy research bulletin. April 2009. Issue 15 Emergency Management: Taking a Health Perspective. http://www.hc-sc.gc.ca/sr-sr/alt_formats/hpb-dgps/pdf/pubs/hpr-rps/bull/2009-emergency-urgence/2009-emergency-urgence-eng.pdf. Accessed: June 28, 2010.
7. CBC News: Canada's worst-ever E. coli contamination Updated Dec. 20, 2004 http://www.cbc.ca/news/background/walkerton. Accessed: June 28, 2010.
8. Canadian Food Inspection Agency: Science and regulation...working together for Canadians. http://www.inspection.gc.ca/english/agen/broch/broche.pdf. Accessed: June 29, 2010.
9. Agriculture and Agri-Food Canada: Mandate. http://www4.agr.gc.ca/AAFC-AAC/display-afficher.do?id=1173965157543&lang=eng. Accessed: June 29, 2010.
10. Canadian Food Inspection Agency: Food. http://www.inspection.gc.ca/english/fssa/fssae.shtml. Accessed: June 29, 2010.
11. Canadian Food Inspection Agency: Hazard analysis critical control points/food safety enhancement program. http://www.inspection.gc.ca/english/fssa/polstrat/haccp/haccpe.shtml. Accessed: June 29, 2010.
12. Canadian Food Inspection Agency: Food safety enhancement program manual. http://www.inspection.gc.ca/english/fssa/polstrat/haccp/manue/tablee.shtml. Accessed: June 29, 2010.
13. Canadian Food Inspection Agency: Meat and poultry products. http://www.inspection.gc.ca/english/fssa/meavia/meaviae.shtml. Accessed: June 29, 2010.
14. Health Canada: Drinking water. http://www.hc-sc.gc.ca/ewh-semt/water-eau/drink-potab/index-eng.php. Accessed: June 29, 2010.
15. Health Canada: It's your health, unpasteurized fruit juice and cider. http://www.hc-sc.gc.ca/hl-vs/alt_formats/pacrb-dgapcr/pdf/iyh-vsv/food-aliment/juice-jus-eng.pdf. Accessed: June 29, 2010.

16. Health Canada: Tip sheet for raw milk. http://www.hc-sc.gc.ca/fn-an/securit/kitchen-cuisine/raw-milk-lait-cru-eng.php. Accessed: June 29, 2010.

17. Canadian Food Inspection Agency: E. coli O157:H7: Food safety facts. http://www.inspection.gc.ca/english/fssa/concen/cause/ecolie.pdf. Accessed: June 29, 2010.

18. Canadian Food Inspection Agency: Animal diseases: Trichinellosis. http://www.inspection.gc.ca/english/anima/disemala/trich/trichfse.shtml. Accessed: April, 2010.

19. Canadian Food Inspection Agency: Fact sheet—mycotoxins. http://www.inspection.gc.ca/english/anima/feebet/pol/mycoe.shtml. Accessed: April, 2010.

20. Canadian Food Inspection Agency: Everyday safe food handling practices. http://www.inspection.gc.ca/english/fssa/concen/tipcon/eveprae.shtml. Accessed: April, 2010.

21. Canadian Food Inspection Agency: Food safety facts on microwave ovens. http://www.inspection.gc.ca/english/fssa/concen/tipcon/microe.shtml. Accessed: April, 2010.

22. Picklesimer P: Scientists weigh in on the 5-second rule. ACES News. University of Illinois at Champaign-Urbana, College of Agricultural, Consumer and Environmental Sciences, 2003. http://www.aces.uiuc.edu/news/stories/news2467.html.

23. U.S. Department of Agriculture, Food Safety and Inspection Service: Keeping food safe during an emergency. *Fact sheets: Emergency preparedness*. 2006. http://www.fsis.usda.gov/Fact_Sheets/Keeping_Food_Safe_During_an_Emergency/index.asp.

24. Government of Ontario: Safe food handling. http://www.health.gov.on.ca/english/public/pub/foodsafe/pdf/foodhandl.pdf. Accessed: June 30, 2010.

25. Prescott LM and others: *Microbiology* 6th ed. Boston: McGraw-Hill Publishing Company, 2005.

26. Canadian Food Inspection Agency: Fact sheet–food irradiation. http://www.inspection.gc.ca/english/fssa/concen/tipcon/irrade.shtml. Accessed: April, 2010.

27. Centers for Disease Control and Prevention, Division of Bacterial and Mycotic Diseases: Food irradiation, 2005, http://www.cdc.gov/ncidod/dmbd/diseaseinfo/foodirradiation.htm.

28. International Food Information Council and U.S. Food and Drug Administration: *Food ingredients and colors*. 2004. http://www.cfsan.fda.gov/~dms/foodic.html; http://vm.cfsan.fda.gov/%7Edms/dalbook.html.

29. Health Canada: Sulphites. http://www.hc-sc.gc.ca/fn-an/securit/allerg/fa-aa/allergen_sulphites-sulfites-eng.php. Accessed: June 30, 2010.

30. Health Canada: Food and nutrition – food additives. http://www.hc-sc.gc.ca/fn-an/securit/addit/index-eng.php. Accessed: April 2010.

31. Health Canada: Survey of benzene in soft drinks and other beverage products. http://www.hc-sc.gc.ca/fn-an/surveill/other-autre/benzene_survey_enquete-eng.php. Accessed: June 30, 2010.

32. Food and Drug Administration: *FDA statement: Benzene in soft drinks*. 2006. http://www.fda.gov/bbs/topics/NEWS/2006/NEW01355.html. Accessed: June 9, 2006.

33. Environmental Protection Agency: *Pesticides: Topical & chemical fact sheets*. The EPA and food security. Updated 2006. http://www.epa.gov/pesticides/factsheets/securty.htm.

34. Health Canada: Pesticides and pest management. http://www.hc-sc.gc.ca/cps-spc/pest/index-eng.php. Accessed: June 30, 2010.

35. Department of Health and Human Services, Centers for Disease Control and Prevention: *Third national report on human exposure to environmental chemicals*. 2005. ttp://www.cdc.gov/exposurereport/3rd/pdf/thirdreport.pdf.

36. Canadian Cancer Society: Pesticides and cancer. http://www.cancer.ca/canada-wide/prevention/specific%20environmental%20contaminants/pesticides/pesticide%20exposure%20and%20cancer.aspx?sc_lang=en. Accessed: June 30, 2010.

37. Blair A and others: Disease and injury among participants in the Agricultural Health Study. *Journal of Agricultural Safety and Health* 11:141, 2005.

Chapter 13

1. Otten JJ and others (eds.): Institute of Medicine: *Dietary Reference Intakes: The essential guide to nutrient requirements*. Washington, DC: National Academies Press, 2006.

2. Statistics Canada: Leading causes of death. March 31, 2009. http://www.statcan.gc.ca/daily-quotidien/090331/dq090331g-eng.htm. Accessed: July 1, 2010.

3. Thame M and others: Fetal growth is directly related to maternal anthropometry and placental volume. European Journal of Clinical Nutrition 58:894, 2004.

4. Martin JA and others: Births: Final data for 2004. *National Vital Statistics Reports* 55:1, 2006.

5. Polmamus B and others: Births: Final data for 2004 report. Atlanta: U.S. Department of Health and Human Services, Centers for Disease Control and Prevention, 2006. http://www.cdc.gov/pednss.

6. Greaves L and others: *A best practices review of smoking cessation interventions for pregnant and postpartum girls and women*. Vancouver: British Columbia Centre of Excellence for Women's Health. 2003.

7. World Health Agency: Bulletin of the World Health Organization. 4 January 2010. http://www.who.int/bulletin/releases/NFM0110.pdf. Accessed: July 1, 2010.

8. Public Health Agency of Canada: Measuring up – a health surveillance update on Canadian children and youth. http://www.phac-aspc.gc.ca/publicat/meas-haut/mu_c_e.html. Accessed: February 2010.

9. Tucker J, McGuire W: Epidemiology of preterm birth. *British Medical Journal* 329:675, 2004.

10. Neville MC, McManaman JL: Milk secretion and composition. In *Neonatal nutrition and metabolism*. 2nd ed. Thureen P, Hay W (eds.) Cambridge University Press, 2006.

11. The Society of Obstetricians and Gynaecologists of Canada: Nausea and vomiting in pregnancy. http://www.sogc.org/health/pregnancy_e.asp. Accessed: April 2010.

12. Widmaier E and others: *Vander's human physiology* 10th ed. Boston: McGraw-Hill Publishing Company, 2006

13. Health Canada: Prenatal nutrition guidelines for health professionals: Iron. Cat.: H164-109/1-2009E-PDF. http://www.hc-sc.gc.ca/fn-an/pubs/nutrition/guide-prenatal-eng.php. Accessed: July 1, 2010.

14. Health Canada: Human health risk assessment of mercury in fish and health benefits of fish consumption. http://www.hc-sc.gc.ca/fn-an/pubs/mercur/merc_fish_poisson.eng.php. Accessed: April 2010.

15. Arendas K and others: Canada obesity in pregnancy: Pre-conceptional to postpartum consequences. *Journal of Obstetrics and Gynaecology*, June 2008. http://www.sogc.org/jogc/abstracts/full/200806_Obstetrics_1.pdf. Accessed: July 2, 2010.

16. The Society of Obstetricians and Gynaecologists of Canada: http://www.sogc.org/health/pregnancy-multiple_e.asp. Accessed: April 2010.

17. Statistics Canada: Weight gain during pregnancy: Findings. http://www.statcan.gc.ca/pub/82-003-x/2010002/article/11145/findings-resultats-eng.htm. Accessed: July 2, 2010.
18. Stotland NE and others: Gestational weight gain and adverse neonatal outcome among term infants. *Obstetrics and Gynecology* 108:635, 2006.
19. Chang J and others: Pregnancy-related mortality surveillance—United States, 1991–1999. *Morbidity and Mortality Weekly Report: Surveillance Summaries* 52:1, 2003.
20. Arora S and others: Major factors influencing breastfeeding rates: Mother's perception of father's attitude and milk supply. *Pediatrics* 106:67, 2000.
21. National Library of Medicine, National Institutes of Health: Preeclampsia. *MedLine Plus*. 2005. http://www.nlm.nih.gov/medlineplus/ency/article/000898.htm.
22. Roberts CL and others: Hypertensive disorders in pregnancy: A population-based study. *Medical Journal of Australia* 182:332, 2005.
23. Statistics Canada: Pregnancy outcomes by province or territory of residence. http://www40.statcan.ca/l01/cst01/hlth64a-eng.htm. Accessed: July 4, 2010.
24. Health Canada: Healthy living. healthy babies: Sudden infant death syndrome. http://www.hc-sc.gc.ca/hl-vs/babies-bebes/sids-smsn/index-eng.php. Accessed: April 2010.
25. Davies, GAL and others. Joint SOGC/CSEP Clinical Practice Guideline. Exercise in pregnancy and the postpartum period. http://www.sogc.org/guidelines/public/129E-JCPG-June2003.pdf. Accessed: April 2010.
26. The National Women's Health Information Center, U.S. Department of Health and Human Services, Office on Women's Health: *Benefits of breastfeeding*. 2005. http://www.4woman.gov/Breastfeeding/index.cfm?page=227.
27. Daudelin M and others: Breastfeeding and life from birth to 40 years. *Canadian Journal of Public Health* 71(4):267-268, 1980.
28. Health Canada: Nutrition for healthy term infants – statement of the joint working group: Canadian Paediatric Society, Dietitians of Canada and Health Canada. http://www.hc-sc.gc.ca/fn-an/pubs/infant-nourrisson/nut_infant_nourrisson_term-eng.php. Accessed: April 2010.
29. Mayer-Davis EJ and others: Breast-feeding and risk for childhood obesity. *Diabetes Care* 29:2231, 2006.
30. Hurst N: Breastfeeding after breast augmentation. *Journal of Human Lactation* 19:70, 2003.
31. Canadian Breastfeeding Foundation: http://www.canadianbreastfeedingfoundation.org/index.html. Accessed: April 2010.
32. World Health Organization: Ten facts of breastfeeding. http://www.who.int/features/factfiles/breastfeeding/en. Accessed April 2010.
33. Saarela T and others: Macronutrient and energy contents of human milk fractions during the first six months of lactation. *Acta Paediatricia* 94(9):1176, 2005.
34. Fomon SJ: Infant feeding in the 20th century: Formula and beikost. *Journal of Nutrition* 131:409S, 2001.
35. American Dietetic Association: Start healthy feeding guidelines. 2005 http://www.eatright.org/ada/files/infant_book.pdf. Accessed: November 26, 2006.
36. Gidding SS and others: Dietary recommendations for children and adolescents: A guide for practitioners. *Pediatrics* 117:544, 2006.
37. *Eating Well with Canada's Food Guide:* http://www.hc-sc.gc.ca/fn-an/alt_formats/hpfb-dgpsa/pdf/food-guide-aliment/print_eatwell_bienmang-eng.pdf. Accessed: April 2010.
38. Touger-Decker R, van Loveren C: Sugars and dental caries. *American Journal of Clinical Nutrition* 78:881S, 2003.
39. Canning, P.M. and others: Prevalence of overweight and obesity in a provincial population of Canadian preschool children. *Canadian Medical Association Journal* 171(3): August 3, 2004; 171 (3). doi:10.1503/cmaj.1040075.
40. Ogden CL and others: Prevalence of overweight and obesity in the United States, 1999–2004. *Journal of the American Medical Association* 295:1549, 2006.
41. Heart and Stroke Foundation: Position statement overweight, obesity, and heart disease and stroke http://www.heartandstroke.com/site/c.ikIQLcMWJtE/b.3799193/k.A1E1/Position_Statements__Overweight_obesity_and_heart_disease_and_stroke.htm. Accessed: July 5, 2010.
42. Mark AE and other: Television viewing, computer use and total screen time in Canadian youth. *Paediatrics & Child Health* 11(9):595-9, 2006.
43. Goran MI and others: Obesity and risk of type 2 diabetes and cardiovascular disease in children and adolescents. *The Journal of Clinical Endocrinology & Metabolism* 88:1417, 2003.
44. Health Canada: 2009. Do Canadian children meet their nutrient requirements through food intake alone? Cat. H164-112/1-2009E-PDF.
45. Rampersaud GC and others: Breakfast habits, nutritional status, body weight, and academic performance in children and adolescents. *Journal of the American Dietetic Association* 105:743, 2005.
46. Carrière G: Parent and child factors associated with youth obesity. Statistics Canada, Catalogue 82-003. November 3, 2003. http://www.statcan.gc.ca/pub/82-003-s/2003000/pdf/82-003-s2003003-eng.pdf. Accessed: July 5, 2010.
47. Health Resources and Services Administration, Maternal and Child Health Bureau: Physical activity and overweight. *Child Health USA 2005*. http://www.mchb.hrsa.gov/mchirc/chusa_05/healthstat/adolescents/0321pao.htm.
48. Centers for Disease Control and Prevention: *Overweight and obesity: Childhood overweight*. 2006. http://www.cdc.gov/nccdphp/dnpa/obesity/childhood/index.htm.
49. Campagna, P. D., Amero, M., Arthur, M., Durant, M. A., Murphy, R., Porter, J., Rehman, L., Thompson, A., Wadsworth, L: (2006). Physical activity levels and dietary intake of children and youth in the province of Nova Scotia – 2005. Report for the Nova Scotia Department of Health Promotion and Protection and the Nova Scotia Department of Education.
50. Saladin KS: *Anatomy & physiology 4th ed.* Boston: McGraw-Hill Publishing Company, 2010.
51. American Academy of Dermatologists: *Frequently asked questions about acne*. http://www.skincarephysicians.com/acnenet/FAQ.html#1. Accessed: November 13, 2006.
52. Canadian Society for Exercise Physiology (CSEP) and ParticipACTION: Fact sheet – new physical activity recommendations. http://www.csep.ca/CMFiles/PAMGpdfs/CSEP_PAC%20-%20Fact%20Sheet%20-%20EN.pdf. Accessed: June 30, 2010.
53. McMahan CA and others: Pathobiological determinants of atherosclerosis in youth risk scores are associated with early and advanced atherosclerosis. *Pediatrics* 118:1447, 2006.
54. Position of the American Dietetic Association and Dietitians of Canada: Vegetarian diets. *Journal of the American Dietetic Association* 103:748, 2003.
55. Statistics Canada: Life expectancy. http://www.statcan.gc.ca/pub/82-229-x/2009001/demo/lif-eng.htm. Accessed: July 6, 2010.

56. The Public Health Agency of Canada: Healthy aging in Canada: A new vision, a vital investment, from evidence to action—a background paper. http://www.phac-aspc.gc.ca/seniors-aines/alt-formats/pdf/publications/pro/healthy-sante/haging_newvision/vision-rpt_e.pdf. Accessed: July 6, 2010.

57. Leitch, K: *Reaching for the Top: A Report by the Advisor on Healthy Children and Youth, 2007.* http://www.hcsc.gc.ca/hl-vs/alt_formats/hpb-dgps/pdf/child-enfant/2007-advisor-conseillere/advisor-conseillere-eng.pdf.

58. Chernoff R: Micronutrient requirements in older women. *American Journal of Clinical Nutrition* 81:1240S, 2005.

59. Foote JA and others: Older adults need guidance to meet nutritional recommendations. *Journal of the American College of Nutrition* 19:628, 2000.

60. Pesonen J and others: High bone mineral density among perimenopausal women. *Osteoporosis International* 16:1899, 2005.

61. Armstrong, Bob: All Smiles. WAVE Winnipeg's health and wellness magazine http://www.wrha.mb.ca/wave/2010/06/all-smiles.php. Accessed: July 6, 2010.

62. Hung H-C and others: Tooth loss and dietary intake. *Journal of the American Dental Association* 134:1185, 2003.

63. Balluz LS and others: Vitamin or supplement use among adults. Behavioral Risk Factor Surveillance System, 13 States, 2001. *Public Health Reports* 120:117, 2005.

64. Wan H. and others: 65+ in the United States: 2005, U.S. Census Bureau, Current Population Reports, p23-209. U.S. Government Printing Office, Washington, D.C., 2005.

65. Mood Disorders Association of Ontario: Seniors and depression. http://www.mooddisorders.on.ca/pdf/SeniorsDepression_final.pdf. Accessed: July 6, 2010.

Glossary

A

absorption process by which substances are taken up from the GI tract and enter the bloodstream or the lymph

Acceptable Macronutrient Distribution Ranges (AMDRs) macronutrient intake ranges that are nutritionally adequate and may reduce the risk of diet-related chronic diseases

acid-base balance maintaining the proper pH of body fluids

acid group acid portion of a compound

acids substances that donate hydrogen ions

added sugars sugars and syrups added to foods during processing or preparation

adenosine diphosphate (ADP) high-energy compound, by-product of ATP use

adenosine triphosphate (ATP) high-energy compound that stores energy, major direct energy source for cells

Adequate Intakes (AIs) standard established when sufficient scientific evidence is not available to establish an RDA; an AI can be used as a goal for usual intake by an individual

adipose cells fat cells that store triglycerides

adolescence life stage in which a child matures physically into an adult

aerobic conditions that require free oxygen

aerobic exercise physical activities that involve sustained, rhythmic contractions of large muscle groups

aldosterone hormone that participates in sodium and water conservation

alpha-linolenic acid essential fatty acid

alpha-tocopherol vitamin E

alternative sweeteners substances that sweeten foods while providing few or no kilocalories

amino acids nitrogen-containing chemical units that comprise proteins

amino or **nitrogen-containing group** portion of an amino acid that contains nitrogen

anaerobic conditions that lack free oxygen

anatomy scientific study of cells and other body structures

anecdotes personal reports of experiences

android obesity condition characterized by excessive abdominal fat

anemia disorder characterized by too few red blood cells and poor oxygen transport in blood

anencephaly type of neural tube defect in which the brain does not form properly or is missing

anorexia nervosa (AN) severe psychological disturbance characterized by self-imposed starvation

anthropology within the context of nutrition, the study of how communities and cultures use food as part of daily life and religious or spiritual celebrations

antibodies infection-fighting proteins

antidiuretic hormone (ADH) hormone that participates in water conservation

antioxidant substance that protects other compounds from being damaged or destroyed by certain environmental factors; gives up electrons to radicals to protect cells

appetite a psychological desire for food, which can exist in the absence of hunger

arteries vessels that carry blood away from the heart

arteriosclerosis condition that results from atherosclerosis and is characterized by loss of arterial flexibility

ascorbic acid vitamin C

atherosclerosis long-term disease process in which plaques build up inside arterial walls

B

bacteria simple single-celled microorganisms

bariatric medicine medical specialty that focuses on the treatment of obesity

basal metabolism minimal number of kilocalories the body uses to support vital activities after fasting and resting for 12 hours

bases substances that accept hydrogen ions

beriberi thiamin deficiency disease

beta-carotene carotenoid that the body can convert to vitamin A

bile emulsifier that aids lipid digestion

bioavailability extent to which the digestive tract absorbs a nutrient and how well the body uses it

bioelectrical impedance technique of estimating body composition in which a device measures the conduction of a weak electrical current through the body

biological activity describes vitamin's degree of potency or effects in the body

biology study of living organisms

body mass index (BMI) numerical value of relationship between body weight and risk of certain chronic health problems

buffer solution that resists changes in pH under certain conditions

bulimia nervosa eating disorder characterized by cyclic episodes of bingeing and calorie-restrictive dieting

C

caffeine naturally occurring stimulant drug

calcitonin hormone secreted by the thyroid gland when blood calcium levels are too high

capillaries smallest blood vessels

carbohydrate loading practice of manipulating physical activity and dietary patterns to increase muscle glycogen stores

carbohydrates class of nutrients that is a major source of energy for the body

carcinogens cancer-causing substances

cardiovascular disease (CVD) group of diseases that affect the heart and blood vessels

carotenemia yellowing of the skin that results from excess beta-carotene in the body

carotenoids yellow-orange pigments in fruits and vegetables

case-control study type of study in which individuals who have a health condition are compared with individuals who have similar characteristics but do not have the condition

casein major protein in cow's milk

cell smallest functioning structural unit in a living organism

chemical bond attraction that holds atoms together

chemical reactions process that changes the atomic arrangements of molecules

chemistry study of the composition and characteristics of matter and changes that can occur to it

cholecystokinin (CCK) hormone that stimulates the gallbladder to release bile and pancreas to secrete digestive enzymes

cholesterol lipid found in animal foods and precursor for steroid hormones, bile, and vitamin D

choline water-soluble compound in lecithin

chylomicron lipoprotein formed by intestinal cells

chyme mixture of gastric juice and partially digested food
coenzyme small molecule that interacts with enzymes, enabling the enzymes to function
cofactor ion or molecule that catalyzes chemical reactions
collagen fibrous protein that gives strength to connective tissue
colloidal osmatic pressure role of blood proteins attracting and holding fluid in the bloodstream
colostrum initial form of breast milk that contains anti-infective properties
colour additives dyes, pigments, or other substances that provide colour to food
complex carbohydrates (polysaccharides) compounds comprised of 10 or more monosaccharides bonded together
compounds molecules that contain two or more different elements
conception moment when a sperm enters an egg
connective tissue type of cells that hold together, protect, and support organs
contaminated food item that is impure or unsafe for human consumption
control group group being studied whose treatment differs from that of a treatment group, such as not receiving any treatment or receiving a placebo
coronary artery disease (CAD) a major form of CVD
correlation relationship between variables
cretinism condition affecting infants of women who were iodide deficient during pregnancy
cross-contamination unintentional transfer of pathogenic microbes from one food to another
cytochromes group of proteins involved in the release of energy from macronutrients

D

Daily Values (DVs) set of nutrient intake standards developed for labelling purposes
deamination removal of the nitrogen-containing group from an amino acid
defended body weight scientific notion that body fat content is genetically predetermined
deficiency disease state of health that occurs when a nutrient is missing from the diet
dehydration body water depletion
denaturation altering a protein's natural shape and function by exposing it to conditions such as heat, acids, and physical agitation
diabetes mellitus group of serious chronic diseases characterized by abnormal glucose, fat, and protein metabolism
diastolic pressure pressure in an artery that occurs when the ventricles relax between contractions
diet typical pattern of food choices
dietary fibre (fibre) indigestible plant material; most types are polysaccharides
Dietary Reference Intakes (DRIs) a set of energy and nutrient reference intake standards for a healthy population of North Americans
dietary supplements products that contain one or more ingredients, such as vitamins, minerals, or phytochemicals provided in a capsule, tablet, powder, or formula, that is not a conventional food product
digestion process by which large ingested molecules are mechanically and chemically broken down
disaccharide simple sugar comprised of two monosaccharides
diuretic substance that increases urine production
diverticula abnormal, tiny sacs that form in wall of colon
DNA molecule that contains coded instructions for synthesizing proteins
double-blind study experimental design in which neither the participants nor the researchers are aware of each participant's assignment
dual-energy X-ray absorptiometry (DXA) technique of estimating body composition that involves scanning the body with multiple low-energy X-rays
duodenum first segment of the small intestine

E

eating disorders psychological disturbances that lead to certain physiological changes and serious health complications
EATracker Dietitians of Canada interactive Internet dietary analysis, menu planning, and physical activity tool
edema accumulation of fluid in tissues
electrolytes ions that conduct electricity when they are dissolved in a solution
electrons small negatively charged particles that surround the nucleus of an atom
element each type of atom; substance that cannot be separated into simpler substances by ordinary chemical or physical means
embolus thrombus or part of a plaque that breaks free and travels through the bloodstream
embryo human organism from 14 days to 8 weeks after conception
empty-calorie describes food or beverage that is a poor source of micronutrients in relation to its energy value
emulsifier substance that helps water-soluble and water-insoluble compounds mix with each other
energy capacity to perform work
energy density energy value of a food in relation to the food's weight
energy equilibrium calorie intake equals calorie output
energy intake calories from foods and beverages that contain macronutrients and ethanol
energy output calories cells use to carry out their activities
enrichment addition of vitamins and minerals to food products such as cereal grains to replace those lost during processing or refinement
enterohepatic circulation process that recycles bile salts in the body
enzyme protein that speeds the rate of a chemical reaction but is not altered during the process
epidemiology study of disease rates among different population groups
epiglottis flap of tissue that folds down over the windpipe to keep food from entering the respiratory system during swallowing
epinephrine hormone produced by adrenal glands; also called adrenalin
epithelial cells cells that form protective tissues that line the body
epithelial tissue cells that line every body surface
ergogenic aids foods, devices, dietary supplements, or drugs used to improve physical performance
esophagus tubular structure of the GI tract that connects the pharynx with the stomach
essential amino acids amino acids the body cannot make or make enough to meet its needs
essential fatty acids lipids that must be supplied by the diet
essential nutrient nutrient that must be supplied by food or we will perish
Estimated Average Requirement (EAR) amount of a nutrient that meets the needs of 50% of healthy people in a life stage/gender group
Estimated Energy Requirement (EER) average daily energy intake that meets the needs of a healthy person maintaining his or her weight
estrogen hormone needed for normal bone development and maintenance
exercise physical activities that are usually planned and structured for a purpose
extracellular water water that surrounds cells or is in blood
extrusion reflex involuntary response in which a young infant thrusts its tongue forward when a solid or semisolid object is placed in its mouth

F

fad trendy practice that has widespread appeal for a period, but then becomes no longer fashionable
fat-free mass lean tissues
fat-soluble vitamins vitamins A, D, E, and K

female athlete triad condition characterized by disordered eating, lack of menstrual periods, and osteoporosis
fermentation process used to preserve or produce a variety of foods, including pickles and wine
fetus human organism from 8 weeks after conception until birth
fibre group of substances made by plants that humans do not digest but provide some health benefits
folic acid and **folacin** forms of folate
food additive any substance that becomes incorporated into food during production, packaging, transport, or storage
Food and Nutrition Board (FNB) group of nutrition scientists who develop DRIs
food-borne illness infection caused by microscopic disease-causing agents in food
food insecurity situation in which individuals or families are concerned about running out of food or not having enough money to buy more food
food intoxication illness that results when poisons produced by certain microbes contaminate food and irritate the intestinal tract
fortification addition of supplemental nutrients to commonly eaten foods during their manufacturing process
fructose monosaccharide in fruits, honey, and certain vegetables; "levulose" or "fruit sugar"
fungi simple organisms that live on dead or decaying organic matter
fungicides substances used to limit the spread of fungi

G

galactose monosaccharide that is a component of lactose
gastroesophageal sphincter section of esophagus next to the stomach that controls the opening to the stomach
gastrointestinal (GI) tract muscular tube that extends from the mouth to the anus
gene portion of DNA
genetic endowment inherited physical characteristics that can affect physical performance
genetic modification techniques that alter an organism's DNA
ghrelin hormone that stimulates eating behaviour
glucagon hormone that helps regulate blood glucose levels
glucose monosaccharide that is a primary fuel for muscles and other cells; "dextrose" or "blood sugar"
glycemic index (**GI**); **glycemic load** (**GL**) standards that indicate the body's insulin response to a carbohydrate-containing food
glycogen storage polysaccharide in animals
glycogenolysis glycogen breakdown
glycolysis first stage of glucose oxidation
goitrogens compounds that inhibit iodide metabolism by the thyroid gland
gynoid obesity condition characterized by excessive subcutaneous fat

H

H^+ hydrogen ion chemical formula
heartburn or **gastroesphageal reflux disease** backflow of irritating stomach contents into the esophagus
heat cramps heat-related illness characterized by painful muscle contractions
heat exhaustion heat-related illness that can occur after intense exercise
heatstroke most dangerous form of heat-related illness
heme iron form of iron in hemoglobin and myoglobin
hemoglobin iron-containing protein in red blood cells that transports oxygen to tissues and some carbon dioxide away from tissues
hemolysis disintegration of red blood cells
herbicides substances used to destroy weeds
hereditary hemochromatosis (HHC) common inherited disorder characterized by excess iron absorption
high-density lipoprotein (**HDL**) lipoprotein that transports cholesterol away from tissues and to the liver, where it can be eliminated
high-quality (complete) protein protein that contains all nine essential amino acids in amounts that support the growth
high sensitivity C-reactive protein (**hs-CRP**) protein produced primarily by the liver in response to inflammation; a marker for CVD
homeostasis relatively constant internal environment in the body that is critical for good health and survival
homocysteine amino acid that is a toxic by-product of methionine metabolism and plays a role in the development of atherosclerosis
hormones chemical messengers that convey information to target cells and that regulate body processes and responses
human physiology the study of how the body functions
hunger uncomfortable feeling that drives a person to consume food based on a physiological need for nourishment
hydration water status
hydrocarbon chain chain of carbon atoms bonded to each other and to hydrogen atoms
hydrogenation food manufacturing process that adds hydrogen atoms to liquid vegetable oil forming trans fats
hydrophilic part of molecule that attracts water
hydrophobic part of molecule that avoids water and attracts lipids
hypercalcemia condition characterized by higher than normal concentration of calcium in blood
hyperglycemia abnormally high blood glucose level
hypoglycemia condition that occurs when the blood glucose level is abnormally low
hypertension condition characterized by abnormally high blood pressure levels that persist
hyperthermia very high body temperature
hypothesis possible explanation about an observation that guides scientific research

I

ileum last segment of the small intestine
infant formula synthetic food that simulates human milk
insecticides substances used to control or kill insects
insensible perspiration body water that passes through the skin and not from sweat glands
insoluble fibre forms of dietary fibre that generally do not dissolve in water
insulin hormone that helps regulate blood glucose levels
intracellular water water that is inside cells
intrinsic factor (IF) substance produced in the stomach that facilitates intestinal absorption of vitamin B-12
ion atoms or group of atoms that has a positive or negative charge, due to the loss or gain of one or more electrons
iron deficiency condition characterized by low body stores of iron

J

jejunum middle segment of the small intestine

K

keratin tough protein found in hair, nails, and the outermost layers of skin
ketones chemicals that result from incomplete fat breakdown
kilocalorie or **Calorie** heat energy needed to raise the temperature of 1 litre of water 1° Celsius; measure of food energy
kwashiorkor form of protein-energy malnutrition (PEM) that results from consuming adequate energy and incomplete protein

L

lactase enzyme that splits lactose molecule
lactation milk production
lacteal lymph vessel in villus that absorbs most lipids
lactic acid compound formed from pyruvate during anaerobic metabolism
lactoovovegetarian vegetarian who consumes milk products and eggs for animal protein
lactose disaccharide comprised of a glucose and a galactose molecule; "milk sugar"
lactose intolerance inability to digest lactose properly
lactovegetarian vegetarian who consumes milk and milk products for animal protein
legumes plants that produce pods with a single row of seeds
leptin hormone that reduces hunger and inhibits fat storage in the body
life expectancy length of time an average person born in a specific year can expect to live
lifespan maximum number of years an organism can live
lifestyle way of living
linoleic acid essential fatty acid
lipases enzymes that break down lipids
lipids class of nutrients that do not dissolve in water
lipolysis fat breakdown
lipoprotein water-soluble structure that transports lipids through the bloodstream
lipoprotein lipase enzyme in capillary walls that breaks down triglycerides
liposuction surgical method of reducing the size of local fat deposits
low-birth weight (LBW) infant infant generally weighing less than 2.5 kg (5½ lbs.) at birth
low-density lipoprotein (LDL) lipoprotein that carries cholesterol into tissues
low-quality (incomplete) protein protein that lacks or has inadequate amounts of one or more of the essential amino acids
lumen open space within the small and large intestines
lymph fluid in the lymphatic system

M

macronutrients nutrients needed in gram amounts daily and that provide energy; carbohydrates, proteins, and fats
major minerals essential mineral elements required in amounts of 100 mg or more per day
malnutrition state of health that occurs when the body is improperly nourished
maltose disaccharide comprised of two glucose molecules; "malt sugar"
marasmus starvation
megadose amount of a micronutrient that is at least 10 times the Recommended Dietary Allowance (RDA)
metabolic syndrome condition that increases risk of type 2 diabetes and CVD
metabolic water water formed by cells as a metabolic by-product
metabolism the sum of all chemical reactions occurring in living cells
micelle water-soluble molecules containing bile, phospholipid, free fatty acids, and monoglycerides, which move lipid into the intestinal absorptive cells from the lumen of the GI tract
micronutrients vitamins and minerals
minerals elements that are found in the earth's crust
mitochondria organelles that generate ATP energy from macronutrients
moderation obtaining adequate amounts of nutrients while balancing calorie intake with calorie expenditure
molecule matter that forms when two or more atoms interact and are held together by a chemical bond
monoglyceride single fatty acid attached to a glycerol backbone
monosaccharide simple sugar that is the basic molecule of carbohydrates
monounsaturated fatty acid fatty acid that has one double bond within the carbon chain
morning sickness nausea and vomiting associated with pregnancy
mucus fluid that lubricates and protects certain cells
myocardial infarction heart attack
myoglobin iron-containing protein in muscle cells that controls oxygen uptake from red blood cells

N

negative energy balance calorie intake is less than calorie output
negative nitrogen balance state in which the body loses more nitrogen than it retains
neural tube embryonic structure that eventually develops into the brain and spinal cord
nitrogen balance (equilibrium) balancing nitrogen intake with nitrogen losses
nonessential amino acids group of amino acids that the body can make
nonexercise activity thermogenesis (NEAT) involuntary skeletal muscular activities such as fidgeting
nonheme iron form of iron in vegetables, grains, meats, and supplements
nonnutritive sweeteners group of synthetic compounds that are intensely sweet tasting compared to sugar
nutrient-dense describes food or beverage that has more vitamins and minerals in relation to its energy value
nutrients life-sustaining substances in food
nutrition scientific study of nutrients, chemicals that are in food that are necessary for life, and how the body uses them
nutritive sweetener sweetener that contributes energy to foods

O

obesity or **overweight** condition characterized by excessive body fat
omega-3 fatty acid type of polyunsaturated fatty acid
omnivore organism that can digest and absorb nutrients from plants, animals, fungi, and bacteria
orexins peptides that may contribute to hunger in humans
organ collection of tissues that perform a specific function
organ system collection of organs that work together to perform a major function
organelles structures in cells that perform specialized functions
organic foods foods produced without the use of antibiotics, hormones, synthetic fertilizers and pesticides, genetic improvements, or spoilage-killing radiation
osmosis movement of water through a selectively permeable membrane
osteoblasts bone cells that add bone to where the tissue is needed
osteoclasts bone cells that tear down bone tissue where it is not needed
osteomalacia adult rickets
osteoporosis chronic disease characterized by bones with low mass and reduced structure
ovovegetarian vegetarian who eats eggs for animal protein
oxidizing agent or **oxidant** substance that removes electrons from atoms or molecules
oxytocin hormone that elicits the let-down response and causes the uterus to contract

P

pancreatic amylase enzyme secreted by pancreas that breaks down starch into maltose molecules
pancreatic lipase digestive enzyme that removes two fatty acids from each triglyceride molecule
parasite organism that lives in or on another organism, often deriving nourishment from its host
parathyroid hormone (PTH) hormone secreted by parathyroid glands when blood calcium levels are too low

pasteurization process that kills the pathogens in foods and beverages as well as many microbes responsible for spoilage
pathogens disease-causing microbes
peak bone mass level of maximum bone density achieved in early adulthood
peer review expert critical analysis of a research article prior to its publication
pellagra niacin deficiency disease
pepsin gastric enzyme that breaks down proteins into polypeptides
peptide bond chemical attraction that connects two amino acids together
peptides small chains of amino acids
peristalsis muscular contractions of the gastrointestinal tract
pernicious anemia condition associated with vitamin B-12 deficiency that is characterized by nerve damage and megaloblastic red blood cells
pesticide substance that people use to kill or control unwanted insects, weeds, or other organisms
pH measure of the acidity or alkalinity of a solution
phosphocreatine (**PCr**) high-energy compound used to reform ATP under anaerobic conditions
phospholipid type of lipid needed to make cell membranes and for proper functioning of nerve cells
physical activity movement resulting from contraction of skeletal muscles
physical fitness ability to perform moderate- to vigorous-intensity activities without becoming excessively fatigued
physiological dose amount of a nutrient that is within the range of safe intake and enables the body to function optimally
physiology scientific study of the functioning of cells and other body structures
phytochemicals compounds made by plants that are not nutrients
pica practice of craving and/or eating nonfood items
placebo fake treatment, such as a sham pill, injection, or medical procedure
placebo effect response to a placebo
placenta organ of pregnancy that connects the uterus to the embryo/fetus via the umbilical cord
polypeptides proteins comprised of 50 or more amino acids
polyunsaturated fatty acid fatty acid that has two or more double bonds within the carbon chain
portal vein vein that collects nutrients from the intestinal tract and delivers them to the liver
positive energy balance calorie intake is greater than calorie output
positive nitrogen balance state in which the body retains more nitrogen than it loses
pregnancy-induced hypertension (**PIH**) type of hypertension that can develop during pregnancy
prehypertension persistent systolic blood pressure readings of 120 mm Hg to 139 mm Hg and diastolic readings of 80 mm Hg to 89 mm Hg
prenatal care specialized health care for pregnant women
prenatal period time between conception and birth; pregnancy
preterm infant born before 37 weeks of pregnancy
prolactin hormone that stimulates milk production after delivery
prooxidant substance that promotes free radical production
prospective study type of study that follows a group of healthy people over time to determine characteristics associated with the development of diseases
protein complementation the process of combining incomplete plant-based protein sources to provide all the essential amino acids
protein-energy malnutrition (**PEM**) condition that results from chronic lack of food or poor food choices
proteins large complex organic molecules made up of amino acids
protein turnover cellular process of breaking down proteins and recycling their amino acids
protons positively charged particles in the nucleus of an atom
protozoans single-celled microorganisms that have complex cell structures
provitamins vitamin precursors that do not function in the body until converted to active forms
pseudoscience presentation of information masquerading as factual and obtained by scientific methods
psychology study of the brain and human behaviour, which helps us understand what influences the decisions people make regarding diet and lifestyle
pyruvate compound that results from anaerobic breakdown of glucose

Q

quackery promotion of useless medical treatments

R

radical substance with an unpaired electron
Recommended Dietary Allowance (**RDA**) standards for recommending daily intakes of several nutrients for most healthy individuals
rectum lower section of the large intestine
requirement smallest amount of a nutrient that maintains a defined level of health
resting metabolic rate (**RMR**) body's rate of energy use a few hours after resting and eating
retinol (**preformed vitamin A**) most active form of vitamin A in the body
retrospective study type of study that determines factors that may have contributed to the development of disease
R group (side chain) part of amino acid that determines the molecule's physical and chemical properties
rickets vitamin D deficiency disorder in children
risk factor personal characteristic that increases a person's chances of developing a disease
rodenticides substances used to kill mice and rats

S

salivary amylase enzyme secreted by salivary glands that begins starch digestion
salt substance that forms when an acid combines with a base
satiety feeling that enough food has been eaten to delay the next eating episode and/or reduce subsequent food intake
saturated fatty acid fatty acid that has each carbon atom within the chain filled with hydrogen atoms
scurvy vitamin C deficiency disease
selectively permeable membrane barrier that allows the passage of certain substances and prevents the movement of other substances
senescence declining organ functioning and increased vulnerability
set-point theory scientific notion that body fat content is genetically predetermined
shelf life period of time that a food can be stored before it spoils
simple diffusion molecular movement from a region of higher to lower concentration
skinfold thickness measurements technique of estimating body composition in which calipers are used to measure the width of skinfolds at multiple body sites
solubility describes how easily a substance dissolves in a liquid solvent
soluble fibre forms of dietary fibre that dissolve or swell in water
solute lesser component of a solution that is dissolves in the solvent
solution evenly distributed mixture of two or more compounds
solvent primary component of a solution
spina bifida type of neural tube defect in which the spine does not form properly before birth, and it fails to enclose the spinal cord
starch storage polysaccharide in plants

sterilization process that kills or destroys all microorganisms and viruses
sterols/stanols types of lipids made by plants
sucrase enzyme that splits sucrose molecule
sucrose disaccharide comprised of a glucose and a fructose molecule; "table sugar"
sugars group of simple carbohydrates
syndrome group of signs and symptoms that occur together and indicate a specific health problem
systolic pressure maximum blood pressure within an artery that occurs when the ventricles contract

T

target heart rate zone heart rate range that reflects intensity of physical exertion
teratogen an agent that causes birth defects
testimonial personal endorsement of a product
tetrahydrofolic acid (THFA) folate coenzyme
thermic effect of food (TEF) energy used to digest foods and beverages as well as absorb and further process the macronutrients
thrombus fixed bunch of clots that remains in place
thyroid hormone hormone that controls the metabolic rate
tissues collection of cells that perform a specific function
Tolerable Upper Intake Level (**Upper Level** or **UL**) standard representing the highest average amount of a nutrient that is unlikely to be harmful when consumed daily
tolerances maximum amounts of pesticide residues that can be in or on each treated food crop
total body fat essential and storage fat
total water intake water in beverages and foods
trace minerals essential mineral elements required in amounts that are less than 100 mg per day
trans fats unsaturated fatty acids that have a trans double bond
transamination transfer of the nitrogen-containing group from an unneeded amino acid to a carbon skeleton to form an amino acid
treatment or **experimental group** group being studied that receives a treatment
triglyceride lipid that has three fatty acids attached to a three-carbon compound called glycerol; the form in which most fat in foods and in our body is found

U

ultratrace minerals mineral elements not classified as essential nutrients but that may have physiological functions
underwater weighing technique of estimating body composition that involves comparing weight on land to weight when completely submerged in a tank of water
underweight describes person with a BMI of less than 18.5
unintentional food additives substances that are accidentally in foods
unsaturated fatty acid fatty acid that is missing hydrogen atoms and has one or more double bonds within the carbon chain
upper-body obesity condition characterized by excessive abdominal fat
urea waste product of amino acid metabolism
uterus female reproductive organ that protects the developing organism during pregnancy

V

variable personal characteristic or other factor that changes and can influence an outcome
vegan vegetarian who eats only plant foods
vegetarians people who eat plant-based diets
veins vessels that return blood to the heart
very-low density lipoprotein (**VLDL**) lipoprotein that carries much of the triglycerides in the bloodstream
villi (singular, villus) tiny fingerlike projections of the small intestinal lining that participate in digesting and absorbing food
virus microbe consisting of a piece of genetic material coated with protein
vitamin complex organic molecule that regulates a variety of responses in the body

W

water intoxication condition that occurs when too much water is consumed in a short time period or the kidneys have difficulty filtering water from blood
water-soluble vitamins thiamin, riboflavin, niacin, vitamin B-6, pantothenic acid, folate, biotin, vitamin B-12, choline, and vitamin C
weaning gradual process of shifting from breast-feeding or bottle-feeding to drinking from a cup and eating solid foods
Wernicke-Korsakoff syndrome degenerative brain disorder resulting from thiamin deficiency that occurs primarily among alcoholics

X

xerophthalmia condition affecting the eyes that results from vitamin A deficiency

Credits

Chapter 1

Opener: © BananaStock/PunchStock; **1.1:** © Getty Images; **1.2 left & right:** © Rubberball Productions; **Page 5:** © Greg Kuchik/Getty Images; **1.3 left:** © C Squared Studios/Getty Images; **1.3 right:** © Brand X Pictures/PunchStock; **Table 1.3 (Apple):** © Burke/Triolo Productions/Getty Images; **Table 1.3 (Black Grapes):** © PhotoAlto/PunchStock; **Table 1.3 (Red Grapes):** © Jules Frazier/Getty Images; **Table 1.3 (Strawberry):** © Burke/Triolo Productions/Getty Images; **Table 1.3 (Red Onion):** © C Squared Studios/Getty Images; **Table 1.3 (Garlic):** © Stockdisc/PunchStock; **Table 1.3 (Carrots):** © Photodisc/Getty Images; **Table 1.3 (Chile Pepper):** © Royalty-Free/Corbis; **Table 1.3 (Peppers & Broccoli):** © Photodisc/Getty Images; **Table 1.3 (Coffee Beans):** © Photodisc/PunchStock; **Table 1.3 (Lemon):** © Photodisc/Getty Images; **Table 1.3 (Oranges and Juice):** © Royalty-Free/Corbis; **Page 8:** © Nancy R. Cohen/Getty Images; **Page 10:** © Her Majesty the Queen in Right of Canada, represented by the Minister of Health Canada, 2007; **1.4:** Public Health Agency of Canada, 2010. Reproduced with the permissions of the Minister of Public Works and Government Services Canada, 2010 ©; **Table 1.5:** © Royalty-Free/Corbis; © Hermera Technologies/Alamy; **Page 12:** © Burke/Triolo/Brand X Pictures/Jupiter Images; **Table 1.6:** © The McGraw-Hill Companies, Inc./Christopher Kerrigan, photographer; **1.5a:** © Ed Carey/Cole Group/Getty Images; **1.5b-d:** © The McGraw-Hill Companies, Inc./Christopher Kerrigan, photographer; **Page 14 (Pumpkin Pie):** © Royalty-Free/Corbis; **1.6 left:** © The McGraw-Hill Companies, Inc./Christopher Kerrigan, photographer; **1.6 right:** © Pixtal/SuperStock; **1.7 left:** © Royalty-Free/Corbis; **1.7 right:** © Burke/Triolo Productions/Getty Images; **Page 16 (Brownies):** © Michael Lamotte/Cole Group/Getty Images; **1.9 left:** © Photodisc/PunchStock; **1.9 right:** © The McGraw-Hill Companies, Inc./Michael Scott, photographer; **Page 19:** © Nancy R. Cohen/Getty Images; **1.10:** © The McGraw-Hill Companies, Inc./Lars A. Niki, photographer; **1.B:** © Digitial Vision/PunchStock; **1.C:** Courtesy of the Centers for Disease Control/Dr. Lyle Conrad; **1.D:** © Getty Images; **1.E:** © Comstock/Alamy; **1.E (Kernels):** © Don Farrall/Getty Images: **Page 24 (Spices):** © Royalty-Free/Corbis; **Page 25 (Cornbread):** © Michael Lamotte/Cole Group/Getty Images; **Page 23 (Echinacea flower):** © Brand X Pictures/PunchStock; **Page 25 left:** © Photodisc/Getty Images; **Page 25 (Raspberries):** © PhotoAlto/PunchStock; **Page 25 (Kale):** © Stockdisc/PunchStock; **Page 25 (Eggs):** © Image Source/PunchStock; **Page 25 (Peas):** © Burke/Triolo Productions/Getty Images; **Page 25 (Coke):** © Royalty-Free/Corbis; **Page 26:** © Stockdisc/PunchStock.

Chapter 2

Opener: Courtesy of the Waring Historical Library, MUSC, Charleston, S.C.; **Page 29 (Cabbage):** © Burke Triolo Productions/Getty Images; **Page 29 (Potatoes):** © Ingram Publishing/Alamy; **2.1:** © NIBSC/Photo Researchers, Inc.; **2.3:** Cathieking/Dreamstime.com; **Page 32:** © Digital Vision/PunchStock; **Page 33 left:** © Photodisc/Getty Images; **2.4:** Russ Hanson/ARS/SDA; **Page 34 top:** © Getty Images; **Page 34 bottom:** © Stockbyte/Getty Images; **Page 35:** Used with permission from Dietitians of Canada www.dcjournal.ca; **2.5:** acestock / GetStock.com; **Page 37 (Garlic):** © Photodisc/Getty Images; **Page 37 (Chocolate):** © The McGraw-Hill Companies, Inc./Ken Cavanagh, photographer; **Page 37 (Rice):** © The McGraw-Hill Companies, Inc./Jacques Cornell, photographer; **Page 38:** © Wendy Schiff; **2.6 left & right:** World Health Organization (WHO); **Page 39 bottom:** © Cleo Photography; **Page 40 (Doctor):** © Stockdisc/Punchstock; **Page 40 (Pills):** © Photodisc; **2.7:** © Wendy Schiff; **Table 2.1 top:** © copyright HON 2007. Health on the Net Foundation; **Table 2.1 bottom:** © Photodisc/Punchstock; **Page 44:** © Rick Eglinton/GetStock.com; **Page 47:** © Michael Lamotte/Cole Group/Getty Images; **Page 48 left:** © Photodisc/Getty Images; **Page 48 right:** © Stockdisc/PunchStock; **Page 49:** © Digital Vision/PunchStock.

Chapter 3

Opener: © Paul Irish/GetStock.com; **Page 52:** © Digital Archive Japan/Alamy; **Page 54:** © LARRY LEFEVER/Grant Heilman Photography; **Page 55 top:** © D. Hurst/Alamy; **Page 55 bottom:** © LARRY LEFEVER/Grant Heilman Photography; **Page 56 top:** © Photodisc/Getty Images; **Page 56 left:** © Cleo Photography; **Page 56 bottom:** © Maximilian Stock Ltd./FoodPix/jupiterimages.com; **3.4:** © The McGraw-Hill Companies, Inc./Christopher Kerrigan, photographer; **Page 58:** © Her Majesty the Queen in Right of Canada, represented by the Minister of Health Canada, 2007; **3.5, 3.6:** © Her Majesty the Queen in Right of Canada, represented by the Minister of Health Canada, 2007; **Page 63:** © Jules Frazier/Getty Images; **Page 64 (Cheese):** © Photodisc/Getty Images; **Page 64 (Candies):** © PhotoLink/Getty Images; **Page 65 (Fruit):** © John A. Rizzo/Getty Images; **Page 65 (Food basket):** © C Squared Studios/Getty Images; **Page 65 (Salt):** © C Squared Studios/Getty Images; **Page 66 (Wine):** © Jules Frazier/Getty Images; **Page 66 (Hand-washing):** © Royalty-Free/Corbis; **3.8:** Reprinted with permission from Dietitians of Canada www.dietitians.ca; **3.9:** © Cleo Photography; **Page 72:** © Foodcollection.com/Alamy; **3.10:** © McGraw-Hill Ryerson, Ltd./Kara Stahl; **3.11:** © Martin Lee/GetStock.com; **3.12:** © Cleo Photography; **3.A:** foodfolio/Getstock; **3.B:** © Oldways Preservation & Exchange Trust; **Page 78:** © Burke/Triolo Productions/Getty Images; **Page 79 left:** © Photodisc/Punchstock; **Page 79 right:** © Her Majesty the Queen in Right of Canada, represented by the Minister of Health Canada, 2007; **Page 80 bottom:** © Her Majesty the Queen in Right of Canada, represented by the Minister of Health Canada, 2007; **Page 81 (Seeds):** © Royalty-Free/Corbis; **Page 81 bottom: ham:** © Royalty-Free/Corbis; **egg:** © The McGraw-Hill Companies, Inc./Ken Karp, photographer; **Page 82 top left:** © D. Hurst/Alamy; **Page 82 bottom left:** © Royalty-Free/Corbis; **Page 82 bottom right:** © Stockdisc/PunchStock; **Page 83:** © Photodisc/Getty Images.

Chapter 4

Opener: © The McGraw-Hill Companies, Inc./Joanne Brummett, artwork; **4.3:** © Wendy Schiff; **4.5 (Lemon) & (Wine):** © Burke/Triolo Productions/Getty Images; **4.5 (Cola):** © Royalty-Free/Corbis; **4.5 (Tomato) & (Banana):** © Stockdisc/PunchStock; **4.5 (Coffee):** © Royalty-Free/Corbis; **4.5 (Milk):** © The McGraw-Hill Companies, Inc./Bob Coyle, photographer; **4.5 (Egg):** © Siede Preis/Getty Images; **4.5 (Baking Soda):** © The McGraw-Hill Companies, Inc./

Stephen Frisch, photographer; **4.5 (Ammonia):** © The McGraw-Hill Companies, Inc./Jacques Cornell, photographer; **4.5 (Oven cleaner):** © The McGraw-Hill Companies, Inc./Ken Karp, photographer; **Page 88 bottom left:** © The McGraw-Hill Companies, Inc./Stephen Frisch, photographer; **4.6:** © Phil Degginger; **4.8:** © Wendy Schiff; **Page 98 left:** © Royalty-Free/Corbis; **4.25:** © Dr. G. W. Willis/Visuals Unlimited; **Page 102 left:** © Lee W. Wilcox; **Page 103:** © Martin Lee/GetStock.com; **Page 104:** Brand X Pictures; **Page 105 top:** © Royalty-Free/Corbis; **4.A:** © David M. Martin, M.D./Photo Researchers, Inc.; **Page 109 left:** © Wendy Schiff; **Page 109 right:** © Jonelle Weaver/Getty Images; **Page 110 left:** © Wendy Schiff; **Page 110 right:** © Stockdisc/PunchStock.

Chapter 5

Opener: © Ryan McVay/Getty Images; **Page 115:** © StockFood/SuperStock; **Page 116:** © Cleo Photography; **Page 117 top:** © Wendy Schiff; **5.4:** © Wendy Schiff; **Page 118:** © Wendy Schiff; **5.5:** © Photodisc/PunchStock; **5.6:** © Wendy Schiff; **Table 5.5 (Rice):** © The McGraw-Hill Companies, Inc./Jacques Cornell, photographer; **Table 5.5 (Beans):** © Royalty-Free/Corbis; **Table 5.5 (Banana):** © Stockdisc/PunchStock; **Table 5.5 (Lemon) & (Apple):** © Burke/Triolo Productions/Getty Images; **5.7:** © Cole Group/Getty Images; **Table 5.6 (Carrots):** © C Squared Studios/Getty Images; **Table 5.6 (Lettuce) & (Raspberries):** © Burke/Triolo Productions/Getty Images; **Table 5.6 (Potato):** © The McGraw-Hill Companies, Inc./Christopher Kerrigan, photographer; **5.11:** Adapted from Statistics Canada, *Overview of Canadians' Eating Habits, 2004* (Nutrition: Findings from the Canadian Community Health Survey), 82-620-MIE2006002, January 29, 2010 (http://www.statcan.gc.ca/pub/82-620-m/82-620-m2006002-eng.pdf); **Page 125 (Fruits):** © Digital Vision/Getty Images; **Page 125 (Juice):** © The McGraw-Hill Companies, Inc./Ken Karp, photographer; **Page 125 (Cola):** © Royalty-Free/Corbis; **5.12:** © Cleo Photography; **Page 127 top:** © Royalty-Free/Corbis; **Page 17 bottom:** © PhotoLink/Getty Images; **5.13:** © Nick Rowe/Getty Images; **Page 130:** Reprinted with permission from Canadian Diabetes Association, www.diabetes.ca; **Page 131 top & bottom:** © PhotoLink/Getty Images; **Page 132:** © The McGraw-Hill Companies, Inc./Lars A. Niki, photographer; **Table 5.9:** Reprinted with permission from Canadian Diabetes Association; **Page 133 top:** © Royalty-Free/Corbis; **5.14:** © Cleo Photography; **5.15:** © DU CANE MEDICAL IMAGING LTD/Photo Researchers, Inc.; **Page 137 left & right:** © Photodisc/Getty Images; **Page 138 left:** © Steve Russell/GetStock.com; **Page 138 right:** © Royalty-Free/Corbis; **Page 139 top left:** © Comstock/PunchStock; **Page 139 bottom:** © PhotoLink/Getty Images; **Page 140:** © Photodisc/Getty Images; **Page 141 left:** © C Squared Studios/Getty Images; **Page 141 right:** © Kevin Sanchez/Cole Group/Getty Images; **Page 142:** © C Squared Studios/Getty Images; **Page 144 left:** © Burke/Triolo Productions/Getty Images; **Page 144 right:** © Stockdisc/PunchStock; **Page 145:** © Burke/Triolo Productions/Getty Images.

Chapter 6

Opener: Carlosdelacalle/Dreamstime.com/GetStock.com; **Page 147 bottom:** © Cathy Melloan/PhotoEdit Inc.; **Page 149:** © John A. Rizzo/Getty Images; **Table 6.1 (Oils):** © The McGraw-Hill Companies, Inc./Elite Images, photographer; **Page 152:** © Wendy Schiff; **Table 6.2:** © Royalty-Free/Corbis; **Page 159:** © The McGraw-Hill Companies, Inc./John Flournoy, photographer; **6.14:** © Cleo Photography; **6.16a&b:** © Ed Reschke; **Page 162:** © The McGraw-Hill Companies, Inc./Gary He, photographer; **Page 165:** © Royalty-Free/Corbis; **6.20:** Oldways Presentation & Exchange Trust, 2000. Courtesy of Oldways (www.oldwayspt.org); **Page 167:** © C Squared Studios/Getty Images; **Page 168:** © Royalty-Free/Corbis; **Page 169:** © Ingram Publishing/Alamy; **Table 6.7 top:** © C Squared Studios/Getty Images; **Table 6.7 middle:** © John A. Rizzo/Getty Images; **Table 6.7 bottom:** © Nancy R. Cohen/Getty Images; **Page 171:** © Wendy Schiff; **Page 172:** © Ryan McVay/Getty Images; **6.B:** © The McGraw-Hill Companies, Inc./Jill Braaten, photographer; **Page 176 left:** © Allen Ross Photography; **Page 176 right:** Gwinnet County Police Department/Courtesy of the Centers for Disease Control; **6.F:** © Arthur Glauberman/Photo Researchers, Inc.; **6.G:** PhotoSlinger/Getstock.com; **Page 180:** © Burke/Triolo Productions/Getty Images; **Page 181:** © Photodisc/PunchStock; **Page 182:** © Burke/Triolo Productions/Getty Images; **Page 183 top:** © Royalty-Free/Corbis; **Page 183 bottom:** © Wendy Schiff; **Page 184:** © John A. Rizzo/Getty Images; **Page 185:** © Cleo Photography; **Page 186:** © Spike Mafford/Getty Images; **Page 187:** © Burke/Triolo Productions/Getty Images; **Page 188 left:** © Photodisc/Getty Images; **Page 188 right:** © Stockdisc/PunchStock; **Page 189:** © Burke/Triolo Productions/Getty Images.

Chapter 7

Opener: © The McGraw-Hill Companies, Inc./Gary He, photographer; Table 7.2 (Pizza) & (Tofu): © C Squared Studios/Getty Images; **Table 7.2 (Ham):** © Burke/Triolo Productions/Getty Images; **Table 7.2 (Beans):** © Royalty-Free/Corbis; **Table 7.2 (Peas):** © Getty Images; **Table 7.2 (Bagel):** © Photodisc/Getty Images; **Table 7.2 (Soup):** © John A. Rizzo/Getty Images; **7.3 left:** © C Squared Studios/Getty Images; **7.3 right:** © Photodisc/PunchStock; **Page 194 bottom:** © Wendy Schiff; **Page 195:** © Cleo Photography; **7.8:** © Dr. Stanley Flegler/Visuals Unlimited/Getty Images; **Page 199:** © liquidlibrary/PictureQuest; **Page 200 top:** © PhotoAlto/PunchStock; **Page 200 bottom:** © liquidlibrary/PictureQuest; **Page 202:** © IAN BODDY/SCIENCE PHOTO LIBRARY/Photo Researchers, Inc.; **Page 203 top:** National Institute for Allergy and Infectious Disease (NIAID)/NIH; **Page 203 bottom:** © C Squared Studios/Getty Images; **Page 204:** © Karl Weatherley/Getty Images; **7.14 (Roast) & (Fish):** © Photodisc/PunchStock; **7.14 (Turkey):** © Paul Poplis/StockFood Creative/Getty Images; **7.14 (Rice):** © The McGraw-Hill Companies, Inc./Jacques Cornell, photographer; **7.14 (Bread):** © C Squared Studios/Getty Images; **7.14 (Beans):** © Burke/Triolo Productions/Getty Images; **7.14 (Egg):** © Siede Preis/Getty Images; **7.14 (Nuts):** © C Squared Studios/Getty Images; **7.14 (Dairy):** © Photodisc/Getty Images; **Page 205 right:** Scott Bauer/ARS/USDA; **7.15:** © Cleo Photography; **Page 207 top:** © PhotoLink/Getty Images; **Page 207 bottom:** © Jonelle Weaver/Getty Images; **Page 208 top:** © Digital Vision/PunchStock; **7.16 left:** © C Squared Studios/Getty Images; **7.16 center:** © Royalty-Free/Corbis; **7.16 right:** © C Squared Studios/Getty Images; **Page 209 bottom left:** © Mitch Hrdlicka/Getty Images; **Page 210:** © Jonelle Weaver/Getty Images; **Page 211 top:** © Cleo Photography; **Page 211 bottom:** © Keith Ovregaard/Cole Group/Getty Images; **Page 212:** © Jonelle Weaver/Getty Images; **Page 213:** © The McGraw-Hill Companies, Inc./Gary He, photographer; **7.17, 7.17 inset, 7.18:** Courtesy of the Centers for Disease Control/Dr. Lyle Conrad; **Page 216:** © Getty Images; **Page 217:** © Mitch Hrdlicka/Getty Images; **Page 218:** © Keith Ovregaard/Cole Group/Getty Images; **Page 219 left:** © The McGraw-Hill Companies, Inc./Jacques Cornell, photographer; **Page 219 right:** © Wendy Schiff; **Page 220:** © Michael Lamotte/Cole Group/Getty Images; **Page 221 (Salad):** © PhotoLink/Getty Images; **Page 221 (Yogourts):** © The McGraw-Hill Companies, Inc./Bob Coyle, photographer; **Page 221 (Bread):** © Digital Vision/Getty Images; **Page 222 left:** © Ingram Publishing/Alamy; **Page 222 right:** © Stockdisc/PunchStock; **Page 223:** © Photodisc/Getty Images.

Chapter 8

Opener: © The McGraw-Hill Companies, Inc.; **Page 225:** © C Squared Studios/Getty Images; **Page**

226: © Royalty-Free/Corbis; **Page 227:** © Jules Frazier/Getty Images; **Page 230 (Vegetables):** © Ingram Publishing/Alamy; **Page 230 (Dressing):** © Comstock/PunchStock; **Page 231:** USDA Photo by Bill Tarpening; **Page 232 top:** © Photodisc/Getty Images; **8.4:** © Wendy Schiff; **8.5:** © Ed Carey/Cole Group/Getty Images; **Table 8.2 (Oil):** © The McGraw-Hill Companies, Inc./ Jacques Cornell, photographer; **Table 8.2 (Milk):** © The McGraw-Hill Companies, Inc./Ken Karp, photographer; **Table 8.2 (Broccoli):** © Stockdisc/ PunchStock; **Table 8.2 (Nuts) & (Salmon):** © C Squared Studios/Getty Images; **Table 8.2 (Kale):** © Stockdisc/PunchStock; **Page 235:** © Photodisc/Getty Images; **Page 236:** © Nick Rowe/Getty Images; **Page 237 top, 8.8 (Pumpkin):** © Ingram Publishing/Alamy; **8.8 (Carrot):** © Photodisc/Getty Images; **8.8 (Papaya):** © Burke/Triolo Productions/Getty Images; **8.9:** *A Colour Atlas and Text of Nutritional Disorders* by Dr. Donald D. McLaren (Mosby-Wolfe Europe Ltd.); **Page 238 bottom:** © PhotoLink/Getty Images; **8.10:** *A Colour Atlas and Text of Nutritional Disorders* by Dr. Donald D. McLaren (Mosby-Wolfe Europe Ltd.); **Page 240:** © Jackson Vereen/Cole Group/Getty Images; **8.13 (Fish):** © Digital Vision/ Getty Images; **8.13 (Milk):** © The McGraw-Hill Companies, Inc./Ken Karp, photographer; **8.13 (Mushrooms):** © C Squared Studios/Getty Images; **Page 242:** © Peter Cade/Getty Images; **8.16:** © Ken Gillespie Photography/GetStock; **8.17 (Mango):** © Stockdisc/PunchStock; **8.17 (Asparagus) & (Sardines):** © Burke/Triolo Productions/Getty Images; **Page 246 (Cornflakes):** © Photodisc/PunchStock; **Page 246 (Mushroom):** © Burke/Triolo Productions/Getty Images; **Page 246 (Orange):** © Dennis Gray/Cole Group/Getty Images; **Page 246 (Spinach):** © Royalty-Free/Corbis; **8.20:** © Digital Vision/Getty Images; **8.21 (Ham):** © Royalty-Free/Corbis; **8.21 (Juice):** © Photodisc/Getty Images; **8.21 (Peas):** © C Squared Studios/Getty Images; **8.22:** Courtesy of the Centers for Disease Control; **8.23 (Cereal):** © Photodisc/PunchStock; **8.23 (Taco) & (Spinach):** © Royalty-Free/Corbis; **8.24 (Cereal):** © Comstock/PunchStock; **8.24 (Chicken):** © Michael Lamotte/Cole Group/Getty Images; **8.24 (Peanuts):** © C Squared Studios/Getty Images; **Page 250:** © Mireille Vautier/Alamy; **8.25:** Courtesy of the Centers for Disease Control; **Page 251 bottom:** © C Squared Studios/Getty Images; **8.27 (Potato):** © Royalty-Free/Corbis; **8.27 (Salmon):** © C Squared Studios/Getty Images; **8.27 (Banana):** © Stockdisc/PunchStock; **Page 252 bottom:** © Wendy Schiff; **Page 253 top:** Peggy Greb/ARS/USDA; **8.28 (Rice):** © Jules Frazier/Getty Images; **8.28 (Asparagus):** © Burke/ Triolo Productions/Getty Images; **8.28 (Juice):** © Photodisc/Getty Images; **8.29 top:** © Dr. R. King/ Photo Researchers, Inc.; **8.29 bottom:** © Dr. E. Walker/Photo Researchers, Inc.; **8.30a:** © Claude Edelmann/Photo Researchers, Inc.; **8.30b:** © Wellcome Trust/Custom Medical Stock Photo; **8.32 (Sardines):** © Burke/Triolo Productions/ Getty Images; **8.32 (Soy Milk):** © Wendy Schiff; **8.32 (Burger):** © Burke/Triolo Productions/Getty Images; **Page 258:** © Cleo Photography; **Page 259:** Courtesy of the Centers for Disease Control; **8.34 (Peppers):** © Jules Frazier/Getty Images; **8.34 (Strawberries):** © Burke/Triolo Productions/ Getty Images; **8.34 (Kiwi):** © Ingram Publishing/ Alamy; **Page 261 top:** © Wendy Schiff; **Page 261 bottom:** © Comstock Images/PictureQuest; **Page 263:** © Photodisc/Getty Images; **Page 267:** © C Squared Studios/Getty Images; **Page 268:** © Digital Vision/Getty Images; **Page 269:** © Mitch Hrdlicka/Getty Images; **Page 270:** © Greg Kuchik/ Getty Images; **Page 271:** © Stockdisc/PunchStock; **Page 272 left:** © C Squared Studios/Getty Images; **Page 272 right:** © Burke/Triolo Productions/Getty Images; **Page 273:** © The McGraw-Hill Companies, Inc./Ken Karp, photographer.

Chapter 9

Opener: SSGT Jason M. Carter, USMC/DoD Media; **Page 275:** © Comstock Images/PictureQuest; **Page 276:** © Royalty-Free/Corbis; **Table 9.1 (Lettuce):** © Stockdisc/PunchStock; **Table 9.1 (Tomatoes):** © Burke/Triolo Productions/Getty Images; **9.6:** © Stephen J. Krasemann/Photo Researchers, Inc.; **Page 282 top:** © Photodisc/ Getty Images; **Page 282 bottom:** © Comstock/ PunchStock; **Page 283 top:** U.S. Air Force photo by Tech. Sgt. Mike Buytas; **Page 283 bottom:** TSGT Lance Cheung, USAF/DoD Media; **Page 284:** © Photodisc/PunchStock; **Table 9.3 (Cereal):** © Photodisc/PunchStock; **Table 9.3 (Salad):** © Ingram Publishing/Alamy; **Table 9.3 (Oat Seeds):** © Siede Preis/Getty Images; **Table 9.3 (Peanut Butter):** © Burke/Triolo Productions/ Getty Images; **9.8:** © Royalty-Free/Corbis; **9.10:** © Michael Klein/Peter Arnold, Inc.; **Page 289 top:** © Comstock/Alamy; **9.12 (Cereal):** © Photodisc/ PunchStock; **9.12 (Sardines):** © Burke/Triolo Productions/Getty Images; **9.12 (Milk):** © The McGraw-Hill Companies, Inc./Ken Karp, photographer; **9.13:** © Wendy Schiff; **9.14:** © Her Majesty the Queen in Right of Canada, represented by the Minister of Health Canada, 2007. This publication may be used without permission. No changes permitted. HC Pub.: 4651 Cat.:H164-38/1-2007E ISBN: 0-662-44467-1; **Page 292 top, middle:** © Wendy Schiff; **9.15:** © Yoav Levy/Phototake.com; **Page 293:** © Dynamic Graphics/JupiterImages; **Page 294:** © Jonelle Weaver/Getty Images; **9.16 (Soup):** © John A. Rizzo/Getty Images; **9.16 (Ham) & (Pickle):** © Burke/Triolo Productions/Getty Images; **Page 297 bottom:** Adapted from: USDA: *Home and Garden Bulletin*, No. 232-6, April 1986; **Page 298:** © Photodisc/Getty Images; **Page 299:** © Cleo Photography; **Page 300:** © The McGraw-Hill Companies, Inc./Ken Karp, photographer; **9.17 (Potato):** © Royalty-Free/Corbis; **9.17 (Papaya):** © Burke/Triolo Productions/Getty Images; **9.17 (Melon):** © C Squared Studios/Getty Images; **9.18:** © Her Majesty the Queen in Right of Canada, represented by the Minister of Health Canada, 2007. This publication may be used without permission. No changes permitted. HC Pub.: 4651 Cat.:H164-38/1-2007E ISBN: 0-662-44467-1; **9.19 (Spinach):** © Burke/Triolo Productions/Getty Images; **9.19 (Nuts):** © C Squared Studios/Getty Images; **9.19 (Yam):** © Stockdisc/PunchStock; **9.20:** © Her Majesty the Queen in Right of Canada, represented by the Minister of Health Canada, 2007. This publication may be used without permission. No changes permitted. HC Pub.: 4651 Cat.:H164-38/1-2007E ISBN: 0-662-44467-1; **Page 306:** © C Squared Studios/Getty Images; **Table 9.9 (Shrimp):** © John A. Rizzo/Getty Images; **Table 9.9 (Mushrooms):** © C Squared Studios/Getty Images; **Table 9.9 (Beans) & (Spinach):** © Royalty-Free/Corbis; **9.21 (Oatmeal):** © Comstock/PunchStock; **9.21 (Beans):** © Wendy Schiff; **9.21 (Chicken):** © Ernie Friedlander/Cole Group/Getty Images; **9.22:** © Her Majesty the Queen in Right of Canada, represented by the Minister of Health Canada, 2007. This publication may be used without permission. No changes permitted. HC Pub.: 4651 Cat.:H164-38/1-2007E ISBN: 0-662-44467-1; **Page 310:** © C Squared Studios/Getty Images; **9.23 left:** © Dr. R. King/ Photo Researchers, Inc.; **9.23 right:** © Gladden Willis, M.D./Visuals Unlimited; **Page 311 top:** © liquidlibrary/PictureQuest; **Page 311 bottom:** © Wendy Schiff; **Page 312 top:** Courtesy of The Hospital for Sick Children; **9.24:** Dr. Ananda S. Prasad/American Journal of Medicine; **Page 313 top:** © Cleo Photography; **9.25 (Oysters):** © Wendy Schiff; **9.25 (Crab) & (Pecans):** © C Squared Studios/Getty Images; **9.26:** © Her Majesty the Queen in Right of Canada, represented by the Minister of Health Canada, 2007. This publication may be used without permission. No changes permitted. HC Pub.: 4651 Cat.:H164-38/1-2007E ISBN: 0-662-44467-1; **Page 316 top:** © Cleo Photography; **9.28 (Milk):** © The McGraw-Hill Companies, Inc./Ken Karp, photographer; **9.28 (Shrimp):** © Ingram Publishing/Alamy; **9.28 (Egg):** © Siede Preis/Getty Images; **Page 317:** © Burke/Triolo Productions/ Getty Images; **9.29 (Sunflower Seeds):** © The McGraw-Hill Companies, Inc./Jacques Cornell, photographer; **9.29 (Egg):** © Burke/Triolo Productions/Getty Images; **9.29 (Mushrooms):** © C Squared Studios/Getty Images; **Page 318 bottom:** © Wendy Schiff; **Page 319:** © Nancy R. Cohen/Getty Images; **Page 320:** © M. Freeman/

PhotoLink/Getty Images; **Page 321:** © The McGraw-Hill Companies, Inc./Gary He, photographer; **Page 322 (Glass of Water):** © John A. Rizzo/Getty Images; **Page 322 (Bottle of Water):** © Photodisc/Getty Images; **Page 323 (Groceries):** © Burke/Triolo Productions/Getty Images; **Page 323 (Apple):** © C Squared Studios/Getty Images; **Page 324:** © David Buffington/Getty Images; **Page 326 (Smoothie):** © Jonelle Weaver/Getty Images; **Page 326 (Strawberries):** © Burke/Triolo Productions/Getty Images; **Page 327:** © Jonelle Weaver/Getty Images; **Page 328 left:** © Burke/Triolo Productions/Getty Images; **Page 328 right:** © Stockdisc/PunchStock; **Page 329:** © Siede Preis/Getty Images.

Chapter 10

Opener: © 2009 Jupiterimages Corporation; **Page 331:** © Adam Crowley/Getty Images; **Page 332:** © Photodisc/Getty Images; **10.2:** © Gladden Willis, M.D./Visuals Unlimited; **10.3:** © Rich O'Quihn, University of Georgia; **10.4:** DEXA; **10.5:** © David Young-Wolf/PhotoEdit Inc.; **10.6 (photo):** Cathieking/Dreamstime.com; **10.6 (illustration):** Cathieking/Dreamstime.com; **Page 336:** © The McGraw-Hill Companies, Inc./Lars A. Niki, photographer; **Page 337:** © Stockbyte/PunchStock; **Page 339 bottom:** © Photodisc/Getty Images; **Page 342:** © Steve Mason/Getty Images; **Page 343:** © Jules Frazier/Getty Images; **Page 344:** © Royalty-Free/Corbis; **Page 345:** © Digital Vision/PunchStock; **10.13:** © Science VU/Jackson/Visuals Unlimited; **Page 350, Page 351:** © Royalty-Free/Corbis; **Page 352 top:** © Photodisc/Getty Images; **Page 352 bottom:** © The McGraw-Hill Companies, Inc./Lars A. Niki, photographer; **Page 354:** © Photodisc/PunchStock; **Page 355 both:** © Wendy Schiff; **Page 356 top:** © The McGraw-Hill Companies, Inc./Andrew Resek, photographer; **Page 356 bottom:** © Wendy Schiff; **Page 357:** © David Buffington/Getty Images; **Page 358 top:** © liquidlibrary/PictureQuest; **Page 358 (Bananas):** © Burke/Triolo Productions/Getty Images; **Page 358 (Apple):** © Photodisc/Getty Images; **Page 358 (Raisins):** © The McGraw-Hill Companies, Inc./Jacques Cornell, photographer; **Page 359 top:** © Wendy Schiff; **Page 359 bottom:** © Ryan McVay/Getty Images; **10.17:** © Girishh/Alamy; **Page 363:** © The McGraw-Hill Companies, Inc./Lars A. Niki, photographer; **10.18:** © AP/Wide World Photos; **Page 366:** © Dynamic Images/Jupiter Images; **Page 367:** © fStop/Getty Images; **Page 368:** © The McGraw-Hill Companies, Inc./Lars A. Niki, photographer; **Page 369:** © Stockbyte/PunchStock; **Page 371:** © David Buffington/Getty Images; **Page 372 top:** © Digital Vision/Getty Images; **Page 372 bottom:** © Royalty-Free/Corbis; **Page 372:** © Comstock/PunchStock; **Page 374:** © Photodisc/Getty Images; **Page 375:** © PhotoLink/Getty Images; **Page 376 left:** © Scott T. Baxter/Getty Images; **Page 376 right:** © Stockdisc/PunchStock; **Page 377:** © Ryan McVay/Getty Images.

Chapter 11

Opener: © AP/Wide World Photos; **Page 379:** © Sean Thompson/Photodisc/Getty Images; **11.1:** © Royalty-Free/Corbis; **11.2:** © Wendy Schiff; **Page 381 bottom, Page 386:** © Ryan McVay/Getty Images; **Page 388 top:** LCPL Richard A. Burkdall, USMC/DoD Media; **Page 388 bottom:** © Digital Vision/Punchstock; **Page 390:** Mario Beauregard/CPI/The Canadian Press; **Table 11.2 (Bread):** © John A. Rizzo/Getty Images; **Table 11.2 (Lettuce):** © Burke/Triolo Productions/Getty Images; **Table 11.2 (Cookies):** © John A. Rizzo/Getty Images; **Table 11.2 (Pasta):** © Royalty-Free/Corbis; **Table 11.2 (Oranges):** © Dennis Gray/Cole Group/Getty Images; **Table 11.2 (Celery):** © Burke/Triolo Productions/Getty Images; **Table 11.3:** © Jonelle Weaver/Getty Images; **Table 11.4:** © Wendy Schiff; **Page 394 top:** © D. Fischer & P. Lyons/Cole Group/Getty Images; **Page 394 bottom:** © Keith Ovregaard/Cole Group/Getty Images; **Table 11.5:** © Wendy Schiff; **Page 397 top:** LCPL Casey N. Thurston, USMC/DoD Media; **Page 397 bottom:** © Wendy Schiff; **Page 398 left:** © Javier Pierini/Getty Images; **Page 398 (Salt):** © C Squared Studios/Getty Images; **Page 398 (Juice):** © The McGraw-Hill Companies, Inc./Ken Karp, photographer; **Page 398 (Sugar):** © Royalty-Free/Corbis; **Page 400 top:** © Comstock/Alamy; **Page 400 bottom:** © Nick Koudis/Getty Images; **Table 11.8 (Tea):** © John A. Rizzo/Getty Images; **Table 11.8 (Coffee):** © John A. Rizzo/Getty Images; **Page 403:** © Royalty-Free/Corbis; **Page 403:** © Jeff Maloney/Getty Images; **11.A:** © Wendy Schiff; **Page 405:** © The McGraw-Hill Companies, Inc./Ken Cavanagh, photographer; **Page 406 left:** © Wendy Schiff; **Page 406 right:** © Ed Carey/Cole Group/Getty Images; **Page 407 top:** © Royalty-Free/Corbis; **Page 407 bottom:** © Stockdisc/PunchStock; **Page 408:** © John A. Rizzo/Getty Images; **Page 409:** © Royalty-Free/Corbis.

Chapter 12

Opener (E. Coli): Courtesy of the Centers for Disease Control/National Escherichia, Shigella, Vibrio Reference Unit at CDC; **Opener (Salad):** © Wendy Schiff; **Page 411:** © The McGraw-Hill Companies, Inc.; **Page 412:** © Lucas Oleniuk/GetStock.com; **Page 407 top:** © PhotoAlto/PictureQuest; **Page 407 bottom:** © Dynamic Graphics Group/IT Stock Free/Alamy; **Page 414 left & right:** Courtesy of the Centers for Disease Control; **Table 12.1 (Sausages):** © Burke/Triolo Productions/Getty Images; **Table 12.1 (Oysters):** © John A. Rizzo/Getty Images; **Table 12.1 (Cheese):** © J. Glenn/Cole Group/Getty Images; **Page 416 left:** © Eye of Science/Photo Researchers, Inc.; **Page 416 right:** © Burke/Triolo Productions/Getty Images; **Table 12.2:** © Royalty-Free/Corbis; **12.1:** F.P. Williams, U.S. EPA; **Page 418 bottom:** From M. Schaechter, G. Medoff, & D. Schlessinger (Eds) *Mechanisms of Microbial Disease*, 1989. Williams and Wilkins; **Page 419 (Mushrooms):** © The McGraw-Hill Companies, Inc./Stephen P. Lynch, photographer; **Page 419 (Cheese):** © Stockbyte/PunchStock; **12.3:** © PhotoLink/Getty Images; **Page 420 bottom:** © Royalty-Free/Corbis; **Page 421 bottom:** © The McGraw-Hill Companies, Inc./Rick Brady, photographer; **Page 422:** James Gathany/Courtesy of the Centers for Disease Control; **12.7, 12.8:** © Wendy Schiff; **Page 424 top:** © Royalty-Free/Corbis; **Page 424 bottom:** USDA; **Table 12.6:** © C Squared Studios/Getty Images; **12.9:** USDA, Be Food Safe Campaign; **Page 427 right:** © BananaStock/PunchStock; **Page 427 (Grapes):** © C Squared Studios/Getty Images; **Page 427 (Raisins):** © The McGraw-Hill Companies, Inc./Jacques Cornell, photographer; **Table 12.7 (Pickles):** © Kevin Sanchez/Cole Group/Getty Images; **Table 12.7 (Dried Fruits):** © C Squared Studios/Getty Images; **Table 12.7 (Spam):** © The McGraw-Hill Companies, Inc./Elite Images, photographer; **Table 12.7 (Cheese):** © Burke/Triolo Productions/Getty Images; **12.10:** Photo by Stephen Ausmus/ARS/USDA; **Page 430:** Photo by Jocelyn Augustino/FEMA; **Page 431:** © Wendy Schiff; **Page 433:** © Photodisc/Getty Images; **Page 434:** Photo by Tim McCabe, courtesy of the USDA Natural Resources Conservation Service; 12.12: ARS/USDA; **Page 436:** © Brand X Pictures/PunchStock; **12.B:** Courtesy of Katadyn North America; **Page 439:** © Steve Cole/Getty Images; **Page 440:** Courtesy of National Cancer Institute; **Page 441 left:** © Stockdisc/PunchStock; **Page 441 right:** © Comstock Images/PictureQuest; **Page 442:** © Kevin Sanchez/Cole Group/Getty Images; **Page 443:** © Royalty-Free/Corbis.

Chapter 13

Opener: © Wendy Schiff; **Page 445:** © Brand X Pictures/PunchStock; **13.1 (both):** Lennart Nilsson/Albert Bonniers Forlag AB; **13.2, Page 448:** © Royalty-Free/Corbis; **Table 13.1 (Cereal):** © The McGraw-Hill Companies, Inc./John Flournoy photographer; **Table 13.1 (Juice):** © The McGraw-Hill Companies, Inc./Emily & David Tietz, photographers; **Table 13.1 (Beans):** © Royalty-Free/Corbis; **Page 451:** © Comstock/PunchStock; **Page 453:** © Stockbyte; **Page 454:** © Elinamanninen/Dreamstime.com; **13.5a:**

© Photodisc/Getty Images; **13.5b:** © Brand X Pictures/PunchStock; **Page 456:** © Photodisc/Getty Images; **13.6:** © Royalty-Free/Corbis; **Page 453:** © Wendy Schiff; **13.8:** © Cleo Photography; **Table 13.5 left:** © Royalty-Free/Corbis; **Table 13.5 right:** © Cleo Photography; **Page 461 top:** © C Squared Studios/Getty Images; **Page 461 bottom:** © Creatas/PictureQuest; **Page 462 left:** © Wendy Schiff; **Page 462 right:** © McGraw-Hill Companies; **13.9:** © Creatas/PictureQuest; **Page 463 left:** © Royalty-Free/Corbis; **Page 463 bottom:** © BananaStock/PictureQuest; **13.10:** © E. Gill/Custom Medical Stock Photo; **13.11:** USDA Photo by Ken Hammond; **13.12:** © BananaStock/PunchStock; **Page 466 left:** © Image Source/PunchStock; **Page 466 right:** © BananaStock/PunchStock; **Page 467:** © Pixtal/age fotostock; **Page 468:** © Photodisc/Getty Images; **Page 469, Page 470:** © BananaStock/PunchStock; **Page 471:** © The McGraw-Hill Companies, Inc./Ken Cavanagh, photographer; **13.14:** © Purestock/Getty Images; **Page 474:** © Fancy Photography/Veer; **Page 475 top:** © Wendy Schiff; **13.16:** © Eric Fougére/Kipa/Corbis; **13.17:** © Steve Mason/Getty Images; **Page 478 bottom:** © Steve Cole/Getty Images; **Page 479, 13.18:** USDA Photo by Ken Hammond; **13.A:** © Bettmann/Corbis; **Page 482:** © Brand X Pictures/PunchStock; **Page 483:** © Royalty-Free/Corbis; **Page 484, Page 485:** © Wendy Schiff; **Page 486 left:** © Brand X Pictures/Jupiter Images; **Page 486 right:** © Stockdisc/PunchStock; **Page 487:** © Royalty-Free/Corbis.

Appendices

Page A-1: © Burke/Triolo Productions/Getty Images; **Page A-3:** © Hermera Technologies/Alamy; **Pages B.1, B.2, B.3, B.4, B.5:** © Her Majesty the Queen in Right of Canada, represented by the Minister of Health Canada, 2007; **Page A-14:** © C Squared Studios/Getty Images; **Page A-16:** © Royalty-Free/Corbis; **Page A-21 bottom:** © The McGraw-Hill Companies, Inc./Ken Karp, photographer; **Page A-23:** Used with permission from Dietitians of Canada www.dcjournal.ca.

Chapter Icons

Quiz Yourself Icon: © The McGraw-Hill Companies, Inc./Ken Karp, photographer; **A-head Icon:** © Stockdisc/PunchStock; **Food & Nutrition Tip Icon:** © Jules Frazier/Getty Images; **Did You Know? Icon:** © Comstock/PunchStock; **Concept Checkpoint Icon:** © M. Lamotte/Cole Group/Getty Images; **Personal Dietary Analysis Icon:** © Digital Vision/Getty Images; **Chapter Highlight Icon:** © Photodisc/PunchStock; **Recipe Box Icon:** © C Squared Studios/Getty Images; **Critical Thinking Icon:** © The McGraw-Hill Companies, Inc./Ken Karp, photographer; **Summary and Multiple Choice Icons:** © C Squared Studios/Getty Images.

Index

A

B

C

D

E

F

G

M

N

P

T

X

Y

Z

Dietary Reference Intakes (DRIs): Recommended Intakes for Individuals, Vitamins

Food and Nutrition Board, Institute of Medicine, National Academies

Life Stage Group	Vitamin A (μg/d)[a]	Vitamin C (mg/d)	Vitamin D (μg/d)[b,c]	Vitamin E (mg/d)[d]	Vitamin K (μg/d)	Thiamin (mg/d)	Riboflavin (mg/d)	Niacin (mg/d)[e]	Vitamin B_6 (mg/d)	Folate (μg/d)[f]	Vitamin B-12 (μg/d)	Pantothenic Acid (mg/d)	Biotin (μg/d)	Choline (mg/d)[g]
Infants														
0–6 mo	400*	40*	5*	4*	2.0*	0.2*	0.3*	2*	0.1*	65*	0.4*	1.7*	5*	125*
7–12 mo	500*	50*	5*	5*	2.5*	0.3*	0.4*	4*	0.3*	80*	0.5*	1.8*	6*	150*
Children														
1–3 y	300	15	5*	6	30*	0.5	0.5	6	0.5	150	0.9	2*	8*	200*
4–8 y	400	25	5*	7	55*	0.6	0.6	8	0.6	200	1.2	3*	12*	250*
Males														
9–13 y	600	45	5*	11	60*	0.9	0.9	12	1.0	300	1.8	4*	20*	375*
14–18 y	900	75	5*	15	75*	1.2	1.3	16	1.3	400	2.4	5*	25*	550*
19–30 y	900	90	5*	15	120*	1.2	1.3	16	1.3	400	2.4	5*	30*	550*
31–50 y	900	90	5*	15	120*	1.2	1.3	16	1.3	400	2.4	5*	30*	550*
51–70 y	900	90	10*	15	120*	1.2	1.3	16	1.7	400	2.4[h]	5*	30*	550*
>70 y	900	90	15*	15	120*	1.2	1.3	16	1.7	400	2.4[h]	5*	30*	550*
Females														
9–13 y	600	45	5*	11	60*	0.9	0.9	12	1.0	300	1.8	4*	20*	375*
14–18 y	700	65	5*	15	75*	1.0	1.0	14	1.2	400[i]	2.4	5*	25*	400*
19–30 y	700	75	5*	15	90*	1.1	1.1	14	1.3	400[i]	2.4	5*	30*	425*
31–50 y	700	75	5*	15	90*	1.1	1.1	14	1.3	400[i]	2.4	5*	30*	425*
51–70 y	700	75	10*	15	90*	1.1	1.1	14	1.5	400	2.4[h]	5*	30*	425*
>70 y	700	75	15*	15	90*	1.1	1.1	14	1.5	400	2.4[h]	5*	30*	425*
Pregnancy														
≤18 y	750	80	5*	15	75*	1.4	1.4	18	1.9	600[j]	2.6	6*	30*	450*
19–30 y	770	85	5*	15	90*	1.4	1.4	18	1.9	600[j]	2.6	6*	30*	450*
31–50 y	770	85	5*	15	90*	1.4	1.4	18	1.9	600[j]	2.6	6*	30*	450*
Lactation														
≤18 y	1,200	115	5*	19	75*	1.4	1.6	17	2.0	500	2.8	7*	35*	550*
19–30 y	1,300	120	5*	19	90*	1.4	1.6	17	2.0	500	2.8	7*	35*	550*
31–50 y	1,300	120	5*	19	90*	1.4	1.6	17	2.0	500	2.8	7*	35*	550*

mg = milligram, μg = microgram

NOTE: This table (taken from the DRI reports, see www.nap.edu) presents Recommended Dietary Allowances (RDAs) in **bold type** and Adequate Intakes (AIs) in ordinary type followed by an asterisk (*). RDAs and AIs may both be used as goals for individual intake. RDAs are set to meet the needs of almost all (97 to 98 percent) individuals in a group. For healthy breast-fed infants, the AI is the mean intake. The AI for other life stage and gender groups is believed to cover needs of all individuals in the group, but lack of data or uncertainty in the data prevent being able to specify with confidence the percentage of individuals covered by this intake.

[a]As retinol activity equivalents (RAEs). 1 RAE = 1 μg retinol, 12 μg b-carotene, 24 μg a-carotene, or 24 μg b-cryptoxanthin. To calculate RAEs from REs of provitamin A carotenoids in foods, divide the REs by 2. For preformed vitamin A in foods or supplements and for provitamin A carotenoids in supplements, 1 RE = 1 RAE.

[b]cholecalciferol 1 μg cholecalciferol = 40 IU vitamin D.

[c]In the absence of adequate exposure to sunlight.

[d]As a-tocopherol. a-Tocopherol includes RRR-a-tocopherol, the only form of a-tocopherol that occurs naturally in foods, and the 2R-stereoisomeric forms of a-tocopherol (RRR-, RSR-, RRS-, and RSS-a-tocopherol) that occur in fortified foods and supplements. It does not include the 2S-stereoisomeric forms of a-tocopherol (SRR-, SSR-, SRS-, and SSS-a-tocopherol), also found in fortified foods and supplements.

[e]As niacin equivalents (NE). 1 mg of niacin = 60 mg of tryptophan; 0–6 months = preformed niacin (not NE).

[f]As dietary folate equivalents (DFE). 1 DFE = 1 μg food folate = 0.6 μg of folic acid from fortified food or as a supplement consumed with food = 0.5 μg of a supplement taken on an empty stomach.

[g]Although AIs have been set for choline, there are few data to assess whether a dietary supply of choline is needed at all stages of the life cycle, and it may be that the choline requirement can be met by endogenous synthesis at some of these stages.

[h]Because 10 to 30 percent of older people may malabsorb food-bound B-12, it is advisable for those older than 50 years to meet their RDA mainly by consuming foods fortified with B-12 or a supplement containing B-12.

[i]In view of evidence linking folate intake with neural tube defects in the fetus, it is recommended that all women capable of becoming pregnant consume 400 μg from supplements or fortified foods in addition to intake of food folate from a varied diet.

[j]It is assumed that women will continue consuming 400 μg from supplements or fortified food until their pregnancy is confirmed and they enter prenatal care, which ordinarily occurs after the end of the periconceptional period—the critical time for formation of the neural tube.

Dietary Reference Intakes (DRIs): Recommended Intakes for Individuals, Elements

Food and Nutrition Board, Institute of Medicine, National Academies

Life Stage Group	Calcium (mg/d)	Chromium (μg/d)	Copper (μg/d)	Fluoride (mg/d)	Iodine (μg/d)	Iron (mg/d)	Magnesium (mg/d)	Manganese (mg/d)	Molybdenum (μg/d)	Phosphorus (mg/d)	Selenium (μg/d)	Zinc (mg/d)
Infants												
0–6 mo	210*	0.2*	200*	0.01*	110*	0.27*	30*	0.003*	2*	100*	15*	2*
7–12 mo	270*	5.5*	220*	0.5*	130*	**11**	75*	0.6*	3*	275*	20*	**3**
Children												
1–3 y	500*	11*	**340**	0.7*	**90**	**7**	**80**	1.2*	**17**	**460**	**20**	**3**
4–8 y	800*	15*	**440**	1*	**90**	**10**	**130**	1.5*	**22**	**500**	**30**	**5**
Males												
9–13 y	1,300*	25*	**700**	2*	**120**	**8**	**240**	1.9*	**34**	**1,250**	**40**	**8**
14–18 y	1,300*	35*	**890**	3*	**150**	**11**	**410**	2.2*	**43**	**1,250**	**55**	**11**
19–30 y	1,000*	35*	**900**	4*	**150**	**8**	**400**	2.3*	**45**	**700**	**55**	**11**
31–50 y	1,000*	35*	**900**	4*	**150**	**8**	**420**	2.3*	**45**	**700**	**55**	**11**
51–70 y	1,200*	30*	**900**	4*	**150**	**8**	**420**	2.3*	**45**	**700**	**55**	**11**
>70 y	1,200*	30*	**900**	4*	**150**	**8**	**420**	2.3*	**45**	**700**	**55**	**11**
Females												
9–13 y	1,300*	21*	**700**	2*	**120**	**8**	**240**	1.6*	**34**	**1,250**	**40**	**8**
14–18 y	1,300*	24*	**890**	3*	**150**	**15**	**360**	1.6*	**43**	**1,250**	**55**	**9**
19–30 y	1,000*	25*	**900**	3*	**150**	**18**	**310**	1.8*	**45**	**700**	**55**	**8**
31–50 y	1,000*	25*	**900**	3*	**150**	**18**	**320**	1.8*	**45**	**700**	**55**	**8**
51–70 y	1,200*	20*	**900**	3*	**150**	**8**	**320**	1.8*	**45**	**700**	**55**	**8**
>70 y	1,200*	20*	**900**	3*	**150**	**8**	**320**	1.8*	**45**	**700**	**55**	**8**
Pregnancy												
≤18 y	1,300*	29*	**1,000**	3*	**220**	**27**	**400**	2.0*	**50**	**1,250**	**60**	**12**
19–30 y	1,000*	30*	**1,000**	3*	**220**	**27**	**350**	2.0*	**50**	**700**	**60**	**11**
31–50 y	1,000*	30*	**1,000**	3*	**220**	**27**	**360**	2.0*	**50**	**700**	**60**	**11**
Lactation												
≤18 y	1,300*	44*	**1,300**	3*	**290**	**10**	**360**	2.6*	**50**	**1,250**	**70**	**13**
19–30 y	1,000*	45*	**1,300**	3*	**290**	**9**	**310**	2.6*	**50**	**700**	**70**	**12**
31–50 y	1,000*	45*	**1,300**	3*	**290**	**9**	**320**	2.6*	**50**	**700**	**70**	**12**

NOTE: This table presents Recommended Dietary Allowances (RDAs) in **bold type** and Adequate Intakes (AIs) in ordinary type followed by an asterisk (*). RDAs and AIs may both be used as goals for individual intake. RDAs are set to meet the needs of almost all (97 to 98 percent) individuals in a group. For healthy breast-fed infants, the AI is the mean intake. The AI for other life stage and gender groups is believed to cover needs of all individuals in the group, but lack of data or uncertainty in the data prevent being able to specify with confidence the percentage of individuals covered by this intake.

SOURCES: *Dietary Reference Intakes for Calcium, Phosphorus, Magnesium, Vitamin D, and Fluoride* (1997); *Dietary Reference Intakes for Thiamin, Riboflavin, Niacin, Vitamin B-6, Folate, Vitamin B-12, Pantothenic Acid, Biotin, and Choline* (1998); *Dietary Reference Intakes for Vitamin C, Vitamin E, Selenium, and Carotenoids* (2000); and *Dietary Reference Intakes for Vitamin A, Vitamin K, Arsenic, Boron, Chromium, Copper, Iodine, Iron, Manganese, Molybdenum, Nickel, Silicon, Vanadium, and Zinc* (2001). These reports may be accessed via www.nap.edu.

Dietary Reference Intakes (DRIs): Recommended intakes for Individuals, Macronutrients

Food and Nutrition Board, Institute of Medicine, National Academies

Life Stage Group	Carbohydrate (g/d)	Total Fibre (g/d)	Fat (g/d)	Linoleic Acid (g/d)	α-Linolenic Acid (g/d)	Protein[a] (g/d)
Infants						
0–6 mo	60*	ND	31*	4.4*	0.5*	9.1*
7–12 mo	95*	ND	30*	4.6*	0.5*	**13.5**
Children						
1–3 y	**130**	19*	ND[b]	7*	0.7*	**13**
4–8 y	**130**	25*	ND	10*	0.9*	**19**
Males						
9–13 y	**130**	31*	ND	12*	1.2*	**34**
14–18 y	**130**	38*	ND	16*	1.6*	**52**
19–30 y	**130**	38*	ND	17*	1.6*	**56**
31–50 y	**130**	38*	ND	17*	1.6*	**56**
51–70 y	**130**	30*	ND	14*	1.6*	**56**
>70 y	**130**	30*	ND	14*	1.6*	**56**
Females						
9–13 y	**130**	26*	ND	10*	1.0*	**34**
14–18 y	**130**	26*	ND	11*	1.1*	**46**
19–30 y	**130**	25*	ND	12*	1.1*	**46**
31–50 y	**130**	25*	ND	12*	1.1*	**46**
51–70 y	**130**	21*	ND	11*	1.1*	**46**
>70 y	**130**	21*	ND	11*	1.1*	**46**
Pregnancy						
14–18 y	**175**	28*	ND	13*	1.4*	**71**
19–30 y	**175**	28*	ND	13*	1.4*	**71**
31–50 y	**175**	28*	ND	13*	1.4*	**71**
Lactation						
14–18 y	**210**	29*	ND	13*	1.3*	**71**
19–30 y	**210**	29*	ND	13*	1.3*	**71**
31–50 y	**210**	29*	ND	13*	1.3*	**71**

NOTE: This table presents Recommended Dietary Allowances (RDAs) in **bold type** and Adequate Intakes (AIs) in ordinary type followed by an asterisk (*). RDAs and AIs may both be used as goals for individual intake. RDAs are set to meet the needs of a most all (97 to 98 percent) individuals in a group. For healthy breast-fed infants, the AI is the mean intake. The AI for other life stage and gender groups is believed to cover needs of all individuals in the group, but lack of data or uncertainty in the data prevent being able to specify with confidence the percentage of individuals covered by this intake.

[a]Based on 0.8g protein/kg body weight for reference body weight.

[b]ND = not determinable at this time

SOURCES: *Dietary Reference Intakes for Energy, Carbohydrate, Fiber, Fat, Fatty Acids, Cholesterol, Protein, and Amino Acids* (2002). This report may be accessed via www.nap.edu.

Dietary Reference Intakes (DRIs): Recommended Intakes for Individuals, Electrolytes, and Water

Food and Nutrition Board, Institute of Medicine, National Academies

Life Stage Group	Sodium (mg/d)	Potassium (mg/d)	Chloride (mg/d)	Water (L/d)
Infants				
0–6 mo	120*	400*	180*	0.7*
7–12 mo	370*	700*	570*	0.8*
Children				
1–3 y	1,000*	3,000*	1,500*	1.3*
4–8 y	1,200*	3,800*	1,900*	1.7*
Males				
9–13 y	1,500*	4,500*	2,300*	2.4*
14–18 y	1,500*	4,700*	2,300*	3.3*
19–30 y	1,500*	4,700*	2,300*	3.7*
31–50 y	1,500*	4,700*	2,300*	3.7*
51–70 y	1,300*	4,700*	2,000*	3.7*
> 70 y	1,200*	4,700*	1,800*	3.7*
Females				
9–13 y	1,500*	4,500*	2,300*	2.1*
14–18 y	1,500*	4,700*	2,300*	2.3*
19–30 y	1,500*	4,700*	2,300*	2.7*
31–50 y	1,500*	4,700*	2,300*	2.7*
51–70 y	1,300*	4,700*	2,000*	2.7*
> 70 y	1,200*	4,700*	1,800*	2.7*
Pregnancy				
14–18 y	1,500*	4,700*	2,300*	3.0*
19–50 y	1,500*	4,700*	2,300*	3.0*
Lactation				
14–18 y	1,500*	5,100*	2,300*	3.8*
19–50 y	1,500*	5,100*	2,300*	3.8*

NOTE: The table is adapted from the DRI reports. See www.nap.edu. Adequate Intakes (AIs) are followed by an asterisk (*). These may be used as a goal for individual intake. For healthy breast-fed infants, the AI is the average intake. The AI for other life stage and gender groups is believed to cover the needs of all individuals in the group, but lack of data prevent being able to specify with confidence the percentage of individuals covered by this intake; therefore, no Recommended Dietary Allowance (RDA) was set.

SOURCE: *Dietary Reference Intakes for Water, Potassium, Sodium, Chloride, and Sulfate.* This report may be accessed via www.nap.edu.

Acceptable Macronutrient Distribution Ranges

Macronutrient	Range (percent of energy) Children, 1–3 y	Children, 4–18 y	Adults
Fat	30–40	25–35	20–35
omega-6 polyunsaturated fats (linoleic acid)	5–10	5–10	5–10
omega-3 polyunsaturated fats[a] (α-linolenic acid)	0.6–1.2	0.6–1.2	0.6–1.2
Carbohydrate	45–65	45–65	45–65
Protein	5–20	10–30	10–35

[a]Approximately 10% of the total can come from longer-chain n-3 fatty acids.

SOURCE: *Dietary Reference Intakes for Energy, Carbohydrate, Fiber, Fat, Fatty Acids, Cholesterol, Protein, and Amino Acids (2002).* The report may be accessed via www.nap.edu.

Dietary Reference Intakes (DRIs): Tolerable Upper Intake Levels (UL[a]), Vitamins

Food and Nutrition Board, Institute of Medicine, National Academies

Life Stage Group	Vitamin A (μg/d)[b]	Vitamin C (mg/d)	Vitamin D (μg/d)	Vitamin E (mg/d)[c,d]	Vitamin K	Thiamin	Riboflavin	Niacin (mg/d)[d]	Vitamin B-6 (mg/d)	Folate (μg/d)[d]	Vitamin B-12	Pantothenic Acid	Biotin	Choline (g/d)	Carotenoids[e]
Infants															
0–6 mo	600	ND	25	ND	ND	ND	ND	ND	ND	ND	ND	ND	ND	ND	ND
7–12 mo	600	ND	25	ND	ND	ND	ND	ND	ND	ND	ND	ND	ND	ND	ND
Children															
1–3 y	600	400	50	200	ND	ND	ND	10	30	300	ND	ND	ND	1.0	ND
4–8 y	900	650	50	300	ND	ND	ND	15	40	400	ND	ND	ND	1.0	ND
Males, Females															
9–13 y	1,700	1,200	50	600	ND	ND	ND	20	60	600	ND	ND	ND	2.0	ND
14–18 y	2,800	1,800	50	800	ND	ND	ND	30	80	800	ND	ND	ND	3.0	ND
19–70 y	3,000	2,000	50	1,000	ND	ND	ND	35	100	1,000	ND	ND	ND	3.5	ND
> 70 y	3,000	2,000	50	1,000	ND	ND	ND	35	100	1,000	ND	ND	ND	3.5	ND
Pregnancy															
≤ 18 y	2,800	1,800	50	800	ND	ND	ND	30	80	800	ND	ND	ND	3.0	ND
19–50 y	3,000	2,000	50	1,000	ND	ND	ND	35	100	1,000	ND	ND	ND	3.5	ND
Lactation															
≤ 18 y	2,800	1,800	50	800	ND	ND	ND	30	80	800	ND	ND	ND	3.0	ND
19–50 y	3,000	2,000	50	1,000	ND	ND	ND	35	100	1,000	ND	ND	ND	3.5	ND

[a]UL = The maximum level of daily nutrient intake likely to pose no risk of adverse effects. Unless otherwise specified, the UL represents total intake from food, water, and supplements. Due to lack of suitable data, ULs could not be established for vitamin K, thiamin, riboflavin, vitamin B-12, pantothenic acid, biotin, or carotenoids. In the absence of ULs, extra caution may be warranted in consuming levels above recommended intakes.

[b]As preformed vitamin A only.

[c]As α-tocopherol; applies to any form of supplemental α-tocopherol.

[d]The ULs for vitamin E, niacin, and folate apply to synthetic forms obtained from supplements, fortified foods, or a combination of the two.

[e]β-Carotene supplements are advised only to serve as a provitamin A source for individuals at risk of vitamin A deficiency.

[f]ND = Not determinable due to lack of data of adverse effects in this age group and concern with regard to lack of ability to handle excess amounts. Source of intake should be from food only to prevent high levels of intake.

SOURCES: *Dietary Reference Intakes for Calcium, Phosphorus, Magnesium, Vitamin D, and Fluoride* (1997); *Dietary Reference Intakes for Thiamin, Riboflavin, Niacin, Vitamin B-6, Folate, Vitamin B-12, Pantothenic Acid, Biotin, and Chlorine* (1998); *Dietary Reference Intakes for Vitamin C, Vitamin E, Selenium, and Carotenoids* (2000); and *Dietary Reference Intakes for Vitamin A, Vitamin K, Arsenic, Boron, Chromium, Copper, Iodine, Iron, Manganese, Molybdenum, Nickel, Silicon, Vanadium, and Zinc* (2001). These reports may be accessed via www.nap.edu.

Dietary Reference Intakes (DRIs): Tolerable Upper Intake Levels (UL[a]), Elements and Electrolytes[b,c]

Food and Nutrition Board, Institute of Medicine, National Academies

Life Stage Group	Arsenic[b]	Boron (mg/d)	Calcium (g/d)	Copper (mg/d)	Fluoride (mg/d)	Iodine (mg/d)	Iron (mg/d)	Magnesium (mg/d)[d]	Manganese (mg/d)	Molybdenum (mg/d)	Nickel (mg/d)	Phosphorus (g/d)	Selenium (mg/d)	Vanadium (mg/d)[e]	Zinc (mg/d)	Sodium (mg/d)	Chloride (mg/d)
Infants																	
0–6 mo	ND[f]	ND	ND	ND	0.7	ND	40	ND	ND	ND	ND	ND	45	ND	4	ND	ND
7–12 mo	ND	ND	ND	ND	0.9	ND	40	ND	ND	ND	ND	ND	60	ND	5	ND	ND
Children																	
1–3 y	ND	3	2.5	1,000	1.3	200	40	65	2	300	0.2	3	90	ND	7	1,500	2,300
4–8 y	ND	6	2.5	3,000	2.2	300	40	110	3	600	0.3	3	150	ND	12	1,900	2,900
Males, Females																	
9–13 y	ND	11	2.5	5,000	10	600	40	350	6	1,100	0.6	4	280	ND	23	2,200	3,400
14–18 y	ND	17	2.5	8,000	10	900	45	350	9	1,700	1.0	4	400	ND	34	2,300	3,600
19–70 y	ND	20	2.5	10,000	10	1,100	45	350	11	2,000	1.0	4	400	1.8	40	2,300	3,600
.70 y	ND	20	2.5	10,000	10	1,100	45	350	11	2,000	1.0	3	400	1.8	40	2,300	3,600
Pregnancy																	
#18 y	ND	17	2.5	8,000	10	900	45	350	9	1,700	1.0	3.5	400	ND	34	2,300	3,600
19–50 y	ND	20	2.5	10,000	10	1,100	45	350	11	2,000	1.0	3.5	400	ND	40	2,300	3,600
Lactation																	
#18 y	ND	17	2.5	8,000	10	900	45	350	9	1,700	1.0	4	400	ND	34	2,300	3,600
19–50 y	ND	20	2.5	10,000	10	1,100	45	350	11	2,000	1.0	4	400	ND	40	2,300	3,600

[a]UL 5 The maximum level of daily nutrient intake that is likely to pose no risk of adverse effects. Unless otherwise specified, the UL represents total intake from food, water, and supplements. Due to lack of suitable data, ULs could not be established for arsenic, chromium, and silicon. In the absence of ULs, extra caution may be warranted in consuming levels above recommended intakes.

[b]Although a UL was not determined for arsenic, there is no justification for adding arsenic to food or supplements.

[c]Although silicon has not been shown to cause adverse effects in humans, there is no justification for adding silicon to supplements.

[d]The ULs for magnesium represent intake from a pharmacological agent only and do not include intake from food and water.

[e]Although vanadium in food has not been shown to cause adverse effects in humans, there is no justification for adding vanadium to food and vanadium supplements should be used with caution. The UL is based on adverse effects in laboratory animals and this data could be used to set a UL for adults but not children and adolescents.

[f]ND 5 Not determinable due to lack of data of adverse effects in this age group and concern with regard to lack of ability to handle excess amounts. Source of intake should be from food only to prevent high levels of intake.

SOURCES: Dietary Reference Intakes for Calcium, Phosphorus, Magnesium, Vitamin D, and Fluoride (1997); Dietary Reference Intakes for Thiamin, Riboflavin, Niacin, Vitamin B-6, Folate, Vitamin B-12, Pantothenic Acid, Biotin, and Choline (1998); Dietary Reference Intakes for Vitamin C, Vitamin E, Selenium, and Carotenoids (2000); Dietary Reference Intakes for Vitamin A, Vitamin K, Arsenic, Boron, Chromium, Copper, Iodine, Iron, Manganese, Molybdenum, Nickel, Silicon, Vanadium, and Zinc (2001); and Dietary Reference Intakes for Water, Potassium, Sodium, Chloride, and Sulfate (2004). These reports may be accessed via www.nap.edu.